Fifty Years

Fifty Years

¶ Being a Retrospective Collection of
Novels, Novellas, Tales, Drama, Poetry, and
Reportage and Essays *(Whether Literary,
Musical, Contemplative, Historical, Biographical,
Argumentative, or Gastronomical)*
¶ All Drawn from Volumes Issued during
the Last Half-Century by
ALFRED and BLANCHE KNOPF
Over This Sign and Device

Illinois Central College
Learning Resouce Center

¶ *The Whole Selected,
Assembled, and Edited, with an Introduction
and Sundry Commentaries, by*

Clifton Fadiman

NEW YORK: Alfred·A·Knopf
1965

L. C catalog card number: 65-11119

THIS IS A BORZOI BOOK,
PUBLISHED BY ALFRED A. KNOPF, INC.

FIRST EDITION

iii

Contents

DRAMA

REPORTAGE AND ESSAYS

VERSE

Illustrations

Introduction

1: A View from the Fiftieth Year

IN THE ART WORLD an exhibition of paintings mirroring an entire career is called a Retrospective. This book, however incomplete, is also a Retrospective, marking a few milestones in the long professional life of an artist. A pair of artists, rather, for when one says Alfred A. Knopf, Inc., one says also Blanche, Alfred's wife, partner, and now president of the company.

Mr. Knopf, not given to overstatement, might tut-tut the word "artist." Yet broadly it fits.

Fifty years ago, in May 1915, he founded the firm which more than any other has influenced American book publishing in a manner most knowledgeable judges deem admirable. It was started not as a playboy's exercise but as a business. It has remained one, with attention methodically paid to the superior attractions of black ink over red. But within a few years after its inception the young Alfred Knopf had made clear, first to himself, then to the public, that this business could also be a profession. A profession involves adherence—sometimes explicit, as in the Hippocratic Oath, sometimes tacit—to a set of standards, not necessarily running counter to the demands of the marketplace yet erected above and beyond them. In this sense Mr. Knopf is a professional, like any good doctor, teacher, or lawyer. But we refer also to the teacher's *art*, the physician's *art*. I suggest that, just as Mr. Knopf has made a profession out of a business, so he has made an art out of a profession.

Though in twenty-five years there will probably be none, there are today other American publishers of whom the same may be said. Of Alfred and Blanche Knopf it may be said with great assurance. The assurance roots in the fact that they have striven to be something more than honest brokers mediating between author and audience. Like all publishers, they have sponsored mediocre books as well as some downright poor ones. But as the professional eye scrutinizes the thousands of titles issued over the Borzoi imprint, what it sees is not a row of books ranging from the trivial to the great. Even the great ones are hardly to the point, for other publishers have courageously backed writers as distinguished as those of the house of Knopf. What the professional eye perceives is a linked series of creative acts.

Not primary acts, for these only the writers themselves could perform. But nonetheless creative. Not simple reactions to the demands of the day or the pressures of the market, but expressions—conscious, confident, and at times even a trifle arrogant—of a whole personality.

All who, like the writer of these lines, have been or are book publishers salute, with an unsettling feeling of envy and gratitude, these creative acts. What were they? First, the Borzoi revolution in book design and manufacture, now an old story, in the twenties a radically new one. Second, the discovery of virtually a continentful of European high literature, and its transmission, as daring as it was systematic, to our shores—an act followed in later years by similar ones with respect to Latin America and Japan. Third, the organized effort to publish, often at a commercial loss, first-rate books in fields intimately tied to the personal interests of the Knopfs: historical scholarship, music, gastronomy, oenology, conservation. Finally, the sponsorship over an eleven-year period of *The American Mercury*, which, as the *Pequod* did for Ishmael, constituted the Harvard and Yale of a whole generation of young Americans.

I have tabulated only four among many specific creative acts. There remain two others with less precise outlines.

The first (one boggles over a word so sadly vulgarized since the assassination of President Kennedy) was the formation of a style. The Knopf style became as identifiable as that of Gibbon or El Greco, whether displayed in the minor alteration of a colophon design or the deliberate issue at a loss, year after year, of the (so far) twelve volumes of Professor Lawrence Gipson's monumental *British Empire before the American Revolution*. At best this style is marked by the aristocratic virtues; at worst—in the old days—by a certain amusing rather than offensive hauteur. In a sense much of the Knopf output may be said to have been signed by the publisher.

The second creative gesture was perhaps less an act than a relationship, as tenuous as it was distinguished, between the house of Knopf and the authors it has sheltered. This has little to do with financial generosity. The Knopfs do not buy authors via checkbook, their contracts are drawn with care, their advertising and promotion stop short of the grandiose, their best-seller record is only moderate. It has little to do with flattery or hand-holding; whatever attitudes Mr. Knopf has struck in the past have included none requiring a flexibly hinged knee. Nor is he a "smart" publisher, shrewd in the amenities of the cocktail rout, the celebrity corroboree, and the ritual stroking of critics and reviewers.

Under these circumstances why for so many years was it the ambition of so many serious young writers to "make the Knopf list"? Without invidiousness I would suggest that as a general rule the relationship between Alfred Knopf and an author was and is that between two rather old-fashioned gentlemen, or, as the case might be, between a gentleman and a lady. Mr. Knopf respects his authors so much that he lets them alone, on the assumption that they know their business and he his. The Knopfs number, among their close friends, many of their authors. They also number, among their acquaintances, many of their authors. The family note is not forced. The atmosphere is, if you like, nineteenth-century and perhaps more English than American—certainly more English than New Yorkish. Most intangibly it is an atmosphere in which floats continually suspended an implicit respect for the high estate of good literature.

The forging of a unique publishing style; the quiet elaboration of a classically restrained relationship between author and publisher; the conception and hardheaded development of a series of major creative acts: these, in my view and that of many, entitle the Knopfs to be called not only first-rate publishers but that finer thing, first-rate practitioners of the Art of Publishing.

2: Abstract and Brief Chronicle

FOR A FULL ACCOUNT of the history of the firm we must await the memoirs on which Mr. Knopf is currently reported working. However, the reader may wish to note a few of the major movements that marked its course.

Alfred A. Knopf was born in New York City on September 12, 1892. As the nineteenth century did not really die until June 28, 1914, the first twenty-two years of his life were enclosed within it, a circumstance reflected in his general stance and demeanor.

It is curious that a strikingly large number of men who later achieved distinction lost one or more parents early in their lives. Alfred's mother died when he was four, so that the influence of his father, Samuel, an advertising executive and business consultant of great authority and horsepower, was perhaps reinforced.[1] After conventional

---

[1] I remember Sam clearly. Forty-one years ago I worked briefly for the Knopfs, who then included Mr. Knopf senior. Florid, full-faced, awesomely mustachioed, Sam was a man whose ability matched his irascibility. He functioned as a kind of super-watchdog, or German shepherd, tolerating no waste of any kind, especially of time. I recall, for example, his uncanny flair for gauging just how long an employee might legitimately linger in the men's room. By some extrasensory perception he always knew who was there. To this day, as with Jim Hawkins and the sharp voice of Captain Flint, I can hear ringing in my ears Sam's peremptory rap-rap-rap on the door and his parade-ground rasp: "Fadiman, stop wasting my time in there!" I might add that at this period I was probably the most inefficient stockboy and minor production assistant in the annals of American book publishing, a fact which Alfred, an accurate judge of competence, recognized by paying me ten dollars a week. A difference of opinion finally parted us. Mr. Knopf thought he should run his business and I thought, privately, I should. This divergence left little room for compromise.

preparation in the public schools and the Mackenzie School, Alfred in 1908 entered Columbia College. He made friends with a few professors, a proclivity continued to the present day, but was otherwise unimpressed with the place. In 1912 he accepted a B.A.

His original intention had been to enter Harvard Law School in the fall. He would have made a good lawyer (or for that matter a good musical impresario or college president), but a summer trip to England may have tipped the scales in favor of the book business. He was the guest of John and Ada Galsworthy, dined at the Garrick with Granville Barker, met Alfred Ollivant (and later W. H. Hudson), and, sitting in Dan Rider's bookshop, watched and overheard the easily overhearable Frank Harris (whose mustache I remember as a dead ringer for Sam's), Katherine Mansfield, Haldane MacFall, and other literary figures.

Home again after a *Wanderjahr*, or rather *Halbjahr*, he got a job at eight dollars per week[2] with Doubleday, Page & Company in the accounting department. (He has never quite lost a knack for double-entry bookkeeping.) During his Doubleday period, though still only twenty, he contrived to bring the neglected Joseph Conrad to the attention of the American public. Indeed, a good professional judge, George H. Doran, credited him with virtually "discovering" Conrad. There followed fourteen months with Mr. Mitchell Kennerley, a pioneering bookman of delicate taste and notable unreliability. The experience must have been decisive. In the spring of 1915, with capital that today might float a really glamorous publisher's wingding, he opened his own office, or rather his own desk, lent him by Sam, who dominated a suite in the Candler Building on West Forty-second Street. By the end of the summer he had a room of his own, rental forty-five dollars a month. He also had a young assistant named Blanche Wolf.

His first publication was an English version, for which no crying need existed, of four plays by Emile Augier. (It is characteristic of Mr. Knopf to recall that the book was set in Cheltenham monotype, "a face I have never since had the courage to use.") Of the first season's eleven books, ten were translations. This circumstance was only in small part a prefiguring of Mr. Knopf's flair for the then unexplored European market. Rather does it support the case that a young publisher publishes what he can. However, one of the eleven was a reissue (here we come upon the first show of genius) of W. H. Hudson's *Green Mansions*, with an introduction by the John Galsworthy in whose Devonshire cottage Mr. Knopf had four years previously stayed overnight. By a trick of our incomprehensible copyright law *Green Mansions*, though twenty years old and published in the United States twelve years before, lay quietly in the public domain. Of this fact Mr. Knopf took advantage only technically, for he paid W. H. Hudson royalties (the book was a non-sensational success) sufficient to keep the author in modest comfort during his declining years.

[2] Two dollars *less* than he later paid me.

Green Mansions was the start. The list grew, headed by Joseph Hergesheimer, whom the young Knopf had gently magnetized away from Mitchell Kennerley. Names now effulgent, then only in the course of establishment, began to appear: H. L. Mencken, Carl Van Vechten, George Jean Nathan, Clarence Day, Sigrid Undset, Knut Hamsun, Willa Cather, Ezra Pound, T. S. Eliot, Max Beerbohm, Somerset Maugham (*The Land of the Blessed Virgin*, 1920), Katherine Mansfield, E. M. Forster, Wallace Stevens, J. Middleton Murry, Julian Huxley, Robert Graves, Walter de la Mare, Edith Sitwell, John Crowe Ransom, Thomas Mann (who in perspective may emerge as the greatest novelist of the first half of the century), and one of the half-dozen finest short-story writers ever to use the language, A. E. Coppard.

The list soon began to reflect and has continued to reflect the influence of the first and more interesting of the two mergers in which Mr. Knopf has been involved. In 1916 he married Blanche Wolf. Blanche brought to the firm certain remarkable talents in part complementary to those of her husband: linguistic abilities (her French is virtually part of her); a lively social flair, based on a sense of the creative possibilities that lie in conversation; a passion for travel; a deep interest in the entire spectrum of Continental and Latin American literature. When she and Alfred made their first joint grand tour of Europe, it was Blanche who signed up André Gide. Other European writers for whose appearance on the list she is largely or wholly responsible include Jules Romains, Charles Seignobos, Simone de Beauvoir, Sartre, Camus, Freud (*Moses and Monotheism*), Sholokhov, Elsa Morante, Joseph Kessel, Roger Vailland, Ilya Ehrenburg. In recognition of her support of French literature in the United States she was in 1949 named by Ambassador Bonnet a Chevalier of the French Legion of Honor, and was later made Officier.

Her interest in the Latin American scene has been equally fruitful. In 1942 she blazed a trail in South America, a circumstance later reflected in the acquisition of many notable writers, some published—and with full consciousness of the fact—*con amore*. Among the more eminent names are Eduardo Mallea, Germán Arciniegas, Jorge Amado, and Gilberto Freyre. In 1950 she was made a Cavaleiro of the Brazilian National Order of the Southern Cross, and in 1964 was decorated a second time, receiving the rank of Oficial. (Mr. Knopf was simultaneously named Comendador. I am incompetent to interpret the delicate shadings of these Brazilian honorifics.)

Her acquaintance with the world of English letters is perhaps even deeper than that of her husband. At one time or another she has gathered in under her wing such notable names as Hammond Innes, Ivy Compton-Burnett, and especially Elizabeth Bowen.

Mrs. Knopf is slightly built, feminine (without, as many have discovered, any undue softness), and elegant in ambience and *tournure*. There is therefore a mild irony implicit in the fact that she is responsible for the sanguinary emergence on the Knopf list of the three hard-boiled novelists Dashiell Hammett, Raymond Chandler, and James M. Cain, along with such masters of gentle and reflective fantasy as Robert Nathan.

After World War II the European and English end of the firm's activities was left entirely in her hands. There can be no proper proportioning of credit: Alfred and Blanche have worked as a team. It is not unjust to say that she is the only major book publisher of her sex in the world.

On June 4, 1962, Franklin and Marshall College conferred on her an honorary degree of Doctor of Letters. Commencement citations are usually more notable for their colorful rhetoric than for their fidelity to truth, but in this case the concluding words were accurate:

> Her successful career as a publisher, her enlightened understanding of the mutual respect required between author and publisher, her encouragement of promising literary talents have made her one of the most influential women of our time.

Great publishers, like great artists, should have a loamy and productive unconscious. Perhaps unconsciously the Knopfs took advantage of America's coming of age, the farewell to gentility that by 1920 was already an accomplished fact. The new, the revolutionary does not always pay off. In the twenties and thirties it did. The Borzoi colophon[3] began to mean more than the sign of a business. It became the emblem of a warmly receptive attitude to the modern, even the daring note in American and European literature. Intellectually sound and chronologically in phase with the country's development, that attitude was soon wisely adopted by other excellent publishers. Mr. and Mrs. Knopf may, however, feel justified in the personal application of Tennyson's

For all can grow the flower now that I have sown the seed.

By 1925, though only a decade had passed, the Borzoi list already glittered with remarkable Continental figures. Bunin, Hamsun, Undset, Gide, Unamuno, Baroja, Croce, Mann comprise but a few. In 1920 Knopf published T. S. Eliot's revolutionary *Poems,* containing all his work previous to *The Waste Land.* With de la Mare, Belloc, and Hudson there had been set up the underpinnings of a self-respecting juvenile department. (Most juvenile lists insult children, grownups, and often animals.) An educational department flourished, coolly bypassing the conventional academic hackery and marked by such names as Julian Huxley, Charles A. Beard, Graham Wallas, Simon Nelson Patten, Charles Gide, and G. D. H. Cole. A number of impressive sets and series had been printed or imported: the Blue Jade Library, odd, out-of-the-way para-classics; the Tudor Translations; the scholarly *History of Civilization;* an excellent Stephen Crane; a new version of Maupassant.

In 1921 the Knopfs made the first of many trips abroad. It was almost a trail-blazing expedition, for very few American publishers

---

[3] Mrs. Knopf had always hankered after a Russian wolfhound, though later on she remarked, "I wish I'd picked a better dog for our imprint."

up to that time had thought it worthwhile to visit such countries as Germany, Sweden, Denmark, and Norway. In 1921 also appeared one of the earliest of the many Borzoi retrievals from oblivion, the minor classic *The Diary of a Nobody* by George and Weedon Grossmith. First-rate scholars—Bernard Pares, Aubrey Bell, Prince Mirsky, Raymond Pearl—lent solidity and authority to the Borzoi offerings. Alfred's interest in the art of the camera, today developed to the point of high personal competence as a photographer, was reflecting itself in handsome collections of the work of Alvin Langdon Coburn, E. O. Hoppé, and others. *The American Mercury*, whose contribution to our national life some Ph.D. candidate has still to evaluate, was a roaring and at times strident success.

Finally during this decade of apprenticeship the Borzoi revolution in paper, printing, binding, jackets, and ornament hit the book world. Nineteen twenty-six marked the inauguration of the "Note on the Type in Which This Book Is Set." Then considered eccentric or affected, it has since become so much a natural element of the Knopf style that no other publisher has dared imitate it. From the firm's outset Alfred had known what he wanted to do with the externals of books, then drab, tasteless, and parochial. His 1917 fall catalogue boldly announced, "I do no one an injustice when I say that American books are *not* beautiful." He proceeded to make them beautiful. "We haven't much money to spend here," he informed one author, "but we'll take any amount of pains with a book." He did, using stained tops, spine labels, colored endpapers, batik bindings, imported Japanese paper bindings, geometrical ornament (the work of Claude Bragdon), imported papers, and—most important—not resting until he had achieved to his own satisfaction some harmony between text and design. He sought out and gave new opportunities to fine craftsmen, some of them fine artists: Frederic W. Goudy, Bruce Rogers, W. A. Dwiggins, George Salter, Rudolph Ruzicka, Warren Chappell, Paul Rand, Herbert Bayer, and many others. The Knopf revolution was fairly summed up by George Doran: "[He] not only made beautiful books but told the public they were beautiful books and thereby stimulated the public to require a more graceful format."

Though new ones were to be added, the major lines of development were now drawn. The next decade (1926–36) witnessed a deepening of the Knopf interest in scholarship: Charles Diehl, G. G. Coulton, James Westfall Thompson were added to the list; and one enduring classic in its field was published, W. J. Cash's *The Mind of the South*.

Out of the Knopfs' melomania flowed books by Ernest Newman, J. W. N. Sullivan, Henry Cowell, Francis Toye (a classic biography of Verdi), Alfred Einstein, as well as precious memorabilia by great composers such as Berlioz and Rimsky-Korsakov. Mr. Knopf's interest in cellar and table (which in half a century has had only a barely discernible rounding effect on his waistline) reflected itself in gastronomic and oenological literature by G. B. Stern, P. Morton Shand, Charles Walter Berry, André Simon, Paul Reboux, Philip Wagner, and Julian Street.

Fresh names appeared that have lasted to our time and in some cases gain constantly in stature, such as Isaac Babel. With Dashiell Hammett a new school of detective fiction was founded; and E. C. Bentley's *Trent's Last Case*, snatched from limbo, gave us one of the few absolute classics in this fascinating field. Logan Clendening's *The Human Body* (Mr. Knopf, perhaps stimulated by Mencken, has always had a special interest in medical and biological literature) proved a smashing popular success, followed by the almost equally successful *The Human Mind* by Karl Menninger.

At least three towering monuments of the European intellect and imagination belong to this period: in 1927 Sigrid Undset's *Kristin Lavransdatter* trilogy was published complete; in that same year Thomas Mann's *The Magic Mountain* reached an American audience; and in 1926 and 1928 the two volumes of Spengler's still-impressive dark vision of history, *The Decline of the West*, aroused violent and fruitful controversy.

On the other hand, the Knopfs, like other publishers, also enjoyed their triumphs of the *faux bon*, among which I would number *Sorrell and Son* by Warwick Deeping, Charles Morgan's *The Fountain*, and the rhapsodies of Kahlil Gibran, who has probably brought more money into the Borzoi till than any other single author. Mildly baffled by this latter circumstance, Mr. Knopf once remarked, "I haven't met five people who ever read Gibran." One doubts that he has met two who have ever read another of his great fortuitous *succès de tripes*, *This Is My Beloved* by Walter Benton.

Nineteen thirty-seven was signalized by the publication of *The Trial* by Franz Kafka, whom many rank today with Joyce, Mann, and D. H. Lawrence. Near the terminal point of the decade 1937–47 we note a work of a different order but of far more immediate impact—John Hersey's *Hiroshima* (1946). Between these chronological parentheses appear such figures as A. E. Housman (*Last Poems*), the considerably undervalued *Men of Good Will* series by Jules Romains, the publication of Camus and Sartre, the successful launching of a new spy-thriller luminary, Eric Ambler, and the reissue in classic dress of a number of seminal timeless works, of which the Phillips Bradley *Democracy in America* by Alexis de Tocqueville is an outstanding example. The roll of fine books on music lengthened, with Bruno Walter and Joseph Szigeti contributing valuable memoirs.

The acquisition of the great Brazilian sociologist Gilberto Freyre resulted from Blanche Knopf's trip to South America in 1942, the first of several such rewarding expeditions. Veteran Knopf writers continued to increase their reputations: Clarence Day, Robert Nathan, H. L. Mencken, Elizabeth Bowen, Arthur Waley, Wallace Stevens. A new Borzoi interest

—park and land conservation—began to reflect itself in a series of little-remarked but valuable works. In general, despite the dislocation caused by World War II, it was a good decade of publishing.

The most recent phase, that of the last fifteen years or so, shows no diminution of energy, with perhaps a marked increase in "solid" books of enduring value, particularly in the area of American and Latin American history. These years have also been rich in shrewdly chosen excavations of half-buried intellectual landmarks such as Brooks Adams's *The Law of Civilization and Decay*, Walter Bagehot's *Physics and Politics*, Frederick Law Olmsted's *The Cotton Kingdom*, and Ford Madox Ford's tetralogy *Parade's End*. Many publishers take seriously their duty not only to supply the new but to transmit by timely revivals the complex literary heritage of the past. In this endeavor the Knopfs have always been in the vanguard. The small but important world of genuinely serious readers owes them a debt of gratitude.

During the last two decades the house has developed certain additional interests. There has been an energetic exploitation of Americana, signalized by the publication of a series of classic eighteenth- and nineteenth-century memoirs and travel diaries. Our neighbor to the north has not been neglected, as witness not only many historical and expository volumes but the welcome given to new imaginative writers such as Margaret Laurence (three of whose books were published on the same day, an unusual gesture in publishing). The field of law and jurisprudence has been cultivated, evidenced by volumes from the pens of Learned Hand, Robert H. Jackson, Curtis Bok, and Hugo L. Black. Another special interest has been the theory of history, an area enriched by the searching reflections of Louis Gottschalk, Edward Hallett Carr, Marc Bloch, and Page Smith. In poetry the names of Wallace Stevens and T. S. Eliot have been followed by others less illustrious but of high achievement nonetheless: Theodore Roethke, Randall Jarrell, W. S. Merwin, John Updike, William Meredith, and W. D. Snodgrass. Japanese literature is represented by what is now a rather long list of novelists and tale-tellers, including Kobo Abé, Yukio Mishima, Jiro Osaragi, and Junichiro Tanizaki, the last-named regarded by able judges as a probable future Nobel laureate.

To the first-rate general publisher the old Terentian tag should apply: *humani nil a me alienum puto*. To be catholic in one's interests might seem to entail a certain blandness of mind. But in the case of a fine publisher it is the true base of his creativity. Specialist publishers have their value, of course, but it is on the broad general stream of the whole human tradition that the great generalist publisher launches the varied navy of his volumes. What is remarkable about the Knopfs is not that they publish books of many kinds, or even good books of many kinds. Here they can claim no more credit than is due several of their colleagues. What is remarkable is that Alfred, now seventy-three, and Blanche, whose years suffice to enhance her authority without reducing her energy, have continued to pioneer new fields, welcome new names, and instruct themselves in new disciplines, though it would have been easy enough to recline on the soft pillow of their back list and their faithful house authors. A book publisher who keeps a sharp watch not only on the growth of his business but on the growth of his mind becomes, without ceasing to be a publisher, something of higher value to his fellow citizens. He assumes the functions of a kind of non-systematic yet effective educator, a teacher without classroom or curriculum.

3: Point Score

WHEN GENERAL MOTORS issues an annual statement showing a greater net profit than any other American company, it deserves to be called Number One, for the making of money is the avowed, proper, and sole reason for its existence. Book publishers cannot be so graded. The largest is not the "best," the smallest not the "worst." Indeed there is no reliable yardstick. Distinction, taste, intelligence are not, no matter what certain psychologists tell us, accurately measurable.

Nonetheless there are some pointer readings in the world of book publishing. Their interpretation varies but only within fairly definite limits.

Thus it can hardly be entirely meaningless that Alfred A. Knopf, Inc., has published more Nobel Prize winners than any of its competitors. Here is the scoreboard to date:

1916	Verner von Heidenstam
1920	Knut Hamsun
1924	Ladislas Reymont
1928	Sigrid Undset
1929	Thomas Mann
1933	Ivan Bunin
1939	F. E. Sillanpää
1944	Johannes V. Jensen
1947	André Gide
1955	Halldór Laxness
1957	Albert Camus
1964	Jean-Paul Sartre (declined)

Some of these names have faded sadly: von Heidenstam,[4] Reymont, Sillanpää.[5] Some are not as widely read as they were in their heyday: Hamsun, Bunin, Jensen. But Undset, Mann, Gide, Camus, Sartre[6] remain

---

[4] Knopf published only one book by von Heidenstam, *The Tree of the Folkungs*, in 1925.

[5] And only one book by Sillanpää, *Meek Heritage*, in 1938.

[6] Some of Sartre's books have been published here under other imprints.

titanic names. To them we might add a few more to which the Knopfs might be said to have a semi- or demi-semi-claim: T. S. Eliot (winner in 1948), whose first volume, *Prufrock and Other Observations*, was published by Harriet Weaver in London in 1917 but whose reputation here really took its start from the issuance by Knopf of *Poems* (1920) and *The Sacred Wood* (1921); Ivo Andrić (winner in 1961), now a Knopf author; and even the 1963 laureate, George Seferis, who has appeared over another imprint but who two years before his victory had been included in a Knopf publication, *Six Poets of Modern Greece*, the poets chosen and translated, with introductory essays, by Edmund Keeley and Philip Sherrard.

The Pulitzer Prize record, not quite as overwhelming, is nonetheless highly distinguished.

Fiction:
- 1923 Willa Cather, *One of Ours*
- 1945 John Hersey, *A Bell for Adano*
- 1951 Conrad Richter, *The Town*
- 1965 Shirley Ann Grau, *The Keepers of the House*

DRAMA:
- 1932 George S. Kaufman, Morrie Ryskind, and Ira Gershwin, *Of Thee I Sing*

HISTORY:
- 1956 Richard Hofstadter, *The Age of Reform*
- 1962 Lawrence H. Gipson, *The Triumphant Empire: Thunder-Clouds Gather in the West*

BIOGRAPHY:
- 1927 Emory Holloway, *Whitman: An Interpretation in Narrative*
- 1944 Carleton Mabee, *The American Leonardo: The Life of Samuel F. B. Morse*
- 1945 Russel Blaine Nye, *George Bancroft: Brahmin Rebel*
- 1946 Linnie Marsh Wolfe, *Son of the Wilderness: A Life of John Muir*
- 1950 Samuel Flagg Bemis, *John Quincy Adams and the Foundations of American Foreign Policy*
- 1961 David Donald, *Charles Sumner and the Coming of the Civil War*

POETRY:
- 1927 Leonora Speyer, *Fiddler's Farewell*
- 1934 Robert Hillyer, *Collected Verse*
- 1955 Wallace Stevens, *Collected Poems*
- 1960 W. D. Snodgrass, *Heart's Needle*

GENERAL NON-FICTION:
- 1964 Richard Hofstadter, *Anti-intellectualism in American Life*

In 1954 Theodore Roethke received the prize for poetry; he had first been published by Knopf.

In the more recently established National Book Awards, Knopf and Random House (with which company Alfred A. Knopf, Inc., was merged in 1960) have been the leading winners, each having published six award-getters. The list of Knopf authors and titles:

> 1951   Poetry: Wallace Stevens, *The Auroras of Autumn*
> 1955   Poetry: Wallace Stevens, *Collected Poems*
> 1961   Fiction: Conrad Richter, *The Waters of Kronos*
> 1962   Fiction: Walker Percy, *The Moviegoer*
> 1964   Fiction: John Updike, *The Centaur*
> 1964   Poetry: John Crowe Ransom, *Selected Poems*

Into this honorable crown of laurels a few other leaves might be woven, such as the 1949 Woodrow Wilson Foundation Award, given to V. O. Key, Jr., for the now standard *Southern Politics in State and Nation*.

Such measuring rods are gross, of course, and not too much should be made of them. To students of the business a more interesting one is Firsts. Here a word of caution: even the best publishers cannot truly weigh the future of a young author; most such extrapolations are merely whimsical. Furthermore, writers who later on fulfill their promise often swim quite by accident into a publisher's net. There are many well-known stories of publishers who had not the remotest idea that they had snaffled a valuable property until the reviewers, the public, and the sales chart told them so. However, the record of Borzoi Firsts is too impressive to be a matter of chance.

Here is a partial and merely representative list of writers (I omit authors of works of scholarship) introduced to our country by the Knopfs or in a few cases established by them here following relatively unnoticed publication under other imprints.

AMERICAN

Clarence Day, with *This Simian World*, 1920

Wallace Stevens, with *Harmonium*, 1923

Elinor Wylie, with her first important novel to attract a considerable audience, *The Orphan Angel*, 1926

Thomas Beer, with *The Fair Rewards*, 1922

Joseph Hergesheimer

Ezra Pound[7]

---

[7] The bibliography of Ezra Pound, now generally considered one of the master literary influences of our century, is as tangled as much of his verse. In Noel Stack's "Select Bibliography," which appears in his *Poet in Exile* (Barnes and Noble, 1964), the first American appearance of Pound in book form is credited to Boni and Liveright with *Poems 1918–1921*. This came out in 1921. But Knopf had published *Lustra of Ezra Pound, with Earlier Poems* in 1917; Pound's (and Ernest Fenollosa's) *"Noh"*

H. L. Mencken

George Jean Nathan

Carl Van Vechten

Max Eastman, with his early books *Journalism Versus Art* and *Colors of Life*

Ed Howe

Conrad Aiken, as far back as 1919 with a book of essays, *Scepticisms: Notes on Contemporary Poetry*

T. S. Eliot, considered as an American; *Poems*, 1920, seems to be his first important appearance in book form.

Willa Cather. Knopf was not her first publisher (her book of stories *The Troll Garden* goes back to 1905 and the well-received *My Ántonia* to 1918), but he may fairly be said to have helped her to the large and faithful Cather reading public with *Youth and the Bright Medusa*, 1920, and *One of Ours*, 1922.

Edmund Wilson, with *The Undertaker's Garland*, co-authored by John Peale Bishop

Walter F. White. White's first novel, *The Fire in the Flint*, 1924, no longer remembered, is nonetheless worth noting as one of the first significant American works of imagination by a Negro. In this field, now so richly cultivated, Knopf pioneered.

Julia Peterkin, with *Green Thursday*, 1924

Dashiell Hammett, with *Red Harvest*, 1929

Conrad Richter, with *The Sea of Grass*, 1937

Raymond Chandler, with *The Big Sleep*, 1939

William Shirer, with *Berlin Diary*, 1941

John Hersey, who was first established as an important writer with *A Bell for Adano*, 1944

Theodore Roethke, with *Open House*, 1941

James Baldwin, with his first novel, *Go Tell It on the Mountain*, 1953

Shirley Ann Grau, with *The Black Prince and Other Stories*, 1955

John Updike, with *The Poorhouse Fair* (1959); his book of verse *The Carpentered Hen* had been published by Harper's the previous year.

William Humphrey, with *Home from the Hill*, 1958

ENGLISH

W. H. Hudson, with the reissue of *Green Mansions*

Wyndham Lewis, with his first novel, *Tarr*, 1918

---

or Accomplishment: A Study of the Classical Stage of Japan in 1917; and *Pavannes and Divisions* in 1918. These may be said to have first brought American notice to Pound as a writer of books, unless primacy is accorded his book of essays *The Spirit of Romance* (1910) or his first version of *The Sonnets and Ballate of Guido Cavalcanti*, which appeared in Boston in 1912. The plain fact is that England (Pound was living in London at the time) discovered our man before we did. But Mr. Knopf was not far behind.

Dorothy Richardson, pioneer, with her *Pilgrimage* series, of the stream-of-consciousness school

Robert Graves, with *Fairies and Fusiliers*, 1918

Walter de la Mare, whose genius as a prose writer was first established here with his masterpiece, *Memoirs of a Midget*, 1921

E. M. Forster, one of the major English novelists of the century, whose first four novels (but not his great popular success, *A Passage to India*) appeared under the Borzoi imprint—*Where Angels Fear to Tread* in 1920[8]

H. M. Tomlinson, with *Old Junk*, 1920

Osbert Sitwell, with *Argonaut and Juggernaut*, 1920

Sacheverell Sitwell, with *Southern Baroque Art*, 1924

Edith Sitwell, with *The Sleeping Beauty*, 1924

Katherine Mansfield, with *Bliss and Other Stories*, 1921

A. E. Coppard, with *Adam and Eve and Pinch Me*, 1922

Arthur Machen, with *The House of Souls*, 1922

David Garnett, with *Lady into Fox*, 1923

T. F. Powys, an odd genius in need of revival, with *The Left Leg*, 1923

John Wain, with *Born in Captivity*, 1954

Alan Sillitoe, with *Saturday Night and Sunday Morning*, 1959

Brendan Behan, with *Borstal Boy*, 1959

EUROPEAN

Knut Hamsun, with *Hunger*, 1920

Sigrid Undset, with *Jenny*, 1921

Thomas Mann, with *Royal Highness*, 1916

André Gide, with *Strait Is the Gate*, 1924

Isaac Babel, with *Red Cavalry*, 1929

Franz Kafka, with *The Castle*, 1930[9]

Ivan Bunin, with *The Gentleman from San Francisco and Other Stories*, 1923

Italo Svevo, with *The Confessions of Zeno*, 1930, a novel that has continued to exert a powerful influence

B. Traven, with *The Death Ship*, 1934

Pío Baroja, with *The City of the Discreet*, 1917

Albert Camus, with *The Stranger*, 1946

Jean-Paul Sartre, with *The Age of Reason*, 1947

Simone de Beauvoir, with *The Blood of Others*, 1948

---

[8] The Forster novels were a Knopf reissue. They had earlier been published by Putnam and had been allowed to go out of print.

[9] Possibly the most forgettable of all forms of writing is the publisher's jacket blurb. But the sentence on the wrapper of *The Castle* should somehow be preserved as one of the most accurate forecasts ever made by a publisher: "*The Castle* is indubitably a major work of art and one which is destined to take its place alongside *Faust*, *Pilgrim's Progress*, and other great allegories of literature."

Prizes and Firsts supply two rough-and-ready measuring rods for estimating a publisher's dimensions. A third might be the extent of his world-mindedness. That the world of literature and scholarship strives toward the condition of unity is a phenomenon to which writers and scholars are sensitive, but to which most book publishers, their eyes fixed on narrower horizons, are not. From the outset Alfred Knopf has assumed an ecumenical point of view and his readers over half a century have been the gainers.

We have already noted the names of perhaps forty writers of non-Anglo-Saxon provenience whose introduction to Americans was arranged by Alfred and Blanche Knopf. But there are literally hundreds of others, reflecting a staggering variety of races and countries. Not all appeared first on the Borzoi list; many later on were sponsored by other houses; and many are represented by only one or two books. But to a generation like our own, which is beginning unconsciously to accept as a psychological datum the unity of culture, it might be interesting to reflect on what part during half a century an alert publishing house may play in furthering that unity. Here then are more names, some famous, some half forgotten, some lost in oblivion, some still to justify their publisher's faith. But all in varying degrees have contributed to the enlargement of the American reader's horizon—and all at one time or another were published by Alfred A. Knopf, Inc. They represent perhaps a tenth of a possible maximum listing.

FRANCE

Jean Giraudoux

Henri de Montherlant

Joseph Kessel

Philippe Soupault

Paul Valéry

Jean Giono

Roger Vailland

Maurice Croiset

Jacques de Morgan

Charles Seignobos

Darius Milhaud

Jacques Ellul

Loys Masson

Pierre Drieu La Rochelle

GERMANY, AUSTRIA, SWITZERLAND

Ludwig Thoma

Arthur Schnitzler

Peter Faecke

Ernst Toller

Elias Canetti

Carl Sternheim

Max Brod

Hans Carossa

Heinrich Mann

Erich Kästner

Friedrich Duerrenmatt

Heimito von Doderer

Ludwig Dehio

Egon Friedell

René Fülöp-Miller

C. W. Ceram

Ingeborg Bachmann

SCANDINAVIA AND ICELAND

Harry Martinson
Dag Hammarskjöld
Olav Duun
Godmundur Kamban
Gunnar Gunnarsson

J. Anker Larsen
Frans G. Bengtsson
Edwin Björkman
Svend Fleuron
Laurids Bruun

SPAIN AND PORTUGAL

Eça de Queiroz
Alves Redol
P. A. de Alarcón
Vicente Blasco-Ibáñez
Azorín

Michel del Castillo
José María Gironella
Miguel de Unamuno
Torcuato Luca de Tena
Luís de Sttau Monteiro

ITALY

Carlo Goldoni
Carlo Levi
Benedetto Croce
Elsa Morante

Franco Venturi
Arturo Castiglioni
Libero Bigiaretti

EGYPT

Waguih Ghali

CZECHOSLOVAKIA

Josef Bor

Josef Toman

POLAND

Stanislaw Przybyszewski
Jerzy Andrzejewski

Leopold Tyrmand

GREECE

Vassilis Vassilikos

HUNGARY

Magda Szabo   Emery Kelen

KOREA

Kim Yong Ik
  (His *The Diving Gourd*, 1963, was the first novel by a Korean to
    be published in the United States.)

LATIN AMERICA

Jorge Amado   Miguel Covarrubias
Germán Arciniegas   Alejo Carpentier
Eduardo Mallea   José Donoso
Graciliano Ramos   Arturo Uslar Pietri
Martín Luís Guzmán   João Guimarães Rosa
Fernando Ortiz

JAPAN

Masuo Kato   Shohei Ooka
Yasunari Kawabata   Eiji Yoshikawa

YIDDISH

Sholom Aleichem   I. B. Singer
I. J. Singer

FINLAND

Aino Kallas

RUSSIA

Alexei Tolstoy   Mikhail Sholokhov
Valeriy Tarsis   Leonid Andreyev
Alexander Herzen   V. M. Garshin
Ilya Ehrenburg   Nikolai Gogol

P. A. Kropotkin
Mark Aldanov
Boris Pilniak
Alexei Remizov
P. D. Ouspensky

Ossip Dymov
Alexander Kornilov
Maxim Gorky
M. Y. Lermontov

4: Profile of the Founder

I BELIEVE there exists a certain misconception of Alfred Knopf. It is interesting if only for the light it throws on what Mencken and Nathan delighted to call The American Credo.

In most of Western Europe (though sparsely in Russia and Germany) there has long flourished a well-recognized human type. No single word or phrase describes him ("man of the world" is too trivial) but he may be thus qualified: He is a gentleman of some substance, though not flagrantly rich. Having from his early years taken it for granted, he sees no reason either to assert or to minimize his superiority to the common run. He also takes for granted that life, whatever its meaning (he is rarely of metaphysical temper), is better enjoyed than suffered. Among the pleasures the long experience of mankind has sifted out as preferable he accords high rank to those afforded by the lively exercise of the mind; by the proper care and tending of the body and even its habiliments and disguises;[1] by converse with the intelligent and the well-bred rather than the boring and the lumpish; by such gifts of art as music and literature; by such gifts of art plus nature as the best food, wine, cigars, and flowers; by the cultivation without regard to the world's opinion of any private idiosyncrasies that cause no pain to others; and by the use of money, again without regard to the world's opinion, to secure these pleasures while one is still in a condition to savor them.

To any common-sense view of human nature such a person does not seem eccentric or extraordinary. In any civilized, moderately complex society, except the totalitarian, he is naturally bound to emerge in moderate numbers and calls for no special comment.

It is therefore curious that when this quite normal type appears in our own country he often excites disproportionate reactions of envy, disapproval, ridicule, or more usually merely undue curiosity. He may be called, according to the mental and moral stance of the caller, a snob, a reactionary, a dandy, a sensualist, or an egoist. Generally, though he may have other and even graver failings, he is none of these, but simply a man who elects good food over bad, good talk over bad, the best of

[1] On this point Mr. Knopf may be perforce relaxing. "Tailoring isn't what it used to be," he remarked not long ago. One is reminded of the venerable Boston gentlewoman who maintained the same with respect to thunderstorms.

the past over the worst of the present. Presumably it is our compound heritage of puritanism and egalitarianism that leads us to suspect men who, equally uninterested in the frantic pursuit or the frantic avoidance of pleasure, calmly recognize and intelligently exploit the goods of this life.

Considering the fact that book publishers are not commonly considered hot copy, Mr. Knopf has been rather extensively written about. In London or Paris he would pass without comment as a good sample of the human type I have described. Here, however, journalists, after paying due respect to his high professional competence, prefer to enlarge upon him as a kind of picturesque phenomenon or lordly eccentric, carrying overtones of the Count d'Orsay, Lucullus, Max Beerbohm, J. P. Morgan, Nero, and the Rothschilds. This sort of thing makes for diverting reading but I think it a little obscures the man or at any rate the man who interests me and should interest the American reading public.

For example, in a series of articles, amusing and informative, that once appeared in *The New Yorker* Geoffrey Hellman referred to Mr. Knopf's "Olympian attitude" toward his authors. Many of these I am acquainted with and I should guess that the complaint is made largely by the coarser-grained or those suffering from some feeling of inferiority. I doubt that John Hersey ever thinks of his publisher as Olympian, and I know that Willa Cather and Henry Mencken did not.

The fact is that we have rather a simplified notion of good manners, tending to equate them with mere amiability. "He's a nice fellow," we say approvingly, unaware that we have said almost nothing. Amiability is only *one* manner, not all of them, nor the only one, nor the best one. It is possible to be well-mannered and yet short with fools as I should conceive Mr. Knopf has often been. (So was, come to think of it, the Olympian Zeus.) Good manners do not prove themselves in a refusal to speak one's mind or to state one's preferences. Indeed they are quite compatible with a certain time-saving brusquerie, demeanor which to the confirmed egalitarian might smack of snobbery or arrogance. Put it thus: Mr. Knopf would have felt comfortable as a guest of the great Whig houses of the early nineteenth century. By the same token he may not be entirely comfortable at his present business address, for Madison Avenue, whose main preoccupation is selling something to someone, is made uneasy by "Olympians," that is, by any attitude not devoted to reducing social friction.

In our society one runs a certain risk if, as happens to be Mr. Knopf's case, one has the port of a *grand seigneur*. Blanche's lifelong friend and Knopf author, the novelist Robert Nathan, once wrote: "Alfred is terrifically majestic. He and Blanche are like Jupiter and Juno. He is the ultimate, she the penultimate, but in her own right just as ultimate." The tone of course is one of affectionate irony, but I believe all Mr. Nathan can really mean is that Mr. Knopf (I prefer not to enter the Juno con-

troversy) has that old-fashioned quality which is not only rare in our
country but rather unpopular. I mean presence. Presence is hard to define. It seems to be linked with the ability to impose oneself without
aggression, indeed without effort, speech, or action. It is not necessarily
associated with the highest achievement (I cannot think of Shakespeare
as having presence and Einstein had little) but it does seem related to
a taken-for-granted self-confidence that has emerged from a long series
of unconscious comparisons with others. Presence is eccentrically distributed. Most of our leading political and industrial figures, to judge from
their television performances, lack it and are glad to lack it, fearing
it might estrange them from their fellow citizens. Because their presence is internalized few writers and artists display it, though Robert
Frost and T. S. Eliot did. John Kennedy had it, Mr. Eisenhower does
not have even a speck of it, nor does President Johnson. De Gaulle has
it, Khrushchev lacked it. Robert Hutchins has it supremely. And
Alfred Knopf has it. It sometimes upsets people.

In his early days it was the seigneurial air that transfixed the be-
holder. (Today he is inexorably taking on the look of a benevolent
uncle.) "My first impression of him remains clear; he resembled a prince
from a Persian miniature," wrote Carl Van Vechten of the young Knopf.
A similar though fancier recollection is preserved in Llewelyn Powys's
Verdict of Bridlegoose (1926): "It was now that my eye for the first
time lit on an individual who seemed curiously to resemble Mr. Knopf
as I remembered him, a dark, handsome man, who had the discreet,
downcast eye and glossy look of an important Oriental official, who, after having witnessed the execution of Haman the son of Hammedatha,
the Agagite, on a gallows fifty cubits high, was, in marabou-feathered
sandals, hastening to present the King and Esther with a bouquet of
Sharon roses." Clarence Day also recorded an Oriental impression:
"His voice rose an octave and we were in the Levant"; whereas to Max
Eastman, himself at the time no mean example of presence, he looked
"more like a Caribbean pirate than a connoisseur of literary art."

These exotic images were not entirely off base. Even today Mr.
Knopf is obviously a man painstakingly designed by the Deity to wear a
guardsman's mustache—indeed his erotic effect on Ouida, had they
ever met, would have been shattering. But beneath the Sassanid mag-
nifico lives an upper bourgeois backed by a *gemütlich* German-Jewish-
American tradition. And beneath the bourgeois lies someone more interesting than either: The man of whom B. W. Huebsch, one of the
finest though not most successful of American publishers, said: "Alfred
Knopf is, first and foremost, an artist." The man of whom Carl Van
Vechten, who, though a photographer, saw behind the picturesque,
said: "I have never known him to desert a friend." The man of whom
Willa Cather said: "He has of course published books he thought very
second-rate, and he has successfully done business with people who
were not congenial to him. But in his own mind he kept the two sets

BLANCHE W. KNOPF

photograph by Blackstone-Shelburne, New York

ALFRED A. KNOPF

copyright Arnold Newman, courtesy of Fortune *magazine*

of values apart, clear and distinct." The man of whom Freeman Tilden[2] remarked: "A thing you have to say of Knopf is that he is integral. He doesn't try to be several other people, and if he doesn't feel in the mood he doesn't invent emotions." Finally the man of whom a friend, most perceptive of all, said: "Alfred is fundamentally extremely humble about himself." As many proud men are.[3]

These plaudits are not recited that I may wallow in what Swinburne called "the noble pleasure of praising"; nor in order to weave a pretty garland of sentiments deemed proper when a man is celebrating the semi-centennial of his career. To my limited knowledge Mr. Knopf has in him no tincture of the saint, though his friends these days are occasionally appalled by unmistakable signs of mellowing. Mr. Knopf can be testy, opinionated, and wrong-headed as can be—in other words, a representative human being. But he is also what Mencken called him in 1940, "the perfect publisher," if we allow some latitude to the adjective. And that is a very fine thing to be, a thing beyond the capacity of a merely shrewd man, a merely tough man, a merely energetic man. Huebsch once wrote: "His catalogue is not a mask, it is his face." That is it.

And so, reading that he enjoys scholarship "like an epicure" and "relishes" history like "rare wines," I must enter a mild demurrer. Such judgments are witty but smack of the parish pump. It is true that, except perhaps in the narrow field of printing and book design, Mr. Knopf is no scholar. No publisher can be or should be a scholar, for simon-pure scholarship claims a life of its own, tolerating little competition. But his interest in scholarship, in our history, in our waters and mountains and forests is, as his publications demonstrate, serious, not epicurean. Aware that they are of different orders of being, he distinguishes clearly between Mann and Upmann.[4] In 1949 he became a member and later chairman of the Advisory Board on National Parks, Historic Sites, Buildings and Monuments of the National Park Service. He attended meetings regularly, and not because he was a *Feinschmecker*

[2] Quoted by John Hersey in an interesting account of Mr. Knopf's "love affair" with our National Park System.

[3] It was a proud but not an arrogant man who on October 21, 1948, in a talk delivered before the Grolier Club, in New York City, summed up his professional life in these casual words: "As for ourselves, the job we've done, as I see it, has been to sell reasonably well books by authors some of whom we honestly believe to be among the great ones of our times; to make those books as good-looking as possible; and to prove the fallacy of the remark I heard so often as a young man that so-and-so's book was too good to sell. Usually it wasn't quite good enough."

[4] I might record here an anecdote which has doubtless been told about others but which I first heard as involving Mr. Knopf, and which I would like to believe is part of his biography. One day, traveling across the continent, he entered the smoking car, took a seat next to a gentleman of pleasant appearance and manners, lighted a cigar, and on an impulse offered one to his neighbor. The gentleman accepted, lit up, and after half a dozen reflective puffs remarked: "A magnificent cigar." Mr. Knopf: "It should be; they are specially put up for me by Upmann." Gentleman: "Indeed? May I ask your name?" Knopf: "Alfred Knopf. May I ask yours?" Gentleman: "Upmann."

of buildings and monuments. One of his colleagues said, "To sit with Alfred at our board meetings, one comes to know his size."

He is a member of the New York State Historical Society, the Westchester County Historical Association, the American Historical Association, the Overseers' Visiting Committee of the English Department of Harvard University,[5] and the Council of the Institute of Early American History and Culture, Williamsburg, Virginia. He is also a corresponding member of the Colonial Society of Massachusetts and the Massachusetts Historical Society, and a trustee of the American Scenic and Historic Preservation Society. I doubt that his motivation is the collecting of lodge buttons. On the other hand, there is no question but that via these voluntary associations a clubbable publisher can pick up an occasional manuscript. I also think he likes clubs, as Dr. Johnson did, because they are one of the transmission belts of civilization. But essentially he likes history and admires historians. It is a passion going back to 1909, when he attended a summer-session course under the late Carlton J. H. Hayes. Not long afterward he joined the American Historical Association.

On July 4, 1964, he received a letter from the president of that association, Julian P. Boyd, inviting—or rather ordering—him to attend a dinner in his honor to be given by its members. The terms in which the invitation was couched are remarkable for the insight they give us into the mind of a genuinely serious book publisher. With the gracious permission of Professor Boyd I quote from it:

> In the first place, say some of our most distinguished historians, you have done more for the cause of history than any other publisher. You have encouraged young men and cajoled or browbeaten established men to produce more and better historical writings than they otherwise would have produced. You have held up the highest standards of literary excellence before them and you have shamed them when they failed to observe those standards. You have clothed their writings in distinguished typographical design and you have worried over vindictive or irresponsible criticism as a mother hen worries about her chicks. In the second place, you have shown beyond all doubt that you really like the company of historians. You have endured crowded lobbies, dull papers, and interminable bores over a long period of time. No other publisher has dared to pay such a price or to pay it without complaint in order to be among people whose concern is with the past. Finally, you have crowned these things not once but many times by giving a long succession of sumptuous feasts, with such foods and wines as probably have not been selected with such discrimination since the Star Chamber Revels, and to these elegant affairs you have invited whole platoons of historians.

Mr. Knopf has often been described in print as a connoisseur of cravats, delphiniums, cigars, Chopin, dogs, fine printing, Moselle wine,

---

[5] Previously, for a term of eighteen years, he served on a similar committee of the History Department.

and *haute cuisine*. That is all true. But none of this connoisseurship entitles him to the respect of his fellow citizens. The kind of thing Professor Boyd is talking about does.

5: A Word about This Book

IN 1936 there appeared a now out-of-print anthology, *The Borzoi Reader*, akin to this one. Edited by Carl Van Doren, it marked the first twenty-one years of Alfred A. Knopf, Inc. More than a quarter-century has now passed and with these years have passed not only the distinguished and lovable editor of *The Borzoi Reader* but far too many of the names that shone upon its table of contents. Of the thirty-two writers represented in 1936 there survive as of this writing only seven: David Garnett, Morrie Ryskind, Julian Huxley, John Crowe Ransom, E. M. Forster, Witter Bynner, and Arthur Waley.

Of these seven, five reappear in the present volume: Julian Huxley, John Crowe Ransom, E. M. Forster, Witter Bynner, and Arthur Waley. Of the remaining twenty-five names fifteen are here again represented though in almost all cases by different examples of their work: Willa Cather, Thomas Mann, Elinor Wylie, Joseph Hergesheimer, Clarence Day, W. H. Hudson, Ernest Newman, H. L. Mencken, Wallace Stevens, Max Beerbohm, D. H. Lawrence, Katherine Mansfield, Walter de la Mare, A. E. Coppard, and Joseph Conrad.

The passage of twenty-nine years since the appearance of *The Borzoi Reader* has done nothing to tarnish these names and in most cases has brought them additional luster. One concludes that Alfred and Blanche Knopf chose and published well. It is a good publisher's function to discover for us the permanent as well as the new.

Fifty Years is not a house book. The choices are the editor's. His taste alone, however it may be judged, determined them. It would be foolish to say that these half-million words represent the "best" of the Knopf output, whose totality, I suppose, comprises about 5,000 separate publications. I must, however, state that I did actually go through, often very superficially, every one of these 5,000 volumes in an honest if somewhat ridiculous attempt not to overlook any writer who had ever appeared over the Borzoi imprint. In the end I had to settle for what I most admired (as is bound to be the case, this was often what I had long been familiar with) and for what I felt would also elicit the admiration of a generation younger than mine. When I say "would" I suppose I mean "should."

At the same time, while this is a personal selection, the nature of things required that there be some representation of most of the commonly accepted divisions of literature. Thus the reader will find complete novels and novellas (seven in all); short stories, one of them, by Alan Sillitoe, of almost novella length; a full-length play; examples of writing in the fields of the oration, the literary essay, the reflective essay, the informal memoir, the philosophic essay, reportage, history, the scientific essay, the letter, autobiography, music criticism, and gastronomy; and finally verse, whether light or serious.

I have of course not in the least tried to provide "something for all tastes." Yet examining the table of contents I am struck by the accidental variety there discoverable. Here are works by Frenchmen, Americans, Germans, Englishmen, a Russian, an Irishman, a New Zealander, a Spaniard, and a Chinese; by a novelist now eighty-six and a novelist now thirty-three; by poets as far apart in vision and technique as A. E. Housman and Wallace Stevens; by charmers like Clarence Day and Jeremiahs like Oswald Spengler. While no attempt has been made to tip the scales in favor of the famous, it does happen that six Nobel Prize winners are represented: Bunin, Camus, Gide, Mann, Sartre (declined), Eliot. Of those who should have received Nobel Prizes but did not three are represented: E. M. Forster, D. H. Lawrence, Joseph Conrad. Most of the book consists of what is normally known as high literature, some of it very high indeed. But there is also some businesslike journalism, some excellent but far from literarily distinguished history, and one example, by Raymond Chandler, of superb work in a pop genre. I have tried to avoid anything which, however interesting for other reasons, distills the musty air of the dated. I believe nothing in this volume dates, though much is set in what is known as the past.

Had more space been available I should have liked to include representative work by a few additional authors: Isaac Babel, George Jean Nathan, V. S. Pritchett, T. F. Powys, Paul Valéry, Dashiell Hammett, Conrad Richter, Robert Nathan, Shirley Ann Grau, Friedrich Duerrenmatt, and especially Kafka's The Castle. But anthological considerations are complex and demanding, and this is the best collection circumstances permitted me to assemble. Rough, inadequate, and of course limited in its dimensions, this book nonetheless can stand as a suggestion of what one publishing house over the wide span of five decades has made available to Americans, and so enriched the culture of which we are a part. I do not think that contribution insignificant.

Preceding each of the volume's five sections the reader will find a brief commentary on its contents, occasionally including a few biographical details. These informal notes may be read or they may be ignored. To speak truth, they were written for my own pleasure. The writers they discuss are quite capable of standing on their own feet, if they are poets, or paragraphs if they are prose writers.

To the staff of Alfred A. Knopf, Inc., and especially to William A. Koshland I record my thanks for much efficient and invaluable assistance.

CLIFTON FADIMAN

Fifty Years

BORZOI
BOOKS
1915
1965

Novels and Novellas

THE FOLLOWING SEVEN PIECES of extended narrative have at least two elements in common. Each, even including Raymond Chandler's thriller, as well as being a fair sample of its author's lifework, is in its own way a masterpiece.

And each, again in its own way, sounds the characteristic note of loss and estrangement we have come to associate with our era. It is noteworthy that the words "stranger," "lost," "farewell," and "death" should occur in four of the seven titles. The last words of *A Lost Lady* express sorrowful affection for a dead friend who had marred her own life. The last words of *The Stranger* are "howls of execration." Thus this complex note is sweetly Virgilian in Willa Cather, modulating in depth until in Albert Camus it suggests that horror which comes of indifference to life.

The gamut of style runs from the brutal side-of-the-mouth vernacular of *Farewell, My Lovely* to the baroque prose, rich in musical returns and variations, of *Death in Venice*. All but *Farewell, My Lovely* turn on a contemplation of the gravest and most central moral issues. We stand here in the presence of truly reflective though not necessarily serene minds.

Ivan Bunin (1870–1953), the first Russian to win the Nobel Prize for Literature, is probably not much read in his native land. Born of landowning nobility, he began his career in 1891 with a book of poems of Parnassian inspiration, following it with a prose volume and many remarkable translations of English literature. In 1903 he was awarded the Pushkin Prize. Fame came to him in 1910 with the publication of the book translated into English in 1923 as *The Village*. World-wide acclaim greeted *The Gentleman from San Francisco*, published in America in that same year. From 1918 to his death he lived a deracinated but productive life in Paris. I think it fair to say that his finest work was completed before his self-imposed exile.

Spiritually anchored in the nineteenth century, Bunin wrote memoirs, criticism, stories, and verse hardly influenced by avant-garde movements. Yet in *The Gentleman from San Francisco*, here reprinted, he seems a modernist. For all its Flaubertian cunning, its Pelions and Ossas of sounding phrases, its jewel-crusted texture, it lives for us as certain nineteenth-century masterpieces, conceived in the same vein, such as *Salammbô*, do not. For here is one of the most troubling of the many parables of our time. Its theme is not only as old as Ecclesiastes, it is Ecclesiastes. Yet the symbolic relation between the coffin in which lies the corpse of the man from San Francisco and the resplendent ship within which that coffin is coffined chills us not only as men but especially as mid-century men. For the tonality of our day too is compound. An infinity of glittering possibilities dazzles our eyes. But beneath the dazzle we sense cold death and ruin, the seeming hollowness of effort in a world of unconsolatory values. It is perhaps not entirely meaningless that T. S. Eliot's "The Love Song of J. Alfred Prufrock" appeared in the United States in 1915. That was the year *The Gentleman from San Francisco* appeared in Russia.

On January 4, 1960, in one of those lunatic motor accidents accepted so calmly by us as part of normal human experience, Albert Camus, forty-seven, with Sartre one of the two leading literary voices of his generation, was cut off in his prime. Algerian-born, he studied philosophy; became a journalist, dramatist, novelist, and stage director; worked with the Resistance during World War II; associated with and then broke with Sartre; won fame with the novel here reprinted, as well as with his essay "The Myth of Sisyphus" and the play *Caligula;* and in 1957—after Kipling, the youngest to win it—was awarded the Nobel Prize for Literature.

In our country *The Stranger* is his most widely read work of fiction. I have chosen it partly because its relative brevity rejoices the heart of the anthologist, but more importantly because it displays his mind, or at least an early phase of it, in the clearest of lights. The book has the outward form of a crime story, turning as it does on a killing, a killer, and his punishment. Beneath this thin disguise lies the real book, which might have used as a title Lermontov's famous *A Hero of Our Time*. There is something of Meursault in most of us, certainly in the unhappiest of us. He is an indifferentist, attached, if at all, only to the simplest and most transient of sensory experiences, uncommitted, disengaged, to use the weary slang of our day. The absurdity of man's plight in a seemingly meaningless universe has been dramatized by many mid-century writers. By few has it been presented with such bitter concision as in this short novel. Meursault's act of violence, much as we may instinctively recoil from it, nevertheless cannot be judged by the simplistic techniques of legality or weighed by a rapidly disintegrating conventional morality.

How then shall we judge it, how weigh it? Is there anything at the end Meursault can cling to? We can cling to? This novel strikes like a sword into the human conscience.

Like Henry James's, Willa Cather's life was lived internally; and her books, like his, are laden with those insights that flow from a temperament that is reflective, ruminative, observant, empathic, and sensitive to the nuances of human behavior. Such a temperament links with literary virtues that are currently unpopular.

Willa Cather, born in Virginia in 1876, was removed when still a child to Nebraska, during the period when the frontier spirit was preparing its farewell. As a young woman she worked on a Pittsburgh newspaper, as a teacher in Allegheny, Pennsylvania, then as a member of the staff of *McClure's Magazine* in New York. She was destined, however, to be a novelist, and the last half of her life, though she moved about to many parts of North America, was essentially that of a withdrawn though never escapist artist. Her books, as far as we are concerned, are her life, which ended in 1947. The North American past was the prime mover of her imagination, whether it dealt with her memories of the immigrant settlers of the Middle West (*O Pioneers!, My Ántonia*) or the early missionary days in New Mexico (*Death Comes for the Archbishop*) or eighteenth-century Quebec (*Shadows on the Rock*). She is often accused of idealizing that past, of surrounding it with a dubious aura of beauty and courage. But before casting a final balance we might well ask ourselves whether our own time, in which beauty and courage have become suspect words, is in a position to make a detached judgment on Willa Cather's vision.

Whatever her final ranking, she was a beautiful writer, master of a lucent, unaggressive English style, fitting like a glove the matters that interested her, suited to no others. She wrote subtler books than the one I have chosen—notably *The Professor's House* and *My Mortal Enemy*, which may well repay future symbol-hunters; but *A Lost Lady*, published over forty years ago, has a curious charm—half idyllic, half elegiac —that is the product of her best talents held in quiet, balanced suspension. *A Lost Lady* examines, though that is a cold word, a virtue now almost historical: honor. Honor that the Captain kept, honor that his wife pitifully lost, yet without forfeiting our sympathy and—this is Willa Cather's small miracle—our love. In this narrowly dimensioned drama, so spare, so simple, "the end of an era, the sunset of the pioneer" is given almost musical expression. The provincial, quite unintellectual yet by no means insensitive society she draws in silverpoint is quite, quite dead. But that circumstance lends to her tale an added dimension, for now *A Lost Lady* has become not only the story of a Nebraska Madame Bovary, but a moving historical novel, standing clear of the detail, the furniture that Willa Cather found so displeasing.

I include it in these pages, not only for its manifest virtues but because it may come as a new book to a new generation of readers. They may find that its unstained good taste, its still, slow movement, its almost Mozartian meditative tone convey certain sensations of pleasure that current fiction, whatever its quality, rarely offers.

By a grotesque accident of the alphabet Raymond Chandler follows Willa Cather in this collection. Their books could feasibly enough have exchanged titles. There the kinship stops.

Since his death Raymond Chandler (1888–1959) has become the center of a minor legend, which is often though not always an indication that a writer has some enduring stuff in him not fully recognized during his lifetime. His posthumous collection *Raymond Chandler Speaking* revealed that he had a reflective and incisive mind, rather infrequently met in writers of thrillers. The critical study by Philip Durham, *Down These Mean Streets a Man Must Go*, takes Chandler seriously, but not too seriously; and the brief appreciation by Lawrence Clark Powell prefacing *The Raymond Chandler Omnibus* (Knopf, 1964) makes unnecessary any extended comment by me.

Born in Chicago, educated in Dulwich College, London, a World War I veteran (Canadian Army), a bank clerk in Vancouver and San Francisco, he finally met his *ville fatale* in 1912. It was Los Angeles, out of which he made his four good novels. His first, *The Big Sleep*, was written in three months when he, a prosperous businessman, decided he could write pulp as good as any *The Black Mask* was then publishing. And so the school of hard-boiled fiction, now in a state of phosphorescent decay, birthed one of its two masters, the other being of course Dashiell Hammett, whose all-bone style stands out in contrast to Chandler's image-laden, raw-colored prose.

I do not think Chandler should be judged by conventional literary standards. This is not fiction, in the sense that Tolstoy or Balzac or Hemingway wrote fiction. It belongs to a genre whose kinship is with other kinds of pop art, including the cartoon, the old radio serial, and what is known as science fiction. It is traditionless, close to the violent unconscious of the American primitive, remote from any moral universe. Of its kind *Farewell, My Lovely* is a masterpiece. Its kind is not even remotely represented elsewhere in this book and the reader must bring to it a sensibility that has nothing to do with what we learn in our English classes in school or college. It belongs to a class of writing for which we have no name. Perhaps *belles-lettres laides* might do.

The long life of André Gide (1869–1951) is less interesting for its literary achievements, though they are many, than for its paradigmatic value. It shows us what forms a human career may take when developed as a series of experiments in thought and sensation. I do not mean that Gide played with his life, only that his ideas, dramatized in over eighty published works, were unremittingly provisional. He felt it almost his duty to try to counterpose idea A against a sequent idea B. For example, the reader of the *récit* (for it is hardly a novel) contained in this book will find in *Strait Is the Gate,* an equally masterly tale, a kind of reverse mirror image of *The Immoralist.*

Gide was the scion of a distinguished Protestant family. Its austerity and repressiveness doubtless influenced his strange, sad, but in some ways beautiful marriage with his cousin Madeleine, as well as his later homosexuality. To his sexual inversion far too much importance has been attached, both by himself and by a (then) shocked public. He made many journeys—to North Africa, to French Equatorial Africa, to the Soviet Union—each of them bearing fruit in a series of books of fiction or social criticism. In his later years he functioned as a kind of dean of French letters, never losing touch with the younger generation, which he felt it was his duty to provoke, stimulate, and trouble. The Nobel Prize fell to him in 1947.

He wrote no indubitably great work, unless it be his *Journals,* which are almost on a level with Rousseau's *Confessions. The Counterfeiters* is probably his most ambitious book, a kind of novelistic hall of mirrors, infinitely convoluted and subtle. As an artist he perhaps came nearest to perfection in such *récits* as *The Pastoral Symphony, Strait Is the Gate,* and *The Immoralist* (1902). The last he describes as "a fruit filled with bitter ashes, like those colocynths of the desert that grow in a parched and burning soil." It is a study, clearly in part autobiographical, of a man who slowly shucks off his old self, discovers a new, yet is left joyless and self-questioning. The homosexuality on which it seems to turn is not the central theme. That kind of immoralism which issues from weakness and inadequate self-comprehension perhaps is. Like all his books, or most of them, it consists of a series of questions rather than answers, of probings into the endless recesses of personality. In a lecture Gide gave around the turn of the century he said, "I am reminded of the 'deep sea' of which Nietzsche speaks, of those unexplored regions of man, full of new dangers and surprises for the heroic navigator." The journey into himself here undertaken by Michel-Gide is rich in dangers and surprises, not all of them of a kind to uplift the heart, nonetheless fascinating.

In the year 1999 there is at least a fair chance that Thomas Mann (1875–1955) will be awarded the palm as the century's greatest writer of imaginative prose. It does not seem disproportionate therefore to represent his work in these pages by as many as three examples, two of them his finest novellas and superb illustrations of his elaborate art.

Thomas Mann came of a prosperous and cultivated Lübeck merchant-class family. His bourgeois background and his artistic bent supplied a fruitful background of conflict, out of which has come some of his best work, including *Death in Venice.* In 1901, when he was only twenty-five, appeared the masterly *Buddenbrooks,* in which the opposition between the demands of normal life (*Leben*) are opposed by the claims of the artistic sensibility (*Geist*). *Buddenbrooks* was far surpassed, however, by *The Magic Mountain* (1924), a symbolic vision of a sick Europe which gains in relevance with every passing year. In 1929 Mann, astonishing no one, was awarded the Nobel Prize. His political convictions, originally rather conservative, underwent a decided change with the advent of Hitler. In 1933 he was compelled to leave his beloved native land. In 1939 he set up residence in the United States, becoming a citizen in 1944. After the war, however, Europe again called to him, and his last years were spent in Switzerland.

His life, though conceived on a smaller scale, has a Goethean rondure and harmony. His genius developed without setback, and each vicissitude, even each tragedy that he experienced, somehow reinforced his creative energies. To have surpassed (in depth though not in readability) *The Magic Mountain* with his overwhelming Biblical tetralogy, *Joseph and His Brothers;* to have been capable of creating *Doctor Faustus* when he was over seventy; to have rung a startling change on his central theme of the artist versus society by issuing the (unfinished) *Confessions of Felix Krull* when he was almost eighty: this is Goethean, Titianesque, Hokusaian.

The two novellas here reprinted are now in the absolute sense classic. No matter how often one rereads *Death in Venice* one is lost in astonishment before the almost infernal art with which Mann orchestrates a half dozen great and perennial themes: the seductions of death and art and carnal love; the undying appeal of pagan antiquity; the call of the primitive, of the South, of the jungle in man's heart; the relation between beauty and disease; the contrasting claims of the quotidian and the transcendental; the esthetic experience as an escape from the frustrations of the will. And all this is somehow arranged in a story of tension and suspense, set to a music beautifully surviving translation.

Some of these themes are subtly varied in *Mario and the Magician.* But in this still deeply disturbing tale the political implications dominate. Not merely a political allegory of Italian fascism, it is relevant to all human situations in which the irrational human will is able to impose itself upon man's more decent instincts. Of all Mann's shorter narratives it is the most uncanny, the most powerful, and perhaps the most subtle. It is also the one in which Mann combines to greatest effect his preoccupations with "magic," with distorted sexuality, with the shortcomings of rationalism, and with the perverse forms love may take—for it is Cipolla's hunger for love that is in the end the instrument of his destruction.

Ivan Bunin

THE GENTLEMAN FROM
SAN FRANCISCO

Alas, alas that great city Babylon,
that mighty city!

THE APOCALYPSE

THE GENTLEMAN FROM San Francisco—neither at Naples nor at Capri had anyone remembered his name—was going to the Old World for two whole years, with wife and daughter, solely for the sake of pleasure.

He was firmly convinced that he was fully entitled to rest, to pleasure, to prolonged and comfortable travel, and to not a little else besides. For such a conviction he had his reasons—that, in the first place, he was rich, and, in the second, that he was only now beginning to live, despite his eight and fifty years. Until now he had not lived, but had merely existed—not at all badly, it is true, but, nevertheless, putting all his hopes on the future. He had labored with never a pause for rest—the coolies, whom he had imported by whole thousands, well knew what this meant! —and finally he saw that much had already been accomplished, that he had almost come abreast of those whom he had at one time set out to emulate, and he decided to enjoy breathing space. It was a custom among the class of people to which he belonged to commence their enjoyment of life with a journey to Europe, to India, to Egypt. He, too, proposed to do the same. Of course he desired, first of all, to reward himself for his years of toil; however, he rejoiced on account of his wife and daughter as well. His wife had never been distinguished for any special sensitiveness to new impressions—but then, all elderly American women are fervid travellers.

As for his daughter—a girl no longer in her first youth, and somewhat sickly—travel was a downright necessity for her: to say nothing of the benefit to her health, were there no fortuitous encounters during travels? It is while travelling that one may at times sit at table with a *milliardaire*, or scrutinize frescoes by his side.

The itinerary worked out by the gentleman from San Francisco was an extensive one. In December and January he hoped to enjoy the sun of Southern Italy, the mountains of antiquity, the *tarantella*, the serenades of strolling singers, and that which men of his age relish with the utmost *finesse*: the love of little, youthful Neapolitaines, even though it be given not entirely without ulterior motives; he contemplated spending the Carnival in Nice, in Monte Carlo, whither the very pick of society gravitates at that time—that very society upon which all the benefits of civilization depend: not merely the cut of tuxedos, but, as well, the stability of thrones, and the declaration of wars, and the prosperity of hotels—Monte Carlo, where some give themselves up with passion to automobile and sail races; others to roulette; a third group to that which it is the custom to call flirting; a fourth, to trap-shooting, in which the pigeons, released from their cotes, soar up most gracefully above emerald-green swards, against the background of a sea that is the color of forget-me-nots—only, in the same minute, to strike against the ground as little, crumpled clods of white. . . . The beginning of March he wanted to devote to Florence; about the time of the Passion of Our Lord to arrive in Rome, in order to hear the *Miserere* there; his plans also embraced Venice, and Paris, and bull-fighting in Seville, and sea-bathing in the British Islands, and Athens, and Constantinople, and Palestine, and Egypt, and even Japan—of course, be it understood, already on the return trip. . . . And everything went very well at first.

It was the end of November; almost as far as Gibraltar it was necessary to navigate through an icy murk, now amidst a blizzard of wet snow; but the ship sailed in all safety and even without rolling; the passengers the steamer was carrying proved to be many, and all of them people of note; the ship—the famous *Atlantida*—resembled the most expensive of European hotels, with all conveniences: an all-night bar, Turkish baths, a newspaper of its own—and life upon it flowed in accordance with a most complicated system of regulations: people got up early, to the sounds of bugles, stridently resounding through the corridors at that dark hour when day was so slowly and inimically dawning over the grayish-green desert of waters, ponderously turbulent in the mist. Putting on their flannel pajamas, the passengers drank coffee, chocolate, cocoa; then they got into marble baths, did their exercises, inducing an appetite and a sense of well-being, performed their toilet for the day, and went to breakfast. Until eleven one was supposed to promenade the decks vigorously, inhaling the fresh coolness of the ocean, or to play at shuffleboard and other games for the sake of arousing the appetite anew, and, at eleven, to seek sustenance in bouillon and sandwiches; having refreshed themselves, the passengers perused their newspaper with gusto and calmly awaited lunch, a meal still more nourishing and varied than the breakfast. The next two hours were sacred to repose—the decks were then encumbered with *chaises longues,* upon which the travellers reclined, covered up with plaids, contemplating the cloud-flecked sky and the foaming hummocks flashing by over the side, or else pleasantly dozing off; at five o'clock, refreshed and put in good spirits, they were drenched with strong fragrant tea, served with cookies; at seven they were apprized by bugle signals of a dinner of nine courses. . . . And thereupon the gentleman from San Francisco, in an access of animal spirits, would hurry to his resplendent *cabine de luxe,* to dress.

In the evening the tiers of the *Atlantida* gaped through the dusk as though they were fiery, countless eyes, and a great multitude of servants worked with especial feverishness in the kitchens, sculleries, and wine vaults. The ocean, heaving on the other side of the walls, was awesome; but none gave it a thought, firmly believing it under the sway of the captain—a red-haired man of monstrous bulk and ponderousness, always seeming sleepy, resembling, in his uniform frock coat, with its golden chevrons, an enormous idol; it was only very rarely that he left his mysterious quarters to appear in public. A siren on the forecastle howled every minute in hellish sullenness and whined in frenzied malice, but not many of the diners heard the siren—it was drowned by the strains of a splendid stringed orchestra, playing exquisitely and ceaselessly in the two-tiered hall, decorated with marble, its floors covered with velvet rugs; festively flooded with the lights of crystal lustres and gilded *girandoles,* filled to overflowing with diamond-bedecked ladies in *décolleté* and men in tuxedos, graceful waiters and deferential *maîtres d'hôtel*—among whom one, who took orders for wines exclusively, even walked about with a chain around his neck, like a lord mayor. A tuxedo and perfect linen made the gentleman from San Francisco appear very much younger. Spare, not tall, clumsily but strongly built, groomed until he shone and moderately animated, he sat in the aureate-pearly refulgence of this pala-tial room, at a table with a bottle of amber Johannisberg, with countless goblets, small and large, of the thinnest glass, with a curly bouquet of curly hyacinths. There was something of the Mongol about his yellowish face with clipped silvery mustache; his large teeth gleamed with gold fillings; his stalwart, bald head glistened like old ivory. Rich, yet in keeping with her years, was the dress of his wife—a big woman, expan-sive and calm; elaborate, yet light and diaphanous, with an innocent frankness, was that of his daughter—tall, slender, with magnificent hair, exquisitely dressed, with breath aromatic from violet cachous and with the tenderest of tiny, rosy pimples about her lips and between her shoulder blades, just the least bit powdered. . . . The dinner lasted for two whole hours, while after dinner there was dancing in the ballroom, during which the men—the gentleman from San Francisco among their number, of course—with their feet cocked up, determined, upon the basis of the

latest political and stock-exchange news, the destinies of nations, smoking
Habana cigars and drinking liqueurs until they were crimson in the face,
seated in the bar, where the waiters were Negroes in red jackets, the
whites of their eyes resembling hard-boiled eggs with the shell off. The
ocean, with a dull roar, was moiling in black mountains on the other side
of the wall; the snow-gale whistled mightily through the sodden rigging;
the whole steamer quivered as it mastered both the gale and the mountains, sundering to either side, as though with a plow, their shifting
masses, that again and again boiled up and reared high, with tails of foam;
the siren, stifled by the fog, was moaning with a deathly anguish; the
lookouts up in their crow's nest froze from the cold and grew dazed from
straining their attention beyond their strength. Like to the grim and
sultry depths of the infernal regions, like to their ultimate, their ninth
circle, was the womb of the steamer, below the water line—that womb
where dully gurgled the gigantic furnaces, devouring with their incandescent maws mountains of hard coal, cast into them by men stripped to
the waist, purple from the flames, and with smarting, filthy sweat pouring
over them; whereas here, in the bar, men threw their legs over the arms
of their chairs with never a care, sipping cognac and liqueurs, and were
wafted among the clouds of spicy smoke as they indulged in well-turned
conversation; in the ballroom everything was radiant with light and
warmth and joy; the dancing couples were now awhirl in waltzes, now
twisting in the tango—and the music insistently, in some delectably
shameless melancholy, was suppliant always of the one, always of the same
thing. . . . There was an ambassador among this brilliant throng—a lean,
modest little old man; there was a great man of riches—clean-shaven,
lanky, of indeterminate years, and with the appearance of a prelate, in his
dress coat of an old-fashioned cut; there was a well-known Spanish
writer; there was a world-celebrated beauty, already just the very least
trifle faded and of an unenviable morality; there was an exquisite couple
in love with each other, whom all watched with curiosity and whose
happiness was unconcealed: *he* danced only with *her*; sang—and with
great ability—only to *her* accompaniment; and everything they did was carried out so charmingly that the captain was the only one who knew that
this pair were hired by Lloyd's to play at love for a good figure, and that
they had been sailing for a long time, now on one ship, now on another.

At Gibraltar everybody was gladdened by the sun—it seemed to be
early spring; a new passenger, whose person aroused the general interest,
made his appearance on board the *Atlantida*—he was the hereditary
prince of a certain Asiatic kingdom, travelling incognito; a little man who
somehow seemed to be all made of wood, even though he was alert in his
movements; broad of face, with narrow eyes, in gold-rimmed spectacles;
a trifle unpleasant through the fact that his skin showed through his
coarse black mustache like that of a cadaver; on the whole, however, he
was charming, unpretentious, and modest. On the Mediterranean Sea
there was a whiff of winter again; the billows ran high, and were as multi-

colored as the tail of a peacock; they had snowy-white crests, lashed up—although the sun was sparkling brightly and the sky was perfectly clear—by a *tramontana*, a chill northern wind from beyond the mountains, that was joyously and madly rushing to meet the ship. . . . Then, on the second day, the sky began to pale, the horizon became covered with mist, land was nearing; Ischia, Capri appeared; through the binoculars Naples—lumps of sugar strewn at the foot of some dove-colored mass— could be seen; while over it and this dove-colored thing were visible the ridges of distant mountains, vaguely glimmering with the dead whiteness of snows. There were a great number of people on deck; many of the ladies and gentlemen had already put on short, light fur coats, with the fur outside; Chinese boys, never contradictory and never speaking above a whisper, bow-legged striplings with pitch-black queues reaching to their heels and with eyelashes as long and thick as those of young girls, were already dragging, little by little, sundry plaids, canes, and portmanteaux and grips of alligator hide toward the companionways. . . . The daughter of the gentleman from San Francisco was standing beside the prince, who had been, through a fortuitous circumstance, presented to her yesterday evening, and she pretended to be looking intently into the distance, in a direction he was pointing out to her, telling, explaining something or other to her, hurriedly and quietly. On account of his height he seemed a boy by contrast with others—he was queer and not at all prepossessing of person, with his spectacles, his derby, his English greatcoat, while his scanty mustache looked just as if it were of horsehair, and the swarthy, thin skin seemed to be drawn tightly over his face, and somehow had the appearance of being lacquered—but the young girl was listening to him, without understanding, in her agitation, what he was saying; her heart was thumping from an incomprehensible rapture before his presence and from pride that he was speaking with her, and not some other; everything about him that was different from others—his lean hands, his clear skin, under which flowed the ancient blood of kings, even his altogether unpretentious, yet somehow distinctively neat, European dress—everything held a secret, inexplicable charm, evoked a feeling of amorousness. As for the gentleman from San Francisco himself—he, in a high silk hat, in gray spats over patent-leather shoes, kept on glancing at the famous beauty, who was standing beside him—a tall blonde of striking figure, her eyes were painted in the latest Parisian fashion; she was holding a diminutive, hunched-up, mangy lapdog on a silver chain and was chattering to it without cease. And the daughter, in some vague embarrassment, tried not to notice her father.

Like all Americans of means, he was very generous on his travels, and, like all of them, believed in the full sincerity and good-will of those who brought him food and drink with such solicitude, who served him from morn till night, forestalling his least wish; of those who guarded his cleanliness and rest, lugged his things around, summoned porters for him, delivered his trunks to hotels. Thus had it been everywhere, thus had it been on the ship, and thus was it to be in Naples as well. Naples grew, and drew nearer; the musicians, the brass of their instruments flashing, had already clustered upon the deck, and suddenly deafened everybody with the triumphant strains of a march; the gigantic captain, in his full-dress uniform, appeared upon his stage, and, like a condescending heathen god, waved his hand amiably to the passengers—and to the gentleman from San Francisco it seemed that it was for him alone that the march so beloved by proud America was thundering, that it was he whom the captain was felicitating upon a safe arrival. And every other passenger felt similarly about himself—or herself. And when the *Atlantida* did finally enter the harbor, had heaved to at the wharf with her many-tiered mass, black with people, and the gangplanks clattered down—what a multitude of porters and their helpers in caps with gold braid, what a multitude of different *commissionaires*, whistling gamins, and strapping ragamuffins with packets of colored postal cards in their hands, made a rush toward the gentleman from San Francisco, with offers of their services! And he smiled, with a kindly contemptuousness, at these ragamuffins, as he went toward the automobile of precisely that hotel where there was a possibility of the prince's stopping as well, and drawled through his teeth, now in English, now in Italian:

"Go away!* *Via!*"

Life at Naples at once assumed its wonted, ordered current: in the early morning, breakfast in the somber dining room with its damp draught from windows opening on some sort of a stony little garden; the sky was usually overcast, holding out but little promise, and there was the usual crowd of guides at the door of the vestibule; then came the first smiles of a warm, rosy sun; there was, from the high hanging balcony, a view of Vesuvius, enveloped to its foot by radiant morning mists, and of silver-and-pearl eddies on the surface of the Bay, and of the delicate contour of Capri against the horizon; one could see tiny burros, harnessed in twos to little carts, running down below over the quay, sticky with mire, and detachments of diminutive soldiers, marching off to somewhere or other to lively and exhilarating music. Next came the procession to the waiting automobile and the slow progress through populous, narrow, and damp corridors of streets, between tall, many-windowed houses; the inspection of lifelessly-clean museums, evenly and pleasantly, yet bleakly, lit, seemingly illuminated by snow; or of cool churches, smelling of wax, which everywhere and always contain the same things: a majestic portal, screened by a heavy curtain of leather, and inside—silence, empty vastness, unobtrusive little flames of a seven-branched candlestick glowing redly in the distant depths, on an altar bedecked with laces; a solitary old woman among the dark wooden pews; slippery tombstones underfoot; and somebody's *Descent from the Cross*—inevitably a celebrated one. At one o'clock there was luncheon upon the mountain of San Martino,

---

* English in the original. The same applies to the other phrases in this story marked with asterisks. [*Trans.*]

where, toward noon, gathered not a few people of the very first quality, and where the daughter of the gentleman from San Francisco had once almost fainted away for joy, because she thought she saw the prince sitting in the hall, although she already knew through the newspapers that he had left for a temporary stay at Rome. At five came tea at the hotel, in the showy salon, so cozy with its rugs and flaming fireplaces; and after that it was already time to get ready for dinner—and once more came the mighty, compelling reverberation of the gong through all the stories; once more the processions in Indian file of ladies in *décolleté*, rustling in their silks upon the staircases and reflected in all the mirrors; once more the palatial dining room, widely and hospitably opened, and the red jackets of the musicians upon their platform, and the black cluster of waiters about the *maître d'hôtel*, who, with a skill out of the ordinary, was ladling some sort of a thick, roseate soup into plates. . . . The dinners, as everywhere else, were the crowning glory of each day; the guests dressed for them as for a rout, and these dinners were so abundant in edibles, and wines, and mineral waters, and sweets, and fruits, that toward eleven o'clock at night the chambermaids were distributing through all the corridors rubber bags with hot water to warm sundry stomachs.

However, the December of that year proved to be not altogether a successful one for Naples; the porters grew confused when one talked with them of the weather, and merely shrugged their shoulders guiltily, muttering that they could not recall such another year—although it was not the first year that they had been forced to mutter this, and to urge in extenuation that "something terrible is happening everywhere"; there were unheard-of storms and torrents of rain on the Riviera; there was snow in Athens; Etna was also all snowed over and was aglow of nights; tourists were fleeing from Palermo in all directions, escaping from the cold. The morning sun deceived the Neapolitans every day that winter: toward noon the sky became gray and a fine rain began falling, but growing heavier and colder all the time; at such times the palms near the entrance of the hotel glistened as though they were of tin, the town seemed especially dirty and cramped, the museums exceedingly alike; the cigar stumps of the corpulent cabmen, whose rubber coats flapped in the wind like wings, seemed to have an insufferable stench, while the energetic snapping of their whips over their scrawny-necked nags was patently false; the footgear of the *signori* sweeping the rails of the tramways seemed horrible; the women, splashing through the mud, their black-haired heads bared to the rain, appeared hideously short-legged; as for the dampness, and the stench of putrid fish from the sea foaming at the quay—they were a matter of course. The gentleman and the lady from San Francisco began quarreling in the morning; their daughter either walked about pale, with a headache, or, coming to life again, went into raptures over everything, and was, at such times, both charming and beautiful: beautiful were those tender and complex emotions which had been awakened within her by meeting that homely man through whose veins flowed uncommon blood; for, after all is said and done, perhaps it is of no real importance just what it is, precisely, that awakens a maiden's soul—whether it be money, or fame, or illustrious ancestry. . . .

Everybody affirmed that things were entirely different in Sorrento, in Capri—there it was both warmer and sunnier, and the lemons were in blossom, and the customs were more honest, and the wine was more natural. And so the family from San Francisco determined to set out with all its trunks to Capri, and, after seeing it all, after treading the stones where the palace of Tiberius had once stood, after visiting the faery-like caverns of the Azure Grotto, and hearing the bagpipers of Abruzzi, who for a whole month preceding Christmas wander over the island and sing the praises of the Virgin Mary, they meant to settle in Sorrento.

On the day of departure—a most memorable one for the family from San Francisco!—there was no sun from the early morning. A heavy fog hid Vesuvius to the very base; this gray fog spread low over the leaden heaving of the sea that was lost to the eye at a distance of a half a mile. Capri was entirely invisible—as though there had never been such a thing in the world. And the little steamer that set out for it was so tossed from side to side that the family from San Francisco was laid prostrate upon the divans in the sorry general cabin of this tub, their feet wrapped up in plaids, and their eyes closed from nausea. Mrs. suffered—so she thought— more than anybody; she was overcome by seasickness several times; it seemed to her that she was dying, whereas the stewardess, who always ran up to her with a small basin—she had been, for many years, day in and day out, rolling on these waves, in freezing weather and in torrid, and yet was still tireless and kind to everybody—merely laughed. Miss was dreadfully pale and held a slice of lemon between her teeth; now she could not have been cheered even by the hope of a chance encounter with the prince at Sorrento, where he intended to be about Christmas. Mr., who was lying on his back, in roomy overcoat and large cap, never unlocked his jaws all the way over; his face had grown darker and his mustache whiter, and his head ached dreadfully: during the last days, thanks to the bad weather, he had been drinking too heavily of evenings, and had too much admired the "living pictures" in dives of *recherché* libertinage. But the rain kept on lashing against the jarring windows, the water from them running down on the divans; the wind, howling, bent the masts, and at times, aided by the onslaught of a wave, careened the little steamer entirely to one side, and then something in the hold would roll with a rumble. During the stops, at Castellammare, at Sorrento, things were a trifle more bearable, but even then the rocking was fearful—the shore, with all its cliffs, gardens, *pigin*,[1] its pink and white hotels and hazy mountains clad in curly greenery, swayed up and down as if on a swing; boats bumped up against the sides of the ship; sailors and steerage passengers were yelling vehemently; somewhere, as though it had been crushed, a baby was wailing and smothering; a raw wind was blowing in at the

[1] Pine groves. [*Trans.*]

door; and, from a swaying boat with a flag of the Hotel Royal, a lisping gamin was screaming, luring travellers: "Kgoya-al! Hotel Kgoya-al! . . ." and the gentleman from San Francisco, feeling that he was an old man— which was but proper—was already thinking with sadness and melancholy of all these Royals, Splendids, Excelsiors, and of these greedy, insignificant mannikins, reeking of garlic, that are called Italians. Once, having opened his eyes and raised himself from the divan, he saw, underneath the craggy steep of the shore, a cluster of stone hovels, mouldy through and through, stuck one on top of another near the very edge of the water, near boats, near all sorts of rags, tins, and brown nets—hovels so miserable, that, at the recollection that this was that very Italy he had come hither to enjoy, he felt despair. . . . Finally, at twilight, the dark mass of the island began to draw near, seemingly bored through and through by little red lights near its base; the wind became softer, warmer, more fragrant; over the abating waves, as opalescent as black oil, golden pythons flowed from the lanterns on the wharf. . . . Then came the sudden rumble of the anchor, and it fell with a splash into the water; the ferocious yells of the boatmen, vying with one another, floated in from all quarters—and at once the heart grew lighter, the lights in the general cabin shone more brightly, a desire arose to eat, to drink, to smoke, to be stirring. . . . Ten minutes later the family from San Francisco had descended into a large boat; within fifteen minutes it had set foot upon the stones of the wharf, and had then got into a bright little railway car and to its buzzing started the ascent of the slope, amid the stakes of the vineyards, half-crumbled stone enclosures, and wet, gnarled orange trees, some of them under coverings of straw—trees with thick, glossy foliage, and aglimmer with the orange fruits; all these objects were sliding downward, past the open windows of the little car, toward the base of the mountain. . . . Sweetly smells the earth of Italy after rain, and her every island has its own, its especial aroma!

The island of Capri was damp and dark on this evening. But now it came into life for an instant; lights sprang up here and there, as always on the steamer's arrival. At the top of the mountain, where stood the station of the funicular, there was another throng of those whose duty lay in receiving fittingly the gentleman from San Francisco. There were other arrivals also, but they merited no attention—several Russians, who had taken up their abode in Capri—absent-minded because of their bookish meditations, unkempt, bearded, spectacled, the collars of their old drap overcoats turned up; and a group of long-legged, long-necked, round-headed German youths in Tyrolean costumes, with canvas knapsacks slung over their shoulders—these latter stood in need of nobody's services, feeling themselves at home everywhere, and were not at all generous in their expenditures. The gentleman from San Francisco, on the other hand, who was calmly keeping aloof from both the one group and the other, was immediately noticed. He and his ladies were bustlingly assisted to get out, some men running ahead of him to show him the way; he was

surrounded anew by urchins, and by those robust Caprian wives who
carry on their heads the portmanteaux and trunks of respectable travellers. The wooden pattens of these women clattered over a *piazetta* that
seemed to belong to some opera, an electric globe swaying above it in the
damp wind; the rabble of urchins burst into sharp, birdlike whistles—and,
as though on a stage, the gentleman from San Francisco proceeded in
their midst toward some medieval arch, underneath houses that had become welded into one mass, beyond which a little echoing street—with
the tuft of a palm above flat roofs on its left, and with blue stars in the
black sky overhead—led slopingly to the grand entrance of the hotel,
glittering ahead. . . . And again it seemed that it was in honor of the
guests from San Francisco that this damp little town of stone on a craggy
little island of the Mediterranean Sea had come to life, that it was they
who had made so happy and affable the proprietor of the hotel, that it
was they only who had been waited for by the Chinese gong, that now
began wailing the summons to dinner through all the stories of the hotel,
the instant they had set foot in the vestibule.

The proprietor, a young man of haughty elegance, who had met
them with a polite and exquisite bow, for a minute dumbfounded the
gentleman from San Francisco: having glanced at him, the gentleman
from San Francisco suddenly recalled that just the night before, among
the rest of the confusion of images that had beset him in his sleep, he had
seen precisely this gentleman—just like him, down to the least detail: in
the same sort of frock with rounded skirts, and with the same pomaded
and painstakingly combed head. Startled, he was almost taken aback; but
since, from long, long before, there was not even a mustard seed of any
sort of so-called mystical emotions left in his soul, his astonishment was
dimmed the same instant, passing through a corridor of the hotel, he
spoke jestingly to his wife and daughter of this strange coincidence of
dream and reality. And only his daughter glanced at him with alarm at
that moment: her heart suddenly contracted from sadness, from a feeling
of their loneliness upon this foreign, dark island—a feeling so strong that
she almost burst into tears. But still she said nothing of her feelings to her
father—as always.

An exalted personage—Rais XVII—who had been visiting Capri, had
just taken his departure, and the guests from San Francisco were given
the same apartments that he had occupied. To them was assigned the
handsomest and most expert chambermaid, a Belgian, whose waist was
slenderly and firmly corseted, and who wore a little starched cap that
looked like a pronged crown; also, the stateliest and most dignified of
flunkies, a fiery-eyed Sicilian, swarthy as coal; and the nimblest of bellboys, the short and stout Luigi—a fellow who was very fond of a joke,
and who had changed many places in his time. And a minute later there
was a slight tap at the door of the room of the gentleman from San
Francisco—the French *maître d'hôtel* had come to find out if the newly
arrived guests would dine, and, in the event of an answer in the affirma-

tive—of which, however, there was no doubt—to inform them that the
carte de jour consisted of crawfish, roast beef, asparagus, pheasants, and
so forth. The floor was still rocking under the gentleman from San Francisco—so badly had the atrocious little Italian steamer tossed him about—
but, without hurrying, with his own hands, although somewhat clumsily
from being unaccustomed to such things, he shut a window that had
banged upon the entrance of the *maître d'hôtel* and had let in the odors of
the distant kitchen and of the wet flowers in the garden, and with a
leisurely precision replied that they would dine, that their table must be
placed at a distance from the door, at the farthest end of the dining room,
that they would drink local wine and champagne—moderately dry and
only slightly chilled. The *maître d'hôtel* concurred in every word of his,
in intonations most varied, having, however, but one significance—that
there was never a doubt, nor could there possibly be any, about the
correctness of the wishes of the gentleman from San Francisco, and that
everything would be carried out punctiliously. In conclusion he inclined
his head, and asked deferentially: "Will that be all, sir?"

And, having received a long-drawn-out "Yes"* in answer, he added
that the *tarantella* would be danced in the vestibule today—the dancers
would be Carmella and Giuseppe, known to all Italy, and to "the entire
world of tourists."

"I have seen her on post cards," said the gentleman from San Francisco in a voice devoid of all expression. "About this Giuseppe, now—is
he her husband?"

"Her cousin, sir," answered the *maître d'hôtel*.

And, after a little wait, after considering something, the gentleman
from San Francisco dismissed him with a nod.

And then he began his preparations anew, as though for a wedding
ceremony: he turned on all the electric lights, filling all the mirrors with
reflections of light and glitter, of furniture and opened trunks; he began
shaving and washing, ringing the bell every minute, while other impatient
rings from his wife's and daughter's rooms floated through the entire
corridor and interrupted his. And Luigi, in his red apron, was rushing
headlong to answer the bell, with an ease peculiar to many stout men, the
while he made grimaces of horror that made the chambermaids, running
by with glazed porcelain pails in their hands, laugh till they cried. Having
knocked on the door with his knuckles, he asked with an assumed timidity, with a respectfulness that verged on idiocy: "*Ha sonato, signore?*
[Did you ring, sir?]"

And from the other side of the door came an unhurried, grating
voice, insultingly polite: "Yes, come in. . . ."*

What were the thoughts, what were the emotions of the gentleman
from San Francisco on this evening, that was of such portent to him? He
felt nothing exceptional—for the trouble in this world is just that everything is apparently all too simple! And even if he had sensed within his
soul that something was impending, he would, nevertheless, have thought

that this thing would not occur for some time to come—in any case, not immediately. Besides that, like everyone who has gone through the rocking of a ship, he wanted very much to eat, was anticipating with enjoyment the first spoonful of soup, the first mouthful of wine, and performed the usual routine of dressing even with a certain degree of exhilaration that left no time for reflections.

Having shaved and washed himself, having inserted several artificial teeth properly, he, standing before a mirror, wetted the remnants of his thick, pearly-gray hair and plastered it down around his swarthy-yellow skull, with brushes set in silver; drew a suit of cream-colored silk underwear over his strong old body, beginning to be full at the waist from excesses in food, and put on silk socks and dancing slippers on his shrivelled, splayed feet; sitting down, he put in order his black trousers, drawn high by black silk braces, as well as his snowy-white shirt, with the bosom bulging out; put the links through the glossy cuffs, and began the torturous pursuit of the collar button underneath the stiffly starched collar. The floor was still swaying beneath him, the tips of his fingers pained him greatly, the collar button at times nipped hard the flabby skin in the hollow under his Adam's apple, but he was persistent and finally, his eyes glittering from the exertion, his face all livid from the collar that was choking his throat—a collar far too tight—he did contrive to accomplish his task, and sat down in exhaustion in front of the pier glass, reflected in it from head to foot, a reflection that was repeated in all the other mirrors.

"Oh, this is dreadful!" he muttered, letting his strong bald head drop, and without trying to understand, without reflecting, just what, precisely, was dreadful; then, with an accustomed and attentive glance, he inspected his stubby fingers, with gouty hardenings at the joints, and his convex nails of an almond color, repeating, with conviction: "This is dreadful. . . ."

But at this point the second gong, sonorously, as in some heathen temple, reverberated through the entire house. And, getting up quickly from his seat, the gentleman from San Francisco drew his collar still tighter with the necktie and his stomach by means of the low-cut vest, put on his tuxedo, drew out his cuffs, scrutinized himself once more in the mirror. . . . This Carmella, swarthy, with eyes which she knew well how to use most effectively, resembling a mulatto woman, clad in a dress of many colors, with the color of orange predominant, must dance exceptionally, he reflected. And, stepping briskly out of his room and walking over the carpet to the next one—his wife's—he asked, loudly, if they would be ready soon.

"In five minutes, Dad!" a girl's voice, ringing and by now gay, responded from the other side of the door.

"Very well," said the gentleman from San Francisco.

And, leisurely, he walked down red-carpeted corridors and staircases, descending in search of the reading room. The servants he met stood aside and hugged the wall to let him pass, but he kept on his way as though he had never even noticed them. An old woman who was late for dinner, already stooping, with milky hair but *décolleté* in a light-gray gown of silk, was hurrying with all her might, but drolly, in a henlike manner, and he easily outstripped her. Near the glass doors of the dining room, where all the guests had already assembled, and were beginning their dinner, he stopped before a little table piled with boxes of cigars and Egyptian cigarettes, took a large Manila cigar, and tossed three *lire* upon the little table; upon the closed veranda he glanced, in passing, through the open window: out of the darkness he felt a breath of the balmy air upon him, thought he saw the tip of an ancient palm that had flung wide across the stars its fronds, which seemed gigantic, heard the distant, even noise of the sea floating in to him. . . . In the reading room—snug, quiet, and illuminated only above the tables, some gray-haired German was standing, rustling the newspapers—unkempt, resembling Ibsen, in round silver spectacles and with the astonished eyes of a madman. Having scrutinized him coldly, the gentleman from San Francisco sat down in a deep leather chair in a corner near a green-shaded lamp, put on his pince-nez, twitching his head because his collar was choking him, and hid himself completely behind the newspaper sheet. He rapidly ran through the headlines of certain items, read a few lines about the never-ceasing Balkan war, with an accustomed gesture turned the newspaper over—when suddenly the lines flared up before him with a glassy glare, his neck became taut, his eyes bulged out, the pince-nez flew off his nose. . . . He lunged forward, tried to swallow some air—and gasped wildly; his lower jaw sank, lighting up his entire mouth with the reflection of the gold fillings; his head dropped back on his shoulder and began to sway; the bosom of his shirt bulged out like a basket—and his whole body, squirming, his heels catching the carpet, slid downward to the floor, desperately struggling with someone.

Had the German not been in the reading room, the personnel of the hotel would have managed, quickly and adroitly, to hush up this dreadful occurrence; instantly, through back passages, seizing him by the head and feet, they would have rushed off the gentleman from San Francisco as far away as possible—and never a soul among the guests would have found out what he had been up to. But the German had dashed out of the reading room with a scream—he had aroused the entire house, the entire dining room. And many jumped up from their meal, overturning their chairs; many, paling, ran toward the reading room. "What—what has happened?" was heard in all languages—and no one gave a sensible answer, no one comprehended anything, since even up to now men are amazed most of all by death, and will not, under any circumstances, believe in it. The proprietor dashed from one guest to another, trying to detain those who were running away and to pacify them with hasty assurances that this was just a trifling occurrence, a slight fainting spell of a certain gentleman from San Francisco. . . . But no one listened to him; many had seen the waiters and bellboys tearing the necktie, the vest, and the rumpled tuxedo off this gentleman, and even, for some reason or other, the dancing slippers off his splayed feet, clad in black silk. But he was still struggling. He was still obdurately wrestling with death; he absolutely refused to yield to her, who had so unexpectedly and churlishly fallen upon him. His head was swaying, he rattled hoarsely, like one with his throat cut; his eyes had rolled up, like a drunkard's. . . . When he was hurriedly carried in and laid upon a bed in room number forty-three—the smallest, the poorest, the dampest, and the coldest, situated at the end of the bottom corridor—his daughter ran in, with her hair down, in a little dressing gown that had flown open, her bosom, raised up by the corset, uncovered; then his wife, big and ponderous, already dressed for dinner—her mouth rounded in terror. . . . But by now he had ceased even to bob his head.

A quarter of an hour later everything in the hotel had assumed some semblance of order. But the evening was irreparably spoiled. Some guests, returning to the dining room, finished their dinner, but in silence, with aggrieved countenances, while the proprietor would approach now one group, now another, shrugging his shoulders in polite yet impotent irritation, feeling himself guilty without guilt, assuring everybody that he understood very well "how unpleasant all this was," and pledging his word that he would take "all measures within his power" to remove this unpleasantness. It was necessary to call off the *tarantella*, all unnecessary electric lights were switched off, the majority of the guests withdrew into the bar, and it became so quiet that one heard distinctly the ticking of the clock in the vestibule, whose sole occupant was a parrot, dully muttering something, fussing in his cage before going to sleep, contriving to doze off at last with one claw ludicrously stretched up to the upper perch. . . . The gentleman from San Francisco was lying upon a cheap iron bed, under coarse woolen blankets, upon which the dull light of a single bulb beat down from the ceiling. An icebag hung down to his moist and cold forehead. The livid face, already dead, was gradually growing cold; the hoarse rattling, expelled from the open mouth, illuminated by the reflection of gold, was growing fainter. This was no longer the gentleman from San Francisco rattling—he no longer existed—but some other. His wife, his daughter, the doctor, and the servants were standing, gazing at him dully. Suddenly, that which they awaited and feared was consummated—the rattling ceased abruptly. And slowly, slowly, before the eyes of all, a pallor flowed over the face of the man who had died, and his features seemed to grow finer, to become irradiated, with a beauty which had been rightfully his in the long ago. . . .

The proprietor entered. *"Già è morto,"* said the doctor to him in a whisper. The proprietor, his face dispassionate, shrugged his shoulders. The wife, down whose cheeks the tears were quietly coursing, walked up to him and timidly said that the deceased ought now to be carried to his own room.

"Oh, no, madam," hastily, correctly, but now without any amiability

and not in English, but in French, retorted the proprietor, who was not at
all interested now in such trifling sums as the arrivals from San Francisco
might leave in his coffers. "That is absolutely impossible, madam," said
he, and added in explanation that he valued the apartments occupied by
them very much; that, were he to carry out her wishes, everybody in
Capri would know it and the tourists would shun those apartments.

The young lady, who had been gazing at him strangely, sat down on
a chair, and, stuffing her mouth with a handkerchief, burst into sobs. The
wife dried her tears immediately, her face flaring up. She adopted a
louder tone, making demands in her own language, and still incredulous
of the fact that all respect for them had been completely lost. The proprietor, with a polite dignity, cut her short: if Madam was not pleased
with the customs of the hotel, he would not venture to detain her; and he
firmly announced that the body must be gotten away this very day, at
dawn, that the police had already been notified, and one of the police
officers would be here very soon and would carry out all the necessary
formalities. Was it possible to secure even a common coffin in Capri?
Madam asks. Regrettably, no—it was beyond possibility, and no one
would be able to make one in time. It would be necessary to have recourse to something else. . . . For instance—English soda water came in
large and long boxes. . . . It was possible to knock the partitions out of
such a box. . . .

At night the whole hotel slept. The window in room number forty-
three was opened—it gave out upon a corner of the garden where, near a
high stone wall with broken glass upon its crest, a phthisic banana tree
was growing; the electric light was switched off; the key was turned in
the door, and everybody went away. The dead man remained in the
darkness—the blue stars looked down upon him from the sky, a cricket
with a pensive insouciance began his song in the wall. . . . In the dimly lit
corridor two chambermaids were seated on a window sill, at some darn-
ing. Luigi, in slippers, entered with a pile of clothing in his arms.

"*Pronto?* [All ready?]" he asked solicitously, in a ringing whisper,
indicating with his eyes the fearsome door at the end of the corridor.
And, he waved his hand airily in that direction. . . . "*Partenza!*" he called
out in a whisper, as though he were speeding a train, the usual phrase used
in Italian depots at the departure of trains—and the chambermaids, choking with silent laughter, let their heads sink on each other's shoulder.

Thereupon, hopping softly, he ran up to the very door, gave it the
merest tap, and, inclining his head to one side, in a low voice, asked with
the utmost deference: "*Ha sonato, signore?*"

And, squeezing his throat, thrusting out his lower jaw, in a grating
voice, slowly and sadly, he answered his own question, as though from
the other side of the door:

"Yes, come in. . . ."*

And at dawn, when it had become light beyond the window of room
number forty-three, and a humid wind had begun to rustle the tattered

leaves of the banana tree; when the blue sky of morning had lifted and spread out over the island of Capri, and the pure and clear-cut summit of Monte Solaro had grown aureate against the sun that was rising beyond the distant blue mountains of Italy; when the stonemasons, who were repairing the tourists' paths on the island, had set out to work—a long box that had formerly been used for soda water was brought to room number forty-three. Soon it became very heavy, and was pressing hard against the knees of the junior porter, who bore it off briskly on a one-horse cab over the white paved highway that was sinuously winding to and fro over the slopes of Capri, among the stone walls and the vineyards, ever downwards, to the very sea. The cabby, a puny little man with reddened eyes, in an old, wretched jacket with short sleeves and in trodden-down shoes, was undergoing the after effects of drink—he had diced the whole night through in a *trattoria*—and kept on lashing his sturdy little horse, tricked out in the Sicilian fashion, with all sorts of little bells livelily jingling upon the bridle with its tufts of colored wool, and upon the brass points of its high pad; with a yard-long feather stuck in its cropped forelock—a feather that shook as the horse ran. The cabby kept silent; he was oppressed by his shiftlessness, his vices—by the fact that he had, that night, lost to the last mite all those coppers with which his pockets had been filled. But the morning was fresh; in air such as this, with the sea all around, under the morning sky, the after effects of drink quickly evaporate, and a man is soon restored to a carefree mood, and the cabby was furthermore consoled by that unexpected sum, the opportunity to earn which had been granted him by some gentleman from San Francisco, whose lifeless head was bobbing from side to side in the box at his back. . . . The little steamer—a beetle lying far down below, against the tender and vivid deep-blue with which the Bay of Naples is so densely and highly flooded—was already blowing its final whistles, which reverberated loudly all over the island, whose every bend, every ridge, every stone, was as distinctly visible from every point as if there were absolutely no such thing as atmosphere. Near the wharf the junior porter was joined by the senior, who was speeding with the daughter and wife of the gentleman from San Francisco in his automobile—they were pale, with eyes hollow from tears and a sleepless night. And ten minutes later the little steamer was again chugging through the water, again running toward Sorrento, toward Castellammare, carrying away from Capri, for all time, the family from San Francisco. . . . And again peace and quiet resumed their reign upon the island.

Upon this island, two thousand years ago, had lived a man who had become completely enmeshed in his cruel and foul deeds, who had for some reason seized the power over millions of people in his hands, and who, having himself lost his head at the senselessness of this power and from the fear of death by assassination, lurking in ambush behind every corner, had committed cruelties beyond all measure—and humankind has remembered him for all time; and those who, in their collusion, just as incomprehensively and, in substance, just as cruelly as he, reign at present in power over this world, gather from all over the earth to gaze upon the ruins of that stone villa where he had dwelt on one of the steepest ascents of the island. On this splendid morning all those who had come to Capri for just this purpose were still sleeping in the hotels, although, toward their entrances, were already being led little mouse-gray burros with red saddles, upon which, after awaking and sating themselves with food, Americans and Germans, men and women, young and old, would again clamber up ponderously this day, and after whom would again run the old Caprian beggar women, with sticks in their gnarled hands—would run over stony paths, and always uphill, up to the very summit of Mount Tiberio. Set at rest by the fact that the dead old man from San Francisco, who had likewise been planning to go with them but instead of that had only frightened them with a *memento mori*, had already been shipped off to Naples, the travellers slept on heavily, and the quiet of the island was still undisturbed, the shops in the city were still shut. The market place on the *piazetta* alone was carrying on traffic—in fish and greens; and the people there were all simple folk, among whom, without anything to do, as always, was standing Lorenzo the boatman, famous all over Italy—a tall old man, a carefree rake and a handsome fellow, who had served more than once as a model to many artists; he had brought, and had already sold for a song two lobsters that he had caught that night and which were already rustling in the apron of the cook of that very hotel where the family from San Francisco had passed the night, and now he could afford to stand in calm idleness even until the evening, looking about him with a kingly bearing (a little trick of his), consciously picturesque with his tatters, clay pipe, and a red woolen *beretta* drooping over one ear.

And, along the precipices of Monte Solaro, upon the ancient Phoenician road, hewn out of the crags, down its stone steps, two mountaineers of Abruzzi were descending from Anacapri. One had bagpipes under his leathern mantle—a large bag made from the skin of a she-goat, with two pipes; the other had something in the nature of wooden Pan's reeds. They went on—and all the land, joyous, splendid, sun-flooded, spread out below them: the stony humps of the island, which was lying almost in its entirety at their feet; and that faery-like deep blue in which it was aswim; and the radiant morning vapors over the sea, toward the east, under the blinding sun that was now beating down hotly, rising ever higher and higher; and, still in their morning vagueness, the mistily azure massive outlines of Italy, of her mountains near and far, whose beauty human speech is impotent to express. . . . Halfway down the pipers slackened their pace: over the path, within a grotto in the craggy side of Monte Solaro, all illumed by the sun, all bathed in its warmth and glow, in snow-white raiment of gypsum, and in a royal crown, golden-rusty from inclement weathers, stood the Mother of God, meek and gracious, her orbs lifted up to heaven, to the eternal and happy abodes of her thrice-blessed Son. The pipers bared their heads, put their reeds to their lips—

and there poured forth their naïve and humbly-jubilant praises to the sun, to the morning, to her, the Immaculate Intercessor for all those who suffer in this evil and beautiful world, and to Him Who had been born of her womb in a cavern at Bethlehem, in a poor shepherd's shelter in the distant land of Judaea. . . .

Meanwhile, the body of the dead old man from San Francisco was returning to its home, to a grave on the shores of the New World. Having gone through many humiliations, through much human neglect, having wandered for a week from one port warehouse to another, it had finally gotten once more on board that same famous ship upon which but so recently, with so much deference, he had been borne to the Old World. But now he was already being concealed from the quick—he was lowered in his tarred coffin deep into the black hold. And once more the ship was sailing on and on upon its long sea voyage. In the nighttime it sailed past the island of Capri, and, to one watching them from the island, there was something sad about the ship's lights, slowly disappearing over the dark sea. But, upon the ship itself, in its brilliant salons resplendent with lustres and marbles, there was a crowded ball that night, as usual.

There was a ball on the second night also, and on the third—again in the midst of a raging snowstorm, whirling over an ocean booming like a funeral mass, and heaving in mountains trapped out in mourning by the silver spindrift. The innumerable fiery eyes of the ship that was retreating into the night and the snow-gale were barely visible for the snow to the Devil watching from the crags of Gibraltar, from the stony gateway of two worlds. The Devil was as enormous as a cliff, but the ship was still more enormous than he; many-tiered, many-funnelled, created by the pride of the New Man with an ancient heart. The snow-gale smote upon its rigging and wide-throated funnels, hoary from the snow, but the ship was steadfast, firm, majestic—and awesome. Upon its topmost deck were reared, in their solitude among the snowy whirlwinds, those snug, dimly lit chambers where, plunged in a light and uneasy slumber, was its ponderous guide who resembled a heathen idol, reigning over the entire ship. He heard the pained howlings and the ferocious squealings of the storm-stifled siren, but soothed himself by the proximity of that which, in the final summing up, was incomprehensible even to himself, that which was on the other side of his wall: that large cabin, which had the appearance of being armored, and was being constantly filled by the mysterious rumbling, quivering, and crisp sputtering of blue flames, flaring up and exploding around the pale-faced operator with a metal half-hoop upon his head. In the very depths, in the underwater womb of the *Atlantida*, were the thirty-thousand-pound masses of boilers and of all sorts of other machinery—dully glittering with steel, hissing out steam and exuding oil and boiling water—of that kitchen, made red hot from infernal furnaces underneath, wherein was brewing the motion of the ship. Forces, fearful in their concentration, were bubbling, were being transmitted to its very keel, into an endlessly long catacomb, into a tunnel, illuminated by electricity, wherein slowly, with an inexorability that was crushing to the human soul, was revolving within its oily couch the gigantean shaft, exactly like a living monster that had stretched itself out in this tunnel. Meanwhile, amidship the *Atlantida,* its warm and luxurious cabins, its dining halls and ballrooms, poured forth radiance and joyousness, were humming with the voices of a well-dressed gathering, were sweetly odorous with fresh flowers, and the strains of the stringed orchestra were their song. And again excruciatingly writhed and at intervals came together among this throng, among this glitter of lights, silks, diamonds, and bared feminine shoulders, the supple pair of hired lovers: the sinfully-modest, very pretty young woman, with eyelashes cast down, with a chaste coiffure, and the well-built young man, with black hair that seemed to be pasted on, with his face pale from powder, shod in the most elegant of patent-leather footgear, clad in a tight-fitting dress coat with long tails—an Adonis who resembled a huge leech. And none knew that, already for a long time, this pair had grown wearied of languishing dissemblingly in their blissful torment to the sounds of the shamelessly-sad music—nor that far, far below, at the bottom of the black hold, stood a tarred coffin, in close proximity to the somber and sultry depths of the ship that was toilsomely overpowering the darkness, the ocean, the snow-storm. . . .

Albert Camus

THE STRANGER

Part One: I

MOTHER DIED TODAY. Or, maybe, yesterday; I can't be sure. The tele-gram from the Home says: YOUR MOTHER PASSED AWAY. FUNERAL TOMORROW. DEEP SYMPATHY. Which leaves the matter doubtful; it could have been yesterday.

The Home for Aged Persons is at Marengo, some fifty miles from Algiers. With the two-o'clock bus I should get there well before night-fall. Then I can spend the night there, keeping the usual vigil beside the body, and be back here by tomorrow evening. I have fixed up with my employer for two days' leave; obviously, under the circumstances, he couldn't refuse. Still, I had an idea he looked annoyed, and I said, without thinking: "Sorry, sir, but it's not my fault, you know."

Afterwards it struck me I needn't have said that. I had no reason to excuse myself; it was up to him to express his sympathy and so forth. Probably he will do so the day after tomorrow, when he sees me in black. For the present, it's almost as if Mother weren't really dead. The funeral will bring it home to me, put an official seal on it, so to speak. . . .

I took the two-o'clock bus. It was a blazing hot afternoon. I'd lunched, as usual, at Céleste's restaurant. Everyone was most kind, and Céleste said to me, "There's no one like a mother." When I left they came with me to the door. It was something of a rush, getting away, as at the last moment I had to call in at Emmanuel's place to borrow his black tie and mourning band. He lost his uncle a few months ago.

I had to run to catch the bus. I suppose it was my hurrying like that,

ALBERT CAMUS

photograph by Karsh

WILLA CATHER

photograph by Steichen

what with the glare off the road and from the sky, the reek of gasoline, and the jolts, that made me feel so drowsy. Anyhow, I slept most of the way. When I woke I was leaning against a soldier; he grinned and asked me if I'd come from a long way off, and I just nodded, to cut things short. I wasn't in a mood for talking.

The Home is a little over a mile from the village. I went there on foot. I asked to be allowed to see Mother at once, but the doorkeeper told me I must see the warden first. He wasn't free, and I had to wait a bit. The doorkeeper chatted with me while I waited; then he led me to the office. The warden was a very small man, with gray hair, and a Legion of Honor rosette in his buttonhole. He gave me a long look with his watery blue eyes. Then we shook hands, and he held mine so long that I began to feel embarrassed. After that he consulted a register on his table, and said:

"Madame Meursault entered the Home three years ago. She had no private means and depended entirely on you."

I had a feeling he was blaming me for something, and started to explain. But he cut me short.

"There's no need to excuse yourself, my boy. I've looked up the record and obviously you weren't in a position to see that she was properly cared for. She needed someone to be with her all the time, and young men in jobs like yours don't get too much pay. In any case, she was much happier in the Home."

I said, "Yes, sir; I'm sure of that."

Then he added: "She had good friends here, you know, old folks like herself, and one gets on better with people of one's own generation. You're much too young; you couldn't have been much of a companion to her."

That was so. When we lived together, Mother was always watching me, but we hardly ever talked. During her first few weeks at the Home she used to cry a good deal. But that was only because she hadn't settled down. After a month or two she'd have cried if she'd been told to leave the Home. Because this, too, would have been a wrench. That was why, during the last year, I seldom went to see her. Also, it would have meant losing my Sunday—not to mention the trouble of going to the bus, getting my ticket, and spending two hours on the journey each way.

The warden went on talking, but I didn't pay much attention. Finally he said:

"Now, I suppose you'd like to see your mother?"

I rose without replying, and he led the way to the door. As we were going down the stairs he explained:

"I've had the body moved to our little mortuary—so as not to upset the other old people, you understand. Every time there's a death here, they're in a nervous state for two or three days. Which means, of course, extra work and worry for our staff."

We crossed a courtyard where there were a number of old men, talking amongst themselves in little groups. They fell silent as we came up with them. Then, behind our backs, the chattering began again. Their voices reminded me of parakeets in a cage, only the sound wasn't quite so shrill. The warden stopped outside the entrance of a small, low building.

"So here I leave you, Monsieur Meursault. If you want me for anything, you'll find me in my office. We propose to have the funeral tomorrow morning. That will enable you to spend the night beside your mother's coffin, as no doubt you would wish to do. Just one more thing; I gathered from your mother's friends that she wished to be buried with the rites of the Church. I've made arrangements for this; but I thought I should let you know."

I thanked him. So far as I knew, my mother, though not a professed atheist, had never given a thought to religion in her life.

I entered the mortuary. It was a bright, spotlessly clean room, with whitewashed walls and a big skylight. The furniture consisted of some chairs and trestles. Two of the latter stood open in the center of the room and the coffin rested on them. The lid was in place, but the screws had been given only a few turns and their nickeled heads stuck out above the wood, which was stained dark walnut. An Arab woman—a nurse, I supposed—was sitting beside the bier; she was wearing a blue smock and had a rather gaudy scarf wound round her hair.

Just then the keeper came up behind me. He'd evidently been running, as he was a little out of breath.

"We put the lid on, but I was told to unscrew it when you came, so that you could see her."

While he was going up to the coffin I told him not to trouble.

"Eh? What's that?" he exclaimed. "You don't want me to . . . ?"

"No," I said.

He put back the screwdriver in his pocket and stared at me. I realized then that I shouldn't have said, "No," and it made me rather embarrassed. After eying me for some moments he asked:

"Why not?" But he didn't sound reproachful; he simply wanted to know.

"Well, really I couldn't say," I answered.

He began twiddling his white mustache; then, without looking at me, said gently:

"I understand."

He was a pleasant-looking man, with blue eyes and ruddy cheeks. He drew up a chair for me near the coffin, and seated himself just behind. The nurse got up and moved toward the door. As she was going by, the keeper whispered in my ear:

"It's a tumor she has, poor thing."

I looked at her more carefully and I noticed that she had a bandage round her head, just below her eyes. It lay quite flat across the bridge of her nose, and one saw hardly anything of her face except that strip of whiteness.

As soon as she had gone, the keeper rose.

"Now I'll leave you to yourself."

I don't know whether I made some gesture, but instead of going he halted behind my chair. The sensation of someone posted at my back made me uncomfortable. The sun was getting low and the whole room was flooded with a pleasant, mellow light. Two hornets were buzzing overhead, against the skylight. I was so sleepy I could hardly keep my eyes open. Without looking round, I asked the keeper how long he'd been at the Home. "Five years." The answer came so pat that one could have thought he'd been expecting my question.

That started him off, and he became quite chatty. If anyone had told him ten years ago that he'd end his days as doorkeeper at a home at Marengo, he'd never have believed it. He was sixty-four, he said, and hailed from Paris.

When he said that, I broke in. "Ah, you don't come from here?"

I remembered then that, before taking me to the warden, he'd told me something about Mother. He had said she'd have to be buried mighty quickly because of the heat in these parts, especially down in the plain. "At Paris they keep the body for three days, sometimes four." After that he had mentioned that he'd spent the best part of his life in Paris, and could never manage to forget it. "Here," he had said, "things have to go with a rush, like. You've hardly time to get used to the idea that some-one's dead, before you're hauled off to the funeral." "That's enough," his wife had put in. "You didn't ought to say such things to the poor young gentleman." The old fellow had blushed and begun to apologize. I told him it was quite all right. As a matter of fact, I found it rather interesting, what he'd been telling me; I hadn't thought of that before.

Now he went on to say that he'd entered the Home as an ordinary inmate. But he was still quite hale and hearty, and when the keeper's job fell vacant, he offered to take it on.

I pointed out that, even so, he was really an inmate like the others, but he wouldn't hear of it. He was "an official, like." I'd been struck before by his habit of saying "they" or, less often, "them old folks," when referring to inmates no older than himself. Still, I could see his point of view. As doorkeeper he had a certain standing, and some author-ity over the rest of them.

Just then the nurse returned. Night had fallen very quickly; all of a sudden, it seemed, the sky went black above the skylight. The keeper switched on the lamps, and I was almost blinded by the blaze of light.

He suggested I should go to the refectory for dinner, but I wasn't hungry. Then he proposed bringing me a mug of *café au lait*. As I am very partial to *café au lait* I said, "Thanks," and a few minutes later he came back with a tray. I drank the coffee, and then I wanted a cigarette. But I wasn't sure if I should smoke, under the circumstances—in Mother's presence. I thought it over; really, it didn't seem to matter, so I offered the keeper a cigarette, and we both smoked.

After a while he started talking again.

"You know, your mother's friends will be coming soon, to keep vigil
with you beside the body. We always have a 'vigil' here, when anyone
dies. I'd better go and get some chairs and a pot of black coffee."

The glare off the white walls was making my eyes smart, and I asked
him if he couldn't turn off one of the lamps. "Nothing doing," he said.
They'd arranged the lights like that; either one had them all on or none at
all. After that I didn't pay much more attention to him. He went out,
brought some chairs, and set them out round the coffin. On one he placed
a coffeepot and ten or a dozen cups. Then he sat down facing me, on the
far side of Mother. The nurse was at the other end of the room, with her
back to me. I couldn't see what she was doing, but by the way her arms
moved I guessed that she was knitting. I was feeling very comfortable;
the coffee had warmed me up, and through the open door came scents of
flowers and breaths of cool night air. I think I dozed off for a while.

I was awakened by an odd rustling in my ears. After having had my
eyes closed, I had a feeling that the light had grown even stronger than
before. There wasn't a trace of shadow anywhere, and every object, each
curve or angle, seemed to score its outline on one's eyes. The old people,
Mother's friends, were coming in. I counted ten in all, gliding almost
soundlessly through the bleak white glare. None of the chairs creaked
when they sat down. Never in my life had I seen anyone so clearly as I
saw these people; not a detail of their clothes or features escaped me. And
yet I couldn't hear them, and it was hard to believe they really existed.

Nearly all the women wore aprons, and the strings drawn tight
round their waists made their big stomachs bulge still more. I'd never yet
noticed what big paunches old women usually have. Most of the men,
however, were as thin as rakes, and they all carried sticks. What struck
me most about their faces was that one couldn't see their eyes, only a dull
glow in a sort of nest of wrinkles.

On sitting down, they looked at me, and wagged their heads awkwardly, their lips sucked in between their toothless gums. I couldn't
decide if they were greeting me and trying to say something, or if it was
due to some infirmity of age. I inclined to think that they were greeting
me, after their fashion, but it had a queer effect, seeing all those old
fellows grouped round the keeper, solemnly eying me and dandling their
heads from side to side. For a moment I had an absurd impression that
they had come to sit in judgment on me.

A few minutes later one of the women started weeping. She was in
the second row and I couldn't see her face because of another woman in
front. At regular intervals she emitted a little choking sob; one had a
feeling she would never stop. The others didn't seem to notice. They sat
in silence, slumped in their chairs, staring at the coffin or at their walking
sticks or any object just in front of them, and never took their eyes off it.
And still the woman sobbed. I was rather surprised, as I didn't know who
she was. I wanted her to stop crying, but dared not speak to her. After a
while the keeper bent toward her and whispered in her ear; but she

merely shook her head, mumbled something I couldn't catch, and went on sobbing as steadily as before.

The keeper got up and moved his chair beside mine. At first he kept silent; then, without looking at me, he explained.

"She was devoted to your mother. She says your mother was her only friend in the world, and now she's all alone."

I had nothing to say, and the silence lasted quite a while. Presently the woman's sighs and sobs became less frequent, and, after blowing her nose and snuffling for some minutes, she, too, fell silent.

I'd ceased feeling sleepy, but I was very tired and my legs were aching badly. And now I realized that the silence of these people was telling on my nerves. The only sound was a rather queer one; it came only now and then, and at first I was puzzled by it. However, after listening attentively, I guessed what it was; the old men were sucking at the insides of their cheeks, and this caused the odd, wheezing noises that had mystified me. They were so much absorbed in their thoughts that they didn't know what they were up to. I even had an impression that the dead body in their midst meant nothing at all to them. But now I suspect that I was mistaken about this.

We all drank the coffee, which the keeper handed round. After that, I can't remember much; somehow the night went by. I can recall only one moment; I had opened my eyes and I saw the old men sleeping hunched up on their chairs, with one exception. Resting his chin on his hands clasped round his stick, he was staring hard at me, as if he had been waiting for me to wake. Then I fell asleep again. I woke up after a bit, because the ache in my legs had developed into a sort of cramp.

There was a glimmer of dawn above the skylight. A minute or two later one of the old men woke up and coughed repeatedly. He spat into a big check handkerchief, and each time he spat it sounded as if he were retching. This woke the others, and the keeper told them it was time to make a move. They all got up at once. Their faces were ashen gray after the long, uneasy vigil. To my surprise each of them shook hands with me, as though this night together, in which we hadn't exchanged a word, had created a kind of intimacy between us.

I was quite done in. The keeper took me to his room, and I tidied myself up a bit. He gave me some more "white" coffee, and it seemed to do me good. When I went out, the sun was up and the sky mottled red above the hills between Marengo and the sea. A morning breeze was blowing and it had a pleasant salty tang. There was the promise of a very fine day. I hadn't been in the country for ages, and I caught myself thinking what an agreeable walk I could have had, if it hadn't been for Mother.

As it was, I waited in the courtyard, under a plane tree. I sniffed the smells of the cool earth and found I wasn't sleepy any more. Then I thought of the other fellows in the office. At this hour they'd be getting up, preparing to go to work; for me this was always the worst hour of the day. I went on thinking, like this, for ten minutes or so; then the sound of a bell inside the building attracted my attention. I could see movements behind the windows; then all was calm again. The sun had risen a little higher and was beginning to warm my feet. The keeper came across the yard and said the warden wished to see me. I went to his office and he got me to sign some document. I noticed that he was in black, with pin-stripe trousers. He picked up the telephone receiver and looked at me.

"The undertaker's men arrived some moments ago, and they will be going to the mortuary to screw down the coffin. Shall I tell them to wait, for you to have a last glimpse of your mother?"

"No," I said.

He spoke into the receiver, lowering his voice.

"That's all right, Figeac. Tell the men to go there now."

He then informed me that he was going to attend the funeral, and I thanked him. Sitting down behind his desk, he crossed his short legs and leaned back. Besides the nurse on duty, he told me, he and I would be the only mourners at the funeral. It was a rule of the Home that inmates shouldn't attend funerals, though there was no objection to letting some of them sit up beside the coffin, the night before.

"It's for their own sakes," he explained, "to spare their feelings. But in this particular instance I've given permission to an old friend of your mother to come with us. His name is Thomas Pérez." The warden smiled. "It's a rather touching little story in its way. He and your mother had become almost inseparable. The other old people used to tease Pérez about having a fiancée. 'When are you going to marry her?' they'd ask. He'd turn it with a laugh. It was a standing joke, in fact. So, as you can guess, he feels very badly about your mother's death. I thought I couldn't decently refuse him permission to attend the funeral. But, on our medical officer's advice, I forbade him to sit up beside the body last night."

For some time we sat there without speaking. Then the warden got up and went to the window. Presently he said:

"Ah, there's the padre from Marengo. He's a bit ahead of time."

He warned me that it would take us a good three quarters of an hour, walking to the church, which was in the village. Then we went downstairs.

The priest was waiting just outside the mortuary door. With him were two acolytes, one of whom had a censer. The priest was stooping over him, adjusting the length of the silver chain on which it hung. When he saw us he straightened up and said a few words to me, addressing me as, "My son." Then he led the way into the mortuary.

I noticed at once that four men in black were standing behind the coffin and the screws in the lid had now been driven home. At the same moment I heard the warden remark that the hearse had arrived, and the priest starting his prayers. Then everybody made a move. Holding a strip of black cloth, the four men approached the coffin, while the priest, the boys, and myself filed out. A lady I hadn't seen before was standing by the door. "This is Monsieur Meursault," the warden said to her. I didn't catch her name, but I gathered she was a nursing sister attached to the Home. When I was introduced, she bowed, without the trace of a smile on her long, gaunt face. We stood aside from the doorway to let the coffin by; then, following the bearers down a corridor, we came to the front entrance, where a hearse was waiting. Oblong, glossy, varnished black all over, it vaguely reminded me of the pen trays in the office.

Beside the hearse stood a quaintly dressed little man, whose duty it was, I understood, to supervise the funeral, as a sort of master of ceremonies. Near him, looking constrained, almost bashful, was old M. Pérez, my mother's special friend. He wore a soft felt hat with a pudding-basin crown and a very wide brim—he whisked it off the moment the coffin emerged from the doorway—trousers that concertina'd on his shoes, a black tie much too small for his high white double collar. Under a bulbous, pimply nose, his lips were trembling. But what caught my attention most was his ears; pendulous, scarlet ears that showed up like blobs of sealing wax on the pallor of his cheeks and were framed in wisps of silky white hair.

The undertaker's factotum shepherded us to our places, with the priest in front of the hearse, and the four men in black on each side of it. The warden and myself came next, and, bringing up the rear, old Pérez and the nurse.

The sky was already a blaze of light, and the air stoking up rapidly. I felt the first waves of heat lapping my back, and my dark suit made things worse. I couldn't imagine why we waited so long for getting under way. Old Pérez, who had put on his hat, took it off again. I had turned slightly in his direction and was looking at him when the warden started telling me more about him. I remember his saying that old Pérez and my mother used often to have a longish stroll together in the cool of the evening; sometimes they went as far as the village, accompanied by a nurse, of course.

I looked at the countryside, at the long lines of cypresses sloping up toward the skyline and the hills, the hot red soil dappled with vivid green, and here and there a lonely house sharply outlined against the light—and I could understand Mother's feelings. Evenings in these parts must be a sort of mournful solace. Now, in the full glare of the morning sun, with everything shimmering in the heat haze, there was something inhuman, discouraging, about this landscape.

At last we made a move. Only then I noticed that Pérez had a slight limp. The old chap steadily lost ground as the hearse gained speed. One of the men beside it, too, fell back and drew level with me. I was surprised to see how quickly the sun was climbing up the sky, and just then it struck me that for quite a while the air had been throbbing with the hum of insects and the rustle of grass warming up. Sweat was running down my face. As I had no hat I tried to fan myself with my handkerchief.

The undertaker's man turned to me and said something that I didn't catch. At that same time he wiped the crown of his head with a handkerchief that he held in his left hand, while with his right he tilted up his hat. I asked him what he'd said. He pointed upward.

"Sun's pretty bad today, ain't it?"

"Yes," I said.

After a while he asked: "Is it your mother we're burying?"

"Yes," I said again.

"What was her age?"

"Well, she was getting on." As a matter of fact, I didn't know exactly how old she was.

After that he kept silent. Looking back, I saw Pérez limping along some fifty yards behind. He was swinging his big felt hat at arm's length, trying to make the pace. I also had a look at the warden. He was walking with carefully measured steps, economizing every gesture. Beads of perspiration glistened on his forehead, but he didn't wipe them off.

I had an impression that our little procession was moving slightly faster. Wherever I looked I saw the same sun-drenched countryside, and the sky was so dazzling that I dared not raise my eyes. Presently we struck a patch of freshly tarred road. A shimmer of heat played over it and one's feet squelched at each step, leaving bright black gashes. In front, the coachman's glossy black hat looked like a lump of the same sticky substance, poised above the hearse. It gave one a queer, dreamlike impression, that blue-white glare overhead and all this blackness round one: the sleek black of the hearse, the dull black of the men's clothes, and the silvery-black gashes in the road. And then there were the smells, smells of hot leather and horse dung from the hearse, veined with whiffs of incense smoke. What with these and the hangover from a poor night's sleep, I found my eyes and thoughts growing blurred.

I looked back again. Pérez seemed very far away now, almost hidden by the heat haze; then, abruptly, he disappeared altogether. After puzzling over it for a bit, I guessed that he had turned off the road into the fields. Then I noticed that there was a bend of the road a little way ahead. Obviously Pérez, who knew the district well, had taken a short cut, so as to catch up with us. He rejoined us soon after we were round the bend; then began to lose ground again. He took another short cut and met us again farther on; in fact, this happened several times during the next half-hour. But soon I lost interest in his movements; my temples were throbbing and I could hardly drag myself along.

After that everything went with a rush; and also with such precision and matter-of-factness that I remember hardly any details. Except that when we were on the outskirts of the village the nurse said something to me. Her voice took me by surprise; it didn't match her face at all; it was musical and slightly tremulous. What she said was: "If you go too slowly there's the risk of a heatstroke. But, if you go too fast, you perspire, and the cold air in the church gives you a chill." I saw her point; either way one was in for it.

Some other memories of the funeral have stuck in my mind. The old boy's face, for instance, when he caught up with us for the last time, just outside the village. His eyes were streaming with tears, of exhaustion or distress, or both together. But because of the wrinkles they couldn't flow down. They spread out, crisscrossed, and formed a smooth gloss on the old, worn face.

And I can remember the look of the church, the villagers in the street, the red geraniums on the graves, Pérez's fainting fit—he crumpled up like a rag doll—the tawny-red earth pattering on Mother's coffin, the bits of white roots mixed up with it; then more people, voices, the wait outside a café for the bus, the rumble of the engine, and my little thrill of pleasure when we entered the first brightly lit streets of Algiers, and I pictured myself going straight to bed and sleeping twelve hours at a stretch.

II

ON WAKING I understood why my employer had looked rather cross when I asked for my two days off; it's a Saturday today. I hadn't thought of this at the time; it only struck me when I was getting out of bed. Obviously he had seen that it would mean my getting four days' holiday straight off, and one couldn't expect him to like that. Still, for one thing, it wasn't my fault if Mother was buried yesterday and not today; and then, again, I'd have had my Saturday and Sunday off in any case. But naturally this didn't prevent me from seeing my employer's point.

Getting up was an effort, as I'd been really exhausted by the previous day's experiences. While shaving, I wondered how to spend the morning, and decided that a swim would do me good. So I caught the streetcar that goes down to the harbor.

It was quite like old times; a lot of young people were in the swimming pool, amongst them Marie Cardona, who used to be a typist at the office. I was rather keen on her in those days, and I fancy she liked me, too. But she was with us so short a time that nothing came of it.

While I was helping her to climb on to a raft, I let my hand stray over her breasts. Then she lay flat on the raft, while I trod water. After a moment she turned and looked at me. Her hair was over her eyes and she was laughing. I clambered up on to the raft, beside her. The air was pleasantly warm, and, half jokingly, I let my head sink back upon her lap. She didn't seem to mind, so I let it stay there. I had the sky full in my eyes, all blue and gold, and I could feel Marie's stomach rising and falling gently under my head. We must have stayed a good half-hour on the raft, both of us half asleep. When the sun got too hot she dived off and I followed. I caught up with her, put my arm round her waist, and we swam side by side. She was still laughing.

While we were drying ourselves on the edge of the swimming pool she said: "I'm browner than you." I asked her if she'd come to the movies with me that evening. She laughed again and said, "Yes," if I'd take her to the comedy everybody was talking about, the one with Fernandel in it.

When we had dressed, she stared at my black tie and asked if I was in mourning. I explained that my mother had died. "When?" she asked, and I said, "Yesterday." She made no remark, though I thought she shrank away a little. I was just going to explain to her that it wasn't my fault, but I checked myself, as I remembered having said the same thing to my employer, and realizing then it sounded rather foolish. Still, foolish or not, somehow one can't help feeling a bit guilty, I suppose.

Anyhow, by evening Marie had forgotten all about it. The film was funny in parts, but some of it was downright stupid. She pressed her leg against mine while we were in the picture house, and I was fondling her breast. Toward the end of the show I kissed her, but rather clumsily. Afterward she came back with me to my place.

When I woke up, Marie had gone. She'd told me her aunt expected her first thing in the morning. I remembered it was a Sunday, and that put me off; I've never cared for Sundays. So I turned my head and lazily sniffed the smell of brine that Marie's head had left on the pillow. I slept until ten. After that I stayed in bed until noon, smoking cigarettes. I decided not to lunch at Céleste's restaurant as I usually did; they'd be sure to pester me with questions, and I dislike being questioned. So I fried some eggs and ate them off the pan. I did without bread as there wasn't any left, and I couldn't be bothered going down to buy it.

After lunch I felt at loose ends and roamed about the little flat. It suited us well enough when Mother was with me, but now that I was by myself it was too large and I'd moved the dining table into my bedroom. That was now the only room I used; it had all the furniture I needed: a brass bedstead, a dressing table, some cane chairs whose seats had more or less caved in, a wardrobe with a tarnished mirror. The rest of the flat was never used, so I didn't trouble to look after it.

A bit later, for want of anything better to do, I picked up an old newspaper that was lying on the floor and read it. There was an advertisement of Kruschen Salts and I cut it out and pasted it into an album where I keep things that amuse me in the papers. Then I washed my hands and, as a last resource, went out on to the balcony.

My bedroom overlooks the main street of our district. Though it was a fine afternoon, the paving blocks were black and glistening. What few people were about seemed in an absurd hurry. First of all there came a family going for their Sunday-afternoon walk; two small boys in sailor suits, with short trousers hardly down to their knees, and looking rather uneasy in their Sunday best; then a little girl with a big pink bow and black patent-leather shoes. Behind them was their mother, an enormously fat woman in a brown silk dress, and their father, a dapper little man, whom I knew by sight. He had a straw hat, a walking stick, and a butterfly tie. Seeing him beside his wife, I understood why people said he came of a good family and had married beneath him.

Next came a group of young fellows, the local "bloods," with sleek oiled hair, red ties, coats cut very tight at the waist, braided pockets, and square-toed shoes. I guessed they were going to one of the big theaters in the center of the town. That was why they had started out so early and were hurrying to the streetcar stop, laughing and talking at the top of their voices.

After they had passed, the street gradually emptied. By this time all the matinees must have begun. Only a few shopkeepers and cats remained about. Above the sycamores bordering the road the sky was cloudless, but the light was soft. The tobacconist on the other side of the street brought a chair out on to the pavement in front of his door and sat astride it, resting his arms on the back. The streetcars which a few minutes before had been crowded were now almost empty. In the little café, Chez Pierrot, beside the tobacconist's, the waiter was sweeping up the sawdust in the empty restaurant. A typical Sunday afternoon. . . .

I turned my chair round and seated myself like the tobacconist, as it was more comfortable that way. After smoking a couple of cigarettes I went back to the room, got a tablet of chocolate, and returned to the window to eat it. Soon after, the sky clouded over, and I thought a summer storm was coming. However, the clouds gradually lifted. All the same, they had left in the street a sort of threat of rain, which made it darker. I stayed watching the sky for quite a while.

At five there was a loud clanging of streetcars. They were coming from the stadium in our suburb where there had been a football match. Even the back platforms were crowded and people were standing on the steps. Then another streetcar brought back the teams. I knew they were the players by the little suitcase each man carried. They were bawling out their team song, "Keep the ball rolling, boys." One of them looked up at me and shouted, "We licked them!" I waved my hand and called back, "Good work!" From now on there was a steady stream of private cars.

The sky had changed again; a reddish glow was spreading up beyond the housetops. As dusk set in, the street grew more crowded. People were returning from their walks, and I noticed the dapper little man with the fat wife amongst the passers-by. Children were whimpering and trailing wearily after their parents. After some minutes the local picture houses disgorged their audiences. I noticed that the young fellows coming from them were taking longer strides and gesturing more vigorously than at ordinary times; doubtless the picture they'd been seeing was of the wild-West variety. Those who had been to the picture houses in the middle of the town came a little later, and looked more sedate, though a few were still laughing. On the whole, however, they seemed languid and exhausted. Some of them remained loitering in the street under my window. A group of girls came by, walking arm in arm. The young men under my window swerved so as to brush against them, and shouted humorous remarks, which made the girls turn their heads and giggle. I recognized them as girls from my part of the town, and two or three of them, whom I knew, looked up and waved to me.

Just then the street lamps came on, all together, and they made the stars that were beginning to glimmer in the night sky paler still. I felt my eyes getting tired, what with the lights and all the movement I'd been watching in the street. There were little pools of brightness under the lamps, and now and then a streetcar passed, lighting up a girl's hair, or a smile, or a silver bangle.

Soon after this, as the streetcars became fewer and the sky showed velvety black above the trees and lamps, the street grew emptier, almost imperceptibly, until a time came when there was nobody to be seen and a cat, the first of the evening, crossed, unhurrying, the deserted street.

It struck me that I'd better see about some dinner. I had been leaning so long on the back of my chair, looking down, that my neck hurt when I straightened myself up. I went down, bought some bread and spaghetti, did my cooking, and ate my meal standing. I'd intended to smoke another cigarette at my window, but the night had turned rather chilly and I decided against it. As I was coming back, after shutting the window, I glanced at the mirror and saw reflected in it a corner of my table with my spirit lamp and some bits of bread beside it. It occurred to me that somehow I'd got through another Sunday, that Mother now was buried, and tomorrow I'd be going back to work as usual. Really, nothing in my life had changed.

III

I HAD A BUSY MORNING in the office. My employer was in a good humor. He even inquired if I wasn't too tired, and followed it up by asking what Mother's age was. I thought a bit, then answered, "Round about sixty," as I didn't want to make a blunder. At which he looked relieved—why, I can't imagine—and seemed to think that closed the matter.

There was a pile of bills of lading waiting on my desk, and I had to go through them all. Before leaving for lunch I washed my hands. I always enjoyed doing this at midday. In the evening it was less pleasant, as the roller towel, after being used by so many people, was sopping wet. I once brought this to my employer's notice. It was regrettable, he agreed—but, to his mind, a mere detail. I left the office building a little later than usual, at half-past twelve, with Emmanuel, who works in the Forwarding Department. Our building overlooks the sea, and we paused for a moment on the steps to look at the shipping in the harbor. The sun was scorching hot. Just then a big truck came up, with a din of chains and backfires from the engine, and Emmanuel suggested we should try to jump it. I started to run. The truck was well away, and we had to chase it for quite a distance. What with the heat and the noise from the engine, I felt half dazed. All I was conscious of was our mad rush along the water front, amongst cranes and winches, with dark hulls of ships alongside and masts swaying in the offing. I was the first to catch up with the truck. I took a flying jump, landed safely, and helped Emmanuel to scramble in beside me. We were both of us out of breath, and the bumps of the truck on the roughly laid cobbles made things worse. Emmanuel chuckled, and panted in my ear, "We've made it!"

By the time we reached Céleste's restaurant we were dripping with sweat. Céleste was at his usual place beside the entrance, with his apron bulging on his paunch, his white mustache well to the fore. When he saw me he was sympathetic and "hoped I wasn't feeling too badly." I said, "No," but I was extremely hungry. I ate very quickly and had some coffee to finish up. Then I went to my place and took a short nap, as I'd drunk a glass of wine too many.

When I woke I smoked a cigarette before getting off my bed. I was a bit late and had to run for the streetcar. The office was stifling, and I was kept hard at it all the afternoon. So it came as a relief when we closed down and I was strolling slowly along the wharves in the coolness. The sky was green, and it was pleasant to be out-of-doors after the stuffy office. However, I went straight home, as I had to put some potatoes on to boil.

The hall was dark and, when I was starting up the stairs, I almost bumped into old Salamano, who lived on the same floor as I. As usual, he had his dog with him. For eight years the two had been inseparable. Salamano's spaniel is an ugly brute, afflicted with some skin disease— mange, I suspect; anyhow, it has lost all its hair and its body is covered with brown scabs. Perhaps through living in one small room, cooped up with his dog, Salamano has come to resemble it. His towy hair has gone very thin, and he has reddish blotches on his face. And the dog has developed something of its master's queer hunched-up gait; it always has its muzzle stretched far forward and its nose to the ground. But, oddly enough, though so much alike, they detest each other.

Twice a day, at eleven and six, the old fellow takes his dog for a walk, and for eight years that walk has never varied. You can see them in the rue de Lyon, the dog pulling his master along as hard as he can, till finally the old chap misses a step and nearly falls. Then he beats his dog and calls it names. The dog cowers and lags behind, and it's his master's turn to drag him along. Presently the dog forgets, starts tugging at the leash again, gets another hiding and more abuse. Then they halt on the pavement, the pair of them, and glare at each other; the dog with terror and the man with hatred in his eyes. Every time they're out, this happens. When the dog wants to stop at a lamppost, the old boy won't let him, and drags him on, and the wretched spaniel leaves behind him a trail of little drops. But, if he does it in the room, it means another hiding.

It's been going on like this for eight years, and Céleste always says it's a "crying shame," and something should be done about it; but really one can't be sure. When I met him in the hall, Salamano was bawling at his dog, calling him a bastard, a lousy mongrel, and so forth, and the dog was whining. I said, "Good evening," but the old fellow took no notice and went on cursing. So I thought I'd ask him what the dog had done. Again, he didn't answer, but went on shouting, "You bloody cur!" and the rest of it. I couldn't see very clearly, but he seemed to be fixing something on the dog's collar. I raised my voice a little. Without looking round, he mumbled in a sort of suppressed fury: "He's always in the way, blast him!" Then he started up the stairs, but the dog tried to resist and flattened itself out on the floor, so he had to haul it up on the leash, step by step.

Just then another man who lives on my floor came in from the street. The general idea hereabouts is that he's a pimp. But if you ask him what his job is, he says he's a warehouseman. One thing's sure: he isn't popular in our street. Still, he often has a word for me, and drops in sometimes for a short talk in my room, because I listen to him. As a matter of fact, I find what he says quite interesting. So, really I've no reason for freezing him off. His name is Sintès; Raymond Sintès. He's short and thick-set, has a nose like a boxer's, and always dresses very sprucely. He, too, once said to me, referring to Salamano, that it was "a damned shame," and asked me if I wasn't disgusted by the way the old man served his dog. I answered: "No."

We went up the stairs together, Sintès and I, and when I was turning in at my door, he said:

"Look here! How about having some grub with me? I've a black pudding and some wine."

It struck me that this would save my having to cook my dinner, so I said, "Thanks very much."

He, too, has only one room, and a little kitchen without a window. I saw a pink-and-white plaster angel above his bed, and some photos of sporting champions and naked girls pinned to the opposite wall. The bed hadn't been made and the room was dirty. He began by lighting a paraffin lamp; then fumbled in his pocket and produced a rather grimy bandage, which he wrapped round his right hand. I asked him what the trouble was. He told me he'd been having a roughhouse with a fellow who'd annoyed him.

"I'm not one who looks for trouble," he explained, "only I'm a bit short-tempered. That fellow said to me, challenging-like, 'Come down off that streetcar, if you're a man.' I says, 'You keep quiet, I ain't done nothing to you.' Then he said I hadn't any guts. Well, that settled it. I got down off the streetcar and I said to him, 'You better keep your mouth shut, or I'll shut it for you.' 'I'd like to see you try!' says he. Then I gave him one across the face, and laid him out good and proper. After a bit I started to help him get up, but all he did was to kick at me from where he lay. So I gave him one with my knee and a couple more swipes. He was bleeding like a pig when I'd done with him. I asked him if he'd had enough, and he said, 'Yes.' "

Sintès was busy fixing his bandage while he talked, and I was sitting on the bed.

"So you see," he said, "it wasn't my fault; he was asking for it, wasn't he?"

I nodded, and he added:

"As a matter of fact, I rather want to ask your advice about something; it's connected with this business. You've knocked about the world a bit, and I daresay you can help me. And then I'll be your pal for life; I never forget anyone who does me a good turn."

When I made no comment, he asked me if I'd like us to be pals. I replied that I had no objection, and that appeared to satisfy him. He got out the black pudding, cooked it in a frying pan, then laid the table, putting out two bottles of wine. While he was doing this he didn't speak.

We started dinner, and then he began telling me the whole story, hesitating a bit at first.

"There's a girl behind it—as usual. We slept together pretty regular. I was keeping her, as a matter of fact, and she cost me a tidy sum. That fellow I knocked down is her brother."

Noticing that I said nothing, he added that he knew what the neighbors said about him, but it was a filthy lie. He had his principles like everybody else, and a job in a warehouse.

"Well," he said, "to go on with my story . . . I found out one day that she was letting me down." He gave her enough money to keep her going, without extravagance, though; he paid the rent of her room and twenty francs a day for food. "Three hundred francs for rent, and six hundred for her grub, with a little present thrown in now and then, a pair of stockings or what not. Say, a thousand francs a month. But that wasn't enough for my fine lady; she was always grumbling that she couldn't make both ends meet with what I gave her. So one day I says to her, 'Look here, why not get a job for a few hours a day? That'd make things easier for me, too. I bought you a new dress this month, I pay your rent and give you twenty francs a day. But you go and waste your money at the café with a pack of girls. You give them coffee and sugar. And, of course, the money comes out of my pocket. I treat you on the square, and that's how you pay me back.' But she wouldn't hear of working, though she kept on saying she couldn't make do with what I gave her. And then one day I found out she was doing me dirt."

He went on to explain that he'd found a lottery ticket in her bag, and, when he asked where the money'd come from to buy it, she wouldn't tell him. Then, another time, he'd found a pawn ticket for two bracelets that he'd never set eyes on.

"So I knew there was dirty work going on, and I told her I'd have nothing more to do with her. But, first, I gave her a good hiding, and I told her some home truths. I said that there was only one thing inter-

ested her and that was getting into bed with men whenever she'd the
chance. And I warned her straight, 'You'll be sorry one day, my girl, and
wish you'd got me back. All the girls in the street, they're jealous of
your luck in having me to keep you.' "

He'd beaten her till the blood came. Before that he'd never beaten her.
"Well, not hard, anyhow; only affectionately-like. She'd howl a bit, and
I had to shut the window. Then, of course, it ended as per usual. But this
time I'm done with her. Only, to my mind, I ain't punished her enough.
See what I mean?"

He explained that it was about this he wanted my advice. The lamp
was smoking, and he stopped pacing up and down the room, to lower the
wick. I just listened, without speaking. I'd had a whole bottle of wine to
myself and my head was buzzing. As I'd used up my cigarettes I was
smoking Raymond's. Some late streetcars passed, and the last noises of
the street died off with them. Raymond went on talking. What bored
him was that he had "a sort of lech on her" as he called it. But he was
quite determined to teach her a lesson.

His first idea, he said, had been to take her to a hotel, and then call in
the special police. He'd persuade them to put her on the register as a
"common prostitute," and that would make her wild. Then he'd looked
up some friends of his in the underworld, fellows who kept tarts for
what they could make out of them, but they had practically nothing to
suggest. Still, as he pointed out, that sort of thing should have been right
up their street; what's the good of being in that line if you don't know
how to treat a girl who's let you down? When he told them that, they
suggested he should "brand" her. But that wasn't what he wanted, either.
It would need a lot of thinking out. . . . But, first, he'd like to ask me
something. Before he asked it, though, he'd like to have my opinion of
the story he'd been telling, in a general way.

I said I hadn't any, but I'd found it interesting.

Did I think she really had done him dirt?

I had to admit it looked like that. Then he asked me if I didn't think
she should be punished and what I'd do if I were in his shoes. I told him
one could never be quite sure how to act in such cases, but I quite
understood his wanting her to suffer for it.

I drank some more wine, while Raymond lit another cigarette and
began explaining what he proposed to do. He wanted to write her a
letter, "a real stinker, that'll get her on the raw," and at the same time
make her repent of what she'd done. Then, when she came back, he'd go
to bed with her and, just when she was "properly primed up," he'd spit
in her face and throw her out of the room. I agreed it wasn't a bad plan;
it would punish her, all right.

But, Raymond told me, he didn't feel up to writing the kind of letter
that was needed, and that was where I could help. When I didn't say
anything, he asked me if I'd mind doing it right away, and I said, "No,"
I'd have a shot at it.

He drank off a glass of wine and stood up. Then he pushed aside the plates and the bit of cold pudding that was left, to make room on the table. After carefully wiping the oilcloth, he got a sheet of squared paper from the drawer of his bedside table; after that, an envelope, a small red wooden penholder, and a square inkpot with purple ink in it. The moment he mentioned the girl's name I knew she was a Moor.

I wrote the letter. I didn't take much trouble over it, but I wanted to satisfy Raymond, as I'd no reason not to satisfy him. Then I read out what I'd written. Puffing at his cigarette, he listened, nodding now and then. "Read it again, please," he said. He seemed delighted. "That's the stuff," he chuckled. "I could tell you was a brainy sort, old boy, and you know what's what."

At first I hardly noticed that "old boy." It came back to me when he slapped me on the shoulder and said, "So now we're pals, ain't we?" I kept silence and he said it again. I didn't care one way or the other, but as he seemed so set on it, I nodded and said, "Yes."

He put the letter into the envelope and we finished off the wine. Then both of us smoked for some minutes, without speaking. The street was quite quiet, except when now and again a car passed. Finally, I remarked that it was getting late, and Raymond agreed. "Time's gone mighty fast this evening," he added, and in a way that was true. I wanted to be in bed, only it was such an effort making a move. I must have looked tired, for Raymond said to me, "You mustn't let things get you down." At first I didn't catch his meaning. Then he explained that he had heard of my mother's death; anyhow, he said, that was something bound to happen one day or another. I appreciated that, and told him so.

When I rose, Raymond shook hands very warmly, remarking that men always understood each other. After closing the door behind me I lingered for some moments on the landing. The whole building was as quiet as the grave, a dank, dark smell rising from the well hole of the stairs. I could hear nothing but the blood throbbing in my ears, and for a while I stood still, listening to it. Then the dog began to moan in old Salamano's room, and through the sleep-bound house the little plaintive sound rose slowly, like a flower growing out of the silence and the darkness.

IV

I HAD A BUSY TIME in the office throughout the week. Raymond dropped in once to tell me he'd sent off the letter. I went to the pictures twice with Emmanuel, who doesn't always understand what's happening on the screen and asks me to explain it. Yesterday was Saturday, and Marie came as we'd arranged. She had a very pretty dress, with red and white stripes, and leather sandals, and I couldn't take my eyes off her.

One could see the outline of her firm little breasts, and her sun-tanned face was like a velvety brown flower. We took the bus and went to a beach I know, some miles out of Algiers. It's just a strip of sand between two rocky spurs, with a line of rushes at the back, along the tide line. At four o'clock the sun wasn't too hot, but the water was pleasantly tepid, and small, languid ripples were creeping up the sand.

Marie taught me a new game. The idea was, while one swam, to suck in the spray off the waves and, when one's mouth was full of foam, to lie on one's back and spout it out against the sky. It made a sort of frothy haze that melted into the air or fell back in a warm shower on one's cheeks. But very soon my mouth was smarting with all the salt I'd drawn in; then Marie came up and hugged me in the water, and pressed her mouth to mine. Her tongue cooled my lips, and we let the waves roll us about for a minute or two before swimming back to the beach.

When we had finished dressing, Marie looked hard at me. Her eyes were sparkling. I kissed her; after that neither of us spoke for quite a while. I pressed her to my side as we scrambled up the foreshore. Both of us were in a hurry to catch the bus, get back to my place, and tumble on to the bed. I'd left my window open, and it was pleasant to feel the cool night air flowing over our sunburned bodies.

Marie said she was free next morning, so I proposed she should have luncheon with me. She agreed, and I went down to buy some meat. On my way back I heard a woman's voice in Raymond's room. A little later old Salamano started grumbling at his dog and presently there was a sound of boots and paws on the wooden stairs; then, "Filthy brute! Get on, you cur!" and the two of them went out into the street. I told Marie about the old man's habits, and it made her laugh. She was wearing one of my pajama suits, and had the sleeves rolled up. When she laughed I wanted her again. A moment later she asked me if I loved her. I said that sort of question had no meaning, really; but I supposed I didn't. She looked sad for a bit, but when we were getting our lunch ready she brightened up and started laughing, and when she laughs I always want to kiss her. It was just then that the row started in Raymond's room.

First we heard a woman saying something in a high-pitched voice; then Raymond bawling at her, "You let me down, you bitch! I'll learn you to let me down!" There came some thuds, then a piercing scream—it made one's blood run cold—and in a moment there was a crowd of people on the landing. Marie and I went to see. The woman was still screaming and Raymond still knocking her about. Marie said, wasn't it horrible! I didn't answer anything. Then she asked me to go and fetch a policeman, but I told her I didn't like policemen. However, one turned up presently; the lodger on the second floor, a plumber, came up with him. When he banged on the door the noise stopped inside the room. He knocked again, and, after a moment, the woman started crying, and Raymond opened the door. He had a cigarette dangling from his under-lip and a rather sickly smile.

"Your name?" Raymond gave his name. "Take that cigarette out of your mouth when you're talking to me," the policeman said gruffly. Raymond hesitated, glanced at me, and kept the cigarette in his mouth. The policeman promptly swung his arm and gave him a good hard smack on the left cheek. The cigarette shot from his lips and dropped a yard away. Raymond made a wry face, but said nothing for a moment. Then in a humble tone he asked if he mightn't pick up his cigarette.

The officer said, "Yes," and added: "But don't you forget next time that we don't stand for any nonsense, not from guys like you."

Meanwhile the girl went on sobbing and repeating: "He hit me, the coward. He's a pimp."

"Excuse me, officer," Raymond put in, "but is that in order, calling a man a pimp in the presence of witnesses?"

The policeman told him to shut his trap.

Raymond then turned to the girl. "Don't you worry, my pet. We'll meet again."

"That's enough," the policeman said, and told the girl to go away. Raymond was to stay in his room till summoned to the police station. "You ought to be ashamed of yourself," the policeman added, "getting so tight you can't stand steady. Why, you're shaking all over!"

"I'm not tight," Raymond explained. "Only when I see you standing there and looking at me, I can't help trembling. That's only natural."

Then he closed his door, and we all went away. Marie and I finished getting our lunch ready. But she hadn't any appetite, and I ate nearly all. She left at one, and then I had a nap.

Toward three there was a knock at my door and Raymond came in. He sat down on the edge of my bed and for a minute or two said nothing. I asked him how it had gone off. He said it had all gone quite smoothly at first, as per program; only then she'd slapped his face and he'd seen red, and started thrashing her. As for what happened after that, he needn't tell me, as I was there.

"Well," I said, "you taught her a lesson, all right, and that's what you wanted, isn't it?"

He agreed, and pointed out that whatever the police did, that wouldn't change the fact she'd had her punishment. As for the police, he knew exactly how to handle them. But he'd like to know if I'd expected him to return the blow when the policeman hit him.

I told him I hadn't expected anything whatsoever and, anyhow, I had no use for the police. Raymond seemed pleased and asked if I'd like to come out for a stroll with him. I got up from the bed and started brushing my hair. Then Raymond said that what he really wanted was for me to act as his witness. I told him I had no objection; only I didn't know what he expected me to say.

"It's quite simple," he replied. "You've only got to tell them that the girl had let me down."

So I agreed to be his witness.

We went out together, and Raymond stood me a brandy in a café. Then we had a game of billiards; it was a close game and I lost by only a few points. After that he proposed going to a brothel, but I refused; I didn't feel like it. As we were walking slowly back he told me how pleased he was at having paid out his mistress so satisfactorily. He made himself extremely amiable to me, and I quite enjoyed our walk.

When we were nearly home I saw old Salamano on the doorstep; he seemed very excited. I noticed that his dog wasn't with him. He was turning like a teetotum, looking in all directions, and sometimes peering into the darkness of the hall with his little bloodshot eyes. Then he'd mutter something to himself and start gazing up and down the street again.

Raymond asked him what was wrong, but he didn't answer at once. Then I heard him grunt, "The bastard! The filthy cur!" When I asked him where his dog was, he scowled at me and snapped out, "Gone!" A moment later, all of a sudden, he launched out into it.

"I'd taken him to the Parade Ground as usual. There was a fair on, and you could hardly move for the crowd. I stopped at one of the booths to look at the Handcuff King. When I turned to go, the dog was gone. I'd been meaning to get a smaller collar, but I never thought the brute could slip it and get away like that."

Raymond assured him the dog would find its way home, and told him stories of dogs that had traveled miles and miles to get back to their masters. But this seemed to make the old fellow even more worried than before.

"Don't you understand, they'll do away with him; the police, I mean. It's not likely anyone will take him in and look after him; with all those scabs he puts everybody off."

I told him that there was a pound at the police station, where stray dogs are taken. His dog was certain to be there and he could get it back on payment of a small charge. He asked me how much the charge was, but there I couldn't help him. Then he flew into a rage again.

"Is it likely I'd give money for a mutt like that? No damned fear! They can kill him, for all I care." And he went on calling his dog the usual names.

Raymond gave a laugh and turned into the hall. I followed him upstairs, and we parted on the landing. A minute or two later I heard Salamano's footsteps and a knock on my door.

When I opened it, he halted for a moment in the doorway.

"Excuse me . . . I hope I'm not disturbing you."

I asked him in, but he shook his head. He was staring at his toe caps, and the gnarled old hands were trembling. Without meeting my eyes, he started talking.

"They won't really take him from me, will they, Monsieur Meursault? Surely they wouldn't do a thing like that. If they do—I don't know what will become of me."

I told him that, so far as I knew, they kept stray dogs in the pound for three days, waiting for their owners to call for them. After that they disposed of the dogs as they thought fit.

He stared at me in silence for a moment, then said, "Good evening." After that I heard him pacing up and down his room for quite a while. Then his bed creaked. Through the wall there came to me a little wheezing sound, and I guessed that he was weeping. For some reason, I don't know what, I began thinking of Mother. But I had to get up early next day; so, as I wasn't feeling hungry, I did without supper, and went straight to bed.

V

RAYMOND RANG ME UP at the office. He said that a friend of his—to whom he'd spoken about me—invited me to spend next Sunday at his little seaside bungalow just outside Algiers. I told him I'd have been delighted; only I had promised to spend Sunday with a girl. Raymond promptly replied that she could come, too. In fact, his friend's wife would be very pleased not to be the only woman in a party of men.

I'd have liked to hang up at once, as my employer doesn't approve of my using the office phone for private calls. But Raymond asked me to hold on; he had something else to tell me, and that was why he'd rung me up, though he could have waited till the evening to pass on the invitation.

"It's like this," he said. "I've been shadowed all the morning by some Arabs. One of them's the brother of that girl I had the row with. If you see him hanging round the house when you come back, pass me the word."

I promised to do so.

Just then my employer sent for me. For a moment I felt uneasy, as I expected he was going to tell me to stick to my work and not waste time chattering with friends over the phone. However, it was nothing of the kind. He wanted to discuss a project he had in view, though so far he'd come to no decision. It was to open a branch at Paris, so as to be able to deal with the big companies on the spot, without postal delays, and he wanted to know if I'd like a post there.

"You're a young man," he said, "and I'm pretty sure you'd enjoy living in Paris. And, of course, you could travel about France for some months in the year."

I told him I was quite prepared to go; but really I didn't care much one way or the other.

He then asked if a "change of life," as he called it, didn't appeal to me, and I answered that one never changed his way of life; one life was as good as another, and my present one suited me quite well.

At this he looked rather hurt, and told me that I always shilly-shallied, and that I lacked ambition—a grave defect, to his mind, when one was in business.

I returned to my work. I'd have preferred not to vex him, but I saw no reason for "changing my life." By and large it wasn't an unpleasant one. As a student I'd had plenty of ambition of the kind he meant. But, when I had to drop my studies, I very soon realized all that was pretty futile.

Marie came that evening and asked me if I'd marry her. I said I didn't mind; if she was keen on it, we'd get married.

Then she asked me again if I loved her. I replied, much as before, that her question meant nothing or next to nothing—but I supposed I didn't.

"If that's how you feel," she said, "why marry me?"

I explained that it had no importance really, but, if it would give her pleasure, we could get married right away. I pointed out that, anyhow, the suggestion came from her; as for me, I'd merely said, "Yes."

Then she remarked that marriage was a serious matter.

To which I answered: "No."

She kept silent after that, staring at me in a curious way. Then she asked:

"Suppose another girl had asked you to marry her—I mean, a girl you liked in the same way as you like me—would you have said 'Yes' to her, too?"

"Naturally."

Then she said she wondered if she really loved me or not. I, of course, couldn't enlighten her as to that. And, after another silence, she murmured something about my being "a queer fellow." "And I daresay that's why I love you," she added. "But maybe that's why one day I'll come to hate you."

To which I had nothing to say, so I said nothing.

She thought for a bit, then started smiling and, taking my arm, repeated that she was in earnest; she really wanted to marry me.

"All right," I answered. "We'll get married whenever you like." I then mentioned the proposal made by my employer, and Marie said she'd love to go to Paris.

When I told her I'd lived in Paris for a while, she asked me what it was like.

"A dingy sort of town, to my mind. Masses of pigeons and dark courtyards. And the people have washed-out, white faces."

Then we went for a walk all the way across the town by the main streets. The women were good-lookers, and I asked Marie if she, too, noticed this. She said, "Yes," and that she saw what I meant. After that we said nothing for some minutes. However, as I didn't want her to leave me, I suggested we should dine together at Céleste's. She'd have loved to dine with me, she said, only she was booked up for the evening. We were near my place, and I said, *"Au revoir,* then."

She looked me in the eyes.

"Don't you want to know what I'm doing this evening?"

I did want to know, but I hadn't thought of asking her, and I guessed she was making a grievance of it. I must have looked embarrassed, for suddenly she started laughing and bent toward me, pouting her lips for a kiss.

I went by myself to Céleste's. When I had just started my dinner an odd-looking little woman came in and asked if she might sit at my table. Of course she might. She had a chubby face like a ripe apple, bright eyes, and moved in a curiously jerky way, as if she were on wires. After taking off her close-fitting jacket she sat down and started studying the bill of fare with a sort of rapt attention. Then she called Céleste and gave her order, very fast but quite distinctly; one didn't lose a word. While waiting for the hors d'oeuvre she opened her bag, took out a slip of paper and a pencil, and added up the bill in advance. Diving into her bag again, she produced a purse and took from it the exact sum, plus a small tip, and placed it on the cloth in front of her.

Just then the waiter brought the hors d'oeuvre, which she proceeded to wolf down voraciously. While waiting for the next course, she produced another pencil, this time a blue one, from her bag, and the radio magazine for the coming week, and started making ticks against almost all the items of the daily programs. There were a dozen pages in the magazine, and she continued studying them closely throughout the meal. When I'd finished mine she was still ticking off items with the same meticulous attention. Then she rose, put on her jacket again with the same abrupt, robotlike gestures, and walked briskly out of the restaurant.

Having nothing better to do, I followed her for a short distance. Keeping on the curb of the pavement, she walked straight ahead, never swerving or looking back, and it was extraordinary how fast she covered the ground, considering her smallness. In fact, the pace was too much for me, and I soon lost sight of her and turned back homeward. For a moment the "little robot" (as I thought of her) had much impressed me, but I soon forgot about her.

As I was turning in at my door I ran into old Salamano. I asked him into my room, and he informed me that his dog was definitely lost. He'd been to the pound to inquire, but it wasn't there, and the staff told him it had probably been run over. When he asked them whether it was any use inquiring about it at the police station, they said the police had more important things to attend to than keeping records of stray dogs run over in the streets. I suggested he should get another dog, but, reasonably enough, he pointed out that he'd become used to this one, and it wouldn't be the same thing.

I was seated on my bed, with my legs up, and Salamano on a chair beside the table, facing me, his hands spread on his knees. He had kept on his battered felt hat and was mumbling away behind his draggled yellowish mustache. I found him rather boring, but I had nothing to do and didn't feel sleepy. So, to keep the conversation going, I asked some questions about his dog—how long he had had it and so forth. He told me he had got it soon after his wife's death. He'd married rather late in life. When a young man, he wanted to go on the stage; during his military service he'd often played in the regimental theatricals and acted rather well, so everybody said. However, finally, he had taken a job in the railway, and he didn't regret it, as now he had a small pension. He and his wife had never hit it off very well, but they'd got used to each other, and when she died he felt lonely. One of his mates on the railway whose bitch had just had pups had offered him one, and he had taken it, as a companion. He'd had to feed it from the bottle at first. But, as a dog's life is shorter than a man's, they'd grown old together, so to speak.

"He was a cantankerous brute," Salamano said. "Now and then we had some proper set-tos, he and I. But he was a good mutt all the same."

I said he looked well bred, and that evidently pleased the old man.

"Ah, but you should have seen him before his illness!" he said. "He had a wonderful coat; in fact, that was his best point, really. I tried hard to cure him; every mortal night after he got that skin disease I rubbed an ointment in. But his real trouble was old age, and there's no curing that."

Just then I yawned, and the old man said he'd better make a move. I told him he could stay, and that I was sorry about what had happened to his dog. He thanked me, and mentioned that my mother had been very fond of his dog. He referred to her as "your poor mother," and was afraid I must be feeling her death terribly. When I said nothing he added hastily and with a rather embarrassed air that some of the people in the street said nasty things about me because I'd sent my mother to the Home. But he, of course, knew better; he knew how devoted to my mother I had always been.

I answered—why, I still don't know—that it surprised me to learn I'd produced such a bad impression. As I couldn't afford to keep her here, it seemed the obvious thing to do, to send her to a home. "In any case," I added, "for years she'd never had a word to say to me, and I could see she was moping, with no one to talk to."

"Yes," he said, "and at a home one makes friends, anyhow."

He got up, saying it was high time for him to be in bed, and added that life was going to be a bit of a problem for him, under the new conditions. For the first time since I'd known him he held out his hand to me—rather shyly, I thought—and I could feel the scales on his skin. Just as he was going out of the door, he turned and, smiling a little, said:

"Let's hope the dogs won't bark again tonight. I always think it's mine I hear. . . ."

VI

IT WAS AN EFFORT waking up that Sunday morning; Marie had to jog my shoulders and shout my name. As we wanted to get into the water early, we didn't trouble about breakfast. My head was aching slightly and my first cigarette had a bitter taste. Marie told me I looked like a mourner at a funeral, and I certainly did feel very limp. She was wearing a white dress and had her hair loose. I told her she looked quite ravishing like that, and she laughed happily.

On our way out we banged on Raymond's door, and he shouted that he'd be with us in a jiffy. We went down to the street and, because of my being rather under the weather and our having kept the blind down in my room, the glare of the morning sun hit me in the eyes like a clenched fist.

Marie, however, was almost dancing with delight, and kept on repeating, "What a heavenly day!" After a few minutes I was feeling better, and noticed that I was hungry. I mentioned this to Marie, but she paid no attention. She was carrying an oilcloth bag in which she had stowed our bathing kit and a towel. Presently we heard Raymond shutting his door. He was wearing blue trousers, a short-sleeved white shirt, and a straw hat. I noticed that his forearms were rather hairy, but the skin was very white beneath. The straw hat made Marie giggle. Personally, I was rather put off by his getup. He seemed in high spirits and was whistling as he came down the stairs. He greeted me with, "Hello, old boy!" and addressed Marie as "Mademoiselle."

On the previous evening we had visited the police station, where I gave evidence for Raymond—about the girl's having been false to him. So they let him off with a warning. They didn't check my statement.

After some talk on the doorstep we decided to take the bus. The beach was within easy walking distance, but the sooner we got there the better. Just as we were starting for the bus stop, Raymond plucked my sleeve and told me to look across the street. I saw some Arabs lounging against the tobacconist's window. They were staring at us silently, in the special way these people have—as if we were blocks of stone or dead trees. Raymond whispered that the second Arab from the left was "his man," and I thought he looked rather worried. However, he assured me that all that was ancient history. Marie, who hadn't followed his remarks, asked, "What is it?"

I explained that those Arabs across the way had a grudge against Raymond. She insisted on our going at once. Then Raymond laughed, and squared his shoulders. The young lady was quite right, he said. There was no point in hanging about here. Halfway to the bus stop he glanced back over his shoulder and said the Arabs weren't following. I, too, looked back. They were exactly as before, gazing in the same vague way at the spot where we had been.

When we were in the bus, Raymond, who now seemed quite at ease, kept making jokes to amuse Marie. I could see he was attracted by her, but she had hardly a word for him. Now and again she would catch my eye and smile.

We alighted just outside Algiers. The beach is not far from the bus stop; one has only to cross a patch of highland, a sort of plateau, which overlooks the sea and shelves down steeply to the sands. The ground here was covered with yellowish pebbles and wild lilies that showed snow-white against the blue of the sky, which had already the hard, metallic glint it gets on very hot days. Marie amused herself swishing her bag against the flowers and sending the petals showering in all directions. Then we walked between two rows of little houses with wooden balconies and green or white palings. Some of them were half hidden in clumps of tamarisks; others rose naked from the stony plateau. Before we came to the end of it, the sea was in full view; it lay smooth as a mirror, and in the distance a big headland jutted out over its black reflection. Through the still air came the faint buzz of a motor engine and we saw a fishing boat very far out, gliding almost imperceptibly across the dazzling smoothness.

Marie picked some rock irises. Going down the steep path leading to the sea, we saw some bathers already on the sands.

Raymond's friend owned a small wooden bungalow at the near end of the beach. Its back rested against the cliffside, while the front stood on piles, which the water was already lapping. Raymond introduced us to his friend, whose name was Masson. He was tall, broad-shouldered, and thick-set; his wife was a plump, cheerful little woman who spoke with a Paris accent.

Masson promptly told us to make ourselves at home. He had gone out fishing, he said, first thing in the morning, and there would be fried fish for lunch. I congratulated him on his little bungalow, and he said he always spent his week ends and holidays here. "With the missus, needless to say," he added. I glanced at her, and noticed that she and Marie seemed to be getting on well together; laughing and chattering away. For the first time, perhaps, I seriously considered the possibility of my marrying her.

Masson wanted to have a swim at once, but his wife and Raymond were disinclined to move. So only the three of us, Marie, Masson, and myself, went down to the beach. Marie promptly plunged in, but Masson and I waited for a bit. He was rather slow of speech and had, I noticed, a habit of saying "and what's more" between his phrases—even when the second added nothing really to the first. Talking of Marie, he said: "She's an awfully pretty girl, and what's more, charming."

But I soon ceased paying attention to this trick of his; I was basking in the sunlight, which, I noticed, was making me feel much better. The sand was beginning to stoke up underfoot and, though I was eager for a dip, I postponed it for a minute or two more. At last I said to Masson: "Shall we go in now?" and plunged. Masson walked in gingerly and only began to swim when he was out of his depth. He swam hand over hand and made slow headway, so I left him behind and caught up with Marie. The water was cold and I felt all the better for it. We swam a long way out, Marie and I, side by side, and it was pleasant feeling how our movements matched, hers and mine, and how we were both in the same mood, enjoying every moment.

Once we were out in the open, we lay on our backs and, as I gazed up at the sky, I could feel the sun drawing up the film of salt water on my lips and cheeks. We saw Masson swim back to the beach and slump down on the sand under the sun. In the distance he looked enormous, like a stranded whale. Then Marie proposed that we should swim tandem. She went ahead and I put my arms round her waist, from behind, and while she drew me forward with her arm strokes, I kicked out behind to help us on.

That sound of little splashes had been in my ears for so long that I began to feel I'd had enough of it. So I let go of Marie and swam back at an easy pace, taking long, deep breaths. When I made the beach I stretched myself belly downward beside Masson, resting my face on the sand. I told him "it was fine" here, and he agreed. Presently Marie came back. I raised my head to watch her approach. She was glistening with brine and holding her hair back. Then she lay down beside me, and what with the combined warmth of our bodies and the sun, I felt myself dropping off to sleep.

After a while Marie tugged my arm and said Masson had gone to his place; it must be nearly lunchtime. I rose at once, as I was feeling hungry, but Marie told me I hadn't kissed her once since the early morning. That was so—though I'd wanted to, several times. "Let's go into the water again," she said, and we ran into the sea and lay flat amongst the ripples for a moment. Then we swam a few strokes, and when we were almost out of our depth she flung her arms round me and hugged me. I felt her legs twining round mine, and my senses tingled.

When we got back, Masson was on the steps of his bungalow, shouting to us to come. I told him I was ravenously hungry, and he promptly turned to his wife and said he'd taken quite a fancy to me. The bread was excellent, and I had my full share of the fish. Then came some steak and potato chips. None of us spoke while eating. Masson drank a lot of wine and kept refilling my glass the moment it was empty. By the time coffee was handed round I was feeling slightly muzzy, and I started smoking one cigarette after another. Masson, Raymond, and I discussed a plan of spending the whole of August on the beach together, sharing expenses.

Suddenly Marie exclaimed: "I say! Do you know the time? It's only half-past eleven!"

We were all surprised at that, and Masson remarked that we'd had a very early lunch, but really lunch was a movable feast, you had it when you felt like it.

This set Marie laughing. I don't know why. I suspect she'd drunk a bit too much.

Then Masson asked if I'd like to come with him for a stroll on the beach.

"My wife always has a nap after lunch," he said. "Personally I find it doesn't agree with me; what I need is a short walk. I'm always telling her it's much better for the health. But, of course, she's entitled to her own opinion."

Marie proposed to stay and help with the washing up. Mme Masson smiled and said that, in that case, the first thing was to get the men out of the way. So we went out together, the three of us.

The light was almost vertical and the glare from the water seared one's eyes. The beach was quite deserted now. One could hear a faint tinkle of knives and forks and crockery in the shacks and bungalows lining the foreshore. Heat was welling up from the rocks, and one could hardly breathe.

At first Raymond and Masson talked of things and people I didn't know. I gathered that they'd been acquainted for some time and had even lived together for a while. We went down to the water's edge and walked along it; now and then a longer wave wet our canvas shoes. I wasn't thinking of anything, as all that sunlight beating down on my bare head made me feel half asleep.

Just then Raymond said something to Masson that I didn't quite catch. But at the same moment I noticed two Arabs in blue dungarees a long way down the beach, coming in our direction. I gave Raymond a look and he nodded, saying, "That's him." We walked steadily on. Masson wondered how they'd managed to track us here. My impression was that they had seen us taking the bus and noticed Marie's oilcloth bathing bag; but I didn't say anything.

Though the Arabs walked quite slowly, they were much nearer already. We didn't change our pace, but Raymond said:

"Listen! If there's a roughhouse, you, Masson, take on the second one. I'll tackle the fellow who's after me. And you, Meursault, stand by to help if another one comes up, and lay him out."

I said, "Right," and Masson put his hands in his pockets.

The sand was as hot as fire, and I could have sworn it was glowing red. The distance between us and the Arabs was steadily decreasing. When we were only a few steps away the Arabs halted. Masson and I slowed down, while Raymond went straight up to his man. I couldn't hear what he said, but I saw the native lowering his head, as if to butt him in the chest. Raymond lashed out promptly and shouted to Masson to come. Masson went up to the man he had been marking and struck him twice with all his might. The fellow fell flat into the water and stayed there some seconds with bubbles coming up to the surface round his head. Meanwhile Raymond had been slogging the other man, whose face was streaming with blood. He glanced at me over his shoulder and shouted:

"Just you watch! I ain't finished with him yet!"

"Look out!" I cried. "He's got a knife."

I spoke too late. The man had gashed Raymond's arm and his mouth as well.

Masson sprang forward. The other Arab got up from the water and placed himself behind the fellow with the knife. We didn't dare to move. The two natives backed away slowly, keeping us at bay with the knife and never taking their eyes off us. When they were at a safe distance they swung round and took to their heels. We stood stock-still, with the sunlight beating down on us. Blood was dripping from Raymond's wounded arm, which he was squeezing hard above the elbow.

Masson remarked that there was a doctor who always spent his Sundays here, and Raymond said: "Good. Let's go to him at once." He could hardly get the words out, as the blood from his other wound made bubbles in his mouth.

We each gave him an arm and helped him back to the bungalow. Once we were there he told us the wounds weren't so very deep and he could walk to where the doctor was. Marie had gone quite pale, and Mme Masson was in tears.

Masson and Raymond went off to the doctor's while I was left behind at the bungalow to explain matters to the women. I didn't much relish the task and soon dried up and started smoking, staring at the sea.

Raymond came back at about half-past one, accompanied by Masson. He had his arm bandaged and a strip of sticking plaster on the corner of his mouth. The doctor had assured him it was nothing serious, but he was looking very glum. Masson tried to make him laugh, but without success.

Presently Raymond said he was going for a stroll on the beach. I asked him where he proposed to go, and he mumbled something about "wanting to take the air." We—Masson and I—then said we'd go with him, but he flew into a rage and told us to mind our own business. Masson said we mustn't insist, seeing the state he was in. However, when he went out, I followed him.

It was like a furnace outside, with the sunlight splintering into flakes of fire on the sand and sea. We walked for quite a while, and I had an idea that Raymond had a definite idea where he was going; but probably I was mistaken about this.

At the end of the beach we came to a small stream that had cut a channel in the sand, after coming out from behind a biggish rock. There we found our two Arabs again, lying on the sand in their blue dungarees. They looked harmless enough, as if they didn't bear any malice, and neither made any move when we approached. The man who had slashed

Raymond stared at him without speaking. The other man was blowing down a little reed and extracting from it three notes of the scale, which he played over and over again, while he watched us from the corner of an eye.

For a while nobody moved; it was all sunlight and silence except for the tinkle of the stream and those three little lonely sounds. Then Raymond put his hand to his revolver pocket, but the Arabs still didn't move. I noticed the man playing on the reed had his big toes splayed out almost at right angles to his feet.

Still keeping his eyes on his man, Raymond said to me: "Shall I plug him one?"

I thought quickly. If I told him not to, considering the mood he was in, he might very well fly into a temper and use his gun. So I said the first thing that came into my head.

"He hasn't spoken to you yet. It would be a lowdown trick to shoot him like that, in cold blood."

Again, for some moments one heard nothing but the tinkle of the stream and the flute notes weaving through the hot, still air.

"Well," Raymond said at last, "if that's how you feel, I'd better say something insulting, and if he answers back I'll loose off."

"Right," I said. "Only, if he doesn't get out his knife you've no business to fire."

Raymond was beginning to fidget. The Arab with the reed went on playing, and both of them watched all our movements.

"Listen," I said to Raymond. "You take on the fellow on the right, and give me your revolver. If the other one starts making trouble or gets out his knife, I'll shoot."

The sun glinted on Raymond's revolver as he handed it to me. But nobody made a move yet; it was just as if everything had closed in on us so that we couldn't stir. We could only watch each other, never lowering our eyes; the whole world seemed to have come to a standstill on this little strip of sand between the sunlight and the sea, the twofold silence of the reed and stream. And just then it crossed my mind that one might fire, or not fire—and it would come to absolutely the same thing.

Then, all of a sudden, the Arabs vanished; they'd slipped like lizards under cover of the rock. So Raymond and I turned and walked back. He seemed happier, and began talking about the bus to catch for our return.

When we reached the bungalow Raymond promptly went up the wooden steps, but I halted on the bottom one. The light seemed thudding in my head and I couldn't face the effort needed to go up the steps and make myself amiable to the women. But the heat was so great that it was just as bad staying where I was, under that flood of blinding light falling from the sky. To stay, or to make a move—it came to much the same. After a moment I returned to the beach, and started walking.

There was the same red glare as far as eye could reach, and small waves were lapping the hot sand in little, flurried gasps. As I slowly walked toward the boulders at the end of the beach I could feel my temples swelling under the impact of the light. It pressed itself on me, trying to check my progress. And each time I felt a hot blast strike my forehead, I gritted my teeth, I clenched my fists in my trouser pockets and keyed up every nerve to fend off the sun and the dark befuddlement it was pouring into me. Whenever a blade of vivid light shot upward from a bit of shell or broken glass lying on the sand, my jaws set hard. I wasn't going to be beaten, and I walked steadily on.

The small black hump of rock came into view far down the beach. It was rimmed by a dazzling sheen of light and feathery spray, but I was thinking of the cold, clear stream behind it, and longing to hear again the tinkle of running water. Anything to be rid of the glare, the sight of women in tears, the strain and effort—and to retrieve the pool of shadow by the rock and its cool silence!

But when I came nearer I saw that Raymond's Arab had returned. He was by himself this time, lying on his back, his hands behind his head, his face shaded by the rock while the sun beat on the rest of his body. One could see his dungarees steaming in the heat. I was rather taken aback; my impression had been that the incident was closed, and I hadn't given a thought to it on my way here.

On seeing me, the Arab raised himself a little, and his hand went to his pocket. Naturally, I gripped Raymond's revolver in the pocket of my coat. Then the Arab let himself sink back again, but without taking his hand from his pocket. I was some distance off, at least ten yards, and most of the time I saw him as a blurred dark form wobbling in the heat haze. Sometimes, however, I had glimpses of his eyes glowing between the half-closed lids. The sound of the waves was even lazier, feebler, than at noon. But the light hadn't changed; it was pounding as fiercely as ever on the long stretch of sand that ended at the rock. For two hours the sun seemed to have made no progress; becalmed in a sea of molten steel. Far out on the horizon a steamer was passing; I could just make out from the corner of an eye the small black moving patch, while I kept my gaze fixed on the Arab.

It struck me that all I had to do was to turn, walk away, and think no more about it. But the whole beach, pulsing with heat, was pressing on my back. I took some steps toward the stream. The Arab didn't move. After all, there was still some distance between us. Perhaps because of the shadow on his face, he seemed to be grinning at me.

I waited. The heat was beginning to scorch my cheeks; beads of sweat were gathering in my eyebrows. It was just the same sort of heat as at my mother's funeral, and I had the same disagreeable sensations—especially in my forehead, where all the veins seemed to be bursting through the skin. I couldn't stand it any longer, and took another step forward. I knew it was a fool thing to do; I wouldn't get out of the sun by moving on a yard or so. But I took that step, just one step, forward. And then the Arab drew his knife and held it up toward me, athwart the sunlight.

A shaft of light shot upward from the steel, and I felt as if a long, thin blade transfixed my forehead. At the same moment all the sweat that had accumulated in my eyebrows splashed down on my eyelids, covering them with a warm film of moisture. Beneath a veil of brine and tears my eyes were blinded; I was conscious only of the cymbals of the sun clashing on my skull, and, less distinctly, of the keen blade of light flashing up from the knife, scarring my eyelashes, and gouging into my eyeballs.

Then everything began to reel before my eyes, a fiery gust came from the sea, while the sky cracked in two, from end to end, and a great sheet of flame poured down through the rift. Every nerve in my body was a steel spring, and my grip closed on the revolver. The trigger gave, and the smooth underbelly of the butt jogged my palm. And so, with that crisp, whipcrack sound, it all began. I shook off my sweat and the clinging veil of light. I knew I'd shattered the balance of the day, the spacious calm of this beach on which I had been happy. But I fired four shots more into the inert body, on which they left no visible trace. And each successive shot was another loud, fateful rap on the door of my undoing.

Part Two: I

I WAS QUESTIONED several times immediately after my arrest. But they were all formal examinations, as to my identity and so forth. At the first of these, which took place at the police station, nobody seemed to have much interest in the case. However, when I was brought before the examining magistrate a week later, I noticed that he eyed me with distinct curiosity. Like the others, he began by asking my name, address, and occupation, the date and place of my birth. Then he inquired if I had chosen a lawyer to defend me. I answered, "No," I hadn't thought about it, and asked him if it was really necessary for me to have one.

"Why do you ask that?" he said. I replied that I regarded my case as very simple. He smiled. "Well, it may seem so to you. But we've got to abide by the law, and, if you don't engage a lawyer, the court will have to appoint one for you."

It struck me as an excellent arrangement that the authorities should see to details of this kind, and I told him so. He nodded, and agreed that the Code was all that could be desired.

At first I didn't take him quite seriously. The room in which he interviewed me was much like an ordinary sitting room, with curtained windows, and a single lamp standing on the desk. Its light fell on the armchair in which he'd had me sit, while his own face stayed in shadow.

I had read descriptions of such scenes in books, and at first it all seemed like a game. After our conversation, however, I had a good look at him. He was a tall man with clean-cut features, deep-set blue eyes, a big gray mustache, and abundant, almost snow-white hair, and he gave me the impression of being highly intelligent and, on the whole, likable enough. There was only one thing that put one off: his mouth had now and then a rather ugly twist; but it seemed to be only a sort of nervous tic. When leaving, I very nearly held out my hand and said, "Good-by"; just in time I remembered that I'd killed a man.

Next day a lawyer came to my cell; a small, plump, youngish man with sleek black hair. In spite of the heat—I was in my shirt sleeves—he was wearing a dark suit, stiff collar, and a rather showy tie, with broad black and white stripes. After depositing his brief case on my bed, he introduced himself, and added that he'd perused the record of my case with the utmost care. His opinion was that it would need cautious handling, but there was every prospect of my getting off, provided I followed his advice. I thanked him, and he said: "Good. Now let's get down to it."

Sitting on the bed, he said that they'd been making investigations into my private life. They had learned that my mother died recently in a home. Inquiries had been conducted at Marengo and the police informed that I'd shown "great callousness" at my mother's funeral.

"You must understand," the lawyer said, "that I don't relish having to question you about such a matter. But it has much importance, and, unless I find some way of answering the charge of 'callousness,' I shall be handicapped in conducting your defense. And that is where you, and only you, can help me."

He went on to ask if I had felt grief on that "sad occasion." The question struck me as an odd one; I'd have been much embarrassed if I'd had to ask anyone a thing like that.

I answered that, of recent years, I'd rather lost the habit of noting my feelings, and hardly knew what to answer. I could truthfully say I'd been quite fond of Mother—but really that didn't mean much. All normal people, I added as on afterthought, had more or less desired the death of those they loved, at some time or another.

Here the lawyer interrupted me, looking greatly perturbed.

"You must promise me not to say anything of that sort at the trial, or to the examining magistrate."

I promised, to satisfy him, but I explained that my physical condition at any given moment often influenced my feelings. For instance, on the day I attended Mother's funeral, I was fagged out and only half awake. So, really, I hardly took stock of what was happening. Anyhow, I could assure him of one thing: that I'd rather Mother hadn't died.

The lawyer, however, looked displeased. "That's not enough," he said curtly.

After considering for a bit he asked me if he could say that on that day I had kept my feelings under control.

"No," I said. "That wouldn't be true."

He gave me a queer look, as if I slightly revolted him; then informed me, in an almost hostile tone, that in any case the head of the Home and some of the staff would be cited as witnesses.

"And that might do you a very nasty turn," he concluded.

When I suggested that Mother's death had no connection with the charge against me, he merely replied that this remark showed I'd never had any dealings with the law.

Soon after this he left, looking quite vexed. I wished he had stayed longer and I could have explained that I desired his sympathy, not for him to make a better job of my defense, but, if I might put it so, spontaneously. I could see that I got on his nerves; he couldn't make me out, and, naturally enough, this irritated him. Once or twice I had a mind to assure him that I was just like everybody else; quite an ordinary person. But really that would have served no great purpose, and I let it go—out of laziness as much as anything else.

Later in the day I was taken again to the examining magistrate's office. It was two in the afternoon and, this time, the room was flooded with light—there was only a thin curtain on the window—and extremely hot.

After inviting me to sit down, the magistrate informed me in a very polite tone that, "owing to unforeseen circumstances," my lawyer was unable to be present. I should be quite entitled, he added, to reserve my answers to his questions until my lawyer could attend.

To this I replied that I could answer for myself. He pressed a bell push on his desk and a young clerk came in and seated himself just behind me. Then we—I and the magistrate—settled back in our chairs and the examination began. He led off by remarking that I had the reputation of being a taciturn, rather self-centered person, and he'd like to know what I had to say to that. I answered:

"Well, I rarely have anything much to say. So, naturally I keep my mouth shut."

He smiled as on the previous occasion, and agreed that that was the best of reasons. "In any case," he added, "it has little or no importance."

After a short silence he suddenly leaned forward, looked me in the eyes, and said, raising his voice a little:

"What really interests me is—you!"

I wasn't quite clear what he meant, so I made no comment.

"There are several things," he continued, "that puzzle me about your crime. I feel sure that you will help me to understand them."

When I replied that really it was quite simple, he asked me to give him an account of what I'd done that day. As a matter of fact, I had already told him at our first interview—in a summary sort of way, of course—about Raymond, the beach, our swim, the fight, then the beach again, and the five shots I'd fired. But I went over it all again, and after each phrase he nodded. "Quite so, quite so." When I described the body lying on the sand, he nodded more emphatically, and said, "Good!" I was tired of repeating the same story; I felt as if I'd never talked so much in all my life before.

After another silence he stood up and said he'd like to help me; I interested him, and, with God's help, he would do something for me in my trouble. But, first, he must put a few more questions.

He began by asking bluntly if I'd loved my mother.

"Yes," I replied, "like everybody else." The clerk behind me, who had been typing away at a steady pace, must just then have hit the wrong keys, as I heard him pushing the carrier back and crossing something out.

Next, without any apparent logical connection, the magistrate sprang another question.

"Why did you fire five consecutive shots?"

I thought for a bit; then explained that they weren't quite consecutive. I fired one at first, and the other four after a short interval.

"Why did you pause between the first and second shot?"

I seemed to see it hovering again before my eyes, the red glow of the beach, and to feel that fiery breath on my cheeks—and, this time, I made no answer.

During the silence that followed, the magistrate kept fidgeting, running his fingers through his hair, half rising, then sitting down again. Finally, planting his elbows on the desk, he bent toward me with a queer expression.

"But why, *why* did you go on firing at a prostrate man?"

Again I found nothing to reply.

The magistrate drew his hand across his forehead and repeated in a slightly different tone:

"I ask you '*Why?*' I insist on your telling me."

I still kept silent.

Suddenly he rose, walked to a file cabinet standing against the opposite wall, pulled a drawer open, and took from it a silver crucifix, which he was waving as he came back to the desk.

"Do you know who this is?" His voice had changed completely; it was vibrant with emotion.

"Of course I do," I answered.

That seemed to start him off; he began speaking at a great pace. He told me he believed in God, and that even the worst of sinners could obtain forgiveness of Him. But first he must repent, and become like a little child, with a simple, trustful heart, open to conviction. He was leaning right across the table, brandishing his crucifix before my eyes.

As a matter of fact, I had great difficulty in following his remarks, as, for one thing, the office was so stiflingly hot and big flies were buzzing around and settling on my cheeks; also because he rather alarmed me. Of course, I realized it was absurd to feel like this, considering that, after all, it was I who was the criminal. However, as he continued talking, I did my best to understand, and I gathered that there was only one point in my confession that badly needed clearing up—the fact that I'd waited before firing a second time. All the rest was, so to speak, quite in order; but that completely baffled him.

I started to tell him that he was wrong in insisting on this; the point was of quite minor importance. But, before I could get the words out, he had drawn himself up to his full height and was asking me very earnestly if I believed in God. When I said, "No," he plumped down into his chair indignantly.

That was unthinkable, he said; all men believe in God, even those who reject Him. Of this he was absolutely sure; if ever he came to doubt it, his life would lose all meaning. "Do you wish," he asked indignantly, "my life to have no meaning?" Really I couldn't see how my wishes came into it, and I told him as much.

While I was talking, he thrust the crucifix again just under my nose and shouted: "I, anyhow, am a Christian. And I pray Him to forgive you for your sins. My poor young man, how can you not believe that He suffered for your sake?"

I noticed that his manner seemed genuinely solicitous when he said, "My poor young man"—but I was beginning to have enough of it. The room was growing steadily hotter.

As I usually do when I want to get rid of someone whose conversation bores me, I pretended to agree. At which, rather to my surprise, his face lit up.

"You see! You see! Now won't you own that you believe and put your trust in Him?"

I must have shaken my head again, for he sank back in his chair, looking limp and dejected.

For some moments there was a silence during which the typewriter, which had been clicking away all the time we talked, caught up with the last remark. Then he looked at me intently and rather sadly.

"Never in all my experience have I known a soul so case-hardened as yours," he said in a low tone. "All the criminals who have come before me until now wept when they saw this symbol of our Lord's sufferings."

I was on the point of replying that was precisely because they *were* criminals. But then I realized that I, too, came under that description. Somehow it was an idea to which I never could get reconciled.

To indicate, presumably, that the interview was over, the magistrate stood up. In the same weary tone he asked me a last question: Did I regret what I had done?

After thinking a bit, I said that what I felt was less regret than a kind of vexation—I couldn't find a better word for it. But he didn't seem to understand. . . . This was as far as things went at that day's interview.

I came before the magistrate many times more, but on these occasions my lawyer always accompanied me. The examinations were confined to asking me to amplify my previous statements. Or else the magistrate and my lawyer discussed technicalities. At such times they took very little notice of me, and, in any case, the tone of the examinations changed as time went on. The magistrate seemed to have lost interest in me, and to have come to some sort of decision about my case. He never mentioned God again or displayed any of the religious fervor I had found so embarrassing at our first interview. The result was that our relations became more cordial. After a few questions, followed by an exchange of remarks with the lawyer, the magistrate closed the interview. My case was "taking its course," as he put it. Sometimes, too, the conversation was of a general order, and the magistrate and lawyer encouraged me to join in it. I began to breathe more freely. Neither of the two men, at these times, showed the least hostility toward me, and everything went so smoothly, so amiably, that I had an absurd impression of being "one of the family." I can honestly say that during the eleven months these examinations lasted I got so used to them that I was almost surprised at having ever enjoyed anything better than those rare moments when the magistrate, after escorting me to the door of the office, would pat my shoulder and say in a friendly tone: "Well, Mr. Antichrist, that's all for the present!" After which I was made over to my jailers.

II

THERE ARE SOME THINGS of which I've never cared to talk. And, a few days after I'd been sent to prison, I decided that this phase of my life was one of them. However, as time went by, I came to feel that this aversion had no real substance. In point of fact, during those early days, I was hardly conscious of being in prison; I had always a vague hope that something would turn up, some agreeable surprise.

The change came soon after Marie's first and only visit. From the day when I got her letter telling me they wouldn't let her come to see me any more, because she wasn't my wife—it was from that day that I realized that this cell was my last home, a dead end, so to speak.

On the day of my arrest they put me in a biggish room with several other prisoners, mostly Arabs. They grinned when they saw me enter, and asked me what I'd done. I told them I'd killed an Arab, and they kept mum for a while. But presently night began to fall, and one of them explained to me how to lay out my sleeping mat. By rolling up one end one makes a sort of bolster. All night I felt bugs crawling over my face.

Some days later I was put by myself in a cell, where I slept on a plank bed hinged to the wall. The only other furniture was a latrine bucket and a tin basin. The prison stands on rising ground, and through my little window I had glimpses of the sea. One day when I was hanging on the bars, straining my eyes toward the sunlight playing on the waves, a jailer entered and said I had a visitor. I thought it must be Marie, and so it was.

To go to the Visitors' Room, I was taken along a corridor, then up a flight of steps, then along another corridor. It was a very large room, lit by a big bow window, and divided into three compartments by high iron grilles running transversally. Between the two grilles there was a gap of some thirty feet, a sort of no man's land between the prisoners and their friends. I was led to a point exactly opposite Marie, who was wearing her striped dress. On my side of the rails were about a dozen other prisoners, Arabs for the most part. On Marie's side were mostly Moorish women. She was wedged between a small old woman with tight-set lips and a fat matron, without a hat, who was talking shrilly and gesticulated all the time. Because of the distance between the visitors and prisoners I found I, too, had to raise my voice.

When I came into the room the babel of voices echoing on the bare walls, and the sunlight streaming in, flooding everything in a harsh white glare, made me feel quite dizzy. After the relative darkness and the silence of my cell it took me some moments to get used to these conditions. After a bit, however, I came to see each face quite clearly, lit up as if a spotlight played on it.

I noticed a prison official seated at each end of the no man's land between the grilles. The native prisoners and their relations on the other side were squatting opposite each other. They didn't raise their voices and, in spite of the din, managed to converse almost in whispers. This murmur of voices coming from below made a sort of accompaniment to the conversations going on above their heads. I took stock of all this very quickly and moved a step forward toward Marie. She was pressing her brown, sun-tanned face to the bars and smiling as hard as she could. I thought she was looking very pretty, but somehow couldn't bring myself to tell her so.

"Well?" she asked, pitching her voice very high. "What about it? Are you all right, have you everything you want?"

"Oh, yes. I've everything I want."

We were silent for some moments; Marie went on smiling. The fat woman was bawling at the prisoner beside me, her husband presumably, a tall, fair, pleasant-looking man.

"Jeanne refused to have him," she yelled.

"That's just too bad," the man replied.

"Yes, and I told her you'd take him back the moment you got out; but she wouldn't hear of it."

Marie shouted across the gap that Raymond sent me his best wishes, and I said, "Thanks." But my voice was drowned by my neighbor's, asking "if he was quite fit."

The fat woman gave a laugh. "Fit? I should say he is! The picture of health."

Meanwhile the prisoner on my left, a youngster with thin, girlish hands, never said a word. His eyes, I noticed, were fixed on the little old woman opposite him, and she returned his gaze with a sort of hungry passion. But I had to stop looking at them as Marie was shouting to me that we mustn't lose hope.

"Certainly not," I answered. My gaze fell on her shoulders, and I had a sudden longing to squeeze them, through the thin dress. Its silky texture fascinated me, and I had a feeling that the hope she spoke of centered on it, somehow. I imagine something of the same sort was in Marie's mind, for she went on smiling, looking straight at me.

"It'll all come right, you'll see, and then we shall get married."

All I could see of her now was the white flash of her teeth, and the little puckers round her eyes. I answered: "Do you really think so?" but chiefly because I felt it up to me to answer something.

She started talking very fast in the same high-pitched voice.

"Yes, you'll be acquitted, and we'll go bathing again, Sundays."

The woman beside me was still yelling away, telling her husband that she'd left a basket for him in the prison office. She gave a list of the things she'd brought and told him to mind and check them carefully, as some had cost quite a lot. The youngster on my other side and his mother were still gazing mournfully at each other, and the murmur of the Arabs droned on below us. The light outside seemed to be surging up against the window, seeping through, and smearing the faces of the people facing it with a coat of yellow oil.

I began to feel slightly squeamish, and wished I could leave. The strident voice beside me was jarring on my ears. But, on the other hand, I wanted to have the most I could of Marie's company. I've no idea how much time passed. I remember Marie's describing to me her work, with that set smile always on her face. There wasn't a moment's letup in the noise—shouts, conversations, and always that muttering undertone. The only oasis of silence was made by the young fellow and the old woman gazing into each other's eyes.

Then, one by one, the Arabs were led away; almost everyone fell silent when the first one left. The little old woman pressed herself against the bars and at the same moment a jailer tapped her son's shoulder. He called, "*Au revoir*, Mother," and, slipping her hand between the bars, she gave him a small, slow wave with it.

No sooner was she gone than a man, hat in hand, took her place. A prisoner was led up to the empty place beside me, and the two started a brisk exchange of remarks—not loud, however, as the room had become relatively quiet. Someone came and called away the man on my right, and his wife shouted at him—she didn't seem to realize it was no longer necessary to shout—"Now, mind you look after yourself, dear, and don't do anything rash!"

My turn came next. Marie threw me a kiss. I looked back as I walked away. She hadn't moved; her face was still pressed to the rails, her lips still parted in that tense, twisted smile.

Soon after this I had a letter from her. And it was then that the things I've never liked to talk about began. Not that they were particularly terrible; I've no wish to exaggerate and I suffered less than others. Still, there was one thing in those early days that was really irksome: my habit of thinking like a free man. For instance, I would suddenly be seized with a desire to go down to the beach for a swim. And merely to have imagined the sound of ripples at my feet, the smooth feel of the water on my body as I struck out, and the wonderful sensation of relief it gave brought home still more cruelly the narrowness of my cell.

Still, that phase lasted a few months only. Afterward, I had prisoner's thoughts. I waited for the daily walk in the courtyard or a visit from my lawyer. As for the rest of the time, I managed quite well, really. I've often thought that had I been compelled to live in the trunk of a dead tree, with nothing to do but gaze up at the patch of sky just overhead, I'd have got used to it by degrees. I'd have learned to watch for the passing of birds or drifting clouds, as I had come to watch for my lawyer's odd neckties, or, in another world, to wait patiently till Sunday for a spell of love-making with Marie. Well, here, anyhow, I wasn't penned in a hollow tree trunk. There were others in the world worse off than I. I remembered it had been one of Mother's pet ideas— she was always voicing it—that in the long run one gets used to anything.

Usually, however, I didn't think things out so far. Those first months were trying, of course; but the very effort I had to make helped me through them. For instance, I was plagued by the desire for a woman —which was natural enough, considering my age. I never thought of Marie especially. I was obsessed by thoughts of this woman or that, of all the ones I'd had, all the circumstances under which I'd loved them; so much so that the cell grew crowded with their faces, ghosts of my old passions. That unsettled me, no doubt; but, at least, it served to kill time.

I gradually became quite friendly with the chief jailer, who went the rounds with the kitchen hands at mealtimes. It was he who brought up the subject of women. "That's what the men here grumble about most," he told me.

I said I felt like that myself. "There's something unfair about it," I added, "like hitting a man when he's down."

"But that's the whole point of it," he said; "that's why you fellows are kept in prison."

"I don't follow."

"Liberty," he said, "means that. You're being deprived of your liberty."

It had never before struck me in that light, but I saw his point. "That's true," I said. "Otherwise it wouldn't be a punishment."

The jailer nodded. "Yes, you're different, you can use your brains. The others can't. Still, those fellows find a way out; they do it by themselves." With which remark the jailer left my cell. Next day I did like the others.

The lack of cigarettes, too, was a trial. When I was brought to the prison, they took away my belt, my shoelaces, and the contents of my pockets, including my cigarettes. Once I had been given a cell to myself I asked to be given back, anyhow, the cigarettes. Smoking was forbidden, they informed me. That, perhaps, was what got me down the most; in fact, I suffered really badly during the first few days. I even tore off splinters from my plank bed and sucked them. All day long I felt faint and bilious. It passed my understanding why I shouldn't be allowed even to smoke; it could have done no one any harm. Later on, I understood the idea behind it; this privation, too, was part of my punishment. But, by the time I understood, I'd lost the craving, so it had ceased to be a punishment.

Except for these privations I wasn't too unhappy. Yet again, the whole problem was: how to kill time. After a while, however, once I'd learned the trick of remembering things, I never had a moment's boredom. Sometimes I would exercise my memory on my bedroom and, starting from a corner, make the round, noting every object I saw on the way. At first it was over in a minute or two. But each time I repeated the experience, it took a little longer. I made a point of visualizing every piece of furniture, and each article upon or in it, and then every detail of each article, and finally the details of the details, so to speak: a tiny dent or incrustation, or a chipped edge, and the exact grain and color of the woodwork. At the same time I forced myself to keep my inventory in mind from start to finish, in the right order and omitting no item. With the result that, after a few weeks, I could spend hours merely in listing the objects in my bedroom. I found that the more I thought, the more details, half-forgotten or malobserved, floated up from my memory. There seemed no end to them.

So I learned that even after a single day's experience of the outside world a man could easily live a hundred years in prison. He'd have laid up enough memories never to be bored. Obviously, in one way, this was a compensation.

Then there was sleep. To begin with, I slept badly at night and never in the day. But gradually my nights became better, and I managed to doze off in the daytime as well. In fact, during the last months, I must have slept sixteen or eighteen hours out of the twenty-four. So there remained only six hours to fill—with meals, relieving nature, my memories . . . and the story of the Czech.

One day, when inspecting my straw mattress, I found a bit of newspaper stuck to its underside. The paper was yellow with age, almost transparent, but I could still make out the letter print. It was the story of a crime. The first part was missing, but I gathered that its scene was some village in Czechoslovakia. One of the villagers had left his home to try his luck abroad. After twenty-five years, having made a fortune, he returned to his country with his wife and child. Meanwhile his mother and sister had been running a small hotel in the village where he was born. He decided to give them a surprise and, leaving his wife and child in another inn, he went to stay at his mother's place, booking a room under an assumed name. His mother and sister completely failed to recognize him. At dinner that evening he showed them a large sum of money he had on him, and in the course of the night they slaughtered him with a hammer. After taking the money they flung the body into the river. Next morning his wife came and, without thinking, betrayed the guest's identity. His mother hanged herself. His sister threw herself into a well. I must have read that story thousands of times. In one way it sounded most unlikely; in another, it was plausible enough. Anyhow, to my mind, the man was asking for trouble; one shouldn't play fool tricks of that sort.

So, what with long bouts of sleep, my memories, readings of that scrap of newspaper, the tides of light and darkness, the days slipped by. I'd read, of course, that in jail one ends up by losing track of time. But this had never meant anything definite to me. I hadn't grasped how days could be at once long and short. Long, no doubt, as periods to live through, but so distended that they ended up by overlapping on each other. In fact, I never thought of days as such; only the words "yesterday" and "tomorrow" still kept some meaning.

When, one morning, the jailer informed me I'd now been six months in jail, I believed him—but the words conveyed nothing to my mind. To me it seemed like one and the same day that had been going on since I'd been in my cell, and that I'd been doing the same thing all the time.

After the jailer left me I shined up my tin pannikin and studied my face in it. My expression was terribly serious, I thought, even when I tried to smile. I held the pannikin at different angles, but always my face had the same mournful, tense expression.

The sun was setting and it was the hour of which I'd rather not speak—"the nameless hour," I called it—when evening sounds were creeping up from all the floors of the prison in a sort of stealthy procession. I went to the barred window and in the last rays looked once again at my reflected face. It was as serious as before; and that wasn't surprising, as just then I was feeling serious. But, at the same time, I heard something that I hadn't heard for months. It was the sound of a voice; my own voice, there was no mistaking it. And I recognized it as the voice that for many a day of late had been sounding in my ears. So I knew that all this time I'd been talking to myself.

And something I'd been told came back; a remark made by the nurse at Mother's funeral. No, there was no way out, and no one can imagine what the evenings are like in prison.

III

On the whole I can't say that those months passed slowly; another summer was on its way almost before I realized the first was over. And I knew that with the first really hot days something new was in store for me. My case was down for the last sessions of the Assize Court, and those sessions were due to end some time in June.

The day on which my trial started was one of brilliant sunshine. My lawyer assured me the case would take only two or three days. "From what I hear," he added, "the court will dispatch your case as quickly as possible, as it isn't the most important one on the Cause List. There's a case of parricide immediately after, which will take them some time."

They came for me at half-past seven in the morning and I was conveyed to the law courts in a prison van. The two policemen led me into a small room that smelled of darkness. We sat near a door through which came sounds of voices, shouts, chairs scraping on the floor; a vague hubbub which reminded me of one of those small-town "socials" when, after the concert's over, the hall is cleared for dancing.

One of my policemen told me the judges hadn't arrived yet, and offered me a cigarette, which I declined. After a bit he asked me if I was feeling nervous. I said, "No," and that the prospect of witnessing a trial rather interested me; I'd never had occasion to attend one before.

"Maybe," the other policeman said. "But after an hour or two one's had enough of it."

After a while a small electric bell purred in the room. They unfastened my handcuffs, opened the door, and led me to the prisoner's dock.

There was a great crowd in the courtroom. Though the Venetian blinds were down, light was filtering through the chinks, and the air stiflingly hot already. The windows had been kept shut. I sat down, and the police officers took their stand on each side of my chair.

It was then that I noticed a row of faces opposite me. These people were staring hard at me, and I guessed they were the jury. But somehow I didn't see them as individuals. I felt as you do just after boarding a streetcar and you're conscious of all the people on the opposite seat staring at you in the hope of finding something in your appearance to amuse them. Of course, I knew this was an absurd comparison; what these people were looking for in me wasn't anything to laugh at, but signs of criminality. Still, the difference wasn't so very great, and, anyhow, that's the idea I got.

What with the crowd and the stuffiness of the air I was feeling a bit dizzy. I ran my eyes round the courtroom but couldn't recognize any of the faces. At first I could hardly believe that all these people had come on my account. It was such a new experience, being a focus of interest; in the ordinary way no one ever paid much attention to me.

"What a crush!" I remarked to the policeman on my left, and he explained that the newspapers were responsible for it.

He pointed to a group of men at a table just below the jury box. "There they are!"

"Who?" I asked, and he replied, "The press." One of them, he added, was an old friend of his.

A moment later the man he'd mentioned looked our way and, coming to the dock, shook hands warmly with the policeman. The journalist was an elderly man with a rather grim expression, but his manner was quite pleasant. Just then I noticed that almost all the people in the courtroom were greeting each other, exchanging remarks and forming groups —behaving, in fact, as in a club where the company of others of one's own tastes and standing makes one feel at ease. That, no doubt, explained the odd impression I had of being *de trop* here, a sort of gate-crasher.

However, the journalist addressed me quite amiably, and said he hoped all would go well for me. I thanked him, and he added with a smile:

"You know, we've been featuring you a bit. We're always rather short of copy in the summer, and there's been precious little to write about except your case and the one that's coming on after it. I expect you've heard about it; it's a case of parricide."

He drew my attention to one of the group at the press table, a plump, small man with huge black-rimmed glasses, who made me think of an overfed weasel.

"That fellow's the special correspondent of one of the Paris dailies. As a matter of fact, he didn't come on your account. He was sent for the parricide case, but they've asked him to cover yours as well."

It was on the tip of my tongue to say, "That was very kind of them," but then I thought it would sound silly. With a friendly wave of his hand he left us, and for some minutes nothing happened.

Then, accompanied by some colleagues, my lawyer bustled in, in his gown. He went up to the press table and shook hands with the journalists. They remained laughing and chatting together, all seemingly very much at home here, until a bell rang shrilly and everyone went to his place. My lawyer came up to me, shook hands, and advised me to answer all the questions as briefly as possible, not to volunteer information, and to rely on him to see me through.

I heard a chair scrape on my left, and a tall, thin man wearing pince-nez settled the folds of his red gown as he took his seat. The Public Prosecutor, I gathered. A clerk of the court announced that Their Honors were entering, and at the same moment two big electric fans started buzzing overhead. Three judges, two in black and the third in scarlet, with brief cases under their arms, entered and walked briskly to the bench, which was several feet above the level of the courtroom floor. The man in scarlet took the central, high-backed chair, placed his cap of office on the table, ran a handkerchief over his small bald crown, and announced that the hearing would now begin.

The journalists had their fountain pens ready; they all wore the same expression of slightly ironical indifference, with the exception of one, a much younger man than his colleagues, in gray flannels with a blue tie, who, leaving his pen on the table, was gazing hard at me. He had a plain, rather chunky face; what held my attention was his eyes, very pale, clear eyes, riveted on me, though not betraying any definite emotion. For a moment I had an odd impression, as if I were being scrutinized by myself. That—and the fact that I was unfamiliar with court procedure—may explain why I didn't follow very well the opening phases: the drawing of lots for the jury, the various questions put by the presiding judge to the Prosecutor, the foreman of the jury, and my counsel (each time he spoke all the jurymen's heads swung round together toward the bench), the hurried reading of the charge sheet, in the course of which I recognized some familiar names of people and places; then some supplementary questions put to my lawyer.

Next, the Judge announced that the court would call over the witness list. Some of the names read out by the clerk rather surprised me. From amongst the crowd, which until now I had seen as a mere blur of faces, rose, one after the other, Raymond, Masson, Salamano, the doorkeeper from the Home, old Pérez, and Marie, who gave me a little nervous wave of her hand before following the others out by a side door. I was thinking how strange it was I hadn't noticed any of them before when I heard the last name called, that of Céleste. As he rose, I noticed beside him the quaint little woman with a mannish coat and brisk, decided air, who had shared my table at the restaurant. She had her eyes fixed on me, I noticed. But I hadn't time to wonder about her; the Judge had started speaking again.

He said that the trial proper was about to begin, and he need hardly say that he expected the public to refrain from any demonstration whatsoever. He explained that he was there to supervise the proceedings, as a sort of umpire, and he would take a scrupulously impartial view of the case. The verdict of the jury would be interpreted by him in a spirit of justice. Finally, at the least sign of a disturbance he would have the court cleared.

The day was stoking up. Some of the public were fanning themselves with newspapers, and there was a constant rustle of crumpled paper. On a sign from the presiding judge the clerk of the court brought three fans of plaited straw, which the three judges promptly put in action.

My examination began at once. The Judge questioned me quite calmly and even, I thought, with a hint of cordiality. For the nth time I was asked to give particulars of my identity and, though heartily sick of this formality, I realized that it was natural enough; after all, it would be a shocking thing for the court to be trying the wrong man.

The Judge then launched into an account of what I'd done, stopping after every two or three sentences to ask me, "Is that correct?" To which I always replied, "Yes, sir," as my lawyer had advised me. It was a long business, as the Judge lingered on each detail. Meanwhile the journalists scribbled busily away. But I was sometimes conscious of the eyes of the youngest fixed on me; also those of the queer little robot woman. The jurymen, however, were all gazing at the red-robed judge, and I was again reminded of the row of passengers on one side of a tram. Presently he gave a slight cough, turned some pages of his file, and, still fanning his face, addressed me gravely.

He now proposed, he said, to trench on certain matters which, on a superficial view, might seem foreign to the case, but actually were highly relevant. I guessed that he was going to talk about Mother, and at the same moment realized how odious I would find this. His first question was: Why had I sent my mother to an institution? I replied that the reason was simple; I hadn't enough money to see that she was properly looked after at home. Then he asked if the parting hadn't caused me distress. I explained that neither Mother nor I expected much of one another—or, for that matter, of anybody else; so both of us had got used to the new conditions easily enough. The Judge then said that he had no wish to press the point, and asked the Prosecutor if he could think of any more questions that should be put to me at this stage.

The Prosecutor, who had his back half turned to me, said, without looking in my direction, that, subject to His Honor's approval, he would like to know if I'd gone back to the stream with the intention of killing the Arab. I said, "No." In that case, why had I taken a revolver with me, and why go back precisely to that spot? I said it was a matter of pure chance. The Prosecutor then observed in a nasty tone: "Very good. That will be all for the present."

I couldn't quite follow what came next. Anyhow after some palavering among the bench, the Prosecutor, and my counsel, the presiding judge announced that the court would now rise; there was an adjournment till the afternoon, when evidence would be taken.

Almost before I knew what was happening I was rushed out to the prison van, which drove me back, and I was given my midday meal. After a short time, just enough for me to realize how tired I was feeling, they came for me. I was back in the same room, confronting the same faces, and the whole thing started again. But the heat had meanwhile much increased, and by some miracle fans had been procured for everyone: the jury, my lawyer, the Prosecutor, and some of the journalists, too. The young man and the robot woman were still at their places. But they were not fanning themselves and, as before, they never took their eyes off me.

I wiped the sweat from my face, but I was barely conscious of where or who I was until I heard the warden of the Home called to the witness box. When asked if my mother had complained about my conduct, he said, "Yes," but that didn't mean much; almost all the inmates of the Home had grievances against their relatives. The Judge asked him to be more explicit; did she reproach me with having sent her to the Home, and he said, "Yes," again. But this time he didn't qualify his answer.

To another question he replied that on the day of the funeral he was somewhat surprised by my calmness. Asked to explain what he meant by "my calmness," the warden lowered his eyes and stared at his shoes for a moment. Then he explained that I hadn't wanted to see Mother's body, or shed a single tear, and that I'd left immediately the funeral ended, without lingering at her grave. Another thing had surprised him. One of the undertaker's men told him that I didn't know my mother's age. There was a short silence; then the Judge asked him if he might take it that he was referring to the prisoner in the dock. The warden seemed puzzled by this, and the Judge explained: "It's a formal question. I am bound to put it."

The Prosecutor was then asked if he had any questions to put, and he answered loudly: "Certainly not! I have all I want." His tone and the look of triumph on his face, as he glanced at me, were so marked that I felt as I hadn't felt for ages. I had a foolish desire to burst into tears. For the first time I'd realized how all these people loathed me.

After asking the jury and my lawyer if they had any questions, the Judge heard the doorkeeper's evidence. On stepping into the box the man threw a glance at me, then looked away. Replying to questions, he said that I'd declined to see Mother's body, I'd smoked cigarettes and slept, and drunk *café au lait*. It was then I felt a sort of wave of indignation spreading through the courtroom, and for the first time I understood that I was guilty. They got the doorkeeper to repeat what he had said about the coffee and my smoking.

The Prosecutor turned to me again, with a gloating look in his eyes. My counsel asked the doorkeeper if he, too, hadn't smoked. But the Prosecutor took strong exception to this. "I'd like to know," he cried indignantly, "who is on trial in this court. Or does my friend think that by aspersing a witness for the prosecution he will shake the evidence, the abundant and cogent evidence, against his client?" None the less, the Judge told the doorkeeper to answer the question.

The old fellow fidgeted a bit. Then, "Well, I know I didn't ought to have done it," he mumbled, "but I did take a cigarette from the young gentleman when he offered it—just out of politeness."

The Judge asked me if I had any comment to make. "None," I said, "except that the witness is quite right. It's true I offered him a cigarette."

The doorkeeper looked at me with surprise and a sort of gratitude. Then, after hemming and hawing for a bit, he volunteered the statement that it was he who'd suggested I should have some coffee.

My lawyer was exultant. "The jury will appreciate," he said, "the importance of this admission."

The Prosecutor, however, was promptly on his feet again. "Quite so," he boomed above our heads. "The jury will appreciate it. And they will draw the conclusion that, though a third party might inadvertently offer him a cup of coffee, the prisoner, in common decency, should have refused it, if only out of respect for the dead body of the poor woman who had brought him into the world."

After which the doorkeeper went back to his seat.

When Thomas Pérez was called, a court officer had to help him to the box. Pérez stated that, though he had been a great friend of my mother, he had met me once only, on the day of the funeral. Asked how I had behaved that day, he said:

"Well, I was most upset, you know. Far too much upset to notice things. My grief sort of blinded me, I think. It had been a great shock, my dear friend's death; in fact, I fainted during the funeral. So I didn't hardly notice the young gentleman at all."

The Prosecutor asked him to tell the court if he'd seen me weep. And when Pérez answered, "No," added emphatically: "I trust the jury will take note of this reply."

My lawyer rose at once, and asked Pérez in a tone that seemed to me needlessly aggressive:

"Now, think well, my man! Can you swear you saw he didn't shed a tear?"

Pérez answered, "No."

At this some people tittered, and my lawyer, pushing back one sleeve of his gown, said sternly:

"That is typical of the way this case is being conducted. No attempt is being made to elicit the true facts."

The Prosecutor ignored this remark; he was making dabs with his pencil on the cover of his brief, seemingly quite indifferent.

There was a break of five minutes, during which my lawyer told me the case was going very well indeed. Then Céleste was called. He was announced as a witness for the defense. The defense meant me.

Now and again Céleste threw me a glance; he kept squeezing his Panama hat between his hands as he gave evidence. He was in his best suit, the one he wore when sometimes of a Sunday he went with me to the races. But evidently he hadn't been able to get his collar on; the top of his shirt, I noticed, was secured only by a brass stud. Asked if I was one of his customers, he said, "Yes, and a friend as well." Asked to state his opinion of me, he said that I was "all right" and, when told to explain what he meant by that, he replied that everyone knew what that meant. "Was I a secretive sort of man?" "No," he answered, "I shouldn't call him that. But he isn't one to waste his breath, like a lot of folks."

The Prosecutor asked him if I always settled my monthly bill at his restaurant when he presented it. Céleste laughed. "Oh, he paid on the nail, all right. But the bills were just details-like, between him and me." Then he was asked to say what he thought about the crime. He placed his hands on the rail of the box and one could see he had a speech all ready.

"To my mind it was just an accident, or a stroke of bad luck, if you prefer. And a thing like that takes you off your guard."

He wanted to continue, but the Judge cut him short. "Quite so. That's all, thank you."

For a bit Céleste seemed flabbergasted; then he explained that he hadn't finished what he wanted to say. They told him to continue, but to make it brief.

He only repeated that it was "just an accident."

"That's as it may be," the Judge observed. "But what we are here for is to try such accidents, according to law. You can stand down."

Céleste turned and gazed at me. His eyes were moist and his lips trembling. It was exactly as if he'd said: "Well, I've done my best for you, old man. I'm afraid it hasn't helped much. I'm sorry."

I didn't say anything, or make any movement, but for the first time in my life I wanted to kiss a man.

The Judge repeated his order to stand down, and Céleste returned to his place amongst the crowd. During the rest of the hearing he remained there, leaning forward, elbows on knees and his Panama between his hands, not missing a word of the proceedings.

It was Marie's turn next. She had a hat on and still looked quite pretty, though I much preferred her with her hair free. From where I was I had glimpses of the soft curve of her breasts, and her underlip had the little pout that always fascinated me. She appeared very nervous.

The first question was: How long had she known me? Since the time when she was in our office, she replied. Then the Judge asked her what were the relations between us, and she said she was my girl friend. Answering another question, she admitted promising to marry me. The Prosecutor, who had been studying a document in front of him, asked her rather sharply when our "liaison" had begun. She gave the date. He then observed with a would-be casual air that apparently she meant the day following my mother's funeral. After letting this sink in he remarked in a slightly ironic tone that obviously this was a "delicate topic" and he could enter into the young lady's feelings, but—and here his voice grew sterner—his duty obliged him to waive considerations of delicacy.

After making this announcement he asked Marie to give a full account of our doings on the day when I had "intercourse" with her for the first time. Marie wouldn't answer at first, but the Prosecutor insisted, and then she told him that we had met at the baths, gone together to the pictures, and then to my place. He then informed the court that, as a result of certain statements made by Marie at the proceedings before the magistrate, he had studied the movie programs of that date, and turning to Marie asked her to name the film that we had gone to see. In a very low voice she said it was a picture with Fernandel in it. By the time she had finished, the courtroom was so still you could have heard a pin drop.

Looking very grave, the Prosecutor drew himself up to his full height and, pointing at me, said in such a tone that I could have sworn he was genuinely moved:

"Gentlemen of the jury, I would have you note that on the next day after his mother's funeral that man was visiting the swimming pool, starting a liaison with a girl, and going to see a comic film. That is all I wish to say."

When he sat down there was the same dead silence. Then all of a sudden Marie burst into tears. He'd got it all wrong, she said; it wasn't a bit like that really, he'd bullied her into saying the opposite of what she meant. She knew me very well, and she was sure I hadn't done anything really wrong—and so on. At a sign from the presiding judge, one of the court officers led her away, and the hearing continued.

Hardly anyone seemed to listen to Masson, the next witness. He stated that I was a respectable young fellow; "and, what's more, a very decent chap." Nor did they pay any more attention to Salamano, when he told them how kind I'd always been to his dog, or when, in answer to a question about my mother and myself, he said that Mother and I had very little in common and that explained why I'd fixed up for her to enter the Home. "You've got to understand," he added. "You've got to understand." But no one seemed to understand. He was told to stand down.

Raymond was the next, and last, witness. He gave me a little wave of his hand and led off by saying I was innocent. The Judge rebuked him.

"You are here to give evidence, not your views on the case, and you must confine yourself to answering the questions put you."

He was then asked to make clear his relations with the deceased, and Raymond took this opportunity of explaining that it was he, not I, against whom the dead man had a grudge, because he, Raymond, had beaten up his sister. The Judge asked him if the deceased had no reason to dislike me, too. Raymond told him that my presence on the beach that morning was a pure coincidence.

"How comes it then," the Prosecutor inquired, "that the letter which led up to this tragedy was the prisoner's work?"

Raymond replied that this, too, was due to mere chance.

To which the Prosecutor retorted that in this case "chance" or "mere coincidence" seemed to play a remarkably large part. Was it by chance that I hadn't intervened when Raymond assaulted his mistress? Did this convenient term "chance" account for my having vouched for Raymond at the police station and having made, on that occasion, statements extravagantly favorable to him? In conclusion he asked Raymond to state what were his means of livelihood.

On his describing himself as a warehouseman, the Prosecutor informed the jury it was common knowledge that the witness lived on the immoral earnings of women. I, he said, was this man's intimate friend and associate; in fact, the whole background of the crime was of the most squalid description. And what made it even more odious was the personality of the prisoner, an inhuman monster wholly without a moral sense.

Raymond began to expostulate, and my lawyer, too, protested. They were told that the Prosecutor must be allowed to finish his remarks.

"I have nearly done," he said; then turned to Raymond. "Was the prisoner your friend?"

"Certainly. We were the best of pals, as they say."

The Prosecutor then put me the same question. I looked hard at Raymond, and he did not turn away.

Then, "Yes," I answered.

The Prosecutor turned toward the jury.

"Not only did the man before you in the dock indulge in the most shameful orgies on the day following his mother's death. He killed a man cold-bloodedly, in pursuance of some sordid vendetta in the underworld of prostitutes and pimps. That, gentlemen of the jury, is the type of man the prisoner is."

No sooner had he sat down than my lawyer, out of all patience, raised his arms so high that his sleeves fell back, showing the full length of his starched shirt cuffs.

"Is my client on trial for having buried his mother, or for killing a man?" he asked.

There were some titters in court. But then the Prosecutor sprang to his feet and, draping his gown round him, said he was amazed at his friend's ingenuousness in failing to see that between these two elements of the case there was a vital link. They hung together psychologically, if he might put it so. "In short," he concluded, speaking with great vehemence, "I accuse the prisoner of behaving at his mother's funeral in a way that showed he was already a criminal at heart."

These words seemed to take much effect on the jury and public. My lawyer merely shrugged his shoulders and wiped the sweat from his forehead. But obviously he was rattled, and I had a feeling things weren't going well for me.

Soon after this incident the court rose. As I was being taken from the courthouse to the prison van, I was conscious for a few brief moments of the once familiar feel of a summer evening out-of-doors. And, sitting in the darkness of my moving cell, I recognized, echoing in my tired brain, all the characteristic sounds of a town I'd loved, and of a certain hour of the day which I had always particularly enjoyed. The shouts of newspaper boys in the already languid air, the last calls of birds in the public garden, the cries of sandwich vendors, the screech of streetcars at the steep corners of the upper town, and that faint rustling overhead as darkness sifted down upon the harbor—all these sounds made my return to prison like a blind man's journey along a route whose every inch he knows by heart.

Yes, this was the evening hour when—how long ago it seemed!—I always felt so well content with life. Then, what awaited me was a night of easy, dreamless sleep. This was the same hour, but with a difference; I was returning to a cell, and what awaited me was a night haunted by forebodings of the coming day. And so I learned that familiar paths traced in the dusk of summer evenings may lead as well to prisons as to innocent, untroubled sleep.

IV

It is always interesting, even in the prisoner's dock, to hear oneself being talked about. And certainly in the speeches of my lawyer and the prosecuting counsel a great deal was said about me; more, in fact, about me personally than about my crime.

Really there wasn't any very great difference between the two speeches. Counsel for the defense raised his arms to heaven and pleaded guilty, but with extenuating circumstances. The Prosecutor made similar gestures; he agreed that I was guilty, but denied extenuating circumstances.

One thing about this phase of the trial was rather irksome. Quite often, interested as I was in what they had to say, I was tempted to put in a word, myself. But my lawyer had advised me not to. "You won't do your case any good by talking," he had warned me. In fact, there seemed to be a conspiracy to exclude me from the proceedings; I wasn't to have any say and my fate was to be decided out of hand.

It was quite an effort at times for me to refrain from cutting them all short, and saying: "But, damn it all, who's on trial in this court, I'd like to know? It's a serious matter for a man, being accused of murder. And I've something really important to tell you."

However, on second thoughts, I found I had nothing to say. In any case, I must admit that hearing oneself talked about loses its interest very soon. The Prosecutor's speech, especially, began to bore me before he was halfway through it. The only things that really caught my attention were occasional phrases, his gestures, and some elaborate tirades—but these were isolated patches.

What he was aiming at, I gathered, was to show that my crime was premeditated. I remember his saying at one moment, "I can prove this, gentlemen of the jury, to the hilt. First, you have the facts of the crime; which are as clear as daylight. And then you have what I may call the night side of this case, the dark workings of a criminal mentality."

He began by summing up the facts, from my mother's death onward. He stressed my heartlessness, my inability to state Mother's age, my visit to the swimming pool where I met Marie, our matinee at the pictures where a Fernandel film was showing, and finally my return with Marie to my rooms. I didn't quite follow his remarks at first, as he kept on mentioning "the prisoner's mistress," whereas for me she was just "Marie." Then he came to the subject of Raymond. It seemed to me that his way of treating the facts showed a certain shrewdness. All he said sounded quite plausible. I'd written the letter in collusion with Raymond so as to entice his mistress to his room and subject her to ill-treatment by a man "of more than dubious reputation." Then, on the beach, I'd provoked a brawl with Raymond's enemies, in the course of which Raymond was wounded. I'd asked him for his revolver and gone back by myself with the intention of using it. Then I'd shot the Arab. After the first shot I waited. Then, "to be certain of making a good job of it," I fired four more shots deliberately, point-blank, and in cold blood, at my victim.

"That is my case," he said. "I have described to you the series of events which led this man to kill the deceased, fully aware of what he was doing. I emphasize this point. We are not concerned with an act of homicide committed on a sudden impulse which might serve as extenuation. I ask you to note, gentlemen of the jury, that the prisoner is an educated man. You will have observed the way in which he answered my questions; he is intelligent and he knows the value of words. And I repeat that it is quite impossible to assume that, when he committed the crime, he was unaware what he was doing."

I noticed that he laid stress on my "intelligence." It puzzled me rather why what would count as a good point in an ordinary person should be used against an accused man as an overwhelming proof of his guilt. While thinking this over, I missed what he said next, until I heard him exclaim indignantly: "And has he uttered a word of regret for his most odious crime? Not one word, gentlemen. Not once in the course of these proceedings did this man show the least contrition."

Turning toward the dock, he pointed a finger at me, and went on in the same strain. I really couldn't understand why he harped on this point so much. Of course, I had to own that he was right; I didn't feel much regret for what I'd done. Still, to my mind he overdid it, and I'd have liked to have a chance of explaining to him, in a quite friendly, almost affectionate way, that I have never been able really to regret anything in all my life. I've always been far too much absorbed in the present moment, or the immediate future, to think back. Of course, in the position into which I had been forced, there was no question of my speaking to anyone in that tone. I hadn't the right to show any friendly feeling or possess good intentions. And I tried to follow what came next, as the Prosecutor was now considering what he called my "soul."

He said he'd studied it closely—and had found a blank, "literally nothing, gentlemen of the jury." Really, he said, I had no soul, there was nothing human about me, not one of those moral qualities which normal men possess had any place in my mentality. "No doubt," he added, "we should not reproach him with this. We cannot blame a man for lacking what it was never in his power to acquire. But in a criminal court the wholly passive ideal of tolerance must give place to a sterner, loftier ideal, that of justice. Especially when this lack of every decent instinct is such as that of the man before you, a menace to society." He proceeded to discuss my conduct toward my mother, repeating what he had said in the course of the hearing. But he spoke at much greater length of my crime—at such length, indeed, that I lost the thread and was conscious only of the steadily increasing heat.

A moment came when the Prosecutor paused and, after a short silence, said in a low, vibrant voice: "This same court, gentlemen, will be called on to try tomorrow that most odious of crimes, the murder of a father by his son." To his mind, such a crime was almost unimaginable. But, he ventured to hope, justice would be meted out without paltering. And yet, he made bold to say, the horror that even the crime of parricide inspired in him paled beside the loathing inspired by my callousness.

"This man, who is morally guilty of his mother's death, is no less unfit to have a place in the community than that other man who did to death the father that begat him. And, indeed, the one crime led on to the other; the first of these two criminals, the man in the dock, set a precedent, if I may put it so, and authorized the second crime. Yes, gentlemen, I am convinced"—here he raised his voice a tone—"that you will not find I am exaggerating the case against the prisoner when I say that he is also guilty of the murder to be tried tomorrow in this court. And I look to you for a verdict accordingly."

The Prosecutor paused again, to wipe the sweat off his face. He then explained that his duty was a painful one, but he would do it without flinching. "This man has, I repeat, no place in a community whose basic principles he flouts without compunction. Nor, heartless as he is, has he any claim to mercy. I ask you to impose the extreme penalty of the law; and I ask it without a qualm. In the course of a long career, in which it has often been my duty to ask for a capital sentence, never have I felt that painful duty weigh so little on my mind as in the present case. In demanding a verdict of murder without extenuating circumstances, I am following not only the dictates of my conscience and a sacred obligation, but also those of the natural and righteous indignation I feel at the sight of a criminal devoid of the least spark of human feeling."

When the Prosecutor sat down there was a longish silence. Personally I was quite overcome by the heat and my amazement at what I had been hearing. The presiding judge gave a short cough, and asked me in a very low tone if I had anything to say. I rose, and as I felt in the mood to speak, I said the first thing that crossed my mind: that I'd had no intention of killing the Arab. The Judge replied that this statement would be taken into consideration by the court. Meanwhile he would be glad to hear, before my counsel addressed the court, what were the motives of my crime. So far, he must admit, he hadn't fully understood the grounds of my defense.

I tried to explain that it was because of the sun, but I spoke too quickly and ran my words into each other. I was only too conscious that it sounded nonsensical, and, in fact, I heard people tittering.

My lawyer shrugged his shoulders. Then he was directed to address the court, in his turn. But all he did was to point out the lateness of the hour and to ask for an adjournment till the following afternoon. To this the judge agreed.

When I was brought back next day, the electric fans were still churning up the heavy air and the jurymen plying their gaudy little fans in a sort of steady rhythm. The speech for the defense seemed to me interminable. At one moment, however, I pricked up my ears; it was when I heard him saying: "It is true I killed a man." He went on in the same strain, saying "I" when he referred to me. It seemed so queer that I bent toward the policeman on my right and asked him to explain. He told me to shut up; then, after a moment, whispered: "They all do that." It seemed to me that the idea behind it was still further to exclude me from the case, to put me off the map, so to speak, by substituting the lawyer for myself. Anyway, it hardly mattered; I already felt worlds away from this courtroom and its tedious "proceedings."

My lawyer, in any case, struck me as feeble to the point of being ridiculous. He hurried through his plea of provocation, and then he, too, started in about my soul. But I had an impression that he had much less talent than the Prosecutor.

"I, too," he said, "have closely studied this man's soul; but, unlike my learned friend for the prosecution, I have found something there. Indeed, I may say that I have read the prisoner's mind like an open book." What he had read there was that I was an excellent young fellow, a steady, conscientious worker who did his best by his employer; that I was popular with everyone and sympathetic in others' troubles. According to him I was a dutiful son, who had supported his mother as long as he was able. After anxious consideration I had reached the conclusion that, by entering a home, the old lady would have comforts that my means didn't permit me to provide for her. "I am astounded, gentlemen," he added, "by the attitude taken up by my learned friend in referring to this Home. Surely if proof be needed of the excellence of such institutions, we need only remember that they are promoted and financed by a government department." I noticed that he made no reference to the funeral, and this seemed to me a serious omission. But, what with his long-windedness, the endless days and hours they had been discussing my "soul," and the rest of it, I found that my mind had gone blurred; everything was dissolving into a grayish, watery haze.

Only one incident stands out; toward the end, while my counsel rambled on, I heard the tin trumpet of an ice-cream vendor in the street,

a small, shrill sound cutting across the flow of words. And then a rush of
memories went through my mind—memories of a life which was mine
no longer and had once provided me with the surest, humblest pleasures:
warm smells of summer, my favorite streets, the sky at evening, Marie's
dresses and her laugh. The futility of what was happening here seemed
to take me by the throat, I felt like vomiting, and I had only one idea: to
get it over, to go back to my cell, and sleep . . . and sleep.

Dimly I heard my counsel making his last appeal.

"Gentlemen of the jury, surely you will not send to his death a
decent, hard-working young man, because for one tragic moment he lost
his self-control? Is he not sufficiently punished by the lifelong remorse
that is to be his lot? I confidently await your verdict, the only verdict
possible—that of homicide with extenuating circumstances."

The court rose, and the lawyer sat down, looking thoroughly exhausted. Some of his colleagues came to him and shook his hand. "You
put up a magnificent show, old man," I heard one of them say. Another
lawyer even called me to witness: "Fine, wasn't it?" I agreed, but insin-
cerely; I was far too tired to judge if it had been "fine" or otherwise.

Meanwhile the day was ending and the heat becoming less intense.
By some vague sounds that reached me from the street I knew that the
cool of the evening had set in. We all sat on, waiting. And what we all
were waiting for really concerned nobody but me. I looked round the
courtroom. It was exactly as it had been on the first day. I met the eyes
of the journalist in gray and the robot woman. This reminded me that
not once during the whole hearing had I tried to catch Marie's eye. It
wasn't that I'd forgotten her; only I was too preoccupied. I saw her now,
seated between Céleste and Raymond. She gave me a little wave of her
hand, as if to say, "At last!" She was smiling, but I could tell that she was
rather anxious. But my heart seemed turned to stone, and I couldn't even
return her smile.

The judges came back to their seats. Someone read out to the jury,
very rapidly, a string of questions. I caught a word here and there.
"Murder of malice aforethought . . . Provocation . . . Extenuating circumstances." The jury went out, and I was taken to the little room
where I had already waited. My lawyer came to see me; he was very
talkative and showed more cordiality and confidence than ever before.
He assured me that all would go well and I'd get off with a few years'
imprisonment or transportation. I asked him what were the chances of
getting the sentence quashed. He said there was no chance of that. He
had not raised any point of law, as this was apt to prejudice the jury.
And it was difficult to get a judgment quashed except on technical
grounds. I saw his point, and agreed. Looking at the matter dispassion-
ately, I shared his view. Otherwise there would be no end to litigation.
"In any case," the lawyer said, "you can appeal in the ordinary way. But
I'm convinced the verdict will be favorable."

We waited for quite a while, a good three quarters of an hour, I should say. Then a bell rang. My lawyer left me, saying:

"The foreman of the jury will read out the answers. You will be called on after that to hear the judgment."

Some doors banged. I heard people hurrying down flights of steps, but couldn't tell whether they were near by or distant. Then I heard a voice droning away in the courtroom.

When the bell rang again and I stepped back into the dock, the silence of the courtroom closed in round me, and with the silence came a queer sensation when I noticed that, for the first time, the young journalist kept his eyes averted. I didn't look in Marie's direction. In fact, I had no time to look, as the presiding judge had already started pronouncing a rigmarole to the effect that "in the name of the French people" I was to be decapitated in some public place.

It seemed to me then that I could interpret the look on the faces of those present; it was one of almost respectful sympathy. The policemen, too, handled me very gently. The lawyer placed his hand on my wrist. I had stopped thinking altogether. I heard the Judge's voice asking if I had anything more to say. After thinking for a moment, I answered, "No." Then the policemen led me out.

V

I HAVE JUST REFUSED, for the third time, to see the prison chaplain. I have nothing to say to him, don't feel like talking—and shall be seeing him quite soon enough, anyway. The only thing that interests me now is the problem of circumventing the machine, learning if the inevitable admits a loophole.

They have moved me to another cell. In this one, lying on my back, I can see the sky, and there is nothing else to see. All my time is spent in watching the slowly changing colors of the sky, as day moves on to night. I put my hands behind my head, gaze up, and wait.

This problem of a loophole obsesses me; I am always wondering if there have been cases of condemned prisoners' escaping from the implacable machinery of justice at the last moment, breaking through the police cordon, vanishing in the nick of time before the guillotine falls. Often and often I blame myself for not having given more attention to accounts of public executions. One should always take an interest in such matters. There's never any knowing what one may come to. Like everyone else I'd read descriptions of executions in the papers. But technical books dealing with this subject must certainly exist; only I'd never felt sufficiently interested to look them up. And in these books I might have

found escape stories. Surely they'd have told me that in one case, anyhow, the wheels had stopped; that once, if only once, in that inexorable
march of events, chance or luck had played a happy part. Just once! In a
way I think that single instance would have satisfied me. My emotion
would have done the rest. The papers often talk of "a debt owed to
society"—a debt which, according to them, must be paid by the offender.
But talk of that sort doesn't touch the imagination. No, the one thing
that counted for me was the possibility of making a dash for it and
defeating their bloodthirsty rite; of a mad stampede to freedom that
would anyhow give me a moment's hope, the gambler's last throw.
Naturally, all that "hope" could come to was to be knocked down at the
corner of a street or picked off by a bullet in my back. But, all things
considered, even this luxury was forbidden me; I was caught in the
rattrap irrevocably.

Try as I might, I couldn't stomach this brutal certitude. For really,
when one came to think of it, there was a disproportion between the
judgment on which it was based and the unalterable sequence of events
starting from the moment when the judgment was delivered. The fact
that the verdict was read out at eight P.M. rather than at five, the fact
that it might have been quite different, that it was given by men who
change their underclothes, and was credited to so vague an entity as the
"French people"—for that matter, why not to the Chinese or the German people?—all these facts seemed to deprive the court's decision of
much of its gravity. Yet I could but recognize that, from the moment
the verdict was given, its effects became as cogent, as tangible, as, for
example, this wall against which I was lying, pressing my back to it.

When such thoughts crossed my mind, I remembered a story
Mother used to tell me about my father. I never set eyes on him. Perhaps
the only things I really knew about him were what Mother had told me.
One of these was that he'd gone to see a murderer executed. The mere
thought of it turned his stomach. But he'd seen it through and, on coming home, was violently sick. At the time, I found my father's conduct
rather disgusting. But now I understood; it was so natural. How had I
failed to recognize that nothing was more important than an execution;
that, viewed from one angle, it's the only thing that can genuinely interest a man? And I decided that, if ever I got out of jail, I'd attend every
execution that took place. I was unwise, no doubt, even to consider this
possibility. For, the moment I'd pictured myself in freedom, standing
behind a double rank of policemen—on the right side of the line, so to
speak—the mere thought of being an onlooker who comes to see the
show, and can go home and vomit afterward, flooded my mind with a
wild, absurd exultation. It was a stupid thing to let my imagination run
away with me like that; a moment later I had a shivering fit and had to
wrap myself closely in my blanket. But my teeth went on chattering;
nothing would stop them.

Still, obviously, one can't be sensible all the time. Another equally ridiculous fancy of mine was to frame new laws, altering the penalties. What was wanted, to my mind, was to give the criminal a chance, if only a dog's chance; say, one chance in a thousand. There might be some drugs, or combination of drugs, which would kill the patient (I thought of him as "the patient") nine hundred and ninety-nine times in a thousand. That he should know this was, of course, essential. For after taking much thought, calmly, I came to the conclusion that what was wrong about the guillotine was that the condemned man had no chance at all, absolutely none. In fact, the patient's death had been ordained irrevocably. It was a foregone conclusion. If by some fluke the knife didn't do its job, they started again. So it came to this, that— against the grain, no doubt—the condemned man had to hope the apparatus was in good working order! This, I thought, was a flaw in the system; and, on the face of it, my view was sound enough. On the other hand, I had to admit it proved the efficiency of the system. It came to this; the man under sentence was obliged to collaborate mentally, it was in his interest that all should go off without a hitch.

Another thing I had to recognize was that, until now, I'd had wrong ideas on the subject. For some reason I'd always supposed that one had to go up steps and climb on to a scaffold, to be guillotined. Probably that was because of the 1789 Revolution; I mean, what I'd learned about it at school, and the pictures I had seen. Then one morning I remembered a photograph the newspapers had featured on the occasion of the execution of a famous criminal. Actually the apparatus stood on the ground; there was nothing very impressing about it, and it was much narrower than I'd imagined. It struck me as rather odd that picture had escaped my memory until now. What had struck me at the time was the neat appearance of the guillotine; its shining surfaces and finish reminded me of some laboratory instrument. One always has exaggerated ideas about what one doesn't know. Now I had to admit it seemed a very simple process, getting guillotined; the machine is on the same level as the man, and he walks toward it as he steps forward to meet somebody he knows. In a sense, that, too, was disappointing. The business of climbing a scaffold, leaving the world below, so to speak, gave something for a man's imagination to get hold of. But, as it was, the machine dominated everything; they killed you discreetly, with a hint of shame and much efficiency.

There were two other things about which I was always thinking: the dawn and my appeal. However, I did my best to keep my mind off these thoughts. I lay down, looked up at the sky, and forced myself to study it. When the light began to turn green I knew that night was coming. Another thing I did to deflect the course of my thoughts was to listen to my heart. I couldn't imagine that this faint throbbing which had been with me for so long would ever cease. Imagination has never been one of my strong points. Still, I tried to picture a moment when the beating of my heart no longer echoed in my head. But, in vain. The dawn and my appeal were still there. And I ended by believing it was a silly thing to try to force one's thoughts out of their natural groove.

They always came for one at dawn; that much I knew. So, really, all my nights were spent in waiting for that dawn. I have never liked being taken by surprise. When something happens to me I want to be ready for it. That's why I got into the habit of sleeping off and on in the daytime and watching through the night for the first hint of daybreak in the dark dome above. The worst period of the night was that vague hour when, I knew, they usually come; once it was after midnight I waited, listening intently. Never before had my ears perceived so many noises, such tiny sounds. Still, I must say I was lucky in one respect; never during any of those periods did I hear footsteps. Mother used to say that however miserable one is, there's always something to be thankful for. And each morning, when the sky brightened and light began to flood my cell, I agreed with her. Because I might just as well have heard footsteps, and felt my heart shattered into bits. Even though the faintest rustle sent me hurrying to the door and, pressing an ear to the rough, cold wood, I listened so intently that I could hear my breathing, quick and hoarse like a dog's panting—even so there was an end; my heart hadn't split, and I knew I had another twenty-four hours' respite.

Then all day there was my appeal to think about. I made the most of this idea, studying my effects so as to squeeze out the maximum of consolation. Thus, I always began by assuming the worst; my appeal was dismissed. That meant, of course, I was to die. Sooner than others, obviously. "But," I reminded myself, "it's common knowledge that life isn't worth living, anyhow." And, on a wide view, I could see that it makes little difference whether one dies at the age of thirty or threescore and ten—since, in either case, other men and women will continue living, the world will go on as before. Also, whether I died now or forty years hence, this business of dying had to be got through, inevitably. Still, somehow this line of thought wasn't as consoling as it should have been; the idea of all those years of life in hand was a galling reminder! However, I could argue myself out of it, by picturing what would have been my feelings when my term was up, and death had cornered me. Once you're up against it, the precise manner of your death has obviously small importance. Therefore—but it was hard not to lose the thread of the argument leading up to that "therefore"—I should be prepared to face the dismissal of my appeal.

At this stage, but only at this stage, I had, so to speak, the *right*, and accordingly I gave myself leave, to consider the other alternative; that my appeal was successful. And then the trouble was to calm down that sudden rush of joy racing through my body and even bringing tears to my eyes. But it was up to me to bring my nerves to heel and steady my mind; for, even in considering this possibility, I had to keep some order in my thoughts, so as to make my consolations, as regards the first alternative, more plausible. When I'd succeeded, I had earned a good hour's peace of mind; and that, anyhow, was something.

It was at one of these moments that I refused once again to see the chaplain. I was lying down and could mark the summer evening coming on by a soft golden glow spreading across the sky. I had just turned down my appeal, and felt my blood circulating with slow, steady throbs. No, I didn't want to see the chaplain. . . . Then I did something I hadn't done for quite a while; I fell to thinking about Marie. She hadn't written for ages; probably, I surmised, she had grown tired of being the mistress of a man sentenced to death. Or she might be ill, or dead. After all, such things happen. How could I have known about it, since, apart from our two bodies, separated now, there was no link between us, nothing to remind us of each other? Supposing she were dead, her memory would mean nothing; I couldn't feel an interest in a dead girl. This seemed to me quite normal; just as I realized people would soon forget me once I was dead. I couldn't even say that this was hard to stomach; really, there's no idea to which one doesn't get acclimatized in time.

My thoughts had reached this point when the chaplain walked in, unannounced. I couldn't help giving a start on seeing him. He noticed this evidently, as he promptly told me not to be alarmed. I reminded him that usually his visits were at another hour, and for a pretty grim occasion. This, he replied, was just a friendly visit; it had no concern with my appeal, about which he knew nothing. Then he sat down on my bed, asking me to sit beside him. I refused—not because I had anything against him; he seemed a mild, amiable man.

He remained quite still at first, his arms resting on his knees, his eyes fixed on his hands. They were slender but sinewy hands, which made me think of two nimble little animals. Then he gently rubbed them together. He stayed so long in the same position that for a while I almost forgot he was there.

All of a sudden he jerked his head up and looked me in the eyes. "Why," he asked, "don't you let me come to see you?"

I explained that I didn't believe in God.

"Are you really so sure of that?"

I said I saw no point in troubling my head about the matter; whether I believed or didn't was, to my mind, a question of so little importance.

He then leaned back against the wall, laying his hands flat on his thighs. Almost without seeming to address me, he remarked that he'd often noticed one fancies one is quite sure about something, when in point of fact one isn't. When I said nothing, he looked at me again, and asked:

"Don't you agree?"

I said that seemed quite possible. But, though I mightn't be so sure about what interested me, I was absolutely sure about what didn't interest me. And the question he had raised didn't interest me at all.

He looked away and, without altering his posture, asked if it was because I felt utterly desperate that I spoke like this. I explained that it wasn't despair I felt, but fear—which was natural enough.

"In that case," he said firmly, "God can help you. All the men I've seen in your position turned to Him in their time of trouble."

Obviously, I replied, they were at liberty to do so, if they felt like it. I, however, didn't want to be helped, and I hadn't time to work up interest for something that didn't interest me.

He fluttered his hands fretfully; then, sitting up, smoothed out his cassock. When this was done he began talking again, addressing me as "my friend." It wasn't because I'd been condemned to death, he said, that he spoke to me in this way. In his opinion every man on the earth was under sentence of death.

There, I interrupted him; that wasn't the same thing, I pointed out, and, what's more, could be no consolation.

He nodded. "Maybe. Still, if you don't die soon, you'll die one day. And then the same question will arise. How will you face that terrible, final hour?"

I replied that I'd face it exactly as I was facing it now.

Thereat he stood up, and looked me straight in the eyes. It was a trick I knew well. I used to amuse myself trying it on Emmanuel and Céleste, and nine times out of ten they'd look away uncomfortably. I could see the chaplain was an old hand at it, as his gaze never faltered. And his voice was quite steady when he said: "Have you no hope at all? Do you really think that when you die you die outright, and nothing remains?"

I said: "Yes."

He dropped his eyes and sat down again. He was truly sorry for me, he said. It must make life unbearable for a man, to think as I did.

The priest was beginning to bore me, and, resting a shoulder on the wall, just beneath the little skylight, I looked away. Though I didn't trouble much to follow what he said, I gathered he was questioning me again. Presently his tone became agitated, urgent, and, as I realized that he was genuinely distressed, I began to pay more attention.

He said he felt convinced my appeal would succeed, but I was saddled with a load of guilt, of which I must get rid. In his view man's justice was a vain thing; only God's justice mattered. I pointed out that the former had condemned me. Yes, he agreed, but it hadn't absolved me from my sin. I told him that I wasn't conscious of any "sin"; all I knew was that I'd been guilty of a criminal offense. Well, I was paying the penalty of that offense, and no one had the right to expect anything more of me.

Just then he got up again, and it struck me that if he wanted to move in this tiny cell, almost the only choice lay between standing up and sitting down. I was staring at the floor. He took a single step toward me, and halted, as if he didn't dare to come nearer. Then he looked up through the bars at the sky.

"You're mistaken, my son," he said gravely. "There's more that might be required of you. And perhaps it *will* be required of you."

"What do you mean?"

"You might be asked to see . . ."

"To see what?"

Slowly the priest gazed round my cell, and I was struck by the sadness of his voice when he replied:

"These stone walls, I know it only too well, are steeped in human suffering. I've never been able to look at them without a shudder. And yet—believe me, I am speaking from the depths of my heart—I *know* that even the wretchedest amongst you have sometimes seen, taking form against that grayness, a divine face. It's that face you are asked to see."

This roused me a little. I informed him that I'd been staring at those walls for months; there was nobody, nothing in the world, I knew better than I knew them. And once upon a time, perhaps, I used to try to see a face. But it was a sun-gold face, lit up with desire—Marie's face. I had no luck; I'd never seen it, and now I'd given up trying. Indeed, I'd never seen anything "taking form," as he called it, against those gray walls.

The chaplain gazed at me with a sort of sadness. I now had my back to the wall and light was flowing over my forehead. He muttered some words I didn't catch; then abruptly asked if he might kiss me. I said, "No." Then he turned, came up to the wall, and slowly drew his hand along it.

"Do you really love these earthly things so very much?" he asked in a low voice.

I made no reply.

For quite a while he kept his eyes averted. His presence was getting more and more irksome, and I was on the point of telling him to go, and leave me in peace, when all of a sudden he swung round on me, and burst out passionately:

"No! No! I refuse to believe it. I'm sure you've often wished there was an afterlife."

Of course I had, I told him. Everybody has that wish at times. But that had no more importance than wishing to be rich, or to swim very fast, or to have a better-shaped mouth. It was in the same order of things. I was going on in the same vein, when he cut in with a question. How did I picture the life after the grave?

I fairly bawled out at him: " A life in which I can remember this life on earth. That's all I want of it." And in the same breath I told him I'd had enough of his company.

But, apparently, he had more to say on the subject of God. I went close up to him and made a last attempt to explain that I'd very little time left, and I wasn't going to waste it on God.

Then he tried to change the subject by asking me why I hadn't once addressed him as "Father," seeing that he was a priest. That irritated me still more, and I told him he wasn't my father; quite the contrary, he was on the others' side.

"No, no, my son," he said, laying his hand on my shoulder. "I'm on *your* side, though you don't realize it—because your heart is hardened. But I shall pray for you."

Then, I don't know how it was, but something seemed to break inside me, and I started yelling at the top of my voice. I hurled insults at him, I told him not to waste his rotten prayers on me; it was better to burn than to disappear. I'd taken him by the neckband of his cassock, and, in a sort of ecstasy of joy and rage, I poured out on him all the thoughts that had been simmering in my brain. He seemed so cocksure, you see. And yet none of his certainties was worth one strand of a woman's hair. Living as he did, like a corpse, he couldn't even be sure of being alive. It might look as if my hands were empty. Actually, I was sure of myself, sure about everything, far surer than he; sure of my present life and of the death that was coming. That, no doubt, was all I had; but at least that certainty was something I could get my teeth into—just as it had got its teeth into me. I'd been right, I was still right, I was always right. I'd passed my life in a certain way, and I might have passed it in a different way, if I'd felt like it. I'd acted thus, and I hadn't acted otherwise; I hadn't done x, whereas I had done y or z. And what did that mean? That, all the time, I'd been waiting for this present moment, for that dawn, tomorrow's or another day's, which was to justify me. Nothing, nothing had the least importance, and I knew quite well why. He, too, knew why. From the dark horizon of my future a sort of slow, persistent breeze had been blowing toward me, all my life long, from the years that were to come. And on its way that breeze had leveled out all the ideas that people tried to foist on me in the equally unreal years I then was living through. What difference could they make to me, the deaths of others, or a mother's love, or his God; or the way a man decides to live, the fate he thinks he chooses, since one and the same fate was bound to "choose" not only me but thousands of millions of privileged people who, like him, called themselves my brothers. Surely, surely he must see that? Every man alive was privileged; there was only one class of men, the privileged class. All alike would be condemned to die one day; his turn, too, would come like the others'. And what difference could it make if, after being charged with murder, he were executed because he didn't weep at his mother's funeral, since it all came to the same thing in the end? The same thing for Salamano's wife and for Salamano's dog. That little robot woman was as "guilty" as the girl from Paris who had married Masson, or as Marie, who wanted me to marry her. What did it matter if Raymond was as much my pal as Céleste, who was a far worthier man? What did it matter if at this very moment Marie was kissing a new boy friend? As a condemned man himself, couldn't he grasp what I meant by that dark wind blowing from my future? . . .

I had been shouting so much that I'd lost my breath, and just then the jailers rushed in and started trying to release the chaplain from my grip. One of them made as if to strike me. The chaplain quietened them down, then gazed at me for a moment without speaking. I could see tears in his eyes. Then he turned and left the cell.

Once he'd gone, I felt calm again. But all this excitement had exhausted me and I dropped heavily on to my sleeping plank. I must have had a longish sleep, for, when I woke, the stars were shining down on my face. Sounds of the countryside came faintly in, and the cool night air, veined with smells of earth and salt, fanned my cheeks. The marvelous peace of the sleepbound summer night flooded through me like a tide. Then, just on the edge of daybreak, I heard a steamer's siren. People were starting on a voyage to a world which had ceased to concern me forever. Almost for the first time in many months I thought of my mother. And now, it seemed to me, I understood why at her life's end she had taken on a "fiancé"; why she'd played at making a fresh start. There, too, in that Home where lives were flickering out, the dusk came as a mournful solace. With death so near, Mother must have felt like someone on the brink of freedom, ready to start life all over again. No one, no one in the world had any right to weep for her. And I, too, felt ready to start life all over again. It was as if that great rush of anger had washed me clean, emptied me of hope, and, gazing up at the dark sky spangled with its signs and stars, for the first time, the first, I laid my heart open to the benign indifference of the universe. To feel it so like myself, indeed, so brotherly, made me realize that I'd been happy, and that I was happy still. For all to be accomplished, for me to feel less lonely, all that remained to hope was that on the day of my execution there should be a huge crowd of spectators and that they should greet me with howls of execration.

Willa Cather

A LOST LADY

> *. . . Come, my coach!*
> *Good night, ladies; good night, sweet ladies*
> *Good night, good night.*

Part One: I

THIRTY OR FORTY YEARS AGO, in one of those grey towns along the Burlington railroad, which are so much greyer today than they were then, there was a house well known from Omaha to Denver for its hospitality and for a certain charm of atmosphere. Well known, that is to say, to the railroad aristocracy of that time; men who had to do with the railroad itself, or with one of the "land companies" which were its by-products. In those days it was enough to say of a man that he was "connected with the Burlington." There were the directors, the general managers, vice-presidents, superintendents, whose names we all knew; and their younger brothers or nephews were auditors, freight agents, departmental assistants. Everyone "connected" with the Road, even the large cattle- and grain-shippers, had annual passes; they and their families rode about over the line a great deal. There were then two distinct social strata in the prairie States; the homesteaders and hand-workers who were there to make a living, and the bankers and gentlemen ranchers who came from the Atlantic seaboard to invest money and to "develop our great West," as they used to tell us.

When the Burlington men were travelling back and forth on business not very urgent, they found it agreeable to drop off the express and spend a night in a pleasant house where their importance was delicately recognized; and no house was pleasanter than that of Captain Daniel Forrester, at Sweet Water. Captain Forrester was himself a railroad man, a contractor, who had built hundreds of miles of road for the Burlington,—over the sage brush and cattle country, and on up into the Black Hills.

The Forrester place, as everyone called it, was not at all remarkable; the people who lived there made it seem much larger and finer than it was. The house stood on a low round hill, nearly a mile east of town; a white house with a wing, and sharp-sloping roofs to shed the snow. It was encircled by porches, too narrow for modern notions of comfort, supported by the fussy, fragile pillars of that time, when every honest stick of timber was tortured by the turning-lathe into something hideous. Stripped of its vines and denuded of its shrubbery, the house would probably have been ugly enough. It stood close into a fine cottonwood grove that threw sheltering arms to left and right and grew all down the hillside behind it. Thus placed on the hill, against its bristling grove, it was the first thing one saw on coming into Sweet Water by rail, and the last thing one saw on departing.

To approach Captain Forrester's property, you had first to get over a wide, sandy creek which flowed along the eastern edge of the town. Crossing this by the foot-bridge or the ford, you entered the Captain's private lane, bordered by Lombardy poplars, with wide meadows lying on either side. Just at the foot of the hill on which the house sat, one crossed a second creek by the stout wooden road-bridge. This stream traced artless loops and curves through the broad meadows that were half pasture land, half marsh. Anyone but Captain Forrester would have drained the bottom land and made it into highly productive fields. But he had selected this place long ago because it looked beautiful to him, and he happened to like the way the creek wound through his pasture, with mint and joint-grass and twinkling willows along its banks. He was well off for those times, and he had no children. He could afford to humour his fancies.

When the Captain drove friends from Omaha or Denver over from the station in his democrat wagon, it gratified him to hear these gentlemen admire his fine stock, grazing in the meadows on either side of his lane. And when they reached the top of the hill, it gratified him to see men who were older than himself leap nimbly to the ground and run up the front steps as Mrs. Forrester came out on the porch to greet them. Even the hardest and coldest of his friends, a certain narrow-faced Lincoln banker, became animated when he took her hand, tried to meet the gay challenge in her eyes and to reply cleverly to the droll word of greeting on her lips.

She was always there, just outside the front door, to welcome their visitors, having been warned of their approach by the sound of hoofs and the rumble of wheels on the wooden bridge. If she happened to be in the kitchen, helping her Bohemian cook, she came out in her apron, waving a buttery iron spoon, or shook cherry-stained fingers at the new arrival. She never stopped to pin up a lock; she was attractive in dishabille, and she knew it. She had been known to rush to the door in her dressing-gown, brush in hand and her long black hair rippling over her shoulders, to welcome Cyrus Dalzell, president of the Colorado & Utah; and that great man had never felt more flattered. In his eyes, and in the eyes of the admiring middle-aged men who visited there, whatever Mrs. Forrester chose to do was "lady-like" because she did it. They could not imagine her in any dress or situation in which she would not be charming. Captain Forrester himself, a man of few words, told Judge Pommeroy that he had never seen her look more captivating than on the day when she was chased by the new bull in the pasture. She had forgotten about the bull and gone into the meadow to gather wild flowers. He heard her scream, and as he ran puffing down the hill, she was scudding along the edge of the marshes like a hare, beside herself with laughter, and stubbornly clinging to the crimson parasol that had made all the trouble.

Mrs. Forrester was twenty-five years younger than her husband, and she was his second wife. He married her in California and brought her to Sweet Water a bride. They called the place home even then, when they lived there but a few months out of each year. But later, after the Captain's terrible fall with his horse in the mountains, which broke him so that he could no longer build railroads, he and his wife retired to the house on the hill. He grew old there,—and even she, alas! grew older.

II

But we will begin this story with a summer morning long ago, when Mrs. Forrester was still a young woman, and Sweet Water was a town of which great things were expected. That morning she was standing in the deep bay window of her parlour, arranging old-fashioned blush roses in a glass bowl. Glancing up, she saw a group of little boys coming along the driveway, barefoot, with fishing-poles and lunch-baskets. She knew most of them; there was Niel Herbert, Judge Pommeroy's nephew, a handsome boy of twelve whom she liked; and polite George Adams, son of a gentleman rancher from Lowell, Massachusetts. The others were just little boys from the town; the butcher's red-headed son, the leading grocer's fat brown twins, Ed Elliott (whose flirtatious old father kept a shoe store and was the Don Juan of the lower world of Sweet Water), and the two sons of the German tailor,—pale, freckled lads with ragged clothes and ragged rust-coloured hair, from whom she sometimes bought game or catfish when they appeared silent and spook-like at her kitchen door and thinly asked if she would "care for any fish this morning."

As the boys came up the hill she saw them hesitate and consult together. "You ask her, Niel."

"You'd better, George. She goes to your house all the time, and she barely knows me to speak to."

As they paused before the three steps which led up to the front porch, Mrs. Forrester came to the door and nodded graciously, one of the pink roses in her hand.

"Good-morning, boys. Off for a picnic?"

George Adams stepped forward and solemnly took off his big straw hat. "Good-morning, Mrs. Forrester. Please may we fish and wade down in the marsh and have our lunch in the grove?"

"Certainly. You have a lovely day. How long has school been out? Don't you miss it? I'm sure Niel does. Judge Pommeroy tells me he's very studious."

The boys laughed, and Niel looked unhappy.

"Run along, and be sure you don't leave the gate into the pasture open. Mr. Forrester hates to have the cattle get in on his blue grass."

The boys went quietly round the house to the gate into the grove, then ran shouting down the grassy slopes under the tall trees. Mrs. Forrester watched them from the kitchen window until they disappeared behind the roll of the hill. She turned to her Bohemian cook.

"Mary, when you are baking this morning, put in a pan of cookies for those boys. I'll take them down when they are having their lunch."

The round hill on which the Forrester house stood sloped gently down to the bridge in front, and gently down through the grove behind. But east of the house, where the grove ended, it broke steeply from high grassy banks, like bluffs, to the marsh below. It was thither the boys were bound.

When lunch time came they had done none of the things they meant to do. They had behaved like wild creatures all morning; shouting from the breezy bluffs, dashing down into the silvery marsh through the dewy cobwebs that glistened on the tall weeds, swishing among the pale tan cattails, wading in the sandy creek bed, chasing a striped water snake from the old willow stump where he was sunning himself, cutting sling-shot crotches, throwing themselves on their stomachs to drink at the cool spring that flowed out from under a bank into a thatch of dark watercress. Only the two German boys, Rheinhold and Adolph Blum, withdrew to a still pool where the creek was dammed by a reclining tree trunk, and, in spite of all the noise and splashing about them, managed to catch a few suckers.

The wild roses were wide open and brilliant, the blue-eyed grass was in purple flower, and the silvery milkweed was just coming on. Birds and butterflies darted everywhere. All at once the breeze died, the air grew very hot, the marsh steamed, and the birds disappeared. The boys found they were tired; their shirts stuck to their bodies and their hair to their foreheads. They left the sweltering marsh-meadows for the grove, lay down on the clean grass under the grateful shade of the tall cotton-woods, and spread out their lunch. The Blum boys never brought anything but rye bread and hunks of dry cheese,—their companions wouldn't have touched it on any account. But Thaddeus Grimes, the butcher's red-headed son, was the only one impolite enough to show his scorn. "You live on wienies to home, why don't you never bring none?" he bawled.

"Hush," said Niel Herbert. He pointed to a white figure coming rapidly down through the grove, under the flickering leaf shadows,—Mrs. Forrester, bareheaded, a basket on her arm, her blue-black hair shining in the sun. It was not until years afterward that she began to wear veils and sun hats, though her complexion was never one of her beauties. Her cheeks were pale and rather thin, slightly freckled in summer.

As she approached, George Adams, who had a particular mother, rose, and Niel followed his example.

"Here are some hot cookies for your lunch, boys." She took the napkin off the basket. "Did you catch anything?"

"We didn't fish much. Just ran about," said George.

"I know! You were wading and things." She had a nice way of talking to boys, light and confidential. "I wade down there myself sometimes, when I go down to get flowers. I can't resist it. I pull off my stockings and pick up my skirts, and in I go!" She thrust out a white shoe and shook it.

"But you can swim, can't you, Mrs. Forrester," said George. "Most women can't."

"Oh yes, they can! In California everybody swims. But the Sweet Water doesn't tempt me,—mud and water snakes and blood-suckers—Ugh!" she shivered, laughing.

"We seen a water snake this morning and chased him. A whopper!" Thad Grimes put in.

"Why didn't you kill him? Next time I go wading he'll bite my toes! Now, go on with your lunch. George can leave the basket with Mary as you go out." She left them, and they watched her white figure drifting along the edge of the grove as she stopped here and there to examine the raspberry vines by the fence.

"These are good cookies, all right," said one of the giggly brown Weaver twins. The German boys munched in silence. They were all rather pleased that Mrs. Forrester had come down to them herself, instead of sending Mary. Even rough little Thad Grimes, with his red thatch and catfish mouth—the characteristic feature of all the Grimes brood—knew that Mrs. Forrester was a very special kind of person. George and Niel were already old enough to see for themselves that she was different from the other townswomen, and to reflect upon what it was that made her so. The Blum brothers regarded her humbly from under their pale, chewed-off hair, as one of the rich and great of the world. They realized, more than their companions, that such a fortunate and privileged class was an axiomatic fact in the social order.

The boys had finished their lunch and were lying on the grass talking about how Judge Pommeroy's water spaniel, Fanny, had been poisoned, and who had certainly done it, when they had a second visitor.

"Shut up, boys, there he comes now. That's Poison Ivy," said one of the Weaver twins. "Shut up, we don't want old Roger poisoned."

A well-grown boy of eighteen or nineteen, dressed in a shabby corduroy hunting suit, with a gun and gamebag, had climbed up from the marsh and was coming down the grove between the rows of trees. He walked with a rude, arrogant stride, kicking at the twigs, and carried himself with unnatural erectness, as if he had a steel rod down his back. There was something defiant and suspicious about the way he held his head. He came up to the group and addressed them in a superior, patronizing tone.

"Hullo, kids. What are *you* doing here?"

"Picnic," said Ed Elliott.

"I thought girls went on picnics. Did you bring teacher along? Ain't you kids old enough to hunt yet?"

George Adams looked at him scornfully. "Of course we are. I got a 22 Remington for my last birthday. But we know better than to bring guns over here. You better hide yours, Mr. Ivy, or Mrs. Forrester will come down and tell you to get out."

"She can't see us from the house. And anyhow, she can't say anything to me. I'm just as good as she is."

To this the boys made no reply. Such an assertion was absurd even to fish-mouthed Thad; his father's business depended upon some people being better than others, and ordering better cuts of meat in consequence. If everybody ate round steak like Ivy Peters' family, there would be nothing in the butcher's trade.

The visitor had put his gun and gamebag behind a tree, however, and stood stiffly upright, surveying the group out of his narrow beady eyes and making them all uncomfortable. George and Niel hated to look at Ivy,—and yet his face had a kind of fascination for them. It was red, and the flesh looked hard, as if it were swollen from bee-stings, or from an encounter with poison ivy. This nickname, however, was given him because it was well known that he had "made away" with several other dogs before he had poisoned the Judge's friendly water spaniel. The boys said he took a dislike to a dog and couldn't rest until he made an end of him.

Ivy's red skin was flecked with tiny freckles, like rust spots, and in each of his hard cheeks there was a curly indentation, like a knot in a tree-bole,—two permanent dimples which did anything but soften his countenance. His eyes were very small, and an absence of eyelashes gave his pupils the fixed, unblinking hardness of a snake's or a lizard's. His hands had the same swollen look as his face, were deeply creased across the back and knuckles, as if the skin were stretched too tight. He was an ugly fellow, Ivy Peters, and he liked being ugly.

He began telling the boys that it was too hot to hunt now, but later he meant to steal down to the marsh, where the ducks came at sundown, and bag a few. "I can make off across the corn fields before the old Cap sees me. He's not much on the run."

"He'll complain to your father."

"A whoop my father cares!" The speaker's restless eyes were looking up through the branches. "See that woodpecker tapping; don't mind us a bit. That's nerve!"

"They are protected here, so they're not afraid," said precise George.

"Hump! They'll spoil the old man's grove for him. That tree's full of holes already. Wouldn't he come down easy, now!"

Niel and George Adams sat up. "Don't you dare shoot here, you'll get us all into trouble."

"She'd come right down from the house," cried Ed Elliott.

"Let her come, stuck-up piece! Who's talking about shooting, anyway? There's more ways of killing dogs than choking them with butter."

At this effrontery the boys shot amazed glances at one another, and the brown Weaver twins broke simultaneously into giggles and rolled over on the turf. But Ivy seemed unaware that he was regarded as being especially resourceful where dogs were concerned. He drew from his pocket a metal sling-shot and some round bits of gravel. "I won't kill it. I'll just surprise it, so we can have a look at it."

"Bet you won't hit it!"

"Bet I will!" He fitted the stone to the leather, squinted, and let fly. Sure enough, the woodpecker dropped at his feet. He threw his heavy black felt hat over it. Ivy never wore a straw hat, even in the hottest weather. "Now wait. He'll come to. You'll hear him flutter in a minute."

"It ain't a he, anyhow. It's a female. Anybody would know that," said Niel contemptuously, annoyed that this unpopular boy should come along and spoil their afternoon. He held the fate of his uncle's spaniel against Ivy Peters.

"All right, Miss Female," said Ivy carelessly, intent upon a project of his own. He took from his pocket a little red leather box, and when he opened it the boys saw that it contained curious little instruments: tiny sharp knife blades, hooks, curved needles, a saw, a blow-pipe, and scissors.

"Some of these I got with a taxidermy outfit from the *Youth's Companion*, and some I made myself." He got stiffly down on his knees, —his joints seemed disinclined to bend at all,—and listened beside his hat. "She's as lively as a cricket," he announced. Thrusting his hand suddenly under the brim, he brought out the startled bird. It was not bleeding, and did not seem to be crippled.

"Now, you watch, and I'll show you something," said Ivy. He held the woodpecker's head in a vice made of his thumb and forefinger, enclosing its panting body with his palm. Quick as a flash, as if it were a practised trick, with one of those tiny blades he slit both the eyes that glared in the bird's stupid little head, and instantly released it.

The woodpecker rose in the air with a whirling, corkscrew motion, darted to the right, struck a tree-trunk,—to the left, and struck another. Up and down, backward and forward among the tangle of branches it flew, raking its feathers, falling and recovering itself. The boys stood watching it, indignant and uncomfortable, not knowing what to do. They were not especially sensitive; Thad was always on hand when there was anything doing at the slaughter house, and the Blum boys lived by killing things. They wouldn't have believed they could be so upset by a hurt woodpecker. There was something wild and desperate about the way the darkened creature beat its wings in the branches, whirling in the sunlight and never seeing it, always thrusting its head up and shaking it, as a bird does when it is drinking. Presently it managed to get its feet on the same limb where it had been struck, and seemed to recognize that perch. As if it had learned something by its bruises, it pecked and crept its way along the branch and disappeared into its own hole.

"There," Niel Herbert exclaimed between his teeth, "if I can get it now, I can kill it and put it out of its misery. Let me on your back, Rhein."

Rheinhold was the tallest, and he obediently bent his bony back. The trunk of a cottonwood tree is hard to climb; the bark is rough, and the branches begin a long way up. Niel tore his trousers and scratched his bare legs smartly before he got to the first fork. After recovering breath, he wound his way up toward the woodpecker's hole, which was inconveniently high. He was almost there, his companions below thought him quite safe, when he suddenly lost his balance, turned a somersault in the air, and bumped down on the grass at their feet. There he lay without moving.

"Run for water!"

"Run for Mrs. Forrester! Ask her for whiskey."

"No," said George Adams, "let's carry him up to the house. She will know what to do."

"That's sense," said Ivy Peters. As he was much bigger and stronger than any of the others, he lifted Niel's limp body and started up the hill. It had occurred to him that this would be a fine chance to get inside the Forresters' house and see what it was like, and this he had always wanted to do.

Mary, the cook, saw them coming from the kitchen window, and ran for her mistress. Captain Forrester was in Kansas City that day.

Mrs. Forrester came to the back door. "What's happened? It's Niel, too! Bring him in this way, please."

Ivy Peters followed her, keeping his eyes open, and the rest trooped after him,—all but the Blum boys, who knew that their place was outside the kitchen door. Mrs. Forrester led the way through the butler's pantry, the dining room, the back parlour, to her own bedroom. She threw down the white counterpane, and Ivy laid Niel upon the sheets. Mrs. Forrester was concerned, but not frightened.

"Mary, will you bring the brandy from the sideboard. George, telephone Dr. Dennison to come over at once. Now you other boys run out on the front porch and wait quietly. There are too many of you in here." She knelt by the bed, putting brandy between Niel's white lips with a teaspoon. The little boys withdrew, only Ivy Peters remained standing in the back parlour, just outside the bedroom door, his arms folded across his chest, taking in his surroundings with bold, unblinking eyes.

Mrs. Forrester glanced at him over her shoulder. "Will you wait on the porch, please? You are older than the others, and if anything is needed I can call on you."

Ivy cursed himself, but he had to go. There was something final about her imperious courtesy,—high-and-mighty, he called it. He had intended to sit down in the biggest leather chair and cross his legs and make himself at home; but he found himself on the front porch, put out by that delicately modulated voice as effectually as if he had been kicked out by the brawniest tough in town.

Niel opened his eyes and looked wonderingly about the big, half-darkened room, full of heavy, old-fashioned walnut furniture. He was lying on a white bed with ruffled pillow shams, and Mrs. Forrester was kneeling beside him, bathing his forehead with cologne. Bohemian Mary stood behind her, with a basin of water. "Ouch, my arm!" he muttered, and the perspiration broke out on his face.

"Yes, dear, I'm afraid it's broken. Don't move. Dr. Dennison will be here in a few minutes. It doesn't hurt very much, does it?"

"No'm," he said faintly. He was in pain, but he felt weak and contented. The room was cool and dusky and quiet. At his house everything was horrid when one was sick. . . . What soft fingers Mrs. Forrester had, and what a lovely lady she was. Inside the lace ruffle of her dress he saw her white throat rising and falling so quickly. Suddenly she got up to take off her glittering rings,—she had not thought of them before,—shed them off her fingers with a quick motion as if she were washing her hands, and dropped them into Mary's broad palm. The little boy was thinking that he would probably never be in so nice a place again. The windows went almost down to the baseboard, like doors, and the closed green shutters let in streaks of sunlight that quivered on the polished floor and the silver things on the dresser. The heavy curtains were looped back with thick cords, like ropes. The marble-topped wash-stand was as big as a sideboard. The massive walnut furniture was all inlaid with pale-coloured woods. Niel had a scroll-saw, and this inlay interested him.

"There, he looks better now, doesn't he, Mary?" Mrs. Forrester ran her fingers through his black hair and lightly kissed him on the forehead. Oh, how sweet, how sweet she smelled!

"Wheels on the bridge; it's Dr. Dennison. Go and show him in, Mary."

Dr. Dennison set Niel's arm and took him home in his buggy. Home was not a pleasant place to go to; a frail egg-shell house, set off on the edge of the prairie where people of no consequence lived. Except for the fact that he was Judge Pommeroy's nephew, Niel would have been one of the boys to whom Mrs. Forrester merely nodded brightly as she passed. His father was a widower. A poor relation, a spinster from Kentucky, kept house for them, and Niel thought she was probably the worst house keeper in the world. Their house was usually full of washing in various stages of incompletion,—tubs sitting about with linen soaking,—and the beds were "aired" until any hour in the afternoon when Cousin Sadie happened to think of making them up. She liked to sit down after breakfast and read murder trials, or peruse a well-worn copy of "St. Elmo." Sadie was a good-natured thing and was always running off to help a neighbour, but Niel hated to have anyone come to see them. His father was at home very little, spent all his time at his office. He kept the county abstract books and made farm loans. Having lost his own property, he invested other people's money for them. He was a gentle, agreeable man, young, good-looking, with nice manners, but Niel felt there was an air of failure and defeat about his family. He clung to his maternal uncle, Judge Pommeroy, white-whiskered and portly, who was Captain Forrester's lawyer and a friend of all the great men who visited the Forresters. Niel was proud, like his mother; she died when he was five years old. She had hated the West, and used haughtily to tell her neighbours that she would never think of living anywhere but in Fayette county, Kentucky; that they had only come to Sweet Water to make investments and to "turn the crown into the pound." By that phrase she was still remembered, poor lady.

III

FOR THE NEXT few years Niel saw very little of Mrs. Forrester. She was an excitement that came and went with summer. She and her husband always spent the winter in Denver and Colorado Springs,—left Sweet Water soon after Thanksgiving and did not return until the first of May. He knew that Mrs. Forrester liked him, but she hadn't much time for growing boys. When she had friends staying with her, and gave a picnic supper for them, or a dance in the grove on a moonlight night, Niel was always invited. Coming and going along the road to the marsh with the Blum boys, he sometimes met the Captain driving visitors over in the democrat wagon, and he heard about these people from Black Tom, Judge Pommeroy's faithful negro servant, who went over to wait on the table for Mrs. Forrester when she had a dinner party.

Then came the accident which cut short the Captain's career as a roadbuilder. After that fall with his horse, he lay ill at the Antlers, in Colorado Springs, all winter. In the summer, when Mrs. Forrester brought him home to Sweet Water, he still walked with a cane. He had grown much heavier, seemed encumbered by his own bulk, and never suggested taking a contract for the railroad again. He was able to work in his garden, trimmed his snowball bushes and lilac hedges, devoted a great deal of time to growing roses. He and his wife still went away for the winter, but each year the period of their absence grew shorter.

All this while the town of Sweet Water was changing. Its future no longer looked bright. Successive crop failures had broken the spirit of the farmers. George Adams and his family had gone back to Massachusetts, disillusioned about the West. One by one the other gentlemen ranchers followed their example. The Forresters now had fewer visitors. The Burlington was "drawing in its horns," as people said, and the railroad officials were not stopping off at Sweet Water so often,—were more inclined to hurry past a town where they had sunk money that would never come back.

Niel Herbert's father was one of the first failures to be crowded to the wall. He closed his little house, sent his cousin Sadie back to Kentucky, and went to Denver to accept an office position. He left Niel behind to read law in the office with his uncle. Not that Niel had any taste for the law, but he liked being with Judge Pommeroy, and he might as well stay there as anywhere, for the present. The few thousand dollars his mother had left him would not be his until he was twenty-one.

Niel fitted up a room for himself behind the suite which the Judge retained for his law offices, on the second floor of the most pretentious brick block in town. There he lived with monastic cleanliness and severity, glad to be rid of his cousin and her inconsequential housewifery, and resolved to remain a bachelor, like his uncle. He took care of the offices, which meant that he did the janitor work, and arranged them exactly to suit his taste, making the rooms so attractive that all the Judge's friends, and especially Captain Forrester, dropped in there to talk oftener than ever.

The Judge was proud of his nephew. Niel was now nineteen, a tall, straight, deliberate boy. His features were clear-cut, his grey eyes, so dark that they looked black under his long lashes, were rather moody and challenging. The world did not seem over-bright to young people just then. His reserve, which did not come from embarrassment or vanity, but from a critical habit of mind, made him seem older than he was, and a little cold.

.   .   .

One winter afternoon, only a few days before Christmas, Niel sat writing in the back office, at the long table where he usually worked or trifled, surrounded by the Judge's fine law library and solemn steel engravings of statesmen and jurists. His uncle was at his desk in the front office, engaged in a friendly consultation with one of his country clients. Niel, greatly bored with the notes he was copying, was trying to invent an excuse for getting out on the street, when he became aware of light footsteps coming rapidly down the outside corridor. The door of the front office opened, he heard his uncle rise quickly to his feet, and, at the same moment, heard a woman's laugh,—a soft, musical laugh which rose and descended like a suave scale. He turned in his screw chair so that he could look over his shoulder through the double doors into the front room. Mrs. Forrester stood there, shaking her muff at the Judge and the bewildered Swede farmer. Her quick eye lighted upon a bottle of Bourbon and two glasses on the desk among the papers.

"Is that the way you prepare your cases, Judge? What an example for Niel!" She peeped through the door and nodded to the boy as he rose.

He remained in the back room, however, watching her while she declined the chair the Judge pushed toward her and made a sign of refusal when he politely pointed to the Bourbon. She stood beside his desk in her long sealskin coat and cap, a crimson scarf showing above the collar, a little brown veil with spots tied over her eyes. The veil did not in the least obscure those beautiful eyes, dark and full of light, set under a low white forehead and arching eyebrows. The frosty air had brought no colour to her cheeks,—her skin had always the fragrant, crystalline whiteness of white lilacs. Mrs. Forrester looked at one, and one knew that she was bewitching. It was instantaneous, and it pierced the thickest hide. The Swede farmer was now grinning from ear to ear, and he, too, had shuffled to his feet. There could be no negative encounter, however slight, with Mrs. Forrester. If she merely bowed to you, merely looked at you, it constituted a personal relation. Something about her took hold of one in a flash; one became acutely conscious of her, of her fragility and grace, of her mouth which could say so much without words; of her eyes, lively, laughing, intimate, nearly always a little mocking.

"Will you and Niel dine with us tomorrow evening, Judge? And will you lend me Tom? We've just had a wire. The Ogdens are stopping over with us. They've been East to bring the girl home from school, —she's had mumps or something. They want to get home for Christmas, but they will stop off for two days. Probably Frank Ellinger will come on from Denver."

"No prospect can afford me such pleasure as that of dining with Mrs. Forrester," said the Judge ponderously.

"Thank you!" she bowed playfully and turned toward the double doors. "Niel, could you leave your work long enough to drive me home? Mr. Forrester has been detained at the bank."

Niel put on his wolfskin coat. Mrs. Forrester took him by his shaggy sleeve and went with him quickly down the long corridor and the narrow stairs to the street.

At the hitch-bar stood her cutter, looking like a painted toy among the country sleds and wagons. Niel tucked the buffalo robes about Mrs. Forrester, untied the ponies, and sprang in beside her. Without direction the team started down the frozen main street, where few people were abroad, crossed the creek on the ice, and trotted up the poplar-bordered lane toward the house on the hill. The late afternoon sun burned on the snow-crusted pastures. The poplars looked very tall and straight, pinched up and severe in their winter poverty. Mrs. Forrester chatted to Niel with her face turned toward him, holding her muff up to break the wind.

"I'm counting on you to help me entertain Constance Ogden. Can you take her off my hands day after tomorrow, come over in the afternoon? Your duties as a lawyer aren't very arduous yet?" She smiled teasingly. "What can I do with a miss of nineteen? one who goes to college? I've no learned conversation for her!"

"Surely I haven't!" Niel exclaimed.

"Oh, but you're a boy! Perhaps you can interest her in lighter things. She's considered pretty."

"Do you think she is?"

"I haven't seen her lately. She was striking,—china blue eyes and heaps of yellow hair, not exactly yellow,—what they call an ashen blond, I believe."

Niel had noticed that in describing the charms of other women Mrs. Forrester always made fun of them a little.

They drew up in front of the house. Ben Keezer came round from the kitchen to take the team.

"You are to go back for Mr. Forrester at six, Ben. Niel, come in for a moment and get warm." She drew him through the little storm entry, which protected the front door in winter, into the hall. "Hang up your coat and come along." He followed her through the parlour into the sitting-room, where a little coal grate was burning under the black mantelpiece, and sat down in the big leather chair in which Captain Forrester dozed after his mid-day meal. It was a rather dark room, with walnut bookcases that had carved tops and glass doors. The floor was covered by a red carpet, and the walls were hung with large, old-fashioned engravings; "The House of the Poet on the Last Day of Pompeii," "Shakespeare Reading before Queen Elizabeth."

Mrs. Forrester left him and presently returned carrying a tray with a decanter and sherry glasses. She put it down on her husband's smoking-table, poured out a glass for Niel and one for herself, and perched on the arm of one of the stuffed chairs, where she sat sipping her sherry and stretching her tiny, silver-buckled slippers out toward the glowing coals.

"It's so nice to have you staying on until after Christmas," Niel observed. "You've only been here one other Christmas since I can remember."

"I'm afraid we're staying on all winter this year. Mr. Forrester thinks we can't afford to go away. For some reason, we are extraordinarily poor just now."

"Like everybody else," the boy commented grimly.

"Yes, like everybody else. However, it does no good to be glum about it, does it?" She refilled the two glasses. "I always take a little sherry at this time in the afternoon. At Colorado Springs some of my friends take tea, like the English. But I should feel like an old woman, drinking tea! Besides, sherry is good for my throat." Niel remembered some legend about a weak chest and occasional terrifying hemorrhages. But that seemed doubtful, as one looked at her,—fragile, indeed, but with such light, effervescing vitality. "Perhaps I do seem old to you, Niel, quite old enough for tea and a cap!"

He smiled gravely. "You seem always the same to me, Mrs. Forrester."

"Yes? And how is that?"

"Lovely. Just lovely."

As she bent forward to put down her glass she patted his cheek. "Oh, you'll do very well for Constance!" Then, seriously, "I'm glad if I do, though. I want you to like me well enough to come to see us often this winter. You shall come with your uncle to make a fourth at whist. Mr. Forrester must have his whist in the evening. Do you think he is looking any worse, Niel? It frightens me to see him getting a little uncertain. But there, we must believe in good luck!" She took up the half-empty glass and held it against the light.

Niel liked to see the firelight sparkle on her earrings, long pendants of garnets and seed-pearls in the shape of fleurs-de-lys. She was the only woman he knew who wore earrings; they hung naturally against her thin, triangular cheeks. Captain Forrester, although he had given her handsomer ones, liked to see her wear these, because they had been his mother's. It gratified him to have his wife wear jewels; it meant something to him. She never left off her beautiful rings unless she was in the kitchen.

"A winter in the country may do him good," said Mrs. Forrester, after a silence during which she looked intently into the fire, as if she were trying to read the outcome of their difficulties there. "He loves this place so much. But you and Judge Pommeroy must keep an eye on him when he is in town, Niel. If he looks tired or uncertain, make some excuse and bring him home. He can't carry a drink or two as he used," —she glanced over her shoulder to see that the door into the dining-room was shut. "Once last winter he had been drinking with some old friends at the Antlers,—nothing unusual, just as he always did, as a man must be able to do,—but it was too much for him. When he came out to join me in the carriage, coming down that long walk, you know, he fell.

There was no ice, he didn't slip. It was simply because he was unsteady. He had trouble getting up. I still shiver to think of it. To me, it was as if one of the mountains had fallen down."

A little later Niel went plunging down the hill, looking exultantly into the streak of red sunset. Oh, the winter would not be so bad, this year! How strange that she should be here at all, a woman like her among common people! Not even in Denver had he ever seen another woman so elegant. He had sat in the dining-room of the Brown Palace hotel and watched them as they came down to dinner,—fashionable women from "the East," on their way to California. But he had never found one so attractive and distinguished as Mrs. Forrester. Compared with her, other women were heavy and dull; even the pretty ones seemed lifeless,—they had not that something in their glance that made one's blood tingle. And never elsewhere had he heard anything like her inviting, musical laugh, that was like the distant measures of dance music, heard through opening and shutting doors.

He could remember the very first time he ever saw Mrs. Forrester, when he was a little boy. He had been loitering in front of the Episcopal church one Sunday morning, when a low carriage drove up to the door. Ben Keezer was on the front seat, and on the back seat was a lady, alone, in a black silk dress all puffs and ruffles, and a black hat, carrying a parasol with a carved ivory handle. As the carriage stopped she lifted her dress to alight; out of a swirl of foamy white petticoats she thrust a black, shiny slipper. She stepped lightly to the ground and with a nod to the driver went into the church. The little boy followed her through the open door, saw her enter a pew and kneel. He was proud now that at the first moment he had recognized her as belonging to a different world from any he had ever known.

Niel paused for a moment at the end of the lane to look up at the last skeleton poplar in the long row; just above its pointed tip hung the hollow, silver winter moon.

IV

In PLEASANT WEATHER Judge Pommeroy walked to the Forresters', but on the occasion of the dinner for the Ogdens he engaged the livery-man to take him and his nephew over in one of the town hacks,— vehicles seldom used except for funerals and weddings. They smelled strongly of the stable and contained lap-robes as heavy as lead and as slippery as oiled paper. Niel and his uncle were the only townspeople asked to the Forresters' that evening; they rolled over the creek and up the hill in state, and emerged covered with horsehair.

Captain Forrester met them at the door, his burly figure buttoned up in a frock coat, a flat collar and black string tie under the heavy folds of his neck. He was always clean-shaven except for a drooping dun-coloured moustache. The company stood behind him laughing while Niel caught up the whisk-broom and began dusting roan hairs off his uncle's broadcloth. Mrs. Forrester gave Niel a brushing in turn and then took him into the parlour and introduced him to Mrs. Ogden and her daughter.

The daughter was a rather pretty girl, Niel thought, in a pale pink evening dress which left bare her smooth arms and short, dimpled neck. Her eyes were, as Mrs. Forrester had said, a china blue, rather prominent and inexpressive. Her fleece of ashy-gold hair was bound about her head with silver bands. In spite of her fresh, rose-like complexion, her face was not altogether agreeable. Two dissatisfied lines reached from the corners of her short nose to the corners of her mouth. When she was displeased, even a little, these lines tightened, drew her nose back, and gave her a suspicious, injured expression. Niel sat down by her and did his best, but he found her hard to talk to. She seemed nervous and distracted, kept glancing over her shoulder, and crushing her handkerchief up in her hands. Her mind, clearly, was elsewhere. After a few moments he turned to the mother, who was more easily interested.

Mrs. Ogden was almost unpardonably homely. She had a pear-shaped face, and across her high forehead lay a row of flat, dry curls. Her bluish brown skin was almost the colour of her violet dinner dress. A diamond necklace glittered about her wrinkled throat. Unlike Constance, she seemed thoroughly amiable, but as she talked she tilted her head and "used" her eyes, availing herself of those arch glances which he had supposed only pretty women indulged in. Probably she had long been surrounded by people to whom she was an important personage, and had acquired the manner of a spoiled darling. Niel thought her rather foolish at first, but in a few moments he had got used to her mannerisms and began to like her. He found himself laughing heartily and forgot the discouragement of his failure with the daughter.

Mr. Ogden, a short, weather-beaten man of fifty, with a cast in one eye, a stiff imperial, and twisted moustaches, was noticeably quieter and less expansive than when Niel had met him here on former occasions. He seemed to expect his wife to do the talking. When Mrs. Forrester addressed him, or passed near him, his good eye twinkled and followed her,—while the eye that looked askance remained unchanged and committed itself to nothing.

Suddenly everyone became more lively; the air warmed, and the lamplight seemed to brighten, as a fourth member of the Denver party came in from the dining-room with a glittering tray full of cocktails he had been making. Frank Ellinger was a bachelor of forty, six feet two, with long straight legs, fine shoulders, and a figure that still permitted his white waistcoat to button without a wrinkle under his conspicuously well-cut dinner coat. His black hair, coarse and curly as the filling of a mattress, was grey about the ears, his florid face showed little purple veins about his beaked nose,—a nose like the prow of a ship, with long nostrils. His chin was deeply cleft, his thick curly lips seemed very muscular, very much under his control, and, with his strong white teeth, irregular and curved, gave him the look of a man who could bite an iron rod in two with a snap of his jaws. His whole figure seemed very much alive under his clothes, with a restless, muscular energy that had something of the cruelty of wild animals in it. Niel was very much interested in this man, the hero of many ambiguous stories. He didn't know whether he liked him or not. He knew nothing bad about him, but he felt something evil.

The cocktails were the signal for general conversation, the company drew together in one group. Even Miss Constance seemed less dissatisfied. Ellinger drank his cocktail standing beside her chair, and offered her the cherry in his glass. They were old-fashioned whiskey cocktails. Nobody drank Martinis then; gin was supposed to be the consolation of sailors and inebriate scrub-women.

"Very good, Frank, very good," Captain Forrester pronounced, drawing out a fresh, cologne-scented handkerchief to wipe his moustache. "Are encores in order?" The Captain puffed slightly when he talked. His eyes, always somewhat suffused and bloodshot since his injury, blinked at his friends from under his heavy lids.

"One more round for everybody, Captain." Ellinger brought in from the sideboard a capacious shaker and refilled all the glasses except Miss Ogden's. At her he shook his finger, and offered her the little dish of Maraschino cherries.

"No, I don't want those. I want the one in your glass," she said with a pouty smile. "I like it to taste of something!"

"Constance!" said her mother reprovingly, rolling her eyes at Mrs. Forrester, as if to share with her the charm of such innocence.

"Niel," Mrs. Forrester laughed, "won't you give the child your cherry, too?"

Niel promptly crossed the room and proffered the cherry in the bottom of his glass. She took it with her thumb and fore-finger and dropped it into her own,—where, he was quick to observe, she left it when they went out to dinner. A stubborn piece of pink flesh, he decided, and certainly a fool about a man quite old enough to be her father. He sighed when he saw that he was placed next her at the dinner table.

Captain Forrester still made a commanding figure at the head of his own table, with his napkin tucked under his chin and the work of carving well in hand. Nobody could lay bare the bones of a brace of duck or a twenty-pound turkey more deftly. "What part of the turkey do you prefer, Mrs. Ogden?" If one had a preference, it was gratified, with all the stuffing and gravy that went with it, and the vegetables properly placed. When a plate left Captain Forrester's hands, it was a dinner; the recipient was served, and well served. He served Mrs. Forrester last of the ladies but before the men, and to her, too, he said, "Mrs. Forrester, what part of the turkey shall I give you this evening?" He was a man who did not vary his formulae or his manners. He was no more mobile than his countenance. Niel and Judge Pommeroy had often remarked how much Captain Forrester looked like the pictures of Grover Cleveland. His clumsy dignity covered a deep nature, and a conscience that had never been juggled with. His repose was like that of a mountain. When he laid his fleshy, thick-fingered hand upon a frantic horse, an hysterical woman, an Irish workman out for blood, he brought them peace; something they could not resist. That had been the secret of his management of men. His sanity asked nothing, claimed nothing; it was so simple that it brought a hush over distracted creatures. In the old days, when he was building road in the Black Hills, trouble sometimes broke out in camp when he was absent, staying with Mrs. Forrester at Colorado Springs. He would put down the telegram that announced an insurrection and say to his wife, "Maidy, I must go to the men." And that was all he did,—he went to them.

While the Captain was intent upon his duties as host he talked very little, and Judge Pommeroy and Ellinger kept a lively cross-fire of amusing stories going. Niel, sitting opposite Ellinger, watched him closely. He still couldn't decide whether he liked him or not. In Denver Frank was known as a prince of good fellows; tactful, generous, resourceful, though apt to trim his sails to the wind; a man who good-humouredly bowed to the inevitable, or to the almost-inevitable. He had, when he was younger, been notoriously "wild," but that was not held against him, even by mothers with marriageable daughters, like Mrs. Odgen. Morals were different in those days. Niel had heard his uncle refer to Ellinger's youthful infatuation with a woman called Nell Emerald, a handsome and rather unusual woman who conducted a house properly licensed by the Denver police. Nell Emerald had told an old club man that though she had been out behind young Ellinger's new trotting horse, she "had no respect for a man who would go driving with a prostitute in broad daylight." This story and a dozen like it were often related of Ellinger, and the women laughed over them as heartily as the men. All the while that he was making a scandalous chronicle for himself, young Ellinger had been devotedly caring for an invalid mother, and he was described to strangers as a terribly fast young man and a model son. That combination pleased the taste of the time. Nobody thought the worse of him. Now that his mother was dead, he lived at the Brown Palace hotel, though he still kept her house at Colorado Springs.

When the roast was well under way, Black Tom, very formal in a white waistcoat and high collar, poured the champagne. Captain Forrester lifted his glass, the frail stem between his thick fingers, and glancing round the table at his guests and at Mrs. Forrester, said,

"Happy days!"

It was the toast he always drank at dinner, the invocation he was sure to utter when he took a glass of whiskey with an old friend. Whoever had heard him say it once, liked to hear him say it again. Nobody else could utter those two words as he did, with such gravity and high courtesy. It seemed a solemn moment, seemed to knock at the door of Fate; behind which all days, happy and otherwise, were hidden. Niel drank his wine with a pleasant shiver, thinking that nothing else made life seem so precarious, the future so cryptic and unfathomable, as that brief toast uttered by the massive man, "Happy days!"

Mrs. Ogden turned to the host with her most languishing smile: "Captain Forrester, I want you to tell Constance"—(She was an East Virginia woman, and what she really said was, "Cap'n Forrester, Ah wan' yew to tell," etc. Her vowels seemed to roll about in the same way her eyes did.)—"I want you to tell Constance about how you first found this lovely spot, 'way back in Indian times."

The Captain looked down the table between the candles at Mrs. Forrester, as if to consult her. She smiled and nodded, and her beautiful earrings swung beside her pale cheeks. She was wearing her diamonds tonight, and a black velvet gown. Her husband had archaic ideas about jewels; a man bought them for his wife in acknowledgment of things he could not gracefully utter. They must be costly; they must show that he was able to buy them, and that she was worthy to wear them.

With her approval the Captain began his narrative: a concise account of how he came West a young boy, after serving in the Civil War, and took a job as driver for a freighting company that carried supplies across the plains from Nebraska City to Cherry Creek, as Denver was then called. The freighters, after embarking in that sea of grass six hundred miles in width, lost all count of the days of the week and the month. One day was like another, and all were glorious; good hunting, plenty of antelope and buffalo, boundless sunny sky, boundless plains of waving grass, long fresh-water lagoons yellow with lagoon flowers, where the bison in their periodic migrations stopped to drink and bathe and wallow.

"An ideal life for a young man," the Captain pronounced. Once, when he was driven out of the trail by a wash-out, he rode south on his horse to explore, and found an Indian encampment near the Sweet Water, on this very hill where his house now stood. He was, he said, "greatly taken with the location," and made up his mind that he would one day have a house there. He cut down a young willow tree and drove the stake into the ground to mark the spot where he wished to build. He went away and did not come back for many years; he was helping to lay the first railroad across the plains.

"There were those that were dependent on me," he said. "I had sickness to contend with, and responsibilities. But in all those years I expect there was hardly a day passed that I did not remember the Sweet Water and this hill. When I came here a young man, I had planned it in my mind, pretty much as it is today; where I would dig my well, and where I would plant my grove and my orchard. I planned to build a house that my friends could come to, with a wife like Mrs. Forrester to make it attractive to them. I used to promise myself that some day I would manage it." This part of the story the Captain told not with embarrassment, but with reserve, choosing his words slowly, absently cracking English walnuts with his strong fingers and heaping a little hoard of kernels beside his plate. His friends understood that he was referring to his first marriage, to the poor invalid wife who had never been happy and who had kept his nose to the grindstone.

"When things looked most discouraging," he went on, "I came back here once and bought the place from the railroad company. They took my note. I found my willow stake,—it had rooted and grown into a tree,—and I planted three more to mark the corners of my house. Twelve years later Mrs. Forrester came here with me, shortly after our marriage, and we built our house." Captain Forrester puffed from time to time, but his clear account commanded attention. Something in the way he uttered his unornamented phrases gave them the impressiveness of inscriptions cut in stone.

Mrs. Forrester nodded at him from her end of the table. "And now, tell us your philosophy of life,—this is where it comes in," she laughed teasingly.

The Captain coughed and looked abashed. "I was intending to omit that tonight. Some of our guests have already heard it."

"No, no. It belongs at the end of the story, and if some of us have heard it, we can hear it again. Go on!"

"Well, then, my philosophy is that what you think of and plan for day by day, in spite of yourself, so to speak—you will get. You will get it more or less. That is, unless you are one of the people who get nothing in this world. There are such people. I have lived too much in mining works and construction camps not to know that." He paused as if, though this was too dark a chapter to be gone into, it must have its place, its moment of silent recognition. "If you are not one of those, Constance and Niel, you will accomplish what you dream of most."

"And why? That's the interesting part of it," his wife prompted him.

"Because," he roused himself from his abstraction and looked about at the company, "because a thing that is dreamed of in the way I mean, is already an accomplished fact. All our great West has been developed from such dreams; the homesteader's and the prospector's and the contractor's. We dreamed the railroads across the mountains, just as I dreamed my place on the Sweet Water. All these things will be everyday facts to the coming generation, but to us—" Captain Forrester ended with a sort of grunt. Something forbidding had come into his voice, the lonely, defiant note that is so often heard in the voices of old Indians.

Mrs. Ogden had listened to the story with such sympathy that Niel liked her better than ever, and even the preoccupied Constance seemed able to give it her attention. They rose from the dessert and went into the parlour to arrange the card tables. The Captain still played whist as well as ever. As he brought out a box of his best cigars, he paused before Mrs. Ogden and said, "Is smoke offensive to you, Mrs. Ogden?" When she protested that it was not, he crossed the room to where Constance was talking with Ellinger and asked with the same grave courtesy, "Is smoke offensive to you, Constance?" Had there been half a dozen women present, he would have asked that question of each, probably, and in the same words. It did not bother him to repeat a phrase. If an expression answered his purpose, he saw no reason for varying it.

Mrs. Forrester and Mr. Ogden were to play against Mrs. Ogden and the Captain. "Constance," said Mrs. Forrester as she sat down, "will you play with Niel? I'm told he's very good."

Miss Ogden's short nose flickered up, the lines on either side of it deepened, and she again looked injured. Niel was sure she detested him. He was not going to be done in by her.

"Miss Ogden," he said as he stood beside his chair, deliberately shuffling a pack of cards, "my uncle and I are used to playing together, and probably you are used to playing with Mr. Ellinger. Suppose we try that combination?"

She gave him a quick, suspicious glance from under her yellow eyelashes and flung herself into a chair without so much as answering him. Frank Ellinger came in from the dining-room, where he had been sampling the Captain's French brandy, and took the vacant seat opposite Miss Ogden. "So it's you and me, Connie? Good enough!" he exclaimed, cutting the pack Niel pushed toward him.

Just before midnight Black Tom opened the door and announced that the egg-nog was ready. The card players went into the dining-room, where the punch-bowl stood smoking on the table.

"Constance," said Captain Forrester, "do you sing? I like to hear one of the old songs with the egg-nog."

"Ah'm sorry, Cap'n Forrester. Ah really haven't any voice."

Niel noticed that whenever Constance spoke to the Captain she strained her throat, though he wasn't in the least deaf. He broke in over her refusal. "Uncle can start a song if you coax him, sir."

Judge Pommeroy, after smoothing his silver whiskers and coughing, began "Auld Lang Syne." The others joined in, but they hadn't got to the end of it when a hollow rumbling down on the bridge made them laugh, and everyone ran to the front windows to see the Judge's funeral coach come lurching up the hill, with only one of the side lanterns lit. Mrs. Forrester sent Tom out with a drink for the driver. While Niel and his uncle were putting on their overcoats in the hall, she came up to them and whispered coaxingly to the boy, "Remember, you are coming over tomorrow, at two? I am planning a drive, and I want you to amuse Constance for me."

Niel bit his lip and looked down into Mrs. Forrester's laughing, persuasive eyes. "I'll do it for you, but that's the only reason," he said threateningly.

"I understand, for me! I'll credit it to your account."

The Judge and his nephew rolled away on swaying springs. The Ogdens retired to their rooms upstairs. Mrs. Forrester went to help the Captain divest himself of his frock coat, and put it away for him. Ever since he was hurt he had to be propped high on pillows at night, and he slept in a narrow iron bed, in the alcove which had formerly been his wife's dressing-room. While he was undressing he breathed heavily and sighed, as if he were very tired. He fumbled with his studs, then blew on his fingers and tried again. His wife came to his aid and quickly unbuttoned everything. He did not thank her in words, but submitted gratefully.

When the iron bed creaked at receiving his heavy figure, she called from the big bedroom, "Good-night, Mr. Forrester," and drew the heavy curtains that shut off the alcove. She took off her rings and earrings and was beginning to unfasten her black velvet bodice when, at a tinkle of glass from without, she stopped short. Rehooking the shoulder of her gown, she went to the dining-room, now faintly lit by the coal fire in the back parlour. Frank Ellinger was standing at the sideboard, taking a nightcap. The Forrester French brandy was old, and heavy like a cordial.

"Be careful," she murmured as she approached him, "I have a distinct impression that there is someone on the enclosed stairway. There is a wide crack in the door. Ah, but kittens have claws, these days! Pour me just a little. Thank you. I'll have mine in by the fire."

He followed her into the next room, where she stood by the grate, looking at him in the light of the pale blue flames that ran over the fresh coal, put on to keep the fire.

"You've had a good many brandies, Frank," she said, studying his flushed, masterful face.

"Not too many. I'll need them . . . to-night," he replied meaningly.

She nervously brushed back a lock of hair that had come down a little. "It's not to-night. It's morning. Go to bed and sleep as late as you please. Take care, I heard silk stockings on the stairs. Good-night." She put her hand on the sleeve of his coat; the white fingers clung to the black cloth as bits of paper cling to magnetized iron. Her touch, soft as it was, went through the man, all the feet and inches of him. His broad shoulders lifted on a deep breath. He looked down at her.

Her eyes fell. "Good-night," she said faintly. As she turned quickly away, the train of her velvet dress caught the leg of his broadcloth trousers and dragged with a friction that crackled and threw sparks.

Both started. They stood looking at each other for a moment before she actually slipped through the door. Ellinger remained by the hearth, his arms folded tight over his chest, his curly lips compressed, frowning into the fire.

V

Niel went up the hill the next afternoon, just as the cutter with the two black ponies jingled round the driveway and stopped at the front door. Mrs. Forrester came out on the porch, dressed for a sleigh ride. Ellinger followed her, buttoned up in a long fur-lined coat, showily befrogged down the front, with a glossy astrachan collar. He looked even more powerful and bursting with vigour than last night. His highly-coloured, well-visored countenance shone with a good opinion of himself and of the world.

Mrs. Forrester called to Niel gaily. "We are going down to the Sweet Water to cut cedar boughs for Christmas. Will you keep Constance company? She seems a trifle disappointed at being left behind, but we can't take the big sleigh,—the pole is broken. Be nice to her, there's a good boy!" She pressed his hand, gave him a meaning, confidential smile, and stepped into the sleigh. Ellinger sprang in beside her, and they glided down the hill with a merry tinkle of sleighbells.

Niel found Miss Ogden in the back parlour, playing solitaire by the fire. She was clearly out of humour.

"Come in, Mr. Herbert. I think they might have taken us along, don't you? I want to see the river my own self. I hate bein' shut up in the house!"

"Let's go out, then. Wouldn't you like to see the town?"

Constance seemed not to hear him. She was wrinkling and unwrinkling her short nose, and the restless lines about her mouth were fluttering. "What's to hinder us from getting a sleigh at the livery barn and going down to the Sweet Water? I don't suppose the river's private property?" She gave a nervous, angry laugh and looked hopefully at Niel.

"We couldn't get anything at this hour. The livery teams are all out," he said with firmness.

Constance glanced at him suspiciously, then sat down at the card table and leaned over it, drawing her plump shoulders together. Her fluffy yellow hair was wound round her head like a scarf and held in place by narrow bands of black velvet.

The ponies had crossed the second creek and were trotting down the high road toward the river. Mrs. Forrester expressed her feelings in a laugh full of mischief. "Is she running after us? Where did she get the idea that she was to come? What a relief to get away!" She lifted her chin and sniffed the air. The day was grey, without sun, and the air was still and dry, a warm cold. "Poor Mr. Ogden," she went on, "how much livelier he is without his ladies! They almost extinguish him. Now aren't you glad you never married?"

"I'm certainly glad I never married a homely woman. What does a man do it for, anyway? She had no money,—and he's always had it, or been on the way to it."

"Well, they're off tomorrow. And Connie! You've reduced her to a state of imbecility, really! What an afternoon Niel must be having!" She laughed as if the idea of his predicament delighted her.

"Who's this kid, anyway?" Ellinger asked her to take the reins for a moment while he drew a cigar from his pocket. "He's a trifle stiff. Does he make himself useful?"

"Oh, he's a nice boy, stranded here like the rest of us. I'm going to train him to be very useful. He's devoted to Mr. Forrester. Handsome, don't you think?"

"So-so." They turned into a by-road that wound along the Sweet Water. Ellinger held the ponies in a little and turned down his high astrachan collar. "Let's have a look at you, Marian."

Mrs. Forrester was holding her muff before her face, to catch the flying particles of snow the ponies kicked up. From behind it she glanced at him sidewise. "Well?" she said teasingly.

He put his arm through hers and settled himself low in the sleigh. "You ought to look at me better than that. It's been a devil of a long while since I've seen you."

"Perhaps it's been too long," she murmured. The mocking spark in her eyes softened perceptibly under the long pressure of his arm. "Yes, it's been long," she admitted lightly.

"You didn't answer the letter I wrote you on the eleventh."

"Didn't I? Well, at any rate I answered your telegram." She drew her head away as his face came nearer. "You'll really have to watch the ponies, my dear, or they'll tumble us out in the snow."

"I don't care. I wish they would!" he said between his teeth. "Why didn't you answer my letter?"

"Oh, I don't remember! You don't write so many."

"It's no satisfaction. You won't let me write you love letters. You say it's risky."

"So it is, and foolish. But now you needn't be so careful. Not too careful!" she laughed softly. "When I'm off in the country for a whole winter, alone, and growing older, I like to . . ." she put her hand on his, "to be reminded of pleasanter things."

Ellinger took off his glove with his teeth. His eyes, sweeping the winding road and the low, snow-covered bluffs, had something wolfish in them.

"Be careful, Frank. My rings! You hurt me!"

"Then why didn't you take them off? You used to. Are these your cedars, shall we stop here?"

"No, not here." She spoke very low. "The best ones are farther on, in a deep ravine that winds back into the hills."

Ellinger glanced at her averted head, and his heavy lips twitched in a smile at one corner. The quality of her voice had changed, and he knew the change. They went spinning along the curves of the winding road, saying not a word. Mrs. Forrester sat with her head bent forward, her face half hidden in her muff. At last she told him to stop. To the right of the road he saw a thicket. Behind it a dry water course wound into the bluffs. The tops of the dark, still cedars, just visible from the road, indicated its windings.

"Sit still," he said, "while I take out the horses."

When the blue shadows of approaching dusk were beginning to fall over the snow, one of the Blum boys, slipping quietly along through the timber in search of rabbits, came upon the empty cutter standing in the brush, and near it the two ponies, stamping impatiently where they were tied. Adolph slid back into the thicket and lay down behind a fallen log to see what would happen. Not much ever happened to him but weather.

Presently he heard low voices, coming nearer from the ravine. The big stranger who was visiting at the Forresters' emerged, carrying the buffalo robes on one arm; Mrs. Forrester herself was clinging to the other. They walked slowly, wholly absorbed by what they were saying to each other. When they came up to the sleigh, the man spread the robes on the seat and put his hands under Mrs. Forrester's arms to lift her in. But he did not lift her; he stood for a long while holding her crushed up against his breast, her face hidden in his black overcoat.

"What about those damned cedar boughs?" he asked, after he had put her in and covered her up. "Shall I go back and cut some?"

"It doesn't matter," she murmured.

He reached under the seat for a hatchet and went back to the ravine. Mrs. Forrester sat with her eyes closed, her cheek pillowed on her muff, a faint, soft smile on her lips. The air was still and blue; the Blum boy could almost hear her breathe. When the strokes of the hatchet rang out from the ravine, he could see her eyelids flutter . . . soft shivers went through her body.

The man came back and threw the evergreens into the sleigh. When he got in beside her, she slipped her hand through his arm and settled softly against him. "Drive slowly," she murmured, as if she were talking in her sleep. "It doesn't matter if we are late for dinner. Nothing matters." The ponies trotted off.

The pale Blum boy rose from behind his log and followed the tracks up the ravine. When the orange moon rose over the bluffs, he was still sitting under the cedars, his gun on his knee. While Mrs. Forrester had been waiting there in the sleigh, with her eyes closed, feeling so safe, he could almost have touched her with his hand. He had never seen her before when her mocking eyes and lively manner were not between her and all the world. If it had been Thad Grimes who lay behind that log, now, or Ivy Peters?

But with Adolph Blum her secrets were safe. His mind was feudal; the rich and fortunate were also the privileged. These warm-blooded, quick-breathing people took chances,—followed impulses only dimly understandable to a boy who was wet and weather-chapped all the year; who waded in the mud fishing for cat, or lay in the marsh waiting for wild duck. Mrs. Forrester had never been too haughty to smile at him when he came to the back door with his fish. She never haggled about the price. She treated him like a human being. His little chats with her, her nod and smile when she passed him on the street, were among the pleasantest things he had to remember. She bought game of him in the closed season, and didn't give him away.

VI

It was during that winter, the first one Mrs. Forrester had ever spent in the house on the hill, that Niel came to know her very well. For the Forresters that winter was a sort of isthmus between two estates; soon afterward came a change in their fortunes. And for Niel it was a natural turning-point, since in the autumn he was nineteen, and in the spring he was twenty,—a very great difference.

After the Christmas festivities were over, the whist parties settled into a regular routine. Three evenings a week Judge Pommeroy and his nephew sat down to cards with the Forresters. Sometimes they went over early and dined there. Sometimes they stayed for a late supper after the last rubber. Niel, who had been so content with a bachelor's life, and who had made up his mind that he would never live in a place that was under the control of women, found himself becoming attached to the comforts of a well-conducted house; to the pleasures of the table, to the soft chairs and soft lights and agreeable human voices at the Forresters'. On bitter, windy nights, sitting in his favourite blue chair before the grate, he used to wonder how he could manage to tear himself away, to plunge into the outer darkness, and run down the long frozen road and up the dead street of the town. Captain Forrester was experimenting with bulbs that winter, and had built a little glass conservatory on the south side of the house, off the back parlour. Through January and February the house was full of narcissus and Roman hyacinths, and their heavy, spring-like odour made a part of the enticing comfort of the fireside there.

Where Mrs. Forrester was, dulness was impossible, Niel believed.

The charm of her conversation was not so much in what she said, though she was often witty, but in the quick recognition of her eyes, in the living quality of her voice itself. One could talk with her about the most trivial things, and go away with a high sense of elation. The secret of it, he supposed, was that she couldn't help being interested in people, even very commonplace people. If Mr. Ogden or Mr. Dalzell were not there to tell their best stories for her, then she could be amused by Ivy Peters' ruffianly manners, or the soft compliments of old man Elliott when he sold her a pair of winter shoes. She had a fascinating gift of mimicry. When she mentioned the fat iceman, or Thad Grimes at his meat block, or the Blum boys with their dead rabbits, by a subtle suggestion of their manner she made them seem more individual and vivid than they were in their own person. She often caricatured people to their faces, and they were not offended, but greatly flattered. Nothing pleased one more than to provoke her laughter. Then you felt you were getting on with her. It was her form of commenting, of agreeing with you and appreciating you when you said something interesting,—and it often told you a great deal that was both too direct and too elusive for words.

Long, long afterward, when Niel did not know whether Mrs. Forrester were living or dead, if her image flashed into his mind, it came with a brightness of dark eyes, her pale triangular cheeks with long earrings, and her many-coloured laugh. When he was dull, dull and tired of everything, he used to think that if he could hear that long-lost lady laugh again, he could be gay.

The big storm of the winter came late that year; swept down over Sweet Water the first day of March and beat upon the town for three days and nights. Thirty inches of snow fell, and the cutting wind blew it into whirling drifts. The Forresters were snowed in. Ben Keezer, their man of all work, did not attempt to break a road or even to come over to the town himself. On the third day Niel went to the post-office, got the Captain's leather mail sack with its accumulation of letters, and set off across the creek, plunging into drifts up to his middle, sometimes up to his arm-pits. The fences along the lane were covered, but he broke his trail by keeping between the two lines of poplars. When at last he reached the front porch, Captain Forrester came to the door and let him in.

"Glad to see you, my boy, very glad. It's been a little lonesome for us. You must have had hard work getting over. I certainly appreciate it. Come to the sitting-room fire and dry yourself. We will talk quietly. Mrs. Forrester has gone upstairs to lie down; she's been complaining of a headache."

Niel stood before the fire in his rubber boots, drying his trousers. The Captain did not sit down but opened the glass door into his little conservatory.

"I've something pretty to show you, Niel. All my hyacinths are coming along at once, every colour of the rainbow. The Roman hyacinths, I say, are Mrs. Forrester's. They seem to suit her."

Niel went to the door and looked with keen pleasure at the fresh, watery blossoms. "I was afraid you might lose them this bitter weather, Captain."

"No, these things can stand a good deal of cold. They've been company for us." He stood looking out through the glass at the drifted shrubbery. Niel liked to see him look out over his place. A man's house is his castle, his look seemed to say. "Ben tells me the rabbits have come up to the barn to eat the hay, everything green is covered up. I had him throw a few cabbages out for them, so they won't suffer. Mrs. Forrester has been on the porch every day, feeding the snow birds," he went on, as if talking to himself.

The stair door opened, and Mrs. Forrester came down in her Japanese dressing-gown, looking very pale. The dark shadows under her eyes seemed to mean that she had been losing sleep.

"Oh, it's Niel! How nice of you. And you've brought the mail. Are there any letters for me?"

"Three. Two from Denver and one from California." Her husband gave them to her. "Did you sleep, Maidy?"

"No, but I rested. It's delightful up in the west room, the wind sings and whistles about the eaves. If you'll excuse me, I'll dress and glance at my letters. Stand closer to the fire, Niel. Are you very wet?" When she stopped beside him to feel his clothes, he smelled a sharp odour of spirits. Was she ill, he wondered, or merely so bored that she had been trying to dull herself?

When she came back she had dressed and rearranged her hair.

"Mrs. Forrester," said the Captain in a solicitous tone, "I believe I would like some tea and toast this afternoon, like your English friends, and it would be good for your head. We won't offer Niel anything else."

"Very well. Mary has gone to bed with a toothache, but I will make the tea. Niel can make the toast here by the fire while you read your paper."

She was cheerful now,—tied one of Mary's aprons about Niel's neck and set him down with the toasting fork. He noticed that the Captain, as he read his paper, kept his eye on the sideboard with a certain watchfulness, and when his wife brought the tray with tea, and no sherry, he seemed very much pleased. He drank three cups, and took a second piece of toast.

"You see, Mr. Forrester," she said lightly, "Niel has brought back my appetite. I ate no lunch to-day," turning to the boy, "I've been shut up too long. Is there anything in the papers?"

This meant was there any news concerning the people they knew. The Captain put on his silver-rimmed glasses again and read aloud about the doings of their friends in Denver and Omaha and Kansas City. Mrs.

Forrester sat on a stool by the fire, eating toast and making humorous comments upon the subjects of those solemn paragraphs; the engagement of Miss Erma Salton-Smith, etc.

"At last, thank God! You remember her, Niel. She's been here. I think you danced with her."

"I don't think I do. What is she like?"

"She's exactly like her name. Don't you remember? Tall, very animated, glittering eyes, like the Ancient Mariner's?"

Niel laughed. "Don't you like bright eyes, Mrs. Forrester?"

"Not any others, I don't!" She joined in his laugh so gaily that the Captain looked out over his paper with an expression of satisfaction. He let the journal slowly crumple on his knees, and sat watching the two beside the grate. To him they seemed about the same age. It was a habit with him to think of Mrs. Forrester as very, very young.

She noticed that he was not reading. "Would you like me to light the lamp, Mr. Forrester?"

"No, thank you. The twilight is very pleasant."

It was twilight by now. They heard Mary come downstairs and begin stirring about the kitchen. The Captain, his slippers in the zone of firelight and his heavy shoulders in shadow, snored from time to time. As the room grew dusky, the windows were squares of clear, pale violet, and the shutters ceased to rattle. The wind was dying with the day. Everything was still, except when Bohemian Mary roughly clattered a pan. Mrs. Forrester whispered that she was out of sorts because her sweetheart, Joe Pucelik, hadn't been over to see her. Sunday night was his regular night, and Sunday was the first day of the blizzard. "When she's neglected, her tooth always begins to ache!"

"Well, now that I've got over, he'll have to come, or she will be in a temper."

"Oh, he'll come!" Mrs. Forrester shrugged. "I am blind and deaf, but I'm quite sure she makes it worth his while!" After a few moments she rose. "Come," she whispered, "Mr. Forrester is asleep. Let's run down the hill, there's no one to stop us. I'll slip on my rubber boots. No objections!" She put her fingers on his lips. "Not a word! I can't stand this house a moment longer."

They slipped quietly out of the front door into the cold air which tasted of new-fallen snow. A clear arc of blue and rose colour painted the west, over the buried town. When they reached the rounded breast of the hill, blown almost bare, Mrs. Forrester stood still and drew in deep breaths, looking down over the drifted meadows and the stiff, blue poplars.

"Oh, but it is bleak!" she murmured. "Suppose we should have to stay here all next winter, too, . . . and the next! What will become of me, Niel?" There was fear, unmistakable fright in her voice. "You see there is nothing for me to do. I get no exercise. I don't skate; we didn't in California, and my ankles are weak. I've always danced in the winter, there's plenty of dancing at Colorado Springs. You wouldn't believe how I miss it. I shall dance till I'm eighty. . . . I'll be the waltzing grand-mother! It's good for me, I need it."

They plunged down into the drifts and did not stop again until they reached the wooden bridge.

"See, even the creek is frozen! I thought running water never froze. How long will it be like this?"

"Not long now. In a month you'll see the green begin in the marsh and run over the meadows. It's lovely over here in the spring. And you'll be able to get out tomorrow, Mrs. Forrester. The clouds are thinning. Look, there's the new moon!"

She turned. "Oh, I saw it over the wrong shoulder!"

"No you didn't. You saw it over mine."

She sighed and took his arm. "My dear boy, your shoulders aren't broad enough."

Instantly before his eyes rose the image of a pair of shoulders that were very broad, objectionably broad, clad in a frogged overcoat with an astrachan collar. The intrusion of this third person annoyed him as they went slowly back up the hill.

Curiously enough, it was as Captain Forrester's wife that she most interested Niel, and it was in her relation to her husband that he most admired her. Given her other charming attributes, her comprehension of a man like the railroad-builder, her loyalty to him, stamped her more than anything else. That, he felt, was quality; something that could never become worn or shabby; steel of Damascus. His admiration of Mrs. Forrester went back to that, just as, he felt, she herself went back to it. He rather liked the stories, even the spiteful ones, about the gay life she led in Colorado, and the young men she kept dangling about her every winter. He sometimes thought of the life she might have been living ever since he had known her,—and the one she had chosen to live. From that disparity, he believed, came the subtlest thrill of her fascina-tion. She mocked outrageously at the proprieties she observed, and in-herited the magic of contradictions.

VII

ON THE EVENINGS when there was no whist at the Forresters', Niel usually sat in his room and read,—but not law, as he was supposed to do. The winter before, when the Forresters were away, and one dull day dragged after another, he had come upon a copious diversion, an almost inexhaustible resource. The high, narrow bookcase in the back office, between the double doors and the wall, was filled from top to bottom with rows of solemn looking volumes bound in dark cloth, which were kept apart from the law library; an almost complete set of the Bohn classics, which Judge Pommeroy had bought long ago when he was a student at the University of Virginia. He had brought them West with him, not because he read them a great deal, but because, in his day, a gentleman had such books in his library, just as he had claret in his cellar. Among them was a set of Byron in three volumes, and last winter, apropos of a quotation which Niel didn't recognize, his uncle advised him to read Byron,—all except "Don Juan." That, the Judge remarked, with a deep smile, he "could save until later." Niel, of course, began with "Don Juan." Then he read "Tom Jones" and "Wilhelm Meister" and raced on until he came to Montaigne and a complete translation of Ovid. He hadn't finished yet with these last,—always went back to them after other experiments. These authors seemed to him to know their business. Even in "Don Juan" there was a little "fooling," but with these gentlemen none.

There were philosophical works in the collection, but he did no more than open and glance at them. He had no curiosity about what men had thought; but about what they had felt and lived, he had a great deal. If anyone had told him that these were classics and represented the wisdom of the ages, he would doubtless have let them alone. But ever since he had first found them for himself, he had been living a double life, with all its guilty enjoyments. He read the *Heroides* over and over, and felt that they were the most glowing love stories ever told. He did not think of these books as something invented to beguile the idle hour, but as living creatures, caught in the very behaviour of living,—surprised behind their misleading severity of form and phrase. He was eavesdropping upon the past, being let into the great world that had plunged and glittered and sumptuously sinned long before little Western towns were dreamed of. Those rapt evenings beside the lamp gave him a long perspective, influenced his conception of the people about him, made him know just what he wished his own relations with these people to be. For some reason, his reading made him wish to become an architect. If the Judge had left his Bohn library behind him in Kentucky, his nephew's life might have turned out differently.

Spring came at last, and the Forrester place had never been so lovely. The Captain spent long, happy days among his flowering shrubs, and his wife used to say to visitors, "Yes, you can see Mr. Forrester in a moment; I will send the English gardener to call him."

Early in June, when the Captain's roses were just coming on, his pleasant labors were interrupted. One morning an alarming telegram reached him. He cut it open with his garden shears, came into the house, and asked his wife to telephone for Judge Pommeroy. A savings bank, one in which he was largely interested, had failed in Denver. That evening the Captain and his lawyer went west on the express. The Judge, when he was giving Niel final instructions about the office business, told him he was afraid the Captain was bound to lose a good deal of money.

Mrs. Forrester seemed unaware of any danger; she went to the station to see her husband off, spoke of his errand merely as a "business trip." Niel, however, felt a foreboding gloom. He dreaded poverty for her. She was one of the people who ought always to have money; any retrenchment of their generous way of living would be a hardship for her,—would be unfitting. She would not be herself in straitened circumstances.

Niel took his meals at the town hotel; on the third day after Captain Forrester's departure, he was annoyed to find Frank Ellinger's name on the hotel register. Ellinger did not appear at supper, which meant, of course, that he was dining with Mrs. Forrester, and that the lady herself would get his dinner. She had taken the occasion of the Captain's absence to let Bohemian Mary go to visit her mother on the farm for a week. Niel thought it very bad taste in Ellinger to come to Sweet Water when Captain Forrester was away. He must know that it would stir up the gossips.

Niel had meant to call on Mrs. Forrester that evening, but now he went back to the office instead. He read late, and after he went to bed he slept lightly. He was awakened before dawn by the puffing of the switch engine down at the round house. He tried to muffle his ears in the sheet and go to sleep again, but the sound of escaping steam for some reason excited him. He could not shut out the feeling that it was summer, and that the dawn would soon be flaming gloriously over the Forresters' marsh. He had awakened with that intense, blissful realization of summer which sometimes comes to children in their beds. He rose and dressed quickly. He would get over to the hill before Frank Ellinger could intrude his unwelcome presence, while he was still asleep in the best bedroom of the Wimbleton hotel.

An impulse of affection and guardianship drew Niel up the poplar-bordered road in the early light,—though he did not go near the house itself, but at the second bridge cut round through the meadow and on to the marsh. The sky was burning with the soft pink and silver of a cloudless summer dawn. The heavy, bowed grasses splashed him to the knees. All over the marsh, snow-on-the-mountain, globed with dew, made cool sheets of silver, and the swamp milk-weed spread its flat, raspberry-coloured clusters. There was an almost religious purity about the fresh morning air, the tender sky, the grass and flowers with the sheen of early dew upon them. There was in all living things something limpid and joyous—like the wet, morning call of the birds, flying up through the unstained atmosphere. Out of the saffron east a thin, yellow, wine-like sunshine began to gild the fragrant meadows and the glistening tops of the grove. Niel wondered why he did not often come over like this, to see the day before men and their activities had spoiled it, while the morning was still unsullied, like a gift handed down from the heroic ages.

Under the bluffs that overhung the marsh he came upon thickets of wild roses, with flaming buds, just beginning to open. Where they had opened, their petals were stained with that burning rose-colour which is always gone by noon,—a dye made of sunlight and morning and moisture, so intense that it cannot possibly last . . . must fade, like ecstasy. Niel took out his knife and began to cut the stiff stems, crowded with red thorns.

He would make a bouquet for a lovely lady; a bouquet gathered off the cheeks of morning . . . these roses, only half awake, in the defencelessness of utter beauty. He would leave them just outside one of the French windows of her bedroom. When she opened her shutters to let in the light, she would find them,—and they would perhaps give her a sudden distaste for coarse worldlings like Frank Ellinger.

After tying his flowers with a twist of meadow grass, he went up the hill through the grove and softly round the still house to the north side of Mrs. Forrester's own room, where the door-like green shutters were closed. As he bent to place the flowers on the sill, he heard from within a woman's soft laughter; impatient, indulgent, teasing, eager. Then another laugh, very different, a man's. And it was fat and lazy, —ended in something like a yawn.

Niel found himself at the foot of the hill on the wooden bridge, his face hot, his temples beating, his eyes blind with anger. In his hand he still carried the prickly bunch of wild roses. He threw them over the wire fence into a mudhole the cattle had trampled under the bank of the creek. He did not know whether he had left the house by the driveway or had come down through the shrubbery. In that instant between stooping to the window-sill and rising, he had lost one of the most beautiful things in his life. Before the dew dried, the morning had been wrecked for him; and all subsequent mornings, he told himself bitterly. This day saw the end of that admiration and loyalty that had been like a bloom on his existence. He could never recapture it. It was gone, like the morning freshness of the flowers.

"Lilies that fester," he muttered, "*lilies that fester smell far worse than weeds.*"

Grace, variety, the lovely voice, the sparkle of fun and fancy in those dark eyes; all this was nothing. It was not a moral scruple she had outraged, but an aesthetic ideal. Beautiful women, whose beauty meant more than it said . . . was their brilliancy always fed by something coarse and concealed? Was that their secret?

VIII

NIEL MET HIS UNCLE and Captain Forrester when they alighted from the morning train, and drove over to the house with them. The business on which they had gone to Denver was not referred to until they were sitting with Mrs. Forrester in the front parlour. The windows were open, and the perfume of the mock-orange and of June roses was blowing in from the garden. Captain Forrester introduced the subject, after slowly unfolding his handkerchief and wiping his forehead, and his fleshy neck, around his low collar.

"Maidy," he said, not looking at her, "I've come home a poor man. It took about everything there was to square up. You'll have this place, unencumbered, and my pension; that will be about all. The live-stock will bring in something."

Niel saw that Mrs. Forrester grew very pale, but she smiled and brought her husband his cigar stand. "Oh, well! I expect we can manage, can't we?"

"We can just manage. Not much more. I'm afraid Judge Pommeroy considers I acted foolishly."

"Not at all, Mrs. Forrester," the Judge exclaimed. "He acted just as I hope I would have done in his place. But I am an unmarried man. There were certain securities, government bonds, which Captain Forrester could have turned over to you, but it would have been at the expense of the depositors."

"I've known men to do that," said the Captain heavily, "but I never considered they paid their wives a compliment. If Mrs. Forrester is satisfied, I shall never regret my decision." For the first time his tired, swollen eyes sought his wife's.

"I never question your decisions in business, Mr. Forrester. I know nothing about such things."

The Captain put down the cigar he had taken but not lighted, rose with an effort, and walked over to the bay window, where he stood gazing out over his meadows. "The place looks very nice, Maidy," he said presently. "I see you've watered the roses. They need it, this weather. Now, if you'll excuse me, I'll lie down for a while. I did not sleep well on the train. Niel and the Judge will stay for lunch." He opened the door into Mrs. Forrester's room and closed it behind him.

Judge Pommeroy began to explain to Mrs. Forrester the situation they had faced in Denver. The bank, about which Mrs. Forrester knew nothing but its name, was one which paid good interest on small deposits. The depositors were wage-earners; railroad employés, mechanics, and day labourers, many of whom had at some time worked for Captain Forrester. His was the only well-known name among the bank officers, it was the name which promised security and fair treatment to his old workmen and their friends. The other directors were promising young business men with many irons in the fire. But, the Judge said with evident chagrin, they had refused to come up to the scratch and pay their losses like gentlemen. They claimed that the bank was insolvent, not through unwise investments or mismanagement, but because of a nation-wide financial panic, a shrinking in values that no one could have foreseen. They argued that the fair thing was to share the loss with the depositors; to pay them fifty cents on the dollar, giving long-time notes for twenty-five per cent, settling on a basis of seventy-five per cent.

Captain Forrester had stood firm that not one of the depositors should lose a dollar. The promising young business men had listened to him respectfully, but finally told him they would settle only on their own terms; any additional refunding must be his affair. He sent to the vault for his private steel box, opened it in their presence, and sorted the contents on the table. The government bonds he turned in at once. Judge Pommeroy was sent out to sell the mining stocks and other securities in the open market.

At this part of his narrative the Judge rose and began to pace the floor, twisting the seals on his watchchain. "That was what a man of honour was bound to do, Mrs. Forrester. With five of the directors backing down, he had either to lose his name or save it. The depositors had put their savings into that bank because Captain Forrester was president. To those men with no capital but their back and their two hands, his name meant safety. As he tried to explain to the directors, those deposits were above price; money saved to buy a home, or to take care of a man in sickness, or to send a boy to school. And those young men, bright fellows, well thought of in the community, sat there and looked down their noses and let your husband strip himself down to pledging his life insurance! There was a crowd in the street outside the bank all day, every day; Poles and Swedes and Mexicans, looking scared to death. A lot of them couldn't speak English,—seemed like the only English word they knew was 'Forrester.' As we went in and out we'd hear the Mexicans saying, 'Forrester, Forrester.' It was a torment for me, on your account, Ma'm, to see the Captain strip himself. But, 'pon my honour, I couldn't forbid him. As for those white-livered rascals that sat there,—" the Judge stopped before Mrs. Forrester and ruffled his bushy white hair with both hands, "By God, Madam, I think I've lived too long! In my day the difference between a business man and a scoundrel was bigger than the difference between a white man and a nigger. I wasn't the right one to go out there as the Captain's counsel. One of these smooth members of the bar, like Ivy Peters is getting ready to be, might have saved something for you out of the wreck. But I couldn't use my influence with your husband. To that crowd outside the bank doors his name meant a hundred cents on the dollar, and by God, they got it! I'm proud of him, Ma'm; proud of his acquaintance!"

It was the first time Niel had ever seen Mrs. Forrester flush. A quick pink swept over her face. Her eyes glistened with moisture. "You were quite right, Judge. I wouldn't for the world have had him do otherwise for me. He would never hold up his head again. You see, I know him." As she said this she looked at Niel, on the other side of the room, and her glance was like a delicate and very dignified rebuke to some discourtesy, —though he was not conscious of having shown her any.

When their hostess went out to see about lunch, Judge Pommeroy turned to his nephew. "Son, I'm glad you want to be an architect. I can't see any honourable career for a lawyer, in this new business world that's coming up. Leave the law to boys like Ivy Peters, and get into some clean profession. I wasn't the right man to go with Forrester." He shook his head sadly.

"Will they really be poor?"

"They'll be pinched. It's as he said; they've nothing left but this place."

Mrs. Forrester returned and went to waken her husband for lunch. When she opened the door into her room, they heard stertorous breathing, and she called to them to come quickly. The Captain was stretched upon his iron bed in the antechamber, and Mrs. Forrester was struggling to lift his head.

"Quick, Niel," she panted. "We must get pillows under him. Bring those from my bed."

Niel gently pushed her away. Sweat poured from his face as he got his strength under the Captain's shoulders. It was like lifting a wounded elephant. Judge Pommeroy hurried back to the sitting-room and telephoned Dr. Dennison that Captain Forrester had had a stroke.

A stroke could not finish a man like Daniel Forrester. He was kept in his bed for three weeks, and Niel helped Mrs. Forrester and Ben Keezer take care of him. Although he was at the house so much during that time, he never saw Mrs. Forrester alone,—scarcely saw her at all, indeed. With so much to attend to, she became abstracted, almost impersonal. There were many letters to answer, gifts of fruit and wine and flowers to be acknowledged. Solicitous inquiries came from friends scattered all the way from the Missouri to the mountains. When Mrs. Forrester was not in the Captain's room, or in the kitchen preparing special foods for him, she was at her desk.

One morning while she was seated there, a distinguished visitor arrived. Niel, waiting by the door for the letters he was to take to the post, saw a large, red-whiskered man in a rumpled pongee suit and a panama hat come climbing up the hill; Cyrus Dalzell, president of the Colorado & Utah, who had come over in his private car to enquire for the health of his old friend. Niel warned Mrs. Forrester, and she went to meet the visitor, just as he mounted the steps, wiping his face with a red silk bandanna.

He took both the lady's hands and exclaimed in a warm, deep voice, "Here she is, looking as fresh as a bride! May I claim an old privilege?" He bent his head and kissed her. "I won't be in your way, Marian," he said as they came into the house, "but I had to see for myself how he does, and how you do."

Mr. Dalzell shook hands with Niel, and as he talked he moved about the parlour clumsily and softly, like a brown bear. Mrs. Forrester stopped him to straighten his flowing yellow tie and pull down the back of his wrinkled coat. "It's easy to see that Kitty wasn't with you this morning when you dressed," she laughed.

"Thank you, thank you, my dear. I've got a green porter down there, and he doesn't seem to realize the extent of his duties. No, Kitty wanted to come, but we have two giddy nieces out from Portsmouth, visiting us, and she felt she couldn't. I just had my car hitched on to the tail of the Burlington flyer and came myself. Now tell me about Daniel. Was it a stroke?"

Mrs. Forrester sat down on the sofa beside him and told him about her husband's illness, while he interrupted with sympathetic questions and comments, taking her hand between his large, soft palms and patting it affectionately.

"And now I can go home and tell Kitty that he will soon be as good as ever,—and that you look like you were going to lead the ball tonight. You whisper to Daniel that I've got a couple cases of port down in my car that will build him up faster than anything the doctors give him. And I've brought along a dozen sherry, for a lady that knows a thing or two about wines. And next winter you are both coming out to stay with us at the Springs, for a change of air."

Mrs. Forrester shook her head gently. "Oh, that, I'm afraid, is a pretty dream. But we'll dream it, anyway!" Everything about her had brightened since Cyrus Dalzell came up the hill. Even the long garnet earrings beside her cheeks seemed to flash with a deeper colour, Niel thought. She was a different woman from the one who sat there writing, half an hour ago. Her fingers, as they played on the sleeve of the pongee coat, were light and fluttery as butterfly wings.

"No dream at all, my dear. Kitty has arranged everything. You know how quickly she thinks things out. I am to come for you in my car. We'll get my old porter Jim as a valet for Daniel, and you can just play around and put fresh life into us all. We saw last winter that we couldn't do anything without our Lady Forrester. Nothing came off right without her. If we had a party, we sat down afterward and wondered what in hell we'd had it for. Oh, no, we can't manage without you!"

Tears flashed into her eyes. "That's very dear of you. It's sweet to be remembered when one is away." In her voice there was the heartbreaking sweetness one sometimes hears in lovely, gentle old songs.

IX

AFTER THREE WEEKS the Captain was up and around again. He dragged his left foot, and his left arm was uncertain. Though he recovered his speech, it was thick and clouded; some words he could not pronounce distinctly,—slid over them, dropped out a syllable. Therefore he avoided talking even more than was his habit. The doctor said that unless another brain lesion occurred, he might get on comfortably for some years yet.

In August Niel was to go to Boston to begin coaching for his entrance examinations at the Massachusetts Institute of Technology, where he meant to study architecture. He put off bidding the Forresters goodbye until the very day before he left. His last call was different from any he had ever made there before. Already they began to treat him like a young man. He sat rather stiffly in that parlour where he had been so much at home. The Captain was in his big chair in the bay window, in the full glow of the afternoon sun, saying little, but very friendly. Mrs. Forrester, on the sofa in the shadowy corner of the room, talked about Niel's plans and his journey.

"Is it true that Mary is going to marry Pucelik this fall?" he asked her. "Who will you get to help you?"

"No one, for the present. Ben will do all I can't do. Never mind us. We will pass a quiet winter, like an old country couple,—as we are!" she said lightly.

Niel knew that she faced the winter with terror, but he had never seen her more in command of herself,—or more the mistress of her own house than now, when she was preparing to become the servant of it. He had the feeling, which he never used to have, that her lightness cost her something.

"Don't forget us, but don't mope. Make lots of new friends. You'll never be twenty again. Take a chorus girl out to supper—a pretty one, mind! Don't bother about your allowance. If you got into a scrape, we could manage a little cheque to help you out, couldn't we, Mr. Forrester?"

The Captain puffed and looked amused. "I think we could, Niel, I think so. Don't get up, my boy. You must stay to dinner."

Niel said he couldn't. He hadn't finished packing, and he was leaving on the morning train.

"Then we must have a little something before you go." Captain Forrester rose heavily, with the aid of his cane, and went into the dining-room. He brought back the decanter and filled three glasses with ceremony. Lifting his glass, he paused, as always, and blinked.

"Happy days!"

"Happy days!" echoed Mrs. Forrester, with her loveliest smile, "and every success to Niel!"

Both the Captain and his wife came to the door with him, and stood there on the porch together, where he had so often seen them stand to speed the parting guest. He went down the hill touched and happy. As he passed over the bridge his spirits suddenly fell. Would that chilling doubt always lie in wait for him, down there in the mud, where he had thrown his roses one morning?

He burned to ask her one question, to get the truth out of her and set his mind at rest: What did she do with all her exquisiteness when she was with a man like Ellinger? Where did she put it away? And having put it away, how could she recover herself, and give one—give even him—the sense of tempered steel, a blade that could fence with anyone and never break?

Part Two: I

IT WAS TWO YEARS BEFORE Niel Herbert came home again, and when he came the first acquaintance he met was Ivy Peters. Ivy got on the train at one of the little stations east of Sweet Water, where he had been trying a case. As he strolled through the Pullman he noticed among the passengers a young man in a grey flannel suit, with a silk shirt of one shade of blue and a necktie of another. After regarding this urban figure from the rear for a few seconds, Ivy glanced down at his own clothes with gloating satisfaction. It was a hot day in June, but he wore the black felt hat and ready-made coat of winter weight he had always affected as a boy. He stepped forward, his hands thrust in his pockets.

"Hullo, Niel. Thought I couldn't be mistaken."

Niel looked up and saw the red, bee-stung face, with its two permanent dimples, smiling down at him in contemptuous jocularity.

"Hello, Ivy. I couldn't be mistaken in you, either."

"Coming home to go into business?"

Niel replied that he was coming only for the summer vacation.

"Oh, you're not through school yet? I suppose it takes longer to make an architect than it does to make a shyster. Just as well; there's not much building going on in Sweet Water these days. You'll find a good many changes."

"Won't you sit down?" Niel indicated the neighbouring chair. "You are practising law?"

"Yes, along with a few other things. Have to keep more than one iron in the fire to make a living with us. I farm a little on the side. I rent that meadow-land on the Forrester place. I've drained the old marsh and put it into wheat. My brother John does the work, and I boss the job. It's quite profitable. I pay them a good rent, and they need it. I doubt if they could get along without. Their influential friends don't seem to help them out much. Remember all those chesty old boys the Captain used to drive about in his democrat wagon, and ship in barrels of Bourbon for? Good deal of bluff about all those old-timers. The panic put them out of the game. The Forresters have come down in the world like the rest. You remember how the old man used to put it over us kids and not let us carry a gun in there? I'm just mean enough to like to shoot along that creek a little better than anywhere else, now. There wasn't any harm in the old Captain, but he had the delusion of grandeur. He's happier now that he's like the rest of us and don't have to change his shirt every day." Ivy's unblinking greenish eyes rested upon Niel's haberdashery.

Niel, however, did not notice this. He knew that Ivy wanted him to show disappointment, and he was determined not to do so. He enquired about the Captain's health, pointedly keeping Mrs. Forrester's name out of the conversation.

"He's only about half there . . . seems contented enough. . . . She takes good care of him, I'll say that for her. . . . She seeks consolation, always did, you know . . . too much French brandy . . . but she never neglects him. I don't blame her. Real work comes hard on her."

Niel heard these remarks dully, through the buzz of an idea. He felt that Ivy had drained the marsh quite as much to spite him and Mrs. Forrester as to reclaim the land. Moreover, he seemed to know that until this moment Ivy himself had not realized how much that consideration weighed with him. He and Ivy had disliked each other from childhood, blindly, instinctively, recognizing each other through antipathy, as hostile insects do. By draining the marsh Ivy had obliterated a few acres of something he hated, though he could not name it, and had asserted his power over the people who had loved those unproductive meadows for their idleness and silvery beauty.

After Ivy had gone on into the smoker, Niel sat looking out at the windings of the Sweet Water and playing with his idea. The Old West had been settled by dreamers, great-hearted adventurers who were unpractical to the point of magnificence; a courteous brotherhood, strong in attack but weak in defence, who could conquer but could not hold. Now all the vast territory they had won was to be at the mercy of men like Ivy Peters, who had never dared anything, never risked anything. They would drink up the mirage, dispel the morning freshness, root out the great brooding spirit of freedom, the generous, easy life of the great landholders. The space, the colour, the princely carelessness of the pioneer they would destroy and cut up into profitable bits, as the match factory splinters the primeval forest. All the way from the Missouri to the mountains this generation of shrewd young men, trained to petty economies by hard times, would do exactly what Ivy Peters had done when he drained the Forrester marsh.

II

THE NEXT AFTERNOON Niel found Captain Forrester in the bushy little plot he called his rose garden, seated in a stout hickory chair that could be left out in all weather, his two canes beside him. His attention was fixed upon a red block of Colorado sandstone, set on a granite boulder in the middle of the gravel space around which the roses grew. He showed Niel that this was a sun-dial, and explained it with great pride. Last summer, he said, he sat out here a great deal, with a square board mounted on a post, and marked the length of the shadows by his watch. His friend, Cyrus Dalzell, on one of his visits, took this board away, had the diagram exactly copied on sandstone, and sent it to him, with the column-like boulder that formed its base.

"I think it's likely Mr. Dalzell hunted around among the mountains a good many mornings before he found a natural formation like that," said the Captain. "A pillar, such as they had in Bible times. It's from the Garden of the Gods. Mr. Dalzell has his summer home up there."

The Captain sat with the soles of his boots together, his legs bowed out. Everything about him seemed to have grown heavier and weaker. His face was fatter and smoother; as if the features were running into each other, as when a wax face melts in the heat. An old Panama hat, burned yellow by the sun, shaded his eyes. His brown hands lay on his knees, the fingers well apart, nerveless. His moustache was the same straw colour; Niel remarked to him that it had grown no greyer. The Captain touched his cheek with his palm. "Mrs. Forrester shaved me for awhile. She did it very nicely, but I didn't like to have her do it. Now I use one of these safety razors. I can manage, if I take my time. The barber comes over once a week. Mrs. Forrester is expecting you, Niel. She's down in the grove. She goes down there to rest in the hammock."

Niel went round the house to the gate that gave into the grove. From the top of the hill he could see the hammock slung between two cotton-woods, in the low glade at the farther end, where he had fallen the time he broke his arm. The slender white figure was still, and as he hurried across the grass he saw that a white garden hat lay over her face. He approached quietly and was just wondering if she were asleep, when he heard a soft, delighted laugh, and with a quick movement she threw off the lace hat through which she had been watching him. He stepped forward and caught her suspended figure, hammock and all, in his arms. How light and alive she was! like a bird caught in a net. If only he could rescue her and carry her off like this,—off the earth of sad, inevitable periods, away from age, weariness, adverse fortune!

She showed no impatience to be released, but lay laughing up at him with that gleam of something elegantly wild, something fantastic and tantalizing,—seemingly so artless, really the most finished artifice! She put her hand under his chin as if he were still a boy.

"And how handsome he's grown! Isn't the old Judge proud of you! He called me up last night and began sputtering, 'It's only fair to warn you, Ma'm, that I've a very handsome boy over here.' As if I hadn't known you would be! And now you're a man, and have seen the world! Well, what have you found in it?"

"Nothing so nice as you, Mrs. Forrester."

"Nonsense! You have sweethearts?"

"Perhaps."

"Are they pretty?"

"Why they? Isn't one enough?"

"One is too many. I want you to have half a dozen,—and still save the best for us! One would take everything. If you had her, you would not have come home at all. I wonder if you know how we've looked for you?" She took his hand and turned a seal ring about on his little finger absently. "Every night for weeks, when the lights of the train came swinging in down below the meadows, I've said to myself, 'Niel is coming home; there's that to look forward to.' " She caught herself as she always did when she found that she was telling too much, and finished in a playful tone. "So, you see, you mean a great deal to all of us. Did you find Mr. Forrester?"

"Oh, yes! I had to stop and look at his sun-dial."

She raised herself on her elbow and lowered her voice. "Niel, can you understand it? He isn't childish, as some people say, but he will sit and watch that thing hour after hour. How can anybody like to see time visibly devoured? We are all used to seeing clocks go round, but why does he want to see that shadow creep on that stone? Has he changed much? No? I'm glad you feel so. Now tell me about the Adamses and what George is like."

Niel dropped on the turf and sat with his back against a tree trunk, answering her rapid questions and watching her while he talked. Of course, she was older. In the brilliant sun of the afternoon one saw that her skin was no longer like white lilacs,—it had the ivory tint of gardenias that have just begun to fade. The coil of blue-black hair seemed more than ever too heavy for her head. There were lines,—something strained about the corners of her mouth that used not to be there. But the astonishing thing was how these changes could vanish in a moment, be utterly wiped out in a flash of personality, and one forgot everything about her except herself.

"And tell me, Niel, do women really smoke after dinner now with the men, nice women? I shouldn't like it. It's all very well for actresses, but women can't be attractive if they do everything that men do."

"I think just now it's the fashion for women to make themselves comfortable, before anything else."

Mrs. Forrester glanced at him as if he had said something shocking.

"Ah, that's just it! The two things don't go together. Athletics and going to college and smoking after dinner—Do you like it? Don't men like women to be different from themselves? They used to."

Niel laughed. Yes, that was certainly the idea of Mrs. Forrester's generation.

"Uncle Judge says you don't come to see him any more as you used to, Mrs. Forrester. He misses it."

"My dear boy, I haven't been over to the town for six weeks. I'm always too tired. We have no horse now, and when I do go I have to walk. That house! Nothing is ever done there unless I do it, and nothing ever moves unless I move it. That's why I come down here in the after-noon,—to get where I can't see the house. I can't keep it up as it should be kept, I'm not strong enough. Oh, yes, Ben helps me; he sweeps and beats the rugs and washes windows, but that doesn't get a house very far." Mrs. Forrester sat up suddenly and pinned on her white hat. "We went all the way to Chicago, Niel, to buy that walnut furniture, couldn't find anything at home big and heavy enough. If I'd known that one day I'd have to push it about, I would have been more easily satisfied!" She rose and shook out her rumpled skirts.

They started toward the house, going slowly up the long, grassy undulation between the trees.

"Don't you miss the marsh?" Niel asked suddenly.

She glanced away evasively. "Not much. I would never have time to go there, and we need the money it pays us. And you haven't time to play any more either, Niel. You must hurry and become a successful man. Your uncle is terribly involved. He has been so careless that he's not much better off than we are. Money is a very important thing. Realize that in the beginning; face it, and don't be ridiculous in the end, like so many of us." They stopped by the gate at the top of the hill and looked back at the green alleys and the sharp shadows, at the quivering fans of light that seemed to push the trees farther apart and made Elysian fields underneath them. Mrs. Forrester put her white hand, with all its rings, on Niel's arm.

"Do you really find a kind of pleasure in coming back to us? That's very unusual, I think. At your age I wanted to be with the young and gay. It's nice for us, though." She looked at him with her rarest smile, one he had seldom seen on her face, but always remembered,—a smile with-out archness, without gaiety, full of affection and wistfully sad. And the same thing was in her voice when she spoke those quiet words,—the sudden quietness of deep feeling. She turned quickly away. They went through the gate and around the house to where the Captain sat watch-ing the sunset glory on his roses. His wife touched his shoulder.

"Will you go in, now, Mr. Forrester, or shall I bring your coat?"

"I'll go in. Isn't Niel going to stay for dinner?" "Not this time. He'll come soon, and we'll have a real dinner for him. Will you wait for Mr. Forrester, Niel? I must hurry in and start the fire."

Niel tarried behind and accompanied the Captain's slow progress toward the front of the house. He leaned upon two canes, lifting his feet slowly and putting them down firmly and carefully. He looked like an old tree walking.

Once up the steps and into the parlour, he sank into his big chair and panted heavily. The first whiff of a fresh cigar seemed to restore him. "Can I trouble you to mail some letters for me, Niel, as you go by the post-office?" He produced them from the breast pocket of his summer coat. "Let me see whether Mrs. Forrester has anything to go." Rising, the Captain went into the little hall. There, by the front door, on a table under the hatrack, was a scantily draped figure, an Arab or Egyptian slave girl, holding in her hands a large flat shell from the California coast. Niel remembered noticing that figure the first time he was ever in the house, when Dr. Dennison carried him out through this hallway with his arm in splints. In the days when the Forresters had servants and were sending over to the town several times a day, the letters for the post were always left in this shell. The Captain found one now, and handed it to Niel. It was addressed to Mr. Francis Bosworth Ellinger, Glenwood Springs, Colorado.

For some reason Niel felt embarrassed and tried to slip the letter quickly into his pocket. The Captain, his two canes in one hand, prevented him. He took the pale blue envelope again, and held it out at arm's length, regarding it.

"Mrs. Forrester is a fine penman; have you ever noticed? Always was. If she made me a list of articles to get at the store, I never had to hide it. It was like copper plate. That's exceptional in a woman, Niel."

Niel remembered her hand well enough, he had never seen another in the least like it; long, thin, angular letters, curiously delicate and curiously bold, looped and laced with strokes fine as a hair and perfectly distinct. Her script looked as if it had been done at a high pitch of speed, the pen driven by a perfectly confident dexterity.

"Oh, yes, Captain! I'm never able to take any letters for Mrs. Forrester without looking at them. No one could forget her writing."

"Yes. It's very exceptional." The Captain gave him the envelope, and with his canes went slowly toward his big chair.

Niel had often wondered just how much the Captain knew. Now, as he went down the hill, he felt sure that he knew everything; more than anyone else; all there was to know about Marian Forrester.

III

NIEL HAD PLANNED to do a great deal of reading in the Forresters' grove that summer, but he did not go over so often as he had intended.

The frequent appearance of Ivy Peters about the place irritated him. Ivy visited his new wheat fields on the bottom land very often; and he always took the old path, that led from what was once the marsh, up the steep bank and through the grove. He was likely to appear at any hour, his trousers stuffed into his top-boots, tramping along between the rows of trees with an air of proprietorship. He shut the gate behind the house with a slam and went whistling through the yard. Often he stopped at the kitchen door to call out some pleasantry to Mrs. Forrester. This annoyed Niel, for at that hour of the morning, when she was doing her house-work, Mrs. Forrester was not dressed to receive her inferiors. It was one thing to greet the president of the Colorado & Utah *en déshabille*, but it was another to chatter with a coarse-grained fellow like Ivy Peters in her wrapper and slippers, her sleeves rolled up and her throat bare to his cool, impudent eyes.

Sometimes Ivy strode through the rose plot where Captain Forrester was sitting in the sun,—went by without looking at him, as if there were no one there. If he spoke to the Captain at all, he did so as if he were addressing someone incapable of understanding anything. "Hullo, Captain, ain't afraid this sun will spoil your complexion?" or "Well, Captain, you'll have to get the prayer-meetings to take up this rain question. The drought's damned bad for my wheat."

One morning, as Niel was coming up through the grove, he heard laughter by the gate, and there he saw Ivy, with his gun, talking to Mrs. Forrester. She was bareheaded, her skirts blowing in the wind, her arm through the handle of a big tin bucket that rested on the fence beside her. Ivy stood with his hat on his head, but there was in his attitude that unmistakable something which shows that a man is trying to make him-self agreeable to a woman. He was telling her a funny story, probably an improper one, for it brought out her naughtiest laugh, with something nervous and excited in it, as if he were going too far. At the end of his story Ivy himself broke into his farm-hand guffaw. Mrs. Forrester shook her finger at him and, catching up her pail, ran back into the house. She bent a little with its weight, but Ivy made no offer to carry it for her. He let her trip away with it as if she were a kitchen maid, and that were her business.

Niel emerged from the grove, and stopped where the Captain sat in the garden. "Good-morning, Captain Forrester. Was that Ivy Peters who just went through here? That fellow hasn't the manners of a pig!" he blurted out.

The Captain pointed to Mrs. Forrester's empty chair. "Sit down, Niel, sit down." He drew his handkerchief from his pocket and began polishing his glasses. "No," he said quietly, "he ain't overly polite."

More than if he had complained bitterly, that guarded admission made one feel how much he had been hurt and offended by Ivy's rude-ness. There was something very sad in his voice, and helpless. From his equals, respect had always come to him as his due; from fellows like Ivy he had been able to command it,—to order them off his place, or dismiss them from his employ.

Niel sat down and smoked a cigar with him. They had a long talk about the building of the Black Hills branch of the Burlington. In Boston last winter Niel had met an old mine-owner, who was living in Deadwood when the railroad first came in. When Niel asked him if he had known Daniel Forrester, the old gentleman said, "Forrester? Was he the one with the beautiful wife?"

"You must tell her," said the Captain, stroking the warm surface of his sun-dial. "Yes, indeed. You must tell Mrs. Forrester."

One night in the first week of July, a night of glorious moonlight, Niel found himself unable to read, or to stay indoors at all. He walked aimlessly down the wide, empty street, and crossed the first creek by the foot-bridge. The wide ripe fields, the whole country, seemed like a sleeping garden. One trod the dusty roads softly, not to disturb the deep slumber of the world.

In the Forrester land the scent of sweet clover hung heavy. It had always grown tall and green here ever since Niel could remember; the Captain would never let it be cut until the weeds were mowed in the fall. The black, plume-like shadows of the poplars fell across the lane and over Ivy Peters' wheat fields. As he walked on, Niel saw a white figure standing on the bridge over the second creek, motionless in the clear moonlight. He hurried forward. Mrs. Forrester was looking down at the water where it flowed bright over the pebbles. He came up beside her. "The Captain is asleep?"

"Oh, yes, long ago! He sleeps well, thank heaven! After I tuck him in, I have nothing more to worry about."

While they were standing there, talking in low voices, they heard a heavy door slam on the hill. Mrs. Forrester started and looked back over her shoulder. A man emerged from the shadow of the house and came striding down the drive-way. Ivy Peters stepped upon the bridge.

"Good evening," he said to Mrs. Forrester, neither calling her by name nor removing his hat. "I see you have company. I've just been up looking at the old barn, to see if the stalls are fit to put horses in there tomorrow. I'm going to start cutting wheat in the morning, and we'll have to put the horses in your stable at noon. We'd lose time taking them back to town."

"Why, certainly. The horses can go in our barn. I'm sure Mr. Forrester would have no objection." She spoke as if he had asked her permission.

"Oh!" Ivy shrugged. "The men will begin down here at six o'clock. I won't get over till about ten, and I have to meet a client at my office at three. Maybe you could give me some lunch, to save time."

His impudence made her smile. "Very well, then; I invite you to lunch. We lunch at one."

"Thanks. It will help me out." As if he had forgotten himself, he lifted his hat, and went down the lane swinging it in his hand.

Niel stood looking after him. "Why do you allow him to speak to you like that, Mrs. Forrester? If you'll let me, I'll give him a beating and teach him how to speak to you."

"No, no, Niel! Remember, we have to get along with Ivy Peters, we simply have to!" There was a note of anxiety in her voice, and she caught his arm.

"You don't have to take anything from him, or to stand his bad manners. Anybody else would pay you as much for the land as he does."

"But he has a lease for five years, and he could make it very disagreeable for us, don't you see? Besides," she spoke hurriedly, "there's more than that. He's invested a little money for me in Wyoming, in land. He gets splendid land from the Indians some way, for next to nothing. Don't tell your uncle; I've no doubt it's crooked. But the Judge is like Mr. Forrester; his methods don't work nowadays. He will never get us out of debt, dear man! He can't get himself out. Ivy Peters is terribly smart, you know. He owns half the town already."

"Not quite," said Niel grimly. "He's got hold of a good deal of property. He'll take advantage of anybody's necessity. You know he's utterly unscrupulous, don't you? Why didn't you let Mr. Dalzell, or some of your other old friends, invest your money for you?"

"Oh, it was too little! Only a few hundred dollars I'd saved on the housekeeping. They would put it into something safe, at six per cent. I know you don't like Ivy,—and he knows it! He's always at his worst before you. He's not so bad as—as his face, for instance!" She laughed nervously. "He honestly wants to help us out of the hole we're in. Coming and going all the time, as he does, he sees everything, and I really think he hates to have me work so hard."

"Next time you have anything to invest, you let me take it to Mr. Dalzell and explain. I'll promise to do as well by you as Ivy Peters can."

Mrs. Forrester took his arm and drew him into the lane. "But, my dear boy, you know nothing about these business schemes You're not clever that way,—it's one of the things I love you for. I don't admire people who cheat Indians. Indeed I don't!" She shook her head vehemently.

"Mrs. Forrester, rascality isn't the only thing that succeeds in business."

"It succeeds faster than anything else, though," she murmured absently. They walked as far as the end of the lane and turned back again. Mrs. Forrester's hand tightened on his arm. She began speaking abruptly. "You see, two years, three years, more of this, and I could still go back to California—and live again. But after that . . . Perhaps people think I've settled down to grow old gracefully, but I've not. I feel such a power to live in me, Niel." Her slender fingers gripped his wrist. "It's grown by being held back. Last winter I was with the Dalzells at Glenwood Springs for three weeks (I owe *that* to Ivy Peters; he looked after things here, and his sister kept house for Mr. Forrester), and I was surprised at myself. I could dance all night and not feel tired. I could ride horseback all day and be ready for a dinner party in the evening. I had no clothes, of course; old evening dresses with yards and yards of satin and velvet in them, that Mrs. Dalzell's sewing woman made over. But I looked well enough! Yes, I did. I always know how I'm looking, and I looked well enough. The men thought so. I looked happier than any woman there. They were nearly all younger, much. But they seemed dull, bored to death. After a glass or two of champagne they went to sleep and had nothing to say! I always look better after the first glass,—it gives me a little colour, it's the only thing that does. I accepted the Dalzells' invitation with a purpose; I wanted to see whether I had anything left worth saving. And I have, I tell you! You would hardly believe it, I could hardly believe it, but I still have!"

By this time they had reached the bridge, a bare white floor in the moonlight. Mrs. Forrester had been quickening her pace all the while. "So that's what I'm struggling for, to get out of this hole,"—she looked about as if she had fallen into a deep well,—"out of it! When I'm alone here for months together, I plan and plot. If it weren't for that—"

As Niel walked back to his room behind the law offices, he felt frightened for her. When women began to talk about still feeling young, didn't it mean that something had broken? Two or three years, she said. He shivered. Only yesterday old Dr. Dennison had proudly told him that Captain Forrester might live a dozen. "We are keeping his general health up remarkably, and he was originally a man of iron."

What hope was there for her? He could still feel her hand upon his arm, as she urged him faster and faster up the lane.

IV

The weather was dry and intensely hot for several weeks, and then, at the end of July, thunder-storms and torrential rains broke upon the Sweet Water valley. The river burst out of its banks, all the creeks were up, and the stubble of Ivy Peters' wheat fields lay under water. A wide lake and two rushing creeks now separated the Forresters from the town. Ben Keezer rode over to them every day to do the chores and to take them their mail. One evening Ben, with his slicker and leather mailbag, had just come out of the post-office and was preparing to mount his horse, when Niel Herbert stopped him to ask in a low voice whether he had got the Denver paper.

"Oh, yes. I always wait for the papers. She likes to have them to read of an evening. Guess it's pretty lonesome over there." He swung into his saddle and splashed off. Niel walked slowly around to the hotel for dinner. He had found something very disconcerting in the Denver paper: Frank Ellinger's picture on the society page, along with Constance Ogden's. They had been married yesterday at Colorado Springs, and were stopping at the Antlers.

After supper Niel put on his rubber coat and started for the Forresters'. When he reached the first creek, he found that the foot-bridge had been washed out from the far bank and lay obliquely in the stream, battered at by the yellow current which might at any moment carry it away. One could not cross the ford without a horse. He looked irresolutely across the submerged bottom lands. The house was dark, no lights in the parlour windows. The rain was beginning to fall again. Perhaps she had rather be alone tonight. He would go over tomorrow.

He went back to the law office and tried to make himself comfortable, though the place was in distracting disorder. The continued rain had set one of the chimneys leaking, had brought down streams of soot and black water and flooded the stove and the Judge's once handsome Brussels carpet. The tinner had been there all afternoon, trying to find what was the matter with the flue, cutting a new sheet-iron drawer to fit under the stove-pipe. But at six o'clock he had gone away, leaving tools and sheets of metal lying about. The rooms were damp and cold. Niel put on a heavy sweater, since he could not have a fire, lit the big coal-oil lamp, and sat down with a book. When at last he looked at his watch, it was nearly midnight, and he had been reading three hours. He would have another pipe, and go to bed. He had scarcely lit it, when he heard quick, hurrying footsteps in the echoing corridor outside. He got to the door in an instant, was there to open it before Mrs. Forrester had time to knock. He caught her by the arm and pulled her in.

Everything but her wet, white face was hidden by a black rubber hat and a coat that was much too big for her. Streams of water trickled from the coat, and when she opened it he saw that she was drenched to the waist,—her black dress clung in a muddy pulp about her.

"Mrs. Forrester," he cried, "you can't have crossed the creek! It's up to a horse's belly in the ford."

"I came over the bridge, what's left of it. It shook under me, but I'm not heavy." She threw off her hat and wiped the water from her face with her hands.

"Why didn't you ask Ben to bring you over on his horse? Here, please swallow this."

She pushed his hand aside. "Wait. Afterwards. Ben? I didn't think until after he was gone. It's the telephone I want, long distance. Get me Colorado Springs, the Antlers, quick!"

Then Niel noticed that she smelled strong of spirits; it steamed above the smell of rubber and creek mud and wet cloth. She snatched up the desk telephone, but he gently took it from her.

"I'll get them for you, but you're in no condition to talk now; you're out of breath. Do you really want to talk tonight? You know Mrs. Beasley will hear every word you say." Mrs. Beasley was the Sweet Water central, and an indefatigable reporter of everything that went over the wires.

Mrs. Forrester, sitting in his uncle's desk chair, tapped the carpet with the toe of her rubber boot. "Do hurry, please," she said in that polite, warning tone of which even Ivy Peters was afraid.

Niel aroused the sleepy central and put in the call. "She asks whom you wish to speak to?"

"Frank Ellinger. Say Judge Pommeroy's office wishes to speak to him."

Niel began soothing Mrs. Beasley at the other end. "No, not the management, Mrs. Beasley, one of the guests. Frank Ellinger," he spelled the name. "Yes. Judge Pommeroy's office wants to talk to him. I'll be right here. As soon as you can, please."

He put down the instrument. "I'd rather, you know, publish anything in the town paper than telephone it through Mrs. Beasley." Mrs. Forrester paid no heed to him, did not look at him, sat staring at the wall. "I can't see why you didn't call me up and ask me to bring a horse over for you, if you felt you must get to a long distance telephone tonight."

"Yes; I didn't think of it. I only knew I had to get over here, and I was afraid something might stop me." She was watching the telephone as if it were alive. Her eyes were shrunk to hard points. Her brows, drawn together in an acute angle, kept twitching in the frown which held them, —the singular frown of one overcome by alcohol or fatigue, who is holding on to consciousness by the strength of a single purpose. Her blue lips, the black shadows under her eyes, made her look as if some poison were at work in her body.

They waited and waited. Niel understood that she did not wish him to talk. Her mind was struggling with something, with every blink of her lashes she seemed to face it anew. Presently she rose as if she could bear the suspense no longer and went over to the window, leaned against it.

"Did you leave Captain Forrester alone?" Niel asked suddenly.

"Yes. Nothing will happen over there. Nothing ever *does* happen!" she answered wildly, wringing her hands.

The telephone buzzed. Mrs. Forrester darted toward the desk, but Niel lifted the instrument in his left hand and barred her way with his right. "Try to be calm, Mrs. Forrester. When I get Ellinger I will let you talk to him,—and central will hear every word you say, remember."

After some exchanges with the Colorado office, he pointed her to the chair. "Sit down and I'll give it to you. He is on the wire."

He did not dare to leave her alone, though it was awkward enough to be a listener. He walked to the window and stood with his back to the desk where she was sitting.

"Is that you, Frank? This is Marian. I won't keep you a moment. You were asleep? So early? That's not like you. You've reformed already, haven't you? That's what marriage does, they say. No, I wasn't altogether surprised. You might have taken me into your confidence, though. Haven't I deserved it?"

A long, listening pause. Niel stared stupidly at the dark window. He had steeled his nerves for wild reproaches. The voice he heard behind him was her most charming; playful, affectionate, intimate, with a thrill of pleasant excitement that warmed its slight formality and burned through the common-place words like the colour in an opal. He simply held his breath while she fluttered on:

"Where shall you go for your honeymoon? Oh, I'm very sorry! So soon . . . You must take good care of her. Give her my love. . . . I should think California, at this time of the year, might be right . . ."

It went on like this for some minutes. The voice, it seemed to Niel, was that of a woman, young, beautiful, happy,—warm and at her ease, sitting in her own drawing-room and talking on a stormy night to a dear friend far away.

"Oh, unusually well, for me. Stop and see for yourself. You will be going to Omaha on business next week, before California. Oh, yes, you will! Stop off between trains. You know how welcome you are, always."

A long pause. An exclamation from Mrs. Forrester made Niel turn sharply round. Now it was coming! Her voice was darkening with every word. "I think I understand you. You are not speaking from your own room? What, from the office booth? Oh, then I understand you very well indeed!" Niel looked about in alarm. It was time to stop her, but how? The voice went on.

"Play safe! When have you ever played anything else? You know, Frank, the truth is that you're a coward; a great, hulking coward. Do you hear me? I want you to hear! . . . You've got a safe thing at last, I should think; safe and pasty! How much stock did you get with it? A big block, I hope! Now let me tell you the truth: I don't want you to come here! I never want to see you again while I live, and I forbid you to come and look at me when I'm dead. I don't want your hateful eyes to look at my dead face. Do you hear me? Why don't you answer me? Don't dare to hang up the receiver, you coward! Oh, you big . . . Frank, Frank, say something! Oh, he's shut me off, I can't hear him!"

She flung the receiver down, dropped her head on the desk, and broke into heavy, groaning sobs. Niel stood over her and waited with composure. For once he had been quick enough; he had saved her. The moment that quivering passion of hatred and wrong leaped into her voice, he had taken the big shears left by the tinner and cut the insulated wire behind the desk. Her reproaches had got no farther than this room.

When the sobs ceased he touched her shoulder. He shook her, but there was no response. She was asleep, sunk in a heavy stupor. Her hands and face were so cold that he thought there could not be a drop of warm blood left in her body. He carried her into his room, cut off her drenched clothing, wrapped her in his bathrobe and put her into his own bed. She was absolutely unconscious. He blew out the light, locked her in, and left the building, going as fast as he could to Judge Pommeroy's cottage. He roused his uncle and briefly explained the situation.

"Can you dress and go down to the office for the rest of the night, Uncle Judge? Someone must be with her. And I'll get over to the Captain at once; he certainly oughtn't to be left alone. If she could get across the bridge, I guess I can. By the way, she began talking wild, and I cut the telephone wire behind your desk. So keep an eye on it. It might make trouble on a stormy night like this. I'll get a livery hack and take Mrs. Forrester home in the morning, before the town is awake."

When daylight began to break Niel went into Captain Forrester's room and told him that his wife had been sent for in the night to answer a long distance telephone call, and that now he was going to bring her home.

The Captain lay propped up on three big pillows. Since his face had grown fat and relaxed, its ruggedness had changed to an almost Asiatic smoothness. He looked like a wise old Chinese mandarin as he lay listening to the young man's fantastic story with perfect composure, merely blinking and saying, "Thank you, Niel, thank you."

As Niel went through the sleeping town on his way to the livery barn, he saw the short, plump figure of Mrs. Beasley, like a boiled pudding sewed up in a blue kimono, waddling through the feathery asparagus bed behind the telephone office. She had already been next door to tell her neighbour Molly Tucker, the seamstress, the story of her exciting night.

V

Soon afterward, when Captain Forrester had another stroke, Mrs. Beasley and Molly Tucker and their friends were perfectly agreed that it was a judgment upon his wife. No judgment could have been crueller. Under the care of him, now that he was helpless, Mrs. Forrester quite went to pieces.

Even after their misfortunes had begun to come upon them, she had maintained her old reserve. She had asked nothing and accepted nothing. Her demeanour toward the townspeople was always the same; easy, cordial, and impersonal. Her own friends had moved away long ago,—all except Judge Pommeroy and Dr. Dennison. When any of the housewives from the town came to call, she met them in the parlour, chatted with them in the smiling, careless manner they could never break through, and they got no further. They still felt they must put on their best dress and carry a card-case when they went to the Forresters'.

But now that the Captain was helpless, everything changed. She could hold off the curious no longer. The townswomen brought soups and custards for the invalid. When they came to sit out the night with him, she turned the house over to them. She was worn out; so exhausted that she was dull to what went on about her. The Mrs. Beasleys and Molly Tuckers had their chance at last. They went in and out of Mrs. Forrester's kitchen as familiarly as they did out of one another's. They rummaged through the linen closet to find more sheets, pried about in the attic and cellar. They went over the house like ants, the house where they had never before got past the parlour; and they found they had been fooled all these years. There was nothing remarkable about the place at all! The kitchen was inconvenient, the sink was smelly. The carpets were worn, the curtains faded, the clumsy, old-fashioned furniture they wouldn't have had for a gift, and the upstairs bed-rooms were full of dust and cobwebs.

Judge Pommeroy remarked to his nephew that he had never seen these women look so wide-awake, so important and pleased with themselves, as now when he encountered them bustling about the Forrester place. The Captain's illness had the effect of a social revival, like a new club or a church society. The creatures grew bolder and bolder,—and Mrs. Forrester, apparently, had no power of resistance. She drudged in the kitchen, slept, half-dressed, in one of the chambers upstairs, kept herself going on black coffee and brandy. All the bars were down. She had ceased to care about anything.

As the women came and went through the lane, Niel sometimes overheard snatches of their conversation.

"Why didn't she sell some of that silver? All those platters and covered dishes stuck away with the tarnish of years on them!"

"I wouldn't mind having some of her linen. There's a chest full of double damask upstairs, every tablecloth long enough to make two. Did you ever see anything like the wine glasses! I'll bet there's not as many in both saloons put together. If she has a sale after he's gone, I'll buy a dozen champagne glasses; they're nice to serve sherbet in."

"There are nine dozen glasses," said Molly Tucker, "counting them for beer and whiskey. If there is a sale, I've a mind to bid in a couple of them green ones, with long stems, for mantel ornaments. But she'll never sell 'em all, unless she can get the saloons to take 'em."

Ed Elliott's mother laughed. "She'll never sell 'em, as long as she's got anything to put in 'em."

"The cellar will go dry, some day."

"I guess there's always plenty that will get it for such as her. I never go there now that I don't smell it on her. I went over late the other night, and she was on her knees, washing up the kitchen floor. Her eyes were glassy. She kept washing the place around the ice-box over and over, till it made me nervous. I said, 'Mrs. Forrester, I think you've washed that place several times already.'"

"Was she confused?"

"Not a particle! She laughed and said she was often absent-minded."

Mrs. Elliott's companions laughed, too, and agreed that absent-minded was a good expression.

Niel repeated this conversation to his uncle. "Uncle," he declared, "I don't see how I can go back to Boston and leave the Forresters. I'd like to chuck school for a year, and see them through. I want to go over there and clear those gossips out. Could you stay at the hotel for a few weeks, and let me have Black Tom? With him to help me, I'd send every one of those women trotting down the lane."

It was arranged quietly, and at once. Tom was put in the kitchen, and Niel himself took charge of the nursing. He met the women with firmness: they were very kind, but now nothing was needed. The Doctor had said the house must be absolutely quiet and that the invalid must see no one.

Once the house was tranquil, Mrs. Forrester went to bed and slept for the better part of a week. The Captain himself improved. On his good days he could be put into a wheel-chair and rolled out into his garden to enjoy the September sunlight and the last of his briar roses.

"Thank you, Niel, thank you, Tom," he often said when they lifted him into his chair. "I value this quiet very highly." If a day came when they thought he ought not to go out, he was sad and disappointed.

"Better get him out, no matter what," said Mrs. Forrester. "He likes to look at his place. That, and his cigar, are the only pleasures he has left."

When she was rested and in command of herself again, she took her place in the kitchen, and Black Tom went back to the Judge.

At night, when he was alone, when Mrs. Forrester had gone to bed and the Captain was resting quietly, Niel found a kind of solemn happiness in his vigils. It had been hard to give up that year; most of his classmates were younger than he. It had cost him something, but now that he had taken the step, he was glad. As he put in the night hours, sitting first in one chair and then in another, reading, smoking, getting a lunch to keep himself awake, he had the satisfaction of those who keep faith. He liked being alone with the old things that had seemed so beautiful to him in his childhood. These were still the most comfortable chairs in the world, and he would never like any pictures so well as "William Tell's Chapel" and "The House of the Tragic Poet." No card-table was so good for solitaire as this old one with a stone top, mosaic in the pattern of a chess-board, which one of the Captain's friends had brought him from Naples. No other house could take the place of this one in his life.

He had time to think of many things; of himself and of his old friends here. He had noticed that often when Mrs. Forrester was about her work, the Captain would call to her, "Maidy, Maidy," and she would reply, "Yes, Mr. Forrester," from wherever she happened to be, but without coming to him,—as if she knew that when he called to her in that tone he was not asking for anything. He wanted to know if she were near, perhaps; or, perhaps, he merely liked to call her name and to hear her answer. The longer Niel was with Captain Forrester in those peaceful closing days of his life, the more he felt that the Captain knew his wife better even than she knew herself; and that, knowing her, he,—to use one of his own expressions,—valued her.

VI

CAPTAIN FORRESTER'S death, which occurred early in December, was "telegraphic news," the only State news that the discouraged town of Sweet Water had furnished for a long while. Flowers and telegrams came from east and west, but it happened that none of the Captain's closest friends could come to his funeral. Mr. Dalzell was in California, the president of the Burlington railroad was travelling in Europe. The others were far away or in uncertain health. Dr. Dennison and Judge Pommeroy were the only two of his intimates among the pallbearers.

On the morning of the funeral, when the Captain was already in his coffin, and the undertaker was in the parlour setting up chairs, Niel heard a knocking at the kitchen door. There he found Adolph Blum, carrying a large white box.

"Niel," he said, "will you please give these to Mrs. Forrester, and tell her they are from Rhein and me, for the Captain?"

Adolph was in his old working clothes, the only clothes he had, probably, with a knitted comforter about his neck. Niel knew he wouldn't come to the funeral, so he said:

"Won't you come in and see him, 'Dolph? He looks just like himself."

Adolph hesitated, but he caught sight of the undertaker's man, through the parlour bay-window, and said, "No, thank you, Niel," thrust his red hands into his jacket pockets, and walked away.

Niel took the flowers out of the box, a great armful of yellow roses, which must have cost the price of many a dead rabbit. He carried them upstairs, where Mrs. Forrester was lying down.

"These are from the Blum boys," he said. "Adolph just brought them to the kitchen door."

Mrs. Forrester looked at them, then turned away her head on the pillow, her lips trembling. It was the only time that day he saw her pale composure break.

The funeral was large. Old settlers and farmer folk came from all over the county to follow the pioneer's body to the grave. As Niel and his uncle were driving back from the cemetery with Mrs. Forrester, she spoke for the first time since they had left the house. "Judge Pommeroy," she said quietly, "I think I will have Mr. Forrester's sun-dial taken over and put above his grave. I can have an inscription cut on the base. It seems more appropriate for him than any stone we could buy. And I will plant some of his own rose-bushes beside it."

When they got back to the house it was four o'clock, and she insisted upon making tea for them. "I would like it myself, and it is better to be doing something. Wait for me in the parlour. And, Niel, move the things back as we always have them."

The grey day was darkening, and as the three sat having their tea in the bay-window, swift squalls of snow were falling over the wide meadows between the hill and the town, and the creaking of the big cottonwoods about the house seemed to say that winter had come.

VII

ONE MORNING IN April, Niel was alone in the law office. His uncle had been ill with rheumatic fever for a long while, and he had been attending to the routine of business.

The door opened, and a figure stood there, strange and yet familiar, —he had to think a moment before he realized that it was Orville Ogden, who used to come to Sweet Water so often, but who had not been seen there now for several years. He didn't look a day older; one eye was still direct and clear, the other clouded and oblique. He still wore a stiff imperial and twisted moustache, the grey colour of old beeswax, and his thin hair was brushed heroically up over the bald spot.

"This is Judge Pommeroy's nephew, isn't it? I can't think of your name, my boy, but I remember you. Is the Judge out?"

"Please be seated, Mr. Ogden. My uncle is ill. He hasn't been at the office for several months. He's had really a very bad time of it. Is there anything I can do for you?"

"Oh, I'm sorry to hear that! I'm sorry." He spoke as if he were. "I guess all we fellows are getting older, whether we like it or not. It made a great difference when Daniel Forrester went." Mr. Ogden took off his overcoat, put his hat and gloves neatly on the desk, and then seemed somewhat at a loss. "What is your uncle's trouble?" he asked suddenly.

Niel told him. "I was to have gone back to school this winter, but uncle begged me to stay and look after things for him. There was no one here he wanted to entrust his business to."

"I see, I see," said Mr. Ogden thoughtfully. "Then you do attend to his business for the present?" He paused and reflected. "Yes, there was something that I wanted to take up with him. I am stopping off for a few hours only, between trains. I might speak to you about it, and you could consult your uncle and write me in Chicago. It's a confidential matter, and concerns another person."

Niel assured him of his discretion, but Mr. Ogden seemed to find the subject difficult to approach. He looked very grave and slowly lit a cigar.

"It is simply," he said at last, "a rather delicate suggestion I wish to make to your uncle about one of his clients. I have several friends in the Government at Washington just at present, friends who would go out of their way to serve me. I have been thinking that we might manage it to get a special increase of pension for Mrs. Forrester. I am due in Chicago this week, and after my business there is finished, I would be quite willing to go on to Washington to see what can be done; provided, of course, that no one, least of all your uncle's client, knows of my activity in the matter."

Niel flushed. "I'm sorry, Mr. Ogden," he brought out, "but Mrs. Forrester is no longer a client of my uncle's. After the Captain's death, she saw fit to take her business away from him."

Mr. Ogden's normal eye became as blank as the other.

"What's that? He isn't her lawyer? Why, for twenty years—"

"I know that, sir. She didn't treat him with much consideration. She transferred her business very abruptly."

"To whom, may I ask?"

"To a lawyer here in town; Ivy Peters."

"Peters? I never heard of him."

"No, you wouldn't have. He wasn't one of the people who went to the Forrester house in the old days. He's one of the younger generation, a few years older than I. He rented part of the Forresters' land for several years before the Captain's death,—was their tenant. That was how Mrs. Forrester came to know him. She thinks him a good business man."

Mr. Ogden frowned. "And is he?"

"Some people think so."

"Is he trustworthy?"

"Far from it. He takes the cases nobody else will take. He may treat Mrs. Forrester honestly. But if he does, it will not be from principle."

"This is very distressing news. Go on with your work, my boy. I must think this over." Mr. Ogden rose and walked about the room, his hands behind him. Niel turned to an unfinished letter on his desk, in order to leave his visitor the more free.

Mr. Ogden's position, he understood, was a difficult one. He had been devoted to Mrs. Forrester, and before Constance had made up her mind to marry Frank Ellinger, before the mother and daughter began to angle for him, Mr. Ogden had come to the Forresters' more frequently than any of their Denver friends. He hadn't been back, Niel believed, since that Christmas party when he and his family were there with Ellinger. Very soon afterward he must have seen what his women-folk were up to; and whether he approved or disapproved, he must have decided that there was nothing for him to do but to keep out. It hadn't been the Forresters' reversal of fortune that had kept him away. One

could see that he was deeply troubled, that he had her heavily on his mind.

Niel had finished his letter and was beginning another, when Mr. Ogden stopped beside his desk, where he stood twisting his imperial lighter and tighter. "You say this young lawyer is unprincipled? Sometimes rascals have a soft spot, a sentiment, where women are concerned."

Niel stared. He immediately thought of Ivy's dimples.

"A soft spot? A sentiment? Mr. Ogden, why not go to his office? A glance would convince you."

"Oh, that's not necessary! I understand." He looked out of the window, from which he could just see the tree-tops of the Forrester grove, and murmured, "Poor lady! So misguided. She ought to have advice from some of Daniel's friends." He took out his watch and consulted it, turning something over in his mind. His train was due in an hour, he said. Nothing could be done at present. In a few moments he left the office.

Afterward, Niel felt sure that when Mr. Ogden stood there uncertainly, watch in hand, he was considering an interview with Mrs. Forrester. He had wanted to go to her, and had given it up. Was he afraid of his women-folk? Or was it another kind of cowardice, the fear of losing a pleasant memory, of finding her changed and marred, a dread of something that would throw a disenchanting light upon the past? Niel had heard his uncle say that Mr. Ogden admired pretty women, though he had married a homely one, and that in his deep, non-committal way he was very gallant. Perhaps, with a little encouragement, he would have gone to see Mrs. Forrester, and he might have helped her. The fact that he had done nothing to bring this about, made Niel realize how much his own feeling toward that lady had changed.

It was Mrs. Forrester herself who had changed. Since her husband's death she seemed to have become another woman. For years Niel and his uncle, the Dalzells and all her friends, had thought of the Captain as a drag upon his wife; a care that drained her and dimmed her and kept her from being all that she might be. But without him, she was like a ship without ballast, driven hither and thither by every wind. She was flighty and perverse. She seemed to have lost her faculty of discrimination; her power of easily and graciously keeping everyone in his proper place.

Ivy Peters had been in Wyoming at the time of Captain Forrester's illness and death,—called away by a telegram which announced that oil had been discovered near his land-holdings. He returned soon after the Captain's funeral, however, and was seen about the Forrester place more than ever. As there was nothing to be done on his fields in the winter, he had amused himself by pulling down the old barn after office hours. One was likely to come upon him, smoking his cigar on the front porch as if he owned the place. He often spent the evening there, playing cards with Mrs. Forrester or talking about his business projects. He had not made his fortune yet, but he was on the way to it. Occasionally he took a

friend or two, some of the town boys, over to dine at Mrs. Forrester's. The boys' mothers and sweethearts were greatly scandalized. "Now she's after the young ones," said Ed Elliott's mother. "She's getting childish."

At last Niel had a plain talk with Mrs. Forrester. He told her that people were gossiping about Ivy's being there so much. He had heard comments even on the street.

"But I can't bother about their talk. They have always talked about me, always will. Mr. Peters is my lawyer and my tenant; I have to see him, and I'm certainly not going to his office. I can't sit in the house alone every evening and knit. If you came to see me any oftener than you do, that would make talk. You are still younger than Ivy,—and better-looking! Did that never occur to you?"

"I wish you wouldn't talk to me like that," he said coldly. "Mrs. Forrester, why don't you go away? to California, to people of your own kind. You know this town is no place for you."

"I mean to, just as soon as I can sell this place. It's all I have, and if I leave it to tenants it will run down, and I can't sell it to advantage. That's why Ivy is here so much, he's trying to make the place presentable; pulling down the old barn that had become an eyesore, putting new boards in the porch floor where the old ones had rotted. Next summer, I am going to paint the house. Unless I keep the place up, I can never get my price for it." She talked nervously, with exaggerated earnestness, as if she were trying to persuade herself.

"And what are you asking for it now, Mrs. Forrester?"

"Twenty thousand dollars."

"You'll never get it. At least, not until times have greatly changed."

"That's what your uncle said. He wouldn't attempt to sell it for more than twelve. That's why I had to put it into other hands. Times have changed, but he doesn't realize it. Mr. Forrester himself told me it would be worth that. Ivy says he can get me twenty thousand, or if not, he will take it off my hands as soon as his investments begin to bring in returns."

"And in the meantime, you are simply wasting your life here."

"Not altogether." She looked at him with pleading plausibility. "I am getting rested after a long strain. And while I wait, I'm finding new friends among the young men,—those your age, and a little younger. I've wanted for a long while to do something for the boys of this town, but my hands were full. I hate to see them growing up like savages, when all they need is a civilized house to come to, and a woman to give them a few hints. They've never had a chance. You wouldn't be the boy you are if you'd never gone to Boston,—and you've always had older friends who'd seen better days. Suppose you had grown up like Ed Elliott and Joe Simpson?"

"I flatter myself I wouldn't be exactly like them, if I had! However, there is no use discussing it, if you've thought it over and made up your

mind. I spoke of it because I thought you mightn't realize how it strikes the townspeople."

"I know!" She tossed her head. Her eyes glittered, but there was no mirth in them,—it was more like hysterical defiance. "I know; they call me the Merry Widow. I rather like it!"

Niel left the house without further argument, and though that was three weeks ago, he had not been back since. Mrs. Forrester had called to see his uncle in the meantime. The Judge was as courtly as ever in his manner toward her, but he was deeply hurt by her defection, and his cherishing care for her would never be revived. He had attended to all Captain Forrester's business for twenty years, and since the failure of the Denver bank had never deducted a penny for fees from the money entrusted to him. Mrs. Forrester had treated him very badly. She had given him no warning. One day Ivy Peters had come into the office with a written order from her, requesting that an accounting, and all funds and securities, be turned over to him. Since then she had never spoken of the matter to the Judge,—or to Niel, save in that conversation about the sale of the property.

VIII

ONE MORNING WHEN A warm May wind was whirling the dust up the street, Mrs. Forrester came smiling into Judge Pommeroy's office, wearing a new spring bonnet, and a short black velvet cape, fastened at the neck with a bunch of violets. "Please be nice enough to notice my new clothes, Niel," she said coaxingly. "They are the first I've had in years and years."

He told her they were very pretty.

"And aren't you glad I have some at last?" she smiled enquiringly through her veil. "I feel as if you weren't going to be cross with me today, and would do what I ask you. It's nothing very troublesome. I want you to come to dinner Friday night. If you come, there will be eight of us, counting Annie Peters. They are all boys you know, and if you don't like them, you ought to! Yes, you ought to!" she nodded at him severely. "Since you mind what people say, Niel, aren't you afraid they'll be saying you're a snob, just because you've been to Boston and seen a little of the world? You mustn't be so stiff, so—so superior! It isn't becoming, at your age." She drew her brows down into a level frown so like his own that he laughed. He had almost forgotten her old talent for mimicry.

"What do you want me for? You used always to say it was no good asking people who didn't mix."

"You can mix well enough, if you take the trouble. And this time you will, for me. Won't you?"

When she was gone, Niel was angry with himself for having been persuaded.

On Friday evening he was the last guest to arrive. It was a warm night, after a hot day. The windows were open, and the perfume of the lilacs came into the dusky parlour where the boys were sitting about in chairs that seemed too big for them. A lamp was burning in the dining-room, and there Ivy Peters stood at the side-board, mixing cocktails. His sister Annie was in the kitchen, helping the hostess. Mrs. Forrester came in for a moment to greet Niel, then excused herself and hurried back to Annie Peters. Through the open door he saw that the silver dishes had reappeared on the dinner table, and the candlesticks and flowers. The young men who sat about in the twilight would not know the difference, he thought, if she had furnished her table that morning, from the stock in Wernz's queensware store. Their conception of a really fine dinner service was one "hand painted" by a sister or sweetheart. Each boy sat with his legs crossed, one tan shoe swinging in the air and displaying a tan silk sock. They were talking about clothes; Joe Simpson, who had just inherited his father's clothing business, was eager to tell them what the summer styles would be.

Ivy Peters came in, shaking his drinks. "You fellows are like a bunch of girls,—always talking about what you are going to wear and how you can spend your money. Simpson wouldn't get rich very fast if you all wore your clothes as long as I do. When did I get this suit, Joe?"

"Oh, about the year I graduated from High School, I guess!"

They all laughed at Ivy. No matter what he did or said, they laughed,—in recognition of his general success.

Mrs. Forrester came back, fanning herself with a little sandalwood fan, and when she appeared the boys rose,—in alarm, one might have thought, from the suddenness of it. That much, at any rate, she had succeeded in teaching them.

"Are your cocktails ready, Ivy? You will have to wait for me a moment, while I put some powder on my nose. If I'd known how hot it would be tonight, I'm afraid I wouldn't have had a roast for you. I'm browner than the ducks. You can pour them though. I won't be long."

She disappeared into her own room, and the boys sat down with the same surprising promptness. Ivy Peters carried the tray about, and they held their glasses before them, waiting for Mrs. Forrester. When she came, she took Niel's arm and led him into the dining-room. "Did you notice," she whispered to him, "how they hold their glasses? What is it they do to a little glass to make it look so vulgar? Nobody could ever teach them to pick one up and drink out of it, not if there were tea in it!"

Aloud she said, "Niel, will you light the candles for me? And then take the head of the table, please. You can carve ducks?"

"Not so well as—as my uncle does," he murmured, carefully putting back a candle-shade.

"Nor as Mr. Forrester did? I don't ask that. Nobody can carve now as men used to. But you can get them apart, I suppose? The place at your right is for Annie Peters. She is bringing in the dinner for me. Be seated, gentlemen!" with a little mocking bow and a swinging of earrings.

While Niel was carving the ducks, Annie slipped into the chair beside him, her naturally red face glowing from the heat of the stove. She was several years younger than her brother, whom she obeyed unquestioningly in everything. She had an extremely bad complexion and pale yellow hair with white lights in it, exactly the colour of molasses taffy that has been pulled until it glistens. During the dinner she did not once speak, except to say, "Thank you," or "No, thank you." Nobody but Mrs. Forrester talked much until the first helping of duck was consumed. The boys had not yet learned to do two things at once. They paused only to ask their hostess if she "would care for the jelly," or to answer her questions.

Niel studied Mrs. Forrester between the candles, as she nodded encouragingly to one and another, trying to "draw them out," laughing at Roy Jones' heavy jokes, or congratulating Joe Simpson upon his new dignity as a business man with a business of his own. The long earrings swung beside the thin cheeks that were none the better, he thought, for the rouge she had put on them when she went to her room just before dinner. It improved some women, but not her,—at least, not tonight, when her eyes were hollow with fatigue, and she looked pinched and worn as he had never seen her. He sighed as he thought how much work it meant to cook a dinner like this for eight people,—and a beefsteak with potatoes would have pleased them better! They didn't really like this kind of food at all. Why did she do it? How would she feel about it tonight, when she sank dead weary into bed, after these stupid boys had said good-night, and their yellow shoes had carried them down the hill?

She was not eating anything, she was using up all her vitality to electrify these heavy lads into speech. Niel felt that he must help her, or at least try to. He addressed them one after another with energy and determination; he tried baseball, politics, scandal, the corn crop. They answered him with monosyllables or exclamations. He soon realized that they didn't want his polite remarks; they wanted more duck, and to be let alone with it.

Dinner was soon over, at any rate. The hostess' attempts to prolong it were unavailing. The salad and frozen pudding were dispatched as promptly as the roast had been. The guests went into the parlour and lit cigars.

Mrs. Forrester had the old-fashioned notion that men should be alone after dinner. She did not join them for half an hour. Perhaps she had lain down upstairs, for she looked a little rested. The boys were talking now, discussing a camping trip Ed Elliott was going to take in the mountains. They were giving him advice about camp outfits, trout flies, mixtures to keep off mosquitoes.

"I'll tell you, boys," said Mrs. Forrester, when she had listened to them for a moment, "when I go back to California, I intend to have a summer cabin up in the Sierras, and I invite you, one and all, to visit me. You'll have to work for your keep, you understand; cut the firewood and bring the water and wash the pots and pans, and go out and catch fish for breakfast. Ivy can bring his gun and shoot game for us, and I'll bake bread in an iron pot, the old trappers' way, if I haven't forgotten how. Will you come?"

"You bet we will! You know those mountains by heart, I expect?" said Ed Elliott.

She smiled and shook her head. "It would take a life-time to do that, Ed, more than a life-time. The Sierras,—there's no end to them, and they're magnificent."

Niel turned to her. "Have you ever told the boys how it was you first met Captain Forrester in the mountains out there? If they haven't heard the story, I think they would like it."

"Really, would you? Well, once upon a time, when I was a very young girl, I was spending the summer at a camp in the mountains, with friends of my father's."

She began there, but that was not the beginning of the story; long ago Niel had heard from his uncle that the beginning was a scandal and a murder. When Marian Ormsby was nineteen, she was engaged to Ned Montgomery, a gaudy young millionaire of the Gold Coast. A few weeks before the date set for their marriage, Montgomery was shot and killed in the lobby of a San Francisco hotel by the husband of another woman. The subsequent trial involved a great deal of publicity, and Marian was hurried away from curious eyes and sent up into the mountains until the affair should blow over.

Tonight Mrs. Forrester began with "Once upon a time." Sitting at one end of the big sofa, her slippers on a foot-stool and her head in shadow, she stirred the air before her face with the sandalwood fan as she talked, the rings glittering on her white fingers. She told them how Captain Forrester, then a widower, had come up to the camp to visit her father's partner. She had noticed him very little,—she was off every day with the young men. One afternoon she had persuaded young Fred Harney, an intrepid mountain climber, to take her down the face of Eagle Cliff. They were almost down, and were creeping over a projecting ledge, when the rope broke, and they dropped to the bottom. Harney fell on the rocks and was killed instantly. The girl was caught in a pine tree, which arrested her fall. Both her legs were broken, and she lay in the canyon all night in the bitter cold, swept by the icy canyon draught. Nobody at the camp knew where to look for the two missing members of the party,—they had stolen off alone for their foolhardy adventure. Nobody worried, because Harney knew all the trails and could not get lost. In the morning, however, when they were still missing, search parties went out. It was Captain Forrester's party that found

Marian, and got her out by the lower trail. The trail was so steep and narrow, the turns round the jutting ledges so sharp, that it was impossible to take her out on a litter. The men took turns carrying her, hugging the canyon walls with their shoulders as they crept along. With her broken legs hanging, she suffered terribly,—fainted again and again. But she noticed that she suffered less when Captain Forrester carried her, and that he took all the most dangerous places on the trail himself. "I could feel his heart pump and his muscles strain," she said, "when he balanced himself and me on the rocks. I knew that if we fell, we'd go together; he would never drop me."

They got back to camp, and everything possible was done for her, but by the time a surgeon could be got up from San Francisco, her fractures had begun to knit and had to be broken over again.

"It was Captain Forrester I wanted to hold my hand when the surgeon had to do things to me. You remember, Niel, he always boasted that I never screamed when they were carrying me up the trail. He stayed at the camp until I could begin to walk, holding to his arm. When he asked me to marry him, he didn't have to ask twice. Do you wonder?" She looked with a smile about the circle, and drew her finger-tips absently across her forehead as if to brush away something,—the past, or the present, who could tell?

The boys were genuinely moved. While she was answering their questions, Niel thought about the first time he ever heard her tell that story: Mr. Dalzell had stopped off with a party of friends from Chicago; Marshall Field and the president of the Union Pacific were among them, he remembered, and they were going through in Mr. Dalzell's private car to hunt in the Black Hills. She had, after all, not changed so much since then. Niel felt tonight that the right man could save her, even now. She was still her indomitable self, going through her old part,—but only the stage-hands were left to listen to her. All those who had shared in fine undertakings and bright occasions were gone.

IX

WITH THE SUMMER MONTHS Judge Pommeroy's health improved, and as soon as he was able to be back in his office, Niel began to plan to return to Boston. He would get there the first of August and would go to work with a tutor to make up for the months he had lost. It was a melancholy time for him. He was in a fever of impatience to be gone, and yet he felt that he was going away forever, and was making the final break with everything that had been dear to him in his boyhood. The people, the very country itself, were changing so fast that there would be nothing to come back to.

He had seen the end of an era, the sunset of the pioneer. He had come upon it when already its glory was nearly spent. So in the buffalo times a traveller used to come upon the embers of a hunter's fire on the prairie, after the hunter was up and gone; the coals would be trampled out, but the ground was warm, and the flattened grass where he had slept and where his pony had grazed, told the story.

This was the very end of the road-making West; the men who had put plains and mountains under the iron harness were old; some were poor, and even the successful ones were hunting for rest and a brief reprieve from death. It was already gone, that age; nothing could ever bring it back. The taste and smell and song of it, the visions those men had seen in the air and followed,—these he had caught in a kind of afterglow in their own faces,—and this would always be his.

It was what he most held against Mrs. Forrester; that she was not willing to immolate herself, like the widow of all these great men, and die with the pioneer period to which she belonged; that she preferred life on any terms. In the end, Niel went away without bidding her good-bye. He went away with weary contempt for her in his heart.

It happened like this,—had scarcely the dignity of an episode. It was nothing, and yet it was everything. Going over to see her one summer evening, he stopped a moment by the dining-room window to look at the honeysuckle. The dining-room door was open into the kitchen, and there Mrs. Forrester stood at a table, making pastry. Ivy Peters came in at the kitchen door, walked up behind her, and unconcernedly put both arms around her, his hands meeting over her breast. She did not move, did not look up, but went on rolling out pastry.

Niel went down the hill. "For the last time," he said, as he crossed the bridge in the evening light, "for the last time." And it was even so; he never went up the poplar-bordered road again. He had given her a year of his life, and she had thrown it away. He had helped the Captain to die peacefully, he believed; and now it was the Captain who seemed the reality. All those years he had thought it was Mrs. Forrester who made that house so different from any other. But ever since the Captain's death it was a house where old friends, like his uncle, were betrayed and cast off, where common fellows behaved after their kind and knew a common woman when they saw her.

If he had not had the nature of a spaniel, he told himself, he would never have gone back after the first time. It took two doses to cure him. Well, he had had them! Nothing she could ever do would in the least matter to him again.

He had news of her now and then, as long as his uncle lived. *"Mrs. Forrester's name is everywhere coupled with Ivy Peters'," the Judge wrote. "She does not look happy, and I fear her health is failing, but she has put herself in such a position that her husband's friends cannot help her."*

And again: *"Of Mrs. Forrester, no news is good news. She is sadly broken."*

After his uncle's death, Niel heard that Ivy Peters had at last bought the Forrester place, and had brought a wife from Wyoming to live there. Mrs. Forrester had gone West,—people supposed to California.

It was years before Niel could think of her without chagrin. But eventually, after she had drifted out of his ken, when he did not know if Daniel Forrester's widow were living or dead, Daniel Forrester's wife returned to him, a bright, impersonal memory.

He came to be very glad that he had known her, and that she had had a hand in breaking him in to life. He has known pretty women and clever ones since then,—but never one like her, as she was in her best days. Her eyes, when they laughed for a moment into one's own, seemed to promise a wild delight that he has not found in life. "I know where it is," they seemed to say, "I could show you!" He would like to call up the shade of the young Mrs. Forrester, as the witch of Endor called up Samuel's, and challenge it, demand the secret of that ardour; ask her whether she had really found some ever-blooming, ever-burning, ever-piercing joy, or whether it was all fine play-acting. Probably she had found no more than another; but she had always the power of suggesting things much lovelier than herself, as the perfume of a single flower may call up the whole sweetness of spring.

Niel was destined to hear once again of his long-lost lady. One evening as he was going into the dining-room of a Chicago hotel, a broad-shouldered man with an open, sunbrowned face, approached him and introduced himself as one of the boys who had grown up in Sweet Water.

"I'm Ed Elliott, and I thought it must be you. Could we take a table together? I promised an old friend of yours to give you a message, if I ever ran across you. You remember Mrs. Forrester? Well, I saw her again, twelve years after she left Sweet Water,—down in Buenos Ayres." They sat down and ordered dinner.

"Yes, I was in South America on business. I'm a mining engineer, I spent some time in Buenos Ayres. One evening there was a banquet of some sort at one of the big hotels, and I happened to step out of the bar, just as a car drove up to the entrance where the guests were going in. I paid no attention until one of the ladies laughed. I recognized her by her laugh,—that hadn't changed a particle. She was all done up in furs, with a scarf over her head, but I saw her eyes, and then I was sure. I stepped up and spoke to her. She seemed glad to see me, made me go into the hotel, and talked to me until her husband came to drag her away to the dinner. Oh, yes, she was married again,—to a rich, cranky old Englishman; Henry Collins was his name. He was born down there, she told me, but she met him in California. She told me they lived on a big stock ranch and had come down in their car for this banquet. I made inquiries afterward and found the old fellow was quite a character; had been married twice before, once to a Brazilian woman. People said he was rich, but quarrelsome and rather stingy. She seemed to have everything, though. They travelled in a fine French car, and she had brought her maid along, and he had his valet. No, she hadn't changed as much as you'd think. She was a good deal made up, of course, like most of the women down there; plenty of powder, and a little red, too, I guess. Her hair was black, blacker than I remembered it; looked as if she dyed it. She invited me to visit them on their estate, and so did the old man, when he came to get her. She asked about everybody, and said, 'If you ever meet Niel Herbert, give him my love, and tell him I often think of him.' She said again, 'Tell him things have turned out well for me. Mr. Collins is the kindest of husbands.' I called at your office in New York on my way back from South America, but you were somewhere in Europe. It was remarkable, how she'd come up again. She seemed pretty well gone to pieces before she left Sweet Water."

"Do you suppose," said Niel, "that she could be living still? I'd almost make the trip to see her."

"No, she died about three years ago. I know that for certain. After she left Sweet Water, wherever she was, she always sent a cheque to the Grand Army Post every year to have flowers put on Captain Forrester's grave for Decoration Day. Three years ago the Post got letter from the old Englishman, with a draft for the future care of Captain Forrester's grave, '*in memory of my late wife, Marian Forrester Collins.*' "

"So we may feel sure that she was well cared for, to the very end," said Niel. "Thank God for that!"

"I knew you'd feel that way," said Ed Elliott, as a warm wave of feeling passed over his face. "I did!"

Raymond Chandler

FAREWELL, MY LOVELY

1

IT WAS ONE OF THE MIXED BLOCKS over on Central Avenue, the blocks that are not yet all Negro. I had just come out of a three-chair barber shop where an agency thought a relief barber named Dimitrios Aleidis might be working. It was a small matter. His wife said she was willing to spend a little money to have him come home.

I never found him, but Mrs. Aleidis never paid me any money either.

It was a warm day, almost the end of March, and I stood outside the barber shop looking up at the jutting neon sign of a second floor dine and dice emporium called Florian's. A man was looking up at the sign too. He was looking up at the dusty windows with a sort of ecstatic fixity of expression, like a hunky immigrant catching his first sight of the Statue of Liberty. He was a big man but not more than six feet five inches tall and not wider than a beer truck. He was about ten feet away from me. His arms hung loose at his sides and a forgotten cigar smoked behind his enormous fingers.

Slim quiet Negroes passed up and down the street and stared at him with darting side glances. He was worth looking at. He wore a shaggy borsalino hat, a rough gray sports coat with white golf balls on it for buttons, a brown shirt, a yellow tie, pleated gray flannel slacks and alligator shoes with white explosions on the toes. From his outer breast pocket cascaded a show handkerchief of the same brilliant yellow as his tie. There were a couple of colored feathers tucked into the band of his hat, but he didn't really need them. Even on Central Avenue, not the quietest dressed street in the world, he looked about as inconspicuous as a tarantula on a slice of angel food.

Published 1940. Copyright 1940 by Raymond Chandler.

His skin was pale and he needed a shave. He would always need a shave. He had curly black hair and heavy eyebrows that almost met over his thick nose. His ears were small and neat for a man of that size and his eyes had a shine close to tears that gray eyes often seem to have. He stood like a statue, and after a long time he smiled.

He moved slowly across the sidewalk to the double swinging doors which shut off the stairs to the second floor. He pushed them open, cast a cool expressionless glance up and down the street, and moved inside. If he had been a smaller man and more quietly dressed, I might have thought he was going to pull a stick-up. But not in those clothes, and not with that hat, and that frame.

The doors swung back outwards and almost settled to a stop. Before they had entirely stopped moving they opened again, violently, outwards. Something sailed across the sidewalk and landed in the gutter between two parked cars. It landed on its hands and knees and made a high keening noise like a cornered rat. It got up slowly, retrieved a hat and stepped back onto the sidewalk. It was a thin, narrow-shouldered brown youth in a lilac colored suit and a carnation. It had slick black hair. It kept its mouth open and whined for a moment. People stared at it vaguely. Then it settled its hat jauntily, sidled over to the wall and walked silently splayfooted off along the block.

Silence. Traffic resumed. I walked along to the double doors and stood in front of them. They were motionless now. It wasn't any of my business. So I pushed them open and looked in.

A hand I could have sat in came out of the dimness and took hold of my shoulder and squashed it to a pulp. Then the hand moved me through the doors and casually lifted me up a step. The large face looked at me. A deep soft voice said to me, quietly:

"Smokes in here, huh? Tie that for me, pal."

It was dark in there. It was quiet. From up above came vague sounds of humanity, but we were alone on the stairs. The big man stared at me solemnly and went on wrecking my shoulder with his hand.

"A dinge," he said. "I just thrown him out. You seen me throw him out?"

He let go of my shoulder. The bone didn't seem to be broken, but the arm was numb.

"It's that kind of a place," I said, rubbing my shoulder. "What did you expect?"

"Don't say that, pal," the big man purred softly, like four tigers after dinner. "Velma used to work here. Little Velma."

He reached for my shoulder again. I tried to dodge him but he was as fast as a cat. He began to chew my muscles up some more with his iron fingers.

"Yeah," he said. "Little Velma. I ain't seen her in eight years. You say this here is a dinge joint?"

I croaked that it was.

He lifted me up two more steps. I wrenched myself loose and tried for a little elbow room. I wasn't wearing a gun. Looking for Dimitrios Aleidis hadn't seemed to require it. I doubted if it would do me any good. The big man would probably take it away from me and eat it.

"Go on up and see for yourself," I said, trying to keep the agony out of my voice.

He let go of me again. He looked at me with a sort of sadness in his gray eyes. "I'm feelin' good," he said. "I wouldn't want anybody to fuss with me. Let's you and me go on up and maybe nibble a couple."

"They won't serve you. I told you it's a colored joint."

"I ain't seen Velma in eight years," he said in his deep sad voice. "Eight long years since I said goodby. She ain't wrote to me in six. But she'll have reason. She used to work here. Cute she was. Let's you and me go on up, huh?"

"All right," I yelled. "I'll go up with you. Just lay off carrying me. Let me walk. I'm fine. I'm all grown up. I go to the bathroom alone and everything. Just don't carry me."

"Little Velma used to work here," he said gently. He wasn't listening to me.

We went on up the stairs. He let me walk. My shoulder ached. The back of my neck was wet.

2

Two MORE SWING DOORS closed off the head of the stairs from whatever was beyond. The big man pushed them open lightly with his thumbs and we went into the room. It was a long narrow room, not very clean, not very bright, not very cheerful. In the corner a group of Negroes chanted and chattered in the cone of light over a crap table. There was a bar against the right hand wall. The rest of the room was mostly small round tables. There were a few customers, men and women, all Negroes.

The chanting at the crap table stopped dead and the light over it jerked out. There was a sudden silence as heavy as a water-logged boat. Eyes looked at us, chestnut colored eyes, set in faces that ranged from gray to deep black. Heads turned slowly and the eyes in them glistened and stared in the dead alien silence of another race.

A large, thick-necked Negro was leaning against the end of the bar with pink garters on his shirt sleeves and pink and white suspenders crossing his broad back. He had bouncer written all over him. He put his lifted foot down slowly and turned slowly and stared at us, spreading his feet gently and moving a broad tongue along his lips. He had a battered face that looked as if it had been hit by everything but the bucket of a dragline. It was scarred, flattened, thickened, checkered, and welted. It was a face that had nothing to fear. Everything had been done to it that anybody could think of.

The short crinkled hair had a touch of gray. One ear had lost the lobe.

The Negro was heavy and wide. He had big heavy legs and they looked a little bowed, which is unusual in a Negro. He moved his tongue some more and smiled and moved his body. He came towards us in a loose fighter's crouch. The big man waited for him silently.

The Negro with the pink garters on his arms put a massive brown hand against the big man's chest. Large as it was, the hand looked like a stud. The big man didn't move. The bouncer smiled gently.

"No white folks, brother. Jes' fo' the colored people. I'se sorry."

The big man moved his small sad gray eyes and looked around the room. His cheeks flushed a little. "Shine box," he said angrily, under his breath. He raised his voice. "Where's Velma at?" he asked the bouncer.

The bouncer didn't quite laugh. He studied the big man's clothes, his brown shirt and yellow tie, his rough gray coat and the white golf balls on it. He moved his thick head around delicately and studied all this from various angles. He looked down at the alligator shoes. He chuckled lightly. He seemed amused. I felt a little sorry for him. He spoke softly again.

"Velma you says? No Velma heah, brother. No hooch, no gals, no nothing. Jes' the scram, white boy, jes' the scram."

"Velma used to work here," the big man said. He spoke almost dreamily, as if he was all by himself, out in the woods, picking johnny-jump-ups. I got my handkerchief out and wiped the back of my neck again.

The bouncer laughed suddenly. "Shuah," he said, throwing a quick look back over his shoulder at his public. "Velma used to work heah. But Velma don't work heah no mo'. She done reti'ed. Haw, Haw."

"Kind of take your goddamned mitt off my shirt," the big man said.

The bouncer frowned. He was not used to being talked to like that. He took his hand off the shirt and doubled it into a fist about the size and color of a large eggplant. He had his job, his reputation for toughness, his public esteem to consider. He considered them for a second and made a mistake. He swung the fist very hard and short with a sudden outward jerk of the elbow and hit the big man on the side of the jaw. A soft sigh went around the room.

It was a good punch. The shoulder dropped and the body swung behind it. There was a lot of weight in that punch and the man who landed it had had plenty of practice. The big man didn't move his head more than an inch. He didn't try to block the punch. He took it, shook himself lightly, made a quiet sound in his throat and took hold of the bouncer by the throat.

The bouncer tried to knee him in the groin. The big man turned him in the air and slid his gaudy shoes apart on the scaly linoleum that covered the floor. He bent the bouncer backwards and shifted his right hand to the bouncer's belt. The belt broke like a piece of butcher's string. The big man put his enormous hands flat against the bouncer's spine and heaved. He threw him clear across the room, spinning and staggering and flailing with his arms. Three men jumped out of the way. The bouncer went over with a table and smacked into the baseboard with a crash that must have been heard in Denver. His legs twitched. Then he lay still.

"Some guys," the big man said, "has got wrong ideas about when to get tough." He turned to me. "Yeah," he said. "Let's you and me nibble one."

We went over to the bar. The customers, by ones and twos and threes, became quiet shadows that drifted soundless across the floor, soundless through the doors at the head of the stairs. Soundless as shadows on grass. They didn't even let the doors swing.

We leaned against the bar. "Whiskey sour," the big man said. "Call yours."

"Whiskey sour," I said.

We had whiskey sours.

The big man licked his whiskey sour impassively down the side of the thick squat glass. He stared solemnly at the barman, a thin, worried-looking Negro in a white coat who moved as if his feet hurt him.

"*You* know where Velma is?"

"Velma, you says?" the barman whined. "I ain't seen her 'round heah lately. Not right lately, nossuh."

"How long you been here?"

"Let's see," the barman put his towel down and wrinkled his forehead and started to count on his fingers. "'Bout ten months, I reckon. 'Bout a yeah. 'Bout—"

"Make your mind up," the big man said.

The barman goggled and his Adam's apple flopped around like a headless chicken.

"How long's this coop been a dinge joint?" the big man demanded gruffly.

"Says which?"

The big man made a fist into which his whiskey sour glass melted almost out of sight.

"Five years anyway," I said. "This fellow wouldn't know anything about a white girl named Velma. Nobody here would."

The big man looked at me as if I had just hatched out. His whiskey sour hadn't seemed to improve his temper.

"Who the hell asked you to stick your face in?" he asked me.

I smiled. I made it a big warm friendly smile. "I'm the fellow that came in with you. Remember?"

He grinned back then, a flat white grin without meaning. "Whiskey sour," he told the barman. "Shake them fleas outa your pants. Service."

The barman scuttled around, rolling the whites of his eyes. I put my back against the bar and looked at the room. It was now empty, save for the barman, the big man and myself, and the bouncer crushed over against the wall. The bouncer was moving. He was moving slowly as if with great pain and effort. He was crawling softly along the baseboard like a fly with one wing. He was moving behind the tables, wearily, a man suddenly old, suddenly disillusioned. I watched him move. The barman put down two more whiskey sours. I turned to the bar. The big man glanced casually over at the crawling bouncer and then paid no further attention to him.

"There ain't nothing left of the joint," he complained. "They was a little stage and band and cute little rooms where a guy could have fun. Velma did some warbling. A redhead she was. Cute as lace pants. We was to of been married when they hung the frame on me."

I took my second whiskey sour. I was beginning to have enough of the adventure. "What frame?" I asked.

"Where you figure I been them eight years I said about?"

"Catching butterflies."

He prodded his chest with a forefinger like a banana. "In the caboose. Malloy is the name. They call me Moose Malloy, on account of I'm large. The Great Bend bank job. Forty grand. Solo job. Ain't that something?"

"You going to spend it now?"

He gave me a sharp look. There was a noise behind us. The bouncer was on his feet again, weaving a little. He had his hand on the knob of a dark door over behind the crap table. He got the door open, half fell through. The door clattered shut. A lock clicked.

"Where's that go?" Moose Malloy demanded.

The barman's eyes floated in his head, focused with difficulty on the door through which the bouncer had stumbled.

"Tha—tha's Mistah Montgomery's office, suh. He's the boss. He's got his office back there."

"He might know," the big man said. He drank his drink at a gulp. "He better not crack wise neither. Two more of the same."

He crossed the room slowly, lightfooted, without a care in the world. His enormous back hid the door. It was locked. He shook it and a piece of the panel flew off to one side. He went through and shut the door behind him.

There was silence. I looked at the barman. The barman looked at me. His eyes became thoughtful. He polished the counter and sighed and leaned down with his right arm.

I reached across the counter and took hold of the arm. It was thin, brittle. I held it and smiled at him.

"What you got down there, bo?"

He licked his lips. He leaned on my arm, and said nothing. Grayness invaded his shining face.

"This guy is tough," I said. "And he's liable to go mean. Drinks do that to him. He's looking for a girl he used to know. This place used to be a white establishment. Get the idea?"

The barman licked his lips.

"He's been away a long time," I said. "Eight years. He doesn't seem to realize how long that is, although I'd expect him to think it a life time. He thinks the people here should know where his girl is. Get the idea?"

The barman said slowly: "I thought you was with him."

"I couldn't help myself. He asked me a question down below and then dragged me up. I never saw him before. But I didn't feel like being thrown over any houses. What you got down there?"

"Got me a sawed-off," the barman said.

"Tsk. That's illegal," I whispered. "Listen, you and I are together. Got anything else?"

"Got me a gat," the barman said. "In a cigar box. Leggo my arm."

"That's fine," I said. "Now move along a bit. Easy now. Sideways. This isn't the time to pull the artillery."

"Says you," the barman sneered, putting his tired weight against my arm. "Says—"

He stopped. His eyes rolled. His head jerked.

There was a dull flat sound at the back of the place, behind the closed door beyond the crap table. It might have been a slammed door. I didn't think it was. The barman didn't think so either.

The barman froze. His mouth drooled. I listened. No other sound. I started quickly for the end of the counter. I had listened too long.

The door at the back opened with a bang and Moose Malloy came through it with a smooth heavy lunge and stopped dead, his feet planted and a wide pale grin on his face.

A Colt Army .45 looked like a toy pistol in his hand.

"Don't nobody try to fancy pants," he said cozily. "Freeze the mitts on the bar."

The barman and I put our hands on the bar.

Moose Malloy looked the room over with a raking glance. His grin was taut, nailed on. He shifted his feet and moved silently across the room. He looked like a man who could take a bank single-handed—even in those clothes.

He came to the bar. "Rise up, nigger," he said softly. The barman put his hands high in the air. The big man stepped on my back and prowled me over carefully with his left hand. His breath was hot on my neck. It went away.

"Mister Montgomery didn't know where Velma was neither," he said. "He tried to tell me—with this." His hard hand patted the gun. I turned slowly and looked at him. "Yeah," he said. "You'll know me. You ain't forgetting me, pal. Just tell them johns not to get careless is all." He waggled the gun. "Well so long, punks. I gotta catch a street car."

He started towards the head of the stairs.

"You didn't pay for the drinks," I said.

He stopped and looked at me carefully.

"Maybe you got something there," he said, "but I wouldn't squeeze it too hard."

He moved on, slipped through the double doors, and his steps sounded remotely going down the stairs.

The barman stooped. I jumped around behind the counter and jostled him out of the way. A sawed-off shotgun lay under a towel on a shelf under the bar. Beside it was a cigar box. In the cigar box was a .38 automatic. I took both of them. The barman pressed back against the tier of glasses behind the bar.

I went back around the end of the bar and across the room to the gaping door behind the crap table. There was a hallway behind it, L-shaped, almost lightless. The bouncer lay sprawled on its floor unconscious, with a knife in his hand. I leaned down and pulled the knife loose and threw it down a back stairway. The bouncer breathed stertorously and his hand was limp.

I stepped over him and opened a door marked "Office" in flaked black paint.

There was a small scarred desk close to a partly boarded-up window. The torso of a man was bolt upright in the chair. The chair had a high back which just reached to the nape of the man's neck. His head was folded back over the high back of the chair so that his nose pointed at the boarded-up window. Just folded, like a handkerchief or a hinge.

A drawer of the desk was open at the man's right. Inside it was a newspaper with a smear of oil in the middle. The gun would have come from there. It had probably seemed like a good idea at the time, but the position of Mr. Montgomery's head proved that the idea had been wrong.

There was a telephone on the desk. I laid the sawed-off shotgun down and went over to lock the door before I called the police. I felt safer that way and Mr. Montgomery didn't seem to mind.

When the prowl car boys stamped up the stairs, the bouncer and the barman had disappeared and I had the place to myself.

3

A MAN NAMED NULTY GOT THE CASE, a lean-jawed sourpuss with long yellow hands which he kept folded over his kneecaps most of the time he talked to me. He was a detective-lieutenant attached to the 77th Street Division and we talked in a bare room with two small desks against opposite walls and room to move between them, if two people didn't try it at once. Dirty brown linoleum covered the floor and the smell of old cigar butts hung in the air. Nulty's shirt was frayed and his coat sleeves had been turned in at the cuffs. He looked poor enough to be honest, but he didn't look like a man who could deal with Moose Malloy.

He lit half of a cigar and threw the match on the floor, where a lot of company was waiting for it. His voice said bitterly:

"Shines. Another shine killing. That's what I rate after eighteen years in this man's police department. No pix, no space, not even four lines in the want-ad section."

I didn't say anything. He picked my card up and read it again and threw it down.

"Philip Marlowe, Private Investigator. One of those guys, huh? Jesus, you look tough enough. What was you doing all that time?"

"All what time?"

"All the time this Malloy was twisting the neck of this smoke."

"Oh, that happened in another room," I said. "Malloy hadn't promised me he was going to break anybody's neck."

"Ride me," Nulty said bitterly. "Okey, go ahead and ride me. Everybody else does. What's another one matter? Poor old Nulty. Let's go on up and throw a couple of nifties at him. Always good for a laugh, Nulty is."

"I'm not trying to ride anybody," I said. "That's the way it happened—in another room."

"Oh, sure," Nulty said through a fan of rank cigar smoke. "I was down there and saw, didn't I? Don't you pack no rod?"

"Not on that kind of a job."

"What kind of a job?"

"I was looking for a barber who had run away from his wife. She thought he could be persuaded to come home."

"You mean a dinge?"

"No, a Greek."

"Okey," Nulty said and spit into his wastebasket. "Okey. You met the big guy how?"

"I told you already. I just happened to be there. He threw a Negro out of the doors of Florian's and I unwisely poked my head in to see what was happening. So he took me upstairs."

"You mean he stuck you up?"

"No, he didn't have the gun then. At least, he didn't show one. He took the gun away from Montgomery, probably. He just picked me up. I'm kind of cute sometimes."

"I wouldn't know," Nulty said. "You seem to pick up awful easy."

"All right," I said. "Why argue? I've seen the guy and you haven't. He could wear you or me for a watch charm. I didn't know he had killed anybody until after he left. I heard a shot, but I got the idea somebody had got scared and shot at Malloy and then Malloy took the gun away from whoever did it."

"And why would you get an idea like that?" Nulty asked almost suavely. "He used a gun to take that bank, didn't he?"

"Consider the kind of clothes he was wearing. He didn't go there to kill anybody; not dressed like that. He went there to look for this girl named Velma that had been his girl before he was pinched for the bank job. She worked there at Florian's or whatever place was there when it was still a white joint. He was pinched there. You'll get him all right."

"Sure," Nulty said. "With that size and them clothes. Easy."

"He might have another suit," I said. "And a car and a hideout and money and friends. But you'll get him."

Nulty spit in the wastebasket again. "I'll get him," he said, "about the time I get my third set of teeth. How many guys is put on it? One. Listen, you know why? No space. One time there was five smokes carved Harlem sunsets on each other down on East Eighty-four. One of them was cold already. There was blood on the furniture, blood on the walls, blood even on the ceiling. I go down and outside the house a guy that works on the *Chronicle*, a newshawk, is coming off the porch and getting into his car. He makes a face at us and says, 'Aw, hell, shines,' and gets in his heap and goes away. Don't even go in the house."

"Maybe he's a parole breaker," I said. "You'd get some co-opera-tion on that. But pick him up nice or he'll knock off a brace of prowlies for you. Then you'll get space."

"And I wouldn't have the case no more neither," Nulty sneered.

The phone rang on his desk. He listened to it and smiled sor-rowfully. He hung up and scribbled on a pad and there was a faint gleam in his eyes, a light far back in a dusty corridor.

"Hell, they got him. That was Records. Got his prints, mug and everything. Jesus, that's a little something anyway." He read from his pad. "Jesus, this is a man. Six five and one-half, two hundred sixty-four pounds, without his necktie. Jesus, that's a boy. Well, the hell with him. They got him on the air now. Probably at the end of the hot car list. Ain't nothing to do but just wait." He threw his cigar into a spittoon.

"Try looking for the girl," I said. "Velma. Malloy will be looking for her. That's what started it all. Try Velma."

"You try her," Nulty said. "I ain't been in a joy house in twenty years."

I stood up. "Okey," I said, and started for the door.

"Hey, wait a minute," Nulty said. "I was only kidding. You ain't awful busy, are you?"

I rolled a cigarette around in my fingers and looked at him and waited by the door.

"I mean you got time to sort of take a gander around for this dame. That's a good idea you had there. You might pick something up. You can work under glass."

"What's in it for me?"

He spread his yellow hands sadly. His smile was as cunning as a broken mousetrap. "You been in jams with us boys before. Don't tell me no. I heard different. Next time it ain't doing you any harm to have a pal."

"What good is it going to do me?"

"Listen," Nulty urged. "I'm just a quiet guy. But any guy in the department can do you a lot of good."

"Is this for love—or are you paying anything in money?"

"No money," Nulty said, and wrinkled his sad yellow nose. "But I'm needing a little credit bad. Since the last shake-up, things is really tough. I wouldn't forget it, pal. Not ever."

I looked at my watch. "Okey, if I think of anything, it's yours. And when you get the mug, I'll identify it for you. After lunch." We shook hands and I went down the mud-colored hall and stairway to the front of the building and my car.

It was two hours since Moose Malloy had left Florian's with the Army Colt in his hand. I ate lunch at a drugstore, bought a pint of bourbon, and drove eastward to Central Avenue and north on Central again. The hunch I had was as vague as the heat waves that danced above the sidewalk.

Nothing made it my business except curiosity. But strictly speaking, I hadn't had any business in a month. Even a no-charge job was a change.

4

FLORIAN'S WAS CLOSED UP, OF COURSE. An obvious plainclothesman sat in front of it in a car, reading a paper with one eye. I didn't know why they bothered. Nobody there knew anything about Moose Malloy. The bouncer and the barman had not been found. Nobody on the block knew anything about them, for talking purposes.

I drove past slowly and parked around the corner and sat looking at a Negro hotel which was diagonally across the block from Florian's and beyond the nearest intersection. It was called the Hotel Sans Souci. I got out and walked back across the intersection and went into it. Two rows of hard empty chairs stared at each other across a strip of tan fiber carpet. A desk was back in the dimness and behind the desk a baldheaded man had his eyes shut and his soft brown hands clasped peacefully on the desk in front of him. He dozed, or appeared to. He wore an Ascot tie that looked as if it had been tied about the year 1880. The green stone in his stickpin was not quite as large as an apple. His large loose chin was folded down gently on the tie, and his folded hands were peaceful and clean, with manicured nails, and gray halfmoons in the purple of the nails.

A metal embossed sign at his elbow said: "This Hotel is Under the Protection of The International Consolidated Agencies, Ltd. Inc."

When the peaceful brown man opened one eye at me thoughtfully I pointed at the sign.

"H.P.D. man checking up. Any trouble here?"

H.P.D. means Hotel Protective Department, which is the department of a large agency that looks after check bouncers and people who move out by the back stairs leaving unpaid bills and second-hand suitcases full of bricks.

"Trouble, brother," the clerk said in a high sonorous voice, "is something we is fresh out of." He lowered his voice four or five notches and added: "What was the name again?"

"Marlowe. Philip Marlowe—"

"A nice name, brother. Clean and cheerful. You're looking right well today." He lowered his voice again. "But you ain't no H.P.D. man. Ain't seen one in years." He unfolded his hands and pointed languidly at the sign. "I acquired that second-hand, brother, just for the effect."

"Okey," I said. I leaned on the counter and started to spin a half dollar on the bare, scarred wood of the counter.

"Heard what happened over at Florian's this morning?"

"Brother, I forgit." Both his eyes were open now and he was watching the blur of light made by the spinning coin.

"The boss got bumped off," I said. "Man named Montgomery. Somebody broke his neck."

"May the Lawd receive his soul, brother." Down went the voice again. "Cop?"

"Private—on a confidential lay. And I know a man who can keep things confidential when I see one."

He studied me, then closed his eyes and thought. He reopened them cautiously and stared at the spinning coin. He couldn't resist looking at it.

"Who done it?" he asked softly. "Who fixed Sam?"

"A tough guy out of the jailhouse got sore because it wasn't a white joint. It used to be, it seems. Maybe you remember?"

He said nothing. The coin fell over with a light ringing whirr and lay still.

"Call your play," I said. "I'll read you a chapter of the Bible or buy you a drink. Say which."

"Brother, I kind of like to read my Bible in the seclusion of my family." His eyes were bright, toadlike, steady.

"Maybe you've just had lunch," I said.

"Lunch," he said, "is something a man of my shape and disposition aims to do without." Down went the voice. "Come 'round this here side of the desk."

I went around and drew the flat pint of bonded bourbon out of my pocket and put it on the shelf. I went back to the front of the desk. He bent over and examined it. He looked satisfied.

"Brother, this don't buy you nothing at all," he said. "But I is pleased to take a light snifter in your company."

He opened the bottle, put two small glasses on the desk and quietly poured each full to the brim. He lifted one, sniffed it carefully, and poured it down his throat with his little finger lifted.

He tasted it, thought about it, nodded and said: "This come out of the correct bottle, brother. In what manner can I be of service to you? There ain't a crack in the sidewalk 'round here I don't know by its first name. Yessuh, this liquor has been keepin' the right company." He refilled his glass.

I told him what had happened at Florian's and why. He stared at me solemnly and shook his bald head.

"A nice quiet place Sam run too," he said. "Ain't nobody been knifed there in a month."

"When Florian's was a white joint some six or eight years ago or less, what was the name of it?"

"Electric signs come kind of high, brother."

I nodded. "I thought it might have had the same name. Malloy would probably have said something if the name had been changed. But who ran it?"

"I'm a mite surprised at you, brother. The name of that pore sinner was Florian. Mike Florian—"

"And what happened to Mike Florian?"

The Negro spread his gentle brown hands. His voice was sonorous and sad. "Daid, brother. Gathered to the Lawd. Nineteen hundred and thirty-four, maybe thirty-five. I ain't precise on that. A wasted life, brother, and a case of pickled kidneys, I heard say. The ungodly man drops like a polled steer, brother, but mercy waits for him up yonder." His voice went down to the business level. "Damn if I know why."

"Who did he leave behind him? Pour another drink."

He corked the bottle firmly and pushed it across the counter. "Two is all, brother—before sundown. I thank you. Your method of approach is soothin' to a man's dignity . . . Left a widow. Name of Jessie."

"What happened to her?"

"The pursuit of knowledge, brother, is the askin' of many questions. I ain't heard. Try the phone book."

There was a booth in the dark corner of the lobby. I went over and shut the door far enough to put the light on. I looked up the name in the chained and battered book. No Florian in it at all. I went back to the desk.

"No soap," I said.

The Negro bent regretfully and heaved a city directory up on top of the desk and pushed it towards me. He closed his eyes. He was getting bored. There was a Jessie Florian, Widow, in the book. She lived at 1644 West 54th Place. I wondered what I had been using for brains all my life.

I wrote the address down on a piece of paper and pushed the directory back across the desk. The Negro put it back where he had found it, shook hands with me, then folded his hands on the desk exactly where they had been when I came in. His eyes drooped slowly and he appeared to fall asleep.

The incident for him was over. Halfway to the door I shot a glance back at him. His eyes were closed and he breathed softly and regularly, blowing a little with his lips at the end of each breath. His bald head shone.

I went out of the Hotel Sans Souci and crossed the street to my car. It looked too easy. It looked much too easy.

5

1644 WEST 54TH PLACE was a dried-out brown house with a dried-out brown lawn in front of it. There was a large bare patch around a tough-looking palm tree. On the porch stood one lonely wooden rocker, and the afternoon breeze made the unpruned shoots of last year's poinsettias tap-tap against the cracked stucco wall. A line of stiff yellowish half-washed clothes jittered on a rusty wire in the side yard.

I drove on a quarter block, parked my car across the street and walked back.

The bell didn't work so I rapped on the wooden margin of the screen door. Slow steps shuffled and the door opened and I was looking into dimness at a blowsy woman who was blowing her nose as she opened the door. Her face was gray and puffy. She had weedy hair of that vague color which is neither brown nor blond, that hasn't enough life in it to be ginger, and isn't clean enough to be gray. Her body was thick in a shapeless outing flannel bathrobe many moons past color and design. It was just something around her body. Her toes were large and obvious in a pair of man's slippers of scuffed brown leather.

I said: "Mrs. Florian? Mrs. Jessie Florian?"

"Uh-huh," the voice dragged itself out of her throat like a sick man getting out of bed.

"You are the Mrs. Florian whose husband once ran a place of entertainment on Central Avenue? Mike Florian?"

She thumbed a wick of hair past her large ear. Her eyes glittered with surprise. Her heavy clogged voice said:

"Wha-what? My goodness sakes alive. Mike's been gone these five years. Who did you say you was?"

The screen door was still shut and hooked.

"I'm a detective," I said. "I'd like a little information."

She stared at me a long dreary minute. Then with effort she unhooked the door and turned away from it.

"Come on in then. I ain't had time to get cleaned up yet," she whined. "Cops, huh?"

I stepped through the door and hooked the screen again. A large handsome cabinet radio droned to the left of the door in the corner of the room. It was the only decent piece of furniture the place had. It looked brand new. Everything else was junk—dirty overstuffed pieces, a wooden rocker that matched the one on the porch, a square arch into a dining room with a stained table, finger marks all over the swing door to the kitchen beyond. A couple of frayed lamps with once gaudy shades that were now as gay as superannuated streetwalkers.

The woman sat down in the rocker and flopped her slippers and looked at me. I looked at the radio and sat down on the end of a davenport. She saw me looking at it. A bogus heartiness, as weak as a China-man's tea, moved into her face and voice. "All the comp'ny I got," she said. Then she tittered. "Mike ain't done nothing new, has he? I don't get cops calling on me much."

Her titter contained a loose alcoholic overtone. I leaned back against something hard, felt for it and brought up an empty quart gin bottle. The woman tittered again.

"A joke that was," she said. "But I hope to Christ they's enough cheap blondes where he is. He never got enough of them here."

"I was thinking more about a redhead," I said.

"I guess he could use a few of them too." Her eyes, it seemed to me, were not so vague now. "I don't call to mind. Any special redhead?"

"Yes. A girl named Velma. I don't know what last name she used except that it wouldn't be her real one. I'm trying to trace her for her folks. Your place on Central is a colored place now, although they haven't changed the name, and of course the people there never heard of her. So I thought of you."

"Her folks taken their time getting around to it—looking for her," the woman said thoughtfully.

"There's a little money involved. Not much. I guess they have to get her in order to touch it. Money sharpens the memory."

"So does liquor," the woman said. "Kind of hot today, ain't it? You said you was a copper though." Cunning eyes, steady attentive face. The feet in the man's slippers didn't move.

I held up the dead soldier and shook it. Then I threw it to one side and reached back on my hip for the pint of bond bourbon the Negro hotel clerk and I had barely tapped. I held it out on my knee. The woman's eyes became fixed in an incredulous stare. Then suspicion climbed all over her face, like a kitten, but not so playfully.

"You ain't no copper," she said softly. "No copper ever bought a drink of that stuff. What's the gag, mister?"

She blew her nose again, on one of the dirtiest handkerchiefs I ever saw. Her eyes stayed on the bottle. Suspicion fought with thirst, and thirst was winning. It always does.

"This Velma was an entertainer, a singer. You wouldn't know her? I don't suppose you went there much."

Seaweed colored eyes stayed on the bottle. A coated tongue coiled on her lips.

"Man, that's liquor," she sighed. "I don't give a damn who you are. Just hold it careful, mister. This ain't no time to drop anything."

She got up and waddled out of the room and come back with two thick smeared glasses.

"No fixin's. Just what you brought is all," she said.

I poured her a slug that would have made me float over a wall. She reached for it hungrily and put it down her throat like an aspirin tablet and looked at the bottle. I poured her another and a smaller one for me. She took it over to her rocker. Her eyes had turned two shades browner already.

"Man, this stuff dies painless with me," she said and sat down. "It never knows what hit it. What was we talkin' about?"

"A redhaired girl named Velma who used to work in your place on Central Avenue."

"Yeah." She used her second drink. I went over and stood the bottle on an end beside her. She reached for it. "Yeah. Who you say you was?"

I took out a card and gave it to her. She read it with her tongue and lips, dropped it on a table beside her and set her empty glass on it.

"Oh, a private guy. You ain't said that, mister." She waggled a finger at me with gay reproach. "But your liquor says you're an all right guy at that. Here's to crime." She poured a third drink for herself and drank it down.

I sat down and rolled a cigarette around in my fingers and waited. She either knew something or she didn't. If she knew something, she either would tell me or she wouldn't. It was that simple.

"Cute little redhead," she said slowly and thickly. "Yeah, I remember her. Song and dance. Nice legs and generous with 'em. She went off somewheres. How would I know what them tramps do?"

"Well, I didn't really think you would know," I said. "But it was natural to come and ask you, Mrs. Florian. Help yourself to the whiskey —I could run out for more when we need it."

"You ain't drinkin'," she said suddenly.

I put my hand around my glass and swallowed what was in it slowly enough to make it seem more than it was.

"Where's her folks at?" she asked suddenly.

"What does that matter?"

"Okey," she sneered. "All cops is the same. Okey, handsome. A guy that buys me a drink is a pal." She reached for the bottle and set up Number 4. "I shouldn't ought to barber with you. But when I like a guy, the ceiling's the limit." She simpered. She was as cute as a washtub. "Hold onto your chair and don't step on no snakes," she said. "I got me an idea."

She got up out of the rocker, sneezed, almost lost the bathrobe, slapped it back against her stomach and stared at me coldly.

"No peekin'," she said, and went out of the room again, hitting the door frame with her shoulder.

I heard her fumbling steps going into the back part of the house.

The poinsettia shoots tap-tapped dully against the front wall. The clothes line creaked vaguely at the side of the house. The ice cream peddler went by ringing his bell. The big new handsome radio in the corner whispered of dancing and love with a deep soft throbbing note like the catch in a torch singer's voice.

Then from the back of the house there were various types of crashing sounds. A chair seemed to fall over backwards, a bureau drawer was pulled out too far and crashed to the floor, there was fumbling and thudding and muttered thick language. Then the slow click of a lock and the squeak of a trunk top going up. More fumbling and banging. A tray landed on the floor. I got up from the davenport and sneaked into the dining room and from that into a short hall. I looked around the edge of an open door.

She was in there swaying in front of the trunk, making grabs at what was in it, and then throwing her hair back over her forehead with anger. She was drunker than she thought. She leaned down and steadied herself on the trunk and coughed and sighed. Then she went down on her thick knees and plunged both hands into the trunk and groped.

They came up holding something unsteadily. A thick package tied with faded pink tape. Slowly, clumsily, she undid the tape. She slipped an envelope out of the package and leaned down again to thrust the envelope out of sight into the right-hand side of the trunk. She retied the tape with fumbling fingers.

I sneaked back the way I had come and sat down on the davenport. Breathing stertorous noises, the woman came back into the living room and stood swaying in the doorway with the tape-tied package.

She grinned at me triumphantly, tossed the package and it fell somewhere near my feet. She waddled back to the rocker and sat down and reached for the whiskey.

I picked the package off the floor and untied the faded pink tape.

"Look 'em over," the woman grunted. "Photos. Newspaper stills. Not that them tramps ever got in no newspapers except by way of the police blotter. People from the joint they are. They're all the bastard left me—them and his old clothes."

I leafed through the bunch of shiny photographs of men and women in professional poses. The men had sharp foxy faces and racetrack clothes or eccentric clownlike makeup. Hoofers and comics from the filling station circuit. Not many of them would ever get west of Main Street. You would find them in tanktown vaudeville acts, cleaned up, or down in the cheap burlesque houses, as dirty as the law allowed and once in a while just enough dirtier for a raid and a noisy police court trial, and then back in their shows again, grinning, sadistically filthy and as rank as the smell of stale sweat. The women had good legs and displayed their inside curves more than Will Hays would have liked. But their faces were as thread-bare as a bookkeeper's office coat. Blondes, brunettes, large cowlike eyes with a peasant dullness in them. Small sharp eyes with urchin greed in them. One or two of the faces obviously vicious. One or two of them might have had red hair. You couldn't tell from the photographs. I looked them over casually, without interest and tied the tape again.

"I wouldn't know any of these," I said. "Why am I looking at them?"

She leered over the bottle her right hand was grappling with unstead-ily. "Ain't you looking for Velma?"

"Is she one of these?"

Thick cunning played on her face, had no fun there and went some-where else. "Ain't you got a photo of her—from her folks?"

"No."

That troubled her. Every girl has a photo somewhere, if it's only in short dresses with a bow in her hair. I should have had it.

"I ain't beginnin' to like you again," the woman said almost quietly.

I stood up with my glass and went over and put it down beside hers on the end table.

"Pour me a drink before you kill the bottle."

She reached for the glass and I turned and walked swiftly through the square arch into the dining room, into the hall, into the cluttered bedroom with the open trunk and the spilled tray. A voice shouted be-hind me. I plunged ahead down into the right side of the trunk, felt an envelope and brought it up swiftly.

She was out of her chair when I got back to the living room, but she had only taken two or three steps. Her eyes had a peculiar glassiness. A murderous glassiness.

"Sit down," I snarled at her deliberately. "You're not dealing with a simple-minded lug like Moose Malloy this time."

It was a shot more or less in the dark, and it didn't hit anything. She blinked twice and tried to lift her nose with her upper lip. Some dirty teeth showed in a rabbit leer.

"Moose? The Moose? What about him?" she gulped.

"He's loose," I said. "Out of jail. He's wandering, with a forty-five gun in his hand. He killed a nigger over on Central this morning because he wouldn't tell him where Velma was. Now he's looking for the fink that turned him up eight years ago."

A white look smeared the woman's face. She pushed the bottle against her lips and gurgled at it. Some of the whiskey ran down her chin.

"And the cops are looking for *him*," she said and laughed. "Cops. Yah!"

A lovely old woman. I liked being with her. I liked getting her drunk for my own sordid purposes. I was a swell guy. I enjoyed being me. You

find almost anything under your hand in my business, but I was beginning to be a little sick at my stomach.

I opened the envelope my hand was clutching and drew out a glazed
still. It was like the others but it was different, much nicer. The girl wore
a Pierrot costume from the waist up. Under the white conical hat with a
black pompon on the top, her fluffed out hair had a dark tinge that might
have been red. The face was in profile but the visible eye seemed to have
gaiety in it. I wouldn't say the face was lovely and unspoiled, I'm not that
good at faces. But it was pretty. People had been nice to that face, or nice
enough for their circle. Yet it was a very ordinary face and its prettiness
was strictly assembly line. You would see a dozen faces like it on a city
block in the noon hour.

Below the waist the photo was mostly legs and very nice legs at that.
It was signed across the lower right hand corner: "Always yours—Velma
Valento."

I held it up in front of the Florian woman, out of her reach. She
lunged but came short.

"Why hide it?" I asked.

She made no sound except thick breathing. I slipped the photo back
into the envelope and the envelope into my pocket.

"Why hide it?" I asked again. "What makes it different from the
others? Where is she?"

"She's dead," the woman said. "She was a good kid, but she's dead,
copper. Beat it."

The tawny mangled brows worked up and down. Her hand opened
and the whiskey bottle slid to the carpet and began to gurgle. I bent to
pick it up. She tried to kick me in the face. I stepped away from her.

"And that still doesn't say why you hid it," I told her. "When did
she die? How?"

"I am a poor sick old woman," she grunted. "Get away from me,
you son of a bitch."

I stood there looking at her, not saying anything, not thinking of
anything particular to say. I stepped over to her side after a moment and
put the flat bottle, now almost empty, on the table at her side.

She was staring down at the carpet. The radio droned pleasantly in
the corner. A car went by outside. A fly buzzed in a window. After
a long time she moved one lip over the other and spoke to the floor, a
meaningless jumble of words from which nothing emerged. Then she
laughed and threw her head back and drooled. Then her right hand
reached for the bottle and it rattled against her teeth as she drained it.
When it was empty she held it up and shook it and threw it at me. It
went off in the corner somewhere, skidding along the carpet and bringing
up with a thud against the baseboard.

She leered at me once more, then her eyes closed and she began to

It might have been an act, but I didn't care. Suddenly I had enough
of the scene, too much of it, far too much of it.

I picked my hat off the davenport and went over to the door and opened it and went out past the screen. The radio still droned in the corner and the woman still snored gently in her chair. I threw a quick look back at her before I closed the door, then shut it, opened it again silently and looked again.

Her eyes were still shut but something gleamed below the lids. I went down the steps, along the cracked walk to the street.

In the next house a window curtain was drawn aside and a narrow intent face was close to the glass, peering, an old woman's face with white hair and a sharp nose.

Old Nosey checking up on the neighbors. There's always at least one like her to the block. I waved a hand at her. The curtain fell.

I went back to my car and got into it and drove back to the 77th Street Division, and climbed upstairs to Nulty's smelly little cubbyhole of an office on the second floor.

6

NULTY DIDN'T SEEM TO HAVE MOVED. He sat in his chair in the same attitude of sour patience. But there were two more cigar stubs in his ashtray and the floor was a little thicker in burnt matches.

I sat down at the vacant desk and Nulty turned over a photo that was lying face down on his desk and handed it to me. It was a police mug, front and profile, with a fingerprint classification underneath. It was Malloy all right, taken in a strong light, and looking as if he had no more eyebrows than a French roll.

"That's the boy." I passed it back.

"We got a wire from Oregon State pen on him," Nulty said. "All time served except his copper. Things look better. We got him cornered. A prowl car was talking to a conductor at the end of the Seventh Street line. The conductor mentioned a guy that size, looking like that. He got off Third and Alexandria. What he'll do is break into some big house where the folks are away. Lots of 'em there, old-fashioned places too far downtown now and hard to rent. He'll break in one and we got him bottled. What you been doing?"

"Was he wearing a fancy hat and white golf balls on his jacket?"

Nulty frowned and twisted his hands on his kneecaps. "No, a blue suit. Maybe brown."

"Sure it wasn't a sarong?"

"Huh? Oh yeah, funny. Remind me to laugh on my day off."

I said: "That wasn't the Moose. He wouldn't ride a street car. He had money. Look at the clothes he was wearing. He couldn't wear stock sizes. They must have been made to order."

"Okey, ride me," Nulty scowled. "What you been doing?"

"What you ought to have done. This place called Florian's was under the same name when it was a white night trap. I talked to a Negro hotelman who knows the neighborhood. The sign was expensive so the shines just went on using it when they took over. The man's name was Mike Florian. He's dead some years, but his widow is still around. She lives at 1644 West 54th Place. Her name is Jessie Florian. She's not in the phone book, but she is in the city directory."

"Well, what do I do—date her up?" Nulty asked.

"I did it for you. I took in a pint of bourbon with me. She's a charming middle-aged lady with a face like a bucket of mud and if she has washed her hair since Coolidge's second term, I'll eat my spare tire, rim and all."

"Skip the wisecracks," Nulty said.

"I asked Mrs. Florian about Velma. You remember, Mr. Nulty, the redhead named Velma that Moose Malloy was looking for? I'm not tiring you, am I, Mr. Nulty?"

"What you sore about?"

"You wouldn't understand. Mrs. Florian said she didn't remember Velma. Her home is very shabby except for a new radio, worth seventy or eighty dollars."

"You ain't told me why that's something I should start screaming about."

"Mrs. Florian—Jessie to me—said her husband left her nothing but his old clothes and a bunch of stills of the gang who worked at his joint from time to time. I plied her with liquor and she is a girl who will take a drink if she has to knock you down to get the bottle. After the third or fourth she went into her modest bedroom and threw things around and dug the bunch of stills out of the bottom of an old trunk. But I was watching her without her knowing it and she slipped one out of the packet and hid it. So after a while I snuck in there and grabbed it."

I reached into my pocket and laid the Pierrot girl on his desk. He lifted it and stared at it and his lips quirked at the corners.

"Cute," he said. "Cute enough. I could of used a piece of that once. Haw, haw. Velma Valento, huh? What happened to this doll?"

"Mrs. Florian says she died—but that hardly explains why she hid the photo."

"It don't do at that. Why did she hide it?"

"She wouldn't tell me. In the end, after I told her about the Moose being out, she seemed to take a dislike to me. That seems impossible, doesn't it?"

"Go on," Nulty said.

"That's all. I've told you the facts and given you the exhibit. If you can't get somewhere on this set-up, nothing I could say would help."

"Where would I get? It's still a shine killing. Wait'll we get the Moose. Hell, it's eight years since he saw the girl unless she visited him in the pen."

"All right," I said. "But don't forget he's looking for her and he's a man who would bear down. By the way, he was in for a bank job. That means a reward. Who got it?"

"I don't know," Nulty said. "Maybe I could find out. Why?"

"Somebody turned him up. Maybe he knows who. That would be another job he would give time to." I stood up. "Well, goodby and good luck."

"You walking out on me?"

I went over to the door. "I have to go home and take a bath and gargle my throat and get my nails manicured."

"You ain't sick, are you?"

"Just dirty," I said. "Very, very dirty."

"Well, what's your hurry? Sit down a minute." He leaned back and hooked his thumbs in his vest, which made him look a little more like a cop, but didn't make him look any more magnetic.

"No hurry," I said. "No hurry at all. There's nothing more I can do. Apparently this Velma is dead, if Mrs. Florian is telling the truth—and I don't at the moment know of any reason why she would lie about it. That was all I was interested in."

"Yeah," Nulty said suspiciously—from force of habit.

"And you have Moose Malloy all sewed up anyway, and that's that. So I'll just run on home now and go about the business of trying to earn a living."

"We might miss out on the Moose," Nulty said. "Guys get away once in a while. Even big guys." His eyes were suspicious also, insofar as they contained any expression at all. "How much she slip you?"

"What?"

"How much this old lady slip you to lay off?"

"Lay off what?"

"Whatever it is you're layin' off from now on." He moved his thumbs from his armholes and placed them together in front of his vest and pushed them against each other. He smiled.

"Oh, for Christ's sake," I said, and went out of the office, leaving his mouth open.

When I was about a yard from the door, I went back and opened it again quietly and looked in. He was sitting in the same position, pushing his thumbs at each other. But he wasn't smiling any more. He looked worried. His mouth was still open.

He didn't move or look up. I didn't know whether he heard me or not. I shut the door again and went away.

7

THEY HAD REMBRANDT on the calendar that year, a rather smeary self-portrait due to imperfectly registered color plate. It showed him holding a smeared palette with a dirty thumb and wearing a tam-o'-shanter which wasn't any too clean either. His other hand held a brush poised in the air, as if he might be going to do a little work after a while, if somebody made a down payment. His face was aging, saggy, full of the disgust of life and the thickening effects of liquor. But it had a hard cheerfulness that I liked, and the eyes were as bright as drops of dew.

I was looking at him across my office desk at about four-thirty when the phone rang and I heard a cool, supercilious voice that sounded as if it thought it was pretty good. It said drawlingly, after I had answered:

"You are Philip Marlowe, a private detective?"

"Check."

"Oh—you mean, yes. You have been recommended to me as a man who can be trusted to keep his mouth shut. I should like you to come to my house at seven o'clock this evening. We can discuss a matter. My name is Lindsay Marriott and I live at 4212 Cabrillo Street, Montemar Vista. Do you know where that is?"

"I know where Montemar Vista is, Mr. Marriott."

"Yes. Well, Cabrillo Street is rather hard to find. The streets down here are all laid out in a pattern of interesting but intricate curves. I should suggest that you walk up the steps from the sidewalk cafe. If you do that, Cabrillo is the third street you come to and my house is the only one on the block. At seven then?"

"What is the nature of the employment, Mr. Marriott?"

"I should prefer not to discuss that over the phone."

"Can't you give me some idea? Montemar Vista is quite a distance."

"I shall be glad to pay your expenses, if we don't agree. Are you particular about the nature of the employment?"

"Not as long as it's legitimate."

The voice grew icicles. "I should not have called you, if it were not."

A Harvard boy. Nice use of the subjunctive mood. The end of my foot itched, but my bank account was still trying to crawl under a duck. I put honey into my voice and said: "Many thanks for calling me, Mr. Marriott. I'll be there."

He hung up and that was that. I thought Mr. Rembrandt had a faint sneer on his face. I got the office bottle out of the deep drawer of the desk and took a short drink. That took the sneer out of Mr. Rembrandt in a hurry.

A wedge of sunlight slipped over the edge of the desk and fell noiselessly to the carpet. Traffic lights bong-bonged outside on the boulevard, interurban cars pounded by, a typewriter clacked monotonously in the lawyer's office beyond the party wall. I had filled and lit a pipe when the telephone rang again.

It was Nulty this time. His voice sounded full of baked potato. "Well, I guess I ain't quite bright at that," he said, when he knew who he was talking to. "I miss one. Malloy went to see that Florian dame."

I held the phone tight enough to crack it. My upper lip suddenly felt a little cold. "Go on. I thought you had him cornered."

"Was some other guy. Malloy ain't around there at all. We get a call from some old window-peeker on West Fifty-four. Two guys was to see the Florian dame. Number One parked the other side of the street and acted kind of cagey. Looked the dump over good before he went in. Was it about an hour. Six feet, dark hair, medium heavy built. Come out quiet."

"He had liquor on his breath too," I said.

"Oh, sure. That was you, wasn't it? Well, Number Two was the Moose. Guy in loud clothes as big as a house. He come in a car too but the old lady don't get the license, can't read the number that far off. This was about an hour after you was there, she says. He goes in fast and is in about five minutes only. Just before he gets back in his car he takes a big gat out and spins the chamber. I guess that's what the old lady saw he done. That's why she calls up. She don't hear no shots though, inside the house."

"That must have been a big disappointment," I said.

"Yeah. A nifty. Remind me to laugh on my day off. The old lady misses one too. The prowl boys go down there and don't get no answer on the door, so they walk in, the front door not being locked. Nobody's dead on the floor. Nobody's home. The Florian dame has skipped out. So they stop by next door and tell the old lady and she's sore as a boil on account of she didn't see the Florian dame go out. So they report back and go on about the job. So about an hour, maybe hour and a half after that, the old lady phones in again and says Mrs. Florian is home again. So they give the call to me and I ask her what makes that important and she hangs up in my face."

Nulty paused to collect a little breath and wait for my comments. I didn't have any. After a moment he went on grumbling.

"What you make of it?"

"Nothing much. The Moose would be likely to go by there, of course. He must have known Mrs. Florian pretty well. Naturally he wouldn't stick around very long. He would be afraid the law might be wise to Mrs. Florian."

"What I figure," Nulty said calmly, "maybe I should go over and see her—kind of find out where she went to."

"That's a good idea," I said. "If you can get somebody to lift you out of your chair."

"Huh? Oh, another nifty. It don't make a lot of difference any more now though. I guess I won't bother."

"All right," I said. "Let's have it whatever it is."

He chuckled. "We got Malloy all lined up. We really got him this time. We make him at Girard, headed north in a rented hack. He gassed up there and the service station kid recognized him from the description we broadcast a while back. He said everything jibed except Malloy had changed to a dark suit. We got county and state law on it. If he goes on north we get him at the Ventura line, and if he slides over to the Ridge Route, he has to stop at Castaic for his check ticket. If he don't stop, they phone ahead and block the road. We don't want no cops shot up, if we can help it. That sound good?"

"It sounds all right," I said. "If it really is Malloy, and if he does exactly what you expect him to do."

Nulty cleared his throat carefully. "Yeah. What you doing on it—just in case?"

"Nothing. Why should I be doing anything on it?"

"You got along pretty good with that Florian dame. Maybe she would have some more ideas."

"All you need to find out is a full bottle," I said.

"You handled her real nice. Maybe you ought to kind of spend a little more time on her."

"I thought this was a police job."

"Oh sure. Was your idea about the girl though."

"That seems to be out—unless the Florian is lying about it."

"Dames lie about anything—just for practice," Nulty said grimly. "You ain't real busy, huh?"

"I've got a job to do. It came in since I saw you. A job where I get paid. I'm sorry."

"Walking out, huh?"

"I wouldn't put it that way. I just have to work to earn a living."

"Okey, pal. If that's the way you feel about it, okey."

"I don't feel any way about it," I almost yelled. "I just don't have time to stooge for you or any other cop."

"Okey, get sore," Nulty said, and hung up.

I held the dead phone and snarled into it: "Seventeen hundred and fifty cops in this town and they want me to do their leg work for them."

I dropped the phone into its cradle and took another drink from the office bottle.

After a while I went down to the lobby of the building to buy an evening paper. Nulty was right in one thing at least. The Montgomery killing hadn't even made the want-ad section so far.

I left the office again in time for an early dinner.

8

I GOT DOWN TO Montemar Vista as the light began to fade, but there was still a fine sparkle on the water and the surf was breaking far out in long smooth curves. A group of pelicans was flying bomber formation just under the creaming lip of the waves. A lonely yacht was taking in toward the yacht harbor at Bay City. Beyond it the huge emptiness of the Pacific was purple-gray.

Montemar Vista was a few dozen houses of various sizes and shapes hanging by their teeth and eyebrows to a spur of mountain and looking as if a good sneeze would drop them down among the box lunches on the beach.

Above the beach the highway ran under a wide concrete arch which was in fact a pedestrian bridge. From the inner end of this a flight of concrete steps with a thick galvanized handrail on one side ran straight as a ruler up the side of the mountain. Beyond the arch the sidewalk cafe my client had spoken of, was bright and cheerful inside, but the iron-legged tile-topped tables outside under the striped awning were empty save for a single dark woman in slacks who smoked and stared moodily out to sea, with a bottle of beer in front of her. A fox terrier was using one of the iron chairs for a lamppost. She chided the dog absently as I drove past and gave the sidewalk cafe my business to the extent of using its parking space.

I walked back through the arch and started up the steps. It was a nice walk if you liked grunting. There were two hundred and eighty steps up to Cabrillo Street. They were drifted over with windblown sand and the handrail was as cold and wet as a toad's belly.

When I reached the top the sparkle had gone from the water and a seagull with a broken trailing leg was twisting against the offsea breeze. I sat down on the damp cold top step and shook the sand out of my shoes and waited for my pulse to come down into the low hundreds. When I was breathing more or less normally again I shook my shirt loose from my back and went along to the lighted house which was the only one within yelling distance of the steps.

It was a nice little house with a salt-tarnished spiral of staircase going up to the front door and an imitation coachlamp for a porchlight. The garage was underneath and to one side. Its door was lifted up and rolled back and the light of the porchlamp shone obliquely on a huge black battleship of a car with chromium trimmings, a coyote tail tied to the Winged Victory on the radiator cap and engraved initials where the emblem should be. The car had a right-hand drive and looked as if had cost more than the house.

I went up the spiral steps, looked for a bell, and used a knocker in the shape of a tiger's head. Its clatter was swallowed in the early evening fog. I heard no steps in the house. My damp shirt felt like an icepack on my back. The door opened silently, and I was looking at a tall blond man in a white flannel suit with a violet satin scarf around his neck.

There was a cornflower in the lapel of his white coat and his pale blue eyes looked faded out by comparison. The violet scarf was loose enough to show that he wore no tie and that he had a thick, soft brown neck, like the neck of a strong woman. His features were a little on the heavy side, but handsome, he had an inch more of height than I had, which made him six feet one. His blond hair was arranged, by art or nature, in three precise blond ledges which reminded me of steps, so that I didn't like them. I wouldn't have liked them anyway. Apart from all this he had the general appearance of a lad who would wear a white flannel suit with a violet scarf around his neck and a cornflower in his lapel.

He cleared his throat lightly and looked past my shoulder at the darkening sea. His cool supercilious voice said: "Yes?"

"Seven o'clock," I said. "On the dot."

"Oh yes. Let me see, your name is—" he paused and frowned in the effort of memory. The effect was as phony as the pedigree of a used car. I let him work at it for a minute, then I said:

"Philip Marlowe. The same as it was this afternoon."

He gave me a quick darting frown, as if perhaps something ought to be done about that. Then he stepped back and said coldly:

"Ah yes. Quite so. Come in, Marlowe. My house boy is away this evening."

He opened the door wide with a fingertip, as though opening the door himself dirtied him a little.

I went in past him and smelled perfume. He closed the door. The entrance put us on a low balcony with a metal railing that ran around three sides of a big studio living room. The fourth side contained a big fireplace and two doors. A fire was crackling in the fireplace. The balcony was lined with bookshelves and there were pieces of glazed metallic looking bits of sculpture on pedestals.

We went down three steps to the main part of the living room. The carpet almost tickled my ankles. There was a concert grand piano, closed down. On one corner of it stood a tall silver vase on a strip of peach-colored velvet, and a single yellow rose in the vase. There was plenty of nice soft furniture, a great many floor cushions, some with golden tassels and some just naked. It was a nice room, if you didn't get rough. There was a wide damask covered divan in a shadowy corner, like a casting couch. It was the kind of room where people sit with their feet in their laps and sip absinthe through lumps of sugar and talk with high affected voices and sometimes just squeak. It was a room where anything could happen except work.

Mr. Lindsay Marriott arranged himself in the curve of the grand piano, leaned over to sniff at the yellow rose, then opened a French enamel cigarette case and lit a long brown cigarette with a gold tip. I sat down on a pink chair and hoped I wouldn't leave a mark on it. I lit a Camel, blew smoke through my nose and looked at a piece of black shiny metal on a stand. It showed a full, smooth curve with a shallow fold in it and two protuberances on the curve. I stared at it. Marriott saw me staring at it.

"An interesting bit," he said negligently, "I picked it up just the other day. Asta Dial's *Spirit of Dawn*."

"I thought it was Klopstein's *Two Warts on a Fanny*," I said.

Mr. Lindsay Marriott's face looked as if he had swallowed a bee. He smoothed it out with an effort.

"You have a somewhat peculiar sense of humor," he said.

"Not peculiar," I said. "Just uninhibited."

"Yes," he said very coldly. "Yes—of course. I've no doubt . . . Well, what I wished to see you about is, as a matter of fact, a very slight matter indeed. Hardly worth bringing you down here for. I am meeting a couple of men tonight and paying them some money. I thought I might as well have someone with me. You carry a gun?"

"At times. Yes," I said. I looked at the dimple in his broad, fleshy chin. You could have lost a marble in it.

"I shan't want you to carry that. Nothing of that sort at all. This is a purely business transaction."

"I hardly ever shoot anybody," I said. "A matter of blackmail?"

He frowned. "Certainly not. I'm not in the habit of giving people grounds for blackmail."

"It happens to the nicest people. I might say particularly to the nicest people."

He waved his cigarette. His aquamarine eyes had a faintly thoughtful expression, but his lips smiled. The kind of smile that goes with a silk noose.

He blew some more smoke and tilted his head back. This accentuated the soft firm lines of his throat. His eyes came down slowly and studied me.

"I'm meeting these men—most probably—in a rather lonely place. I don't know where yet. I expect a call giving me the particulars. I have to be ready to leave at once. It won't be very far away from here. That's the understanding."

"You've been making this deal some time?"

"Three or four days, as a matter of fact."

"You left your bodyguard problem until pretty late."

He thought that over. He snicked some dark ash from his cigarette. "That's true. I had some difficulty making my mind up. It would be better for me to go alone, although nothing has been said definitely about my having someone with me. On the other hand I'm not much of a hero."

"They know you by sight, of course?"

"I—I'm not sure. I shall be carrying a large amount of money and it is not my money. I'm acting for a friend. I shouldn't feel justified in letting it out of my possession, of course."

I snubbed out my cigarette and leaned back in the pink chair and twiddled my thumbs. "How much money—and what for?"

"Well, really—" It was a fairly nice smile now, but I still didn't like it. "I can't go into that."

"You just want me to go along and hold your hat?"

His hand jerked again and some ash fell off on his white cuff. He shook it off and stared down at the place where it had been.

"I'm afraid I don't like your manner," he said, using the edge of his voice.

"I've had complaints about it," I said. "But nothing seems to do any good. Let's look at this job a little. You want a bodyguard, but he can't wear a gun. You want a helper, but he isn't supposed to know what he's supposed to do. You want me to risk my neck without knowing why or what for or what the risk is. What are you offering for all this?"

"I hadn't really got around to thinking about it." His cheekbones were dusky red.

"Do you suppose you could get around to thinking about it?"

He leaned forward gracefully and smiled between his teeth. "How would you like a swift punch on the nose?"

I grinned and stood up and put my hat on. I started across the carpet towards the front door, but not very fast.

His voice snapped at my back. "I'm offering you a hundred dollars for a few hours of your time. If that isn't enough, say so. There's no risk. Some jewels were taken from a friend of mine in a holdup—and I'm buying them back. Sit down and don't be so touchy."

I went back to the pink chair and sat down again.

"All right," I said. "Let's hear about it."

We stared at each other for all of ten seconds. "Have you ever heard of Fei Tsui jade?" he asked slowly, and lit another of his dark cigarettes.

"No."

"It's the only really valuable kind. Other kinds are valuable to some extent for the material, but chiefly for the workmanship on them. Fei Tsui is valuable in itself. All known deposits were exhausted hundreds of years ago. A friend of mine owns a necklace of sixty beads of about six carats each, intricately carved. Worth eighty or ninety thousand dollars. The Chinese government has a very slightly larger one valued at a hundred and twenty-five thousand. My friend's necklace was taken in a holdup a few nights ago. I was present, but quite helpless. I had driven my friend to an evening party and later to the Trocadero and we were on our way back to her home from there. A car brushed the left front fender and stopped, as I thought, to apologize. Instead of that it was a very quick and very neat holdup. Either three or four men, I really saw only two, but I'm sure another stayed in the car behind the wheel, and I thought I saw a glimpse of still a fourth at the rear window. My friend was wearing the jade necklace. They took that and two rings and a bracelet. The one who seemed to be the leader looked the things over without any apparent hurry under a small flashlight. Then he handed one of the rings back and said that would give us an idea what kind of people we were dealing with and to wait for a phone call before reporting to the police or the insurance company. So we obeyed their instructions.

There's plenty of that sort of thing going on, of course. You keep the affair to yourself and pay ransom, or you never see your jewels again. If they're fully insured, perhaps you don't mind, but if they happen to be rare pieces, you would rather pay ransom."

I nodded. "And this jade necklace is something that can't be picked up every day."

He slid a finger along the polished surface of the piano with a dreamy expression, as if touching smooth things pleased him.

"Very much so. It's irreplaceable. She shouldn't have worn it out—ever. But she's a reckless sort of woman. The other things were good but ordinary."

"Uh-huh. How much are you paying?"

"Eight thousand dollars. It's dirt cheap. But if my friend couldn't get another like it, these thugs couldn't very easily dispose of it either. It's probably known to every one in the trade, all over the country."

"This friend of yours—does she have a name?"

"I'd prefer not to mention it at the moment."

"What are the arrangements?"

He looked at me along his pale eyes. I thought he seemed a bit scared, but I didn't know him very well. Maybe it was a hangover. The hand that held the dark cigarette couldn't keep still.

"We have been negotiating by telephone for several days—through me. Everything is settled except the time and place of meeting. It is to be sometime tonight. I shall presently be getting a call to tell me of that. It will not be very far away, they say, and I must be prepared to leave at once. I suppose that is so that no plant could be arranged. With the police, I mean."

"Uh-huh. Is the money marked? I suppose it *is* money?"

"Currency, of course. Twenty-dollar bills. No, why should it be marked?"

"It can be done so that it takes black light to detect it. No reason—except that the cops like to break up these gangs—if they can get any co-operation. Some of the money might turn up on some lad with a record."

He wrinkled his brow thoughtfully. "I'm afraid I don't know what black light is."

"Ultra-violet. It makes certain metallic inks glisten in the dark. I could get it done for you."

"I'm afraid there isn't time for that now," he said shortly.

"That's one of the things that worries me."

"Why?"

"Why you only called me this afternoon. Why you picked on me. Who told you about me?"

He laughed. His laugh was rather boyish, but not a very young boy. "Well, as a matter of fact I'll have to confess I merely picked your name at random out of the phone book. You see I hadn't intended to have anyone go with me. Then this afternoon I got to thinking why not."

I lit another of my squashed cigarettes and watched his throat muscles. "What's the plan?"

He spread his hands. "Simply to go where I am told, hand over the package of money, and receive back the jade necklace."

"Uh-huh."

"You seem fond of that expression."

"What expression?"

"Uh-huh."

"Where will I be—in the back of the car?"

"I suppose so. It's a big car. You could easily hide in the back of it."

"Listen," I said slowly. "You plan to go out with me hidden in your car to a destination you are to get over the phone some time tonight. You will have eight grand in currency on you and with that you are supposed to buy back a jade necklace worth ten or twelve times that much. What you will probably get will be a package you won't be allowed to open—providing you get anything at all. It's just as likely they will simply take your money, count it over in some other place, and mail you the necklace, if they feel bighearted. There's nothing to prevent them double-crossing you. Certainly nothing I could do would stop them. These are heist guys. They're tough. They might even knock you on the head—not hard—just enough to delay you while they go on their way."

"Well, as a matter of fact, I'm a little afraid of something like that," he said quietly, and his eyes twitched. "I suppose that's really why I wanted somebody with me."

"Did they put a flash on you when they pulled the stickup?"

He shook his head, no.

"No matter. They've had a dozen chances to look you over since. They probably knew all about you before that anyway. These jobs are cased. They're cased the way a dentist cases your tooth for a gold inlay. You go out with this dame much?"

"Well—not infrequently," he said stiffly.

"Married?"

"Look here," he snapped. "Suppose we leave the lady out of this entirely."

"Okey," I said. "But the more I know the fewer cups I break. I ought to walk away from this job, Marriott. I really ought. If the boys want to play ball, you don't need me. If they don't want to play ball, I can't do anything about it."

"All I want is your company," he said quickly.

I shrugged and spread my hands. "Okey—but I drive the car and carry the money—and you do the hiding in the back. We're about the same height. If there's any question, we'll just tell them the truth. Nothing to lose by it."

"No." He bit his lip.

"I'm getting a hundred dollars for doing nothing. If anybody gets conked, it ought to be me."

He frowned and shook his head, but after quite a long time his face cleared slowly and he smiled.

"Very well," he said slowly. "I don't suppose it matters much. We'll be together. Would you care for a spot of brandy?"

"Uh-huh. And you might bring me my hundred bucks. I like to feel money."

He moved away like a dancer, his body almost motionless from the waist up.

The phone rang as he was on his way out. It was in a little alcove off the living room proper, cut into the balcony. It wasn't the call we were thinking about though. He sounded too affectionate.

He danced back after a while with a bottle of Five-Star Martell and five nice crisp twenty-dollar bills. That made it a nice evening—so far.

9

THE HOUSE WAS VERY STILL. Far off there was a sound which might have been beating surf or cars zooming along a highway, or wind in pine trees. It was the sea, of course, breaking far down below. I sat there and listened to it and thought long, careful thoughts.

The phone rang four times within the next hour and a half. The big one came at eight minutes past ten. Marriott talked briefly, in a very low voice, cradled the instrument without a sound and stood up with a sort of hushed movement. His face looked drawn. He had changed to dark clothes now. He walked silently back into the room and poured himself a stiff drink in a brandy glass. He held it against the light a moment with a queer unhappy smile, swirled it once quickly and tilted his head back to pour it down his throat.

"Well—we're all set, Marlowe. Ready?"

"That's all I've been all evening. Where do we go?"

"A place called Purissima Canyon."

"I never heard of it."

"I'll get a map." He got one and spread it out quickly and the light blinked in his brassy hair as he bent over it. Then he pointed with his finger. The place was one of the many canyons off the foothill boulevard that turns into town from the coast highway north of Bay City. I had a vague idea where it was, but no more. It seemed to be at the end of a street called Camino de la Costa.

"It will be not more than twelve minutes from here," Marriott said quickly. "We'd better get moving. We only have twenty minutes to play with."

He handed me a light colored overcoat which made me a fine target. It fitted pretty well. I wore my own hat. I had a gun under my arm, but I hadn't told him about that.

While I put the coat on, he went on talking in a light nervous voice and dancing on his hands the thick manila envelope with the eight grand in it.

"Purissima Canyon has a sort of level shelf at the inner end of it, they say. This is walled off from the road by a white fence of four-by-fours, but you can just squeeze by. A dirt road winds down into a little hollow and we are to wait there without lights. There are no houses around."

"We?"

"Well, I mean 'I'—theoretically."

"Oh."

He handed me the manila envelope and I opened it up and looked at what was inside. It was money all right, a huge wad of currency. I didn't count it. I snapped the rubber around again and stuffed the packet down inside my overcoat. It almost caved in a rib.

We went to the door and Marriott switched off all the lights. He opened the front door cautiously and peered out at the foggy air. We went out and down the salt-tarnished spiral stairway to the street level and the garage.

It was a little foggy, the way it always is down there at night. I had to start up the windshield wiper for a while.

The big foreign car drove itself, but I held the wheel for the sake of appearances.

For two minutes we figure-eighted back and forth across the face of the mountain and then popped out right beside the sidewalk cafe. I could understand now why Marriott had told me to walk up the steps. I could have driven about in those curving, twisting streets for hours without making any more yardage than an angleworm in a bait can.

On the highway the lights of the streaming cars made an almost solid beam in both directions. The big cornpoppers were rolling north growling as they went and festooned all over with green and yellow overhang lights. Three minutes of that and we turned inland, by a big service station, and wound along the flank of the foothills. It got quiet. There was loneliness and the smell of kelp and the smell of wild sage from the hills. A yellow window hung here and there, all by itself, like the last orange. Cars passed, spraying the pavement with cold white light, then growled off into the darkness again. Wisps of fog chased the stars down the sky.

Marriott leaned forward from the dark rear seat and said:

"Those lights off to the right are the Belvedere Beach Club. The next canyon is Las Pulgas and the next after that Purissima. We turn right at the top of the second rise." His voice was hushed and taut.

I grunted and kept on driving. "Keep your head down," I said over my shoulder. "We may be watched all the way. This car sticks out like spats at an Iowa picnic. Could be the boys don't like your being twins."

We went down into a hollow at the inward end of a canyon and then

up on the high ground and after a little while down again and up again.
Then Marriott's tight voice said in my ear:

"Next street on the right. The house with the square turret. Turn
beside that."

"You didn't help them pick this place out, did you?"

"Hardly," he said, and laughed grimly. "I just happen to know these
canyons pretty well."

I swung the car to the right past a big corner house with a square
white turret topped with round tiles. The headlights sprayed for an instant on a street sign that read: Camino de la Costa. We slid down a broad
avenue lined with unfinished electroliers and weed-grown sidewalks.
Some realtor's dream had turned into a hangover there. Crickets chirped
and bullfrogs whooped in the darkness behind the overgrown sidewalks.
Marriott's car was that silent.

There was a house to a block, then a house to two blocks, then no
houses at all. A vague window or two was still lighted, but the people
around there seemed to go to bed with the chickens. Then the paved
avenue ended abruptly in a dirt road packed as hard as concrete in dry
weather. The dirt road narrowed and dropped slowly downhill between
walls of brush. The lights of the Belvedere Beach Club hung in the air to
the right and far ahead there was a gleam of moving water. The acrid
smell of the sage filled the night. Then a white painted barrier loomed
across the dirt road and Marriott spoke at my shoulder again.

"I don't think you can get past it," he said. "The space doesn't look
wide enough."

I cut the noiseless motor, dimmed the lights and sat there, listening.
Nothing. I switched the lights off altogether and got out of the car. The
crickets stopped chirping. For a little while the silence was so complete
that I could hear the sound of tires on the highway at the bottom of the
cliffs, a mile away. Then one by one the crickets started up again until the
night was full of them.

"Sit tight. I'm going down there and have a look see," I whispered
into the back of the car.

I touched the gun butt inside my coat and walked forward. There
was more room between the brush and the end of the white barrier than
there had seemed to be from the car. Someone had hacked the brush
away and there were car marks in the dirt. Probably kids going down
there to neck on warm nights. I went on past the barrier. The road
dropped and curved. Below was darkness and a vague far off sea-sound.
And the lights of cars on the highway. I went on. The road ended in a
shallow bowl entirely surrounded by brush. It was empty. There seemed
to be no way into it but the way I had come. I stood there in the silence
and listened.

Minute passed slowly after minute, but I kept on waiting for some
new sound. None came. I seemed to have that hollow entirely to myself.

I looked across to the lighted beach club. From its upper windows a man with a good night glass could probably cover this spot fairly well. He could see a car come and go, see who got out of it, whether there was a group of men or just one. Sitting in a dark room with a good night glass you can see a lot more detail than you would think possible.

I turned to go back up the hill. From the base of a bush a cricket chirped loud enough to make me jump. I went on up around the curve and past the white barricade. Still nothing. The black car stood dimly shining against a grayness which was neither darkness nor light. I went over to it and put a foot on the running board beside the driver's seat.

"Looks like a tryout," I said under my breath, but loud enough for Marriott to hear me from the back of the car. "Just to see if you obey orders."

There was a vague movement behind but he didn't answer. I went on trying to see something besides bushes.

Whoever it was had a nice easy shot at the back of my head. Afterwards I thought I might have heard the swish of a sap. Maybe you always think that—afterwards.

10

"FOUR MINUTES," THE VOICE SAID. "Five, possibly six. They must have moved quick and quiet. He didn't even let out a yell."

I opened my eyes and looked fuzzily at a cold star. I was lying on my back. I felt sick.

The voice said: "It could have been a little longer. Maybe even eight minutes altogether. They must have been in the brush, right where the car stopped. The guy scared easily. They must have thrown a small light in his face and he passed out—just from panic. The pansy."

There was silence. I got up on one knee. Pains shot from the back of my head clear to my ankles.

"Then one of them got into the car," the voice said, "and waited for you to come back. The others hid again. They must have figured he would be afraid to come alone. Or something in his voice made them suspicious, when they talked to him on the phone."

I balanced myself woozily on the flat of my hands, listening.

"Yeah, that was about how it was," the voice said.

It was my voice. I was talking to myself, coming out of it. I was trying to figure the thing out subconsciously.

"Shut up, you dimwit," I said, and stopped talking to myself.

Far off the purl of motors, nearer the chirp of crickets, the peculiar long drawn ee-ee-ee of tree frogs. I didn't think I was going to like those sounds any more.

I lifted a hand off the ground and tried to shake the sticky sage ooze off it, then rubbed it on the side of my coat. Nice work, for a hundred dollars. The hand jumped at the inside pocket of the overcoat. No manila envelope, naturally. The hand jumped inside my own suit coat. My wallet was still there. I wondered if my hundred was still in it. Probably not. Something felt heavy against my left ribs. The gun in the shoulder holster.

That was a nice touch. They left me my gun. A nice touch of something or other—like closing a man's eyes after you knife him.

I felt the back of my head. My hat was still on. I took it off, not without discomfort and felt the head underneath. Good old head, I'd had it a long time. It was a little soft now, a little pulpy, and more than a little tender. But a pretty light sapping at that. The hat had helped. I could still use the head. I could use it another year anyway.

I put my right hand back on the ground and took the left off and swivelled it around until I could see my watch. The illuminated dial showed 10.56, as nearly as I could focus on it.

The call had come at 10.08. Marriott had talked maybe two minutes. Another four had got us out of the house. Time passes very slowly when you are actually doing something. I mean, you can go through a lot of movements in very few minutes. Is that what I mean? What the hell do I care what I mean? Okey, better men than me have meant less. Okey, what I mean is, that would be 10.15, say. The place was about twelve minutes away. 10.27. I get out, walk down in the hollow, spend at the most eight minutes fooling around and come on back up to get my head treated. 10.35. Give me a minute to fall down and hit the ground with my face. The reason I hit it with my face, I got my chin scraped. It hurts. It feels scraped. That way I know it's scraped. No, I can't see it. I don't have to see it. It's my chin and I know whether it's scraped or not. Maybe you want to make something of it. Okey, shut up and let me think. What with? . . .

The watch showed 10.56 p.m. That meant I had been out for twenty minutes.

Twenty minutes' sleep. Just a nice doze. In that time I had muffed a job and lost eight thousand dollars. Well, why not? In twenty minutes you can sink a battleship, down three or four planes, hold a double execution. You can die, get married, get fired and find a new job, have a tooth pulled, have your tonsils out. In twenty minutes you can even get up in the morning. You can get a glass of water at a night club—maybe.

Twenty minutes' sleep. That's a long time. Especially on a cold night, out in the open. I began to shiver.

I was still on my knees. The smell of the sage was beginning to bother me. The sticky ooze from which wild bees get their honey. Honey was sweet, much too sweet. My stomach took a whirl. I clamped my teeth tight and just managed to keep it down my throat. Cold sweat stood out in lumps on my forehead, but I shivered just the same. I got up on one foot, then on both feet, straightened up, wobbling a little. I felt like an amputated leg.

I turned slowly. The car was gone. The dirt road stretched empty, back up the shallow hill towards the paved street, the end of Camino de la Costa. To the left the barrier of white-painted four-by-fours stood out against the darkness. Beyond the low wall of brush the pale glow in the sky would be the lights of Bay City. And over farther to the right and near by were the lights of the Belvedere Club.

I went over where the car had stood and got a fountain pen flash unclipped from my pocket and poked the little light down at the ground. The soil was red loam, very hard in dry weather, but the weather was not bone dry. There was a little fog in the air, and enough of the moisture had settled on the surface of the ground to show where the car had stood. I could see, very faint, the tread marks of the heavy ten-ply Vogue tires. I put the light on them and bent over and the pain made my head dizzy. I started to follow the tracks. They went straight ahead for a dozen feet, then swung over to the left. They didn't turn. They went towards the gap at the left hand end of the white barricade. Then I lost them.

I went over to the barricade and shone the little light on the brush. Fresh-broken twigs. I went through the gap, on down the curving road. The ground was still softer here. More marks of the heavy tires. I went on down, rounded the curve and was at the edge of the hollow closed in by brush.

It was there all right, the chromium and glossy paint shining a little even in the dark, and the red reflector glass of the tail-lights shining back at the pencil flash. It was there, silent, lightless, all the doors shut. I went towards it slowly, gritting my teeth at every step. I opened one of the rear doors and put the beam of the flash inside. Empty. The front was empty too. The ignition was off. The key hung in the lock on a thin chain. No torn upholstery, no scarred glass, no blood, no bodies. Everything neat and orderly. I shut the doors and circled the car slowly, looking for a sign and not finding any.

A sound froze me.

A motor throbbed above the rim of the brush. I didn't jump more than a foot. The flash in my hand went out. A gun slid into my hand all by itself. Then headlight beams tilted up towards the sky, then tilted down again. The motor sounded like a small car. It had that contented sound that comes with moisture in the air.

The lights tilted down still more and got brighter. A car was coming down the curve of the dirt road. It came two-thirds of the way and then stopped. A spotlight clicked on and swung out to the side, held there for a long moment, went out again. The car came on down the hill. I slipped the gun out of my pocket and crouched behind the motor of Marriott's car.

A small coupe of no particular shape or color slid into the hollow and turned so that its headlights raked the sedan from one end to the other. I got my head down in a hurry. The lights swept above me like a sword. The coupe stopped. The motor died. The headlights died. Silence. Then a door opened and a light foot touched the ground. More silence. Even the crickets were silent. Then a beam of light cut the darkness low down, parallel to the ground and only a few inches above it. The beam swept, and there was no way I could get my ankles out of it quickly enough. the beam stopped on my feet. Silence. The beam came up and raked the top of the hood again.

Then a laugh. It was a girl's laugh. Strained, taut as a mandolin wire. A strange sound in that place. The white beam shot under the car again and settled on my feet.

The voice said, not quite shrilly: "All right, you. Come out of there with your hands up and very damned empty. You're covered."

I didn't move.

The light wavered a little, as though the hand that held it wavered. It swept slowly along the hood once more. The voice stabbed at me again.

"Listen, stranger. I'm holding a ten shot automatic. I can shoot straight. Both your feet are vulnerable. What do you bid?"

"Put it up—or I'll blow it out of your hand!" I snarled. My voice sounded like somebody tearing slats off a chicken coop.

"Oh—a hardboiled gentleman." There was a quaver in the voice, a nice little quaver. Then it hardened again. "Coming out? I'll count three. Look at the odds I'm giving you—twelve fat cylinders, maybe sixteen. But your feet will hurt. And ankle bones take years and years to get well and sometimes they never do really—"

I straightened up slowly and looked into the beam of the flashlight.

"I talk too much when I'm scared too," I said.

"Don't—don't move another inch! Who are you?"

I moved around the front of the car towards her. When I was six feet from the slim dark figure behind the flash I stopped. The flash glared at me steadily.

"You stay right there," the girl snapped angrily, after I had stopped. "Who are you?"

"Let's see your gun."

She held it forward into the light. It was pointed at my stomach. It was a little gun, it looked like a small Colt vest pocket automatic.

"Oh, that," I said. "That toy. It doesn't either hold ten shots. It holds six. It's just a little bitty gun, a butterfly gun. They shoot butterflies with them. Shame on you for telling a deliberate lie like that."

"Are you crazy?"

"Me? I've been sapped by a holdup man. I might be a little goofy."

"Is that—is that your car?"

"No."

"Who are you?"

"What were you looking at back there with your spotlight?"

"I get it. You ask the answers. He-man stuff. I was looking at a man."

"Does he have blond hair in waves?"

"Not now," she said quietly. "He might have had—once."

That jarred me. Somehow I hadn't expected it. "I didn't see him," I said lamely. "I was following the tire marks with a flashlight down the hill. Is he badly hurt?" I went another step towards her. The little gun jumped at me and the flash held steady.

"Take it easy," she said quietly. "Very easy. Your friend is dead."

I didn't say anything for a moment. Then I said: "All right, let's go look at him."

"Let's stand right here and not move and you tell me who you are and what happened." The voice was crisp. It was not afraid. It meant what it said.

"Marlowe. Philip Marlowe. An investigator. Private."

"That's who you are—if it's true. Prove it."

"I'm going to take my wallet out."

"I don't think so. Just leave your hands where they happen to be. We'll skip the proof for the time being. What's your story?"

"This man may not be dead."

"He's dead all right. With his brains on his face. The story, mister. Make it fast."

"As I said—he may not be dead. We'll go look at him." I moved one foot forward.

"Move and I'll drill you!" she snapped.

I moved the other foot forward. The flash jumped about a little. I think she took a step back.

"You take some awful chances, mister," she said quietly. "All right, go on ahead and I'll follow. You look like a sick man. If it hadn't been for that—"

"You'd have shot me. I've been sapped. It always makes me a little dark under the eyes."

"A nice sense of humor—like a morgue attendant," she almost wailed.

I turned away from the light and immediately it shone on the ground in front of me. I walked past the little coupe, an ordinary little car, clean and shiny under the misty starlight. I went on, up the dirt road, around the curve. The steps were close behind me and the flashlight guided me. There was no sound anywhere now except our steps and the girl's breathing. I didn't hear mine.

11

HALFWAY UP THE SLOPE I looked off to the right and saw his foot. She swung the light. Then I saw all of him. I ought to have seen him as I came down, but I had been bent over, peering at the ground with the fountain pen flash, trying to read tire marks by a light the size of a quarter.

"Give me the flash," I said and reached back.

She put it into my hand, without a word. I went down on a knee. The ground felt cold and damp through the cloth.

He lay smeared to the ground, on his back, at the base of a bush, in that bag-of-clothes position that always means the same thing. His face was a face I had never seen before. His hair was dark with blood, the beautiful blond ledges were tangled with blood and some thick grayish ooze, like primeval slime.

The girl behind me breathed hard, but she didn't speak. I held the light on his face. He had been beaten to a pulp. One of his hands was flung out in a frozen gesture, the fingers curled. His overcoat was half twisted under him, as though he had rolled as he fell. His legs were crossed. There was a trickle as black as dirty oil at the corner of his mouth.

"Hold the flash on him," I said, passing it back to her. "If it doesn't make you sick."

She took it and held it without a word, as steady as an old homicide veteran. I got my fountain pen flash out again and started to go through his pockets, trying not to move him.

"You shouldn't do that," she said tensely. "You shouldn't touch him until the police come."

"That's right," I said. "And the prowl car boys are not supposed to touch him until the K-car men come and they're not supposed to touch him until the coroner's examiner sees him and the photographers have photographed him and the fingerprint man has taken his prints. And do you know how long all that is liable to take out here? A couple of hours."

"All right," she said. "I suppose you're always right. I guess you must be that kind of person. Somebody must have hated him to smash his head in like that."

"I don't suppose it was personal," I growled. "Some people just like to smash heads."

"Seeing that I don't know what it's all about, I couldn't guess," she said tartly.

I went through his clothes. He had loose silver and bills in one trouser pocket, a tooled leather keycase in the other, also a small knife. His left hip pocket yielded a small billfold with more currency, insurance cards, a driver's license, a couple of receipts. In his coat loose match folders, a gold pencil clipped to a pocket, two thin cambric handkerchiefs as fine and white as dry powdered snow. Then the enamel cigarette case from which I had seen him take his brown gold-tipped cigarettes. They were South American, from Montevideo. And in the other inside pocket a second cigarette case I hadn't seen before. It was made of embroidered silk, a dragon on each side, a frame of imitation tortoise-shell so thin it was hardly there at all. I tickled the catch open and looked in at three oversized Russian cigarettes under the band of elastic. I pinched one. They felt old and dry and loose. They had hollow mouthpieces.

"He smoked the others," I said over my shoulder. "These must have been for a lady friend. He would be a lad who would have a lot of lady friends."

The girl was bent over, breathing on my neck now. "Didn't you know him?"

"I only met him tonight. He hired me for a bodyguard."

"Some bodyguard."

I didn't say anything to that.

"I'm sorry," she almost whispered. "Of course I don't know the circumstances. Do you suppose those could be jujus? Can I look?"

I passed the embroidered case back to her.

"I knew a guy once who smoked jujus," she said. "Three highballs and three sticks of tea and it took a pipe wrench to get him off the chandelier."

"Hold the light steady."

There was a rustling pause. Then she spoke again.

"I'm sorry." She handed the case down again and I slipped it back in his pocket. That seemed to be all. All it proved was that he hadn't been cleaned out.

I stood up and took my wallet out. The five twenties were still in it.

"High class boys," I said. "They only took the large money."

The flash was drooping to the ground. I put my wallet away again, clipped my own small flash to my pocket and reached suddenly for the little gun she was still holding in the same hand with the flashlight. She dropped the flashlight, but I got the gun. She stepped back quickly and I reached down for the light. I put it on her face for a moment, then snapped it off.

"You didn't have to be rough," she said, putting her hands down into the pockets of a long rough coat with flaring shoulders. "I didn't think you killed him."

I liked the cool quiet of her voice. I liked her nerve. We stood in the darkness, face to face, not saying anything for a moment. I could see the brush and light in the sky.

I put the light on her face and she blinked. It was a small neat vibrant face with large eyes. A face with bone under the skin, fine drawn like a Cremona violin. A very nice face.

"Your hair's red," I said. "You look Irish."

"And my name's Riordan. So what? Put that light out. It's not red, it's auburn."

I put it out. "What's your first name?"

"Anne. And don't call me Annie."

"What are you doing around here?"

"Sometimes at night I go riding. Just restless. I live alone. I'm an orphan. I know all this neighborhood like a book. I just happened to be riding along and noticed a light flickering down in the hollow. It seemed a little cold for young love. And they don't use lights, do they?"

"I never did. You take some awful chances, Miss Riordan."

"I think I said the same about you. I had a gun. I wasn't afraid. There's no law against going down there."

"Uh-huh. Only the law of self preservation. Here. It's not my night to be clever. I suppose you have a permit for the gun." I held it out to her, butt first.

She took it and tucked it down into her pocket. "Strange how curious people can be, isn't it? I write a little. Feature articles."

"Any money in it?"

"Very damned little. What were you looking for—in his pockets?"

"Nothing in particular. I'm a great guy to snoop around. We had eight thousand dollars to buy back some stolen jewelry for a lady. We got hijacked. Why they killed him I don't know. He didn't strike me as a fellow who would put up much of a fight. And I didn't hear a fight. I was down in the hollow when he was jumped. He was in the car, up above. We were supposed to drive down into the hollow but there didn't seem to be room for the car without scratching it up. So I went down there on foot and while I was down there they must have stuck him up. Then one of them got into the car and dry-gulched me. I thought he was still in the car, of course."

"That doesn't make you so terribly dumb," she said.

"There was something wrong with the job from the start. I could feel it. But I needed the money. Now I have to go to the cops and eat dirt. Will you drive me to Montemar Vista? I left my car there. He lived there."

"Sure. But shouldn't somebody stay with him? You could take my car—or I could go call the cops."

I looked at the dial of my watch. The faintly glowing hands said that it was getting towards midnight.

"No."

"Why not?"

"I don't know why not. I just feel it that way. I'll play it alone."

She said nothing. We went back down the hill and got into her little car and she started it and jockeyed it around without lights and drove it back up the hill and eased it past the barrier. A block away she sprang the lights on.

My head ached. We didn't speak until we came level with the first house on the paved part of the street. Then she said:

"You need a drink. Why not go back to my house and have one? You can phone the law from there. They have to come from West Los Angeles anyway. There's nothing up here but a fire station."

"Just keep on going down to the coast. I'll play it solo."

"But why? I'm not afraid of them. My story might help you."

"I don't want any help. I've got to think. I want to be by myself for a while."

"I—okey," she said.

She made a vague sound in her throat and turned on to the boulevard. We came to the service station at the coast highway and turned north to Montemar Vista and the sidewalk cafe there. It was lit up like a luxury liner. The girl pulled over on to the shoulder and I got out and stood holding the door.

I fumbled a card out of my wallet and passed it in to her. "Some day you may need a strong back," I said. "Let me know. But don't call me if it's brain work."

She tapped the card on the wheel and said slowly: "You'll find me in the Bay City phone book. 819 Twenty-fifth Street. Come around and pin a putty medal on me for minding my own business. I think you're still woozy from that crack on the head."

She swung her car swiftly around on the highway and I watched its twin tail-lights fade into the dark.

I walked past the arch and the sidewalk cafe into the parking space and got into my car. A bar was right in front of me and I was shaking again. But it seemed smarter to walk into the West Los Angeles police station the way I did twenty minutes later, as cold as a frog and as green as the back of a new dollar bill.

12

It was an hour and a half later. The body had been taken away, the ground gone over, and I had told my story three or four times. We sat, four of us, in the day captain's room at the West Los Angeles station. The building was quiet except for a drunk in a cell who kept giving the Australian bush call while he waited to go downtown for sunrise court.

A hard white light inside a glass reflector shone down on the flat topped table on which were spread the things that had come from Lindsay Marriott's pockets, things now that seemed as dead and homeless as their owner. The man across the table from me was named Randall and he was from Central Homicide in Los Angeles. He was a thin quiet man of fifty with smooth creamy gray hair, cold eyes, a distant manner. He wore a dark red tie with black spots on it and the spots kept dancing in front of my eyes. Behind him, beyond the cone of light two beefy men lounged like bodyguards, each of them watching one of my ears.

I fumbled a cigarette around in my fingers and lit it and didn't like the taste of it. I sat watching it burn between my fingers. I felt about eighty years old and slipping fast.

Randall said coldly: "The oftener you tell this story the sillier it sounds. This man Marriott had been negotiating for days, no doubt, about this payoff and then just a few hours before the final meeting he calls up a perfect stranger and hires him to go with him as a bodyguard."

"Not exactly as a bodyguard," I said. "I didn't even tell him I had a gun. Just for company."

"Where did he hear of you?"

"First he said a mutual friend. Then that he just picked my name out of the book."

Randall poked gently among the stuff on the table and detached a white card with an air of touching something not quite clean. He pushed it along the wood.

"He had your card. Your business card."

I glanced at the card. It had come out of his billfold, together with a number of other cards I hadn't bothered to examine back there in the hollow of Purissima Canyon. It was one of my cards all right. It looked rather dirty at that, for a man like Marriott. There was a round smear across one corner.

"Sure," I said. "I hand those out whenever I get a chance. Naturally."

"Marriott let you carry the money," Randall said. "Eight thousand dollars. He was rather a trusting soul."

I drew on my cigarette and blew the smoke towards the ceiling. The light hurt my eyes. The back of my head ached.

"I don't have the eight thousand dollars," I said. "Sorry."

"No. You wouldn't be here, if you had the money. Or would you?" There was a cold sneer on his face now, but it looked artificial.

"I'd do a lot for eight thousand dollars," I said. "But if I wanted to kill a man with a sap, I'd only hit him twice at the most—on the back of the head."

He nodded slightly. One of the dicks behind him spit into the waste-basket.

"That's one of the puzzling features. It looks like an amateur job, but of course it might be meant to look like an amateur job. The money was not Marriott's, was it?"

"I don't know. I got the impression not, but that was just an impression. He wouldn't tell me who the lady in the case was."

"We don't know anything about Marriott—yet," Randall said slowly. "I suppose it's at least possible he meant to steal the eight thousand himself."

"Huh?" I felt surprised. I probably looked surprised. Nothing changed in Randall's smooth face.

"Did you count the money?"

"Of course not. He just gave me a package. There was money in it and it looked like a lot. He said it was eight grand. Why would he want to steal it from me when he already had it before I came on the scene?"

Randall looked at a corner of the ceiling and drew his mouth down at the corners. He shrugged.

"Go back a bit," he said. "Somebody had stuck up Marriott and a lady and taken this jade necklace and stuff and had later offered to sell it back for what seems like a pretty small amount, in view of its supposed value. Marriott was to handle the payoff. He thought of handling it alone and we don't know whether the other parties made a point of that or whether it was mentioned. Usually in cases like that they are rather fussy. But Marriott evidently decided it was all right to have you along. Both of you figured you were dealing with an organized gang and that they would play ball within the limits of their trade. Marriott was scared. That would be natural enough. He wanted company. You were the company. But you are a complete stranger to him, just a name on a card handed to him by some unknown party, said by him to be a mutual friend. Then at the last minute Marriott decides to have you carry the money and do the talking while he hides in the car. You say that was your idea, but he may have been hoping you would suggest it, and if you didn't suggest it, he would have had the idea himself."

"He didn't like the idea at first," I said.

Randall shrugged again. "He pretended not to like the idea—but he gave in. So finally he gets a call and off you go to the place he describes. All this is coming from Marriott. None of it is known to you independently. When you get there, there seems to be nobody about. You are supposed to drive down into that hollow, but it doesn't look to be room enough for the big car. It wasn't, as a matter of fact, because the car was pretty badly scratched on the left side. So you get out and walk down into the hollow, see and hear nothing, wait a few minutes, come back to the car and then somebody in the car socks you on the back of the head. Now suppose Marriott wanted that money and wanted to make you the fall guy—wouldn't he have acted just the way he did?"

"It's a swell theory," I said. "Marriott socked me, took the money, then he got sorry and beat his brains out, after first burying the money under a bush."

Randall looked at me woodenly. "He had an accomplice of course. Both of you were supposed to be knocked out, and the accomplice would beat it with the money. Only the accomplice double-crossed Marriott by killing him. He didn't have to kill you because you didn't know him."

I looked at him with admiration and ground out my cigarette stub in a wooden tray that had once had a glass lining in it but hadn't any more.

"It fits the facts—so far as we know them," Randall said calmly. "It's no sillier than any other theory we could think up at the moment."

"It doesn't fit one fact—that I was socked from the car, does it? That would make me suspect Marriott of having socked me—other things being equal. Although I didn't suspect him after he was killed."

"The way you were socked fits best of all," Randall said. "You didn't tell Marriott you had a gun, but he may have seen the bulge under your arm or at least suspected you had a gun. In that case he would want to hit you when you suspected nothing. And you wouldn't suspect anything from the back of the car."

"Okey," I said. "You win. It's a good theory, always supposing the money was not Marriott's and that he wanted to steal it and that he had an accomplice. So his plan is that we both wake up with bumps on our heads and the money is gone and we say so sorry and I go home and forget all about it. Is that how it ends? I mean is that how he expected it to end? It had to look good to him too, didn't it?"

Randall smiled wryly. "I don't like it myself. I was just trying it out. It fits the facts—as far as I know them, which is not far."

"We don't know enough to even start theorizing," I said. "Why not assume he was telling the truth and that he perhaps recognized one of the stick-up men?"

"You say you heard no struggle, no cry?"

"No. But he could have been grabbed quickly, by the throat. Or he could have been too scared to cry out when they jumped him. Say they were watching from the bushes and saw me go down the hill. I went some distance, you know. A good hundred feet. They go over to look into the car and see Marriott. Somebody sticks a gun in his face and makes him get out—quietly. Then he's sapped down. But something he says, or some way he looks, makes them think he has recognized somebody."

"In the dark?"

"Yes," I said. "It must have been something like that. Some voices stay in your mind. Even in the dark people are recognized."

Randall shook his head. "If this was an organized gang of jewel thieves, they wouldn't kill without a lot of provocation." He stopped suddenly and his eyes got a glazed look. He closed his mouth very slowly, very tight. He had an idea. "Hijack," he said.

I nodded. "I think that's an idea."

"There's another thing," he said. "How did you get here?"

"I drove my car."

"Where was your car?"

"Down at Montemar Vista, in the parking lot by the sidewalk cafe."

He looked at me very thoughtfully. The two dicks behind him looked at me suspiciously. The drunk in the cells tried to yodel, but his voice cracked and that discouraged him. He began to cry.

"I walked back to the highway," I said. "I flagged a car. A girl was driving it alone. She stopped and took me down."

"Some girl," Randall said. "It was late at night, on a lonely road, and she stopped."

"Yeah. Some of them will do that. I didn't get to know her, but she seemed nice." I stared at them, knowing they didn't believe me and wondering why I was lying about it.

"It was a small car," I said. "A Chevvy coupe. I didn't get the license number."

"Haw, he didn't get the license number," one of the dicks said and spat into the wastebasket again.

Randall leaned forward and stared at me carefully. "If you're holding anything back with the idea of working on this case yourself to make yourself a little publicity, I'd forget it, Marlowe. I don't like all the points

in your story and I'm going to give you the night to think it over.
Tomorrow I'll probably ask you for a sworn statement. In the meantime
let me give you a tip. This is a murder and a police job and we wouldn't
want your help, even if it was good. All we want from you is facts. Get
me?"

"Sure. Can I go home now? I don't feel any too well."

"You can go home now." His eyes were icy.

I got up and started towards the door in a dead silence. When I had
gone four steps Randall cleared his throat and said carelessly:

"Oh, one small point. Did you notice what kind of cigarettes Marriott smoked?"

I turned. "Yes. Brown ones. South American, in a French enamel
case."

He leaned forward and pushed the embroidered silk case out of the
pile of junk on the table and then pulled it towards him.

"Ever see this one before?"

"Sure. I was just looking at it."

"I mean, earlier this evening."

"I believe I did," I said. "Lying around somewhere. Why?"

"You didn't search the body?"

"Okey," I said. "Yes, I looked through his pockets. That was in one
of them. I'm sorry. Just professional curiosity. I didn't disturb anything.
After all he was my client."

Randall took hold of the embroidered case with both hands and
opened it. He sat looking into it. It was empty. The three cigarettes were
gone.

I bit hard on my teeth and kept the tired look on my face. It was not
easy.

"Did you see him smoke a cigarette out of this?"

"No."

Randall nodded coolly. "It's empty as you see. But it was in his
pocket just the same. There's a little dust in it. I'm going to have it
examined under a microscope. I'm not sure, but I have an idea it's
marihuana."

I said: "If he had any of those, I should think he would have smoked
a couple tonight. He needed something to cheer him up."

Randall closed the case carefully and pushed it away.

"That's all," he said. "And keep your nose clean."

I went out.

The fog had cleared off outside and the stars were as bright as
artificial stars of chromium on a sky of black velvet. I drove fast. I needed
a drink badly and the bars were closed.

13

I GOT UP AT NINE, drank three cups of black coffee, bathed the back of my head with ice-water and read the two morning papers that had been thrown against the apartment door. There was a paragraph and a bit about Moose Malloy, in Part II, but Nulty didn't get his name mentioned. There was nothing about Lindsay Marriott, unless it was on the society page.

I dressed and ate two soft boiled eggs and drank a fourth cup of coffee and looked myself over in the mirror. I still looked a little shadowy under the eyes. I had the door open to leave when the phone rang.

It was Nulty. He sounded mean.

"Marlowe?"

"Yeah. Did you get him?"

"Oh sure. We got him." He stopped to snarl. "On the Ventura line, like I said. Boy, did we have fun! Six foot six, built like a coffer dam, on his way to Frisco to see the Fair. He had five quarts of hooch in the front seat of the rent car, and he was drinking out of another one as he rode along, doing a quiet seventy. All we had to go up against him with was two county cops with guns and blackjacks."

He paused and I turned over a few witty sayings in my mind, but none of them seemed amusing at the moment. Nulty went on:

"So he done exercises with the cops and when they was tired enough to go to sleep, he pulled one side off their car, threw the radio into the ditch, opened a fresh bottle of hooch, and went to sleep hisself. After a while the boys snapped out of it and bounced blackjacks off his head for about ten minutes before he noticed it. When he began to get sore they got handcuffs on him. It was easy. We got him in the icebox now, drunk driving, drunk in auto, assaulting police officer in performance of duty, two counts, malicious damage to official property, attempted escape from custody, assault less than mayhem, disturbing the peace, and parking on a state highway. Fun, ain't it?"

"What's the gag?" I asked. "You didn't tell me all that just to gloat."

"It was the wrong guy," Nulty said savagely. "This bird is named Stoyanoffsky and he lives in Hemet and he just got through working as a sandhog on the San Jack tunnel. Got a wife and four kids. Boy, is she sore. What you doing on Malloy?"

"Nothing. I have a headache."

"Any time you get a little free time—"

"I don't think so," I said. "Thanks just the same. When is the inquest on the nigger coming up?"

"Why bother?" Nulty sneered, and hung up.

I drove down to Hollywood Boulevard and put my car in the parking space beside the building and rode up to my floor. I opened the door of the little reception room which I always left unlocked, in case I had a client and the client wanted to wait.

Miss Anne Riordan looked up from a magazine and smiled at me.

She was wearing a tobacco brown suit with a high-necked white sweater inside it. Her hair by daylight was pure auburn and on it she wore a hat with a crown the size of a whiskey glass and a brim you could have wrapped the week's laundry in. She wore it at an angle of approximately forty-five degrees, so that the edge of the brim just missed her shoulder. In spite of that it looked smart. Perhaps because of that.

She was about twenty-eight years old. She had a rather narrow forehead of more height than is considered elegant. Her nose was small and inquisitive, her upper lip a shade too long and her mouth more than a shade too wide. Her eyes were gray-blue with flecks of gold in them. She had a nice smile. She looked as if she had slept well. It was a nice face, a face you get to like. Pretty, but not so pretty that you would have to wear brass knuckles every time you took it out.

"I didn't know just what your office hours were," she said. "So I waited. I gather that your secretary is not here today."

"I don't have a secretary."

I went across and unlocked the inner door, then switched on the buzzer that rang on the outer door. "Let's go into my private thinking parlor."

She passed in front of me with a vague scent of very dry sandalwood and stood looking at the five green filing cases, the shabby rust-red rug, the half-dusted furniture, and the not too clean net curtains.

"I should think you would want somebody to answer the phone," she said. "And once in a while to send your curtains to the cleaners."

"I'll send them out come St. Swithin's Day. Have a chair. I might miss a few unimportant jobs. And a lot of leg art. I save money."

"I see," she said demurely, and placed a large suede bag carefully on the corner of the glass-topped desk. She leaned back and took one of my cigarettes. I burned my finger with a paper match lighting it for her.

She blew a fan of smoke and smiled through it. Nice teeth, rather large.

"You probably didn't expect to see me again so soon. How is your head?"

"Poorly. No, I didn't."

"Were the police nice to you?"

"About the way they always are."

"I'm not keeping you from anything important, am I?"

"No."

"All the same I don't think you're very pleased to see me."

I filled a pipe and reached for the packet of paper matches. I lit the pipe carefully. She watched that with approval. Pipe smokers were solid men. She was going to be disappointed in me.

"I tried to leave you out of it," I said. "I don't know why exactly.

It's no business of mine any more anyhow. I ate my dirt last night and banged myself to sleep with a bottle and now it's a police case: I've been warned to leave it alone."

"The reason you left me out of it," she said calmly, "was that you didn't think the police would believe just mere idle curiosity took me down into that hollow last night. They would suspect some guilty reason and hammer at me until I was a wreck."

"How do you know I didn't think the same thing?"

"Cops are just people," she said irrelevantly.

"They start out that way, I've heard."

"Oh—cynical this morning." She looked around the office with an idle but raking glance. "Do you do pretty well in here? I mean financially? I mean, do you make a lot of money—with this kind of furniture?"

I grunted.

"Or should I try minding my own business and not asking impertinent questions?"

"Would it work, if you tried it?"

"Now we're both doing it. Tell me, why did you cover up for me last night? Was it on account of I have reddish hair and a beautiful figure?"

I didn't say anything.

"Let's try this one," she said cheerfully. "Would you like to know who that jade necklace belonged to?"

I could feel my face getting stiff. I thought hard but I couldn't remember for sure. And then suddenly I could. I hadn't said a word to her about a jade necklace.

I reached for the matches and relit my pipe. "Not very much," I said. "Why?"

"Because I know."

"Uh-huh."

"What do you do when you get real talkative—wiggle your toes?"

"All right," I growled. "You came here to tell me. Go ahead and tell me."

Her blue eyes widened and for a moment I thought they looked a little moist. She took her lower lip between her teeth and held it that way while she stared down at the desk. Then she shrugged and let go of her lip and smiled at me candidly.

"Oh I know I'm just a damned inquisitive wench. But there's a strain of bloodhound in me. My father was a cop. His name was Cliff Riordan and he was police chief of Bay City for seven years. I suppose that's what's the matter."

"I seem to remember. What happened to him?"

"He was fired. It broke his heart. A mob of gamblers headed by a man named Laird Brunette elected themselves a mayor. So they put Dad in charge of the Bureau of Records and Identification, which in Bay City is about the size of a tea-bag. So Dad quit and pottered around for a couple of years and then died. And Mother died soon after him. So I've been alone for two years."

"I'm sorry," I said.

She ground out her cigarette. It had no lipstick on it. "The only reason I'm boring you with this is that it makes it easy for me to get along with policemen. I suppose I ought to have told you last night. So this morning I found out who had charge of the case and went to see him. He was a little sore at you at first."

"That's all right," I said. "If I had told him the truth on all points, he still wouldn't have believed me. All he will do is chew one of my ears off."

She looked hurt. I got up and opened the other window. The noise of the traffic from the boulevard came in in waves, like nausea. I felt lousy. I opened the deep drawer of the desk and got the office bottle out and poured myself a drink.

Miss Riordan watched me with disapproval. I was no longer a solid man. She didn't say anything. I drank the drink and put the bottle away again and sat down.

"You didn't offer me one," she said coolly.

"Sorry. It's only eleven o'clock or less. I didn't think you looked the type."

Her eyes crinkled at the corners. "Is that a compliment?"

"In my circle, yes."

She thought that over. It didn't mean anything to her. It didn't mean anything to me either when I thought it over. But the drink made me feel a lot better.

She leaned forward and scraped her gloves slowly across the glass of the desk. "You wouldn't want to hire an assistant, would you? Not if it only cost you a kind word now and then?"

"No."

She nodded. "I thought probably you wouldn't. I'd better just give you my information and go on home."

I didn't say anything. I lit my pipe again. It makes you look thoughtful when you are not thinking.

"First of all, it occurred to me that a jade necklace like that would be a museum piece and would be well known," she said.

I held the match in the air, still burning and watching the flame crawl close to my fingers. Then I blew it out softly and dropped it in the tray and said:

"I didn't say anything to you about a jade necklace."

"No, but Lieutenant Randall did."

"Somebody ought to sew buttons on his face."

"He knew my father. I promised not to tell."

"You're telling me."

"You knew already, silly."

Her hand suddenly flew up as if it was going to fly to her mouth, but it only rose halfway and then fell back slowly and her eyes widened. It was a good act, but I knew something else about her that spoiled it.

"You *did* know, didn't you?" She breathed the words, hushedly.

"I thought it was diamonds. A bracelet, a pair of earrings, a pendant, three rings, one of the rings with emeralds too."

"Not funny," she said. "Not even fast."

"Fei Tsui jade. Very rare. Carved beads about six carats apiece, sixty of them. Worth eighty thousand dollars."

"You have such nice brown eyes," she said. "And you think you're tough."

"Well, who does it belong to and how did you find out?"

"I found out very simply. I thought the best jeweler in town would probably know, so I went and asked the manager of Block's. I told him I was a writer and wanted to do an article on rare jade—you know the line."

"So he believed your red hair and your beautiful figure."

She flushed clear to the temples. "Well, he told me anyway. It belongs to a rich lady who lives in Bay City, in an estate on the canyon. Mrs. Lewin Lockridge Grayle. Her husband is an investment banker or something, enormously rich, worth about twenty millions. He used to own a radio station in Beverly Hills, Station KFDK, and Mrs. Grayle used to work there. He married her five years ago. She's a ravishing blonde. Mr. Grayle is elderly, liverish, stays home and takes calomel while Mrs. Grayle goes places and has a good time."

"This manager of Block's," I said. "He's a fellow that gets around."

"Oh, I didn't get all that from him, silly. Just about the necklace. The rest I got from Giddy Gertie Arbogast."

I reached into the deep drawer and brought the office bottle up again.

"You're not going to turn out to be one of those drunken detectives, are you?" she asked anxiously.

"Why not? They always solve their cases and they never even sweat. Get on with the story."

"Giddy Gertie is the society editor of the *Chronicle*. I've known him for years. He weighs two hundred and wears a Hitler mustache. He got out his morgue file on the Grayles. Look."

She reached into her bag and slid a photograph across the desk, a five-by-three glazed still.

It was a blonde. A blonde to make a bishop kick a hole in a stained glass window. She was wearing street clothes that looked black and white, and a hat to match and she was a little haughty, but not too much. Whatever you needed, wherever you happened to be—she had it. About thirty years old.

I poured a fast drink and burned my throat getting it down. "Take it away," I said. "I'll start jumping."

"Why, I got it for you. You'll want to see her, won't you?"

I looked at it again. Then I slid it under the blotter. "How about tonight at eleven?"

"Listen, this isn't just a bunch of gag lines, Mr. Marlowe. I called her up. She'll see you. On business."

"It may start out that way."

She made an impatient gesture, so I stopped fooling around and got my battle-scarred frown back on my face. "What will she see me about?"

"Her necklace, of course. It was like this. I called her up and had a lot of trouble getting to talk to her, of course, but finally I did. Then I gave her the song and dance I had given the nice man at Block's and it didn't take. She sounded as if she had a hangover. She said something about talking to her secretary, but I managed to keep her on the phone and ask her if it was true she had a Fei Tsui jade necklace. After a while she said, yes. I asked if I might see it. She said, what for? I said my piece over again and it didn't take any better than the first time. I could hear her yawning and bawling somebody outside the mouthpiece for putting me on. Then I said I was working for Philip Marlowe. She said 'So what?' Just like that."

"Incredible. But all the society dames talk like tramps nowadays."

"I wouldn't know," Miss Riordan said sweetly. "Probably some of them *are* tramps. So I asked her if she had a phone with no extension and she said what business was it of mine. But the funny thing was she hadn't hung up on me."

"She had the jade on her mind and she didn't know what you were leading up to. And she may have heard from Randall already."

Miss Riordan shook her head. "No. I called him later and he didn't know who owned the necklace until I told him. He was quite surprised that I had found out."

"He'll get used to you," I said. "He'll probably have to. What then?"

"So I said to Mrs. Grayle: 'You'd still like it back, wouldn't you?' Just like that. I didn't know any other way to say. I had to say something that would jar her a bit. It did. She gave me another number in a hurry. And I called that and I said I'd like to see her. She seemed surprised. So I had to tell her the story. She didn't like it. But she had been wondering why she hadn't heard from Marriott. I guess she thought he had gone south with the money or something. So I'm to see her at two o'clock. Then I'll tell her about you and how nice and discreet you are and how you would be a good man to help her get it back, if there's any chance and so on. She's already interested."

I didn't say anything. I just stared at her. She looked hurt. "What's the matter? Did I do right?"

"Can't you get it through your head that this is a police case now and that I've been warned to stay off it?"

"Mrs. Grayle has a perfect right to employ you, if she wants to."

"To do what?"

She snapped and unsnapped her bag impatiently. "Oh, my goodness

—a woman like that—with her looks—can't you see—" She stopped and bit her lip. "What kind of man was Marriott?"

"I hardly knew him. I thought he was a bit of a pansy. I didn't like him very well."

"Was he a man who would be attractive to women?"

"Some women. Others would want to spit."

"Well, it looks as if he might have been attractive to Mrs. Grayle. She went out with him."

"She probably goes out with a hundred men. There's very little chance to get the necklace now."

"Why?"

I got up and walked to the end of the office and slapped the wall with the flat of my hand, hard. The clacking typewriter on the other side stopped for a moment, and then went on. I looked down through the open window into the shaft between my building and the Mansion House Hotel. The coffee shop smell was strong enough to build a garage on. I went back to my desk, dropped the bottle of whiskey back into the drawer, shut the drawer and sat down again. I lit my pipe for the eighth or ninth time and looked carefully across the half-dusted glass to Miss Riordan's grave and honest little face.

You could get to like that face a lot. Glamoured up blondes were a dime a dozen, but that was a face that would wear. I smiled at it.

"Listen, Anne. Killing Marriott was a dumb mistake. The gang behind this holdup would never pull anything like that. What must have happened was that some gowed-up run they took along for a gun-holder lost his head. Marriott made a false move and some punk beat him down and it was done so quickly nothing could be done to prevent it. Here is an organized mob with inside information on jewels and the movements of the women that wear them. They ask moderate returns and they would play ball. But here also is a back alley murder that doesn't fit at all. My idea is that whoever did it is a dead man hours ago, with weights on his ankles, deep in the Pacific Ocean. And either the jade went down with him or else they have some idea of its real value and they have cached it away in a place where it will stay for a long time—maybe for years before they dare bring it out again. Or, if the gang is big enough, it may show up on the other side of the world. The eight thousand they asked seems pretty low if they really know the value of the jade. But it would be hard to sell. I'm sure of one thing. They never meant to murder anybody."

Anne Riordan was listening to me with her lips slightly parted and a rapt expression on her face, as if she was looking at the Dalai Lhama.

She closed her mouth slowly and nodded once. "You're wonderful," she said softly. "But you're nuts."

She stood up and gathered her bag to her. "Will you go to see her or won't you?"

"Randall can't stop me—if it comes from her."

"All right. I'm going to see another society editor and get some more dope on the Grayles if I can. About her love life. She would have one, wouldn't she?"

The face framed in auburn hair was wistful.

"Who hasn't?" I sneered.

"*I* never had. Not really."

I reached up and shut my mouth with my hand. She gave me a sharp look and moved towards the door.

"You've forgotten something," I said.

She stopped and turned. "What?" She looked all over the top of the desk.

"You know damn well what."

She came back to the desk and leaned across it earnestly. "Why would they kill the man that killed Marriott, if they don't go in for murder?"

"Because he would be the type that would get picked up sometime and would talk—when they took his dope away from him. I mean they wouldn't kill a customer."

"What makes you so sure the killer took dope?"

"I'm not sure. I just said that. Most punks do."

"Oh." She straightened up and nodded and smiled. "I guess you mean these," she said and reached quickly into her bag and laid a small tissue bag package on the desk.

I reached for it, pulled a rubber band off it carefully and opened up the paper. On it lay three long thick Russian cigarettes with paper mouthpieces. I looked at her and didn't say anything.

"I know I shouldn't have taken them," she said almost breathlessly. "But I knew they were jujus. They usually come in plain papers but lately around Bay City they have been putting them out like this. I've seen several. I thought it was kind of mean for the poor man to be found dead with marihuana cigarettes in his pocket."

"You ought to have taken the case too," I said quietly. "There was dust in it. And it being empty was suspicious."

"I couldn't—with you there. I—I almost went back and did. But I didn't quite have the courage. Did it get you in wrong?"

"No," I lied. "Why should it?"

"I'm glad of that," she said wistfully.

"Why didn't you throw them away?"

She thought about it, her bag clutched to her side, her wide-brimmed absurd hat tilted so that it hid one eye.

"I guess it must be because I'm a cop's daughter," she said at last. "You just don't throw away evidence." Her smile was frail and guilty and her cheeks were flushed. I shrugged.

"Well—" the word hung in the air, like smoke in a closed room. Her lips stayed parted after saying it. I let it hang. The flush on her face deepened.

"I'm horribly sorry. I shouldn't have done it."
I passed that too.
She went very quickly to the door and out.

14

I POKED AT ONE OF THE LONG Russian cigarettes with a finger, then laid
them in a neat row, side by side and squeaked my chair. You just don't
throw away evidence. So they were evidence. Evidence of what? That a
man occasionally smoked a stick of tea, a man who looked as if any touch
of the exotic would appeal to him. On the other hand lots of tough guys
smoked marihuana, also lots of band musicians and high school kids, and
nice girls who had given up trying. American hasheesh. A weed that
would grow anywhere. Unlawful to cultivate now. That meant a lot in a
country as big as the U.S.A.

I sat there and puffed my pipe and listened to the clacking typewriter behind the wall of my office and the bong-bong of the traffic lights
changing on Hollywood Boulevard and spring rustling in the air, like a
paper bag blowing along a concrete sidewalk.

They were pretty big cigarettes, but a lot of Russians are, and
marihuana is a coarse leaf. Indian hemp. American hasheesh. Evidence.
God, what hats the women wear. My head ached. Nuts.

I got my penknife out and opened the small sharp blade, the one I
didn't clean my pipe with, and reached for one of them. That's what a
police chemist would do. Slit one down the middle and examine the stuff
under a microscope, to start with. There might just happen to be something unusual about it. Not very likely, but what the hell, he was paid by
the month.

I slit one down the middle. The mouthpiece part was pretty tough to
slit. Okey, I was a tough guy, I slit it anyway. See if can you stop me.

Out of the mouthpiece shiny segments of rolled thin cardboard
partly straightened themselves and had printing on them. I sat up straight
and pawed for them. I tried to spread them out on the desk in order, but
they slid around on the desk. I grabbed another of the cigarettes and
squinted inside the mouthpiece. Then I went to work with the blade of
the pocket knife in a different way. I pinched the cigarette down to the
place where the mouthpieces began. The paper was thin all the way, you
could feel the grain of what was underneath. So I cut the mouthpiece
off carefully and then still more carefully cut through the mouthpiece
longways, but only just enough. It opened out and there was another card
underneath, rolled up, not touched this time.

I spread it out fondly. It was a man's calling card. Thin pale ivory,
just off white. Engraved on that were delicately shaded words. In the
lower left hand corner a Stillwood Heights telephone number. In the

lower right hand corner the legend, "By Appointment Only." In the middle, a little larger, but still discreet: "Jules Amthor." Below, a little smaller: "Psychic Consultant."

I took hold of the third cigarette. This time, with a lot of difficulty, I teased the card out without cutting anything. It was the same. I put it back where it had been.

I looked at my watch, put my pipe in an ashtray, and then had to look at my watch again to see what time it was. I rolled the two cut cigarettes and the cut card in part of the tissue paper, the one that was complete with card inside in another part of the tissue paper and locked both little packages away in my desk.

I sat looking at the card. Jules Amthor, Psychic Consultant, By Appointment Only, Stillwood Heights phone number, no address. Three like that rolled inside three sticks of tea, in a Chinese or Japanese silk cigarette case with an imitation tortoise-shell frame, a trade article that might have cost thirty-five to seventy-five cents in any Oriental store, Hooey Phooey Sing—Long Sing Tung, that kind of place, where a nice-mannered Jap hisses at you, laughing heartily when you say that the Moon of Arabia incense smells like the girls in Frisco Sadie's back parlor.

And all this in the pocket of a man who was very dead, and who had another and genuinely expensive cigarette case containing cigarettes which he actually smoked.

He must have forgotten it. It didn't make sense. Perhaps it hadn't belonged to him at all. Perhaps he had picked it up in a hotel lobby. Forgotten he had it on him. Forgotten to turn it in. Jules Amthor, Psychic Consultant.

The phone rang and I answered it absently. The voice had the cool hardness of a cop who thinks he is good. It was Randall. He didn't bark. He was the icy type.

"So you didn't know who that girl was last night? And she picked you up on the boulevard and you walked over to there. Nice lying, Marlowe."

"Maybe you have a daughter and you wouldn't like newscameramen jumping out of bushes and popping flashbulbs in her face."

"You lied to me."

"It was a pleasure."

He was silent a moment, as if deciding something. "We'll let that pass," he said. "I've seen her. She came in and told me her story. She's the daughter of a man I knew and respected, as it happens."

"She told you," I said, "and you told her."

"I told her a little," he said coldly. "For a reason. I'm calling you for the same reason. This investigation is going to be undercover. We have a chance to break this jewel gang and we're going to do it."

"Oh, it's a gang murder this morning. Okey."

"By the way, that was marihuana dust in that funny cigarette case—the one with the dragons on it. Sure you didn't see him smoke one out of it?"

"Quite sure. In my presence he smoked only the others. But he wasn't in my presence all the time."

"I see. Well, that's all. Remember what I told you last night. Don't try getting ideas about this case. All we want from you is silence. Otherwise—"

He paused. I yawned into the mouthpiece.

"I heard that," he snapped. "Perhaps you think I'm not in a position to make that stick. I am. One false move out of you and you'll be locked up as a material witness."

"You mean the papers are not to get the case?"

"They'll get the murder—but they won't know what's behind it."

"Neither do you," I said.

"I've warned you twice now," he said. "The third time is out."

"You're doing a lot of talking," I said, "for a guy that holds cards."

I got the phone hung in my face for that. Okey, the hell with him, let him work at it.

I walked around the office a little to cool off, bought myself a short drink, looked at my watch again and didn't see what time it was, and sat down at the desk once more.

Jules Amthor, Psychic Consultant. Consultations by Appointment Only. Give him enough time and pay him enough money and he'll cure anything from a jaded husband to a grasshopper plague. He would be an expert in frustrated love affairs, women who slept alone and didn't like it, wandering boys and girls who didn't write home, sell the property now or hold it for another year, will this part hurt me with my public or make me seem more versatile? Men would sneak in on him too, big strong guys that roared like lions around their offices and were all cold mush under their vests. But mostly it would be women, fat women that panted and thin women that burned, old women that dreamed and young women that thought they might have Electra complexes, women of all sizes, shapes and ages, but with one thing in common—money. No Thursdays at the County Hospital for Mr. Jules Amthor. Cash on the line for him. Rich bitches who had to be dunned for their milk bills would pay him right now.

A fakeloo artist, a hoopla spreader, and a lad who had his card rolled up inside sticks of tea, found on a dead man.

This was going to be good. I reached for the phone and asked the O-operator for the Stillwood Heights number.

15

A WOMAN'S VOICE ANSWERED, a dry, husky-sounding foreign voice: " 'Allo."

"May I talk to Mr. Amthor?"

"Ah no. I regret. I am ver-ry sor-ry. Amthor never speaks upon the telephone. I am hees secretary. Weel I take the message?"

"What's the address out there? I want to see him."

"Ah, you weesh to consult Amthor professionally? He weel be ver-ry pleased. But he ees ver-ry beesy. When you weesh to see him?"

"Right away. Sometime today."

"Ah," the voice regretted, "that cannot be. The next week per'aps. I weel look at the book."

"Look," I said, "never mind the book. You 'ave the pencil?"

"But certainly I 'ave the pencil. I—"

"Take this down. My name is Philip Marlowe. My address is 615 Cahuenga Building, Hollywood. That's on Hollywood Boulevard near Ivar. My phone number is Glenview 7537." I spelled the hard ones and waited.

"Yes, Meester Marlowe. I 'ave that."

"I want to see Mr. Amthor about a man named Marriott." I spelled that too. "It is very urgent. It is a matter of life and death. I want to see him fast. F-a-s-t—fast. Sudden, in other words. Am I clear?"

"You talk ver-ry strange," the foreign voice said.

"No." I took hold of the phone standard and shook it. "I feel fine. I always talk like that. This is a very queer business. Mr. Amthor will positively want to see me. I'm a private detective. But I don't want to go to the police until I've seen him."

"Ah," the voice got as cool as a cafeteria dinner. "You are of the police, no?"

"Listen," I said. "I am of the police, no. I am a private detective. Confidential. But it is very urgent just the same. You call me back, no? You 'ave the telephone number, yes?"

"Si. I 'ave the telephone number. Meester Marriott—he ees sick?"

"Well, he's not up and around," I said. "So you know him?"

"But no. You say a matter of life and death. Amthor he cure many people—"

"This is one time he flops," I said. "I'll be waiting for a call."

I hung up and lunged for the office bottle. I felt as if I had been through a meat grinder. Ten minutes passed. The phone rang. The voice said:

"Amthor he weel see you at six o'clock."

"That's fine. What's the address?"

"He weel send a car."

"I have a car of my own. Just give me—"

"He weel send a car," the voice said coldly, and the phone clicked in my ear.

I looked at my watch once more. It was more than time for lunch. My stomach burned from the last drink. I wasn't hungry. I lit a cigarette. It tasted like a plumber's handkerchief. I nodded across the office at Mr. Rembrandt, then I reached for my hat and went out. I was halfway to the elevator before the thought hit me. It hit me without any reason or sense, like a dropped brick. I stopped and leaned against the marbled wall and pushed my hat around on my head and suddenly I laughed.

A girl passing me on the way from the elevators back to her work turned and gave me one of those looks which are supposed to make your spine feel like a run in a stocking. I waved my hand at her and went back to my office and grabbed the phone. I called up a man I knew who worked on the Lot Books of a title company.

"Can you find a property by the address alone?" I asked him.

"Sure. We have a cross-index. What is it?"

"1644 West 54th Place. I'd like to know a little something about the condition of the title."

"I'd better call you back. What's that number?"

He called back in about three minutes.

"Get your pencil out," he said. "It's Lot 8 of Block 11 of Caraday's Addition to the Maplewood Tract Number 4. The owner of record, subject to certain things, is Jessie Pierce Florian, widow."

"Yeah. What things?"

"Second half taxes, two ten-year street improvement bonds, one storm drain assessment bond also ten year, none of these delinquents, also a first trust deed of $2600."

"You mean one of those things where they can sell you out on ten minutes' notice?"

"Not quite that quick, but a lot quicker than a mortgage. There's nothing unusual about it except the amount. It's high for that neighborhood, unless it's a new house."

"It's a very old house and in bad repair," I said. "I'd say fifteen hundred would buy the place."

"Then it's distinctly unusual, because the refinancing was done only four years ago."

"Okay, who holds it? Some investment company?"

"No. An individual. Man named Lindsay Marriott, a single man. Okey?"

I forget what I said to him or what thanks I made. They probably sounded like words. I sat there, just staring at the wall.

My stomach suddenly felt fine. I was hungry. I went down to the Mansion House Coffee Shop and ate lunch and got my car out of the parking lot next to my building.

I drove south and east, towards West 54th Place. I didn't carry any liquor with me this time.

16

THE BLOCK LOOKED just as it had looked the day before. The street was empty except for an ice truck, two Fords in driveways, and a swirl of dust going around a corner. I drove slowly past No. 1644 and parked farther along and studied the houses on either side of mine. I walked back and stopped in front of it, looking at the tough palm tree and the drab unwatered scrap of lawn. The house seemed empty, but probably wasn't. It just had that look. The lonely rocker on the front porch stood just where it had stood yesterday. There was a throw-away paper on the walk. I picked it up and slapped it against my leg and then I saw the curtain move next door, in the near front window.

Old Nosey again. I yawned and tilted my hat down. A sharp nose almost flattened itself against the inside of the glass. White hair above it, and eyes that were just eyes from where I stood. I strolled along the sidewalk and the eyes watched me. I turned in towards her house. I climbed the wooden steps and rang the bell.

The door snapped open as if it had been on a spring. She was a tall old bird with a chin like a rabbit. Seen from close her eyes were as sharp as lights on still water. I took my hat off.

"Are you the lady who called the police about Mrs. Florian?"

She stared at me coolly and missed nothing about me, probably not even the mole on my right shoulder blade.

"I ain't sayin' I am, young man, and I ain't sayin' I ain't. Who are you?" It was a high twangy voice, made for talking over an eight party line.

"I'm a detective."

"Land's sakes. Why didn't you say so? What's she done now? I ain't seen a thing and I ain't missed a minute. Henry done all the goin' to the store for me. Ain't been a sound out of there."

She snapped the screen door unhooked and drew me in. The hall smelled of furniture oil. It had a lot of dark furniture that had once been in good style. Stuff with inlaid panels and scollops at the corners. We went into a front room that had cotton lace antimacassars pinned on everything you could stick a pin into.

"Say, didn't I see you before?" she asked suddenly, a note of suspicion crawling around in her voice. "Sure enough I did. You was the man that—"

"That's right. And I'm still a detective. Who's Henry?"

"Oh, he's just a little colored boy that goes errands for me. Well, what you want, young man?" She patted a clean red and white apron and gave me the beady eye. She clicked her store teeth a couple of times for practice.

"Did the officers come here yesterday after they went to Mrs. Florian's house?"

"What officers?"

"The uniformed officers," I said patiently.

"Yes, they was here a minute. They didn't know nothing."

"Describe the big man to me—the one that had a gun and made you call up."

She described him, with complete accuracy. It was Malloy all right.

"What kind of car did he drive?"

"A little car. He couldn't hardly get into it."

"That's all you can say? This man's a murderer!"

Her mouth gaped, but her eyes were pleased. "Land's sakes, I wish I could tell you, young man. But I never knew much about cars. Murder, eh? Folks ain't safe a minute in this town. When I come here twenty-two years ago we didn't lock our doors hardly. Now it's gangsters and crooked police and politicians fightin' each other with machine guns, so I've heard. Scandalous is what it is, young man."

"Yeah. What do you know about Mrs. Florian?"

The small mouth puckered. "She ain't neighborly. Plays her radio loud late nights. Sings. She don't talk to anybody." She leaned forward a little. "I'm not positive, but my opinion is she drinks liquor."

"She have many visitors?"

"She don't have no visitors at all."

"You'd know, of course, Mrs.—"

"Mrs. Morrison. Land's sakes, yes. What else have I got to do but look out of the windows?"

"I bet it's fun. Mrs. Florian has lived here a long time?"

"About ten years, I reckon. Had a husband once. Looked like a bad one to me. He died." She paused and thought. "I guess he died natural," she added. "I never heard different."

"Left her money?"

Her eyes receded and her chin followed them. She sniffed hard. "You been drinkin' liquor," she said coldly.

"I just had a tooth out. The dentist gave it to me."

"I don't hold with it."

"It's bad stuff, except for medicine," I said.

"I don't hold with it for medicine neither."

"I think you're right," I said. "Did he leave her money? Her husband?"

"I wouldn't know." Her mouth was the size of a prune and as smooth. I had lost out.

"Has anybody at all been there since the officers?"

"Ain't seen."

"Thank you very much, Mrs. Morrison. I won't trouble you any more now. You've been very kind and helpful."

I walked out of the room and opened the door. She followed me and cleared her throat and clicked her teeth a couple more times.

"What number should I call?" she asked, relenting a little.

"University 4-5000. Ask for Lieutenant Nulty. What does she live on—relief?"

"This ain't a relief neighborhood," she said coldly.

"I bet that side piece was the admiration of Sioux Falls once," I said, gazing at a carved sideboard that was in the hall because the dining room was too small for it. It had curved ends, thin carved legs, was inlaid all over, and had a painted basket of fruit on the front.

"Mason City," she said softly. "Yessir, we had a nice home once, me and George. Best there was."

I opened the screen door and stepped through it and thanked her again. She was smiling now. Her smile was as sharp as her eyes.

"Gets a registered letter first of every month," she said suddenly.

I turned and waited. She leaned towards me. "I see the mailman go up to the door and get her to sign. First day of every month. Dresses up then and goes out. Don't come home till all hours. Sings half the night. Times I could have called the police it was so loud."

I patted the thin malicious arm.

"You're one in a thousand, Mrs. Morrison," I said. I put my hat on, tipped it to her and left. Halfway down the walk I thought of something and swung back. She was still standing inside the screen door, with the house door open behind her. I went back up on the steps.

"Tomorrow's the first," I said. "First of April. April Fool's Day. Be sure to notice whether she gets her registered letter, will you, Mrs. Morrison?"

The eyes gleamed at me. She began to laugh—a high-pitched old woman's laugh. "April Fool's Day," she tittered. "Maybe she won't get it."

I left her laughing. The sound was like a hen having hiccups.

17

NOBODY ANSWERED MY RING or knock next door. I tried again. The screen door wasn't hooked. I tried the house door. It was unlocked. I stepped inside.

Nothing was changed, not even the smell of gin. There were still no bodies on the floor. A dirty glass stood on the small table beside the chair where Mrs. Florian had sat yesterday. The radio was turned off. I went over to the davenport and felt down behind the cushions. The same dead soldier and another one with him now.

I called out. No answer. Then I thought I heard a long slow unhappy breathing that was half groaning. I went through the arch and sneaked into the little hallway. The bedroom door was partly open and the groaning sound came from behind it. I stuck my head in and looked.

Mrs. Florian was in bed. She was lying flat on her back with a cotton comforter pulled up to her chin. One of the little fluffballs on the comforter was almost in her mouth. Her long yellow face was slack, half dead. Her dirty hair straggled on the pillow. Her eyes opened slowly and looked at me with no expression. The room had a sickening smell of sleep, liquor and dirty clothes. A sixty-nine cent alarm clock ticked on the peeling gray-white paint of the bureau. It ticked loud enough to shake the walls. Above it a mirror showed a distorted view of the woman's face. The trunk from which she had taken the photos was still open.

I said: "Good afternoon, Mrs. Florian. Are you sick?"

She worked her lips together slowly, rubbed one over the other, then slid a tongue out and moistened them and worked her jaws. Her voice came from her mouth sounding like a worn-out phonograph record. Her eyes showed recognition now, but not pleasure.

"You get him?"

"The Moose?"

"Sure."

"Not yet. Soon, I hope."

She screwed her eyes up and then snapped them open as if trying to get rid of a film over them.

"You ought to keep your house locked up," I said. "He might come back."

"You think I'm scared of the Moose, huh?"

"You acted like it when I was talking to you yesterday."

She thought about that. Thinking was weary work. "Got any liquor?"

"No, I didn't bring any today, Mrs. Florian. I was a little low on cash."

"Gin's cheap. It hits."

"I might go out for some in a little while. So you're not afraid of Malloy?"

"Why would I be?"

"Okey, you're not. What *are* you afraid of?"

Light snapped into her eyes, held for a moment, and faded out again. "Aw beat it. You coppers give me an ache in the fanny."

I said nothing. I leaned against the door frame and put a cigarette in my mouth and tried to jerk it up far enough to hit my nose with it. This is harder than it looks.

"Coppers," she said slowly, as if talking to herself, "will never catch that boy. He's good and he's got dough and he's got friends. You're wasting your time, copper."

"Just the routine," I said. "It was practically a self-defense anyway. Where would he be?"

She snickered and wiped her mouth on the cotton comforter.

"Soap now," she said. "Soft stuff. Copper smart. You guys still think it gets you something."

"I like the Moose," I said.

Interest flickered in her eyes. "You known him?"

"I was with him yesterday—when he killed the nigger over on Central."

She opened her mouth wide and laughed her head off without making any more sound than you would make cracking a breadstick. Tears ran out of her eyes and down her face.

"A big strong guy," I said. "Soft-hearted in spots too. Wanted his Velma pretty bad."

The eyes veiled. "Thought it was her folks was looking for her," she said softly.

"They are. But she's dead, you said. Nothing there. Where did she die?"

"Dalhart, Texas. Got a cold and went to the chest and off she went."

"You were there?"

"Hell, no. I just heard."

"Oh. Who told you, Mrs. Florian?"

"Some hoofer. I forget the name right now. Maybe a good stiff drink might help some. I feel like Death Valley."

"And you look like a dead mule," I thought, but didn't say it out loud. "There's just one more thing," I said, "then I'll maybe run out for some gin. I looked up the title to your house, I don't know just why."

She was rigid under the bedclothes, like a wooden woman. Even her eyelids were frozen half down over the clogged iris of her eyes. Her breath stilled.

"There's a rather large trust deed on it," I said. "Considering the low value of property around here. It's held by a man named Lindsay Marriott."

Her eyes blinked rapidly, but nothing else moved. She stared.

"I used to work for him," she said at last. "I used to be a servant in his family. He kind of takes care of me a little."

I took the unlighted cigarette out of my mouth and looked at it aimlessly and stuck it back in.

"Yesterday afternoon, a few hours after I saw you, Mr. Marriott called me up at my office. He offered me a job."

"What kind of job?" Her voice croaked now, badly.

I shrugged. "I can't tell you that. Confidential. I went to see him last night."

"You're a clever son of a bitch," she said thickly and moved a hand under the bedclothes.

I stared at her and said nothing.

"Copper-smart," she sneered.

I ran a hand up and down the door frame. It felt slimy. Just touching it made me want to take a bath.

"Well, that's all," I said smoothly. "I was just wondering how come. Might be nothing at all. Just a coincidence. It just looked as if it might mean something."

"Copper-smart," she said emptily. "Not a real copper at that. Just a cheap shamus."

"I suppose so," I said. "Well, good-by, Mrs. Florian. By the way, I don't think you'll get a registered letter tomorrow morning."

She threw the bedclothes aside and jerked upright with her eyes blazing. Something glittered in her right hand. A small revolver, a Banker's Special. It was old and worn, but looked business-like.

"Tell it," she snarled. "Tell it fast."

I looked at the gun and the gun looked at me. Not too steadily. The hand behind it began to shake, but the eyes still blazed. Saliva bubbled at the corners of her mouth.

"You and I could work together," I said.

The gun and her jaw dropped at the same time. I was inches from the door. While the gun was still dropping, I slid through it and beyond the opening.

"Think it over," I called back.

There was no sound, no sound of any kind.

I went fast back through the hall and dining room and out of the house. My back felt queer as I went down the walk. The muscles crawled.

Nothing happened. I went along the street and got into my car and drove away from there.

The last day of March and hot enough for summer. I felt like taking my coat off as I drove. In front of the 77th Street Station, two prowl car men were scowling at a bent front fender. I went in through the swing doors and found a uniformed lieutenant behind the railing looking over the charge sheet. I asked him if Nulty was upstairs. He said he thought he was, was I a friend of his. I said yes. He said okey, go on up, so I went up the worn stairs and along the corridor and knocked at the door. The voice yelled and I went in.

He was picking his teeth, sitting in one chair with his feet on the other. He was looking at his left thumb, holding it up in front of his eyes and at arm's length. The thumb looked all right to me, but Nulty's stare was gloomy, as if he thought it wouldn't get well.

He lowered it to his thigh and swung his feet to the floor and looked at me instead of at his thumb. He wore a dark gray suit and a mangled cigar end was waiting on the desk for him to get through with the toothpick.

I turned the felt seat cover that lay on the other chair with its straps not fastened to anything, sat down, and put a cigarette in my face.

"You," Nulty said, and looked at his toothpick, to see if it was chewed enough.

"Any luck?"

"Malloy? I ain't on it any more."

"Who is?"

"Nobody ain't. Why? The guy's lammed. We got him on the tele-type and they got readers out. Hell, he'll be in Mexico long gone."

"Well, all he did was kill a Negro," I said. "I guess that's only a misdemeanor."

"You still interested? I thought you was workin'?" His pale eyes moved damply over my face.

"I had a job last night, but it didn't last. Have you still got that Pierrot photo?"

He reached around and pawed under his blotter. He held it out. It still looked pretty. I stared at the face.

"This is really mine," I said. "If you don't need it for the file, I'd like to keep it."

"Should be in the file, I guess," Nulty said. "I forgot about it. Okey, keep it under your hat. I passed the file in."

I put the photo in my breast pocket and stood up. "Well, I guess that's all," I said, a little too airily.

"I smell something," Nulty said coldly.

I looked at the piece of rope on the edge of his desk. His eyes followed my look. He threw the toothpick on the floor and stuck the chewed cigar in his mouth.

"Not this either," he said.

"It's a vague hunch. If it grows more solid, I won't forget you."

"Things is tough. I need a break, pal."

"A man who works as hard as you deserves one," I said.

He struck a match on his thumbnail, looked pleased because it caught the first time, and started inhaling smoke from the cigar.

"I'm laughing," Nulty said sadly, as I went out.

The hall was quiet, the whole building was quiet. Down in front the prowl car men were still looking at their bent fender. I drove back to Hollywood.

The phone was ringing as I stepped into the office. I leaned down over the desk and said, "Yes?"

"Am I addressing Mr. Philip Marlowe?"

"Yes, this is Marlowe."

"This is Mrs. Grayle's residence. Mrs. Lewin Lockridge Grayle. Mrs. Grayle would like to see you here as soon as convenient."

"Where?"

"The address is Number 862 Aster Drive, in Bay City. May I say you will arrive within the hour?"

"Are you Mr. Grayle?"

"Certainly not, sir. I am the butler."

"That's me you hear ringing the door bell," I said.

18

IT WAS CLOSE TO THE OCEAN and you could feel the ocean in the air but you couldn't see water from the front of the place. Aster Drive had a long smooth curve there and the houses on the inland side were just nice houses, but on the canyon side they were great silent estates, with twelve foot walls and wrought-iron gates and ornamental hedges; and inside, if you could get inside, a special brand of sunshine, very quiet, put up in noise-proof containers just for the upper classes.

A man in a dark blue Russian tunic and shiny black puttees and flaring breeches stood in the half-open gates. He was a dark, good-looking lad, with plenty of shoulders and shiny smooth hair and the peak on his rakish cap made a soft shadow over his eyes. He had a cigarette in the corner of his mouth and he held his head tilted a little, as if he liked to keep the smoke out of his nose. One hand had a smooth black gauntlet on it and the other was bare. There was a heavy ring on his third finger.

There was no number in sight, but this should be 862. I stopped my car and leaned out and asked him. It took him a long time to answer. He had to look me over very carefully. Also the car I was driving. He came over to me and as he came he carelessly dropped his ungloved hand towards his hip. It was the kind of carelessness that was meant to be noticed.

He stopped a couple of feet away from my car and looked me over again.

"I'm looking for the Grayle residence," I said.

"This is it. Nobody in."

"I'm expected."

He nodded. His eyes gleamed like water. "Name?"

"Philip Marlowe."

"Wait there." He strolled, without hurry, over to the gates and unlocked an iron door set into one of the massive pillars. There was a telephone inside. He spoke briefly into it, snapped the door shut, and came back to me.

"You have some identification?"

I let him look at the license on the steering post. "That doesn't prove anything," he said. "How do I know it's your car?"

I pulled the key out of the ignition and threw the door open and got out. That put me about a foot from him. He had a nice breath. Haig and Haig at least.

"You've been at the sideboy again," I said.

He smiled. His eyes measured me. I said:

"Listen, I'll talk to the butler over that phone and he'll know my voice. Will that pass me in or do I have to ride on your back?"

"I just work here," he said softly. "If I didn't—" he let the rest hang in the air, and kept on smiling.

"You're a nice lad," I said and patted his shoulder. "Dartmouth or Dannemora?"

"Christ," he said. "Why didn't you say you were a cop?"

We both grinned. He waved his hand and I went in through the half open gate. The drive curved and tall molded hedges of dark green completely screened it from the street and from the house. Through a green gate I saw a Jap gardener at work weeding a huge lawn. He was pulling a piece of weed out of the vast velvet expanse and sneering at it the way Jap gardeners do. Then the tall hedge closed in again and I didn't see anything more for a hundred feet. Then the hedge ended in a wide circle in which half a dozen cars were parked.

One of them was a small coupe. There were a couple of very nice two-tone Buicks of the latest model, good enough to go for the mail in. There was a black limousine, with dull nickel louvres and hubcaps the size of bicycle wheels. There was a long sport phaeton with the top down. A short very wide all-weather concrete driveway led from these to the side entrance of the house.

Off to the left, beyond the parking space there was a sunken garden with a fountain at each of the four corners. The entrance was barred by a wrought-iron gate with a flying Cupid in the middle. There were busts on light pillars and a stone seat with crouching griffins at each end. There was an oblong pool with stone waterlilies in it and a big stone bullfrog sitting on one of the leaves. Still farther a rose colonnade led to a thing like an altar, hedged in at both sides, yet not so completely but that the sun lay in an arabesque along the steps of the altar. And far over to the left there was a wild garden, not very large, with a sundial in the corner near an angle of wall that was built to look like a ruin. And there were flowers. There were a million flowers.

The house itself was not so much. It was smaller than Buckingham Palace, rather gray for California, and probably had fewer windows than the Chrysler Building.

I sneaked over to the side entrance and pressed a bell and somewhere a set of chimes made a deep mellow sound like church bells.

A man in a striped vest and gilt buttons opened the door, bowed, took my hat and was through for the day. Behind him in dimness, a man in striped knife-edge pants and a black coat and wing collar with gray striped tie leaned his gray head forward about half an inch and said: "Mr. Marlowe? If you will come this way, please—"

We went down a hall. It was a very quiet hall. Not a fly buzzed in it. The floor was covered with Oriental rugs and there were paintings along the walls. We turned a corner and there was more hall. A French window showed a gleam of blue water far off and I remembered almost with a shock that we were near the Pacific Ocean and that this house was on the edge of one of the canyons.

The butler reached a door and opened it against voices and stood aside and I went in. It was a nice room with large chesterfields and lounging chairs done in pale yellow leather arranged around a fireplace in front of which, on the glossy but not slippery floor, lay a rug as thin as silk and as old as Aesop's aunt. A jet of flowers glistened in a corner, another on a low table, the walls were of dull painted parchment, there was comfort, space, coziness, a dash of the very modern and a dash of the very old, and three people sitting in a sudden silence watching me cross the floor.

One of them was Anne Riordan, looking just as I had seen her last, except that she was holding a glass of amber fluid in her hand. One was a tall thin sad-faced man with a stony chin and deep eyes and no color in his face but an unhealthy yellow. He was a good sixty, or rather a bad sixty. He wore a dark business suit, a red carnation, and looked subdued.

The third was the blonde. She was dressed to go out, in a pale greenish blue. I didn't pay much attention to her clothes. They were what the guy designed for her and she would go to the right man. The effect was to make her look very young and to make her lapis lazuli eyes look very blue. Her hair was of the gold of old paintings and had been fussed with just enough but not too much. She had a full set of curves which nobody had been able to improve on. The dress was rather plain except for a clasp of diamonds at the throat. Her hands were not small, but they had shape, and the nails were the usual jarring note—almost magenta. She was giving me one of her smiles. She looked as if she smiled easily, but her eyes had a still look, as if they thought slowly and carefully. And her mouth was sensual.

"So nice of you to come," she said. "This is my husband. Mix Mr. Marlowe a drink, honey."

Mr. Grayle shook hands with me. His hand was cold and a little moist. His eyes were sad. He mixed a Scotch and soda and handed it to me.

Then he sat down in a corner and was silent. I drank half of the drink and grinned at Miss Riordan. She looked at me with a sort of absent expression, as if she had another clue.

"Do you think you can do anything for us?" the blonde asked slowly, looking down into her glass. "If you think you can, I'd be delighted. But the loss is rather small, compared with having any more fuss with gangsters and awful people."

"I don't know very much about it really," I said.

"Oh, I hope you can." She gave me a smile I could feel in my hip pocket.

I drank the other half of my drink. I began to feel rested. Mrs. Grayle rang a bell set into the arm of the leather chesterfield and a footman came in. She half pointed to the tray. He looked around and mixed two drinks. Miss Riordan was still playing cute with the same one and apparently Mr. Grayle didn't drink. The footman went out.

Mrs. Grayle and I held our glasses. Mrs. Grayle crossed her legs, a little carelessly.

"I don't know whether I can do anything," I said. "I doubt it. What is there to go on?"

"I'm sure you can." She gave me another smile. "How far did Lin Marriott take you into his confidence?"

She looked sideways at Miss Riordan. Miss Riordan just couldn't catch the look. She kept right on sitting. She looked sideways the other way. Mrs. Grayle looked at her husband. "Do you have to bother with this, honey?"

Mr. Grayle stood up and said he was very glad to have met me and that he would go and lie down for a while. He didn't feel very well. He hoped I would excuse him. He was so polite I wanted to carry him out of the room just to show my appreciation.

He left. He closed the door softly, as if he was afraid to wake a sleeper. Mrs. Grayle looked at the door for a moment and then put the smile back on her face and looked at me.

"Miss Riordan is in your complete confidence, of course."

"Nobody's in my complete confidence, Mrs. Grayle. She happens to know about this case—what there is to know."

"Yes." She drank a sip or two, then finished her glass at a swallow and set it aside.

"To hell with this polite drinking," she said suddenly. "Let's get together on this. You're a very good-looking man to be in your sort of racket."

"It's a smelly business," I said.

"I didn't quite mean that. Is there any money in it—or is that impertinent?"

"There's not much money in it. There's a lot of grief. But there's a lot of fun too. And there's always a chance of a big case."

"How does one get to be a private detective? You don't mind my sizing you up a little? And push that table over here, will you? So I can reach the drinks."

I got up and pushed the huge silver tray on a stand across the glossy floor to her side. She made two more drinks. I still had half of my second.

"Most of us are ex-cops," I said. "I worked for the D.A. for a while. I got fired."

She smiled nicely. "Not for incompetence, I'm sure."

"No, for talking back. Have you had any more phone calls?"

"Well—" She looked at Anne Riordan. She waited. Her look said things.

Anne Riordan stood up. She carried her glass, still full, over to the tray and set it down. "You probably won't run short," she said. "But if you do—and thanks very much for talking to me, Mrs. Grayle. I won't use anything. You have my word for it."

"Heavens, you're not leaving," Mrs. Grayle said with a smile.

Anne Riordan took her lower lip between her teeth and held it there for a moment as if making up her mind whether to bite it off and spit it out or leave it on a while longer.

"Sorry, afraid I'll have to. I don't work for Mr. Marlowe, you know. Just a friend. Good-by, Mrs. Grayle."

The blonde gleamed at her. "I hope you'll drop in again soon. Any time." She pressed the bell twice. That got the butler. He held the door open.

Miss Riordan went out quickly and the door closed. For quite a while after it closed, Mrs. Grayle stared at it with a faint smile. "It's much better this way, don't you think?" she said after an interval of silence. I nodded. "You're probably wondering how she knows so much if she's just a friend," I said. "She's a curious little girl. Some of it she dug out herself, like who you were and who owned the jade necklace. Some of it just happened. She came by last night to that dell where Marriott was killed. She was out riding. She happened to see a light and came down there."

"Oh." Mrs. Grayle lifted a glass quickly and made a face. "It's horrible to think of. Poor Lin. He was rather a heel. Most of one's friends are. But to die like that is awful." She shuddered. Her eyes got large and dark.

"So it's all right about Miss Riordan. She won't talk. Her father was chief of police here for a long time," I said.

"Yes. So she told me. You're not drinking."

"I'm doing what *I* call drinking."

"You and I should get along. Did Lin—Mr. Marriott—tell you how the hold-up happened?"

"Between here and the Trocadero somewhere. He didn't say exactly. Three or four men."

She nodded her golden gleaming head. "Yes. You know there was something rather funny about that holdup. They gave me back one of my rings, rather a nice one, too."

"He told me that."

"Then again I hardly ever wore the jade. After all, it's a museum piece, probably not many like it in the world, a very rare type of jade. Yet they snapped at it. I wouldn't expect them to think it had any value much, would you?"

"They'd know you wouldn't wear it otherwise. Who knew about its value?"

She thought. It was nice to watch her thinking. She still had her legs crossed, and still carelessly.

"All sorts of people, I suppose."

"But they didn't know you would be wearing it that night? Who knew that?"

She shrugged her pale blue shoulders. I tried to keep my eyes where they belonged.

"My maid. But she's had a hundred chances. And I trust her—"

"Why?"

"I don't know. I just trust some people. I trust you."

"Did you trust Marriott?"

Her face got a little hard. Her eyes a little watchful. "Not in some things. In others, yes. There are degrees." She had a nice way of talking, cool, half-cynical, and yet not hard-boiled. She rounded her words well.

"All right—besides the maid. The chauffeur?"

She shook her head, no. "Lin drove me that night, in his own car. I don't think George was around at all. Wasn't it Thursday?"

"I wasn't there. Marriott said four or five days before in telling me about it. Thursday would have been an even week from last night."

"Well, it was Thursday." She reached for my glass and her fingers touched mine a little, and were soft to the touch. "George gets Thursday evening off. That's the usual day, you know." She poured a fat slug of mellow-looking Scotch into my glass and squirted in some fizz-water. It was the kind of liquor you think you can drink forever, and all you do is get reckless. She gave herself the same treatment.

"Lin told you my name?" she asked softly, the eyes still watchful.

"He was careful not to."

"Then he probably misled you a little about the time. Let's see what we have. Maid and chauffeur out. Out of consideration as accomplices, I mean."

"They're not out by me."

"Well, at least I'm trying," she laughed. "Then there's Newton, the butler. He might have seen it on my neck that night. But it hangs down rather low and I was wearing a white fox evening wrap; no, I don't think he could have seen it."

"I bet you looked a dream," I said.

"You're not getting a little tight, are you?"

"I've been known to be soberer."

She put her head back and went off into a peal of laughter. I have only known four women in my life who could do that and still look beautiful. She was one of them.

"Newton is okey," I said. "His type don't run with hoodlums. That's just guessing, though. How about the footman?"

She thought and remembered, then shook her head. "He didn't see me."

"Anybody ask you to wear the jade?"

Her eyes instantly got more guarded. "You're not fooling me a damn bit," she said.

She reached for my glass to refill it. I let her have it, even though it still had an inch to go. I studied the lovely lines of her neck.

When she had filled the glasses and we were playing with them again I said, "Let's get the record straight and then I'll tell you something. Describe the evening."

She looked at her wrist watch, drawing a full length sleeve back to do it. "I ought to be—"

"Let him wait."

Her eyes flashed at that. I liked them that way. "There's such a thing as being just a little too frank," she said.

"Not in my business. Describe the evening. Or have me thrown out on my ear. One or the other. Make your lovely mind up."

"You'd better sit over here beside me."

"I've been thinking that a long time," I said. "ever since you crossed your legs, to be exact."

She pulled her dress down. "These damn things are always up around your neck."

I sat beside her on the yellow leather chesterfield. "Aren't you a pretty fast worker?" she asked quietly.

I didn't answer her.

"Do you do much of this sort of thing?" she asked with a sidelong look.

"Practically none. I'm a Tibetan monk, in my spare time."

"Only you don't have any spare time."

"Let's focus," I said. "Let's get what's left of our minds—or mine—on the problem. How much are you going to pay me?"

"Oh, that's the problem. I thought you were going to get my necklace back. Or try to."

"I have to work in my own way. This way." I took a long drink and it nearly stood me on my head. I swallowed a little air.

"And investigate a murder," I said.

"That has nothing to do with it. I mean that's a police affair, isn't it?"

"Yeah—only the poor guy paid me a hundred bucks to take care of him—and I didn't. Makes me feel guilty. Makes me want to cry. Shall I cry?"

"Have a drink." She poured us some more Scotch. It didn't seem to affect her any more than water affects Boulder Dam.

"Well, where have we got to?" I said, trying to hold my glass so that the whiskey would stay inside it. "No maid, no chauffeur, no butler, no footman. We'll be doing our own laundry next. How did the holdup happen? Your version might have a few details Marriott didn't give me."

She leaned forward and cupped her chin in her hand. She looked serious without looking silly-serious.

"We went to a party in Brentwood Heights. Then Lin suggested we run over to the Troc for a few drinks and a few dances. So we did. They were doing some work on Sunset and it was very dusty. So coming back Lin dropped down to Santa Monica. That took us past a shabby looking hotel called the Hotel Indio, which I happened to notice for some silly meaningless reason. Across the street from it was a beer joint and a car was parked in front of that."

"Only one car—in front of a beer joint?"

"Yes. Only one. It was a very dingy place. Well, this car started up and followed us and of course I thought nothing of that either. There was no reason to. Then before we got to where Santa Monica turns into Arguello Boulevard, Lin said, 'Let's go over the other road' and turned up some curving residential street. Then all of a sudden a car rushed by us and grazed the fender and then pulled over to stop. A man in an overcoat and scarf and hat low on his face came back to apologize. It was a white scarf bunched out and it drew my eyes. It was about all I really saw of him except that he was tall and thin. As soon as he got close—and I remembered afterwards that he didn't walk in our headlights at all—"

"That's natural. Nobody likes to look into headlights. Have a drink. My treat this time."

She was leaning forward, her fine eyebrows—not daubs of paint—drawn together in a frown of thought. I made two drinks. She went on:

"As soon as he got close to the side where Lin was sitting he jerked the scarf up over his nose and a gun was shining at us. 'Stick-up,' he said. 'Be very quiet and everything will be jake.' Then another man came over on the other side."

"In Beverly Hills," I said, "the best policed four square miles in California."

She shrugged. "It happened just the same. They asked for my jewelry and bag. The man with the scarf did. The one on my side never spoke at all. I passed the things across Lin and the man gave me back my bag and one ring. He said to hold off calling the police and insurance people for a while. They would make us a nice smooth easy deal. He said they found it easier to work on a straight percentage. He seemed to have all the time in the world. He said they could work through the insurance people, if they had to, but that meant cutting in a shyster, and they preferred not to. He sounded like a man with some education."

"It might have been Dressed-Up Eddie," I said. "Only he got bumped off in Chicago."

She shrugged. "It happened just the same. They asked for my jew-

"Then they left and we went home and I told Lin to keep quiet about it. The next day I got a call. We have two phones, one with extensions and one in my bedroom with no extensions. The call was on this. It's not listed, of course."

I nodded. "They can buy the number for a few dollars. It's done all the time. Some movie people have to change their numbers every month."

We had a drink.

"I told the man calling to take it up with Lin and he would represent me and if they were not too unreasonable, we might deal. He said okey, and from then on I guess they just stalled long enough to watch us a little. Finally, as you know, we agreed on eight thousand dollars and so forth."

"Could you recognize any of them?"

"Of course not."

"Randall know all this?"

"Of course. Do we have to talk about it any more? It bores me." She gave me the lovely smile.

"Did he make any comment?"

She yawned. "Probably. I forget."

I sat with my empty glass in my hand and thought. She took it away from me and started to fill it again.

I took the refilled glass out of her hand and transferred it to my left and took hold of her left hand with my right. It felt smooth and soft and warm and comforting. It squeezed mine. The muscles in it were strong. She was a well built woman, and no paper flower.

"I think he had an idea," she said. "But he didn't say what it was."

"Anybody would have an idea out of all that," I said.

She turned her head slowly and looked at me. Then she nodded. "You can't miss it, can you?"

"How long have you known him?"

"Oh, years. He used to be an announcer at the station my husband owned. KFDK. That's where I met him. That's where I met my husband too."

"I knew that. But Marriott lived as if he had money. Not riches, but comfortable money."

"He came into some and quit radio business."

"Do you know for a fact he came into money—or was that just something he said?"

She shrugged. She squeezed my hand.

"Or it may not have been very much money and he may have gone through it pretty fast," I squeezed her hand back. "Did he borrow from you?"

"You're a little old-fashioned, aren't you?" She looked down at the hand I was holding.

"I'm still working. And your Scotch is so good it keeps me half-sober. Not that I'd have to be drunk—"

"Yes." She drew her hand out of mine and rubbed it. "You must have quite a clutch—in your spare time. Lin Marriott was a high-class blackmailer, of course. That's obvious. He lived on women."

"He had something on you?"

"Should I tell you?"

"It probably wouldn't be wise."

She laughed. "I will, anyhow. I got a little tight at his house once and passed out. I seldom do. He took some photos of me—with my clothes up to my neck."

"The dirty dog," I said. "Have you got any of them handy?"

She slapped my wrist. She said softly:

"What's your name?"

"Phil. What's yours?"

"Helen. Kiss me."

She fell softly across my lap and I bent down over her face and began to browse on it. She worked her eyelashes and made butterfly kisses on my cheeks. When I got to her mouth it was half open and burning and her tongue was a darting snake between her teeth.

The door opened and Mr. Grayle stepped quietly into the room. I was holding her and didn't have a chance to let go. I lifted my face and looked at him. I felt as cold as Finnegan's feet, the day they buried him.

The blonde in my arms didn't move, didn't even close her lips. She had a half-dreamy, half-sarcastic expression on her face.

Mr. Grayle cleared his throat slightly and said: "I beg your pardon, I'm sure," and went quietly out of the room. There was an infinite sadness in his eyes.

I pushed her away and stood up and got my handkerchief out and mopped my face.

She lay as I had left her, half sideways along the davenport, the skin showing in a generous sweep above one stocking.

"Who was that?" she asked thickly.

"Mr. Grayle."

"Forget him."

I went away from her and sat down in the chair I had sat in when I first came into the room.

After a moment she straightened herself out and sat up and looked at me steadily.

"It's all right. He understands. What the hell can he expect?"

"I guess he knows."

"Well, I tell you it's all right. Isn't that enough? He's a sick man. What the hell—"

"Don't go shrill on me. I don't like shrill women."

She opened a bag lying beside her and took out a small handkerchief and wiped her lips, then looked at her face in a mirror.

"I guess you're right," she said. "Just too much Scotch. Tonight at the Belvedere Club. Ten o'clock." She wasn't looking at me. Her breath was fast.

"Is that a good place?"

"Laird Brunette owns it. I know him pretty well."

"Right," I said. I was still cold. I felt nasty, as if I had picked a poor man's pocket.

She got a lipstick out and touched her lips very lightly and then looked at me along her eyes. She tossed the mirror. I caught it and looked at my face. I worked at it with my handkerchief and stood up to give her back the mirror.

She was leaning back, showing all her throat, looking at me lazily down her eyes.

"What's the matter?"

"Nothing. Ten o'clock at the Belvedere Club. Don't be too magnificent. All I have is a dinner suit. In the bar?"

She nodded, her eyes still lazy.

I went across the room and out, without looking back. The footman met me in the hall and gave me my hat, looking like the Great Stone Face.

19

I WALKED DOWN THE CURVING DRIVEWAY and lost myself in the shadow of the tall trimmed hedges and came to the gates. Another man was

holding the fort now, a husky in plainclothes, an obvious bodyguard. He let me out with a nod.

A horn tooted. Miss Riordan's coupe was drawn up behind my car. I went over there and looked in at her. She looked cool and sarcastic.

She sat there with her hands on the wheel, gloved and slim. She smiled.

"I waited. I suppose it was none of my business. What did you think of her?"

"I bet she snaps a mean garter."

"Do you always have to say things like that?" She flushed bitterly. "Sometimes I hate men. Old men, young men, football players, opera tenors, smart millionaires, beautiful men who are gigolos and almost-heels who are—private detectives."

I grinned at her sadly. "I know I talk too smart. It's in the air nowadays. Who told you he was a gigolo?"

"Who?"

"Don't be obtuse. Marriott."

"Oh, it was a cinch guess. I'm sorry. I don't mean to be nasty. I guess you can snap her garter any time you want to, without much of a struggle. But there's one thing you can be sure of—you're a late comer to the show."

The wide curving street dozed peacefully in the sun. A beautifully painted panel truck slid noiselessly to a stop before a house across the street, then backed a little and went up the driveway to a side entrance. On the side of the panel truck was painted the legend: "Bay City Infant Service."

Anne Riordan leaned towards me, her gray-blue eyes hurt and clouded. Her slightly too long upper lip pouted and then pressed back against her teeth. She made a sharp little sound with her breath.

"Probably you'd like me to mind my own business, is that it? And not have ideas you don't have first. I thought I was helping a little."

"I don't need any help. The police don't want any from me. There's nothing I can do for Mrs. Grayle. She has a yarn about a beer parlor where a car started from and followed them, but what does that amount to? It was a crummy dive on Santa Monica. This was a high-class mob. There was somebody in it that could even tell Fei Tsui jade when he saw it."

"If he wasn't tipped off."

"There's that too," I said, and fumbled a cigarette out of a package. "Either way there's nothing for me in it."

"Not even about psychics?"

I stared rather blankly. "Psychics?"

"My God," she said softly. "And I thought you were a detective."

"There's a hush on part of this," I said. "I've got to watch my step. This Grayle packs a lot of dough in his pants. And law is where you buy it in this town. Look at the funny way the cops are acting. No build-up,

no newspaper handout, no chance for the innocent stranger to step in
with the trifling clue that turns out to be all important. Nothing but
silence and warnings to me to lay off. I don't like it at all."

"You got most of the lipstick off," Anne Riordan said. "I mentioned
psychics. Well, good-by. It was nice to know you—in a way."

She pressed her starter button and jammed her gears in and was gone
in a swirl of dust.

I watched her go. When she was gone I looked across the street. The
man from the panel truck that said Bay City Infant Service came out of
the side door of the house dressed in a uniform so white and stiff and
gleaming that it made me feel clean just to look at it. He was carrying a
carton of some sort. He got into his panel truck and drove away.

I figured he had just changed a diaper.

I got into my own car and looked at my watch before starting up. It
was almost five.

The Scotch, as good enough Scotch will, stayed with me all the way
back to Hollywood. I took the red lights as they came.

"There's a nice little girl," I told myself out loud, in the car, "for a
guy that's interested in a nice little girl." Nobody said anything. "But I'm
not," I said. Nobody said anything to that either. "Ten o'clock at the
Belvedere Club," I said. Somebody said: "Phooey."

It sounded like my voice.

It was a quarter to six when I reached my office again. The building
was very quiet. The typewriter beyond the party wall was stilled. I lit a
pipe and sat down to wait.

20

THE INDIAN SMELLED. He smelled clear across the little reception
room when the buzzer sounded and I opened the door between to see
who it was. He stood just inside the corridor door looking as if he had
been cast in bronze. He was a big man from the waist up and he had a big
chest. He looked like a bum.

He wore a brown suit of which the coat was too small for his
shoulders and his trousers were probably a little tight at the waist. His hat
was at least two sizes too small and had been perspired in freely by
somebody it fitted better than it fitted him. He wore it about where a
house wears a wind vane. His collar had the snug fit of a horse-collar and
was of about the same shade of dirty brown. A tie dangled outside his
buttoned jacket, a black tie which had been tied with a pair of pliers in a
knot the size of a pea. Around his bare and magnificent throat, above the
dirty collar, he wore a wide piece of black ribbon, like an old woman
trying to freshen up her neck.

He had a big flat face and a highbridged fleshy nose that looked as hard as the prow of a cruiser. He had lidless eyes, drooping jowls, the shoulders of a blacksmith and the short and apparently awkward legs of a chimpanzee. I found out later that they were only short.

If he had been cleaned up a little and dressed in a white nightgown, he would have looked like a very wicked Roman senator.

His smell was the earthy smell of primitive man, and not the slimy dirt of cities.

"Huh," he said. "Come quick. Come now."

I backed into my office and wiggled my finger at him and he followed me making as much noise as a fly makes walking on the wall. I sat down behind my desk and squeaked my swivel chair professionally and pointed to the customer's chair on the other side. He didn't sit down. His small black eyes were hostile.

"Come where?" I said.

"Huh. Me Second Planting. Me Hollywood Indian."

"Have a chair, Mr. Planting."

He snorted and his nostrils got very wide. They had been wide enough for mouseholes to start with.

"Name Second Planting. Name no Mister Planting."

"What can I do for you?"

He lifted his voice and began to intone in a deep-chested sonorous boom. "He say come quick. Great white father say come quick. He say me bring you in fiery chariot. He say—"

"Yeah. Cut out the pig Latin," I said. "I'm no schoolmarm at the snake dances."

"Nuts," the Indian said.

We sneered at each other across the desk for a moment. He sneered better than I did. Then he removed his hat with massive disgust and turned it upside down. He rolled a finger around under the sweatband. That turned the sweatband up into view, and it had not been misnamed. He removed a paper clip from the edge and threw a fold of tissue paper on the desk. He pointed at it angrily, with a well-chewed fingernail. His lank hair had a shelf around it, high up, from the too-tight hat.

I unfolded the piece of tissue paper and found a card inside. The card was no news to me. There had been three exactly like it in the mouthpieces of three Russian-appearing cigarettes.

I played with my pipe, stared at the Indian and tried to ride him with my stare. He looked as nervous as a brick wall.

"Okey, what does he want?"

"He want you come quick. Come now. Come in fiery—"

"Nuts," I said.

The Indian liked that. He closed his mouth slowly and winked an eye solemnly and then almost grinned.

"Also it will cost him a hundred bucks as a retainer," I added, trying to look as if that was a nickel.

"Huh?" Suspicious again. Stick to basic English.

"Hundred dollars," I said. "Iron men. Fish. Bucks to the number of one hundred. Me no money, me no come. Savvy?" I began to count a hundred with both hands.

"Huh. Big shot," the Indian sneered.

He worked under his greasy hatband and threw another fold of tissue paper on the desk. I took it and unwound it. It contained a brand new hundred dollar bill.

The Indian put his hat back on his head without bothering to tuck the hatband back in place. It looked only slightly more comic that way. I sat staring at the hundred dollar bill, with my mouth open.

"Psychic is right," I said at last. "A guy that smart I'm afraid of."

"Not got all day," the Indian remarked, conversationally.

I opened my desk and took out a Colt .38 automatic of the type known as Super Match. I hadn't worn it to visit Mrs. Lewin Lockridge Grayle. I stripped my coat off and strapped the leather harness on and tucked the automatic down inside it and strapped the lower strap and put my coat back on again.

This meant as much to the Indian as if I had scratched my neck.

"Gottum car," he said. "Big car."

"I don't like big cars any more," I said. "I gottum own car."

"You come my car," the Indian said threateningly.

"I come your car," I said.

I locked the desk and office up, switched the buzzer off and went out, leaving the reception room door unlocked as usual.

We went along the hall and down in the elevator. The Indian smelled. Even the elevator operator noticed it.

21

THE CAR WAS A DARK BLUE seven-passenger sedan, a Packard of the latest model, custom-built. It was the kind of car you wear your rope pearls in. It was parked by a fire-hydrant and a dark foreign-looking chauffeur with a face of carved wood was behind the wheel. The interior was upholstered in quilted gray chenille. The Indian put me in the back. Sitting there alone I felt like a high-class corpse, laid out by an undertaker with a lot of good taste.

The Indian got in beside the chauffeur and the car turned in the middle of the block and a cop across the street said: "Hey," weakly, as if he didn't mean it, and then bent down quickly to tie his shoe.

We went west, dropped over to Sunset and slid fast and noiseless along that. The Indian sat motionless beside the chauffeur. An occasional whiff of his personality drifted back to me. The driver looked as if he was half asleep but he passed the fast boys in the convertible sedans as though they were being towed. They turned on all the green lights for him. Some drivers are like that. He never missed one.

We curved through the bright mile or two of the Strip, past the antique shops with famous screen names on them, past the windows full of point lace and ancient pewter, past the gleaming new nightclubs with famous chefs and equally famous gambling rooms, run by polished graduates of the Purple Gang, past the Georgian-Colonial vogue, now old hat, past the handsome modernistic buildings in which the Hollywood flesh-peddlers never stop talking money, past a drive-in lunch which somehow didn't belong, even though the girls wore white silk blouses and drum majorettes' shakos and nothing below the hips but glazed kid Hessian boots. Past all this and down a wide smooth curve to the bridle path of Beverly Hills and lights to the south, all colors of the spectrum and crystal clear in an evening without fog, past the shadowed mansions up on the hills to the north, past Beverly Hills altogether and up into the twisting foothill boulevard and the sudden cool dusk and the drift of wind from the sea.

It had been a warm afternoon, but the heat was gone. We whipped past a distant cluster of lighted buildings and an endless series of lighted mansions, not too close to the road. We dipped down to skirt a huge green polo field with another equally huge practice field beside it, soared again to the top of a hill and swung mountainward up a steep hillroad of clean concrete that passed orange groves, some rich man's pet because this is not orange country, and then little by little the lighted windows of the millionaires' homes were gone and the road narrowed and this was Still-wood Heights.

The smell of sage drifted up from a canyon and made me think of a dead man and a moonless sky. Straggly stucco houses were molded flat to the side of the hill, like bas-reliefs. Then there were no more houses, just the still dark foothills with an early star or two above them, and the concrete ribbon of road and a sheer drop on one side into a tangle of scrub oak and manzanita where sometimes you can hear the call of the quails if you stop and keep still and wait. On the other side of the road was a raw clay bank at the edge of which a few unbeatable wild flowers hung on like naughty children that won't go to bed.

Then the road twisted into a hairpin turn and the big tires scratched over loose stones, and the car tore less soundlessly up a long driveway lined with the wild geraniums. At the top of this, faintly lighted, lonely as a lighthouse, stood an eyrie, an eagle's nest, an angular building of stucco and glass brick, raw and modernistic and yet not ugly and altogether a swell place for a psychic consultant to hang out his shingle. Nobody would be able to hear any screams.

The car turned beside the house and a light flicked on over a black door set into the heavy wall. The Indian climbed out grunting and opened the rear door of the car. The chauffeur lit a cigarette with an electric lighter and a harsh smell of tobacco came back to me softly in the evening. I got out.

We went over to the black door. It opened of itself, slowly, almost with menace. Beyond it a narrow hallway probed back into the house. Light glowed from the glass brick walls.

The Indian growled. "Huh. You go in, big shot."

"After you, Mr. Planting."

He scowled and went in and the door closed after us as silently and mysteriously as it had opened. At the end of the narrow hallway we squeezed into a little elevator and the Indian closed the door and pressed a button. We rose softly, without sound. Such smelling as the Indian had done before was a mooncast shadow to what he was doing now.

The elevator stopped, the door opened. There was light and I stepped out into a turret room where the day was still trying to be remembered. There were windows all around it. Far off the sea flickered. Darkness prowled slowly on the hills. There were paneled walls where there were no windows, and rugs on the floor with the soft colors of old Persians, and there was a reception desk that looked as if it had been made of carvings stolen from an ancient church. And behind the desk a woman sat and smiled at me, a dry tight withered smile that would turn to powder if you touched it.

She had sleek coiled hair and a dark, thin, wasted Asiatic face. There were heavy colored stones in her ears and heavy rings on her fingers, including a moonstone and an emerald in a silver setting that may have been a real emerald but somehow managed to look as phony as a dime store slave bracelet. And her hands were dry and dark and not young and not fit for rings.

She spoke. The voice was familiar. "Ah, Meester Marlowe, so ver-ry good of you to come. Amthor he weel be so ver-ry pleased."

I laid the hundred dollar bill the Indian had given me down on the desk. I looked behind me. The Indian had gone down again in the elevator.

"Sorry. It was a nice thought, but I can't take this."

"Amthor he—he weesh to employ you, is it not?" She smiled again. Her lips rustled like tissue paper.

"I'd have to find out what the job is first."

She nodded and got up slowly from behind the desk. She swished before me in a tight dress that fitted her like a mermaid's skin and showed that she had a good figure if you like them four sizes bigger below the waist.

"I weel conduct you," she said.

She pressed a button in the paneling and a door slid open noiselessly. There was a milky glow beyond it, I looked back at her smile before I went through. It was older than Egypt now. The door slid silently shut behind me.

There was nobody in the room.

It was octagonal, draped in black velvet from floor to ceiling, with a high remote black ceiling that may have been of velvet too. In the middle of a coal black lustreless rug stood an octagonal white table, just large enough for two pairs of elbows and in the middle of it a milk white globe on a black stand. The light came from this. How, I couldn't see. On either side of the table there was a white octagonal stool which was a smaller edition of the table. Over against one wall there was one more such stool. There were no windows. There was nothing else in the room, nothing at all. On the walls there was not even a light fixture. If there were other doors, I didn't see them. I looked back at the one by which I had come in. I couldn't see that either.

I stood there for perhaps fifteen seconds with the faint obscure feeling of being watched. There was probably a peephole somewhere, but I couldn't spot it. I gave up trying. I listened to my breath. The room was so still that I could hear it going through my nose, softly, like little curtains rustling.

Then an invisible door on the far side of the room slid open and a man stepped through and the door closed behind him. The man walked straight to the table with his head down and sat on one of the octagonal stools and made a sweeping motion with one of the most beautiful hands I have ever seen.

"Please be seated. Opposite me. Do not smoke and do not fidget. Try to relax, completely. Now how may I serve you?"

I sat down, got a cigarette into my mouth and rolled it along my lips without lighting it. I looked him over. He was thin, tall and straight as a steel rod. He had the palest finest white hair I ever saw. It could have been strained through silk gauze. His skin was as fresh as a rose petal. He might have been thirty-five or sixty-five. He was ageless. His hair was brushed straight back from as good a profile as Barrymore ever had. His eyebrows were coal black, like the walls and ceiling and floor. His eyes were deep, far too deep. They were the depthless drugged eyes of the somnambulist. They were like a well I read about once. It was nine hundred years old, in an old castle. You could drop a stone into it and wait. You could listen and wait and then you would give up waiting and laugh and then just as you were ready to turn away a faint, minute splash would come back up to you from the bottom of that well, so tiny, so remote that you could hardly believe a well like that possible.

His eyes were deep like that. And they were also eyes without expression, without soul, eyes that could watch lions tear a man to pieces and never change, that could watch a man impaled and screaming in the hot sun with his eyelids cut off.

He wore a double-breasted black business suit that had been cut by an artist. He stared vaguely at my fingers.

"Please do not fidget," he said. "It breaks the waves, disturbs my concentration."

"It makes the ice melt, the butter run and the cat squawk," I said.

He smiled the faintest smile in the world. "You didn't come here to be impertinent, I'm sure."

"You seem to forget why I did come. By the way, I gave that hundred dollar bill back to your secretary. I came, as you may recall, about some cigarettes. Russian cigarettes filled with marihuana. With your card rolled in the hollow mouthpieces."

"You wish to find out why that happened?"

"Yeah. I ought to be paying you the hundred dollars."

"That will not be necessary. The answer is simple. There are things I do not know. This is one of them."

For a moment I almost believed him. His face was as smooth as an angel's wing.

"Then why send me a hundred dollars—and a tough Indian that stinks—and a car? By the way, does the Indian have to stink? If he's working for you, couldn't you sort of get him to take a bath?"

"He is a natural medium. They are rare—like diamonds, and like diamonds, are sometimes found in dirty places. I understand you are a private detective?"

"Yes."

"I think you are a very stupid person. You look stupid. You are in a stupid business. And you came here on a stupid mission."

"I get it," I said. "I'm stupid. It sank in after a while."

"And I think I need not detain you any longer."

"You're not detaining me," I said. "I'm detaining you. I want to know why those cards were in those cigarettes."

He shrugged the smallest shrug that could be shrugged. "My cards are available to anybody. I do not give my friends marihuana cigarettes. Your question remains stupid."

"I wonder if this would brighten it up any. The cigarettes were in a cheap Chinese or Japanese case of imitation tortoiseshell. Ever see anything like that?"

"No. Not that I recall."

"I can brighten it up a little more. The case was in the pocket of a man named Lindsay Marriott. Ever hear of him?"

He thought. "Yes. I tried at one time to treat him for camera shyness. He was trying to get into pictures. It was a waste of time. Pictures did not want him."

"I can guess that," I said. "He would photograph like Isadora Duncan. I've still got the big one left. Why did you send me the C-note."

"My dear Mr. Marlowe," he said coldly, "I am no fool. I am in a very sensitive profession. I am a quack. That is to say I do things which the doctors in their small frightened selfish guild cannot accomplish. I am in danger at all times—from people like you. I merely wish to estimate the danger before dealing with it."

"Pretty trivial in my case, huh?"

"It hardly exists," he said politely and made a peculiar motion with his left hand which made my eyes jump at it. Then he put it down very slowly on the white table and looked at it. Then he raised his depthless eyes again and folded his arms.

"Your hearing—"

"I smell it now," I said. "I wasn't thinking of him."

I turned my head to the left. The Indian was sitting on the third white stool against the black velvet.

He had some kind of a white smock on him over his other clothes. He was sitting without a movement, his eyes closed, his head bent forward a little, as if he had been asleep for an hour. His dark strong face was full of shadows.

I looked back at Amthor. He was smiling his minute smile.

"I bet that makes the dowagers shed their false teeth," I said. "What does he do for real money—sit on your knee and sing French songs?"

He made an impatient gesture. "Get to the point, please."

"Last night Marriott hired me to go with him on an expedition that involved paying some money to some crooks at a spot they picked. I got knocked on the head. When I came out of it Marriott had been murdered."

Nothing changed much in Amthor's face. He didn't scream or run up the walls. But for him the reaction was sharp. He unfolded his arms and refolded them the other way. His mouth looked grim. Then he sat like a stone lion outside the Public Library.

"The cigarettes were found on him," I said.

He looked at me coolly. "But not by the police, I take it. Since the police have not been here."

"Correct."

"The hundred dollars," he said very softly, "was hardly enough."

"That depends what you expect to buy with it."

"You have these cigarettes with you?"

"One of them. But they don't prove anything. As you said, anybody could get your cards. I'm just wondering why they were where they were. Any ideas?"

"How well did you know Mr. Marriott?" he asked softly.

"Not at all. But I had ideas about him. They were so obvious they stuck out."

Amthor tapped lightly on the white table. The Indian still slept with his chin on his huge chest, his heavy-lidded eyes tight shut.

"By the way, did you ever meet a Mrs. Grayle, a wealthy lady who lives in Bay City?"

He nodded absently. "Yes, I treated her centers of speech. She had a very slight impediment."

"You did a sweet job on her," I said. "She talks as good as I do now."

That failed to amuse him. He still tapped on the table. I listened to

the taps. Something about them I didn't like. They sounded like a code. He stopped, folded his arms again and leaned back against the air.

"What I like about this job everybody knows everybody," I said. "Mrs. Grayle knew Marriott too."

"How did you find that out?" he asked slowly.

I didn't say anything.

"You will have to tell the police—about those cigarettes," he said.

I shrugged.

"You are wondering why I do not have you thrown out," Amthor said pleasantly. "Second Planting could break your neck like a celery stalk. I am wondering myself. You seem to have some sort of theory. Blackmail I do not pay. It buys nothing—and I have many friends. But naturally there are certain elements which would like to show me in a bad light. Psychiatrists, sex specialists, neurologists, nasty little men with rubber hammers and shelves loaded with the literature of aberrations. And of course they are all—doctors. While I am still a—quack. What is your theory?"

I tried to stare him down, but it couldn't be done. I felt myself licking my lips.

He shrugged lightly. "I can't blame you for wanting to keep it to yourself. This is a matter that I must give thought to. Perhaps you are a much more intelligent man than I thought. I also make mistakes. In the meantime—" He leaned forward and put a hand on each side of the milky globe.

"I think Marriott was a blackmailer of women," I said. "And finger man for a jewel mob. But who told him what women to cultivate—so that he would know their comings and goings, get intimate with them, make love to them, make them load up with the ice and take them out, and then slip to a phone and tell the boys where to operate?"

"That," Amthor said carefully, "is your picture of Marriott—and of me. I am slightly disgusted."

I leaned forward until my face was not more than a foot from his. "You're in a racket. Dress it up all you please and it's still a racket. And it wasn't just the cards, Amthor. As you say, anybody could get those. It wasn't the marihuana. You wouldn't be in a cheap line like that—not with your chances. But on the back of each card there is a blank space. And on blank spaces, or even on written ones, there is sometimes invisible writing."

He smiled bleakly, but I hardly saw it. His hands moved over the milky bowl.

The light went out. The room was as black as Carry Nation's bonnet.

22

I KICKED MY STOOL BACK and stood up and jerked the gun out of the holster under my arm. But it was no good. My coat was buttoned and I was too slow. I'd have been too slow anyway, if it came to shooting anybody.

There was a soundless rush of air and an earthy smell. In the complete darkness the Indian hit me from behind and pinned my arms to my sides. He started to lift me. I could have got the gun out still and fanned the room with blind shots, but I was a long way from friends. It didn't seem as if there was any point in it.

I let go of the gun and took hold of his wrists. They were greasy and hard to hold. The Indian breathed gutturally and set me down with a jar that lifted the top of my head. He had my wrists now, instead of me having his. He twisted them behind me fast and a knee like a corner stone went into my back. He bent me. I can be bent. I'm not the City Hall. He bent me.

I tried to yell, for no reason at all. Breath panted in my throat and couldn't get out. The Indian threw me sideways and got a body scissors on me as I fell. He had me in a barrel. His hands went to my neck. Sometimes I wake up in the night. I feel them there and I smell the smell of him. I feel the breath fighting and losing and the greasy fingers digging in. Then I get up and take a drink and turn the radio on.

I was just about gone when the light flared on again, blood red, on account of the blood in my eyeballs and at the back of them. A face floated around and a hand pawed me delicately, but the other hands stayed on my throat.

A voice said softly, "Let him breathe—a little."

The fingers slackened. I wrenched loose from them. Something that glinted hit me on the side of the jaw.

The voice said softly: "Get him on his feet."

The Indian got me on my feet. He pulled me back against the wall, holding me by both twisted wrists.

"Amateur," the voice said softly and the shiny thing that was as hard and bitter as death hit me again, across the face. Something warm trickled. I licked at it and tasted iron and salt.

A hand explored my wallet. A hand explored all my pockets. The cigarette in tissue paper came out and was unwrapped. It went somewhere in the haze that was in front of me.

"There were three cigarettes?" the voice said gently, and the shining thing hit my jaw again.

"Three," I gulped.

"Just where did you say the others were?"

"In my desk—at the office."

The shiny thing hit me again. "You are probably lying—but I can find out." Keys shone with funny little red lights in front of me. The voice said: "Choke him a little more."

The iron fingers went into my throat. I was strained back against him, against the smell of him and the hard muscles of his stomach. I reached up and took one of his fingers and tried to twist it.

The voice said softly: "Amazing. He's learning."

The glinting thing swayed through the air again. It smacked my jaw, the thing that had once been my jaw.

"Let him go. He's tame," the voice said.

The heavy strong arms dropped away and I swayed forward and took a step and steadied myself. Amthor stood smiling very slightly, almost dreamily in front of me. He held my gun in his delicate, lovely hand. He held it pointed at my chest.

"I could teach you," he said in his soft voice. "But to what purpose? A dirty little man in a dirty little world. One spot of brightness on you and you would still be that. Is it not so?" He smiled, so beautifully.

I swung at his smile with everything I had left.

It wasn't so bad considering. He reeled and blood came out of both his nostrils. Then he caught himself and straightened up and lifted the gun again.

"Sit down, my child," he said softly. "I have visitors coming. I am so glad you hit me. It helps a great deal."

I felt for the white stool and sat down and put my head down on the white table beside the milky globe which was now shining again softly. I stared at it sideways, my face on the table. The light fascinated me. Nice light, nice soft light.

Behind me and around me there was nothing but silence.

I think I went to sleep, just like that, with a bloody face on the table, and a thin beautiful devil with my gun in his hand watching me and smiling.

23

"ALL RIGHT," THE BIG ONE SAID. "You can quit stalling now."

I opened my eyes and sat up.

"Out in the other room, pally."

I stood up, still dreamy. We went somewhere, through a door. Then I saw where it was—the reception room with the windows all around. It was black dark now outside.

The woman with the wrong rings sat at her desk. A man stood beside her.

"Sit here, pally."

He pushed me down. It was a nice chair, straight but comfortable but I wasn't in the mood for it. The woman behind the desk had a notebook open and was reading out loud from it. A short elderly man with a deadpan expression and a gray mustache was listening to her.

Amthor was standing by a window, with his back to the room, looking out at the placid line of the ocean, far off, beyond the pier lights, beyond the world. He looked at it as if he loved it. He half turned his head to look at me once, and I could see that the blood had been washed off his face, but his nose wasn't the nose I had first met, not by two sizes. That made me grin, cracked lips and all.

"You got fun, pally?"

I looked at what made the sound, what was in front of me and what had helped me get where I was. He was a windblown blossom of some two hundred pounds with freckled teeth and the mellow voice of a circus barker. He was tough, fast and he ate red meat. Nobody could push him around. He was the kind of cop who spits on his blackjack every night instead of saying his prayers. But he had humorous eyes.

He stood in front of me splay-legged, holding my open wallet in his hand, making scratches on the leather with his right thumbnail, as if he just liked to spoil things. Little things, if they were all he had. But probably faces would give him more fun.

"Peeper, huh, pally? From the big bad burg, huh? Little spot of blackmail, huh?"

His hat was on the back of his head. He had dusty brown hair darkened by sweat on his forehead. His humorous eyes were flecked with red veins.

My throat felt as though it had been through a mangle. I reached up and felt it. That Indian. He had fingers like pieces of tool steel.

The dark woman stopped reading out of her notebook and closed it. The elderly smallish man with the gray mustache nodded and came over to stand behind the one who was talking to me.

"Cops?" I asked, rubbing my chin.

"What do *you* think, pally?"

Policeman's humor. The small one had a cast in one eye, and it looked half blind.

"Not L.A.," I said, looking at him. "That eye would retire him in Los Angeles."

The big man handed me my wallet. I looked through it. I had all the money still. All the cards. It had everything that belonged in it. I was surprised.

"Say something, pally," the big one said. "Something that would make us get fond of you."

"Give me back my gun."

He leaned forward a little and thought. I could see him thinking. It hurt his corns. "Oh, you want your gun, pally?" He looked sideways at the one with the gray mustache. "He wants his gun," he told him. He looked at me again. "And what would you want your gun for, pally?"

"I want to shoot an Indian."

"Oh, you want to shoot an Indian, pally."

"Yeah—just one Indian, pop."

He looked at the one with the mustache again. "This guy is very tough," he told him. "He wants to shoot an Indian."

"Listen, Hemingway, don't repeat everything I say," I said.

"I think the guy is nuts," the big one said. "He just called me Hemingway. Do you think he is nuts?"

The one with the mustache bit a cigar and said nothing. The tall beautiful man at the window turned slowly and said softly: "I think possibly he is a little unbalanced."

"I can't think of any reason why he should call me Hemingway," the big one said. "My name ain't Hemingway."

The older man said: "I didn't see a gun."

They looked at Amthor. Amthor said: "It's inside. I have it. I'll give it to you, Mr. Blane."

The big man leaned down from his hips and bent his knees a little and breathed in my face. "What for did you call me Hemingway, pally?"

"There are ladies present."

He straightened up again. "You see." He looked at the one with the mustache. The one with the mustache nodded and then turned and walked away, across the room. The sliding door opened. He went in and Amthor followed him.

There was silence. The dark woman looked down at the top of her desk and frowned. The big man looked at my right eyebrow and slowly shook his head from side to side, wonderingly.

The door opened again and the man with the mustache came back. He picked a hat up from somewhere and handed it to me. He took my gun out of his pocket and handed it to me. I knew by the weight it was empty. I tucked it under my arm and stood up.

The big man said: "Let's go, pally. Away from here. I think maybe a little air will help you to get straightened out."

"Okey, Hemingway."

"He's doing that again," the big man said sadly. "Calling me Hemingway on account of there are ladies present. Would you think that would be some kind of dirty crack in his book?"

The man with the mustache said, "Hurry up."

The big man took me by the arm and we went over to the little elevator. It came up. We got into it.

24

AT THE BOTTOM OF THE SHAFT we got out and walked along the narrow hallway and out of the black door. It was crisp clear air outside, high enough to be above the drift of foggy spray from the ocean. I breathed deeply.

The big man still had hold of my arm. There was a car standing there, a plain dark sedan, with private plates.

The big man opened the front door and complained: "It ain't really up to your class, pally. But a little air will set you up fine. Would that be all right with you? We wouldn't want to do anything that you wouldn't like us to do, pally."

"Where's the Indian?"

He shook his head a little and pushed me into the car. I got into the right side of the front seat. "Oh, yeah, the Indian," he said. "You got to shoot him with a bow and arrow. That's the law. We got him in the back of the car."

I looked in the back of the car. It was empty.

"Hell, he ain't there," the big one said. "Somebody must of glommed him off. You can't leave nothing in a unlocked car any more."

"Hurry up," the man with the mustache said, and got into the back seat. Hemingway went around and pushed his hard stomach behind the wheel. He started the car. We turned and drifted off down the driveway lined with wild geraniums. A cold wind lifted off the sea. The stars were too far off. They said nothing.

We reached the bottom of the drive and turned out onto the concrete mountain road and drifted without haste along that.

"How come you don't have a car with you, pally?"

"Amthor sent for me."

"Why would that be, pally?"

"It must have been he wanted to see me."

"This guy is good," Hemingway said. "He figures things out." He spit out of the side of the car and made a turn nicely and let the car ride its motor down the hill. "He says you called him up on the phone and tried to put the bite on him. So he figures he better have a looksee what kind of guy he is doing business with—if he is doing business. So he sends his own car."

"On account of he knows he is going to call some cops he knows and I won't need mine to get home with," I said. "Okey, Hemingway."

"Yeah, that again. Okey. Well he has a dictaphone under his table and his secretary takes it all down and when we come she reads it back to Mister Blane here."

I turned and looked at Mister Blane. He was smoking a cigar, peacefully, as though he had his slippers on. He didn't look at me.

"Like hell she did," I said. "More likely a stock bunch of notes they had all fixed up for a case like that."

"Maybe you would like to tell us why you wanted to see this guy," Hemingway suggested politely.

"You mean while I still have part of my face?"

"Aw, we ain't those kind of boys at all," he said, with a large gesture.

"You know Amthor pretty well, don't you, Hemingway?"

"Mr. Blane kind of knows him. Me, I just do what the orders is."

"Who the hell is Mister Blane?"

"That's the gentleman in the back seat."

"And besides being in the back seat who the hell is he?"

"Why, Jesus, everybody knows Mr. Blane."

"All right," I said, suddenly feeling very weary.

There was a little more silence, more curves, more winding ribbons of concrete, more darkness, and more pain.

The big man said: "Now that we are all between pals and no ladies present we really don't give so much time to why you went back up there, but this Hemingway stuff is what really has me down."

"A gag," I said. "An old, old gag."

"Who is this Hemingway person at all?"

"A guy that keeps saying the same thing over and over until you begin to believe it must be good."

"That must take a hell of a long time," the big man said. "For a private dick you certainly have a wandering kind of mind. Are you still wearing your own teeth?"

"Yeah, with a few plugs in them."

"Well, you certainly have been lucky, pally."

The man in the back seat said: "This is all right. Turn right at the next."

"Check."

Hemingway swung the sedan into a narrow dirt road that edged along the flank of a mountain. We drove along that about a mile. The smell of the sage became overpowering.

"Here," the man in the back seat said.

Hemingway stopped the car and set the brake. He leaned across me and opened the door.

"Well, it's nice to have met you, pally. But don't come back. Anyways not on business. Out."

"I walk home from here?"

The man in the back seat said: "Hurry up."

"Yeah, you walk home from here, pally. Will that be all right with you?"

"Sure, it will give me time to think a few things out. For instance, you boys are not L.A. cops. But one of you is a cop, maybe both of you. I'd say you are Bay City cops. I'm wondering why you were out of your territory."

"Ain't that going to be kind of hard to prove, pally?"

"Goodnight, Hemingway."

He didn't answer. Neither of them spoke. I started to get out of the car and put my foot on the running board and leaned forward, still a little dizzy.

The man in the back seat made a sudden flashing movement that I sensed rather than saw. A pool of darkness opened at my feet and was far, far deeper than the blackest night.

I dived into it. It had no bottom.

25

THE ROOM WAS FULL OF SMOKE.

The smoke hung straight up in the air, in thin lines, straight up and down like a curtain of small clear beads. Two windows seemed to be open in an end wall, but the smoke didn't move. I had never seen the room before. There were bars across the windows.

I was dull, without thought. I felt as if I had slept for a year. But the smoke bothered me. I lay on my back and thought about it. After a long time I took a deep breath that hurt my lungs.

I yelled: "Fire!"

That made me laugh. I didn't know what was funny about it but I began to laugh. I lay there on the bed and laughed. I didn't like the sound of the laugh. It was the laugh of a nut.

The one yell was enough. Steps thumped rapidly outside the room and a key was jammed into a lock and the door swung open. A man jumped in sideways and shut the door after him. His right hand reached toward his hip.

He was a short thick man in a white coat. His eyes had a queer look, black and flat. There were bulbs of gray skin at the outer corners of them.

I turned my head on the hard pillow and yawned.

"Don't count that one, Jack. It slipped out," I said.

He stood there scowling, his right hand hovering towards his right hip. Greenish malignant face and flat black eyes and gray white skin and nose that seemed just a shell.

"Maybe you want some more strait-jacket," he sneered.

"I'm fine, Jack. Just fine. Had a long nap. Dreamed a little, I guess. Where am I?"

"Where you belong."

"Seems like a nice place," I said. "Nice people, nice atmosphere. I guess I'll have me a short nap again."

"Better be just that," he snarled.

He went out. The door shut. The lock clicked. The steps growled into nothing.

He hadn't done the smoke any good. It still hung there in the middle of the room, all across the room. Like a curtain. It didn't dissolve, didn't float off, didn't move. There was air in the room, and I could feel it on my face. But the smoke couldn't feel it. It was a gray web woven by a thousand spiders. I wondered how they had got them to work together.

Cotton flannel pajamas. The kind they have in the County Hospital. No front, not a stitch more than is essential. Coarse, rough material. The neck chafed my throat. My throat was still sore. I began to remember things. I reached up and felt the throat muscles. They were still sore. Just one Indian, pop. Okey, Hemingway. So you want to be a detective? Earn good money. Nine easy lessons. We provide badge. For fifty cents extra we send you a truss.

The throat felt sore but the fingers feeling it didn't feel anything. They might just as well have been a bunch of bananas. I looked at them. They looked like fingers. No good. Mail order fingers. They must have come with the badge and the truss. And the diploma.

It was night. The world outside the windows was a black world. A glass porcelain bowl hung from the middle of the ceiling on three brass chains. There was light in it. It had little colored lumps around the edge, orange and blue alternately. I stared at them. I was tired of the smoke. As I stared they began to open up like little portholes and heads popped out. Tiny heads, but alive, heads like the heads of small dolls, but alive. There was a man in a yachting cap with a Johnnie Walker nose and a fluffy blonde in a picture hat and a thin man with crooked bow tie. He looked like a waiter in a beachtown flytrap. He opened his lips and sneered: "Would you like your steak rare or medium, sir?"

I closed my eyes tight and winked them hard and when I opened them again it was just a sham porcelain bowl on three brass chains.

But the smoke still hung motionless in the moving air.

I took hold of the corner of a rough sheet and wiped the sweat off my face with the numb fingers the correspondence school had sent me after the nine easy lessons, one half in advance, Box Two Million Four Hundred and Sixty Eight Thousand Nine Hundred and Twenty Four, Cedar City, Iowa. Nuts. Completely nuts.

I sat up on the bed and after a while I could reach the floor with my feet. They were bare and they had pins and needles in them. Notions counter on the left, madam. Extra large safety pins on the right. The feet began to feel the floor. I stood up. Too far up. I crouched over, breathing hard and held the side of the bed and a voice that seemed to come from under the bed said over and over again: "You've got the dt's . . . you've got the dt's . . . you've got the dt's."

I started to walk, wobbling like a drunk. There was a bottle of whiskey on a small white enamel table between the two barred windows. It looked like a good shape. It looked about half full. I walked towards it.

There are a lot of nice people in the world, in spite. You can crab over
the morning paper and kick the shins of the guy in the next seat at the
movies and feel mean and discouraged and sneer at the politicians, but
there are a lot of nice people in the world just the same. Take the guy
that left that half bottle of whiskey there. He had a heart as big as one of
Mae West's hips.

I reached it and put both my half-numb hands down on it and hauled
it up to my mouth, sweating as if I was lifting one end of the Golden
Gate Bridge.

I took a long untidy drink. I put the bottle down again, with infinite
care. I tried to lick underneath my chin.

The whiskey had a funny taste. While I was realizing that it had a
funny taste I saw a washbowl jammed into the corner of the wall. I made
it. I just made it. I vomited. Dizzy Dean never threw anything harder.

Time passed—an agony of nausea and staggering and dazedness and
clinging to the edge of the bowl and making animal sounds for help.

It passed. I staggered back to the bed and lay down on my back again
and lay there panting, watching the smoke. The smoke wasn't quite so
clear. Not quite so real. Maybe it was just something back of my eyes.
And then quite suddenly it wasn't there at all and the light from the
porcelain ceiling fixture etched the room sharply.

I sat up again. There was a heavy wooden chair against the wall near
the door. There was another door besides the door the man in the white
coat had come in at. A closet door, probably. It might even have my
clothes in it. The floor was covered with green and gray linoleum in
squares. The walls were painted white. A clean room. The bed on which
I sat was a narrow iron hospital bed, lower than they usually are, and
there were thick leather straps with buckles attached to the sides, about
where a man's wrists and ankles would be.

It was a swell room—to get out of.

I had feeling all over my body now, soreness in my head and throat
and in my arm. I couldn't remember about the arm. I rolled up the sleeve
of the cotton pajama thing and looked at it fuzzily. It was covered with
pin pricks on the skin all the way from the elbow to the shoulder.
Around each was a small discolored patch, about the size of a quarter.

Dope. I had been shot full of dope to keep me quiet. Perhaps scopolamine too, to make me talk. Too much dope for the time. I was having
the French fits coming out of it. Some do, some don't. It all depends how
you are put together. Dope.

That accounted for the smoke and the little heads around the edge of
the ceiling light and the voices and the screwy thoughts and the straps
and bars and the numb fingers and feet. The whiskey was probably part
of somebody's forty-eight-hour liquor cure. They had just left it around
so that I wouldn't miss anything.

I stood up and almost hit the opposite wall with my stomach. That
made me lie down and breathe very gently for quite a long time. I was

tingling all over now and sweating. I could feel little drops of sweat form on my forehead and then slide slowly and carefully down the side of my nose to the corner of my mouth. My tongue licked at them foolishly.

I sat up once more and planted my feet on the floor and stood up.

"Okey, Marlowe," I said between my teeth. "You're a tough guy. Six feet of iron man. One hundred and ninety pounds stripped and with your face washed. Hard muscles and no glass jaw. You can take it. You've been sapped down twice, had your throat choked and been beaten half silly on the jaw with a gun barrel. You've been shot full of hop and kept under it until you're as crazy as two waltzing mice. And what does all that amount to? Routine. Now let's see you do something really tough, like putting your pants on."

I lay down on the bed again.

Time passed again. I don't know how long. I had no watch. They don't make that kind of time in watches anyway.

I sat up. This was getting to be stale. I stood up and started to walk. No fun walking. Makes your heart jump like a nervous cat. Better lie down and go back to sleep. Better take it easy for a while. You're in bad shape, pally. Okey, Hemingway, I'm weak. I couldn't knock over a flower vase. I couldn't break a fingernail.

Nothing doing. I'm walking. I'm tough. I'm getting out of here.

I lay down on the bed again.

The fourth time was a little better. I got across the room and back twice. I went over to the washbowl and rinsed it out and leaned on it and drank water out of the palm of my hand. I kept it down. I waited a little and drank more. Much better.

I walked. I walked. I walked.

Half an hour of walking and my knees were shaking but my head was clear. I drank more water, a lot of water. I almost cried into the bowl while I was drinking it.

I walked back to the bed. It was a lovely bed. It was made of rose-leaves. It was the most beautiful bed in the world. They had got it from Carole Lombard. It was too soft for her. It was worth the rest of my life to lie down in it for two minutes. Beautiful soft bed, beautiful sleep, beautiful eyes closing and lashes falling and the gentle sound of breathing and darkness and rest sunk in deep pillows. . . .

I walked.

They built the Pyramids and got tired of them and pulled them down and ground the stone up to make concrete for Boulder Dam and they built that and brought the water to the Sunny Southland and used it to have a flood with.

I walked all through it. I couldn't be bothered.

I stopped walking. I was ready to talk to somebody.

26

THE CLOSET DOOR WAS LOCKED. The heavy chair was too heavy for me. It was meant to be. I stripped the sheets and pad off the bed and dragged the mattress to one side. There was a mesh spring underneath fastened top and bottom by coil springs of black enameled metal about nine inches long. I went to work on one of them. It was the hardest work I ever did. Ten minutes later I had two bleeding fingers and a loose spring. I swung it. It had a nice balance. It was heavy. It had a whip to it.

And when this was all done I looked across at the whiskey bottle and it would have done just as well, and I had forgotten all about it.

I drank some more water. I rested a little, sitting on the side of the bare springs. Then I went over to the door and put my mouth against the hinge side and yelled:

"Fire! Fire! Fire!"

It was a short wait and a pleasant one. He came running hard along the hallway outside and his key jammed viciously into the lock and twisted hard.

The door jumped open. I was flat against the wall on the opening side. He had the sap out this time, a nice little tool about five inches long, covered with woven brown leather. His eyes popped at the stripped bed and then began to swing around.

I giggled and socked him. I laid the coil spring on the side of his head and he stumbled forward. I followed him down to his knees. I hit him twice more. He made a moaning sound. I took the sap out of his limp hand. He whined.

I used my knee on his face. It hurt my knee. He didn't tell me whether it hurt his face. While he was still groaning I knocked him cold with the sap.

I got the key from the outside of the door and locked it from the inside and went through him. He had more keys. One of them fitted my closet. In it my clothes hung. I went through my pockets. The money was gone from my wallet. I went back to the man with the white coat. He had too much money for his job. I took what I had started with and heaved him on to the bed and strapped him wrist and ankle and stuffed half a yard of sheet into his mouth. He had a smashed nose. I waited long enough to make sure he could breathe through it.

I was sorry for him. A simple hardworking little guy trying to hold his job down and get his weekly pay check. Maybe with a wife and kids. Too bad. And all he had to help him was a sap. It didn't seem fair. I put the doped whiskey down where he could reach it, if his hands hadn't been strapped.

I patted his shoulder. I almost cried over him.

All my clothes, even my gun harness and gun, but no shells in the gun, hung in the closet. I dressed with fumbling fingers, yawning a great deal.

The man on the bed rested. I left him there and locked him in.

Outside was a wide silent hallway with three closed doors. No sounds came from behind any of them. A wine-colored carpet crept down the middle and was as silent as the rest of the house. At the end there was a jog in the hall and then another hall at right angles and the head of a big old-fashioned staircase with white oak bannisters. It curved graciously down into the dim hall below. Two stained glass inner doors ended the lower hall. It was tessellated and thick rugs lay on it. A crack of light seeped past the edge of an almost closed door. But no sound at all.

An old house, built as once they built them and don't build them any more. Standing probably on a quiet street with a rose arbor at the side and plenty of flowers in front. Gracious and cool and quiet in the bright California sun. And inside it who cares, but don't let them scream too loud.

I had my foot out to go down the stairs when I heard a man cough. That jerked me around and I saw there was a half open door along the other hallway at the end. I tiptoed along the runner. I waited, close to the partly open door, but not in it. A wedge of light lay at my feet on the carpet. The man coughed again. It was a deep cough, from a deep chest. It sounded peaceful and at ease. It was none of my business. My business was to get out of there. But any man whose door could be open in that house interested me. He would be a man of position, worth tipping your hat to. I sneaked a little into the wedge of light. A newspaper rustled.

I could see part of a room and it was furnished like a room, not like a cell. There was a dark bureau with a hat on it and some magazines. Windows with lace curtains, a good carpet.

Bed springs creaked heavily. A big guy, like his cough. I reached out fingertips and pushed the door an inch or two. Nothing happened. Nothing ever was slower than my head craning in. I saw the room now, the bed, and the man on it, the ashtray heaped with stubs that overflowed on to a night table and from that to the carpet. A dozen mangled newspapers all over the bed. One of them in a pair of huge hands before a huge face. I saw the hair above the edge of the green paper. Dark, curly—black even—and plenty of it. A line of white skin under it. The paper moved a little more and I didn't breathe and the man on the bed didn't look up.

He needed a shave. He would always need a shave. I had seen him before, over on Central Avenue, in a Negro dive called Florian's. I had seen him in a loud suit with white golf balls on the coat and a whiskey sour in his hand. And I had seen him with an Army Colt looking like a toy in his fist, stepping softly through a broken door. I had seen some of his work and it was the kind of work that stays done.

He coughed again and rolled his buttocks on the bed and yawned bitterly and reached sideways for a frayed pack of cigarettes on the night table. One of them went into his mouth. Light flared at the end of his thumb. Smoke came out of his nose.

"Ah," he said, and the paper went up in front of his face again.

I left him there and went back along the side hall. Mr. Moose Malloy seemed to be in very good hands. I went back to the stairs and down.

A voice murmured behind the almost closed door. I waited for the answering voice. None. It was a telephone conversation. I went over close to the door and listened. It was a low voice, a mere murmur. Nothing carried that meant anything. There was finally a dry clicking sound. Silence continued inside the room after that.

This was the time to leave, to go far away. So I pushed the door open and stepped quietly in.

27

IT WAS AN OFFICE, not small, not large, with a neat professional look. A glass-doored bookcase with heavy books inside. A first aid cabinet on the wall. A white enamel and glass sterilizing cabinet with a lot of hypodermic needles and syringes inside it being cooked. A wide flat desk with a blotter on it, a bronze paper cutter, a pen set, an appointment book, very little else, except the elbows of a man who sat brooding, with his face in his hands.

Between the spread yellow fingers I saw hair the color of wet brown sand, so smooth that it appeared to be painted on his skull. I took three more steps and his eyes must have looked beyond the desk and seen my shoes move. His head came up and he looked at me. Sunken colorless eyes in a parchment-like face. He unclasped his hands and leaned back slowly and looked at me with no expression at all.

Then he spread his hands with a sort of helpless but disapproving gesture and when they came to rest again, one of them was very close to the corner of the desk.

I took two steps more and showed him the blackjack. His index and second finger still moved towards the corner of the desk.

"The buzzer," I said, "won't buy you anything tonight. I put your tough boy to sleep."

His eyes got sleepy. "You have been a very sick man, sir. A very sick man. I can't recommend your being up and about yet."

I said: "The right hand." I snapped the blackjack at it. It coiled into itself like a wounded snake.

I went around the desk grinning without there being anything to grin at. He had a gun in the drawer of course. They always have a gun in the drawer and they always get it too late, if they get it at all. I took it out. It was a .38 automatic, a standard model not as good as mine, but I could use its ammunition. There didn't seem to be any in the drawer. I started to break the magazine out of his.

He moved vaguely, his eyes still sunken and sad.

"Maybe you've got another buzzer under the carpet," I said. "Maybe it rings in the Chief's office down at headquarters. Don't use it. Just for an hour I'm a very tough guy. Anybody comes in that door is walking into a coffin."

"There is no buzzer under the carpet," he said. His voice had the slightest possible foreign accent.

I got his magazine out and my empty one and changed them. I ejected the shell that was in the chamber of his gun and let it lie. I jacked one up into the chamber of mine and went back to the other side of the desk again.

There was a spring lock on the door. I backed towards it and pushed it shut and heard the lock click. There was also a bolt. I turned that.

I went back to the desk and sat in a chair. It took my last ounce of strength.

"Whiskey," I said.

He began to move his hands around.

"Whiskey," I said.

He went to the medicine cabinet and got a flat bottle with a green revenue stamp on it and a glass.

"Two glasses," I said. "I tried your whiskey once. I damn near hit Catalina Island with it."

He brought two small glasses and broke the seal and filled the two glasses.

"You first," I said.

He smiled faintly and raised one of the glasses.

"Your health, sir—what remains of it." He drank. I drank. I reached for the bottle and stood it near me and waited for the heat to get to my heart. My heart began to pound, but it was back up in my chest again, not hanging on a shoelace.

"I had a nightmare," I said. "Silly idea. I dreamed I was tied to a cot and shot full of dope and locked in a barred room. I got very weak. I slept. I had no food. I was a sick man. I was knocked on the head and brought into a place where they did that to me. They took a lot of trouble. I'm not that important."

He said nothing. He watched me. There was a remote speculation in his eyes, as if he wondered how long I would live.

"I woke up and the room was full of smoke," I said. "It was just a hallucination, irritation of the optic nerve or whatever a guy like you would call it. Instead of pink snakes I had smoke. So I yelled and a toughie in a white coat came in and showed me a blackjack. It took me a long time to get ready to take it away from him. I got his keys and my clothes and even took my money out of his pocket. So here I am. All cured. What were you saying?"

"I made no remark," he said.

"Remarks want you to make them," I said. "They have their tongues hanging out waiting to be said. This thing here—" I waved the blackjack lightly, "is a persuader. I had to borrow it from a guy."

"Please give it to me at once," he said with a smile you would get to love. It was like the executioner's smile when he comes to your cell to measure you for the drop. A little friendly, a little paternal, and a little cautious at the same time. You would get to love it if there was any way you could live long enough.

I dropped the blackjack into his palm, his left palm.

"Now the gun, please," he said softly. "You have been a very sick man, Mr. Marlowe. I think I shall have to insist that you go back to bed."

I stared at him.

"I am Dr. Sonderborg," he said, "and I don't want any nonsense."

He laid the blackjack down on the desk in front of him. His smile was as stiff as a frozen fish. His long fingers made movements like dying butterflies.

"The gun, please," he said softly. "I advise strongly—"

"What time is it, warden?"

He looked mildly surprised. I had my wrist watch on now, but it had run down.

"It is almost midnight. Why?"

"What day is it?"

"Why, my dear sir—Sunday evening, of course."

I steadied myself on the desk and tried to think and held the gun close enough to him so that he might try and grab it.

"That's over forty-eight hours. No wonder I had fits. Who brought me here?"

He stared at me and his left hand began to edge towards the gun. He belonged to the Wandering Hand Society. The girls would have had a time with him.

"Don't make me get tough," I whined. "Don't make me lose my beautiful manners and my flawless English. Just tell me how I got here."

He had courage. He grabbed for the gun. It wasn't where he grabbed. I sat back and put it in my lap.

He reddened and grabbed for the whiskey and poured himself another drink and downed it fast. He drew a deep breath and shuddered. He didn't like the taste of liquor. Dopers never do.

"You will be arrested at once, if you leave here," he said sharply. "You were properly committed by an officer of the law—"

"Officers of the law can't do it."

That jarred him, a little. His yellowish face began to work.

"Shake it up and pour it," I said. "Who put me in here, why and how? I'm in a wild mood tonight. I want to go dance in the foam. I hear the banshees calling. I haven't shot a man in a week. Speak out, Dr. Fell. Pluck the antique viol, let the soft music float."

"You are suffering from narcotic poisoning," he said coldly. "You very nearly died. I had to give you digitalis three times. You fought, you screamed, you had to be restrained." His words were coming so fast they were leap-frogging themselves. "If you leave my hospital in this condition, you will get into serious trouble."

"Did you say you were a doctor—a medical doctor?"

"Certainly. I am Dr. Sonderborg, as I told you."

"You don't scream and fight from narcotic poisoning, doc. You just lie in a coma. Try again. And skim it. All I want is the cream. Who put me in your private funny house?"

"But—"

"But me no buts. I'll make a sop of you. I'll drown you in a butt of Malmsey wine. I wish I had a butt of Malmsey wine myself to drown in. Shakespeare. He knew his liquor too. Let's have a little of our medicine." I reached for his glass and poured us a couple more. "Get on with it, Karloff."

"The police put you in here."

"What police?"

"The Bay City police naturally." His restless yellow fingers twisted his glass. "This is Bay City."

"Oh. Did this police have a name?"

"A Sergeant Galbraith, I believe. Not a regular patrol car officer. He and another officer found you wandering outside the house in a dazed condition on Friday night. They brought you in because this place was close. I thought you were an addict who had taken an overdose. But perhaps I was wrong."

"It's a good story. I couldn't prove it wrong. But why keep me here?"

He spread his restless hands. "I have told you again and again that you were a very sick man and still are. What would you expect me to do?"

"I must owe you some money then."

He shrugged. "Naturally. Two hundred dollars."

I pushed my chair back a little. "Dirt cheap. Try and get it."

"If you leave here," he said sharply, "you will be arrested at once."

I leaned back over the desk and breathed in his face. "Not just for going out of here, Karloff. Open that wall safe."

He stood up in a smooth lunge, "This has gone quite far enough."

"You won't open it?"

"I most certainly will not open it."

"This is a gun I'm holding."

He smiled, narrowly and bitterly.

"It's an awful big safe," I said. "New too. This is a fine gun. You won't open it?"

Nothing changed in his face.

"Damn it," I said. "When you have a gun in your hand, people are supposed to do anything you tell them to. It doesn't work, does it?"

He smiled. His smile held a sadistic pleasure. I was slipping back. I was going to collapse.

I staggered at the desk and he waited, his lips parted softly.

I stood leaning there for a long moment, staring into his eyes. Then I grinned. The smile fell off his face like a soiled rag. Sweat stood out on his forehead.

"So long," I said. "I leave you to dirtier hands than mine."

I backed to the door and opened it and went out.

The front doors were unlocked. There was a roofed porch. The garden hummed with flowers. There was a white picket fence and a gate. The house was on a corner. It was a cool, moist night, no moon.

The sign on the corner said Descanso Street. Houses were lighted down the block. I listened for sirens. None came. The other sign said Twenty-third Street. I plowed over to Twenty-fifth Street and started towards the eight-hundred block. No. 819 was Anne Riordan's number. Sanctuary.

I had walked a long time before I realized that I was still holding the gun in my hand. And I had heard no sirens.

I kept on walking. The air did me good, but the whiskey was dying, and it writhed as it died. The block had fir trees along it, and brick houses, and looked like Capitol Hill in Seattle more than Southern California.

There was a light still in No. 819. It had a white porte-cochère, very tiny, pressed against a tall cypress hedge. There were rose bushes in front of the house. I went up the walk. I listened before I pushed the bell. Still no sirens wailing. The bell chimed and after a little while a voice croaked through one of those electrical contraptions that let you talk with your front door locked.

"What is it, please?"

"Marlowe."

Maybe her breath caught, maybe the electrical thing just made that sound being shut off.

The door opened wide and Miss Anne Riordan stood there in a pale green slack suit looking at me. Her eyes went wide and scared. Her face under the glare of the porchlight was suddenly pale.

"My God," she wailed. "You look like Hamlet's father!"

28

THE LIVING ROOM HAD a tan figured rug, white and rose chairs, a black marble fireplace with very tall brass andirons, high bookcases built back into the walls, and rough cream drapes against the lowered venetian blinds.

There was nothing womanish in the room except a full length mirror with a clear sweep of floor in front of it.

I was half-sitting and half-lying in a deep chair with my legs on a footstool. I had had two cups of black coffee, then I had had a drink, then I had had two soft-boiled eggs and a slice of toast broken into them, then some more black coffee with brandy laced in it. I had had all this in the breakfast room, but I couldn't remember what it looked like any more. It was too long ago.

I was in good shape again. I was almost sober and my stomach was bunting towards third base instead of trying for the centerfield flagpole.

Anne Riordan sat opposite me, leaning forward, her neat chin cupped in her neat hand, her eyes dark and shadowy under the fluffed out reddish-brown hair. There was a pencil stuck through her hair. She looked worried. I had told her some of it, but not all. Especially about Moose Malloy I had not told her.

"I thought you were drunk," she said. "I thought you had to be drunk before you came to see me. I thought you had been out with that blonde. I thought—I don't know what I thought."

"I bet you didn't get all this writing," I said, looking around. "Not even if you got paid for what you thought you thought."

"And my dad didn't get it grafting on the cops either," she said. "Like that fat slob they have for chief of police nowadays."

"It's none of my business," I said.

She said: "We had some lots at Del Rey. Just sand lots they suckered him for. And they turned out to be oil lots."

I nodded and drank out of the nice crystal glass I was holding. What was in it had a nice warm taste.

"A fellow could settle down here," I said. "Move right in. Everything set for him."

"If he was that kind of fellow. And anybody wanted him to," she said.

"No butler," I said. "That makes it tough."

She flushed. "But you—you'd rather get your head beaten to a pulp and your arm riddled with dope needles and your chin used for a backboard in a basketball game. God knows there's enough of it."

I didn't say anything. I was too tired.

"At least," she said, "you had the brains to look in those mouthpieces. The way you talked over on Aster Drive I thought you had missed the whole thing."

"Those cards don't mean anything."

Her eyes snapped at me. "You sit there and tell me that after the man had you beaten up by a couple of crooked policemen and thrown in a two-day liquor cure to teach you to mind your own business? Why the thing stands out so far you could break off a yard of it and still have enough left for a baseball bat."

"I ought to have said that one," I said. "Just my style. Crude. What sticks out?"

"That this elegant psychic person is nothing but a high-class mobster. He picks the prospects and milks the minds and then tells the rough boys to go out and get the jewels."

"You really think that?"

She stared at me. I finished my glass and got my weak look on my face again. She ignored it.

"Of course I think it," she said. "And so do you."

"I think it's a little more complicated than that."

Her smile was cozy and acid at the same time. "I beg your pardon. I forgot for the moment you were a detective. It *would* have to be complicated, wouldn't it? I suppose there's a sort of indecency about a simple case."

"It's more complicated than that," I said.

"All right. I'm listening."

"I don't know. I just think so. Can I have one more drink?"

She stood up. "You know, you'll have to taste water sometime, just for the hell of it." She came over and took my glass. "This is going to be the last." She went out of the room and somewhere ice cubes tinkled and I closed my eyes and listened to the small unimportant sounds. I had no business coming here. If they knew as much about me as I suspected, they might come here looking. That would be a mess.

She came back with the glass and her fingers cold from holding the cold glass touched mine and I held them for a moment and then let them go slowly as you let go of a dream when you wake with the sun in your face and have been in an enchanted valley.

She flushed and went back to her chair and sat down and made a lot of business of arranging herself in it.

She lit a cigarette, watching me drink.

"Amthor's a pretty ruthless sort of lad," I said. "But I don't somehow see him as the brain guy of a jewel mob. Perhaps I'm wrong. If he was and he thought I had something on him, I don't think I'd have got out of that dope hospital alive. But he's a man who has things to fear. He didn't get really tough until I began to babble about invisible writing."

She looked at me evenly. "Was there some?"

I grinned. "If there was, I didn't read it."

"That's a funny way to hide nasty remarks about a person, don't you think? In the mouthpieces of cigarettes. Suppose they were never found."

"I think the point is that Marriott feared something and that if anything happened to him, the cards *would* be found. The police would go over anything in his pockets with a fine-tooth comb. That's what bothers me. If Amthor's a crook, nothing would have been left to find."

"You mean if Amthor murdered him—or had him murdered? But

what Marriott knew about Amthor may not have had any direct connection with the murder."

I leaned back and pressed my back into the chair and finished my drink and made believe I was thinking that over. I nodded.

"But the jewel robbery had a connection with the murder. And we're assuming Amthor had a connection with the jewel robbery."

Her eyes were a little sly. "I bet you feel awful," she said. "Wouldn't you like to go to bed?"

"Here?"

She flushed to the roots of her hair. Her chin stuck out. "That was the idea. I'm not a child. Who the devil cares what I do or when or how?"

I put my glass aside and stood up. "One of my rare moments of delicacy is coming over me," I said. "Will you drive me to a taxi stand, if you're not too tired?"

"You damned sap," she said angrily. "You've been beaten to a pulp and shot full of God knows how many kinds of narcotics and I suppose all you need is a night's sleep to get up bright and early and start out being a detective again."

"I thought I'd sleep a little late."

"You ought to be in a hospital, you damn fool!"

I shuddered. "Listen," I said. "I'm not very clear-headed tonight and I don't think I ought to linger around here too long. I haven't a thing on any of these people that I could prove, but they seem to dislike me. Whatever I might say would be my word against the law, and the law in this town seems to be pretty rotten."

"It's a nice town," she said sharply, a little breathlessly. "You can't judge—"

"Okey, it's a nice town. So is Chicago. You could live there a long time and not see a Tommygun. Sure, it's a nice town. It's probably no crookeder than Los Angeles. But you can only buy a piece of a big city. You can buy a town this size all complete, with the original box and tissue paper. That's the difference. And that makes me want out."

She stood up and pushed her chin at me. "You'll go to bed now and right here. I have a spare bedroom and you can turn right in and—"

"Promise to lock your door?"

She flushed and bit her lip. "Sometimes I think you're a world-beater," she said, "and sometimes I think you're the worst heel I ever met."

"On either count would you run me over to where I can get a taxi?"

"You'll stay here," she snapped. "You're not fit. You're a sick man."

"I'm not too sick to have my brain picked," I said nastily.

She ran out of the room so fast she almost tripped over the two steps from the living room up to the hall. She came back in nothing flat with a long flannel coat on over her slack suit and no hat and her reddish hair looking as mad as her face. She opened a side door and threw it away from her, bounced through it and her steps clattered on the driveway. A garage door made a faint sound lifting. A car door opened and slammed shut again. The starter ground and the motor caught and the lights flared past the open French door of the living room.

I picked my hat out of a chair and switched off a couple of lamps and saw that the French door had a Yale lock. I looked back a moment before I closed the door. It was a nice room. It would be a nice room to wear slippers in.

I shut the door and the little car slid up beside me and I went around behind it to get in.

She drove me all the way home, tight-lipped, angry. She drove like a fury. When I got out in front of my apartment house she said goodnight in a frosty voice and swirled the little car in the middle of the street and was gone before I could get my keys out of my pocket.

They locked the lobby door at eleven. I unlocked it and passed into the always musty lobby and along to the stairs and the elevator. I rode up to my floor. Bleak light shone along it. Milk bottles stood in front of service doors. The red fire door loomed at the back. It had an open screen that let in a lazy trickle of air that never quite swept the cooking smell out. I was home in a sleeping world, a world as harmless as a sleeping cat.

I unlocked the door of my apartment and went in and sniffed the smell of it, just standing there, against the door for a little while before I put the light on. A homely smell, a smell of dust and tobacco smoke, the smell of a world where men live, and keep on living.

I undressed and went to bed. I had nightmares and woke out of them sweating. But in the morning I was a well man again.

29

I WAS SITTING ON THE SIDE of my bed in my pajamas, thinking about getting up, but not yet committed. I didn't feel very well, but I didn't feel as sick as I ought to, not as sick as I would feel if I had a salaried job. My head hurt and felt large and hot and my tongue was dry and had gravel on it and my throat was stiff and my jaw was not untender. But I had had worse mornings.

It was a gray morning with high fog, not yet warm but likely to be. I heaved up off the bed and rubbed the pit of my stomach where it was sore from vomiting. My left foot felt fine. It didn't have an ache in it. So I had to kick the corner of the bed with it.

I was still swearing when there was a sharp tap at the door, the kind of bossy knock that makes you want to open the door two inches, emit the succulent raspberry and slam it again.

I opened it a little wider than two inches. Detective-Lieutenant Randall stood there, in a brown gabardine suit, with a pork pie lightweight felt on his head, very neat and clean and solemn and with a nasty look in his eye.

He pushed the door lightly and I stepped away from it. He came in and closed it and looked around. "I've been looking for you for two days," he said. He didn't look at me. His eyes measured the room.

"I've been sick."

He walked around with a light springy step, his creamy gray hair shining, his hat under his arm now, his hands in his pockets. He wasn't a very big man for a cop. He took one hand out of his pocket and placed the hat carefully on top of some magazines.

"Not here," he said.

"In a hospital."

"Which hospital?"

"A pet hospital."

He jerked as if I had slapped his face. Dull color showed behind his skin.

"A little early in the day, isn't it—for that sort of thing?"

I didn't say anything. I lit a cigarette. I took one draw on it and sat down on the bed again, quickly.

"No cure for lads like you, is there?" he said. "Except to throw you in the sneezer."

"I've been a sick man and I haven't had my morning coffee. You can't expect a very high grade of wit."

"I told you not to work on this case."

"You're not God. You're not even Jesus Christ." I took another drag on the cigarette. Somewhere down inside me felt raw, but I liked it a little better.

"You'd be amazed how much trouble I could make you."

"Probably."

"Do you know why I haven't done it so far?"

"Yeah."

"Why?" He was leaning over a little, sharp as a terrier, with that stony look in his eyes they all get sooner or later.

"You couldn't find me."

He leaned back and rocked on his heels. His face shone a little. "I thought you were going to say something else," he said. "And if you said it, I was going to smack you on the button."

"Twenty million dollars wouldn't scare you. But you might get orders."

He breathed hard, with his mouth a little open. Very slowly he got a package of cigarettes out of his pocket and tore the wrapper. His fingers were trembling a little. He put a cigarette between his lips and went over to my magazine table for a match folder. He lit the cigarette carefully, put the match in the ashtray and not on the floor, and inhaled.

"I gave you some advice over the telephone the other day," he said. "Thursday."

"Friday."

"Yes—Friday. It didn't take. I can understand why. But I didn't know at that time you had been holding out evidence. I was just recommending a line of action that seemed like a good idea in this case."

"What evidence?"

He stared at me silently.

"Will you have some coffee?" I asked. "It might make you human."

"No."

"*I* will." I stood up and started for the kitchenette.

"Sit down," Randall snapped. "I'm far from through."

I kept on going out to the kitchenette, ran some water into the kettle and put it on the stove. I took a drink of cold water from the faucet, then another. I came back with a third glass in my hand to stand in the doorway and look at him. He hadn't moved. The veil of his smoke was almost a solid thing to one side of him. He was looking at the floor.

"Why was it wrong to go to Mrs. Grayle when she sent for me?" I asked.

"I wasn't talking about that."

"Yeah, but you were just before."

"She didn't send for you." His eyes lifted and had the stony look still. And the flush still dyed his sharp cheekbones. "You forced yourself on her and talked about scandal and practically blackmailed yourself into a job."

"Funny. As I remember it, we didn't even talk job. I didn't think there was anything in her story. I mean, anything to get my teeth into. Nowhere to start. And of course I supposed she had already told it to you."

"She had. That beer joint on Santa Monica is a crook hideout. But that doesn't mean anything. I couldn't get a thing there. The hotel across the street smells too. Nobody we want. Cheap punks."

"She tell you I forced myself on her?"

He dropped his eyes a little. "No."

I grinned. "Have some coffee?"

"No."

I went back into the kitchenette and made the coffee and waited for it to drip. Randall followed me out this time and stood in the doorway himself.

"This jewel gang has been working in Hollywood and around for a good ten years to my knowledge," he said. "They went too far this time. They killed a man. I think I know why."

"Well, if it's a gang job and you break it, that will be the first gang murder solved since I lived in the town. And I could name and describe at least a dozen."

"It's nice of you to say that, Marlowe."

"Correct me if I'm wrong."

"Damn it," he said irritably. "You're not wrong. There were a couple solved for the record, but they were just rappers. Some punk took it for the high pillow."

"Yeah. Coffee?"

"If I drink some, will you talk to me decently, man to man, without wise-cracking?"

"I'll try. I don't promise to spill all my ideas."

"I can do without those," he said acidly.

"That's a nice suit you're wearing."

The flush dyed his face again. "This suit cost twenty-seven-fifty," he snapped.

"Oh Christ, a sensitive cop," I said, and went back to the stove.

"That smells good. How do you make it?"

I poured. "French drip. Coarse ground coffee. No filter papers." I got the sugar from the closet and the cream from the refrigerator. We sat down on opposite sides of the nook.

"Was that a gag, about your being sick, in a hospital?"

"No gag. I ran into a little trouble—down in Bay City. They took me in. Not the cooler, a private dope and liquor cure."

His eyes got distant. "Bay City, eh? You like it the hard way, don't you, Marlowe?"

"It's not that I like it the hard way. It's that I get it that way. But nothing like this before. I've been sapped twice, the second time by a police officer or a man who looked like one and claimed to be one. I've been beaten with my own gun and choked by a tough Indian. I've been thrown unconscious into this dope hospital and kept there locked up and part of the time probably strapped down. And I couldn't prove any of it, except that I actually do have quite a nice collection of bruises and my left arm has been needled plenty."

He stared hard at the corner of the table. "In Bay City," he said slowly.

"The name's like a song. A song in a dirty bathtub."

"What were you doing down there?"

"I didn't go down there. These cops took me over the line. I went to see a guy in Stillwood Heights. That's in L. A."

"A man named Jules Amthor," he said quietly. "Why did you swipe those cigarettes?"

I looked into my cup. The damned little fool. "It looked funny, him—Marriott—having that extra case. With reefers in it. It seems they make them up like Russian cigarettes down in Bay City with hollow mouthpieces and the Romanoff arms and everything."

He pushed his empty cup at me and I refilled it. His eyes were going over my face line by line, corpuscle by corpuscle, like Sherlock Holmes with his magnifying glass or Thorndyke with his pocket lens.

"You ought to have told me," he said bitterly. He sipped and wiped his lips with one of those fringed things they give you in apartment houses for napkins. "But you didn't swipe them. The girl told me."

"Aw well, hell," I said. "A guy never gets to do anything in this country any more. Always women."

"She likes you," Randall said, like a polite FBI man in a movie, a little sad, but very manly. "Her old man was as straight a cop as ever lost a job. She had no business taking those things. She likes you."

"She's a nice girl. Not my type."

"You don't like them nice?" He had another cigarette going. The smoke was being fanned away from his face by his hand.

"I like smooth shiny girls, hardboiled and loaded with sin."

"They take you to the cleaners," Randall said indifferently.

"Sure. Where else have I ever been? What do you call this session?"

He smiled his first smile of the day. He probably allowed himself four.

"I'm not getting much out of you," he said.

"I'll give you a theory, but you are probably way ahead of me on it. This Marriott was a blackmailer of women, because Mrs. Grayle just about told me so. But he was something else. He was the finger man for the jewel mob. The society finger, the boy who would cultivate the victim and set the stage. He would cultivate women he could take out, get to know them pretty well. Take this holdup a week from Thursday. It smells. If Marriott hadn't been driving the car, or hadn't taken Mrs. Grayle to the Troc or hadn't gone home the way he did, past that beer parlor, the holdup couldn't have been brought off."

"The chauffeur could have been driving," Randall said reasonably. "But that wouldn't have changed things much. Chauffeurs are not getting themselves pushed in the face with lead bullets by holdup men—for ninety a month. But there couldn't be many stick-ups with Marriott alone with women or things would get talked about."

"The whole point of this kind of racket is that things are not talked about," I said. "In consideration for that the stuff is sold back cheap."

Randall leaned back and shook his head. "You'll have to do better than that to interest me. Women talk about anything. It would get around that this Marriott was a kind of tricky guy to go out with."

"It probably did. That's why they knocked him off."

Randall stared at me woodenly. His spoon was stirring air in an empty cup. I reached over and he waved the pot aside. "Go on with that one," he said.

"They used him up. His usefulness was exhausted. It was about time for him to get talked about a little, as you suggest. But you don't quit in those rackets and you don't get your time. So this last holdup was just that for him—the last. Look, they really asked very little for the jade considering its value. And Marriott handled the contact. But all the same Marriott was scared. At the last moment he thought he had better not go alone. And he figured a little trick that if anything did happen to him, something on him would point to a man, a man quite ruthless and clever enough to be the brains of that sort of mob, and a man in an unusual position to get information about rich women. It was a childish sort of trick but it did actually work."

Randall shook his head. "A gang would have stripped him, perhaps even have taken the body out to sea and dumped it."

"No. They wanted the job to look amateurish. They wanted to stay in business. They probably have another finger lined up," I said.

Randall still shook his head. "The man these cigarettes pointed to is not the type. He has a good racket of his own. I've inquired. What did you think of him?"

His eyes were too blank, much too blank. I said: "He looked pretty damned deadly to me. And there's no such thing as too much money, is there? And after all his psychic racket is a temporary racket for any one place. He has a vogue and everybody goes to him and after a while the vogue dies down and the business is licking its shoes. That is, if he's a psychic and nothing else. Just like movie stars. Give him five years. He could work it that long. But give him a couple of ways to use the information he must get out of these women and he's going to make a killing."

"I'll look him up more thoroughly," Randall said with the blank look. "But right now I'm more interested in Marriott. Let's go back farther—much farther. To how you got to know him."

"He just called me up. Picked my name out of the phone book. He said so, at any rate."

"He had your card."

I looked surprised. "Sure. I'd forgotten that."

"Did you ever wonder why he picked *your* name—ignoring that matter of your short memory?"

I stared at him across the top of my coffee cup. I was beginning to like him. He had a lot behind his vest besides his shirt.

"So that's what you really came up for?" I said.

He nodded. "The rest, you know, is just talk." He smiled politely at me and waited.

I poured some more coffee.

Randall leaned over sideways and looked along the cream-colored surface of the table. "A little dust," he said absently, then straightened up and looked me in the eye. "Perhaps I ought to go at this in a little different way," he said. "For instance, I think your hunch about Marriott is probably right. There's twenty-three grand in currency in his safe-deposit box—which we had a hell of a time to locate, by the way. There are also some pretty fair bonds and a trust deed to a property on West Fifty-fourth Place."

He picked a spoon up and rapped it lightly on the edge of his saucer and smiled. "That interest you?" he asked mildly. "The number was 1644 West Fifty-fourth Place."

"Yeah," I said thickly.

"Oh, there was quite a bit of jewelry in Marriott's box too—pretty good stuff. But I don't think he stole it. I think it was very likely given to him. That's one up for you. He was afraid to sell it—on account of the association of thought in his own mind."

I nodded. "He'd feel as if it was stolen."

"Yes. Now that trust deed didn't interest me at all at first, but here's how it works. It's what you fellows are up against in police work. We get all the homicide and doubtful death reports from outlying districts. We're supposed to read them the same day. That's a rule, like you shouldn't search without a warrant or frisk a guy for a gun without reasonable grounds. But we break rules. We have to. I didn't get around to some of the reports until this morning. Then I read one about a killing of a Negro on Central, last Thursday. By a tough ex-con called Moose Malloy. And there was an identifying witness. And sink my putt, if you weren't the witness."

He smiled, softly, his third smile. "Like it?"

"I'm listening."

"This was only this morning, understand. So I looked at the name of the man making the report and I knew him, Nulty. So I knew the case was a flop. Nulty is the kind of guy—well, were you ever up at Crestline?"

"Yeah."

"Well, up near Crestline there's a place where a bunch of old box cars have been made into cabins. I have a cabin up there myself, but not a box car. These box cars were brought up on trucks, believe it or not, and there they stand without any wheels. Now Nulty is the kind of guy who would make a swell brakeman on one of those box cars."

"That's not nice," I said. "A fellow officer."

"So I called Nulty up and he hemmed and hawed around and spit a few times and then he said you had an idea about some girl called Velma something or other that Malloy was sweet on a long time ago and you went to see the widow of the guy that used to own the dive where the killing happened when it was a white joint, and where Malloy and the girl both worked at that time. And her address was 1644 West Fifty-fourth Place, the place Marriott had the trust deed on."

"Yes?"

"So I just thought that was enough coincidence for one morning," Randall said. "And here I am. And so far I've been pretty nice about it."

"The trouble is," I said, "it looks like more than it is. This Velma girl is dead, according to Mrs. Florian. I have her photo."

I went into the living room and reached into my suit-coat and my hand was in midair when it began to feel funny and empty. But they hadn't even taken the photos. I got them out and took them to the kitchen and tossed the Pierrot girl down in front of Randall. He studied it carefully.

"Nobody I ever saw," he said. "That another one?"

"No, this is a newspaper still of Mrs. Grayle. Anne Riordan got it."

He looked at it and nodded. "For twenty million, I'd marry her myself."

"There's something I ought to tell you," I said. "Last night I was so damn mad I had crazy ideas about going down there and trying to bust it alone. This hospital is at Twenty-third and Descanso in Bay City. It's run by a man named Sonderborg who says he's a doctor. He's running a crook hideout on the side. I saw Moose Malloy there last night. In a room."

Randall sat very still, looking at me. "Sure?"

"You couldn't mistake him. He's a big guy, enormous. He doesn't look like anybody you ever saw."

He sat looking at me, without moving. Then very slowly he moved out from under the table and stood up.

"Let's go see this Florian woman."

"How about Malloy?"

He sat down again. "Tell me the whole thing, carefully."

I told him. He listened without taking his eyes off my face. I don't think he even winked. He breathed with his mouth slightly open. His body didn't move. His fingers tapped gently on the edge of the table. When I had finished he said:

"This Dr. Sonderborg—what did he look like?"

"Like a doper, and probably a dope peddler." I described him to Randall as well as I could.

He went quietly into the other room and sat down at the telephone. He dialed his number and spoke quietly for a long time. Then he came back. I had just finished making more coffee and boiling a couple of eggs and making two slices of toast and buttering them. I sat down to eat.

Randall sat down opposite me and leaned his chin in his hand. "I'm having a state narcotics man go down there with a fake complaint and ask to look around. He may get some ideas. He won't get Malloy. Malloy was out of there ten minutes after you left last night. That's one thing you can bet on."

"Why not the Bay City cops?" I put salt on my eggs.

Randall said nothing. When I looked up at him his face was red and uncomfortable.

"For a cop," I said, "you're the most sensitive guy I ever met."

"Hurry up with that eating. We have to go."

"I have to shower and shave and dress after this."

"Couldn't you just go in your pajamas?" he asked acidly.

"So the town is as crooked as all that?" I said.

"It's Laird Brunette's town. They say he put up thirty grand to elect a mayor."

"The fellow that owns the Belvedere Club?"

"And the two gambling boats."

"But it's in our county," I said.

He looked down at his clean, shiny fingernails.

"We'll stop by your office and get those other two reefers," he said.

"If they're still there." He snapped his fingers. "If you'll lend me your keys, I'll do it while you get shaved and dressed."

"We'll go together," I said. "I might have some mail."

He nodded and after a moment sat down and lit another cigarette. I shaved and dressed and we left in Randall's car.

I had some mail, but it wasn't worth reading. The two cut up cigarettes in the desk drawer had not been touched. The office had no look of having been searched.

Randall took the two Russian cigarettes and sniffed at the tobacco and put them away in his pocket.

"He got one card from you," he mused. "There couldn't have been anything on the back of that, so he didn't bother about the others. I guess Amthor is not very much afraid—just thought you were trying to pull something. Let's go."

30

OLD NOSEY POKED HER NOSE an inch outside the front door, sniffed carefully as if there might be an early violet blooming, looked up and down the street with a raking glance, and nodded her white head. Randall and I took our hats off. In that neighborhood that probably ranked you with Valentino. She seemed to remember me.

"Good morning, Mrs. Morrison," I said. "Can we step inside a minute? This is Lieutenant Randall from Headquarters."

"Land's sakes, I'm all flustered. I got a big ironing to do," she said.

"We won't keep you a minute."

She stood back from the door and we slipped past her into her hallway with the side piece from Mason City or wherever it was and from that into the neat living room with the lace curtains at the windows. A smell of ironing came from the back of the house. She shut the door in between as carefully as if it was made of short pie crust.

She had a blue and white apron on this morning. Her eyes were just as sharp and her chin hadn't grown any.

She parked herself about a foot from me and pushed her face forward and looked into my eyes.

"She didn't get it."

I looked wise. I nodded my head and looked at Randall and Randall nodded his head. He went to a window and looked at the side of Mrs. Florian's house. He came back softly, holding his pork pie under his arm, debonair as a French count in a college play.

"She didn't get it," I said.

"Nope, she didn't. Saturday was the first. April Fool's Day. He! He!" She stopped and was about to wipe her eyes with her apron when she remembered it was a rubber apron. That soured her a little. Her mouth got the pruny look.

"When the mailman come by and he didn't go up her walk she run out and called to him. He shook his head and went on. She went back in. She slammed the door so hard I figured a window'd break. Like she was mad."

"I swan," I said.

Old Nosey said to Randall sharply: "Let me see your badge, young man. This young man had a whiskey breath on him t'other day. I ain't never rightly trusted him."

Randall took a gold and blue enamel badge out of his pocket and showed it to her.

"Looks like real police all right," she admitted. "Well, ain't nothing happened over Sunday. She went out for liquor. Come back with two square bottles."

"Gin," I said. "That just gives you an idea. Nice folks don't drink gin."

"Nice folks don't drink no liquor at all," Old Nosey said pointedly.

"Yeah," I said. "Come Monday, that being today, and the mailman went by again. This time she was really sore."

"Kind of smart guesser, ain't you, young man? Can't wait for folks to get their mouth open hardly."

"I'm sorry, Mrs. Morrison. This is an important matter to us—"

"This here young man don't seem to have no trouble keepin' his mouth in place."

"He's married," I said. "He's had practice."

Her face turned a shade of violet that reminded me, unpleasantly, of cyanosis. "Get out of my house afore I call the police!" she shouted.

"There is a police officer standing before you, madam," Randall said shortly. "You are in no danger."

"That's right there is," she admitted. The violet tint began to fade from her face. "I don't take to this man."

"You have company, madam. Mrs. Florian didn't get her registered letter today either—is that it?"

"No." Her voice was sharp and short. Her eyes were furtive. She began to talk rapidly, too rapidly. "People was there last night. I didn't even see them. Folks took me to the picture show. Just as we got back—no, just after they driven off—a car went away from next door. Fast without any lights. I didn't see the number."

She gave me a sharp sidelong look from her furtive eyes. I wondered why they were furtive. I wandered to the window and lifted the lace curtain. An official blue-gray uniform was nearing the house. The man wearing it wore a heavy leather bag over his shoulder and had a vizored cap.

I turned away from the window, grinning.

"You're slipping," I told her rudely. "You'll be playing shortstop in a Class C league next year."

"That's not smart," Randall said coldly.

"Take a look out of the window."

He did and his face hardened. He stood quite still looking at Mrs. Morrison. He was waiting for something, a sound like nothing else on earth. It came in a moment.

It was the sound of something being pushed into the front door mail slot. It might have been a handbill, but it wasn't. There were steps going back down the walk, then along the street, and Randall went to the window again. The mailman didn't stop at Mrs. Florian's house. He went on, his blue-gray back even and calm under the heavy leather pouch.

Randall turned his head and asked with deadly politeness: "How many mail deliveries a morning are there in this district, Mrs. Morrison?"

She tried to face it out. "Just the one," she said sharply—"one mornings and one afternoons."

Her eyes darted this way and that. The rabbit chin was trembling on the edge of something. Her hands clutched at the rubber frill that bordered the blue and white apron.

"The morning delivery just went by," Randall said dreamily. "Registered mail comes by the regular mailman?"

"She always got it Special Delivery," the old voice cracked.

"Oh. But on Saturday she ran out and spoke to the mailman when he didn't stop at her house. And you said nothing about Special Delivery."

It was nice to watch him working—on somebody else.

Her mouth opened wide and her teeth had the nice shiny look that comes from standing all night in a glass of solution. Then suddenly she made a squawking noise and threw the apron over her head and ran out of the room.

He watched the door through which she had gone. It was beyond the arch. He smiled. It was a rather tired smile.

"Neat, and not a bit gaudy," I said. "Next time you play the tough part. I don't like being rough with old ladies—even if they are lying gossips."

He went on smiling. "Same old story." He shrugged. "Police work. Phooey. She started with facts, as she knew facts. But they didn't come fast enough or seem exciting enough. So she tried a little lily-gilding."

He turned and we went out into the hall. A faint noise of sobbing came from the back of the house. For some patient man, long dead, that had been the weapon of final defeat, probably. To me it was just an old woman sobbing, but nothing to be pleased about.

We went quietly out of the house, shut the front door quietly and made sure that the screen door didn't bang. Randall put his hat on and sighed. Then he shrugged, spreading his cool well-kept hands out far from his body. There was a thin sound of sobbing still audible, back in the house.

The mailman's back was two houses down the street.

"Police work," Randall said quietly, under his breath, and twisted his mouth.

We walked across the space to the next house. Mrs. Florian hadn't even taken the wash in. It still jittered, stiff and yellowish on the wire line in the side yard. We went up on the steps and rang the bell. No answer. We knocked. No answer.

"It was unlocked last time," I said.

He tried the door, carefully screening the movement with his body. It was locked this time. We went down off the porch and walked around the house on the side away from Old Nosey. The back porch had a hooked screen. Randall knocked on that. Nothing happened. He came back off the two almost paintless wooden steps and went along the disused and overgrown driveway and opened up a wooden garage. The doors creaked. The garage was full of nothing. There were a few battered old-fashioned trunks not worth breaking up for firewood. Rusted gardening tools, old cans, plenty of those, in cartons. On each side of the doors, in the angle of the wall a nice fat black widow spider sat in its casual untidy web. Randall picked up a piece of wood and killed them absently. He shut the garage up again, walked back along the weedy drive to the front and up the steps of the house on the other side from Old Nosey. Nobody answered his ring or knock.

He came back slowly, looking across the street over his shoulder.

"Back door's easiest," he said. "The old hen next door won't do anything about it now. She's done too much lying."

He went up the two back steps and slid a knife blade neatly into the crack of the door and lifted the hook. That put us in the screen porch. It was full of cans and some of the cans were full of flies.

"Jesus, what a way to live!" he said.

The back door was easy. A five-cent skeleton key turned the lock. But there was a bolt.

"This jars me," I said. "I guess she's beat it. She wouldn't lock up like this. She's too sloppy."

"Your hat's older than mine," Randall said. He looked at the glass panel in the back door. "Lend it to me to push the glass in. Or shall we do a neat job?"

"Kick it in. Who cares around here?"

"Here goes."

He stepped back and lunged at the lock with his leg parallel to the floor. Something cracked idly and the door gave a few inches. We heaved it open and picked a piece of jagged cast metal off the linoleum and laid it politely on the woodstone drainboard, beside about nine empty gin bottles.

Flies buzzed against the closed windows of the kitchen. The place reeked. Randall stood in the middle of the floor, giving it the careful eye.

Then he walked softly through the swing door without touching it except low down with his toe and using that to push it far enough back so that it stayed open. The living room was much as I had remembered it. The radio was off.

"That's a nice radio," Randall said. "Cost money. If it's paid for. Here's something."

He went down on one knee and looked along the carpet. Then he went to the side of the radio and moved a loose cord with his foot. The plug came into view. He bent and studied the knobs on the radio front.

"Yeah," he said. "Smooth and rather large. Pretty smart, that. You don't get prints on a light cord, do you?"

"Shove it in and see if it's turned on."

He reached around and shoved it into the plug in the baseboard. The light went on at once. We waited. The thing hummed for a while and then suddenly a heavy volume of sound began to pour out of the speaker. Randall jumped at the cord and yanked it loose again. The sound was snapped off sharp.

When he straightened his eyes were full of light.

We went swiftly into the bedroom. Mrs. Jessie Pierce Florian lay diagonally across the bed, in a rumpled cotton house dress, with her head close to one end of the footboard. The corner post of the bed was smeared darkly with something the flies liked.

She had been dead long enough.

Randall didn't touch her. He stared down at her for a long time and then looked at me with a wolfish baring of his teeth.

"Brains on her face," he said. "That seems to be the theme song of this case. Only this was done with just a pair of hands. But Jesus what a pair of hands. Look at the neck bruises, the spacing of the finger marks."

"You look at them," I said. I turned away. "Poor old Nulty. It's not just a shine killing any more."

31

A SHINY BLACK BUG with a pink head and pink spots on it crawled slowly along the polished top of Randall's desk and waved a couple of feelers around, as if testing the breeze for a takeoff. It wobbled a little as it crawled, like an old woman carrying too many parcels. A nameless dick sat at another desk and kept talking into an old-fashioned hushaphone telephone mouthpiece, so that his voice sounded like someone whispering in a tunnel. He talked with his eyes half closed, a big scarred hand on the desk in front of him holding a burning cigarette between the knuckles of the first and second fingers.

The bug reached the end of Randall's desk and marched straight off into the air. It fell on its back on the floor, waved a few thin worn legs in the air feebly and then played dead. Nobody cared, so it began waving the legs again and finally struggled over on its face. It trundled slowly off into a corner towards nothing, going nowhere.

The police loudspeaker box on the wall put out a bulletin about a holdup on San Pedro south of Forty-fourth. The holdup was a middle-aged man wearing a dark gray suit and gray felt hat. He was last seen running east on Forty-fourth and then dodging between two houses. "Approach carefully," the announcer said. "This suspect is armed with a .32 caliber revolver and has just held up the proprietor of a Greek restaurant at Number 3966 South San Pedro."

A flat click and the announcer went off the air and another one came on and started to read a hot car list, in a slow monotonous voice that repeated everything twice.

The door opened and Randall came in with a sheaf of letter size typewritten sheets. He walked briskly across the room and sat down across the desk from me and pushed some papers at me.

"Sign four copies," he said.

I signed four copies.

The pink bug reached a corner of the room and put feelers out for a good spot to take off from. It seemed a little discouraged. It went along the baseboard towards another corner. I lit a cigarette and the dick at the hushaphone abruptly got up and went out of the office.

Randall leaned back in his chair, looking just the same as ever, just as cool, just as smooth, just as ready to be nasty or nice as the occasion required.

"I'm telling you a few things," he said, "just so you won't go having any more brainstorms. Just so you won't go master-minding all over the landscape any more. Just so maybe for Christ's sake you will let this one lay."

I waited.

"No prints in the dump," he said. "You know which dump I mean. The cord was jerked to turn the radio off, but she turned it up herself probably. That's pretty obvious. Drunks like loud radios. If you have gloves on to do a killing and you turn up the radio to drown shots or something, you can turn it off the same way. But that wasn't the way it was done. And that woman's neck is broken. She was dead before the guy started to smack her head around. Now why did he start to smack her head around?"

"I'm just listening."

Randall frowned. "He probably didn't know he'd broken her neck. He was sore at her," he said. "Deduction." He smiled sourly.

I blew some smoke and waved it away from my face.

"Well, why was he sore at her? There was a grand reward paid the time he was picked up at Florian's for the bank job in Oregon. It was paid to a shyster who is dead since, but the Florians likely got some of it. Malloy may have suspected that. Maybe he actually knew it. And maybe he was just trying to shake it out of her."

I nodded. It sounded worth a nod. Randall went on:

"He took hold of her neck just once and his fingers didn't slip. If we get him, we might be able to prove by the spacing of the marks that his hands did it. Maybe not. The doc figures it happened last night, fairly early. Motion picture time, anyway. So far we don't tie Malloy to the house last night, not by any neighbors. But it certainly looks like Malloy."

"Yeah," I said. "Malloy all right. He probably didn't mean to kill her, though. He's just too strong."

"That won't help him any," Randall said grimly.

"I suppose not. I just make the point that Malloy does not appear to me to be a killer type. Kill if cornered—but not for pleasure or money—and not women."

"Is that an important point?" he asked dryly.

"Maybe you know enough to know what's important. And what isn't. I don't."

He stared at me long enough for a police announcer to have time to put out another bulletin about the holdup of the Greek restaurant on South San Pedro. The suspect was now in custody. It turned out later that he was a fourteen-year-old Mexican armed with a water-pistol. So much for eye-witnesses.

Randall waited until the announcer stopped and went on:

"We got friendly this morning. Let's stay that way. Go home and lie down and have a good rest. You look pretty peaked. Just let me and the police department handle the Marriott killing and find Moose Malloy and so on."

"I got paid on the Marriott business," I said. "I fell down on the job. Mrs. Grayle has hired me. What do you want me to do—retire and live on my fat?"

He stared at me again. "I know. I'm human. They give you guys licenses, which must mean they expect you to do something with them besides hang them on the wall in your office. On the other hand any acting-captain with a grouch can break you."

"Not with the Grayles behind me."

He studied it. He hated to admit I could be even half right. So he frowned and tapped his desk.

"Just so we understand each other," he said after a pause. "If you crab this case, you'll be in a jam. It may be a jam you can wriggle out of this time. I don't know. But little by little you will build up a body of hostility in this department that will make it damn hard for you to do any work."

"Every private dick faces that every day of his life—unless he's just a divorce man."

"You can't work on murders."

"You've said your piece. I heard you say it. I don't expect to go out and accomplish things a big police department can't accomplish. If I have any small private notions, they are just that—small and private."

He leaned slowly across the desk. His thin restless fingers tap-tapped, like the poinsettia shoots tapping against Mrs. Jessie Florian's front wall. His creamy gray hair shone. His cool steady eyes were on mine.

"Let's go on," he said. "With what there is to tell. Amthor's away on a trip. His wife—and secretary—doesn't know or won't say where. The Indian has also disappeared. Will you sign a complaint against these people?"

"No. I couldn't make it stick."

He looked relieved. "The wife says she never heard of you. As to these two Bay City cops, if that's what they were—that's out of my hands. I'd rather not have the thing any more complicated than it is. One thing I feel pretty sure of—Amthor had nothing to do with Marriott's death. The cigarettes with his card in them were just a plant."

"Doc Sonderborg?"

He spread his hands. "The whole shebang skipped. Men from the D.A.'s office went down there on the quiet. No contact with Bay City at all. The house is locked up and empty. They got in, of course. Some hasty attempt had been made to clean up, but there are prints—plenty of them. It will take a week to work out what we have. There's a wall safe they're working on now. Probably had dope in it—and other things. My guess is that Sonderborg will have a record, not local, somewhere else, for abortion, or treating gunshot wounds or altering finger tips or for illegal use of dope. If it comes under Federal statutes, we'll get a lot of help."

"He said he was a medical doctor," I said.

Randall shrugged. "May have been once. May never have been convicted. There's a guy practicing medicine near Palm Springs right now who was indicted as a dope peddler in Hollywood five years ago. He was as guilty as hell—but the protection worked. He got off. Anything else worrying you?"

"What do you know about Brunette—for telling?"

"Brunette's a gambler. He's making plenty. He's making it an easy way."

"All right," I said, and started to get up. "That sounds reasonable. But it doesn't bring us any nearer to this jewel heist gang that killed Marriott."

"I can't tell you everything, Marlowe."

"I don't expect it," I said. "By the way, Jessie Florian told me—the second time I saw her—that she had been a servant in Marriott's family once. That was why he was sending her money. Anything to support that?"

"Yes. Letters in his safety-deposit box from her thanking him and saying the same thing." He looked as if he was going to lose his temper. "*Now* will you for God's sake go home and mind your own business?"

"Nice of him to take such care of the letters, wasn't it?"

He lifted his eyes until their glance rested on the top of my head. Then he lowered the lids until half the iris was covered. He looked at me like that for a long ten seconds. Then he smiled. He was doing an awful lot of smiling that day. Using up a whole week's supply.

"I have a theory about that," he said. "It's crazy, but it's human nature. Marriott was by the circumstances of his life a threatened man. All crooks are gamblers, more or less, and all gamblers are superstitious—more or less. I think Jessie Florian was Marriott's lucky piece. As long as he took care of her, nothing would happen to him."

I turned my head and looked for the pink-headed bug. He had tried two corners of the room now and was moving off disconsolately towards a third. I went over and picked him up in my handkerchief and carried him back to the desk.

"Look," I said. "This room is eighteen floors above ground. And this little bug climbs all the way up here just to make a friend. Me. *My* luck piece." I folded the bug carefully into the soft part of the handkerchief and tucked the handkerchief into my pocket. Randall was pie-eyed. His mouth moved, but nothing came out of it.

"I wonder whose lucky piece Marriott was," I said.

"Not yours, pal." His voice was acid—cold acid.

"Perhaps not yours either." My voice was just a voice. I went out of the room and shut the door.

I rode the express elevator down to the Spring Street entrance and walked out on the front porch of City Hall and down some steps and over to the flower beds. I put the pink bug down carefully behind a bush.

I wondered, in the taxi going home, how long it would take him to make the Homicide Bureau again.

I got my car out of the garage at the back of the apartment house and ate some lunch in Hollywood before I started down to Bay City. It was a beautiful cool sunny afternoon down at the beach. I left Arguello Boulevard at Third Street and drove over to the City Hall.

32

It was a cheap-looking building for so prosperous a town. It looked more like something out of the Bible belt. Bums sat unmolested in a long row on the retaining wall that kept the front lawn—now mostly Bermuda grass—from falling into the street. The building was of three stories and had an old belfry at the top, and the bell still hanging in the belfry. They had probably rung it for the volunteer fire brigade back in the good old chaw-and-spit days.

The cracked walk and the front steps led to open double doors in which a knot of obvious city hall fixers hung around waiting for something to happen so they could make something else out of it. They all had the well-fed stomachs, the careful eyes, the nice clothes and the reach-me-down manners. They gave me about four inches to get in.

Inside was a long dark hallway that had been mopped the day Mc-Kinley was inaugurated. A wooden sign pointed out the police department Information Desk. A uniformed man dozed behind a pint-sized PBX set into the end of a scarred wooden counter. A plainclothesman with his coat off and his hog's leg looking like a fire plug against his ribs took one eye off his evening paper, bonged a spittoon ten feet away from him, yawned, and said the Chief's office was upstairs at the back.

The second floor was lighter and cleaner, but that didn't mean that it was clean and light. A door on the ocean side, almost at the end of the hall, was lettered: John Wax, Chief of Police. Enter.

Inside there was a low wooden railing and a uniformed man behind it working a typewriter with two fingers and one thumb. He took my card, yawned, said he would see, and managed to drag himself through a mahogany door marked John Wax, Chief of Police. Private. He came back and held the door in the railing for me.

I went on in and shut the door of the inner office. It was cool and large and had windows on three sides. A stained wood desk was set far back like Mussolini's, so that you had to walk across an expanse of blue carpet to get to it, and while you were doing that you would be getting the beady eye.

I walked to the desk. A tilted embossed sign on it read: John Wax, Chief of Police. I figured I might be able to remember the name. I looked at the man behind the desk. No straw was sticking to his hair.

He was a hammered-down heavyweight, with short pink hair and a pink scalp glistening through it. He had small, hungry, heavy-lidded eyes, as restless as fleas. He wore a suit of fawn-colored flannel, a coffee-colored shirt and tie, a diamond ring, a diamond-studded lodge pin in his lapel, and the required three stiff points of handkerchief coming up a little more than the required three inches from his outside breast pocket.

One of his plump hands was holding my card. He read it, turned it over and read the back, which was blank, read the front again, put it down on his desk and laid on it a paperweight in the shape of a bronze monkey, as if he was making sure he wouldn't lose it.

He pushed a pink paw at me. When I gave it back to him, he motioned to a chair.

"Sit down, Mr. Marlowe. I see you are in our business more or less. What can I do for you?"

"A little trouble, Chief. You can straighten it out for me in a minute, if you care to."

"Trouble," he said softly. "A little trouble."

He turned in his chair and crossed his thick legs and gazed thoughtfully towards one of his pairs of windows. That let me see handspun lisle socks and English brogues that looked as if they had been pickled in port wine. Counting what I couldn't see and not counting his wallet he had half a grand on him. I figured his wife had money.

"Trouble," he said, still softly, "is something our little city don't know much about, Mr. Marlowe. Our city is small but very, very clean. I look out of my western windows and I see the Pacific Ocean. Nothing cleaner than that, is there?" He didn't mention the two gambling ships that were hull down on the brass waves just beyond the three-mile limit.

Neither did I. "That's right, Chief," I said.

He threw his chest a couple of inches farther. "I look out of my northern windows and I see the busy bustle of Arguello Boulevard and the lovely California foothills, and in the near foreground one of the nicest little business sections a man could want to know. I look out of my southern windows, which I am looking out of right now, and I see the finest little yacht harbor in the world, for a small yacht harbor. I don't have no eastern windows, but if I did have, I would see a residential section that would make your mouth water. No, sir, trouble is a thing we don't have a lot of on hand in our little town."

"I guess I brought mine with me, Chief. Some of it at least. Do you have a man working for you named Galbraith, a plainclothes sergeant?"

"Why yes, I believe I do," he said, bringing his eyes around. "What about him?"

"Do you have a man working for you that goes like this?" I described the other man, the one who said very little, was short, had a mustache and hit me with a blackjack. "He goes around with Galbraith, very likely. Somebody called him Mister Blane, but that sounded like a phony."

"Quite on the contrary," the fat Chief said as stiffly as a fat man can say anything. "He is my Chief of Detectives. Captain Blane."

"Could I see these two guys in your office?"

He picked my card up and read it again. He laid it down. He waved a soft glistening hand.

"Not without a better reason than you have given me so far," he said suavely.

"I didn't think I could, Chief. Do you happen to know of a man named Jules Amthor? He calls himself a psychic adviser. He lives at the top of a hill in Stillwood Heights."

"No. And Stillwood Heights is not in my territory," the Chief said. His eyes now were the eyes of a man who has other thoughts.

"That's what makes it funny," I said. "You see, I went to call on Mr. Amthor in connection with a client of mine. Mr. Amthor got the idea I was blackmailing him. Probably guys in his line of business get that idea rather easily. He had a tough Indian bodyguard I couldn't handle. So the Indian held me and Amthor beat me up with my own gun. Then he sent for a couple of cops. They happened to be Galbraith and Mister Blane. Could this interest you at all?"

Chief Wax flapped his hands on his desk top very gently. He folded his eyes almost shut, but not quite. The cool gleam of his eyes shone between the thick lids and it shone straight at me. He sat very still, as if listening. Then he opened his eyes and smiled.

"And what happened then?" he inquired, polite as a bouncer at the Stork Club.

"They went through me, took me away in their car, dumped me out on the side of a mountain and socked me with a sap as I got out."

He nodded, as if what I had said was the most natural thing in the world. "And this was in Stillwood Heights," he said softly.

"Yeah."

"You know what I think you are?" He leaned a little over the desk, but not far, on account of his stomach being in the way.

"A liar," I said.

"The door is there," he said, pointing to it with the little finger of his left hand.

I didn't move. I kept on looking at him. When he started to get mad enough to push his buzzer I said: "Let's not both make the same mistake. You think I'm a small time private dick trying to push ten times his own weight, trying to make a charge against a police officer that, even if it was true, the officer would take damn good care couldn't be proved. Not at all. I'm not making any complaints. I think the mistake was natural. I want to square myself with Amthor and I want your man Galbraith to help me do it. Mister Blane needn't bother. Galbraith will be enough. And I'm not here without backing. I have important people behind me."

"How far behind?" the Chief asked and chuckled wittily.

"How far is 862 Aster Drive, where Mr. Merwin Lockridge Grayle lives?"

His face changed so completely that it was as if another man sat in his chair. "Mrs. Grayle happens to be my client," I said.

"Lock the doors," he said. "You're a younger man than I am. Turn the bolt knobs. We'll make a friendly start on this thing. You have an honest face, Marlowe."

I got up and locked the doors. When I got back to the desk along the blue carpet, the Chief had a nice looking bottle out and two glasses. He tossed a handful of cardamom seeds on his blotter and filled both glasses.

We drank. He cracked a few cardamom seeds and we chewed them silently, looking into each other's eyes.

"That tasted right," he said. He refilled the glasses. It was my turn to crack the cardamom seeds. He swept the shells off his blotter to the floor and smiled and leaned back.

"Now let's have it," he said. "Has this job you are doing for Mrs. Grayle anything to do with Amthor?"

"There's a connection. Better check that I'm telling you the truth, though."

"There's that," he said and reached for his phone. Then he took a small book out of his vest and looked up a number. "Campaign contributors," he said and winked. "The Mayor is very insistent that all courtesies be extended. Yes, here it is." He put the book away and dialed.

He had the same trouble with the butler that I had. It made his ears get red. Finally he got her. His ears stayed red. She must have been pretty sharp with him. "She wants to talk to you," he said and pushed the phone across his broad desk.

"This is Phil," I said, winking naughtily at the Chief.

There was a cool provocative laugh. "What are you doing with that fat slob?"

"There's a little drinking being done."

"Do you have to do it with him?"

"At the moment, yes. Business. I said, is there anything new? I guess you know what I mean."

"No. Are you aware, my good fellow, that you stood me up for an hour the other night? Did I strike you as the kind of girl that lets that sort of thing happen to her?"

"I ran into trouble. How about tonight?"

"Let me see—tonight is—what day of the week is it for heaven's sake?"

"I'd better call you," I said. "I may not be able to make it. This is Friday."

"Liar." The soft husky laugh came again. "It's Monday. Same time, same place—and no fooling this time?"

"I'd better call you."

"You'd better be there."

"I can't be sure. Let me call you."

"Hard to get? I see. Perhaps I'm a fool to bother."

"As a matter of fact you are."

"Why?"

"I'm a poor man, but I pay my own way. And it's not quite as soft a way as you would like."

"Damn you, if you're not there—"

"I said I'd call you."

She sighed. "All men are the same."

"So are all women—after the first nine."

She damned me and hung up. The Chief's eyes popped so far out of his head they looked as if they were on stilts.

He filled both glasses with a shaking hand and pushed one at me.

"So it's like that," he said very thoughtfully.

"Her husband doesn't care," I said, "so don't make a note of it."

He looked hurt as he drank his drink. He cracked the cardamom seeds very slowly, very thoughtfully. We drank to each other's baby blue eyes. Regretfully the Chief put the bottle and glasses out of sight and snapped a switch on his call box.

"Have Galbraith come up, if he's in the building. If not, try and get in touch with him for me."

I got up and unlocked the doors and sat down again. We didn't wait long. The side door was tapped on, the Chief called out, and Hemingway stepped into the room.

He walked solidly over to the desk and stopped at the end of it and looked at Chief Wax with the proper expression of tough humility.

"Meet Mr. Philip Marlowe," the Chief said genially. "A private dick from L.A."

Hemingway turned enough to look at me. If he had ever seen me before, nothing in his face showed it. He put a hand out and I put a hand out and he looked at the Chief again.

"Mr. Marlowe has a rather curious story," the Chief said, cunning, like Richelieu behind the arras. "About a man named Amthor who has a place in Stillwood Heights. He's some sort of crystal-gazer. It seems Marlowe went to see him and you and Blane happened in about the same time and there was an argument of some kind. I forget the details." He looked out of his windows with the expression of a man forgetting details.

"Some mistake," Hemingway said. "I never saw this man before."

"There was a mistake, as a matter of fact," the Chief said dreamily. "Rather trifling, but still a mistake. Mr. Marlowe thinks it of slight importance."

Hemingway looked at me again. His face still looked like a stone face.

"In fact he's not even interested in the mistake," the Chief dreamed on. "But he is interested in going to call on this man Amthor who lives in Stillwood Heights. He would like someone with him. I thought of you. He would like someone who would see that he got a square deal. It seems that Mr. Amthor has a very tough Indian bodyguard and Mr. Marlowe is a little inclined to doubt his ability to handle the situation without help. Do you think you could find out where this Amthor lives?"

"Yeah," Hemingway said. "But Stillwood Heights is over the line, Chief. This just a personal favor to a friend of yours?"

"You might put it that way," the Chief said, looking at his left thumb. "We wouldn't want to do anything not strictly legal, of course."

"Yeah," Hemingway said. "No." He coughed. "When do we go?"

The Chief looked at me benevolently. "Now would be okey," I said. "If it suits Mr. Galbraith."

"I do what I'm told," Hemingway said.

The Chief looked him over, feature by feature. He combed him and brushed him with his eyes. "How is Captain Blane today?" he inquired, munching on a cardamom seed.

"Bad shape. Bust appendix," Hemingway said. "Pretty critical."

The Chief shook his head sadly. Then he got hold of the arms of his chair and dragged himself to his feet. He pushed a pink paw across his desk.

"Galbraith will take good care of you, Marlowe. You can rely on that."

"Well, you've certainly been obliging, Chief," I said. "I certainly don't know how to thank you."

"Pshaw! No thanks necessary. Always glad to oblige a friend of a friend, so to speak." He winked at me. Hemingway studied the wink but he didn't say what he added it up to.

We went out, with the Chief's polite murmurs almost carrying us down the office. The door closed. Hemingway looked up and down the hall and then he looked at me.

"You played that one smart, baby," he said. "You must got something we wasn't told about."

33

THE CAR DRIFTED QUIETLY along a quiet street of homes. Arching pepper trees almost met above it to form a green tunnel. The sun twinkled through their upper branches and their narrow light leaves. A sign at the corner said it was Eighteenth Street.

Hemingway was driving and I sat beside him. He drove very slowly, his face heavy with thought.

"How much you tell him?" he asked, making up his mind.

"I told him you and Blane went over there and took me away and tossed me out of the car and socked me on the back of the head. I didn't tell him the rest."

"Not about Twenty-third and Descanso, huh?"

"No."

"Why not?"

"I thought maybe I could get more co-operation from you if I didn't."

"That's a thought. You really want to go over to Stillwood Heights, or was that just a stall?"

"Just a stall. What I really want is for you to tell me why you put me in that funnyhouse and why I was kept there."

Hemingway thought. He thought so hard his cheek muscles made little knots under his grayish skin.

"That Blane," he said. "That sawed-off hunk of shin meat. I didn't mean for him to sap you. I didn't mean for you to walk home neither, not really. It was just an act, on account of we are friends with this swami guy and we kind of keep people from bothering him. You'd be surprised what a lot of people would try to bother him."

"Amazed," I said.

He turned his head. His gray eyes were lumps of ice. Then he looked again through the dusty windshield and did some more thinking.

"Them old cops get sap-hungry once in a while," he said. "They just got to crack a head. Jesus, was I scared. You dropped like a sack of cement. I told Blane plenty. Then we run you over to Sonderborg's place on account of it was a little closer and he was a nice guy and would take care of you."

"Does Amthor know you took me there?"

"Hell, no. It was our idea."

"On account of Sonderborg is such a nice guy and he would take care of me. And no kickback. No chance for a doctor to back up a complaint if I made one. Not that a complaint would have much chance in this sweet little town, if I did make it."

"You going to get tough?" Hemingway asked thoughtfully.

"Not me," I said. "And for once in your life neither are you. Because your job is hanging by a thread. You looked in the Chief's eyes and you saw that. I didn't go in there without credentials, not this trip."

"Okey," Hemingway said and spat out of the window. "I didn't have any idea of getting tough in the first place except just the routine big mouth. What next?"

"Is Blane really sick?"

Hemingway nodded, but somehow failed to look sad. "Sure is. Pain in the gut day before yesterday and it bust on him before they could get his appendix out. He's got a chance—but not too good."

"We certainly hate to lose him," I said. "A fellow like that is an asset to any police force."

Hemingway chewed that one over and spat it out of the car window.

"Okey, next question," he sighed.

"You told me why you took me to Sonderborg's place. You didn't tell me why he kept me there over forty-eight hours, locked up and shot full of dope."

Hemingway braked the car softly over beside the curb. He put his large hands on the lower part of the wheel side by side and gently rubbed the thumbs together.

"I wouldn't have an idea," he said in a far-off voice.

"I had papers on me showing I had a private license," I said. "Keys, some money, a couple of photographs. If he didn't know you boys pretty well, he might think the crack on the head was just a gag to get into his place and look around. But I figure he knows you boys too well for that. So I'm puzzled."

"Stay puzzled, pally. It's a lot safer."

"So it is," I said. "But there's no satisfaction in it."

"You got the L.A. law behind you on this?"

"On this what?"

"On this thinking about Sonderborg."

"Not exactly."

"That don't mean yes or no."

"I'm not that important," I said. "The L.A. law can come in here any time they feel like it—two thirds of them anyway. The Sheriff's boys and the D.A.'s boys. I have a friend in the D.A.'s office. I worked there once. His name is Bernie Ohls. He's Chief Investigator."

"You give it to him?"

"No. I haven't spoken to him in a month."

"Thinking about giving it to him?"

"Not if it interferes with a job I'm doing."

"Private job?"

"Yes."

"Okey, what is it you want?"

"What's Sonderborg's real racket?"

Hemingway took his hands off the wheel and spat out of the window. "We're on a nice street here, ain't we? Nice homes, nice gardens, nice climate. You hear a lot about crooked cops, or do you?"

"Once in a while," I said.

"Okey, how many cops do you find living on a street even as good as this, with nice lawns and flowers? I'd know four or five, all vice squad boys. They get all the gravy. Cops like me live in itty-bitty frame houses on the wrong side of town. Want to see where I live?"

"What would it prove?"

"Listen, pally," the big man said seriously. "You got me on a string, but it could break. Cops don't go crooked for money. Not always, not even often. They get caught in the system. They get you where they have you do what is told them or else. And the guy that sits back there in the nice big corner office, with the nice suit and the nice liquor breath he thinks chewing on them seeds makes smell like violets, only it don't—he ain't giving the orders either. You get me?"

"What kind of a man is the mayor?"

"What kind of guy is a mayor anywhere? A politician. You think he gives the orders? Nuts. You know what's the matter with this country, baby?"

"Too much frozen capital, I heard."

"A guy can't stay honest if he wants to," Hemingway said. "That's what's the matter with this country. He gets chiseled out of his pants if he does. You gotta play the game dirty or you don't eat. A lot of bastards think all we need is ninety thousand FBI men in clean collars and brief cases. Nuts. The percentage would get them just the way it does the rest of us. You know what I think? I think we gotta make this little world all over again. Now take Moral Rearmament. There you've got something. M.R.A. There you've got something, baby."

"If Bay City is a sample of how it works, I'll take aspirin," I said.

"You could get too smart," Hemingway said softly. "You might not think it, but it could be. You could get so smart you couldn't think about anything but bein' smart. Me, I'm just a dumb cop. I take orders. I got a wife and two kids and I do what the big shots say. Blane could tell you things. Me, I'm ignorant."

"Sure Blane has appendicitis? Sure he didn't just shoot himself in the stomach for meanness?"

"Don't be that way," Hemingway complained and slapped his hands up and down on the wheel. "Try and think nice about people."

"About Blane?"

"He's human—just like the rest of us," Hemingway said. "He's a sinner—but he's human."

"What's Sonderborg's racket?"

"Okey, I was just telling you. Maybe I'm wrong. I had you figured for a guy that could be sold a nice idea."

"You don't know what his racket is," I said.

Hemingway took his handkerchief out and wiped his face with it. "Buddy, I hate to admit it," he said. "But you ought to know damn well that if I knew or Blane knew Sonderborg had a racket, either we wouldn't of dumped you in there or you wouldn't ever have come out, not walking. I'm talking about a real bad racket, naturally. Not fluff stuff like telling old women's fortunes out of a crystal ball."

"I don't think I was meant to come out walking," I said. "There's a drug called scopolamine, truth serum, that sometimes makes people talk without their knowing it. It's not sure fire, any more than hypnotism is. But it sometimes works. I think I was being milked in there to find out what I knew. But there are only three ways Sonderborg could have known that there was anything for me to know that might hurt him. Amthor might have told him, or Moose Malloy might have mentioned to him that I went to see Jessie Florian, or he might have thought putting me in there was a police gag."

Hemingway stared at me sadly. "I can't even see your dust," he said. "Who the hell is Moose Malloy?"

"A big hunk that killed a man over on Central Avenue a few days ago. He's on your teletype, if you ever read it. And you probably have a reader on him by now."

"So what?"

"So Sonderborg was hiding him. I saw him there, on a bed reading newspapers, the night I snuck out."

"How'd you get out? Wasn't you locked in?"

"I crocked the orderly with a bed spring. I was lucky."

"This big guy see you?"

"No."

Hemingway kicked the car away from the curb and a solid grin settled on his face. "Let's go collect," he said. "It figures. It figures swell. Sonderborg was hiding hot boys. If they had dough, that is. His set-up was perfect for it. Good money, too."

He kicked the car into motion and whirled around a corner.

"Hell, I thought he sold reefers," he said disgustedly. "With the right protection behind him. But hell, that's a small time racket. A peanut grift."

"Ever hear of the numbers racket? That's a small time racket too—if you're just looking at one piece of it."

Hemingway turned another corner sharply and shook his heavy head. "Right. And pin ball games and bingo houses and horse parlors. But add them all up and give one guy control and it makes sense."

"What guy?"

He went wooden on me again. His mouth shut hard and I could see his teeth were biting at each other inside it. We were on Descanso Street and going east. It was a quiet street even in late afternoon. As we got towards Twenty-third, it became in some vague manner less quiet. Two men were studying a palm tree as if figuring out how to move it. A car was parked near Dr. Sonderborg's place, but nothing showed in it. Halfway down the block a man was reading water meters.

The house was a cheerful spot by daylight. Tea rose begonias made a solid pale mass under the front windows and pansies a blur of color around the base of a white acacia in bloom. A scarlet climbing rose was just opening its buds on a fan-shaped trellis. There was a bed of winter sweet peas and a bronze-green humming bird prodding in them delicately. The house looked like the home of a well-to-do elderly couple who liked to garden. The late afternoon sun on it had a hushed and menacing stillness.

Hemingway slid slowly past the house and a tight little smile tugged at the corners of his mouth. His nose sniffed. He turned the next corner, and looked in his rear view mirror and stepped up the speed of the car.

After three blocks he braked at the side of the street again and turned to give me a hard level stare.

"L.A. law," he said. "One of the guys by the palm tree is called Donnelly. I know him. They got the house covered. So you didn't tell your pal downtown, huh?"

"I said I didn't."

"The Chief'll love this," Hemingway snarled. "They come down here and raid a joint and don't even stop by to say hello."

I said nothing.

"They catch this Moose Malloy?"

I shook my head. "Not so far as I know."

"How the hell far do you know, buddy?" he asked very softly.

"Not far enough. Is there any connection between Amthor and Sonderborg?"

"Not that I know of."

"Who runs this town?"

Silence.

"I heard a gambler named Laird Brunette put up thirty grand to elect the mayor. I heard he owns the Belvedere Club and both the gambling ships out on the water."

"Might be," Hemingway said politely.

"Where can Brunette be found?"

"Why ask me, baby?"

"Where would you make for if you lost your hideout in this town?"

"Mexico."

I laughed. "Okey, will you do me a big favor?"

"Glad to."

"Drive me back downtown."

He started the car away from the curb and tooled it neatly along a shadowed street towards the ocean. The car reached the City Hall and slid around into the police parking zone and I got out.

"Come round and see me some time," Hemingway said. "I'll likely be cleaning spittoons."

He put his big hand out. "No hard feelings?"

"M.R.A.," I said and shook the hand.

He grinned all over. He called me back when I started to walk away. He looked carefully in all directions and leaned his mouth close to my ear.

"Them gambling ships are supposed to be out beyond city and state jurisdiction," he said. "Panama registry. If it was me that was—" he stopped dead, and his bleak eyes began to worry.

"I get it," I said. "I had the same sort of idea. I don't know why I bothered so much to get you to have it with me. But it wouldn't work— not for just one man."

He nodded, and then he smiled. "M.R.A.," he said.

34

I LAY ON MY BACK on a bed in a waterfront hotel and waited for it to get dark. It was a small front room with a hard bed and a mattress slightly thicker than the cotton blanket that covered it. A spring underneath me was broken and stuck into the left side of my back. I lay there and let it prod me.

The reflection of a red neon light glared on the ceiling. When it made the whole room red it would be dark enough to go out. Outside cars honked along the alley they called the Speedway. Feet slithered on the sidewalks below my window. There was a murmur and mutter of coming and going in the air. The air that seeped in through the rusted screens smelled of stale frying fat. Far off a voice of the kind that could be heard far off was shouting: "Get hungry, folks. Get hungry. Nice hot doggies here. Get hungry."

It got darker. I thought; and thought in my mind moved with a kind of sluggish stealthiness, as if it was being watched by bitter and sadistic eyes. I thought of dead eyes looking at a moonless sky, with black blood at the corners of the mouths beneath them. I thought of nasty old women beaten to death against the posts of their dirty beds. I thought of a man with bright blond hair who was afraid and didn't quite know what he was afraid of, who was sensitive enough to know that something was wrong, and too vain or too dull to guess what it was that was wrong. I thought of beautiful rich women who could be had. I thought of nice slim curious girls who lived alone and could be had too, in a different way. I thought of cops, tough cops that could be greased and yet were not by any means all bad, like Hemingway. Fat prosperous cops with Chamber of Commerce voices, like Chief Wax. Slim, smart and deadly cops like Randall, who for all their smartness and deadliness were not free to do a clean job in a clean way. I thought of sour old goats like Nulty who had given up trying. I thought of Indians and psychics and dope doctors.

I thought of lots of things. It got darker. The glare of the red neon sign spread farther and farther across the ceiling. I sat up on the bed and put my feet on the floor and rubbed the back of my neck.

I got up on my feet and went over to the bowl in the corner and threw cold water on my face. After a little while I felt a little better, but very little. I needed a drink, I needed a lot of life insurance, I needed a vacation, I needed a home in the country. What I had was a coat, a hat and a gun. I put them on and went out of the room.

There was no elevator. The hallways smelled and the stairs had grimed rails. I went down them, threw the key on the desk and said I was through. A clerk with a wart on his left eyelid nodded and a Mexican bellhop in a frayed uniform coat came forward from behind the dustiest rubber plant in California to take my bags. I didn't have any bags, so being a Mexican, he opened the door for me and smiled politely just the same.

Outside the narrow street fumed, the sidewalks swarmed with fat stomachs. Across the street a bingo parlor was going full blast and beside it a couple of sailors with girls were coming out of a photographer's shop where they had probably been having their photos taken riding on camels. The voice of the hot dog merchant split the dusk like an axe. A big blue bus blared down the street to the little circle where the street car used to turn on a turntable. I walked that way.

After a while there was a faint smell of ocean. Not very much, but as if they had kept this much just to remind people this had once been a clean open beach where the waves came in and creamed and the wind blew and you could smell something besides hot fat and cold sweat.

The little sidewalk car came trundling along the wide concrete walk. I got on it and rode to the end of the line and got off and sat on a bench where it was quiet and cold and there was a big brown heap of kelp almost at my feet. Out to sea they had turned the lights on in the gambling boats. I got back on the sidewalk car the next time it came and rode back almost to where I had left the hotel. If anybody was tailing me, he was doing it without moving. I didn't think there was. In that clean little city there wouldn't be enough crime for the dicks to be very good shadows.

The black piers glittered their length and then disappeared into the dark background of night and water. You could still smell hot fat, but you could smell the ocean too. The hot dog man droned on:

"Get hungry, folks, get hungry. Nice hot doggies. Get hungry."

I spotted him in a white barbecue stand tickling wienies with a long fork. He was doing a good business even that early in the year. I had to wait sometime to get him alone.

"What's the name of the one farthest out?" I asked, pointing with my nose.

"*Montecito.*" He gave me the level steady look.

"Could a guy with reasonable dough have himself a time there?"

"What kind of a time?"

I laughed, sneeringly, very tough.

"Hot doggies," he chanted. "Nice hot doggies, folks." He dropped his voice. "Women?"

"Nix. I was figuring on a room with a nice sea breeze and good food and nobody to bother me. Kind of vacation."

He moved away. "I can't hear a word you say," he said, and then went into his chant.

He did some more business. I didn't know why I bothered with him. He just had that kind of face. A young couple in shorts came up and bought hot dogs and strolled away with the boy's arm around the girl's brassiere and each eating the other's hot dog.

The man slid a yard towards me and eyed me over. "Right now I should be whistling Roses of Picardy," he said, and paused. "That would cost you," he said.

"How much?"

"Fifty. Not less. Unless they want you for something."

"This used to be a good town," I said. "A cool-off town."

"Thought it still was," he drawled. "But why ask me?"

"I haven't an idea," I said. I threw a dollar bill on his counter. "Put it in the baby's bank," I said. "Or whistle Roses of Picardy."

He snapped the bill, folded it longways, folded it across and folded it again. He laid it on the counter and tucked his middle finger behind his thumb and snapped. The folded bill hit me lightly in the chest and fell noiselessly to the ground. I bent and picked it up and turned quickly. But nobody was behind me that looked like a dick.

I leaned against the counter and laid the dollar bill on it again. "People don't throw money at me," I said. "They hand it to me. Do you mind?"

He took the bill, unfolded it, spread it out and wiped it off with his apron. He punched his cash-register and dropped the bill into the drawer.

"They say money don't stink," he said. "I sometimes wonder."

I didn't say anything. Some more customers did business with him and went away. The night was cooling fast.

"I wouldn't try the *Royal Crown*," the man said. "That's for good little squirrels, that stick to their nuts. You look like dick to me, but that's your angle. I hope you swim good."

I left him, wondering why I had gone to him in the first place. Play the hunch. Play the hunch and get stung. In a little while you wake up with your mouth full of hunches. You can't order a cup of coffee without shutting your eyes and stabbing the menu. Play the hunch.

I walked around and tried to see if anybody walked behind me in any particular way. Then I sought out a restaurant that didn't smell of frying grease and found one with a purple neon sign and a cocktail bar behind a reed curtain. A male cutie with henna'd hair drooped at a bungalow grand piano and tickled the keys lasciviously and sang Stairway to the Stars in a voice with half the steps missing.

I gobbled a dry martini and hurried back through the reed curtain to the dining room.

The eighty-five cent dinner tasted like a discarded mail bag and was served to me by a waiter who looked as if he would slug me for a quarter, cut my throat for six bits, and bury me at sea in a barrel of concrete for a dollar and a half, plus sales tax.

35

It was a long ride for a quarter. The water taxi, an old launch painted up and glassed in for three-quarters of its length, slid through the anchored yachts and around the wide pile of stone which was the end of the breakwater. The swell hit us without warning and bounced the boat like a cork. But there was plenty of room to be sick that early in the evening. All the company I had was three couples and the man who drove the boat, a tough-looking citizen who sat a little on his left hip on account of having a black leather hip-holster inside his right hip pocket. The three couples began to chew each other's faces as soon as we left the shore.

I stared back at the lights of Bay City and tried not to bear down too hard on my dinner. Scattered points of light drew together and became a jeweled bracelet laid out in the show window of the night. Then the brightness faded and they were a soft orange glow appearing and disappearing over the edge of the swell. It was a long smooth even swell with no whitecaps, and just the right amount of heave to make me glad I hadn't pickled my dinner in bar whisky. The taxi slid up and down the swell now with a sinister smoothness, like a cobra dancing. There was cold in the air, the wet cold that sailors never get out of their joints. The red neon pencils that outlined the *Royal Crown* faded off to the left and dimmed in the gliding gray ghosts of the sea, then shone out again, as bright as new marbles.

We gave this one a wide berth. It looked nice from a long way off. A faint music came over the water and music over the water can never be anything but lovely. The *Royal Crown* seemed to ride as steady as a pier on its four hawsers. Its landing stage was lit up like a theater marquee. Then all this faded into remoteness and another, older, smaller boat began to sneak out of the night towards us. It was not much to look at. A converted seagoing freighter with scummed and rusted plates, the super-structure cut down to the boat deck level, and above that two stumpy masts just high enough for a radio antenna. There was light on the *Montecito* also and music floated across the wet dark sea. The spooning couples took their teeth out of each other's necks and stared at the ship and giggled.

The taxi swept around in a wide curve, careened just enough to give the passengers a thrill, and eased up to the hemp fenders along the stage. The taxi's motor idled and backfired in the fog. A lazy searchlight beam swept a circle about fifty yards out from the ship.

The taximan hooked to the stage and a sloe-eyed lad in a blue mess jacket with bright buttons, a bright smile and a gangster mouth, handed the girls up from the taxi. I was last. The casual neat way he looked me over told me something about him. The casual neat way he bumped my shoulder clip told me more.

"Nix," he said softly. "Nix."

He had a smoothly husky voice, a hard Harry straining himself through a silk handkerchief. He jerked his chin at the taximan. The taximan dropped a short loop over a bitt, turned his wheel a little, and climbed out on the stage. He stepped behind me.

"No gats on the boat, laddy. Sorry and all that rot," Mess-jacket purred.

"I could check it. It's just part of my clothes. I'm a fellow who wants to see Brunette, on business."

He seemed mildly amused. "Never heard of him," he smiled. "On your way, bo."

The taximan hooked a wrist through my right arm.

"I want to see Brunette," I said. My voice sounded weak and frail, like an old lady's voice.

"Let's not argue," the sloe-eyed lad said. "We're not in Bay City now, not even in California, and by some good opinions not even in the U.S.A. Beat it."

"Back in the boat," the taximan growled behind me. "I owe you a quarter. Let's go."

I got back into the boat. Mess-jacket looked at me with his silent sleek smile. I watched it until it was no longer a smile, no longer a face, no longer anything but a dark figure against the landing lights. I watched it and hungered. The way back seemed longer. I didn't speak to the taximan and he didn't speak to me. As I got off at the wharf he handed me a quarter.

"Some other night," he said wearily, "when we got more room to bounce you."

Half a dozen customers waiting to get in stared at me, hearing him. I went past them, past the door of the little waiting room on the float, toward the shallow steps at the landward end.

A big redheaded roughneck in dirty sneakers and tarry pants and what was left of a torn blue sailor's jersey and a streak of black down the side of his face straightened from the railing and bumped into me casually.

I stopped. He looked too big. He had three inches on me and thirty pounds. But it was getting to be time for me to put my fist into somebody's teeth even if all I got for it was a wooden arm.

The light was dim and mostly behind him. "What's the matter, pardner?" he drawled. "No soap on the hell ship?"

"Go darn your shirt," I told him. "Your belly is sticking out."

"Could be worse," he said. "The gat's kind of bulgy under the light suit at that."

"What pulls your nose into it?"

"Jesus, nothing at all. Just curiosity. No offense, pal."

"Well, get the hell out of my way then."

"Sure. I'm just resting here."

He smiled a slow tired smile. His voice was soft, dreamy, so delicate for a big man that it was startling. It made me think of another soft-voiced big man I had strangely liked.

"You got the wrong approach," he said sadly. "Just call me Red."

"Step aside, Red. The best people make mistakes. I feel one crawling up my back."

He looked thoughtfully this way and that. He had me angled into a corner of the shelter on the float. We seemed to be more or less alone.

"You want on the *Monty?* Can be done. If you got a reason."

People in gay clothes and gay faces went past us and got into the taxi. I waited for them to pass.

"How much is the reason?"

"Fifty bucks. Ten more if you bleed in my boat."

I started around him.

"Twenty-five," he said softly. "Fifteen if you come back with friends."

"I don't have any friends," I said, and walked away. He didn't try to stop me.

I turned right along the cement walk down which the little electric cars come and go, trundling like baby carriages and blowing little horns that wouldn't startle an expectant mother. At the foot of the first pier there was a flaring bingo parlor, jammed full of people already. I went into it and stood against the wall behind the players, where a lot of other people stood and waited for a place to sit down.

I watched a few numbers go up on the electric indicator, listened to the table men call them off, tried to spot the house players and couldn't, and turned to leave.

A large blueness that smelled of tar took shape beside me. "No got the dough—or just tight with it?" the gentle voice asked in my ear.

I looked at him again. He had the eyes you never see, that you only read about. Violet eyes. Almost purple. Eyes like a girl, a lovely girl. His skin was as soft as silk. Lightly reddened, but it would never tan. It was too delicate. He was bigger than Hemingway and younger, by many years. He was not as big as Moose Malloy, but he looked very fast on his feet. His hair was that shade of red that glints with gold. But except for the eyes he had a plain farmer face, with no stagy kind of handsomeness.

"What's your racket?" he asked. "Private eye?"

"Why do I have to tell you?" I snarled.

"I kind of thought that was it," he said. "Twenty-five too high? No expense account?"

"No."

He sighed. "It was a bum idea I had anyway," he said. "They'll tear you to pieces out there."

"I wouldn't be surprised. What's *your* racket?"

"A dollar here, a dollar there. I was on the cops once. They broke me."

"Why tell me?"

He looked surprised. "It's true."

"You must have been leveling."

He smiled faintly.

"Know a man named Brunette?"

The faint smile stayed on his face. Three bingoes were made in a row. They worked fast in there. A tall beak-faced man with sallow sunken cheeks and a wrinkled suit stepped close to us and leaned against the wall and didn't look at us. Red leaned gently towards him and asked: "Is there something we could tell you, pardner?"

The tall beak-faced man grinned and moved away. Red grinned and shook the building leaning against the wall again.

"I've met a man who could take you," I said.

"I wish there was more," he said gravely. "A big guy costs money. Things ain't scaled for him. He costs to feed, to put clothes on, and he can't sleep with his feet in the bed. Here's how it works. You might not think this is a good place to talk, but it is. Any finks drift along I'll know them and the rest of the crowd is watching those numbers and nothing else. I got a boat with an under-water by-pass. That is, I can borrow one. There's a pier down the line without lights. I know a loading port on the *Monty* I can open. I take a load out there once in a while. There ain't many guys below decks."

"They have a searchlight and lookouts," I said.

"We can make it."

I got my wallet out and slipped a twenty and a five against my stomach and folded them small. The purple eyes watched me without seeming to.

"One way?"

"Fifteen was the word."

"The market took a spurt."

A tarry hand swallowed the bills. He moved silently away. He faded

into the hot darkness outside the doors. The beak-nosed man materialized
at my left side and said quietly:

"I think I know that fellow in sailor clothes. Friend of yours? I think
I seen him before."

I straightened away from the wall and walked away from him without speaking, out of the doors, then left, watching a high head that moved
along from electrolier to electrolier a hundred feet ahead of me. After a
couple of minutes I turned into a space between two concession shacks.
The beak-nosed man appeared, strolling with his eyes on the ground. I
stepped out to his side.

"Good evening," I said. "May I guess your weight for a quarter?" I
leaned against him. There was a gun under the wrinkled coat.

His eyes looked at me without emotion. "Am I goin' to have to pinch
you, son? I'm posted along this stretch to maintain law and order."

"Who's dismaintaining it right now?"

"Your friend had a familiar look to me."

"He ought to. He's a cop."

"Aw hell," the beak-nosed man said patiently. "That's where I seen
him. Good night to you."

He turned and strolled back the way he had come. The tall head was
out of sight now. It didn't worry me. Nothing about that lad would ever
worry me.

I walked on slowly.

36

BEYOND THE ELECTROLIERS, beyond the beat and toot of the small sidewalk cars, beyond the smell of hot fat and popcorn and the shrill children
and the barkers in the peep shows, beyond everything but the smell of the
ocean and the suddenly clear line of the shore and the creaming fall of the
waves into the pebbled spume. I walked almost alone now. The noises
died behind me, the hot dishonest light became a fumbling glare. Then
the lightless finger of a black pier jutted seaward into the dark. This
would be the one. I turned to go out on it.

Red stood up from a box against the beginning of the piles and spoke
upwards to me. "Right," he said. "You go on out to the seasteps. I gotta
go and get her and warm her up."

"Waterfront cop followed me. That guy in the bingo parlor. I had to
stop and speak to him."

"Olson. Pickpocket detail. He's good too. Except once in a while he
will lift a leather and plant it, to keep up his arrest record. That's being a
shade too good, or isn't it?"

"For Bay City I'd say just about right. Let's get going. I'm getting

the wind up. I don't want to blow this fog away. It doesn't look much but it would help a lot."

"It'll last enough to fool a searchlight," Red said. "They got Tommy-guns on that boat deck. You go on out the pier, I'll be along."

He melted into the dark and I went out the dark boards slipping on fish-slimed planking. There was a low dirty railing at the far end. A couple leaned in a corner. They went away, the man swearing.

For ten minutes I listened to the water slapping the piles. A night bird whirred in the dark, the faint grayness of a wing cut across my vision and disappeared. A plane droned high in the ceiling. Then far off a motor barked and roared and kept on roaring like half a dozen truck engines. After a while the sound eased and dropped, then suddenly there was no sound at all.

More minutes passed. I went back to the seasteps and moved down them as cautiously as a cat on a wet floor. A dark shape slid out of the night and something thudded. A voice said: "All set. Get in."

I got into the boat and sat beside him under the screen. The boat slid out over the water. There was no sound from its exhaust now but an angry bubbling along both sides of the shell. Once more the lights of Bay City became something distantly luminous beyond the rise and fall of alien waves. Once more the garish lights of the *Royal Crown* slid off to one side, the ship seeming to preen itself like a fashion model on a revolving platform. And once again the ports of the good ship *Montecito* grew out of the black Pacific and the slow steady sweep of the searchlight turned around it like the beam of a lighthouse.

"I'm scared," I said suddenly. "I'm scared stiff."

Red throttled down the boat and let it slide up and down the swell as though the water moved underneath and the boat stayed in the same place. He turned his face and stared at me.

"I'm afraid of death and despair," I said. "Of dark water and drowned men's faces and skulls with empty eyesockets. I'm afraid of dying, of being nothing, of not finding a man named Brunette."

He chuckled. "You had me going for a minute. You sure give yourself a pep talk. Brunette might be any place. On either of the boats, at the club he owns, back east, Reno, in his slippers at home. That all you want?"

"I want a man named Malloy, a huge brute who got out of the Oregon State pen a while back after an eight-year stretch for bank robbery. He was hiding out in Bay City." I told him about it. I told him a great deal more than I intended to. It must have been his eyes.

At the end he thought and then spoke slowly and what he said had wisps of fog clinging to it, like the beads on a mustache. Maybe that made it seem wiser than it was, maybe not.

"Some of it makes sense," he said. "Some not. Some I wouldn't know about, some I would. If this Sonderborg was running a hideout and peddling reefers and sending boys out to heist jewels off rich ladies with a

wild look in their eyes, it stands to reason that he had an in with the city government, but that don't mean they knew everything he did or that every cop on the force knew he had an in. Could be Blane did and Hemingway, as you call him, didn't. Blane's bad, the other guy is just tough cop, neither bad nor good, neither crooked nor honest, full of guts and just dumb enough, like me, to think being on the cops is a sensible way to make a living. This psychic fellow doesn't figure either way. He bought himself a line of protection in the best market, Bay City, and he used it when he had to. You never know what a guy like that is up to and so you never know what he has on his conscience or is afraid of. Could be he's human and fell for a customer once in a while. Them rich dames are easier to make than paper dolls. So my hunch about your stay in Sonderborg's place is simply that Blane knew Sonderborg would be scared when he found out who you were—and the story they told Sonderborg is probably what he told you, that they found you wandering with your head dizzy—and Sonderborg wouldn't know what to do with you and he would be afraid either to let you go or to knock you off and after long enough Blane would drop around and raise the ante on him. That's all there was to that. It just happened they could use you and they did it. Blane might know about Malloy too. I wouldn't put it past him."

I listened and watched the slow sweep of the searchlight and the coming and going of the water taxi far over to the right.

"I know how these boys figure," Red said. "The trouble with cops is not that they're dumb or crooked or tough, but that they think just being a cop gives them a little something they didn't have before. Maybe it did once, but not any more. They're topped by too many smart minds. That brings us to Brunette. He don't run the town. He couldn't be bothered. He put up big money to elect a mayor so his water taxis wouldn't be bothered. If there was anything in particular he wanted, they would give it to him. Like a while ago one of his friends, a lawyer, was pinched for drunk driving felony and Brunette got the charge reduced to reckless driving. They changed the blotter to do it, and that's a felony too. Which gives you an idea. His racket is gambling and all rackets tie together these days. So he might handle reefers, or touch a percentage from some one of his workers he gave the business to. He might know Sonderborg and he might not. But the jewel heist is out. Figure the work these boys done for eight grand. It's a laugh to think Brunette would have anything to do with that."

"Yeah," I said. "There was a man murdered too—remember?"

"He didn't do that either, nor have it done. If Brunette had that done, you wouldn't have found any body. You never know what might be stitched into a guy's clothes. Why chance it? Look what I'm doing for you for twenty-five bucks. What would Brunette get done with the money *he* has to spend?"

"Would he have a man killed?"

Red thought for a moment. "He might. He probably has. But he's

not a tough guy. These racketeers are a new type. We think about them the way we think about old time yeggs or needled-up punks. Big-mouthed police commissioners on the radio yell that they're all yellow rats, that they'll kill women and babies and howl for mercy if they see a police uniform. They ought to know better than to try to sell the public that stuff. There's yellow cops and there's yellow torpedoes—but damn few of either. And as for the top men, like Brunette—they didn't get there by murdering people. They got there by guts and brains—and they don't have the group courage the cops have either. But above all they're business men. What they do is for money. Just like other business men. Sometimes a guy gets badly in the way. Okey. Out. But they think plenty before they do it. What the hell am I giving a lecture for?"

"A man like Brunette wouldn't hide Malloy," I said. "After he had killed two people."

"No. Not unless there was some other reason than money. Want to go back?"

"No."

Red moved his hands on the wheel. The boat picked up speed. "Don't think I *like* these bastards," he said. "I hate their guts."

37

THE REVOLVING SEARCHLIGHT was a pale mist-ridden finger that barely skimmed the waves a hundred feet or so beyond the ship. It was probably more for show than anything else. Especially at this time in the evening. Anyone who had plans for hijacking the take on one of these gambling boats would need plenty of help and would pull the job about four in the morning, when the crowd was thinned down to a few bitter gamblers, and the crew were all dull with fatigue. Even then it would be a poor way to make money. It had been tried once.

A taxi curved to the landing stage, unloaded, went back shorewards. Red held his speedboat idling just beyond the sweep of the searchlight. If they lifted it a few feet, just for fun—but they didn't. It passed languidly and the dull water glowed with it and the speedboat slid across the line and closed in fast under the overhang, past the two huge scummy stern hawsers. We sidled up to the greasy plates of the hull as coyly as a hotel dick getting set to ease a hustler out of his lobby.

Double iron doors loomed high above us, and they looked too high to reach and too heavy to open even if we could reach them. The speed-boat scuffed the *Montecito's* ancient sides and the swell slapped loosely at the shell under our feet. A big shadow rose in the gloom at my side and a coiled rope slipped upwards through the air, slapped, caught, and the end ran down and splashed in water. Red fished it out with a boathook, pulled it tight and fastened the end to something on the engine cowling. There was just enough fog to make everything seem unreal. The wet air was as cold as the ashes of love.

Red leaned close to me and his breath tickled my ear. "She rides too high. Come a good blow and she'd wave her screws in the air. We got to climb those plates just the same."

"I can hardly wait," I said, shivering.

He put my hands on the wheel, turned it just as he wanted it, set the throttle, and told me to hold the boat just as she was. There was an iron ladder bolted close to the plates, curving with the hull, its rungs probably as slippery as a greased pole.

Going up it looked as tempting as climbing over the cornice of an office building. Red reached for it, after wiping his hands hard on his pants to get some tar on them. He hauled himself up noiselessly, without even a grunt, and his sneakers caught the metal rungs, and he braced his body out almost at right angles to get more traction.

The searchlight beam swept far outside us now. Light bounced off the water and seemed to make my face as obvious as a flare, but nothing happened. Then there was a dull creak of heavy hinges over my head. A faint ghost of yellowish light trickled out into the fog and died. The outline of one half of the loading port showed. It couldn't have been bolted from inside. I wondered why.

The whisper was a mere sound, without meaning. I left the wheel and started up. It was the hardest journey I ever made. It landed me panting and wheezing in a sour hold littered with packing boxes and barrels and coils of rope and clumps of rusted chain. Rats screamed in dark corners. The yellow light came from a narrow door on the far side.

Red put his lips against my ear. "From here we take a straight walk to the boiler room catwalk. They'll have steam in one auxiliary, because they don't have no Diesels on this piece of cheese. There will be probably one guy below. The crew doubles in brass up on the play decks, table men and spotters and waiters and so on. They all got to sign on as something that sounds like ship. From the boiler room I'll show you a ventilator with no grating in it. It goes to the boat deck and the boat deck is out of bounds. But it's all yours—while you live."

"You must have relatives on board," I said.

"Funnier things have happened. Will you come back fast?"

"I ought to make a good splash from the boat deck," I said, and got my wallet out. "I think this rates a little more money. Here. Handle the body as if it was your own."

"You don't owe me nothing more, pardner."

"I'm buying the trip back—even if I don't use it. Take the money before I bust out crying and wet your shirt."

"Need a little help up there?"

"All I need is a silver tongue and the one I have is like a lizard's back."

"Put your dough away," Red said. "You paid me for the trip back. I think you're scared." He took hold of my hand. His was strong, hard, warm and slightly sticky. "I *know* you're scared," he whispered.

"I'll get over it," I said. "One way or another."

He turned away from me with a curious look I couldn't read in that light. I followed him among the cases and barrels, over the raised iron sill of the door, into a long dim passage with the ship smell. We came out of this on to a grilled steel platform, slick with oil, and went down a steel ladder that was hard to hold on to. The slow hiss of the oil burners filled the air now and blanketed all other sound. We turned towards the hiss through mountains of silent iron.

Around a corner we looked at a short dirty wop in a purple silk shirt who sat in a wired-together office chair, under a naked hanging light, and read the evening paper with the aid of a black forefinger and steel-rimmed spectacles that had probably belonged to his grandfather.

Red stepped behind him noiselessly. He said gently:

"Hi, Shorty. How's all the bambinos?"

The Italian opened his mouth with a click and threw a hand at the opening of his purple shirt. Red hit him on the angle of the jaw and caught him. He put him down on the floor gently and began to tear the purple shirt into strips.

"This is going to hurt him more than the poke on the button," Red said softly. "But the idea is a guy going up a ventilator ladder makes a lot of racket down below. Up above they won't hear a thing."

He bound and gagged the Italian neatly and folded his glasses and put them in a safe place and we went along to the ventilator that had no grating in it. I looked up and saw nothing but blackness.

"Good-by," I said.

"Maybe you need a little help."

I shook myself like a wet dog. "I need a company of marines. But either I do it alone or I don't do it. So long."

"How long will you be?" His voice still sounded worried.

"An hour or less."

He stared at me and chewed his lip. Then he nodded. "Sometimes a guy has to," he said. "Drop by that bingo parlor, if you get time."

He walked away softly, took four steps, and came back. "That open loading port," he said. "That might buy you something. Use it." He went quickly.

38

COLD AIR RUSHED DOWN THE VENTILATOR. It seemed a long way to the top. After three minutes that felt like an hour I poked my head out cautiously from the hornlike opening. Canvas-sheeted boats were gray blurs near by. Low voices muttered in the dark. The beam of the searchlight circled slowly. It came from a point still higher, probably a railed platform at the top of one of the stumpy masts. There would be a lad up there with a Tommygun too, perhaps even a light Browning. Cold job, cold comfort when somebody left the loading port unbolted so nicely.

Distantly music throbbed like the phony bass of a cheap radio. Overhead a masthead light and through the higher layers of fog a few bitter stars stared down.

I climbed out of the ventilator, slipped my .38 from my shoulder clip and held it curled against my ribs, hiding it with my sleeve. I walked three silent steps and listened. Nothing happened. The muttering talk had stopped, but not on my account. I placed it now, between two lifeboats. And out of the night and the fog, as it mysteriously does, enough light gathered into one focus to shine on the dark hardness of a machine gun mounted on a high tripod and swung down over the rail. Two men stood near it, motionless, not smoking, and their voices began to mutter again, a quiet whisper that never became words.

I listened to the muttering too long. Another voice spoke clearly behind me.

"Sorry, guests are not allowed on the boat deck."

I turned, not too quickly, and looked at his hands. They were light blurs and empty.

I stepped sideways nodding and the end of a boat hid us. The man followed me gently, his shoes soundless on the damp deck.

"I guess I'm lost," I said.

"I guess you are." He had a youngish voice, not chewed out of marble. "But there's a door at the bottom of the companionway. It has a spring lock on it. It's a good lock. There used to be an open stairway with a chain and a brass sign. We found the livelier element would step over that."

He was talking a long time, either to be nice, or to be waiting. I didn't know which. I said: "Somebody must have left the door open."

The shadowed head nodded. It was lower than mine.

"You can see the spot that puts us in, though. If somebody did leave it open, the boss won't like it a nickel. If somebody didn't, we'd like to know how you got up here. I'm sure you get the idea."

"It seems a simple idea. Let's go down and talk to him about it."

"You come with a party?"

"A very nice party."

"You ought to have stayed with them."

"You know how it is—you turn your head and some other guy is buying her a drink."

He chuckled. Then he moved his chin slightly up and down.

I dropped and did a frogleap sideways and the swish of the blackjack was a long spent sigh in the quiet air. It was getting to be that every blackjack in the neighborhood swung at me automatically. The tall one swore.

I said: "Go ahead and be heroes."

I clicked the safety catch loudly.

Sometimes even a bad scene will rock the house. The tall one stood rooted, and I could see the blackjack swinging at his wrist. The one I had been talking to thought it over without any hurry.

"This won't buy you a thing," he said gravely. "You'll never get off the boat."

"I thought of that. Then I thought how little you'd care."

It was still a bum scene.

"You want what?" he said quietly.

"I have a loud gun," I said. "But it doesn't have to go off. I want to talk to Brunette."

"He went to San Diego on business."

"I'll talk to his stand-in."

"You're quite a lad," the nice one said. "We'll go down. You'll put the heater up before we go through the door."

"I'll put the heater up when I'm sure I'm going through the door."

He laughed lightly. "Go back to your post, Slim. I'll look into this."

He moved lazily in front of me and the tall one appeared to fade into the dark.

"Follow me, then."

We moved Indian file across the deck. We went down brassbound slippery steps. At the bottom was a thick door. He opened it and looked at the lock. He smiled, nodded, held the door for me and I stepped through, pocketing the gun.

The door closed and clicked behind us. He said:

"Quiet evening, so far."

There was a gilded arch in front of us and beyond it a gaming room, not very crowded. It looked much like any other gaming room. At the far end there was a short glass bar and some stools. In the middle a stairway going down and up this the music swelled and faded. I heard roulette wheels. A man was dealing faro to a single customer. There were not more than sixty people in the room. On the faro table there was a pile of yellowbacks that would start a bank. The player was an elderly white-haired man who looked politely attentive to the dealer, but no more.

Two quiet men in dinner jackets came through the archway sauntering, looking at nothing. That had to be expected. They strolled towards us and the short slender man with me waited for them. They were well beyond the arch before they let their hands find their side pockets, looking for cigarettes of course.

"From now on we have to have a little organization here," the short man said. "I don't think you'll mind?"

"You're Brunette," I said suddenly.

He shrugged. "Of course."

"You don't look so tough," I said.

"I hope not."

The two men in dinner jackets edged me gently.

"In here," Brunette said. "We can talk at ease."

He opened the door and they took me into dock.

The room was like a cabin and not like a cabin. Two brass lamps swung in gimbals hung above a dark desk that was not wood, possibly plastic. At the end were two bunks in grained wood. The lower of them was made up and on the top one were half a dozen stacks of phonograph record books. A big combination radio-phonograph stood in the corner. There was a red leather chesterfield, a red carpet, smoking stands, a tabouret with cigarettes and a decanter and glasses, a small bar sitting cattycorners at the opposite end from the bunks.

"Sit down," Brunette said and went around the desk. There were a lot of business-like papers on the desk, with columns of figures, done on a bookkeeping machine. He sat in a tall backed director's chair and tilted it a little and looked me over. Then he stood up again and stripped off his overcoat and scarf and tossed them to one side. He sat down again. He picked a pen up and tickled the lobe of one ear with it. He had a cat smile, but I like cats.

He was neither young nor old, neither fat nor thin. Spending a lot of time on or near the ocean had given him a good healthy complexion. His hair was nut-brown and waved naturally and waved still more at sea. His forehead was narrow and brainy and his eyes held a delicate menace. They were yellowish in color. He had nice hands, not babied to the point of insipidity, but well-kept. His dinner clothes were midnight blue, I judged, because they looked so black. I thought his pearl was a little too large, but that might have been jealousy.

He looked at me for quite a long time before he said: "He has a gun."

One of the velvety tough guys leaned against the middle of my spine with something that was probably not a fishing rod. Exploring hands removed the gun and looked for others.

"Anything else?" a voice asked.

Brunette shook his head. "Not now."

One of the gunners slid my automatic across the desk. Brunette put the pen down and picked up a letter opener and pushed the gun around gently on his blotter.

"Well," he said quietly, looking past my shoulder. "Do I have to explain what I want now?"

One of them went out quickly and shut the door. The other was so still he wasn't there. There was a long easy silence, broken by the distant hum of voices and the deep-toned music and somewhere down below a dull almost imperceptible throbbing.

"Drink?"

"Thanks."

The gorilla mixed a couple at the little bar. He didn't try to hide the glasses while he did it. He placed one on each side of the desk, on black glass scooters.

"Cigarette?"

"Thanks."

"Egyptian all right?"

"Sure."

We lit up. We drank. It tasted like good Scotch. The gorilla didn't drink.

"What I want—" I began.

"Excuse me, but that's rather unimportant, isn't it?"

The soft catlike smile and the lazy half-closing of the yellow eyes.

The door opened and the other one came back and with him was Mess-jacket, gangster mouth and all. He took one look at me and his face went oyster-white.

"He didn't get past me," he said swiftly, curling one end of his lips.

"He had a gun," Brunette said, pushing it with the letter opener. "This gun. He even pushed it into my back more or less, on the boat deck."

"Not past me, boss," Mess-jacket said just as swiftly.

Brunette raised his yellow eyes slightly and smiled at me. "Well?"

"Sweep him out," I said. "Squash him somewhere else."

"I can prove it by the taximan," Mess-jacket snarled.

"You've been off the stage since five-thirty?"

"Not a minute, boss."

"That's no answer. An empire can fall in a minute."

"Not a second, boss."

"But he can be had," I said, and laughed.

Mess-jacket took the smooth gliding step of a boxer and his fist lashed like a whip. It almost reached my temple. There was a dull thud. His fist seemed to melt in midair. He slumped sideways and clawed at a corner of the desk, then rolled on his back. It was nice to see somebody else get sapped for a change.

Brunette went on smiling at me.

"I hope you're not doing him an injustice," Brunette said. "There's still the matter of the door to the companionway."

"Accidentally open."

"Could you think of any other idea?"

"Not in such a crowd."

"I'll talk to you alone," Brunette said, not looking at anyone but me.

The gorilla lifted Mess-jacket by the armpits and dragged him across the cabin and his partner opened an inner door. They went through. The door closed.

"All right," Brunette said. "Who are you and what do you want?"

"I'm a private detective and I want to talk to a man named Moose Malloy."

"Show me you're a private dick."

I showed him. He tossed the wallet back across the desk. His wind-tanned lips continued to smile and the smile was getting stagy.

"I'm investigating a murder," I said. "The murder of a man named Marriott on the bluff near your Belvedere Club last Thursday night. This murder happens to be connected with another murder, of a woman, done by Malloy, an ex-con and bank robber and all-round tough guy."

He nodded. "I'm not asking you yet what it has to do with me. I assume you'll come to that. Suppose you tell me how you got on my boat?"

"I told you."

"It wasn't true," he said gently. "Marlowe is the name? It wasn't true, Marlowe. You know that. The kid down on the stage isn't lying. I pick my men carefully."

"You own a piece of Bay City," I said. "I don't know how big a piece, but enough for what you want. A man named Sonderborg has been running a hideout there. He has been running reefers and stickups and hiding hot boys. Naturally, he couldn't do that without connections. I don't think he could do it without you. Malloy was staying with him. Malloy has left. Malloy is about seven feet tall and hard to hide. I think he could hide nicely on a gambling boat."

"You're simple," Brunette said softly. "Supposing I wanted to hide him, why should I take the risk out here?" He sipped his drink. "After all I'm in another business. It's hard enough to keep a good taxi service running without a lot of trouble. The world is full of places a crook can hide. If he has money. Could you think of a better idea?"

"I could, but to hell with it."

"I can't do anything for you. So how did you get on the boat?"

"I don't care to say."

"I'm afraid I'll have to have you made to say, Marlowe." His teeth glinted in the light from the brass ship's lamps. "After all, it can be done."

"If I tell you, will you get word to Malloy?"

"What word?"

I reached for my wallet lying on the desk and drew a card from it and turned it over. I put the wallet away and got a pencil instead. I wrote five words on the back of the card and pushed it across the desk. Brunette took it and read what I had written on it. "It means nothing to me," he said.

"It will mean something to Malloy."

He leaned back and stared at me. "I don't make you out. You risk your hide to come out here and hand me a card to pass on to some thug I don't even know. There's no sense to it."

"There isn't if you don't know him."

"Why didn't you leave your gun ashore and come aboard the usual way?"

"I forgot the first time. Then I knew that toughie in the mess jacket would never let me on. Then I bumped into a fellow who knew another way."

His yellow eyes lighted as with a new flame. He smiled and said nothing.

"This other fellow is no crook but he's been on the beach with his ears open. You have a loading port that has been unbarred on the inside and you have a ventilator shaft out of which the grating has been removed. There's one man to knock over to get to the boat deck. You'd better check your crew list, Brunette."

He moved his lips softly, one over the other. He looked down at the card again. "Nobody named Malloy is on board this boat," he said. "But if you're telling the truth about that loading port, I'll buy."

"Go and look at it."

He still looked down. "If there's any way I can get word to Malloy, I will. I don't know why I bother."

"Take a look at that loading port."

He sat very still for a moment, then leaned forward and pushed the gun across the desk to me.

"The things I do," he mused, as if he was alone. "I run towns, I elect mayors, I corrupt police, I peddle dope, I hide out crooks, I heist old women strangled with pearls. What a lot of time I have." He laughed shortly. "What a lot of time."

I reached for my gun and tucked it back under my arm.

Brunette stood up. "I promise nothing," he said, eyeing me steadily. "But I believe you."

"Of course not."

"You took a long chance to hear so little."

"Yes."

"Well—" he made a meaningless gesture and then put his hand across the desk.

"Shake hands with a chump," he said softly.

I shook hands with him. His hand was small and firm and a little hot.

"You wouldn't tell me how you found out about this loading port?"

"I can't. But the man who told me is no crook."

"I could make you tell," he said, and immediately shook his head. "No. I believed you once. I'll believe you again. Sit still and have another drink."

He pushed a buzzer. The door at the back opened and one of the nice-tough guys came in.

"Stay here. Give him a drink, if he wants it. No rough stuff."

The torpedo sat down and smiled at me calmly. Brunette went quickly out of the office. I smoked. I finished my drink. The torpedo made me another. I finished that, and another cigarette.

Brunette came back and washed his hands over in the corner, then sat down at his desk again. He jerked his head at the torpedo. The torpedo went out silently.

The yellow eyes studied me. "You win, Marlowe. And I have one hundred and sixty-four men on my crew list. Well—" he shrugged. "You can go back by the taxi. Nobody will bother you. As to your message, I have a few contacts. I'll use them. Good night. I probably should say thanks. For the demonstration."

"Good night," I said, and stood up and went out.

There was a new man on the landing stage. I rode to shore on a different taxi. I went along to the bingo parlor and leaned against the wall in the crowd.

Red came along in a few minutes and leaned beside me against the wall.

"Easy, huh?" Red said softly, against the heavy clear voices of the table men calling the numbers.

"Thanks to you. He bought. He's worried."

Red looked this way and that and turned his lips a little more close to my ear. "Get your man?"

"No. But I'm hoping Brunette will find a way to get him a message."

Red turned his head and looked at the tables again. He yawned and straightened away from the wall. The beak-nosed man was in again. Red stepped over to him and said: "Hiya, Olson," and almost knocked the man off his feet pushing past him.

Olson looked after him sourly and straightened his hat. Then he spat viciously on the floor.

As soon as he had gone, I left the place and went along to the parking lot back towards the tracks where I had left my car.

I drove back to Hollywood and put the car away and went up to the apartment.

I took my shoes off and walked around in my socks feeling the floor with my toes. They would still get numb again once in a while.

Then I sat down on the side of the pulled-down bed and tried to figure time. It couldn't be done. It might take hours or days to find Malloy. He might never be found until the police got him. If they ever did—alive.

39

It was about ten o'clock when I called the Grayle number in Bay City. I thought it would probably be too late to catch her, but it wasn't. I fought my way through a maid and the butler and finally heard her voice on the line. She sounded breezy and well-primed for the evening.

"I promised to call you," I said. "It's a little late, but I've had a lot to do."

"Another stand-up?" Her voice got cool.

"Perhaps not. Does your chauffeur work this late?"

"He works as late as I tell him to."

"How about dropping by to pick me up? I'll be getting squeezed into my commencement suit."

"Nice of you," she drawled. "Should I really bother?" Amthor had certainly done a wonderful job with her centers of speech—if anything had ever been wrong with them.

"I'd show you my etching."

"Just one etching?"

"It's just a single apartment."

"I heard they had such things," she drawled again, then changed her tone. "Don't act so hard to get. You have a lovely build, mister. And don't ever let anyone tell you different. Give me the address again."

I gave it to her and the apartment number. "The lobby door is locked," I said. "But I'll go down and slip the catch."

"That's fine," she said. "I won't have to bring my jimmy."

She hung up, leaving me with a curious feeling of having talked to somebody that didn't exist.

I went down to the lobby and slipped the catch and then took a shower and put my pajamas on and lay down on the bed. I could have slept for a week. I dragged myself up off the bed again and set the catch on the door, which I had forgotten to do, and walked through a deep hard snowdrift out to the kitchenette and laid out glasses and a bottle of liqueur Scotch I had been saving for a really highclass seduction.

I lay down on the bed again. "Pray," I said out loud. "There's nothing left but prayer."

I closed my eyes. The four walls of the room seemed to hold the throb of a boat, the still air seemed to drip with fog and rustle with sea wind. I smelled the rank sour smell of a disused hold. I smelled engine oil and saw a wop in a purple shirt reading under a naked light bulb with his grandfather's spectacles. I climbed and climbed up a ventilator shaft. I climbed the Himalayas and stepped out on top and guys with machine guns were all around me. I talked with a small and somehow very human yellow-eyed man who was a racketeer and probably worse. I thought of the giant with the red hair and the violet eyes, who was probably the nicest man I had ever met.

I stopped thinking. Lights moved behind my closed lids. I was lost in space. I was a gilt-edged sap come back from a vain adventure. I was a hundred dollar package of dynamite that went off with a noise like a pawnbroker looking at a dollar watch. I was a pink-headed bug crawling up the side of the City Hall.

I was asleep.

I woke slowly, unwillingly, and my eyes stared at reflected light on the ceiling from the lamp. Something moved gently in the room.

The movement was furtive and quiet and heavy. I listened to it. Then I turned my head slowly and looked at Moose Malloy. There were shadows and he moved in the shadows, as noiselessly as I had seen him once before. A gun in his hand had a dark oily business-like sheen. His hat was pushed on his black curly hair and his nose sniffed, like the nose of a hunting dog.

He saw me open my eyes. He came softly over to the side of the bed and stood looking down at me.

"I got your note," he said. "I make the joint clean. I don't make no cops outside. If this is a plant, two guys goes out in baskets."

I rolled a little on the bed and he felt swiftly under the pillows. His face was still wide and pale and his deep-set eyes were still somehow gentle. He was wearing an overcoat tonight. It fitted him where it touched. It was burst out in one shoulder seam, probably just getting it on. It would be the largest size they had, but not large enough for Moose Malloy.

"I hoped you'd drop by," I said. "No copper knows anything about this. I just wanted to see you."

"Go on," he said.

He moved sideways to a table and put the gun down and dragged his overcoat off and sat down in my best easy chair. It creaked, but it held. He leaned back slowly and arranged the gun so that it was close to his right hand. He dug a pack of cigarettes out of his pocket and shook one loose and put it into his mouth without touching it with his fingers. A match flared on a thumbnail. The sharp smell of the smoke drifted across the room.

"You ain't sick or anything?" he said.

"Just resting. I had a hard day."

"Door was open. Expecting someone?"

"A dame."

He stared at me thoughtfully.

"Maybe she won't come," I said. "If she does, I'll stall her."

"What dame?"

"Oh, just a dame. If she comes, I'll get rid of her. I'd rather talk to you."

His very faint smile hardly moved his mouth. He puffed his cigarette awkwardly, as if it was too small for his fingers to hold with comfort.

"What made you think I was on the *Monty?*" he asked.

"A Bay City cop. It's a long story and too full of guessing."

"Bay City cops after me?"

"Would that bother you?"

He smiled the faint smile again. He shook his head slightly.

"You killed a woman," I said. "Jessie Florian. That was a mistake."

He thought. Then he nodded. "I'd drop that one," he said quietly.

"But that queered it," I said. "I'm not afraid of you. You're no killer. You didn't mean to kill her. The other one—over on Central—you could have squeezed out of. But not out of beating a woman's head on a bedpost until her brains were on her face."

"You take some awful chances, brother," he said softly.

"The way I've been handled," I said, "I don't know the difference any more. You didn't mean to kill her—did you?"

His eyes were restless. His head was cocked in a listening attitude.

"It's about time you learned your own strength," I said.

"It's too late," he said.

"You wanted her to tell you something," I said. "You took hold of her neck and shook her. She was already dead when you were banging her head against the bedpost."

He stared at me.

"I know what you wanted her to tell you," I said.

"Go ahead."

"There was a cop with me when she was found. I had to break clean."

"How clean?"

"Fairly clean," I said. "But not about tonight."

He stared at me. "Okey, how did you know I was on the *Monty?*" He had asked me that before. He seemed to have forgotten.

"I didn't. But the easiest way to get away would be by water. With the set-up they have in Bay City you could get out to one of the gambling boats. From there you could get clean away. With the right help."

"Laird Brunette is a nice guy," he said emptily. "So I've heard. I never even spoke to him."

"He got the message to you."

"Hell, there's a dozen grapevines that might help him to do that, pal. When do we do what you said on the card? I had a hunch you were leveling. I wouldn't take the chance to come here otherwise. Where do we go?"

He killed his cigarette and watched me. His shadow loomed against the wall, the shadow of a giant. He was so big he seemed unreal.

"What made you think I bumped Jessie Florian?" he asked suddenly.

"The spacing of the finger marks on her neck. The fact that you had something to get out of her, and that you are strong enough to kill people without meaning to."

"The johns tied me to it?"

"I don't know."

"What did I want out of her?"

"You thought she might know where Velma was."

He nodded silently and went on staring at me.

"But she didn't," I said. "Velma was too smart for her."

There was a light knocking at the door.

Malloy leaned forward a little and smiled and picked up his gun. Somebody tried the doorknob. Malloy stood up slowly and leaned forward in a crouch and listened. Then he looked back at me from looking at the door.

I sat up on the bed and put my feet on the floor and stood up. Malloy watched me silently, without a motion. I went over to the door.

"Who is it?" I asked with my lips to the panel.

It was her voice all right. "Open up, silly. It's the Duchess of Windsor."

"Just a second."

I looked back at Malloy. He was frowning. I went over close to him and said in a very low voice: "There's no other way out. Go in the dressing room behind the bed and wait. I'll get rid of her."

He listened and thought. His expression was unreadable. He was a man who had now very little to lose. He was a man who would never know fear. It was not built into even that giant frame. He nodded at last and picked up his hat and coat and moved silently around the bed and into the dressing room. The door closed, but did not shut tight.

I looked around for signs of him. Nothing but a cigarette butt that anybody might have smoked. I went to the room door and opened it. Malloy had set the catch again when he came in.

She stood there half smiling, in the highnecked white fox evening cloak she had told me about. Emerald pendants hung from her ears and almost buried themselves in the soft white fur. Her fingers were curled and soft on the small evening bag she carried.

The smile died off her face when she saw me. She looked me up and down. Her eyes were cold now.

"So it's like that," she said grimly. "Pajamas and dressing gown. To show me his lovely little etching. What a fool I am."

I stood aside and held the door. "It's not like that at all. I was getting dressed and a cop dropped in on me. He just left."

"Randall?"

I nodded. A lie with a nod is still a lie, but it's an easy lie. She hesitated a moment, then moved past me with a swirl of scented fur.

I shut the door. She walked slowly across the room, stared blankly at the wall, then turned quickly.

"Let's understand each other," she said. "I'm not this much of a pushover. I don't go for hall bedroom romance. There was a time in my life when I had too much of it. I like things done with an air."

"Will you have a drink before you go?" I was still leaning against the door, across the room from her.

"Am I going?"

"You gave me the impression you didn't like it here."

"I wanted to make a point. I have to be a little vulgar to make it. I'm not one of these promiscuous bitches. I can be had—but not just by reaching. Yes, I'll take a drink."

I went out into the kitchenette and mixed a couple of drinks with hands that were not too steady. I carried them in and handed her one.

There was no sound from the dressing-room, not even a sound of breathing.

She took the glass and tasted it and looked across it at the far wall. "I don't like men to receive me in their pajamas," she said. "It's a funny thing. I liked you. I liked you a lot. But I could get over it. I have often got over such things."

I nodded and drank.

"Most men are just lousy animals," she said. "In fact it's a pretty lousy world, if you ask me."

"Money must help."

"You think it's going to when you haven't always had money. As a matter of fact it just makes new problems." She smiled curiously. "And you forget how hard the old problems were."

She got out a gold cigarette case from her bag and I went over and held a match for her. She blew a vague plume of smoke and watched it with half-shut eyes.

"Sit close to me," she said suddenly.

"Let's talk a little first."

"About what? Oh—my jade?"

"About murder."

Nothing changed in her face. She blew another plume of smoke, this time more carefully, more slowly. "It's a nasty subject. Do we have to?"

I shrugged.

"Lin Marriott was no saint," she said. "But I still don't want to talk about it."

She stared at me coolly for a long moment and then dipped her hand into her open bag for a handkerchief.

"Personally I don't think he was a finger man for a jewel mob, either," I said. "The police pretend that they think that, but they do a lot of pretending. I don't even think he was a blackmailer, in any real sense. Funny, isn't it?"

"Is it?" The voice was very, very cold now.

"Well, not really," I agreed and drank the rest of my drink. "It was awfully nice of you to come here, Mrs. Grayle. But we seem to have hit the wrong mood. I don't even, for example, think Marriott was killed by a gang. I don't think he was going to that canyon to buy a jade necklace. I don't even think a jade necklace was ever stolen. I think he went to that canyon to be murdered, although he thought he went there to help commit a murder. But Marriott was a very bad murderer."

She leaned forward a little and her smile became just a little glassy. Suddenly, without any real change in her, she ceased to be beautiful. She looked merely like a woman who would have been dangerous a hundred years ago, and twenty years ago daring, but who today was just Grade B Hollywood.

She said nothing, but her right hand was tapping the clasp of her bag.

"A very bad murderer," I said. "Like Shakespeare's Second Murderer in that scene in *King Richard III*. The fellow that had certain dregs of conscience, but still wanted the money, and in the end didn't do the job at all because he couldn't make up his mind. Such murderers are very dangerous. They have to be removed—sometimes with blackjacks."

She smiled. "And who was he about to murder, do you suppose?"

"Me."

"That must be very difficult to believe—that anyone would hate you that much. And you said my jade necklace was never stolen at all. Have you any proof of all this?"

"I didn't say I had. I said I thought these things."

"Then why be such a fool as to talk about them?"

"Proof," I said, "is always a relative thing. It's an overwhelming balance of probabilities. And that's a matter of how they strike you. There was a rather weak motive for murdering me—merely that I was trying to trace a former Central Avenue dive singer at the same time that a convict named Moose Malloy got out of jail and started to look for her too. Perhaps I was helping him find her. Obviously, it was possible to find her, or it wouldn't have been worth while to pretend to Marriott that I had to be killed and killed quickly. And obviously he wouldn't have believed it, if it wasn't so. But there was a much stronger motive for murdering Marriott, which he, out of vanity or love or greed or a mixture of all three, didn't evaluate. He was afraid, but not for himself. He was afraid of violence to which he was a part and for which he could be convicted. But on the other hand he was fighting for his meal ticket. So he took the chance."

I stopped. She nodded and said: "Very interesting. If one knows what you are talking about."

"And one does," I said.

We stared at each other. She had her right hand in her bag again now. I had a good idea what it held. But it hadn't started to come out yet. Every event takes time.

"Let's quit kidding," I said. "We're all alone here. Nothing either of us says has the slightest standing against what the other says. We cancel each other out. A girl who started in the gutter became the wife of a multimillionaire. On the way up a shabby old woman recognized her—probably heard her singing at the radio station and recognized the voice and went to see—and this old woman had to be kept quiet. But she was cheap, therefore she only knew a little. But the man who dealt with her and made her monthly payments and owned a trust deed on her home and could throw her into the gutter any time she got funny—that man knew it all. He was expensive. But that didn't matter either, as long as nobody else knew. But some day a tough guy named Moose Malloy was going to get out of jail and start finding things out about his former sweetie. Because the big sap loved her—and still does. That's what makes it funny, tragic-funny. And about that time a private dick starts nosing in also. So the weak link in the chain, Marriott, is no longer a luxury. He has become a menace. They'll get to him and they'll take him apart. He's that kind of lad. He melts under heat. So he was murdered before he could melt. With a blackjack. By you."

All she did was take her hand out of her bag, with a gun in it. All she did was point it at me and smile. All I did was nothing.

But that wasn't all that was done. Moose Malloy stepped out of the dressing room with the Colt .45 still looking like a toy in his big hairy paw.

He didn't look at me at all. He looked at Mrs. Lewin Lockridge Grayle. He leaned forward and his mouth smiled at her and he spoke to her softly.

"I thought I knew the voice," he said. "I listened to that voice for eight years—all I could remember of it. I kind of liked your hair red, though. Hiya, babe. Long time no see."

She turned the gun.

"Get away from me, you son of a bitch," she said.

He stopped dead and dropped the gun to his side. He was still a couple of feet from her. His breath labored.

"I never thought," he said quietly. "It just came to me out of the blue. *You* turned me in to the cops. *You*. Little Velma."

I threw a pillow, but it was too slow. She shot him five times in the stomach. The bullets made no more sound than fingers going into a glove.

Then she turned the gun and shot at me but it was empty. She dived for Malloy's gun on the floor. I didn't miss with the second pillow. I was around the bed and knocked her away before she got the pillow off her face. I picked the Colt up and went away around the bed again with it.

He was still standing, but he was swaying. His mouth was slack and his hands were fumbling at his body. He went slack at the knees and fell sideways on the bed, with his face down. His gasping breath filled the room.

I had the phone in my hand before she moved. Her eyes were a dead gray, like half-frozen water. She rushed for the door and I didn't try to stop her. She left the door wide, so when I had done phoning I went over and shut it. I turned his head a little on the bed, so he wouldn't smother. He was still alive, but after five in the stomach even a Moose Malloy doesn't live very long.

I went back to the phone and called Randall at his home. "Malloy," I said. "In my apartment. Shot five times in the stomach by Mrs. Grayle. I called the Receiving Hospital. She got away."

"So you had to play clever," was all he said and hung up quickly.

I went back to the bed. Malloy was on his knees beside the bed now, trying to get up, a great wad of bedclothes in one hand. His face poured sweat. His eyelids flickered slowly and the lobes of his ears were dark.

He was still on his knees and still trying to get up when the fast wagon got there. It took four men to get him on the stretcher.

"He has a slight chance—if they're .25's," the fast wagon doctor said just before he went out. "All depends what they hit inside. But he has a chance."

"He wouldn't want it," I said.

He didn't. He died in the night.

40

"You ought to have given a dinner party," Anne Riordan said looking at me across her tan figured rug. "Gleaming silver and crystal, bright crisp linen—if they're still using linen in the places where they give dinner parties—candlelight, the women in their best jewels and the men in white ties, the servants hovering discreetly with the wrapped bottles of wine, the cops looking a little uncomfortable in their hired evening clothes, as who the hell wouldn't, the suspects with their brittle smiles and restless hands, and you at the head of the long table telling all about it, little by little, with your charming light smile and a phony English accent like Philo Vance."

"Yeah," I said. "How about a little something to be holding in my hand while you go on being clever?"

She went out to her kitchen and rattled ice and came back with a couple of tall ones and sat down again.

"The liquor bills of your lady friends must be something fierce," she said and sipped.

"And suddenly the butler fainted," I said. "Only it wasn't the butler who did the murder. He just fainted to be cute."

I inhaled some of my drink. "It's not that kind of story," I said. "It's not lithe and clever. It's just dark and full of blood."

"So she got away?"

I nodded. "So far. She never went home. She must have had a little hideout where she could change her clothes and appearance. After all she lived in peril, like the sailors. She was alone when she came to see me. No chauffeur. She came in a small car and she left it a few dozen blocks away."

"They'll catch her—if they really try."

"Don't be like that. Wilde, the D.A., is on the level. I worked for him once. But if they catch her, what then? They're up against twenty million dollars and a lovely face and either Lee Farrell or Rennenkamp. It's going to be awfully hard to prove she killed Marriott. All they have is what looks like a heavy motive and her past life, if they can trace it. She probably has no record, or she wouldn't have played it this way."

"What about Malloy? If you had told me about him before, I'd have known who she was right away. By the way, how did *you* know? These two photos are not of the same woman."

"No. I doubt if even old lady Florian knew they had been switched on her. She looked kind of surprised when I showed the photo of Velma —the one that had Velma Valento written on it—in front of her nose. But she may have known. She may have just hid it with the idea of selling it to me later on. Knowing it was harmless, a photo of some other girl Marriott substituted."

"That's just guessing."

"It had to be that way. Just as when Marriott called me up and gave me a song and dance about a jewel ransom payoff it had to be because I had been to see Mrs. Florian asking about Velma. And when Marriott was killed, it had to be because he was the weak link in the chain. Mrs. Florian didn't even know Velma had become Mrs. Lewin Lockridge Grayle. She couldn't have. They bought her too cheap. Grayle says they went to Europe to be married and she was married under her real name. He won't tell where or when. He won't tell what her real name was. He won't tell where she is. I don't think he knows, but the cops don't believe that."

"Why won't he tell?" Anne Riordan cupped her chin on the backs of her laced fingers and stared at me with shadowed eyes.

"He's so crazy about her he doesn't care whose lap she sat in."

"I hope she enjoyed sitting in yours," Anne Riordan said acidly.

"She was playing me. She was a little afraid of me. She didn't want to kill me because it's bad business killing a man who is a sort of cop. But she probably would have tried in the end, just as she would have killed Jessie Florian, if Malloy hadn't saved her the trouble."

"I bet it's fun to be played by handsome blondes," Anne Riordan said. "Even if there is a little risk. As, I suppose, there usually is."

I didn't say anything.

"I suppose they can't do anything to her for killing Malloy, because he had a gun."

"No. Not with her pull."

The goldflecked eyes studied me solemnly. "Do you think she meant to kill Malloy?"

"She was afraid of him," I said. "She had turned him in eight years ago. He seemed to know that. But he wouldn't have hurt her. He was in love with her too. Yes, I think she meant to kill anybody she had to kill. She had a lot to fight for. But you can't keep that sort of thing up indefinitely. She took a shot at me in my apartment—but the gun was empty then. She ought to have killed me out on the bluff when she killed Marriott."

"He was in love with her," Anne said softly. "I mean Malloy. It didn't matter to him that she hadn't written to him in six years or ever gone to see him while he was in jail. It didn't matter to him that she had turned him in for a reward. He just bought some fine clothes and started to look for her the first thing when he got out. So she pumped five bullets into him, by way of saying hello. He had killed two people himself, but he was in love with her. What a world."

I finished my drink and got the thirsty look on my face again. She ignored it. She said:

"And she had to tell Grayle where she came from and he didn't care. He went away to marry her under another name and sold his radio station to break contact with anybody who might know her and he gave her everything that money can buy and she gave him—what?"

"That's hard to say." I shook the ice cubes at the bottom of my glass. That didn't get me anything either. "I suppose she gave him a sort of pride that he, a rather old man, could have a young and beautiful and dashing wife. He loved her. What the hell are we talking about it for? These things happen all the time. It didn't make any difference what she did or who she played around with or what she had once been. He loved her."

"Like Moose Malloy," Anne said quietly.

"Let's go riding along the water."

"You didn't tell me about Brunette or the cards that were in those reefers or Amthor or Dr. Sonderborg or that little clue that set you on the path of the great solution."

"I gave Mrs. Florian one of my cards. She put a wet glass on it. Such a card was in Marriott's pockets, wet glass mark and all. Marriott was not a messy man. That was a clue, of sorts. Once you suspected anything it was easy to find out other connections, such as that Marriott owned a trust deed on Mrs. Florian's home, just to keep her in line. As for Amthor, he's a bad hat. They picked him up in a New York hotel and they say he's an international con man. Scotland Yard has his prints, also Paris. How the hell they got all that since yesterday or the day before I don't know. These boys work fast when they feel like it. I think Randall has had this thing taped for days and was afraid I'd step on the tapes. But Amthor had nothing to do with killing anybody. Or with Sonderborg. They haven't found Sonderborg yet. They think he has a record too, but they're not sure until they get him. As for Brunette, you can't get anything on a guy like Brunette. They'll have him before the Grand Jury and he'll refuse to say anything, on his constitutional rights. He doesn't have to bother about his reputation. But there's a nice shakeup here in Bay City. The Chief has been canned and half the detectives have been reduced to acting patrolmen, and a very nice guy named Red Norgaard, who helped me get on the *Montecito*, has got his job back. The mayor is doing all this, changing his pants hourly while the crisis lasts."

"Do you have to say things like that?"

"The Shakespearean touch. Let's go riding. After we've had another drink."

"You can have mine," Anne Riordan said, and got up and brought her untouched drink over to me. She stood in front of me holding it, her eyes wide and a little frightened.

"You're so marvelous," she said. "So brave, so determined and you work for so little money. Everybody pats you over the head and chokes you and smacks your jaw and fills you with morphine, but you just keep right on hitting between tackle and end until they're all worn out. What makes you so wonderful?"

"Go on," I growled. "Spill it."

Anne Riordan said thoughtfully: "I'd like to be kissed, damn you!"

41

IT TOOK OVER THREE MONTHS to find Velma. They wouldn't believe Grayle didn't know where she was and hadn't helped her get away. So every cop and newshawk in the country looked in all the places where money might be hiding her. And money wasn't hiding her at all. Although the way she hid was pretty obvious once it was found out.

One night a Baltimore detective with a camera eye as rare as a pink zebra wandered into a night club and listened to the band and looked at a handsome black-haired, black-browed torcher who could sing as if she meant it. Something in her face struck a chord and the chord went on vibrating.

He went back to Headquarters and got out the Wanted file and started through the pile of readers. When he came to the one he wanted he looked at it a long time. Then he straightened his straw hat on his head and went back to the night club and got hold of the manager. They went back to the dressing rooms behind the shell and the manager knocked on one of the doors. It wasn't locked. The dick pushed the manager aside and went in and locked it.

He must have smelled marihuana because she was smoking it, but he didn't pay any attention then. She was sitting in front of a triple mirror, studying the roots of her hair and eyebrows. They were her own eyebrows. The dick stepped across the room smiling and handed her the reader.

She must have looked at the face on the reader almost as long as the dick had down at Headquarters. There was a lot to think about while she was looking at it. The dick sat down and crossed his legs and lit a cigarette. He had a good eye, but he had over-specialized. He didn't know enough about women.

Finally she laughed a little and said: "You're a smart lad, copper. I thought I had a voice that would be remembered. A friend recognized me by it once, just hearing it on the radio. But I've been singing with this band for a month—twice a week on a network—and nobody gave it a thought."

"I never heard the voice," the dick said and went on smiling.

She said: "I suppose we can't make a deal on this. You know, there's a lot in it, if it's handled right."

"Not with me," the dick said. "Sorry."

"Let's go then," she said and stood up and grabbed up her bag and got her coat from a hanger. She went over to him holding the coat out so he could help her into it. He stood up and held it for her like a gentleman.

She turned and slipped a gun out of her bag and shot him three times through the coat he was holding.

She had two bullets left in the gun when they crashed the door. They got halfway across the room before she used them. She used them both, but the second shot must have been pure reflex. They caught her before she hit the floor, but her head was already hanging by a rag.

"The dick lived until the next day," Randall said, telling me about it. "He talked when he could. That's how we have the dope. I can't understand him being so careless, unless he really was thinking of letting her talk him into a deal of some kind. That would clutter up his mind. But I don't like to think that, of course."

I said I supposed that was so.

"Shot herself clean through the heart—twice," Randall said. "And I've heard experts on the stand say that's impossible, knowing all the time myself that it was. And you know something else?"

"What?"

"She was stupid to shoot that dick. We'd never have convicted her, not with her looks and money and the persecution story these high-priced guys would build up. Poor little girl from a dive climbs to be wife of rich man and the vultures that used to know her won't let her alone. That sort of thing. Hell, Rennenkamp would have half a dozen crummy old burlesque dames in court to sob that they'd blackmailed her for years, and in a way that you couldn't pin anything on them but the jury would go for it. She did a smart thing to run off on her own and leave Grayle out of it, but it would have been smarter to have come home when she was caught."

"Oh you believe now that she left Grayle out of it," I said.

He nodded. I said: "Do you think she had any particular reason for that?"

He stared at me. "I'll go for it, whatever it is."

"She was a killer," I said. "But so was Malloy. And *he* was a long way from being all rat. Maybe that Baltimore dick wasn't so pure as the record shows. Maybe she saw a chance—not to get away—she was tired of dodging by that time—but to give a break to the only man who had ever really given her one."

Randall stared at me with his mouth open and his eyes unconvinced.

"Hell, she didn't have to shoot a cop to do that," he said.

"I'm not saying she was a saint or even a halfway nice girl. Not ever. She wouldn't kill herself until she was cornered. But what she did and the way she did it, kept her from coming back here for trial. Think that over. And who would that trial hurt most? Who would be least able to bear it? And win, lose or draw, who would pay the biggest price for the show? An old man who had loved not wisely, but too well."

Randall said sharply: "That's just sentimental."

"Sure. It sounded like that when I said it. Probably all a mistake anyway. So long. Did my pink bug ever get back up here?"

He didn't know what I was talking about.

I rode down to the street floor and went out on the steps of the City Hall. It was a cool day and very clear. You could see a long way—but not as far as Velma had gone.

André Gide

THE IMMORALIST

> *I will praise thee;*
> *for I am fearfully and wonderfully made*
> PSALMS 139:14

TO
My Comrade and Fellow-Traveler
HENRI GHÉON

Preface

I PRESENT THIS BOOK for what it is worth—a fruit filled with bitter ashes, like those colocynths of the desert that grow in a parched and burning soil. All they can offer to your thirst is a still more cruel fierceness—yet lying on the golden sand they are not without a beauty of their own.

If I had held my hero up as an example, it must be admitted that my success would have been small. The few readers who were disposed to interest themselves in Michel's adventure did so only to reprobate him with all the superiority of their kind hearts. It was not in vain that I had adorned Marceline with so many virtues; they could not forgive Michel for not preferring her to himself.

If I had intended this book to be an indictment of Michel, I should have succeeded as little, for no one was grateful to me for the indignation he felt against my hero; it was as though he felt this indignation in spite of me; it overflowed from Michel onto myself; I seemed indeed within an ace of being confounded with him.

But I intended to make this book as little an indictment as an apology and took care to pass no judgment. The public nowadays will not forgive an author who, after relating an action, does not declare himself either for or against it; more than this, during the very course of the drama they want him to take sides, pronounce in favor either of Alceste or Philinte, of Hamlet or Ophelia, of Faust or Margaret, of Adam or Jehovah. I do not indeed claim that neutrality (I was going to say "indecision") is the certain mark of a great mind; but I believe that many great minds have been very loath to . . . conclude—and that to state a problem clearly is not to suppose it solved in advance.

It is with reluctance that I use the word "problem" here. To tell the truth, in art there are no problems—that are not sufficiently solved by the work of art itself.

If by "problem" one means "drama," shall I say that the one recounted in this book, though the scene of it is laid in my hero's soul, is nevertheless too general to remain circumscribed in his individual adventure. I do not pretend to have invented this "problem"; it existed before my book; whether Michel triumph or succumb, the "problem" will continue to exist, and the author has avoided taking either triumph or defeat for granted.

If certain distinguished minds have refused to see in this drama anything but the exposition of a special case, and in its hero anything but a sufferer from disease, if they have failed to recognize that ideas of very urgent import and very general interest may nevertheless be found in it—the fault lies neither in those ideas nor in that drama, but in the author—in his lack of skill, I should say—though he has put into this book all his passion and all his care, though he has watered it with many tears. But the real interest of a work and the interest taken in it by an ephemeral public are two very different things. A man may, I think, without much conceit, take the risk of not arousing immediate interest in interesting things—he may even prefer this to exciting a momentary delight in a public greedy only for sweets and trifles.

For the rest, I have not tried to prove anything, but only to paint my picture well and to set it in a good light.

(TO THE PRIME MINISTER, MR. D. R.)

Sidi B.M., 30th July 189–

YES, MY DEAR BROTHER, *of course, as you supposed, Michel has confided in us. Here is his story. You asked me to let you have it and I promised to; but now at the last moment I hesitate to send it and the oftener I re-read it the more dreadful it seems. Oh, what, I wonder, will you think of our friend? What, for that matter, do I think of him myself? . . . Are we simply to reprobate him and deny the possibility of turning to good account faculties so manifestly cruel? But I fear there are not a few among us today who would be bold enough to recognize their own features in this tale. Will it be possible to invent some way of employing all this intelligence and strength? Or must they be altogether outlawed?*

In what way can Michel serve society? I admit I cannot guess. . . . He must have some occupation. Will the position and the power you have so deservedly attained enable you to find one? Make haste. Michel is still capable of devotion. Yes, he is so still. But it will soon be only to himself.

I am writing to you under a sky of flawless blue; during the twelve days that Denis, Daniel, and myself have been here, there has not been a single cloud nor the slightest diminution of sunshine. Michel says the weather has been of crystalline clearness for the last two months.

I am neither sad nor cheerful; the air here fills one with a kind of vague excitement and induces a state as far removed from cheerfulness as it is from sorrow; perhaps it is happiness.

We are staying with Michel; we are anxious not leave him; you will understand why when you have read these pages; so we shall await your reply here, in his house; lose no time about it.

You know what ties of friendship bound Michel, Denis, Daniel, and myself together—a friendship which was strong even in our school days, but which every year grew stronger. A kind of pact was concluded between us four—at the first summons of any one of us the other three were to hasten. So when I received that mysterious signal of alarm from Michel, I immediately informed Daniel and Denis, and we all three let everything go and set out.

It is three years since we last saw Michel. He had married and gone traveling with his wife, and at the time of his last stay in Paris, Denis was in Greece, Daniel in Russia, and I, as you know, looking after our sick father. We were not, however, without news, though the account given of him by Silas and Will, who saw him at that time, was, to say the least, surprising. He was no longer the learned Puritan of old days, whose behavior was made awkward by his very earnestness, whose clear and simple gaze had so often checked the looseness of our talk. He was . . . but why forestall what his story will tell you?

Here is his story, then, just as Denis, Daniel, and I heard it. Michel told it to us on his terrace, as we were lying beside him in the dark and the starlight. At the end of his tale we saw day rising over the plain. Michel's house looks down on it and on the village, which is not far off. In the hot weather, and with all its crops reaped, this plain looks like the desert.

Michel's house, though poor and quaint-looking, is charming. In winter it would be cold, for there was no glass in the windows—or rather, there are no windows, but huge holes in the walls. It is so fine that we sleep out of doors on mats.

Let me add that we had a good journey out. We arrived here one evening, gasping with heat, intoxicated with novelty, after having barely stopped on the way, first at Algiers and then at Constantine. At Constantine we took a second train to Sidi B.M., where a little cart was waiting for us. The road comes to an end some way from the village, which is perched on the top of a rock, like certain little hill-towns in Umbria. We climbed up on foot; two mules took our luggage. Approached by the road, Michel's house is the first in the village. It is surrounded by the low walls of a garden—or rather, an enclosure, in which there grow three stunted pomegranate-trees and a superb oleander. A little Kabyle boy ran away at sight of us and scrambled over the wall without more ado.

Michel showed no signs of pleasure as he welcomed us; he was very simple and seemed afraid of any demonstration of tenderness; but on the threshold he stopped and kissed each one of us gravely.

Until night came we barely exchanged a dozen words. An almost excessively frugal dinner was laid for us in a drawing-room where the decorations were so sumptuous that we were astonished by them, though they were afterwards explained by Michel's story. Then he served us coffee, which he made a point of preparing himself; and afterwards we went up onto the terrace, where the view stretched away into infinity, and all three of us, like Job's comforters, sat down and waited, watching and admiring the day's abrupt decline over the incandescent plain.

When it was night Michel said:

First Part: 1

MY DEAR FRIENDS, I knew you were faithful. You have answered my summons as quickly as I should have answered yours. And yet three years have gone by without your seeing me. May your friendship, which has been so proof against absence, be equally proof against the story I am going to tell you. For it was solely to see you, solely that you might listen to me, that I called upon you so suddenly and made you take this journey to my distant abode. The only help I wish for is this—to talk to you. For I have reached a point in my life beyond which I cannot go. Not from weariness, though. But I can no longer understand things. I want . . . I want to talk, I tell you. To know how to free oneself is nothing; the arduous thing is to know what to do with one's freedom. Let me speak of myself; I am going to tell you my life simply, without modesty and without pride, more simply than if I were talking to myself. Listen:

The last time we saw each other, I remember, was in the neighborhood of Angers, in the little country church in which I was married. There were very few people at my wedding, and the presence of real friends turned this commonplace function into something touching. I felt that others were moved, and that in itself was enough to move me. After we left the church, you joined us at my bride's house for a short meal, at which there was neither noise nor laughter; then she and I drove away in a hired carriage, according to the custom by which we always have to associate the idea of a wedding with the vision of a railway station.

I knew my wife very little and thought, without being much distressed by it, that she knew me no better. I had married her without being in love, largely in order to please my father, who, as he lay dying, felt anxious at leaving me alone. I loved my father dearly; engrossed by his last illness, I had thought of nothing else all through that melancholy time but how to make his end easier; and so I pledged my life before I knew what the possibilities of life were. Our betrothal took place at my dying father's bedside, without laughter but not without a certain grave joy, so great was the peace it brought him. If, as I say, I did not love my betrothed, at any rate I had never loved any other woman. This seemed to me sufficient to secure our happiness; and I thought I was giving her the whole of myself, without having any knowledge of what that self was. She was an orphan, as I was, and lived with her two brothers. Her name was Marceline; she was barely twenty; I was four years older.

I have said I did not love her—at any rate, I felt for her nothing of what is generally known as love, but I loved her, if that word may cover a feeling of tenderness, a sort of pity, and a considerable measure of esteem. She was a Catholic and I a Protestant . . . but, thought I, so little of a Protestant! The priest accepted me; I accepted the priest; it all went off without a hitch.

My father was what is called an "atheist"—at least so I suppose, for a kind of invincible shyness, which I imagined he shared, had always made it impossible for me to talk to him about his beliefs. The grave Huguenot teaching which my mother had given me had slowly faded from my mind together with the image of her beauty; you know I was young when I lost her. I did not then suspect how great a hold the early moral lessons of our childhood take on one, nor what marks they leave upon the mind. That kind of austerity for which a taste had been left in me by my mother's way of bringing me up, I now applied wholly to my studies. I was fifteen when I lost her; my father took me in hand, looked after me, and himself instructed me with passionate eagerness. I already knew Latin and Greek well; under him I quickly learned Hebrew, Sanskrit, and finally Persian and Arabic. When I was about twenty I had been so intensively forced that he actually made me his collaborator. It amused him to claim me as his equal and he wanted to show me he was right. The *Essay on Phrygian Cults* which appeared under his name was in reality my work; he scarcely read it over; nothing he had written ever brought him so much praise. He was delighted. As for me, I was a little abashed by the success of this deception. But my reputation was made. The most learned scholars treated me as their colleague. I smile now at all the honors that were paid me. . . . And so I reached the age of twenty-five, having barely cast a glance at anything but books and ruins and knowing nothing of life; I spent all my fervor in my work. I loved a few friends (you were among them), but it was not so much my friends I loved as friendship—it was a craving for high-mindedness that made my devotion to them so great; I cherished in myself each and all of my fine feelings. For the rest, I knew my friends as little as I knew myself. The idea that I might have lived a different existence or that anyone could possibly live differently never for a moment crossed my mind.

My father and I were satisfied with simple things; we both of us spent so little that I reached the age of twenty-five without knowing that we were rich. I imagined, without giving it much thought, that we had just enough to live on. And the habits of economy I had acquired with my father were so great that I felt almost uncomfortable when I learned that we had a great deal more. I was so careless about such matters that even after my father's death, though I was his sole heir, I failed to realize the extent of my fortune; I did so only when our marriage settlements were being drawn up, and at the same time I learned that Marceline brought me next to nothing.

And another thing I was ignorant of—even more important perhaps —was that I had very delicate health. How should I have known this, when I had never put it to the test? I had colds from time to time and neglected them. The excessive tranquillity of the life I led weakened, while at the same time it protected, me. Marceline, on the contrary, seemed strong—that she was stronger than I we were very soon to learn.

On our wedding-day we went straight to Paris and slept in my apartment, where two rooms had been got ready for us. We stayed in Paris only just long enough to do some necessary shopping, then took the train to Marseilles and embarked at once for Tunis.

So many urgent things to be done, so many bewildering events following each other in too rapid succession, the unavoidable agitation of my wedding coming so soon after the more genuine emotion caused by my father's death—all of this had left me exhausted. It was only on the boat that I was able to realize how tired I was. Up till then, every occupation, while increasing my fatigue, had distracted me from feeling it. The enforced leisure on board ship at last enabled me to reflect. For the first time, so it seemed to me.

It was for the first time too that I had consented to forgo my work for any length of time. Up till then I had only allowed myself short holidays. A journey to Spain with my father shortly after my mother's death had, it is true, lasted over a month; another to Germany, six weeks; there were others too, but they had all been student's journeys; my father was never to be distracted from his own particular researches; when I was not accompanying him, I used to read. And yet, we had hardly left Marseilles when memories came back to me of Granada and Seville, of a purer sky, of franker shadows, of dances, of laughter, of songs. That is what we are going to find, I thought. I went up on to the deck and watched Marseilles disappearing in the distance.

Then, suddenly, it occurred to me that I was leaving Marceline a little too much to herself.

She was sitting in the bow; I drew near, and for the first time really looked at her.

Marceline was very pretty. You saw her, so you know. I reproached myself for not having noticed it sooner. I had known her too long to see her with any freshness of vision; our families had been friends for ages; I had seen her grow up; I was accustomed to her grace. . . . For the first time now I was struck with astonishment, it seemed to me so great.

She wore a big veil floating from a simple black straw hat; she was fair, but did not look delicate. Her bodice and skirt were made of the same material—a Scotch plaid which we had chosen together. I had not wanted the gloom of my mourning to overshadow her.

She felt I was looking at her and turned toward me . . . until then I had paid her only the necessary official attentions; I replaced love as best I could by a kind of frigid gallantry, which I saw well enough she found rather tiresome; perhaps at that moment Marceline felt I was looking at her for the first time in a different way. She in her turn looked fixedly at me; then, very tenderly, smiled. I sat down beside her without speaking. I had lived up to then for myself alone, or at any rate in my own fashion; I had married without imagining I should find in my wife anything different from a comrade, without thinking at all definitely that my life might be changed by our union. And now at last I realized that the monologue had come to an end.

We were alone on deck. She held up her face and I gently pressed her to me; she raised her eyes; I kissed her on the eyelids and suddenly felt as I kissed her an unfamiliar kind of pity, which took hold of me so violently that I could not restrain my tears.

"What is it, dear?" said Marceline.

We began to talk. What she said was so charming that it delighted me. I had picked up in one way or another a few ideas on women's silliness. That evening, in her presence, it was myself I thought awkward and stupid.

So the being to whom I had attached my life had a real and individual life of her own! The importance of this thought woke me up several times during the night; several times I sat up in my berth in order to look at Marceline, my wife, asleep in the berth below.

The next morning the sky was splendid; the sea almost perfectly calm. A few leisurely talks lessened our shyness still more. Marriage was really beginning. On the morning of the last day of October we landed in Tunis.

I intended to stay there only a few days. I will confess my folly; in so new a country nothing attracted me except Carthage and a few Roman ruins—Timgad, about which Octave had spoken to me, the mosaics of Sousse, and above all the amphitheater of El Djem, which I decided we must visit without delay. We had first to get to Sousse, and from Sousse take the mail diligence; between there and here I was determined to think nothing worth my attention.

And yet Tunis surprised me greatly. At the touch of new sensations, certain portions of me awoke—certain sleeping faculties, which, from not having as yet been used, had kept all their mysterious freshness. But I was more astonished, more bewildered than amused, and what pleased me most was Marceline's delight.

My fatigue in the meantime was growing greater every day; but I should have thought it shameful to give in to it. I had a bad cough and a curious feeling of discomfort in the upper part of my chest. We are going toward the south, I thought; the heat will put me to rights again.

The Sfax diligence leaves Sousse at eight o'clock in the evening and passes through El Djem at one o'clock in the morning. We had engaged coupé places; I expected to find an uncomfortable shandrydan; the seats, however, were fairly commodious. But oh, the cold! . . . We were both lightly clad and, with a kind of childish confidence in the warmth of southern climes, had taken no wrap with us but a single shawl. As soon as we were out of Sousse and the shelter of its hills, the wind began to blow. It leaped over the plain in great bounds, howling, whistling, coming in by every chink of the door and windows—impossible to protect oneself from it! We were both chilled to the bone when we arrived, and I was exhausted as well by the jolting of the carriage and by my horrible cough, which shook me even worse. What a night! When we got to El Djem, there was no inn, nothing but a frightful native *bordj*. What was to be done? The diligence was going on; the village was asleep; the lugubrious mass of the ruins lowered dimly through the dark immensity of the night; dogs were howling. We went into a room whose walls and floor were made of mud and in which stood two wretched beds. Marceline was shivering with cold, but here at any rate we were out of the wind.

The next day was a dismal one. We were surprised on going out to see a sky that was one unrelieved gray. The wind was still blowing, but less violently than the night before. The diligence passed through again only in the evening. . . . It was a dismal day, I tell you. I went over the amphitheater in a few minutes and found it disappointing; I thought it actually ugly under that dreary sky. Perhaps my fatigue added to my feeling of tedium. Toward the middle of the day, as I had nothing else to do, I went back to the ruins and searched in vain for inscriptions on the stones. Marceline found a place that was sheltered from the wind and sat reading an English book, which by good luck she had brought with her. I went and sat beside her.

"What a melancholy day!" I said. "Aren't you bored?"

"Not particularly. I am reading."

"What made us come to such a place? I hope you are not cold, are you?"

"Not so very. And you? Oh, you must be. How pale you are!"

"No, oh no!"

At night, the wind began again as violently as ever. . . . At last the diligence arrived. We started.

No sooner did the jolting begin than I felt shattered. Marceline, who was very tired, had gone to sleep almost at once on my shoulder. My cough will wake her, I thought, and freeing myself very, very gently, I propped her head against the side of the carriage. In the meantime I had stopped coughing; yes; I had begun to spit instead; this was something new; I brought it up without an effort; it came in little jerks at regular intervals; the sensation was so odd that at first it almost amused me, but I was soon disgusted by the peculiar taste it left in my mouth. My handkerchief was very soon used up. My fingers were covered with it. Should I wake up Marceline? . . . Fortunately I thought of a large silk foulard she was wearing tucked into her belt. I took possession of it quietly. The spitting, which I no longer tried to keep back, came more abundantly and I was extraordinarily relieved by it. It is the end of my cold, I thought. Then, there suddenly came over me a feeling of extreme weakness; everything began to spin round and I thought I was going to faint. Should I wake her up? . . . No, shame! . . . (My puritanical childhood has left me, I think, a hatred of any surrender to bodily weakness—cowardice, I call it.) I controlled myself, made a desperate effort, and finally conquered my giddiness. . . . I felt as if I were at sea again, and the noise of the wheels turned into the sound of the waves. . . . But I had stopped spitting.

Then I sank, overpowered, into a sort of sleep.

When I emerged from it, the sky was already filling with dawn. Marceline was still asleep. We were just getting to Sousse. The foulard I was holding in my hand was dark-colored, so that at first I saw nothing; but when I took out my handkerchief, I saw with stupefaction that it was soaked with blood.

My first thought was to hide the blood from Marceline. But how? I was covered with it; it seemed to be everywhere, on my fingers especially. . . . My nose might perhaps have been bleeding. . . . That's it! If she asks me, I shall say my nose has been bleeding.

Marceline was still asleep. We drew up at the Sousse hotel. She had to get down first and saw nothing. Our two rooms had been kept for us. I was able to dart into mine and wash away every trace of blood. Marceline had seen nothing.

I was feeling very weak, however, and ordered some tea to be brought. And as she was pouring it out, a little pale herself, but very calm and smiling, a kind of irritation seized me to think she had not had the sense to see anything. I felt indeed that I was being unjust, and said to myself that she saw nothing only because I had hidden it from her so cleverly; but I couldn't help it—the feeling grew in me like an instinct, filled me . . . and at last it became too strong; I could contain myself no longer; the words slipped out, as though absent-mindedly:

"I spat blood last night."

She did not utter a sound; she simply turned much paler, tottered, tried to save herself, and fell heavily to the ground.

I sprang to her in a sort of fury: "Marceline! Marceline!" What on earth had I done? Wasn't it enough for *me* to be ill? But, as I have said, I was very weak; I was on the point of fainting myself. I managed, however, to open the door and call. Someone hurried to our help.

I remembered that I had a letter of introduction to an officer in the town, and on the strength of this I sent for the regimental doctor.

Marceline in the meantime had recovered herself and settled down at my bedside, where I lay shivering with fever. The doctor came and examined us both; there was nothing the matter with Marceline, he declared, and she had not been hurt by her fall; *I* was seriously ill; he refused to give a definite opinion and promised to come back before evening.

He came back, smiled at me, talked to me, and prescribed various remedies. I realized that he gave me up for lost. Shall I confess that I felt not the least shock? I was very tired, I simply let myself go. After all, what had life to offer? I had worked faithfully to the end, resolutely and passionately done my duty. The rest . . . oh! what did it matter? thought I, with a certain admiration of my own stoicism. What really pained me was the ugliness of my surroundings. This hotel room is frightful, I thought, and looked at it. Suddenly it occurred to me that in a like room next door was my wife, Marceline; and I heard her speaking. The doctor had not gone; he was talking to her; he was studiously lowering his voice. A little time went by—I must have slept. . . .

When I woke up, Marceline was there. I could see she had been crying. I did not care for life enough to pity myself; but the ugliness of the place vexed me; my eyes rested on her with a pleasure that was almost voluptuous.

She was sitting by me writing. I thought she looked very pretty. I saw her fasten up several letters. Then she got up, drew near my bed, and took my hand tenderly.

"How are you feeling now?" she asked.

I smiled and said sadly: "Shall I get better?"

But she answered at once: "You *shall* get better" with such passionate conviction that it almost brought conviction to me too, and there came over me a kind of confused feeling of all that life might mean, of Marceline's own love—a vague vision of such pathetic beauties that the tears started from my eyes and I wept long and helplessly without trying or wanting to stop.

With what loving violence she managed to get me away from Sousse! How charmingly she protected me, helped me, nursed me! From Sousse to Tunis, from Tunis to Constantine, Marceline was admirable. It

was at Biskra that I was to get well. Her confidence was perfect; never
for a single moment did her zeal slacken. She settled everything, arranged
the starts, engaged the rooms. It was not in her power, alas! to make the
journey less horrible. Several times I thought I should have to stop and
give up. I sweated mortally; I gasped for breath; at times I lost consciousness. At the end of the third day, I arrived at Biskra more dead than alive.

2

WHY SPEAK OF THOSE FIRST DAYS? What remains of them? Their
frightful memory has no tongue. I lost all knowledge of who or where I
was. I can only see Marceline, my wife, my life, bending over the bed
where I lay agonizing. I know that her passionate care, her love, alone
saved me. One day, at last, like a shipwrecked mariner who catches sight
of land, I felt a gleam of life revisit me; I was able to smile at Marceline.
Why should I recall all this? What is important is that Death had touched
me, as people say, with its wing. What is important is that I came to think
it a very astonishing thing to be alive, that every day shone for me, an
unhoped-for light. Before, thought I, I did not understand I was alive. The
thrilling discovery of life was to be mine.

The day came when I was able to get up. I was utterly enchanted by
our home. It was almost nothing but a terrace. What a terrace! My room
and Marceline's opened out onto it; at the further end it was continued
over roofs. From the highest part, one saw palm-trees above the houses;
and above the palm-trees, the desert. On the other side, the terrace ad-
joined the public gardens and was shaded by the branches of the nearest
cassias; lastly, it ran along one side of the courtyard—a small, regular
courtyard, planted regularly with six palm-trees—and came to an end
with the staircase that led down to the courtyard. My room was spacious
and airy; the walls were bare and whitewashed; a little door led to Marceline's room; a large door with glass panes opened onto the terrace.

There the hourless days slipped by. How often in my solitude those
slow-slipping days came back to me! . . . Marceline sits beside me. She is
reading, or sewing, or writing. I am doing nothing—just looking at her. O
Marceline! Marceline! . . . I look. I see the sun; I see the shadow; I see the
line of shadow moving; I have so little to think of that I watch it. I am
still very weak; my breathing is very bad; everything tires me—even
reading; besides, what should I read? Existing is occupation enough.

One morning Marceline came in laughing.

"I have brought you a friend," she said, and I saw come in behind her
a little dark-complexioned Arab. His name was Bachir and he had large
silent eyes that looked at me. They made me feel embarrassed, and that

was enough to tire me. I said nothing, only looked cross. The child, disconcerted by the coldness of my reception, turned to Marceline and, with the coaxing grace of a little animal, nestled up against her, took her hand and kissed it, showing his bare arms as he did so. I noticed that under his thin, white gandourah and patched burnous he was naked.

"Come, sit down there," said Marceline, who had noticed my shyness. "Amuse yourself quietly."

The little fellow sat down on the floor, took a knife and a piece of djerid wood out of the hood of his burnous, and began to slice at it. I think it was a whistle he was trying to make.

After a little time, I ceased to feel uncomfortable. I looked at him; he seemed to have forgotten where he was. His feet were bare; he had charmingly turned ankles and wrists. He handled his wretched knife with amusing dexterity. . . . Was this really going to interest me? . . . His hair was shaved Arab fashion; he wore a shabby chechia on his head with a hole in the place of the tassel. His gandourah, which had slipped down a little, showed his delicate little shoulder. I wanted to touch it. I bent down; he turned round and smiled at me. I signed to him to pass me his whistle, took it and pretended to admire it. After a time he said he must go. Marceline gave him a cake and I a penny.

The next day, for the first time, I felt dull. I seemed to be expecting something. Expecting what? I was listless, restless. At last I could resist no longer.

"Isn't Bachir coming this morning, Marceline?"

"If you like, I'll fetch him."

She left me and went out; after a little she came back alone. What kind of thing had illness made me that I should have felt inclined to cry at seeing her return without Bachir?

"It was too late," she said, "the children had come out of school and dispersed. Some of them are really charming. I think they all know me now."

"Well, at any rate, try and get him to come tomorrow."

Next morning Bachir came back. He sat down in the same way he had done two days before, took out his knife and tried to carve his bit of wood, but it was too hard for him and he finally managed to stick the blade into his thumb. I shuddered with horror, but he laughed, held out his hand for me to see the glistening cut and looked amused at the sight of his blood running. When he laughed, he showed very white teeth; he licked his cut complacently and his tongue was as pink as a cat's. Ah! how well he looked! That was what I had fallen in love with—his health. The health of that little body was a beautiful thing.

The day after, he brought some marbles. He wanted to make me play. Marceline was out or she would have prevented me. I hesitated and looked at Bachir; the little fellow seized my arm, put the marbles into my hand, forced me. The attitude of stooping made me very breathless, but I tried to play all the same. Bachir's pleasure charmed me. At last, however, it was too much for me. I was in a profuse perspiration. I pushed aside the marbles and dropped into an armchair. Bachir, somewhat disturbed, looked at me.

"Ill?" said he sweetly; the quality of his voice was exquisite. Marceline came back at that moment.

"Take him away," I said, "I am tired this morning."

A few hours later I had a hemorrhage. It was while I was taking a laborious walk up and down the terrace; Marceline was busy in her room and fortunately saw nothing. My breathlessness had made me take a deeper respiration than usual and the thing had suddenly come. It had filled my mouth. . . . But it was no longer bright, clear blood as on the first occasion. It was a frightful great clot which I spat on to the ground in disgust.

I took a few tottering steps. I was horribly upset. I was frightened; I was angry. For up till then I had thought that, step by step, recovery was on the way, and that I had nothing to do but wait for it. This brutal accident had thrown me back. The strange thing is that the first hemorrhage had not affected me so much. I now remembered it had left me almost calm. What was the reason for my fear, my horror now? Alas! it was because I had begun to love life.

I returned on my steps, bent down, found the clot, and with a piece of straw picked it up and put it on my handkerchief. It was hideous, almost black in color, sticky, slimy, horrible. . . . I thought of Bachir's beautiful, brilliant flow of blood. . . . And suddenly I was seized with a desire, a craving, something more furious and more imperious than I had ever felt before—to live! I want to live! I *will* live. I clenched my teeth, my hands concentrated my whole being in this wild, grief-stricken endeavor toward existence.

The day before, I had received a letter from T . . . , written in answer to Marceline's anxious inquiries; it was full of medical advice; T . . . had even accompanied his letter with one or two little popular medical pamphlets and a book of a more technical nature, which for that reason seemed to me more serious. I had read the letter carelessly and the printed matter not at all; in the first place I was set against the pamphlets because of their likeness to the moral tracts that used to tease me in my childhood; and then too every kind of advice was irksome to me; and besides, I did not think that *Advice to Tuberculous Patients* or *How to Cure Tuberculosis* in any way concerned me. I did not think I was tuberculous. I inclined to attribute my first hemorrhage to a different cause; or rather, to tell the truth, I did not attribute it to anything; I avoided thinking of it, hardly thought of it at all, and considered myself, if not altogether cured, at least very nearly so. . . . I read the letter; I devoured the book, the pamphlets. Suddenly, with shocking clearness, it became evident to me that I had not been treating myself properly. Hitherto, I had let myself live passively, trusting to the vaguest of hopes; suddenly I perceived my life was attacked—attacked in its very center. An active host of enemies was living within me. I listened to them; I spied on them; I felt them. I should not vanquish them without a struggle . . . and I added half aloud, as if better to convince myself: "It is a matter of will."

I put myself in a state of hostility.

Evening was closing in; I planned my strategy. For some time to come, my recovery was to be my one and only concern; my duty was my health; I must think good, I must call right everything that was salutary to me, forget everything that did not contribute to my cure. Before the evening meal, I had decided on my measures with regard to breathing, exercise, and nourishment.

We used to take our meals in a sort of little kiosk that was surrounded by the terrace on all sides. We were alone, quiet, far from everything, and the intimacy of our meals was delightful. An old Negro used to bring us our food, which was tolerable, from a neighboring hotel. Marceline superintended the menus, ordered one dish or rejected another. . . . Not having much appetite as a rule, I did not mind particularly when the dishes were a failure or the menu insufficient. Marceline, who was herself a small eater, did not know, did not realize that I was not taking enough food. To eat a great deal was the first of my new resolutions. I intended to put it into execution that very evening. I was not able to. We had some sort of uneatable hash, and then a bit of roast meat which was absurdly overdone.

My irritation was so great that I vented it upon Marceline and let myself go in a flood of intemperate words. I blamed her; to listen to me, it was as though she was responsible for the badness of the food. This slight delay in starting on the regime I had decided to adopt seemed of the gravest importance; I forgot the preceding days; the failure of this one meal spoiled everything. I persisted obstinately. Marceline had to go into the town to buy a tin or a jar of anything she could find.

She soon came back with a little terrine, of which I devoured almost the whole contents, as though to prove to us both how much I was in need of more food.

That same evening we settled on the following plan: the meals were to be much better and there were to be more of them—one every three hours, beginning as early as half past six in the morning. An abundant provision of every kind of tinned food was to supplement the deficiencies of the hotel menus.

I could not sleep that night, so excited was I by the vision of my future virtues. I was, I think, a little feverish; there was a bottle of mineral water beside me; I drank a glass, two glasses; the third time, I drank out of the bottle itself and emptied it at a draught. I strengthened my will as one strengthens one's memory by revising a lesson; I instructed my hostility, directed it against all and sundry; I was to fight with everything; my salvation depended on myself alone.

At last I saw the night begin to pale; another day had dawned.

It had been my night of vigil before the battle.

The next day was Sunday. Must I confess that so far I ha[...] little attention to Marceline's religious beliefs? Either from [...] or delicacy, it seemed to me they were no business of mine; [...] did not attach much importance to them. That morning Marce[...] Mass. When she came back, she told me she had been prayi[...] looked at her fixedly and then said as gently as I could:

"You mustn't pray for me, Marceline."

"Why not?" she asked, a little troubled.

"I don't want favors."

"Do you reject the help of God?"

"He would have a right to my gratitude afterwar[...] tions. I don't like them."

To all appearance we were trifling, but we mad[...] importance of our words.

"You will not get well all by yourself, my poor[...]

"If so, it can't be helped." Then, seeing how unl[...] added less roughly:

"You will help me."

3

I AM GOING TO SPEAK at length of my body. I shall speak of it s[...] you will think at first I have forgotten my soul. This omission, as [...] you my story, is intentional; out there, it was a fact. I had not stre[...] enough to keep up a double life. I will think of the spirit and that side[...] things later, I said to myself, when I get better.

I was still far from being well. The slightest thing put me into a perspiration; the slightest thing gave me a cold; my breath was short; sometimes I had a little fever, and often, from early morning, oppressed by a dreadful feeling of lassitude, I remained prostrate in an armchair, indifferent to everything, self-centered, solely occupied in trying to breathe properly. I breathed laboriously, methodically, carefully; my expiration came in two jerks which, with the greatest effort of my will, I could only partially control; for a long time after that, I still had need of all my attention to avoid this.

But what troubled me most was my morbid sensibility to changes of temperature. I think, when I come to reflect on it today, that, in addition to my illness, I was suffering from a general nervous derangement. I cannot otherwise explain a series of phenomena which it seems to me impossible to attribute entirely to a simple condition of tuberculosis. I was always either too hot or too cold; I put on a ridiculous number of clothes, and only stopped shivering when I began to perspire; then, directly I took anything off, I shivered as soon as I stopped perspiring. Certain portions of my body would turn as cold as ice and, in spite of perspiration, felt like marble to the touch; nothing would warm them. I

...ive to cold that if a little water dropped on my feet while I
..., it gave me a relapse; I was equally sensitive to heat. . . . This
... kept and still keep, but now it gives me exquisite enjoyment.
... keen sensibility may, I believe, according as the organism is
... weakly, become a source of delight or discomfort. Everything
... rmerly distressed me is now a delicious pleasure.

... not know how I had managed to sleep up till then with my
... shut; in accordance with T. . .'s advice, I now tried keeping
... pen at night; a little at first; soon I flung them wide; soon it became
... t, a need so great that directly the window was shut, I felt stifled.
... on, with what rapture was I to feel the night wind blow, the moon
... in upon me! . . .

But I am eager to have done with these first stammerings after health.
...eed, thanks to constant attention, to pure air, to better food, I soon
...gan to improve. Up till then, my breathlessness had made me dread the
...airs and I had not dared to leave the terrace; in the last days of January I
...t last went down and ventured into the garden.

Marceline came with me, carrying a shawl. It was three o'clock in
the afternoon. The wind, which is often violent in those parts and which
I had found particularly unpleasant during the last few days, had
dropped. The air was soft and charming.

The public gardens! . . . A very wide path runs through the middle
of them, shaded by two rows of that kind of very tall mimosa which out
there is called cassia. Benches are placed in the shadow of the trees. A
canalized river—one, I mean, that is not wide so much as deep, and almost
straight—flows alongside the path; other smaller channels take the water
from the river and convey it through the gardens to the plants; the thick,
heavy-looking water is the same color as the earth—the color of pinkish,
grayish clay. Hardly any foreigners walk here—only a few Arabs; as they
pass out of the sunlight, their white cloaks take on the color of the shade.

I felt an odd shiver come over me as I stepped into that strange
shade; I wrapped my shawl tighter about me; but it was not an unpleasant
sensation; on the contrary. We sat down on a bench. Marceline was
silent. Some Arabs passed by; then came a troop of children. Marceline
knew several of them; she signed to them and they came up to us. She
told me some of their names; questions and answers passed, smiles, pouts,
little jokes. It all rather irritated me and my feeling of embarrassment
returned. I was tired and perspiring. But must I confess that what made
me most uncomfortable was not the children's presence—it was Marceline's. Yes; however slightly, she was in my way. If I had got up, she
would have followed me; if I had taken off my shawl, she would have
wanted to carry it; if I had put it on again, she would have said: "Are you
cold?" And then, as to talking to the children, I didn't dare to before her;
I saw that she had her favorites; I, in spite of myself, but deliberately,
took more interest in the others.

"Let us go in," I said at last. And I privately resolved to come back to the gardens alone.

The next day, she had to go out about ten o'clock; I took advantage of this. Little Bachir, who rarely failed to come of a morning, carried my shawl; I felt active, light-hearted. We were almost alone in the garden path; I walked slowly, sometimes sat down for a moment, then started off again. Bachir followed, chattering, as faithful and as obsequious as a dog. I reached a part of the canal where the washerwomen come down to wash; there was a flat stone placed in the middle of the stream, and upon it lay a little girl, face downwards, dabbling with her hand in the water; she was busy throwing little odds and ends of sticks and grass into the water and picking them out again. Her bare feet had dipped in the water; there were still traces of wet on them and there her skin showed darker. Bachir went up and spoke to her; she turned round, gave me a smile and answered Bachir in Arabic. "She is my sister," he explained; then he said his mother was coming to wash some clothes and that his little sister was waiting for her. She was called Rhadra in Arabic, which meant "Green." He said all this in a voice that was as charming, as clear, as childlike, as the emotion I felt in hearing it.

"She wants you to give her two sous," he added.

I gave her fifty centimes and prepared to go on, when the mother, the washerwoman, came up. She was a magnificent, heavily built woman, with a high forehead tattooed in blue; she was carrying a basket of linen on her head and was like a Greek caryatid; like a caryatid too, she was simply draped in a wide piece of dark-blue stuff, lifted at the girdle and falling straight to the feet.

As soon as she saw Bachir, she called out to him roughly. He made an angry answer; the little girl joined in and the three of them started a violent dispute. At last Bachir seemed defeated and explained that his mother wanted him that morning; he handed me my shawl sadly and I was obliged to go off by myself.

I had not taken twenty paces when my shawl began to feel unendurably heavy. I sat down, perspiring, on the first bench I came to. I hoped some other boy would come along and relieve me of my burden. The one who soon appeared, and who offered to carry it of his own accord, was a big boy about fourteen years old, as black as a Sudanese and not in the least shy. His name was Ashour. I should have thought him handsome, but that he was blind in one eye. He liked talking; told me where the river came from, and that after running through the public gardens, it flowed into the oasis, which it traversed from end to end. As I listened to him, I forgot my fatigue. Charming as I thought Bachir, I knew him too well by now, and I was glad of a change. I even promised myself to come to the gardens all alone another day and sit on a bench and wait for what some lucky chance might bring. . . .

After a few more short rests, Ashour and I arrived at my door. I wanted to invite him to come in, but I was afraid to, not knowing what Marceline would say.

I found her in the dining-room, busied over a very small boy, so frail and sickly-looking that my first feeling was one of disgust rather than pity. Marceline said rather timidly:

"The poor little thing is ill."

"It's not infectious, I hope. What's the matter with him?"

"I don't exactly know yet. He complains of feeling ill all over. He speaks very little French. When Bachir comes tomorrow, he will be able to interpret. . . . I am making him a little tea."

Then, as if in excuse, and because I stood there without saying anything, "I've known him a long time," she added. "I haven't dared bring him in before; I was afraid of tiring you, or perhaps vexing you."

"Why in the world!" I cried. "Bring in all the children you like, if it amuses you!" And I thought, with a little irritation at not having done so, that I might have perfectly well brought up Ashour.

And yet, as I thought this, I looked at my wife; how maternal and caressing she was! Her tenderness was so touching that the little fellow went off warm and comforted. I spoke of my walk and gently explained to Marceline why I preferred going out alone.

At that time, my nights were generally disturbed by my constantly waking with a start—either frozen with cold or bathed in sweat. That night was a very good one. I hardly woke up at all. The next morning, I was ready to go out by nine o'clock. It was fine; I felt rested, not weak, happy—or rather, amused. The air was calm and warm, but nevertheless I took my shawl to serve as a pretext for making acquaintance with the boy who might turn up to carry it. I have said that the garden ran alongside our terrace, so that I reached it in a moment. It was with rapture I passed into its shade. The air was luminous. The cassias, whose flowers come very early, before their leaves, gave out a delicious scent—or was it from all around me that came the faint, strange perfume, which seemed to enter me by several senses at once and which so uplifted me? I was breathing more easily too, and so I walked more lightly; and yet at the first bench I sat down, but it was because I was excited—dazzled—rather than tired.

I looked. The shadows were transparent and mobile; they did not fall upon the ground—seemed barely to rest on it. Light! Oh, light!

I listened. What did I hear? Nothing; everything; every sound amused me.

I remember a shrub some way off whose bark looked of such a curious texture that I felt obliged to go and feel it. My touch was a caress; it gave me rapture. I remember. . . . Was that the morning that was at last to give me birth?

I had forgotten I was alone, and sat on, expecting nothing, waiting for no one, forgetting the time. Up till that day, so it seemed to me, I had felt so little and thought so much that now I was astonished to find my sensations had become as strong as my thoughts.

I say, "it *seemed* to me," for from the depths of my past childhood, there now awoke in me the glimmerings of a thousand lost sensations. The fact that I was once more aware of my senses enabled me to give them a half fearful recognition. Yes; my reawakened senses now remembered a whole ancient history of their own—recomposed for themselves a vanished past. They were alive! Alive! They had never ceased to live; they discovered that even during those early studious years they had been living their own latent, cunning life.

I met no one that day, and I was glad of it; I took out of my pocket a little Homer, which I had not opened since Marseilles, re-read three lines of the *Odyssey* and learned them by heart; then, finding in their rhythm enough to satisfy me, I dwelled on them awhile with leisurely delight, shut the book, and sat still, trembling, more alive than I had thought it possible to be, my mind benumbed with happiness. . . .

4

IN THE MEANTIME, Marceline, who saw with delight that my health was at last improving, had after a few days begun telling me about the marvelous orchards of the oasis. She was fond of the open air and outdoor exercise. My illness left her enough spare time for long walks, from which she returned glowing with enthusiasm; so far she had not said much about them, as she did not dare invite me to go with her and was afraid of depressing me by an account of delights I was not yet fit to enjoy. But now that I was better, she counted on their attraction to complete my recovery. The pleasure I was again beginning to take in walking and looking about me tempted me to join her. And the next morning we set out together.

She led the way along a path so odd that I have never in any country seen its like. It meanders indolently between two fairly high mud walls; the shape of the gardens they enclose directs its leisurely course; sometimes it winds; sometimes it is broken; a sudden turning as you enter it and you lose your bearings; you cease to know where you came from or where you are going. The water of the river follows the path faithfully and runs alongside one of the walls; the walls are made of the same earth as the path—the same as that of the whole oasis—a pinkish or soft gray clay, which is turned a little darker by the water, which the burning sun crackles, which hardens in the heat and softens with the first shower, so that it becomes a plastic soil that keeps the imprint of every naked foot. Above the walls, palm-trees show. Wood-pigeons went flying into them as we came up. Marceline looked at me.

I forgot my discomfort and fatigue. I walked on in a sort of ecstasy, of silent joy, of elation of the senses and the flesh. At that moment there came a gentle breath of wind; all the palms waved and we saw the tallest of the trees bending; then the whole air grew calm again, and I distinctly heard, coming from behind the wall, the song of a flute. A breach in the wall; we went in.

It was a place full of light and shade; tranquil; it seemed beyond the touch of time; full of silence; full of rustlings—the soft noise of running water that feeds the palms and slips from tree to tree, the quiet call of the pigeons, the song of the flute the boy was playing. He was sitting, almost naked, on the trunk of a fallen palm-tree, watching a herd of goats; our coming did not disturb him; he did not move—stopped playing only for a moment.

I noticed during this brief pause that another flute was answering in the distance. We went on a little, then:

"It's no use going any farther," said Marceline; "these orchards are all alike; possibly at the other end of the oasis they may be a little larger. . . ."

She spread the shawl on the ground. "Sit down and rest," she said.

How long did we stay there? I cannot tell. What mattered time? Marceline was near me; I lay down and put my head on her knees. The song of the flute flowed on, stopped from time to time, went on again; the sound of the water . . . From time to time a goat baa'ed. I shut my eyes; I felt Marceline lay her cool hand on my forehead; I felt the burning sun, gently shaded by the palm-trees; I thought of nothing; what mattered thoughts? I *felt* extraordinarily. . . .

And from time to time there was another noise; I opened my eyes; a little wind was blowing in the palm-trees; it did not come down low enough to reach us—stirred only the highest branches.

The next morning, I returned to the same garden with Marceline; on the evening of the same day, I went back to it alone. The goatherd who played the flute was there. I went up to him; spoke to him. He was called Lassif, was only twelve years old, was a handsome boy. He told me the names of his goats, told me that the little canals are called "seghias"; they do not all run every day, he explained; the water, wisely and parsimoniously distributed, satisfies the thirst of the plants, and is then at once withdrawn. At the foot of each palm the ground is hollowed out into a small cup which holds water enough for the tree's needs; an ingenious system of sluices, which the boy worked for me to see, controls the water, conducts it wherever the ground is thirstiest.

The next day I saw a brother of Lassif's; he was a little older and not so handsome; he was called Lachmi. By means of the kind of ladder made in the trunk of the tree by the old stumps of excised palm leaves he climbed up to the top of a pollarded palm; then he came swiftly down again, showing a golden nudity beneath his floating garment. He brought down a little earthen gourd from the place where the head of the tree had been severed; it had been hung up near the fresh cut in order to collect the palm sap, from which the Arabs make a sweet wine they are extremely fond of. At Lachmi's invitation, I tasted it; but I did not like its sickly, raw, syrupy taste.

The following days I went farther; I saw other gardens, other goatherds, and other goats. As Marceline had said, all these gardens were alike; and yet they were all different.

Sometimes Marceline would still come with me; but more often, as soon as we reached the orchards, I would leave her, persuade her that I was tired, that I wanted to sit down, that she must not wait for me, for she needed more exercise; so that she would finish the walk without me. I stayed behind with the children. I soon knew a great number of them; I had long conversations with them; I learned their games, taught them others, lost all my pennies at pitch and toss. Some of them used to come with me on my walks (every day I walked farther), showed me some new way home, took charge of my coat and my shawl when I happened to have them both with me. Before leaving the children, I used to distribute a handful of pennies among them; sometimes they would follow me, playing all the way, as far as my own door; and finally they would sometimes come in.

Then Marceline on her side brought in others. She brought the boys who went to school, whom she encouraged to work; when school broke up, the good little boys, the quiet little boys came in; those that I brought were different; but they made friends over their games. We took care always to have a store of syrups and sweetmeats on hand. Soon other boys came of their own accord, even uninvited. I remember each one of them; I can see them still. . . .

Toward the end of January, the weather changed suddenly; a cold wind sprang up and my health immediately began to suffer. The great open space that separates the oasis from the town again became impassable, and I was obliged once more to content myself with the public gardens. Then it began to rain—an icy rain, which covered the mountains on the far northern horizon with snow.

I spent those melancholy days beside the fire, gloomily, obstinately, fighting with my illness, which in this vile weather gained upon me. Lugubrious days! I could neither read nor work; the slightest effort brought on the most troublesome perspiration; fixing my thoughts exhausted me; directly I stopped paying attention to my breathing, I suffocated.

During those melancholy days the children were my only distraction. In the rainy weather, only the most familiar came in; their clothes were drenched; they sat round the fire in a circle. A long time would often go by without anything being said. I was too tired, too unwell to do anything but look at them; but the presence of their good health did me good. Those that Marceline petted were weakly, sickly, and too well behaved; I was irritated with her and with them and ended by keeping them at arm's length. To tell the truth, they frightened me.

One morning I had a curious revelation as to my own character; Moktir, the only one of my wife's protégés who did not irritate me (because of his good looks perhaps), was alone with me in my room; up till then, I had not cared much about him, but there was something strange, I thought, in the brilliant and somber expression of his eyes. Some kind of inexplicable curiosity made me watch his movements. I was standing in front of the fire, my two elbows on the mantelpiece, apparently absorbed in a book but, though I had my back turned to him, I could see what he was doing reflected in the glass. Moktir did not know I was watching him and thought I was immersed in my reading. I saw him go noiselessly up to a table where Marceline had laid her work and a little pair of scissors beside it, seize them furtively, and in a twinkling engulf them in the folds of his burnous. My heart beat quickly for a moment, but neither reason nor reflection could arouse in me the smallest feeling of indignation. More than that! I could not manage to persuade myself that the feeling that filled me at the sight was anything but joy.

When I had allowed Moktir ample time for robbing me, I turned round again and spoke to him as if nothing had happened.

Marceline was very fond of this boy; but I do not think it was the fear of grieving her that made me, rather than denounce Moktir, invent some story or other to explain the loss of her scissors.

From that day onwards, Moktir became my favorite.

5

OUR STAY AT BISKRA was not to last much longer. When the February rains were over, the outburst of heat that succeeded them was too violent. After several days of drenching downpour, one morning, suddenly, I woke in an atmosphere of brilliant blue. As soon as I was up, I hurried to the highest part of the terrace. The sky, from one horizon to the other, was cloudless. Mists were rising under the heat of the sun, which was already fierce; the whole oasis was smoking; in the distance could be heard the grumbling of the Oued in flood. The air was so pure and so delicious that I felt better at once. Marceline joined me; we wanted to go out, but that day the mud kept us at home.

A few days later, we went back to Lassif's orchard; the stems of the plants looked heavy, sodden and swollen with water. This African land, whose thirsty season of waiting was not then known to me, had lain submerged for many long days and was now awaking from its winter sleep, drunken with water, bursting with the fresh rise of sap; throughout it rang the wild laughter of an exultant spring which found an echo, a double, as it were, in my own heart. Ashour and Moktir came with us at first; I still enjoyed their slight friendship, which cost me only half a franc a day; but I soon grew tired of them; not now so weak as to need the example of their health, and no longer finding in their play the food necessary to keep my joy alive, I turned the elation of my mind and senses to Marceline. Her gladness made me realize she had been unhappy before. I excused myself like a child for having so often left her to herself, set down my odd, elusive behavior to the score of weakness, and declared that hitherto loving had been too much for me, but that henceforward, as my health grew, so would my love. I spoke truly, but no doubt I was still very weak, for it was not till more than a month later that I desired Marceline.

In the meantime, it was getting hotter every day. There was nothing to keep us at Biskra—except the charm which afterwards called me back there. Our determination to leave was taken suddenly. In three hours our things were packed. The train started next morning at daybreak.

I remember that last night. The moon was nearly full; it streamed into my room by the wide-open window. Marceline was, I think, asleep. I had gone to bed but could not sleep. I felt myself burning with a kind of happy fever—the fever of life itself. . . . I got up, dipped my hands and face in water, then, pushing open the glass doors, went out.

It was already late; not a sound; not a breath; the air itself seemed asleep. The Arab dogs, which yelp all night like jackals, could only just be heard in the distance. Facing me lay the little courtyard; the wall opposite cast a slanting band of shadow across it; the regular palm-trees, bereft of color and life, seemed struck forever motionless. . . . But in sleep there is still some palpitation of life; here, nothing seemed asleep; everything seemed dead. The calm appalled me; and suddenly there rose in me afresh the tragic realization of my life; it came upon me as though to protest, to assert itself, to bewail itself in the silence, so violent, so impetuous, so agonizing almost, that I should have cried aloud, if I could have cried like an animal. I took hold of my hand, I remember—my left hand in my right; I wanted to lift it to my head and I did. What for? To assure myself that I was alive and that I felt the wonder of it. I touched my forehead, my eyelids. Then a shudder seized me. A day will come, thought I, a day will come when I shall not even be strong enough to lift to my lips the very water I most thirst for. . . . I went in, but did not lie down again at once; I wanted to fix that night, to engrave its memory on my mind, to hold and to keep it; undecided as to what I should do, I took a book from my table—it was the Bible—and opened it at random; by stooping over it in the moonlight, I could see to read; I read Christ's words to Peter—those words, alas, which I was never to forget: "When thou wast young, thou girdedst thyself and walkedst whither thou wouldest: but when thou shalt be old, thou shalt stretch forth thy hands . . ." —thou shalt stretch forth thy hands. . . .

The next morning at dawn, we left.

6

I SHALL NOT SPEAK of every stage of the journey. Some of them have left me only a confused recollection; I was sometimes better and sometimes worse in health, still at the mercy of a cold wind and made anxious by the shadow of a cloud; the condition of my nerves too was the cause of frequent trouble; but my lungs at any rate were recovering. Each relapse was shorter and less serious; the attacks were as sharp, but my body was better armed against them.

From Tunis we went to Malta, and from there to Syracuse; I found myself back again on the classic ground whose language and history were known to me. Since the beginning of my illness I had lived without question or role, simply applying myself to the act of living as an animal does or a child. Now that I was less absorbed by my malady, my life became once more certain of itself and conscious. After that long and almost mortal sickness, I had thought I should rise again the same as before and be able without difficulty to reknit my present to my past; in the newness of a strange country it had been possible to deceive myself— but not here; everything brought home to me—though I still thought it astonishing—that I was changed.

When at Syracuse and later, I wanted to start my work again and immerse myself once more in a minute study of the past, I discovered that something had, if not destroyed, at any rate modified my pleasure in it . . . and this something was the feeling of the present. The history of the past had now taken on for me the immobility, the terrifying fixity of the nocturnal shadows in the little courtyard of Biskra—the immobility of death. In old days, I had taken pleasure in this very fixity, which enabled my mind to work with precision; the facts of history all appeared to me like specimens in a museum, or rather like plants in a herbarium, permanently dried, so that it was easy to forget they had once upon a time been juicy with sap and alive in the sun. Nowadays, if I still took any pleasure in history, it was by imagining it in the present. Thus the great political events of the past moved me less than the feeling that began to revive in me for the poets or for a few men of action. At Syracuse, I reread Theocritus and reflected that his goatherds with the beautiful names were the very same as those I had loved at Biskra.

My erudition, which was aroused at every step, became an encumbrance and hampered my joy. I could not see a Greek theater or temple without immediately reconstructing it in my mind. Every thought of the festivals of antiquity made me grieve over the death of the ruin that was left standing in their place; and I had a horror of death.

I ended by avoiding ruins; the noblest monuments of the past were less to me than those sunk gardens of the Latomie whose lemons have the sharp sweetness of oranges—or the shores of the Cyane, still flowing among the papyri as blue as on the day when it wept for Proserpine.

I ended by despising the learning that had at first been my pride; the studies that up to then had been my whole life now seemed to me to have a mere accidental and conventional connection with myself. I found out that I was something different and—oh rapture!—that I had a separate existence of my own. Inasmuch as I was a specialist, I appeared to myself senseless; inasmuch as I was a man, did I know myself at all? I had only just been born and could not as yet know *what* I had been born. It was that I had to find out.

There is nothing more tragic for a man who has been expecting to die than a long convalescence. After that touch from the wing of Death, what seemed important is so no longer; other things become so which had at first seemed unimportant, or which one did not even know existed. The miscellaneous mass of acquired knowledge of every kind that has overlain the mind gets peeled off in places like a mask of paint, exposing the bare skin—the very flesh of the authentic creature that had lain hidden beneath it.

He it was whom I thenceforward set out to discover—that authentic creature, "the old Adam," whom the Gospel had repudiated, whom everything about me—books, masters, parents, and I myself—had begun by attempting to suppress. And he was already coming into view, still in the rough and difficult of discovery, thanks to all that overlay him, but so much the more worthy to be discovered, so much the more valorous. Thenceforward I despised the secondary creature, the creature who was due to teaching, whom education had painted on the surface. These overlays had to be shaken off.

And I compared myself to a palimpsest; I tasted the scholar's joy when he discovers under more recent writing, and on the same paper, a very ancient and infinitely more precious text. What was this occult text? In order to read it, was it not first of all necessary to efface the more recent one?

I was besides no longer the sickly, studious being to whom my early morality, with all its rigidity and restrictions, had been suited. There was more here than a convalescence; there was an increase, a recrudescence of life, the influx of a richer, warmer blood which must of necessity affect my thoughts, touch them one by one, inform them all, stir and color the most remote, delicate, and secret fibers of my being. For, either to strength or to weakness, the creature adapts itself; it constitutes itself according to the powers it possesses; but if these should increase, if they should permit a wider scope, then . . . I did not think all this at the time, and my description gives a false idea of me. In reality, I did not think at all; I never questioned myself; a happy fatalism guided me. I was afraid that too hasty an investigation might disturb the mystery of my slow transformation. I must allow time for the effaced characters to reappear, and not attempt to re-form them. Not so much neglecting my mind, therefore, as allowing it to lie fallow, I gave myself up to the luxurious enjoyment of my own self, of external things, of all existence, which seemed to me divine. We had left Syracuse, and as I ran along the precipitous road that connects Taormina with Mola, I remember shouting aloud, as if my calling could bring him to me: "A new self! A new self!"

My only effort then—an effort which was at that time constant—consisted in systematically condemning and suppressing everything which I believed I owed to my past education and early moral beliefs. Deliberately disdainful of my learning, and in scorn of my scholar's tastes, I refused to visit Agrigentum, and a few days later, on the road to Naples, I passed by the beautiful temple of Pæstum, in which Greece still breathes, and where, two years later, I went to worship some God or other—I no longer know which.

Why do I say "my only effort"? How could I be interested in myself save as a perfectible being? Never before had my will been so tensely strung as in striving after this unknown and vaguely imagined perfection. I employed the whole of my will, indeed, in strengthening and bronzing my body. We had left the coast near Salerno and reached Ravello. There, a keener air, the charm of the rocks, their recesses, their surprises, the unexplored depths of the valleys, all contributed to my strength and enjoyment and gave impetus to my enthusiasm.

Not far from the shore and very near the sky, Ravello lies on an abrupt height facing the flat and distant coast of Pæstum. Under the Norman domination, it was a city of no inconsiderable importance; it is nothing now but a narrow village where I think we were the only strangers. We were lodged in an ancient religious house which had been turned into a hotel; it is situated on the extreme edge of the rock, and its terraces and gardens seemed to hang suspended over an abyss of azure. Over the wall, festooned with creeping vine, one could at first see nothing but the sea; one had to go right up to the wall in order to discover the steep cultivated slope that connects Ravello with the shore by paths that seem more like staircases. Above Ravello, the mountain continues. First come enormous olive and caroub trees, with cyclamen growing in their shadow; then, higher up, Spanish chestnuts in great quantities, cool air, northern plants; lower down, lemon trees near the sea. These are planted in small plots owing to the slope of the ground; they are step gardens, nearly all alike; a narrow path goes from end to end through the middle of each; one enters noiselessly, like a thief; one dreams in their green shadow; their foliage is thick and heavy; no direct ray of sunlight penetrates it; the lemons, like drops of opaque wax, hang perfumed; they are white and greenish in the shade; they are within reach of one's hand, of one's thirst; they are sweet and sharp and refreshing.

The shade was so dense beneath them that I did not dare linger in it after my walk, for exercise still made me perspire. And yet I now managed the steps without being exhausted; I practiced climbing them with my mouth shut; I put greater and greater intervals between my halts; I will go so far without giving in, I used to say to myself; then, the goal reached, I was rewarded by a glow of satisfied pride; I would take a few long deep breaths, and feel as if the air entered my lungs more thoroughly, more efficaciously. I brought all my old assiduity to bear on the care of my body. I began to progress.

I was sometimes astonished that my health came back so quickly. I began to think I had exaggerated the gravity of my condition—to doubt that I had been very ill—to laugh at my blood-spitting—to regret that my recovery had not been more arduous.

In my ignorance of my physical needs, my treatment of myself had at first been very foolish. I now made a patient study of them and came to regard my ingenious exercise of prudence and care as a kind of game. What I still suffered from most was my morbid sensitiveness to the slightest change of temperature. Now that my lungs were cured, I attributed this hyperæsthesia to the nervous debility left me by my illness, and I determined to conquer it. The sight of the beautiful, brown, sunburned skins which some of the carelessly clad peasants at work in the fields showed beneath their open shirts made me long to be like them. One morning, after I had stripped, I looked at myself; my thin arms, my stooping shoulders, which no effort of mine could keep straight, but above all the whiteness of my skin, or rather its entire want of color, shamed me to tears. I dressed quickly and, instead of going down to Amalfi as usual, I turned my steps toward some mossy, grass-grown rocks in a place far from any habitation, far from any road, where I knew no one could see me. When I got there, I undressed slowly. The air was almost sharp, but the sun was burning. I exposed my whole body to its flame. I sat down, lay down, turned myself about. I felt the ground hard beneath me; the waving grass brushed me. Though I was sheltered from the wind, I shivered and thrilled at every breath. Soon a delicious burning enveloped me; my whole being surged up into my skin.

We stayed at Ravello a fortnight; every morning I returned to the same rocks and went on with my cure. I soon found I was wearing a troublesome and unnecessary amount of clothing; my skin having recovered its tone, the constant perspiration ceased and I was able to keep warm without superfluous protection.

On one of the last mornings (we were in the middle of April), I was bolder still. In a hollow of the rocks I have mentioned, there flowed a spring of transparent water. At this very place it fell in a little cascade—not a very abundant one, to be sure, but the fall had hollowed out a deeper basin at its foot in which the water lingered, exquisitely pure and clear. Three times already I had been there, leaned over it, stretched myself along its bank, thirsty and longing; I had gazed at the bottom of polished rock, where not a stain, not a weed was to be seen, and where the sun shot its dancing and iridescent rays. On this fourth day, I came to the spot with my mind already made up. The water looked as bright and as clear as ever, and without pausing to think, I plunged straight in. It struck an instant chill through me, and I jumped out again quickly and flung myself down on the grass in the sun. There was some wild thyme growing near by; I picked some of the sweet-smelling leaves, crushed them in my hands and rubbed my wet but burning body with them. I looked at myself for a long while—with no more shame now—with joy. Although not yet robust, I felt myself capable of becoming so— harmonious, sensuous, almost beautiful.

7

AND SO, IN THE PLACE of all action and all work, I contented myself with physical exercises, which certainly implied a change in my moral outlook, but which I soon began to regard as mere training, as simply a means to an end, and no longer satisfying in themselves.

I will tell you, however, about one other action of mine, though perhaps you will consider it ridiculous, for its very childishness marks the need that then tormented me of showing by some outward sign the change that had come over my inward self: at Amalfi I had my beard and mustache shaved off. Up till that day I had worn them long and my hair cropped close. It had never occurred to me that I could do anything else. And suddenly, on the day when I first stripped myself on the rock, my beard made me feel uncomfortable; it was like a last piece of clothing I could not get rid of; I felt as if it were false; it was carefully cut—not in a point, but square, and it then and there struck me as very ugly and ridiculous. When I got back to my hotel room, I looked at myself in the glass and was displeased with my appearance; I looked like what I had hitherto been—an archæologist—a bookworm. Immediately after lunch, I went down to Amalfi with my mind made up. The town is very small and I could find nothing better than a vulgar little shop in the piazza. It was market day; the place was full; I had to wait interminably; but nothing—neither the suspicious-looking razors, nor the dirty yellow shaving-brush, nor the smell, nor the barber's talk could put me off. When my beard fell beneath his scissors, I felt as though I had taken off a mask. But oh! when I saw myself, the emotion that filled me, and which I tried to keep down, was not pleasure, but fear. I do not criticize this feeling—I record it. I thought myself quite good-looking . . . no, the reason of my fear was a feeling that my mind had been stripped of all disguise, and it suddenly appeared to me redoubtable.

On the other hand, I let my hair grow.

That is all my new and still unoccupied self found to do. I expected it eventually to give birth to actions that would astonish me—but later— later, I said to myself, when it is more fully formed. In the meantime, as I was obliged to live, I was reduced, like Descartes, to a provisional mode of action. This was the reason Marceline did not notice anything. The different look in my eyes, no doubt, and the changed expression of my features, especially on the day when I appeared without my beard, might perhaps have aroused her suspicions, but she already loved me too much to see me as I was; and then I did my best to reassure her. The important thing was that she should not interfere with my renascent life, and to keep it from her eyes I had to dissemble.

For that matter, the man Marceline loved, the man she had married, was not my "new self." So I told myself again and again as an excuse for hiding him. In this way I showed her an image of myself which, by the very fact of its remaining constant and faithful to the past, became every day falser and falser.

For the time being, therefore, my relationship with Marceline remained the same, though it was every day getting more intense by reason of my growing love. My dissimulation (if that expression can be applied to the need I felt of protecting my thoughts from her judgment), my very dissimulation increased that love. I mean that it kept me incessantly occupied with Marceline. At first, perhaps, this necessity for falsehood cost me a little effort; but I soon came to understand that the things that are reputed worst (lying, to mention only one) are only difficult to do as long as one has never done them; but that they become—and very quickly too—easy, pleasant and agreeable to do over again, and soon even natural. So then, as is always the case when one overcomes an initial disgust, I ended by taking pleasure in my dissimulation itself, by protracting it, as if it afforded opportunity for the play of my undiscovered faculties. And every day my life grew richer and fuller, as I advanced toward a riper, more delicious happiness.

8

THE ROAD FROM Ravello to Sorrento is so beautiful that I had no desire that morning to see anything more beautiful on earth. The sun-warmed harshness of the rocks, the air's abundance, the scents, the limpidity, all filled me with the heavenly delight of living, and with such contentment that there seemed to dwell in me nothing but a dancing joy; memories and regrets, hope and desire, future and past were alike silent; I was conscious of nothing in life but what the moment brought, but what the moment carried away.

"O joys of the body!" I exclaimed; "unerring rhythm of the muscles! health! . . ."

I had started early that morning, ahead of Marceline, for her calmer pleasure would have cooled mine, just as her slower pace would have kept me back. She was to join me by carriage at Positano, where we were to lunch.

I was nearing Positano when a noise of wheels, which sounded like the bass accompaniment to a curious kind of singing, made me look round abruptly. At first I could see nothing because of a turn in the road, which in that place follows the edge of the cliff; then a carriage driven at a frantic pace dashed suddenly into view; it was Marceline's. The driver was singing at the top of his voice, standing up on the box and gesticulating violently while he ferociously whipped his frightened horse. What a brute the fellow was! He passed me so quickly that I only just had time to get out of the way, and my shouts failed to make him stop. . . . I rushed after him, but the carriage was going too fast. I was terrified that Marceline would fling herself out of the carriage, and equally so that she would stay in it; a single jolt might have thrown her into the sea. . . . All of a sudden the horse fell down. Marceline jumped out and started running, but I was beside her in a moment. . . . The driver, as soon as he saw me, broke into horrible oaths. I was furious with the man; at his first word of abuse, I rushed at him and flung him brutally from his box. I rolled on the ground with him, but did not lose my advantage; he seemed dazed by his fall and was soon still more so by a blow on the face which I gave him when I saw he meant to bite me. I did not let go of him, however, and pressed with my knee on his chest, while I tried to pinion his arms. I looked at his ugly face, which my fist had made still uglier; he spat, foamed, bled, swore; oh, what a horrible creature! He deserved strangling, I thought. And perhaps I should have strangled him—at any rate, I felt capable of it; and I really believe it was only the thought of the police that prevented me.

I succeeded, not without difficulty, in tying the madman up, and flung him into the carriage like a sack.

Ah, what looks, what kisses Marceline and I exchanged when it was all over. The danger had not been great; but I had had to show my strength, and that in order to protect her. At the moment I felt I could have given my life for her . . . and given it wholly with joy. . . . The horse got up. We left the drunkard at the bottom of the carriage, got onto the box together, and drove as best we could, first to Positano, and then to Sorrento.

It was that night that I first possessed Marceline.

Have you really understood or must I tell you again that I was, as it were, new to things of love? Perhaps it was to its novelty that our wedding night owed its grace. . . . For it seems to me, when I recall it, that that first night of ours was our only one, the expectation and the surprise of love added so much deliciousness to its pleasures—so sufficient is a single night for the expression of the greatest love, and so obstinately does my memory recall that night alone. It was a flashing moment that caught and mingled our souls in its laughter. . . . But I believe there comes a point in love, once and no more, which later on the soul seeks—yes, seeks in vain—to surpass; I believe that happiness wears out in the effort made to recapture it; that nothing is more fatal to happiness than the remembrance of happiness. Alas! I remember that night. . . .

Our hotel was outside the town and surrounded with gardens and orchards; a very large balcony opened out from our room, and the branches of the trees brushed against it. Our wide-open windows let in the dawn freely. I got up and bent tenderly over Marceline. She was asleep; she looked as though she were smiling in her sleep; my greater strength seemed to make me feel her greater delicacy and that her grace was all fragility. Tumultuous thoughts whirled in my brain. I reflected that she was telling the truth when she said I was her all; then: What do I do for her happiness? I thought. Almost all day and every day I abandon her; her every hope is in me, and I neglect her! . . . oh, poor, poor Marceline! My eyes filled with tears. I tried in vain to seek an excuse in my past weakness; what need had I now for so much care and attention, for so much egoism? Was I not now the stronger of the two?

The smile had left her cheeks; daybreak, though it had touched everything else with gold, suddenly showed her to me sad and pale; and perhaps the approach of morning inclined me to be anxious. "Shall I in my turn have to nurse you, fear for you, Marceline?" I inwardly cried. I shuddered, and, overflowing with love, pity, and tenderness, I placed between her closed eyes the gentlest, the most loverlike, the most pious of kisses.

9

THE FEW DAYS WE STAYED at Sorrento were smiling days and very calm. Had I ever enjoyed before such rest, such happiness? Should I ever enjoy them again? . . . I spent almost all my time with Marceline; thinking less of myself, I was able to think more of her, and now took as much pleasure in talking to her as I had before taken in being silent.

I was at first astonished to feel that she looked upon her wandering life, with which I professed myself perfectly satisfied, only as something temporary; but its idleness soon became obvious to me; I agreed it must not last; for the first time, thanks to the leisure left me by my recovered health, there awoke in me a desire for work, and I began to speak seriously of going home; from Marceline's joy, I realized she herself had long been thinking of it.

Meanwhile, when I again began to turn my attention to some of my old historical studies, I found that I no longer took the same pleasure in them. As I have already told you, since my illness I had come to consider this abstract and neutral acquaintance with the past as mere vanity. In other days I had worked at philological research, studying more especially, for instance, the influence of the Goths on the corruption of the Latin language, and had passed over and misunderstood the figures of Theodoric, Cassiodorus, and Amalasontha, and their admirable and astonishing passions, in order to concentrate all my enthusiasm on mere signs—the waste product of their lives.

At present, however, these same signs, and indeed philology as a whole, were nothing more to me than a means of penetrating further into things whose savage grandeur and nobility had begun to dawn on me. I resolved to study this period further, to limit myself for a time to the last years of the empire of the Goths, and to turn to account our coming stay at Ravenna, the scene of its closing agonies.

But shall I confess that the figure of the young king Athalaric was what attracted me most? I pictured to myself this fifteen-year-old boy, worked on in secret by the Goths, in revolt against his mother Amalasontha, rebelling against his Latin education and flinging aside his culture, as a restive horse shakes off a troublesome harness; I saw him preferring the society of the untutored Goths to that of Cassiodorus—too old and too wise—plunging for a few years into a life of violent and unbridled pleasures with rude companions of his own age, and dying at eighteen, rotten and sodden with debauchery. I recognized in this tragic impulse toward a wilder, more natural state, something of what Marceline used to call my "crisis." I tried to find some satisfaction in applying my mind to it, since it no longer occupied my body; and in Athalaric's horrible death, I did my best to read a lesson.

So we settled to spend a fortnight at Ravenna, visit Rome and Florence rapidly, then, giving up Venice and Verona, hurry over the end of our journey and not stop again before reaching Paris. I found a pleasure I had never felt before in talking to Marceline about the future; we were still a little undecided as to how we should spend the summer; we were both tired of traveling and I was in need of absolute quiet for my work; then we thought of a place of mine, situated between Lisieux and Pont-L'Evêque, in the greenest of green Normandy; it had formerly belonged to my mother, and I had passed several summers there with her in my childhood, though I had never gone back to it since her death. My father had left it in charge of a bailiff, an old man by now, who collected the rents and sent them to us regularly. I had kept enchanting memories of a large and very pleasant house standing in a garden watered by running streams; it was called La Morinière; I thought it would be good to live there.

I spoke of spending the following winter in Rome, but as a worker this time, not a tourist. . . . But this last plan was soon upset. Among the number of letters we found waiting for us at Naples was one containing an unexpected piece of information—a chair at the Collège de France had fallen vacant and my name had been several times mentioned in connection with it; it was only a temporary post which would leave me free in the future; the friend who wrote advised me of the few steps to be taken in case I should accept, which he strongly advised me to do. I hesitated to bind myself to what at first seemed to me slavery; but then I reflected that it might be interesting to put forward my ideas on Cassiodorus in a course of lectures. . . . The pleasure I should be giving Marceline finally decided me, and once my decision was taken, I saw only its advantages.

My father had several connections in the learned world of Rome and Florence, with whom I had myself been in correspondence. They gave me every facility for making the necessary researches in Ravenna and elsewhere; I had no thoughts now but for my work. Marceline, by her constant consideration and in a thousand charming ways, did all she could to help me.

Our happiness during those last days of travel was so equable, so calm, that there is nothing to say about it. Men's finest works bear the persistent marks of pain. What would there be in a story of happiness? Only what prepares it, only what destroys it can be told. I have now told you what prepared it.

Second Part: 1

WE ARRIVED AT LA MORINIÈRE in the first days of July, having stayed in Paris only just long enough to do our shopping and pay a very few visits.

La Morinière is situated, as I have told you, between Lisieux and Pont-L'Evêque in the shadiest, wettest country I know. Innumerable narrow coombes and gently rounded hills terminate near the wide "Vallée d'Auge," which then stretches in an uninterrupted plain as far as the sea. There is no horizon; some few copse-woods, filled with mysterious shade, some few fields of corn, but chiefly meadow land—softly sloping pastures, where the lush grass is mown twice a year, where the apple-trees, when the sun is low, join shadow to shadow, where flocks and herds graze untended; in every hollow there is water—pond or pool or river; from every side comes the continual murmur of streams.

Oh, how well I remembered the house! its blue roofs, its walls of stone and brick, its moat, the reflections in the still waters. . . . It was an old house which would easily have lodged a dozen persons; Marceline, three servants, and myself, who occasionally lent a helping hand, found it all we could do to animate a part of it. Our old bailiff, who was called Bocage, had already done his best to prepare some of the rooms; the old furniture awoke from its twenty years' slumber; everything had remained just as I remembered it—the paneling not too dilapidated, the rooms easy to live in. Bocage, to welcome us, had put flowers in all the vases he could lay hands on. He had had the large courtyard and the nearest paths in the park weeded and raked. When we arrived, the sun's last rays were falling on the house, and from the valley facing it a mist had arisen which hovered there motionless, masking and revealing the river. We had not well arrived, when all at once I recognized the scent of the grass; and when I heard the piercing cries of the swallows as they flew round the house, the whole past suddenly rose up, as though it had been lying in wait for my approach to close over and submerge me.

In a few days the house was more or less comfortable; I might have settled down to work; but I delayed, at first still listening to the voice of my past as it recalled its slightest details to my memory, and then too much absorbed by an unwonted emotion. Marceline, a week after our arrival, confided to me that she was expecting a child.

Thenceforward I thought I owed her redoubled care, and that she had a right to greater tenderness than ever; at any rate during the first weeks that followed her confidence, I spent almost every minute of the day in her company. We used to go and sit near the wood, on a bench where in old days I had been used to sit with my mother; there, each moment brought us a richer pleasure, each hour passed with a smoother flow. If no distinct memory of this period of my life stands out for me, it is not because I am less deeply grateful for it—but because everything in it melted and mingled into a state of changeless ease, in which evening joined morning without a break, in which day passed into day without a surprise.

I gradually set to work again with a quiet mind in possession of itself, certain of its strength, looking calmly and confidently to the future; with a will that seemed softened, as though by harkening to the counsels of that temperate land.

There can be no doubt, I thought, that the example of such a land, where everything is ripening toward fruition and harvest, must have the best of influences on me. I looked forward with admiring wonder to the tranquil promise of the great oxen and fat cows that grazed in those opulent meadows. The apple-trees, planted in order on the sunniest slopes of the hillsides, gave hopes this summer of a magnificent crop. I saw in my mind's eye the rich burden of fruit which would soon bow down their branches. From this ordered abundance, this joyous acceptance of service imposed, this smiling cultivation, had arisen a harmony that was the result not of chance but of intention, a rhythm, a beauty, at once human and natural, in which the teeming fecundity of nature and the wise effort of man to regulate it were combined in such perfect agreement that one no longer knew which was more admirable. What would man's effort be worth, thought I, without the savagery of the power it controls? What would the wild rush of these upwelling forces become without the intelligent effort that banks it, curbs it, leads it by such pleasant ways to its outcome of luxury? And I let myself go in a dream of lands where every force should be so regulated, all expenditure so compensated, all exchanges so strict, that the slightest waste would be appreciable; then I applied my dream to life and imagined a code of ethics which should institute the scientific and perfect utilization of a man's self by a controlling intelligence.

Where had my rebelliousness vanished to? Where was it hiding itself? It seemed never to have existed, so tranquil was I. The rising tide of my love had swept it all away.

Meanwhile old Bocage bustled round us; he gave directions, he superintended, he advised; his need of feeling himself indispensable was tiresome in the extreme. In order not to hurt his feelings I had to go over his accounts and listen for hours to his endless explanations. Even that was not enough; I had to visit the estate with him. His sententious truisms, his continual speeches, his evident self-satisfaction, the display he made of his honesty drove me to exasperation; he became more and more persistent and there was nothing I would not have done to recover my liberty, when an unexpected occurrence brought about a change in my relations with him. One evening Bocage announced that he was expecting his son Charles the next day.

I said "Oh!" rather casually, having so far troubled myself very little as to any children Bocage might or might not have; then, seeing that my indifference offended him and that he expected some expression of interest and surprise, "Where has he been?" I asked.

"In a model farm near Alençon," answered Bocage.

"How old is he now? About . . . ?" I went on, calculating the age of this son, of whose existence I had so far been totally unaware, and leaving him time enough to interrupt me. . . .

"Past seventeen," went on Bocage. "He was not much more than four when your father's good lady died. Ah! He's a big lad now; he'll know more than his dad soon. . . ." Once Bocage was started, nothing could stop him, not even the boredom I very plainly showed.

I had forgotten all about this when the next evening Charles, newly arrived from his journey, came to pay his respects to Marceline and me. He was a fine strong young fellow, so exuberantly healthy, so lissom, so well-made, that not even the frightful town clothes he had put on in our honor could make him look ridiculous; his shyness hardly added anything to the fine natural red of his cheeks. He did not look more than fifteen, his eyes were so bright and so childlike; he expressed himself clearly, without embarrassment, and, unlike his father, did not speak when he had nothing to say. I cannot remember what we talked about that first evening; I was so busy looking at him that I found nothing to say and let Marceline do all the talking. But next day, for the first time, I did not wait for old Bocage to come and fetch me, in order to go down to the farm, where I knew they were starting work on a pond that had to be repaired.

This pond—almost as big as a lake—was leaking. The leak had been located and had to be cemented. In order to do this, the pond had first to be drained, a thing that had not been done for fifteen years. It was full of carp and tench, great creatures, some of them, that lay at the bottom of the pond without ever coming up. I wanted to stock the moat with some of these fish and give some to the laborers, so that upon this occasion the pleasure of a fishing party was added to the day's work, as could be seen from the extraordinary animation of the farm; some children from the neighborhood had joined the workers and Marceline herself had promised to come down later.

The water had already been sinking for some time when I got there. Every now and then a great ripple suddenly stirred its surface and the brown backs of the disturbed fish came into sight. The children paddling in the puddles round the edges amused themselves with catching gleaming handfuls of small fry, which they flung into pails of clear water. The water in the pond was muddy and soon became more and more thick and troubled owing to the agitation of the fish. Their abundance was beyond all expectation: four farm laborers, dipping into the water at random, pulled them out in handfuls. I was sorry that Marceline had not arrived and decided to run and fetch her, when a shout signaled the appearance of the first eels. But no one could succeed in catching them, they slipped between the men's fingers. Charles, who up till then had been standing beside his father on the bank, could restrain himself no longer; he took off his shoes and socks in a moment, flung aside his coat and waistcoat, then, tucking up his trousers and shirtsleeves as high as they would go, stepped resolutely into the mud. I immediately did the same.

"Charles!" I cried, "it was a good thing you came back yesterday, wasn't it?" He was already too busy with his fishing to answer, but he looked at me, laughing. I called him after a moment to help me catch a big eel; we joined hands in trying to hold it. . . . Then came another and another; our faces were splashed with mud; sometimes the ooze suddenly gave way beneath us and we sank into it up to our waists; we were soon drenched. In the ardor of the sport, we barely exchanged a shout or two, a word or two; but at the end of the day I became aware I was saying "thou" to Charles, without having any clear idea when I had begun. Our work in common had taught us more about each other than a long conversation. Marceline had not come yet; she did not come at all, but I ceased to regret her absence; I felt as though she would have a little spoiled our pleasure.

Early next morning I went down to the farm to look for Charles. We took our way together to the woods.

As I myself knew very little about my estate and was not much distressed at knowing so little, I was astonished to find how much Charles knew about it and about the way it was farmed; he told me what I was barely aware of, namely, that I had six farmer tenants, that the rents might have amounted to sixteen or eighteen thousand francs, and that if they actually amounted to barely half that sum, it was because almost everything was eaten up by repairs of all sorts and by the payment of middlemen. His way of smiling as he looked at the fields in cultivation soon made me suspect that the management of the estate was not quite so good as I had at first thought and as Bocage had given me to understand; I pressed Charles further on this subject, and the intelligence of practical affairs which had so exasperated me in Bocage amused me in a child like him. We continued our walks day after day; the estate was large and when we had visited every corner of it, we began again with more method. Charles did not hide his irritation at the sight of certain fields, certain pieces of land that were overgrown with gorse, thistles, and weeds; he instilled into me his hatred of fallow land and set me dreaming with him of a better mode of agriculture.

"But," I said to him at first, "who is it that suffers from this lack of cultivation? Isn't it only the farmer himself? However much the profits of his farm vary, his rent still remains the same."

Charles was a little annoyed. "You understand nothing about it," he ventured to say—and I smiled. "You think only of income and won't consider that the capital is deteriorating. Your land is slowly losing its value by being badly cultivated."

"If it were to bring in more by being better cultivated, I expect the farmers would set about it. They are too eager for gain not to make as much profit as they can."

"You are not counting," continued Charles, "the cost of increased labor. These neglected bits of land are sometimes a long way from the farms. True, if they were cultivated, they would bring in nothing or next to nothing, but at any rate they would keep from spoiling."

And so the conversation went on. Sometimes for an hour on end we seemed to be interminably repeating the same things as we walked over the fields; but I listened, and little by little gathered information.

"After all, it's your father's business," I said one day impatiently.

Charles blushed a little. "My father is old," he said; "he has a great deal to do already, seeing to the upkeep of the buildings, collecting the rents and so on. It's not his business to make reforms."

"And what reforms would *you* make?" I asked. But at that he became evasive and pretended he knew nothing about it; it was only by insisting that I forced him to explain.

"I should take away all the uncultivated fields from the tenants," he ended by advising. "If the farmers leave part of their land uncultivated, it's a proof they don't need it all in order to pay you; or if they say they must keep it all, I should raise their rents. All the people hereabouts are idle," he added.

Of the six farms that belonged to me, the one I most liked visiting was situated on a hill that overlooked La Morinière; it was called La Valterie; the farmer who rented it was a pleasant enough fellow and I used to like talking to him. Nearer La Morinière was a farm called the "home farm," which was let on a system that left Bocage, pending the landlord's absence, in possession of part of the cattle. Now that my doubts had been awakened, I began to suspect honest Bocage himself, if not of cheating me, at any rate of allowing other people to cheat me. One stable and one cow-house were, it is true, reserved to me, but it soon dawned upon me that they had merely been invented so as to allow the farmer to feed his cows and horses with my oats and hay. So far, I had listened indulgently to the very unconvincing reports which Bocage gave me from time to time of deaths, malformations, and diseases. I swallowed everything. It had not then occurred to me that it was sufficient for one of the farmer's cows to fall ill for it to become one of my cows, nor that it was sufficient for one of my cows to do well for it to become one of the farmer's; but a few rash remarks of Charles's, a few observations of my own began to enlighten me, and my mind, once given the hint, worked quickly.

Marceline, at my suggestion, went over the accounts minutely, but could find nothing wrong with them; Bocage's honesty was displayed on every page. What was to be done? Let things be. At any rate, I now watched the management of the cattle in a state of suppressed indignation, but without letting it be too obvious.

I had four horses and ten cows—quite enough to be a considerable worry to me. Among my four horses was one which was still called "the colt," though it was more than three years old; it was now being broken in; I was beginning to take an interest in it, when one fine morning I was informed that it was perfectly unmanageable, that it would be impossible ever to do anything with it, and that the best thing would be to get rid of it. As if on purpose to convince me of this, in case I had doubted it, it had been made to break the front of a small cart and had cut its hocks in doing so.

I had much ado that day to keep my temper, but what helped me was Bocage's obvious embarrassment. After all, thought I, he is more weak than anything else; it is the men who are to blame, but they want a guiding hand over them.

I went into the yard to see the colt; one of the men who had been beating it began to stroke it as soon as he heard me coming; I pretended to have seen nothing. I did not know much about horses, but this colt seemed to me a fine animal; it was half-bred, light bay in color and remarkably elegant in shape, with a very bright eye and a very light mane and tail. I made sure it had not been injured, insisted on its cuts being properly dressed, and went away without another word.

That evening, as soon as I saw Charles, I tried to find out what he personally thought of the colt.

"I think he's a perfectly quiet beast," he said, "but they don't know how to manage him; they'll drive him wild."

"And how would *you* manage him?"

"Will you let me have him for a week, Sir? I'll answer for him."

"And what will you do?"

"You will see."

The next morning, Charles took the colt down to a corner of the field that was shaded by a superb walnut-tree and bordered by the river; I went too, together with Marceline. It is one of my most vivid recollections. Charles had tied the colt with a rope a few yards long to a stake firmly planted in the ground. The mettlesome creature had, it seems, objected for some time with great spirit; but now, tired and quieted, it was going round more calmly; the elasticity of its trot was astonishing and as delightful and engaging to watch as a dance. Charles stood in the center of the circle and avoided the rope at every round with a sudden leap, exciting or calming the beast with his voice; he held a long whip in his hand, but I did not see him use it. Everything about his look and movements—his youthfulness, his delight—gave his work the fervent and beautiful aspect of pleasure. Suddenly—I have no idea how—he was astride the animal; it had slackened its pace and then stopped; he had patted it a little, and then, all of a sudden, I saw that he was on its back, sure of himself, barely holding its mane, laughing, leaning forward, still patting and stroking its neck. The colt had hardly resisted for a moment; then it began its even trot again, so handsome, so easy, that I envied Charles and told him so.

"A few days' more training and the saddle won't tickle him at all; in a fortnight, Sir, your lady herself won't be afraid to mount him; he'll be as quiet as a lamb."

It was quite true; a few days later, the horse allowed himself to be stroked, harnessed, led, without any signs of restiveness; and Marceline might really have ridden him if her state of health had permitted.

"You ought to try him yourself, Sir," said Charles.

I should never have done so alone; but Charles suggested saddling another of the farm horses for himself, and the pleasure of accompanying him proved irresistible.

How grateful I was to my mother for having sent me to a riding-school when I was a boy! The recollection of those long-ago lessons stood me in good stead. The sensation of feeling myself on horseback was not too strange; after the first few moments, I had no tremors and felt perfectly at ease. Charles's mount was heavier; it was not pure bred, but far from bad-looking, and above all, Charles rode it well. We got into the habit of going out every day; for choice, we started in the early morning, through grass that was still bright with dew; we rode to the limit of the woods; the dripping hazels, shaken by our passage, drenched us with their showers; suddenly the horizon opened out; there, in front of us, lay the vast Vallée d'Auge and far in the distance could be divined the presence of the sea. We stayed a moment without dismounting; the rising sun colored the mists, parted them, dispersed them; then we set off again at a brisk trot; we lingered a little at the farm, where the work was only just beginning; we enjoyed for a moment the proud pleasure of being earlier than the laborers—of looking down on them; then, abruptly, we left them; I was home again at La Moriniére just as Marceline was beginning to get up.

I used to come in drunk with the open air, dazed with speed, my limbs a little stiff with a delicious fatigue, all health and appetite and freshness. Marceline approved, encouraged my fancy. I went straight to her room, still in my gaiters, and found her lingering in bed, waiting for me; I came bringing with me a scent of wet leaves, which she said she liked. And she listened while I told her of our ride, of the awakening of the fields, of the recommencing of the day's labor. . . . She took as much

delight, it seemed, in feeling me live as in living herself. Soon I trespassed
on this delight too; our rides grew longer, and sometimes I did not come
in till nearly noon.

I kept the afternoons and evenings, however, as much as possible for
the preparation of my lectures. My work on them made good progress; I
was satisfied with it and thought they might perhaps be worth publishing
later as a book. By a kind of natural reaction, the more regular and
orderly my life became and the more pleasure I took in establishing order
about me—the more attracted I felt by the rude ethics of the Goths.
With a boldness for which I was afterwards blamed, I took the line
throughout my lectures of making the apology and eulogy of nonculture;
but, at the same time, in my private life, I was laboriously doing all I could
to control, if not to suppress, everything about me and within me that in
any way suggested it. How far did I not push this wisdom—or this folly?

Two of my tenants whose leases expired at Christmas time came to
me with a request for renewal; it was a matter of signing the usual
preliminary agreement. Strong in Charles's assurances and encouraged by
his daily conversations, I awaited the farmers with resolution. They on
the other hand, equally strong in the conviction that tenants are hard to
replace, began asking for their rents to be lowered. Their stupefaction
was great when I read them the agreement I had myself drawn up, in
which I not only refused to lower the rents but also withdrew from the
farms certain portions of land, which I said they were making no use of.
They pretended at first to take it as a laughing matter—I must be joking.
What could I do with the land? It was worth nothing; and if they made
no use of it, it was because no use could be made of it. . . . Then, seeing I
was serious, they turned obstinate; I was obstinate too. They thought
they would frighten me by threatening to leave. It was what I was waiting for.

"All right! Go if you like! I won't keep you," I said, tearing the
agreement up before their eyes.

So there I was, with more than two hundred acres left on my hands.
I had planned for some time past to give the chief management of this
land to Bocage, thinking that in this way I should be giving it indirectly
to Charles; my intention also was to look after it a good deal myself; but
in reality, I reflected very little about it; the very risk of the undertaking
tempted me. The tenants would not be turning out before Christmas;
between this and then we should have time to look about us. I told
Charles; his delight annoyed me; he could not hide it; it made me feel
more than ever that he was much too young. We were already pressed
for time; it was the season when the reaping of the crops leaves the fields
empty for early ploughing. By an established custom, the outgoing tenant
works side by side with the incoming; the former quits the land bit by
bit, as soon as he has carried his crops. I was afraid the two farmers I had
dismissed would somehow revenge themselves on me; but, on the contrary, they made a pretense of being perfectly amiable (I only learned

later how much they benefited by this). I took advantage of their complaisance to go up to their land—which was soon going to be mine—every morning and evening. Autumn was beginning; more laborers had to be hired to get on with the ploughing and sowing; we had bought harrows, rollers, ploughs; I rode about on horseback, superintending and directing the work, taking pleasure in ordering people about and in using my authority.

Meanwhile, in the neighboring meadows, the apples were being gathered; they dropped from the trees and lay rolling in the thick grass; never had there been a more abundant crop; there were not enough pickers; they had to be brought in from the neighboring villages and taken on for a week; Charles and I sometimes amused ourselves by helping them. Some of the men beat the branches with sticks to bring down the late fruit; the fruit that fell of itself was gathered into separate heaps; often the overripe apples lay bruised and crushed in the long grass so that it was impossible to walk without stepping on them. The smell that rose from the ground was acrid and sickly and mingled with the smell of the ploughed land.

Autumn was advancing. The mornings of the last fine days are the freshest, the most limpid of all. There were times when the moisture-laden atmosphere painted all the distances blue, made them look more distant still, turned a short walk into a day's journey; and the whole country looked bigger; at times again the abnormal transparency of the air brought the horizon closer; it seemed as though it might be reached by one stroke of the wing; and I could not tell which of the two states filled me with a heavier languor. My work was almost finished—at least, so I told myself, as an encouragement to be idle. The time I did not spend at the farm, I spent with Marceline. Together we went out into the garden; we walked slowly, she languidly hanging on my arm; the bench where we went to sit looked over the valley, which the evening gradually filled with light. She had a tender way of leaning against my shoulder; and we would stay so till evening, motionless, speechless, letting the day sink and melt within us. . . . In what a cloak of silence our love had already learned to wrap itself! For already Marceline's love was stronger than words—for sometimes her love was almost an anguish to me. As a breath of wind sometimes ripples the surface of a tranquil pool, the slightest emotion was visible in her face; she was listening now to the new life mysteriously quivering within her, and I leaned over her as over deep transparent waters where, as far as the eye could reach, nothing was to be seen but love. Ah! if this was still happiness, I know I did my best to hold it, as one tries—in vain—to hold the water that slips between one's joined hands; but already I felt, close beside my happiness, something not happiness, something indeed that colored my love, but with the colors of autumn.

Autumn was passing. Every morning the grass was wetter, till it no longer dried in the fringe of the woods on the shady side of the valley; at the first streak of dawn, it was white. The ducks on the waters of the

moat fluttered and flapped their wings; they grew fiercely agitated; sometimes they rose together, calling loudly, and flew in a noisy flight right
round La Morinière. One morning we missed them. Bocage had shut
them up. Charles told me that every autumn at migration time they had
to be shut up in this way. And a few days later the weather changed. One
evening, suddenly, there came a great blast, a breath from the sea, stormy,
steady, bringing with it cold and rain, carrying off the birds of passage.
Marceline's condition, the business of settling into a new apartment, the
work entailed by my lectures, would in any case have soon called us back
to town. The bad weather, which began early, drove us away at once.

It is true that the farm affairs were to bring me back in November. I
was greatly vexed to hear of Bocage's plans for the winter; he told me
that he wished to send Charles back to his model farm, where, so he
declared, he had still a great deal to learn; I talked to him long, used all
the arguments I could think of, but I could not make him budge; at the
outside, he consented to shorten Charles's training by a trifle so as to
allow him to come back a little sooner. Bocage did not conceal from me
that the running of the two farms would be a matter of no small difficulty; but he had in view, so he said, two highly trustworthy peasants
whom he intended to employ; they would be partly farmers, partly tenants, partly laborers; the thing was too unusual in these parts for him
to hope much good would come of it; but, he said, it was my own wish.
This conversation took place toward the end of October. In the first
days of November we moved to Paris.

2

IT WAS IN S . . . STREET, near Passy, that we took up our residence.
The apartment, which had been found for us by one of Marceline's
brothers, and which we had visited when we had last passed through Paris,
was much bigger than the one my father had left me, and Marceline was a
little uneasy, not only at the increased rent, but at all the other expenses
we should certainly be led into. I countered all her fears by pretending I
had a horror of anything temporary; I forced myself to believe in this
feeling and deliberately exaggerated it. Certainly the cost of furnishing
and arranging the apartment would exceed our income for the present
year, but our fortune, which was already large, was sure to increase still
further; I counted on my lectures for this, on the publication of my book,
and, such was my folly, on the profits from my new farms. In consequence, I stopped short at no expense, telling myself at each new one that
here was another tie and thinking also that by these means I should
suppress every vagabond inclination I felt—or feared I might feel—
within me.

For the first few days our time was taken up from morning to night by shopping and other business of the sort; and though eventually Marceline's brother very obligingly offered to do as much as he could for us, it was not long before Marceline felt thoroughly tired out. Then, as soon as we were settled in, instead of resting as she should have done, she felt obliged to receive visitors; they flocked to see us now because we had been absent from Paris during the first days of our marriage, and Marceline, who had become unused to society, was incapable of getting rid of them quickly or of shutting her doors altogether. When I came home in the evening, I found her exhausted, and, though her fatigue, which seemed only natural, caused me no anxiety, I did my best to lessen it; often receiving visits in her stead, which was very little to my taste, and sometimes paying them—which was still less so.

I have never been a brilliant talker; the frivolity, the wit, the spirit of fashionable drawing-rooms, were things in which I could take no pleasure; yet in old days I had frequented some of these salons—but how long ago that seemed! What had happened since then? In other people's company, I felt I was dull, gloomy, unwelcome, at once bored and boring. . . . By a singular piece of ill-luck, you, whom I considered my only real friends, were absent from Paris and not expected back for long. Should I have been able to speak to you more openly? Would you have perhaps understood me better than I did myself? But what did I know at that time of all that was growing up within me, of all I am now telling you about? The future seemed to me absolutely assured and I had never thought myself more master of it.

And even if I had been more perspicacious, what help against myself should I have found in Hubert, Didier, or Maurice, or in all the others whom you know and judge as I do? I very soon discovered, alas, the impossibility of their understanding me. In our very first conversations I found myself forced to impersonate a false character, to resemble the man they imagined I still was; and for convenience's sake, I pretended to have the thoughts and tastes with which they credited me. One cannot both be sincere and seem so.

I was rather more willing to renew my acquaintance with the people of my own profession—archæologists and philologists—but I found very little more pleasure and no more emotion in talking to them than in consulting a good dictionary. I hoped at first to find a rather more direct comprehension of life in one or two novelists and poets; but if they really had such a comprehension, it must be confessed they did not show it; most of them, I thought, did not really live—contented themselves with appearing to live, and were on the verge of considering life merely as a vexatious hindrance to writing. I could not blame them for it; and I do not affirm that the mistake was not mine. . . . As to that, what did I mean by "living"? That is exactly what I wanted to find out. One and another talked cleverly of the different events of life—never of what is at the back of them.

As for the few philosophers whose business it should have been to instruct me, I had long known what to expect of them; whether mathematicians or neo-Kantians, they kept as far away as possible from the disturbing reality and had no more concern for it than the algebraist has for the existence of the quantities he measures.

When I got back to Marceline, I did not conceal from her how tedious I found all these acquaintances.

"They are all alike," I said to her. "When I talk to one, I feel as if I were talking to the whole lot."

"But, my dear," said Marceline, "you can't expect each of them to be different from all the others."

"The greater their likeness to each other, the more unlike they are to me."

And then I went on with a sigh: "Not one of them has managed to be ill. They are alive—they seem to be alive, and yet not to know they are alive. For that matter, since I have been in their company, I have ceased to be alive myself. Today, among other days, what have I done? I had to leave you about nine o'clock. I had just a bare moment for a little reading before I went out; it was the only satisfactory moment of the day. Your brother was waiting for me at the solicitor's, and after the solicitor's, he insisted on sticking to me; I had to see the upholsterer with him; he was really a nuisance at the cabinet-maker's and I only got rid of him at Gaston's; I had lunch in the neighborhood with Philip and then I met Louis at a café and went with him to Theodore's absurd lecture, and paid him compliments when it was over; then, in order to get out of his invitation for Sunday, I had to go with him to Arthur's; then to a water-color exhibition with Arthur; then left cards on Albertine and Julie. . . . I came in thoroughly exhausted and found you as tired as myself, after visits from Adeline, Marthe, Jeanne, and Sophie. . . . And now, in the evening, as I look back on my day, it seems to me so vain and so empty that I long to have it back and live it over again hour by hour—and the thought of it makes me inclined to weep."

And yet I should not have been able to say what I meant by "living," nor whether the very simple secret of my trouble was not that I had acquired a taste for a more spacious, breezier life, one that was less hemmed in, less regardful of others; the secret seemed to me much more mysterious than that; it was the secret, I thought, of one who has known death; for I moved a stranger among ordinary people, like a man who has risen from the grave. And at first I merely felt rather painfully out of my element; but soon I became aware of a very different feeling. I had known no pride, I repeat, when the publication of my essay had brought me such praise. Was it pride now? Perhaps; but at any rate there was no trace of vanity mixed with it. It was rather, for the first time, the consciousness of my own worth. What separated me—distinguished me— from other people was crucial; what no one said, what no one could say but myself, *that* it was my task to say.

My lectures began soon after; the subject was congenial and I poured into the first of them all my newly born passion. Speaking of the later Latin civilization, I depicted artistic culture as welling up in a whole people, like a secretion, which is at first a sign of plethora, of a superabundance of health, but which afterwards stiffens, hardens, forbids the perfect contact of the mind with nature, hides under the persistent appearance of life a diminution of life, turns into an outside sheath, in which the cramped mind languishes and pines, in which at last it dies. Finally, pushing my thought to its logical conclusion, I showed culture, born of life, as the destroyer of life.

The historians criticized a tendency, as they phrased it, to too rapid generalization. Other people blamed my method; and those who complimented me were those who understood me least.

It was at the end of my lecture that I came across Ménalque again for the first time. I had never seen much of him, and shortly before my marriage he had started on one of those distant voyages of discovery which sometimes kept him from us for over a year. In the old days I had never much liked him; he seemed proud, and he took no interest in my existence. I was therefore astonished to see him at my first lecture. His very insolence, which had at first held me aloof from him, pleased me, and I thought the smile he gave me all the more charming because I knew he smiled rarely. Recently, an absurd—a shameful—lawsuit had caused a scandal and given the newspapers a convenient occasion to drag him through the mud; those whom he had offended by his disdain and superiority seized this pretext to revenge themselves; and what irritated them most was that he appeared not to care.

"One must allow other people to be right," he used to say when he was insulted; "it consoles them for not being anything else."

But "good society" was indignant, and people who, as they say, "respect themselves," thought it their duty to turn their backs on him, and so pay him back his contempt. This was an extra encouragement to me; feeling myself attracted by a secret influence, I went up to him and embraced him before everyone.

When they saw to whom I was talking, the last intruders withdrew; I was left alone with Ménalque.

After the irritating criticisms and inept compliments I had been listening to, his few words on the subject of my lecture were very soothing.

"You are burning what you used to adore," said he. "Very good. It is a little late in the day, but never mind, the fire is all the fiercer. I am not sure whether I altogether understand you. You make me curious. I don't much care about talking, but I should like to talk to you. Come and dine with me tonight."

"Dear Ménalque," I answered, "you seem to forget that I am married."

"Yes," he answered, "quite true. The frank cordiality with which you were not afraid to greet me made me think you might be free."

I was afraid I might have wounded him; still more so of seeming weak, and I told him I would join him after dinner.

Ménalque never did more than pass through Paris on his way to somewhere else; he always stayed in a hotel. On this occasion he had had several rooms fitted up for him as a private apartment; he had his own servants, took his meals apart, lived apart; stuffs and hangings of great value which he had brought back from Nepal had been hung on the walls and thrown over the furniture, whose commonplace ugliness was an offense to him. He was dirtying them out, he said, before presenting them to a museum. My haste to rejoin him had been so great that I found him still at table when I came in; as I excused myself for disturbing his meal:

"But I have no intention of letting you disturb it," he said, "and I expect you to let me finish it. If you had come to dinner, I should have given you some Shiraz—the wine that Hafiz celebrated—but it is too late now; one must only drink it fasting; but you'll take some liqueur, won't you?"

I accepted, thinking he would take some too, and when only one glass was brought in, I expressed astonishment.

"Forgive me," he said, "but I hardly ever drink such things."

"Are you afraid of getting drunk?"

"Oh!" replied he, "on the contrary! But I consider sobriety a more powerful intoxication—in which I keep my lucidity."

"And you pour the drink out for others?"

He smiled.

"I cannot," said he, "expect everyone to have my virtues. It's good enough to meet with my vices. . . ."

"You smoke, at any rate?"

"No, not even that. Smoking is an impersonal, negative, too easily achieved kind of drunkenness; what I want from drunkenness is an enhancement, not a diminution of life. But that's enough. Do you know where I have just come from? Biskra. I heard you had been staying there, and I thought I would like to follow up your tracks. What could the blindfolded scholar, the learned bookworm have come to do at Biskra? It's my habit to be discreet only about things that are confided to me; for things that I find out myself, I'll admit that I have an unbounded curiosity. So I searched, poked about, questioned wherever I could. My indiscretion was rewarded, since it has made me wish to meet you again; since instead of the learned man of habit you seemed to be in the old days, I know now that you are . . . it's for you to tell me what."

I felt myself blushing.

"What did you find out about me, Ménalque?"

"Do you want to know? But there's no need to be alarmed! You know your friends and mine well enough to be sure there is no one I can talk to about you. You saw how well your lecture was understood?"

"But," said I, a little impatiently, "there's nothing yet to prove that I can talk to you better than to them. Come on, then! What is it you found out about me?"

"First of all, that you had been ill."

"But there's nothing in that to . . ."

"Oh, yes! That in itself is very important. Then I was told you liked going out alone, without a book (that's what started me wondering), or, when you were not alone, you preferred the company of children to that of your wife. . . . Don't blush like that, or I shan't go on."

"Go on without looking at me."

"One of the children—his name was Moktir, if I remember right—(I have scarcely ever seen a handsomer boy, and never a greater little swindler) seemed to have a good deal to say about you. I enticed him—I bribed him to confide in me . . . not an easy thing to do, as you know, for I think it was only another lie when he said he was not lying that time. . . . Tell me whether what he told me about you is true."

In the meantime, Ménalque had got up and taken a little box out of a drawer.

"Are these scissors yours?" he said, opening the box and taking out a shapeless, twisted, rusty object, which, however, I had little difficulty in recognizing as the pair of scissors Moktir had purloined.

"Yes, they are—they were my wife's scissors."

"He pretends he took them when your head was turned away one day he was alone in the room with you; but that's not the point; he pretends that at the moment he was hiding them in his burnous, he saw you were watching him in the glass and caught the reflection of your eyes looking at him. You saw the theft and said nothing! Moktir was very much astonished at this silence—and so was I."

"And I am too at what you have just said. What! Do you mean to say he knew I had caught him at it?"

"It isn't that that matters; you were trying to be more cunning than he; it's a game at which children like that will always get the better of us. You thought you had him, and in reality, it was he who had you. . . . But that's not what matters. I should like an explanation of your silence."

"I should like one myself."

Some time passed without a word from either of us. Ménalque, who was pacing up and down the room, lighted a cigarette absent-mindedly and then immediately threw it away.

"The fact is," said he, "there's a 'sense,' as people say, a 'sense' which seems to be lacking in you, my dear Michel."

"The 'moral sense,' " said I, forcing myself to smile.

"Oh, no! Simply the sense of property."

"You don't seem to have much of it yourself."

"I have so little of it that, as you see, nothing in this place is mine; not even—or rather, especially not, the bed I sleep on. I have a horror of rest; possessions encourage one to indulge in it, and there's nothing like security for making one fall asleep; I like life well enough to want to live it awake, and so, in the very midst of my riches, I maintain the sensation of a state of precariousness, by which means I aggravate, or at any rate intensify, my life. I will not say I like danger, but I like life to be hazardous, and I want it to demand at every moment the whole of my courage, my happiness, my health. . . ."

"Then what do you blame me for?" I interrupted.

"Oh, how little you understand me, my dear Michel; for once that I am foolish enough to try and make a profession of faith! . . . If I care little for the approbation or disapprobation of men, Michel, it is not in order to approve or disapprove in my turn; those words have very little sense for me. I spoke of myself too much just now. . . . I was carried away by thinking you understood me. . . . I simply meant to say that, for a person who has not got the sense of property, you seem to possess a great deal. Isn't that rather serious?"

"And what is this great deal I possess?"

"Nothing, if you take it in that way. . . . But are you not beginning a course of lectures? Have you not an estate in Normandy? Have you not just settled yourself—and luxuriously too—in an apartment at Passy? You are married? Are you not expecting a child?"

"Well!" said I, impatiently, "it merely proves that I have succeeded in making my life more dangerous than yours."

"Yes, merely," repeated Ménalque ironically; then, turning abruptly, he put out his hand:

"Well, good-bye now; I don't think any more talk tonight would be of much use. But I shall see you again soon."

Some time went by before I saw him again.

Fresh work, fresh preoccupations took up my time; an Italian scholar brought to my notice some new documents he had discovered which were important for my lectures and which I had to study at some length. The feeling that my first lesson had been misunderstood stimulated me to shed a different and more powerful light on the succeeding ones; I was thus led to enunciate as a doctrine what I had at first only tentatively suggested as an ingenious hypothesis. How many assertions owe their strength to the lucky circumstance that as suggestions they were not understood? In my own case, I admit I cannot distinguish what proportion of obstinacy may have mingled with my natural propensity for asserting my opinions. The new things I had to say seemed to me especially urgent because of the difficulty of saying them, and above all of getting them understood.

But, alas, how pale words become when compared with deeds! Was not Ménalque's life, Ménalque's slightest action a thousand times more eloquent than my lectures? How well I understood now that the great philosophers of antiquity, whose teaching was almost wholly moral, worked by example as much as—even more than—by precept!

· · ·

The next time I saw Ménalque was in my own house, nearly three weeks after our first meeting. We had been giving a crowded evening party, and he came in almost at the end of it. In order to avoid being continually disturbed, Marceline and I had settled to be at home on Thursdays; in this way it was easier to keep our doors shut for the rest of the week. Every Thursday evening, then, those people who called themselves our friends used to come and see us; our rooms were large enough to hold a good many guests and they used to stay late. I think that what attracted them most was Marceline's exquisite charm and the pleasure of talking to each other, for as to myself, from the very beginning of these parties, there was nothing I could find either to say or to listen to, and it was with difficulty I concealed my boredom.

That evening, I was wandering aimlessly from the drawing-room to the smoking-room, from the ante-chamber to the library, caught by a sentence here and there, observing very little but looking about me more or less vaguely.

Antoine, Etienne, and Godefroi were discussing the last vote in the Chamber, as they lolled on my wife's elegant armchairs. Hubert and Louis were carelessly turning over some fine etchings from my father's collection, entirely regardless of how they were creasing them. In the smoking-room, Mathias, the better to listen to Leonard, had put his red-hot cigar down on a rosewood table. A glass of curaçao had been spilled on the carpet. Albert was sprawling impudently on a sofa, with his muddy boots dirtying the cover. And the very dust of the air one breathed came from the horrible wear and tear of material objects. . . . A frantic desire seized me to send all my guests packing. Furniture, stuffs, prints, lost all their value for me at the first stain; things stained were things touched by disease, with the mark of death on them. I wanted to save them, to lock them up in a cupboard for my own use alone. How lucky Ménalque is, thought I, to have no possessions! The reason I suffer is that I want to preserve things. But after all, what does it really matter to me? . . .

There was a small, less brilliantly lighted drawing-room, partitioned off by a transparent glass door, and there Marceline was receiving some of her more intimate friends; she was half reclining on a pile of cushions and looked so fearfully pale and tired that I suddenly took fright and vowed that this reception should be the last. It was already late. I was beginning to take out my watch, when I suddenly felt Moktir's little scissors in my pocket.

Why did the little wretch steal them, thought I, if it was only to spoil and destroy them at once?

At that moment someone touched me on the shoulder; I turned quickly; it was Ménalque.

He was almost the only person in evening dress. He had just arrived. He asked me to present him to my wife; I should certainly not have done so of my own accord. Ménalque was distinguished-looking—almost handsome; his face was like a pirate's, barred by an enormous drooping mustache, already quite gray; his eyes shone with a cold flame that denoted courage and decision rather than kindness. He was no sooner standing before Marceline than I knew she had taken a dislike to him. After he had exchanged a few banal words of courtesy with her, I carried him off to the smoking-room.

I had heard that very morning of the new mission on which the Colonial Office was sending him; the newspapers, as they recalled his adventurous career, seemed to have forgotten their recent base insults and now could find no words fine enough to praise him with. Each was more eager than the other to extol and exaggerate his services to his country, to the whole of humanity, as if he never undertook anything but with a humanitarian purpose; and they quoted examples of his abnegation, his devotion, his courage, as if such encomiums might be considered a reward.

I began to congratulate him, but he interrupted me at the first words.

"What! You too, my dear Michel! But *you* didn't begin by insulting me," said he. "Leave all that nonsense to the papers. They seem to be surprised that a man with a certain reputation can still have any virtues at all. They establish distinctions and reserves which I cannot apply to myself, for I exist only as a whole; my only claim is to be natural, and the pleasure I feel in an action, I take as a sign that I ought to do it."

"That may lead far," I said.

"Indeed, I hope so," answered Ménalque. "If only the people we know could persuade themselves of the truth of this! But most of them believe that it is only by constraint they can get any good out of themselves, and so they live in a state of psychological distortion. It is his own self that each of them is most afraid of resembling. Each of them sets up a pattern and imitates it; he doesn't even choose the pattern he imitates; he accepts a pattern that has been chosen for him. And yet I verily believe there are other things to be read in man. But people don't dare to—they don't dare to turn the page. Laws of imitation! Laws of fear, I call them. The fear of finding oneself alone—that is what they suffer from—and so they don't find themselves at all. I detest such moral agoraphobia—the most odious cowardice, I call it. Why, one always has to be alone to invent anything—but they don't want to invent anything. The part in each of us that we feel is different from other people is just the part that is rare, the part that makes our special value—and that is the very thing people try to suppress. They go on imitating. And yet they think they love life."

I let Ménalque speak on; he was saying exactly what I myself had said the month before to Marceline; I ought to have approved him. For what reason, through what moral cowardice did I interrupt him and say, in imitation of Marceline, the very sentence word for word with which she had interrupted me then?

"But, my dear Ménalque, you can't expect each one of them to be different from all the others."

Ménalque stopped speaking abruptly, looked at me oddly and then, as at that very moment Eusèbe came up to take leave, he unceremoniously turned his back on me and went off to talk about some trifle or other to Hector.

The words were no sooner out of my mouth than I realized not only that they were stupid, but worse still, that they might have given Ménalque the impression that I thought his remarks had been pointed at me. It was late; my guests were leaving. When the drawing-room was nearly empty, Ménalque came back to me.

"I can't leave you like this," he said. "No doubt I misunderstood what you said. Let me at least hope so."

"No," I answered, "you did not misunderstand it . . . but it was senseless, and I had no sooner said it than I knew it was foolish. I was sorry, and especially sorry to think it would make you place me among the very people you were attacking and who, I assure you, are as odious to me as to you. I hate people of principle."

"Yes," answered Ménalque, laughing, "there is nothing more detestable in the world. It is impossible to expect any sort of sincerity from them; for they never do anything but what their principles have decreed they should do; or if they do, they think they have done wrong. At the mere suspicion you might be one of them, the words froze on my lips. I felt by my distress what a great affection I have for you; I hoped I was mistaken—not in my affection, but in the conclusion I had drawn."

"Yes, really; your conclusion was wrong."

"Oh! it was, I am sure," said he, suddenly taking my hand. "Listen a moment; I shall soon be going away, but I should like to see you again. My expedition this time will be a longer one and more risky than any of the others; I don't know when I shall come back. I must start in a fortnight's time; no one knows I am leaving so soon; I tell you so in confidence. I start at daybreak. The night before leaving is always a night of terrible heartache for me. Give me a proof that you are not a man of principle; may I count on it that you will spend that last night with me?"

"But we shall see each other again before then," I said, a little astonished.

"No; during the next fortnight I shall be at home to no one. I shall not even be in Paris. Tomorrow I leave for Budapest; in six days' time I must be in Rome. I have friends dotted here and there to whom I must say good-by before leaving. There is one expecting me in Madrid."

"Very well, then, I will pass your night of vigil with you."

"And we will have some Shiraz to drink," said Ménalque.

A few days after this party, Marceline began to feel less well. I have already said she was easily tired; but she did not complain, and as I attributed her fatigue to her condition, I thought it natural and felt no particular anxiety. A rather foolish—or rather ignorant—old doctor had at first been over-reassuring. Some fresh symptoms, however, accompanied by fever, decided me to send for Dr. Tr . . . , who was considered at that time the cleverest specialist in Paris for such cases. He expressed astonishment that I had not called him in sooner and prescribed a strict regime which she ought to have begun to follow some time ago. Marceline had been very courageous, but not very prudent, and had overtired herself. She was told she must now lie up till the date of her confinement, which was expected about the end of January. Feeling no doubt a little anxious and more unwell than she would admit, Marceline consented very meekly to the most tiresome orders. She had a moment's rebellion, however, when Tr . . . prescribed quinine in such heavy doses that she knew it might endanger the child. For three days she obstinately refused to take it; then as her fever increased, she was obliged to submit to that too; but this time it was with deep sadness and as if she were mournfully giving up all hope of the future; the resolution which had hitherto sustained her seemed broken down by a kind of religious resignation, and her condition grew suddenly worse in the days that followed.

I tended her with greater care than ever, did my best to reassure her, and repeated the very words Dr. Tr . . . had used, that he could see nothing very serious in her case; but her extreme anxiety ended by alarming me too. Alas! our happiness was already resting on the dangerous foundations of hope—and hope of what an uncertain future! I, who at first had taken pleasure only in the past, may have one day felt, thought I, the sudden and intoxicating sweetness of a fugitive moment, but the future disenchants the present even more than the present then disenchanted the past; and since our night at Sorrento my whole love, my whole life had been projected into the future.

In the meantime the evening I had promised Ménalque came round; and notwithstanding the reluctance I felt at abandoning Marceline for a whole winter's night, I got her, as best I could, to acknowledge the solemnity of the occasion and the gravity of my promise. Marceline was a little better that evening and yet I was anxious; a nurse took my place beside her. But as soon as I was in the street, my anxiety gained ground; I shook it off, struggled against it, was angry with myself for not being better able to get rid of it; thus I gradually reached a state of excessive tension, of singular excitement, both very unlike and very like the painful uneasiness from which it sprang, but liker still to happiness. It was late and I strode along rapidly; the snow began to fall in thick flakes; I was glad to be breathing a keener air, to be struggling with the cold; I was happy with the wind, the night, the snow against me; I rejoiced in my strength.

Ménalque had heard me coming and came out onto the landing to welcome me. He was waiting for me not without impatience. His face was pale and he looked overwrought. He helped me off with my overcoat and forced me to change my wet boots for some soft Persian slippers. Sweets and cakes were standing on a small table by the fire. There were two lamps, but the light in the room came chiefly from the fire on the hearth. Ménalque immediately inquired after Marceline; for the sake of simplicity I answered that she was very well.

"Are you expecting your child soon?" he went on.

"In a month."

Ménalque bent down toward the fire as if he wished to hide his face. He remained silent. He remained silent so long that at last I felt embarrassed, and as I myself could think of nothing to say either, I got up, took a few steps, and then went up to him and put my hand on his shoulder. Presently, as though he were pursuing his thoughts aloud:

"One must choose," he murmured. "The chief thing is to know what one wants. . . ."

"Don't you want to go?" I asked, in some uncertainty as to what he meant.

"It looks like it."

"Are you hesitating, then?"

"What is the use? You have a wife and child, so stay at home. . . . Of the thousand forms of life, each of us can know but one. It is madness to envy other people's happiness; one would not know what to do with it. Happiness won't come to one ready-made; it has to be made to measure. I am going away tomorrow; yes, I know; I have tried to cut out my happiness to fit me. . . . Keep your calm happiness of hearth and home. . . ."

"*I* cut out my happiness to fit me too," I said, "but I have grown; I am not at ease in my happiness now; sometimes I think it is strangling me. . . ."

"Pooh! You'll get accustomed to it!" said Ménalque. Then he planted himself in front of me and looked deep into my eyes; as I found nothing to say, he smiled rather sadly.

"One imagines one possesses and in reality one is possessed," he went on. "Pour yourself out a glass of Shiraz, dear Michel; you won't often taste it; and eat some of those rose-colored sweets which the Persians take with it. I shall drink with you this evening, forget that I am leaving tomorrow, and talk as if the night were long. . . . Do you know the reason why poetry and philosophy are nothing but dead-letter nowadays? It is because they have severed themselves from life. In Greece, ideas went hand in hand with life; so that the artist's life itself was already a poetic realization, the philosopher's life a putting into action of his philosophy; in this way, as both philosophy and poetry took part in life, instead of remaining unacquainted with each other, philosophy provided food for poetry, and poetry gave expression to philosophy—and the result was admirably persuasive. Nowadays beauty no longer acts; action no longer desires to be beautiful; and wisdom works in a sphere apart."

"But *you* live your wisdom," said I; "why do you not write your memoirs? Or simply," I added, seeing him smile, "recollections of your travels?"

"Because I do not want to recollect," he replied. "I should be afraid of preventing the future and of allowing the past to encroach on me. It is out of the utter forgetfulness of yesterday that I create every new hour's freshness. It is never enough for me to have been happy. I do not believe in dead things and cannot distinguish between being no more and never having been."

These words were too far in advance of my thoughts not to end by irritating me; I should have liked to hang back, to stop him; but I tried in vain to contradict, and besides I was more irritated with myself than with Ménalque. I remained silent therefore, while he, sometimes pacing up and down like a wild beast in a cage, sometimes stooping over the fire, kept up a long and moody silence, or again broke abruptly into words:

"If only our paltry minds," he said, "were able to embalm our memories! But memories keep badly. The most delicate fade and shrivel; the most voluptuous decay; the most delicious are the most dangerous in the end. The things one repents of were at first delicious."

Again a long silence; and then he went on:

"Regrets, remorse, repentance, are past joys seen from behind. I don't like looking backwards and I leave my past behind me as the bird leaves his shade to fly away. Oh, Michel! every joy is always awaiting us, but it must always be the only one; it insists on finding the bed empty and demands from us a widower's welcome. Oh, Michel! every joy is like the manna of the desert which corrupts from one day to the next; it is like the fountain of Ameles, whose waters, says Plato, could never be kept in any vase. . . . Let every moment carry away with it all that it brought."

Ménalque went on speaking for long; I cannot repeat all his words; but many of them were imprinted on my mind the more deeply, the more anxious I was to forget them; not that they taught me much that was new—but they suddenly laid bare my thoughts—thoughts I had shrouded in so many coverings that I had almost hoped to smother them.

And so the night of watching passed.

The next morning, after I had seen Ménalque into the train that carried him away, as I was walking home on my way back to Marceline, I felt horribly sad and full of hatred of his cynical joy; I wanted to believe it was a sham; I tried to deny it. I was angry with myself for not having found anything to say to him in reply; for having said words that might make him doubt my happiness, my love. And I clung to my doubtful happiness—my "calm happiness," as Ménalque had called it; I could not, it was true, banish uneasiness from it, but I assured myself that uneasiness was the very food of love. I imagined the future and saw my child smiling at me; for his sake I would strengthen my character, I would build it up anew. . . . Yes, I walked with a confident step.

Alas! when I got in that morning, I was struck by a sight of unaccustomed disorder. The nurse met me and told me guardedly that my

ANDRÉ GIDE

photograph by Philippe Halsman

RAYMOND CHANDLER

courtesy Houghton Mifflin Company

wife had been seized in the night with bad sickness and pains, though she did not think the term of her confinement was at hand; feeling very ill, she had sent for the doctor; he had arrived post-haste in the night and had not yet left the patient; then, seeing me change color, I suppose, she tried to reassure me, said that things were going much better now, that . . . I rushed to Marceline's room.

The room was darkened and at first I could make out nothing but the doctor, who signed to me to be quiet; then I saw a figure in the dark I did not know. Anxiously, noiselessly, I drew near the bed. Marceline's eyes were shut; she was so terribly pale that at first I thought she was dead; but she turned her head toward me, though without opening her eyes. The unknown figure was in a dark corner of the room, arranging, hiding, various objects; I saw shining instruments, cotton wool; I saw, I thought I saw a cloth stained with blood. . . . I felt I was tottering. I almost fell into the doctor's arms; he held me up. I understood; I was afraid of understanding. . . .

"The child?" I asked anxiously.

He shrugged his shoulders sadly. I lost all sense of what I was doing and flung myself sobbing against the bed. Oh! how suddenly the future had come upon me! The ground had given way abruptly beneath my feet; there was nothing there but an empty hole into which I stumbled headlong.

My recollections here are lost in dark confusion. Marceline, however, seemed at first to recover fairly quickly. The Christmas holidays allowed me a little respite and I was able to spend nearly the whole day with her. I read or wrote in her room, or read aloud to her quietly. I never went out without bringing her back flowers. I remembered the tenderness with which she had nursed me when I was ill, and surrounded her with so much love that sometimes she smiled as though it made her happy. Not a word was exchanged about the melancholy accident that had shattered our hopes. . . .

Then phlebitis declared itself; and when that got better, a clot of blood suddenly set her hovering between life and death. It was night time; I remember leaning over her, feeling my heart stop and go on again with hers. How many nights I watched by her bedside, my eyes obstinately fixed on her, hoping by the strength of my love to instill some of my own life into hers. I no longer thought much about happiness; my single melancholy pleasure was sometimes seeing Marceline smile.

My lectures had begun again. How did I find strength to prepare them, to deliver them? . . . My memory of this time is blurred; I have forgotten how the weeks passed. And yet there was a little incident I must tell you about.

It was one morning, a little after the embolism; I was sitting with Marceline; she seemed a little better, but she was still ordered to keep absolutely motionless; she was not allowed to move even her arms. I bent

over her to give her some drink, and after she had drunk, and as I was still
stooping over her, she begged me, in a voice made weaker still by her
emotion, to open a little box, which she showed me by the direction of
her glance; it was close by, on the table; I opened it and found it full of
ribbons, bits of lace, little ornaments of no value. . . . I wondered what she
wanted. I brought the box to her bedside and took out every object one
by one. Was it this? That? . . . No, not yet; and I felt her getting agitated.
"Oh, Marceline, is it this little rosary you want?"

She tried to smile.

"Are you afraid, then, that I shan't nurse you properly?"

"Oh, my dear," she murmured. And I remembered our conversation
at Biskra, and her timid reproaches when she heard me refuse what she
called "the help of God."

I went on a little roughly: "*I* got well alone all right."

"I prayed for you so much," she answered.

She said the words tenderly, sadly. There was something anxious and
imploring in her look. . . . I took the rosary and slipped it into her weak
hand as it lay on the sheet beside her. A tearful, love-laden glance rewarded me—but I could not answer it; I waited another moment or two,
feeling awkward and embarrassed; finally, not knowing what to do, I said
"Good-by" and left the room, with a feeling of hostility, and as though I
had been turned out of it.

Meanwhile the horrible clot had brought on serious trouble; after her
heart had escaped, it attacked her lungs, brought on congestion, impeded
her breathing, made it short and laborious. I thought she would never get
well. Disease had taken hold of Marceline, never again to leave her; it had
marked her, stained her. Henceforth she was a thing that had been
spoiled.

3

THE WEATHER WAS now becoming warmer. As soon as my lectures
were over, I took Marceline to La Morinière, the doctor having told me
that all immediate danger was past and that nothing would be more likely
to complete her cure than a change to purer air. I myself was in great
need of rest. The nights I had spent nursing her, almost entirely by
myself, the prolonged anxiety, and especially the kind of physical sympathy which had made me at the time of her attack feel the fearful throbbing of her heart in my own breast—all this had exhausted me as much as
if I myself had been ill.

I should have preferred to take Marceline to the mountains, but she
expressed the strongest desire to return to Normandy, declared that
no climate could be better for her, and reminded me that I must not

neglect the two farms of which I had rather rashly assumed the charge. She insisted that as I had made myself responsible for them, it was my business to make them succeed. No sooner had we arrived, therefore, than she urged me to visit the estate immediately. . . . I am not sure that her friendly insistence did not go with a good deal of abnegation; she was afraid, perhaps, that as she still required assistance, I might think myself bound to stay with her and not feel as free as I might wish to. . . . Marceline was better, however; the color had returned to her cheeks, and nothing gave me greater comfort than to feel her smile was less sad; I was able to leave her without uneasiness.

I went then to the farms. The first hay was being made. The scented air, heavy with pollen, at first went to my head like a strong drink. I felt that I had hardly breathed at all since last year, or breathed nothing but dust, so drowned was I in the honeyed sweetness of the atmosphere. The bank on which I seated myself in a kind of intoxication overlooked the house; I saw its blue roofs; I saw the still waters of the moat; all around were fields, some newly mown, others rich with grass; farther on, the curve of the brook; farther again, the woods where last autumn I had so often gone riding with Charles. A sound of singing, which I had been listening to for the last moment or two, drew near; it was the haymakers going home, with a fork or a rake on their shoulders. I recognized nearly all of them, and the unpleasant recollection came to me that I was not there as an enchanted traveler, but as their master. I went up to them, smiled, spoke to them, inquired after each of them in turn. Bocage that morning had already given me a report of the crops; he had indeed kept me regularly informed by letter of everything that went on in the farms. They were not doing so badly—much better than Bocage had led me to expect. But my arrival was being awaited in order to take some important decisions, and during the next few days I devoted myself to farm business to the best of my ability—not taking much pleasure in it, but hoping by this semblance of work to give some stability to my disintegrated life.

As soon as Marceline was well enough to receive visitors, a few friends came to stay with us. They were affectionate, quiet people, and Marceline liked their society, but it had the effect of making me leave the house with more pleasure than usual. I preferred the society of the farm hands; I felt that with them there was more to be learned—not that I questioned them—no; and I hardly know how to express the kind of rapture I felt when I was with them; I seemed to feel things with their senses rather than with my own—and while I knew what our friends were going to say before they opened their mouths, the mere sight of these poor fellows filled me with perpetual amazement.

If at first they appeared as condescending in their answers as I tried to avoid being in my questions, they soon became more tolerant of my presence. I came into closer contact with them. Not content with following them at their work, I wanted to see them at their play; their obtuse thoughts had little interest for me, but I shared their meals, listened to their jokes, fondly watched their pleasures. By a kind of sympathy similar to that which had made my heart throb at the throbs of Marceline's, their alien sensations immediately awoke the echo of my own—no vague echo, but a sharp and precise one. I felt my own arms grow stiff with the mower's stiffness; I was weary with his weariness; the mouthful of cider he drank quenched my thirst; I felt it slip down his throat; one day, one of them, while sharpening his scythe, cut his thumb badly; his pain hurt me to the bone.

And it seemed to me that it was no longer with my sight alone that I became aware of the landscape, but that I *felt* it as well by some sense of touch, which my curious power of sympathy illimitably enlarged.

Bocage's presence was now a nuisance to me; when he came I had to play the master, which I had no longer the least inclination to do. I still gave orders—I had to—still superintended the laborers; but I no longer went on horseback, for fear of looking down on them from too great a height. But notwithstanding the precautions I took to accustom them to my presence and prevent them from feeling ill at ease in it, in theirs I was still filled as before with an evil curiosity. There was a mystery about the existence of each one of them. I always felt that a part of their lives was concealed. What did they do when I was not there? I refused to believe that they had not better ways of amusing themselves. And I credited each of them with a secret which I pertinaciously tried to discover. I went about prowling, following, spying. For preference I fastened on the rudest and roughest among them, as if I expected to find a guiding light shine from their darkness.

One in particular attracted me; he was fairly good-looking, tall, not in the least stupid, but wholly guided by instinct, never acting but on the spur of the moment, blown hither and thither by every passing impulse. He did not belong to the place, and had been taken on by some chance. An excellent worker for two days—and on the third dead drunk. One night I crept furtively down to the barn to see him; he lay sprawling in a heavy, drunken sleep. I stayed looking at him a long time. . . . One fine day, he went as he had come. How much I should have liked to know along what roads! . . . I learned that same evening that Bocage had dismissed him.

I was furious with Bocage and sent for him.

"It seems you have dismissed Pierre," I began. "Will you kindly tell me why?"

He was a little taken aback by my anger, though I tried to moderate it.

"You didn't want to keep a dirty drunkard, did you, Sir? A fellow who led all our best men into mischief!"

"It's my business to know the men I want to keep, not yours."

"A regular waster! No one knew where he came from. It gave the place a bad name. . . . If he had set fire to the barn one night, you mightn't have been so pleased, Sir."

"That's my affair, I tell you. It's my farm, isn't it? I mean to manage it in my own way. In the future, be so good as to give me your reasons before dismissing people."

Bocage, as I have told you, had known me since my childhood. However wounding my tone, he was too much attached to me to be much offended. He did not, in fact, take me sufficiently seriously. The Normandy peasant is too often disinclined to believe anything of which he cannot fathom the motive—that is to say, anything not prompted by interest. Bocage simply considered this quarrel as a piece of absurdity.

I did not want, however, to break off the conversation on a note of blame; feeling I had been too sharp with him, I cast about for something pleasant to add.

"Isn't your son Charles coming back soon?" I ended by asking after a moment's silence.

"I thought you had quite forgotten him, Sir; you seemed to trouble your head about him so little," said Bocage, still rather hurt.

"Forget him, Bocage! How could I, after all we did together last year? I'm counting on him, in fact, to help me with the farms. . . ."

"You're very good, Sir. Charles is coming home in a week's time."

"Well, I'm glad to hear it, Bocage," and I dismissed him.

Bocage was not far wrong; I had not of course forgotten Charles, but I now cared very little about him. How can I explain that, after such vehement camaraderie, my feeling for him now should be so flat and spiritless? The fact is my occupations and tastes were no longer the same as last year. My two farms, I must admit, did not interest me so much as the people employed on them; and if I wanted to foregather with them, Charles would be very much in the way. He was far too reasonable and too respectable. So, notwithstanding the vivid and delightful memories I kept of him, I looked forward with some apprehension to his return.

He returned. Oh, how right I had been to be apprehensive—and how right Ménalque was to repudiate all memories! There entered the room in Charles's place an absurd individual with a bowler hat. Heavens! how changed he was! Embarrassed and constrained though I felt, I tried not to respond too frigidly to the joy he showed at seeing me again; but even his joy was disagreeable to me; it was awkward and, I thought, insincere. I received him in the drawing-room, and as it was late and dark, I could hardly distinguish his face; but when the lamp was brought in, I saw with disgust he had let his whiskers grow.

The conversation that evening was more or less dreary; then, as I knew he would be continually at the farms, I avoided going down to them for almost a week, and fell back on my studies and the society of my guests. And as soon as I began to go out again, I was absorbed by a totally new occupation.

Wood-cutters had invaded the woods. Every year a part of the timber on the estate was sold; the woods were marked off into twelve equal lots which were cut in rotation and every year furnished, besides a few fully grown trees, a certain amount of twelve-year-old copse wood for faggots.

This work was done in the winter, and the wood-cutters were obliged by contract to have the ground cleared before spring. But old Heurtevent, the timber-merchant who directed operations, was so slack that sometimes spring came upon the copses while the wood was still lying on the ground; fresh, delicate shoots could then be seen forcing their way upwards through the dead branches, and when at last the wood-cutters cleared the ground, it was not without destroying many of the young saplings.

That year old Heurtevent's remissness was even greater than we had looked for. In the absence of any other bidder, I had been obliged to let him have the copse wood exceedingly cheap; so that, being assured in any case of a handsome profit, he took very little pains to dispose of the timber which had cost him so little. And from week to week he put off the work with various excuses—a lack of laborers, or bad weather, or a sick horse, or an urgent call for work elsewhere, and so on—with the result that as late as the middle of summer, none of it had been removed.

The year before, this would have irritated me to the highest degree; this year it left me fairly calm; I saw well enough the damage Heurtevent was causing me; but the devastated woods were beautiful; it gave me pleasure to wander in them, tracking and watching the game, startling the snakes, and sometimes sitting by the hour on one of the fallen trunks which still seemed to be living on, with green shoots springing from its wounds.

Then suddenly, about the middle of the last fortnight in August, Heurtevent made up his mind to send his men. Six of them came with orders to finish the work in ten days. The part of the woods that had been cut was that bordering on La Valterie; it was arranged that the wood-cutters should have their food brought them from the farm, in order to expedite the work. The laborer chosen for this task was a curious young rascal called Bute; he had just come back from a term of military service which had utterly demoralized him; but physically he was in admirable condition; he was one of the farm hands I most enjoyed talking to. By this arrangement I was able to see him without going down to the farm. For it was just at that time that I began going out again. For a few days I hardly left the woods except for my meals at La Morinière, and I was very often late for them. I pretended I had to superintend the work, though in reality I only went to see the workers.

Sometimes two of Heurtevent's sons joined the batch of six men; one was about twenty, the other about fifteen years old, long-limbed, wiry, hard-featured young fellows. They had a foreign look about them, and I learned later that their mother was actually a Spanish woman. I was astonished at first that she should have traveled to such distant parts, but Heurtevent had been a rolling stone in his youth and had, it appears, married her in Spain. For this reason he was rather looked askance at in the neighborhood. The first time I saw the younger of the sons was, I remember, on a rainy day; he was alone, sitting on a very high cart, on the top of a great pile of faggots. He was lolling back among the branches, and singing, or rather shouting, a kind of extraordinary song, which was like nothing I had ever heard in our parts. The cart-horses knew the road and followed it without any guidance from him. I cannot tell you the effect this song had on me; for I had never heard its like except in Africa. . . . The boy looked excited—drunk; when I passed, he did not even glance at me. The next day, I learned he was a son of Heurtevent's. It was in order to see him, or rather in the hopes of seeing him, that I spent so much time in the copse. The men by now had very nearly finished clearing it. The young Heurtevents came only three times. They seemed proud, and I could not get a word out of them.

Bute, on the other hand, liked talking; I soon managed to make him understand that there was nothing it was not safe to say to me. Upon this, he let himself go and soon stripped the countryside of every rag of respectability. I lapped up his mysterious secrets with avidity. They surpassed my expectation and yet at the same time failed to satisfy me. Was this what was really grumbling below the surface of appearances or was it merely another kind of hypocrisy? No matter! I questioned Bute as I had questioned the uncouth chronicles of the Goths. Fumes of the abyss rose darkly from his stories, and as I breathed them uneasily and fearfully, my head began to turn. He told me, to begin with, that Heurtevent had relations with his daughter. I was afraid if I showed the slightest disapprobation I should put an end to his confidences; curiosity spurred me on.

"And the mother? Doesn't she object?"

"The mother! She has been dead full twelve years. . . . He used to beat her."

"How many are there in the family?"

"Five children. You've seen the eldest son and the youngest. There's another of sixteen who's delicate and wants to turn priest. And then the eldest daughter has already had two children by the father."

And little by little I learned a good deal more, so that, do what I would, my imagination began to circle round the lurid attractions of Heurtevent's house like a blow-fly round a putrid piece of meat. One night the eldest son had tried to rape a young servant girl, and as she struggled, the father had intervened to help his son and had held her with his huge hands; while the second son went piously on with his prayers on the floor above, and the youngest looked on at the drama as an amused spectator. As far as the rape is concerned, I imagine it was not very difficult, for Bute went on to say that not long after, the servant girl, having acquired a taste for this sort of thing, had tried to seduce the young priest.

"And hasn't she succeeded?" I asked.

"He hasn't given in so far, but he's a bit wobbly," answered Bute.

"Didn't you say there was another daughter?"

"Yes; she picks up as many fellows as she can lay hold of. And all for nothing too. When she's set on it, she wouldn't mind paying herself. But you mustn't carry on at her father's. He would give you what for. He says you can do as you like in your own house, but don't let other people come nosing round! Pierre, the farm hand you sent away, got a nasty knock on the head one night, though he held his tongue about it. Since then, she has her chaps in the home woods."

"Have you had a go yourself?" I asked with an encouraging look.

He dropped his eyes for form's sake and said, chuckling:

"Every now and then." Then, raising his eyes quickly, "So has old Bocage's boy," he added.

"What boy is that?"

"Alcide, the one who sleeps at the farm. Surely you know him, Sir?"

I was simply astounded to hear Bocage had another son.

"It is true," went on Bute, "that last year he was still at his uncle's. But it's very odd you've never met him in the woods, Sir; he poaches in them nearly every night."

Bute said these last words in a lower voice. He looked at me and I saw it was essential to smile. Then Bute seemed satisfied and went on:

"Good Lord, Sir, of course you know your woods are poached. They're so big it doesn't do much harm to anyone."

I looked so far from being displeased that Bute was emboldened to go on, and I think now he was glad to do Bocage an ill turn. He pointed out one or two hollows in the ground in which Alcide had set his snares, and then showed me a place in the hedge where I should be almost certain of catching him. It was a boundary hedge and ran along the top of a bank; there was a narrow opening in it through which Alcide was in the habit of coming about six o'clock in the evening. At this place Bute and I amused ourselves by stretching a copper wire, which we very neatly concealed. Then, having made me swear not to give him away, Bute departed.

For three evenings I waited in vain. I began to think Bute had played me a trick. . . . At last on the fourth evening I heard a light step approaching. My heart began to beat and I had a sudden revelation of the horrible allurement of the poacher's life. . . . The snare was so well set that Alcide walked straight into it. I saw him suddenly fall flat, with his ankle caught in the wire. He tried to save himself, fell down again, and began struggling like a trapped rabbit. But I had hold of him in an instant. He was a wicked-looking youngster, with green eyes, tow-colored hair, and a ferrety expression. He started kicking; then, as I held him so tight that he was unable to move, he tried to bite, and when that failed, he spat out the most extraordinary volley of abuse I have ever heard. In the end I could resist no longer and burst out laughing. At this, he stopped abruptly, looked at me, and went on in a lower tone.

"You brute, you! You've hurt me something horrible."

"Show me where."

He slipped his stocking down over his boot and showed me his ankle, where a slight pink mark was just visible.

"It's nothing at all."

He smiled a little; then, "I shall tell Father," he said in a cunning voice, "that it's *you* who set snares."

"Why, good heavens, it's one of your own!"

"Sure enough, you never set that one."

"Why do you say that?"

"You would never know how to set them as well as that. Just show me how you did it."

"Give me a lesson. . . ."

That evening I came in very late for dinner; no one knew where I was, and Marceline had been anxious. But I did not tell her I had set six snares and, so far from scolding Alcide, had given him ten sous.

The next evening when I went with him to visit the snares, much to my entertainment I found two rabbits caught in them. Of course I let him take them. The shooting season had not yet begun. I wondered what became of the game, as it was impossible to dispose of it openly without the risk of getting into trouble. Alcide refused to tell me. Finally I learned, through Bute again, that Heurtevent was the receiver and his youngest son the go-between between Alcide and him. Was this going to give me an opportunity of a deeper insight into the secrets of that mysterious, unapproachable family? With what passionate eagerness I set about poaching!

I met Alcide every evening; we caught great numbers of rabbits and once even a young roe-deer which still showed some faint signs of life; I cannot recall without horror the delight Alcide took in killing it. We put the deer in a place of safety from which young Heurtevent could take it away at night.

From that moment I no longer cared for going out in the day, when there was so little to attract me in the emptied woods. I even tried to work—melancholy, purposeless work, for I had resigned my temporary lectureship—thankless, dreary work, from which I would be suddenly distracted by the slightest song, the slightest sound coming from the country outside; in every passing cry I heard an invitation. How often I have leaped from my reading and run to the window to see—nothing pass by! How often I have hurried out of doors. . . . The only attention I found possible was that of my five senses.

But when night fell—and it was the season now when night falls early—that was our hour. I had never before guessed its beauty; and I stole out of doors as a thief steals in. I had trained my eyes to be like a night-bird's. I wondered to see the grass taller and more easily stirred, the trees denser. The dark gave everything fresh dimensions, made the ground look distant, lent every surface the quality of depth. The smoothest path looked dangerous. Everywhere one felt the awakening of creatures that lead a life of darkness.

"Where does your father think you are now?"

"In the stables looking after the cattle."

Alcide slept there, I knew, close to the pigeons and the hens; as he was locked in at night, he used to creep out by a hole in the roof. There still hung about his clothes a steamy odor of fowls.

Then, as soon as the game had been collected, he would disappear abruptly into the dark, as if down a trap-door—without a sign of farewell, without a word of tomorrow's rendezvous. I knew that before returning to the farm, where the dogs recognized him and kept silent, he used to meet the Heurtevent boy and deliver his goods. But where? Try as I might, I was never able to find out; threats, bribes, cunning—all failed; the Heurtevents remained inaccessible. I cannot say where my folly showed more triumphantly. Was it in this pursuit of a trivial mystery, which constantly eluded me—or had I even invented the mystery by the mere force of my curiosity? But what did Alcide do when he left me? Did he really sleep at the farm? Or did he simply make the farmer think so? My compromising myself was utterly useless; I merely succeeded in lessening his respect without increasing his confidence—and it both infuriated and distressed me.

After he had disappeared, I suddenly felt myself horribly alone; I went back across the fields, through the dew-drenched grass, my head reeling with darkness, with lawlessness, with anarchy; dripping, muddy, covered with leaves. In the distance there shone from the sleeping house, guiding me like a peaceful beacon, the lamp I had left alight in my study, where Marceline thought I was working, or the lamp of Marceline's own bedroom. I had persuaded her that I should not have been able to sleep without first going out in this way. It was true; I had taken a loathing to my bed. How greatly I should have preferred the barn!

Game was plentiful that year; rabbits, hares, pheasants succeeded each other. After three evenings, Bute, seeing that everything was going so well, took it into his head to join us.

On the sixth of our poaching expeditions, we found only two of the twelve snares we had set; somebody had made a clearance during the daytime. Bute asked me for five francs to buy some more copper wire, as ordinary wire was no use.

The next morning I had the gratification of seeing my ten snares at Bocage's house and I was obliged to compliment him on his zeal. What annoyed me most was that the year before I had foolishly offered fifty centimes for every snare that was brought in; I had therefore to give Bocage five francs. In the meantime Bute had bought some more wire with the five francs I had given him. Four days later, the same story! Ten fresh snares were brought in; another five francs to Bute; another five francs to Bocage. And as I congratulated him:

"It's not me you must congratulate, Sir, it's Alcide," he said.

"No, really?" said I. Too much astonishment might have given me away. I controlled myself.

"Yes," went on Bocage; "it can't be helped, Sir, I'm growing old.

The lad looks around the woods instead of me; he knows them very well;
he can tell better than I can where to look out for the snares."

"I'm sure he can, Bocage."

"So out of the fifty centimes you give me, I let him have twenty-
five."

"He certainly deserves it. What! Twenty snares in five days! Excellent work! The poachers had better be careful. I wager they'll lie low
now."

"Oh, no, Sir. The more one takes, the more one finds. Game is very
dear this year, and for the few sous it costs them . . ."

I had been so completely diddled that I felt almost inclined to suspect
old Bocage himself of having a hand in the game. And what specially
vexed me in the business was not so much Alcide's threefold traffic as his
deceitfulness. And then what did he and Bute do with the money? I
didn't know. I should never know anything about creatures like them.
They would always lie; they would go on deceiving me for the sake of
deceiving. That evening I gave Bute ten francs instead of five and warned
him it was for the last time, that if the snares were taken again, so much
the worse, but I should not go on.

The next day up came Bocage; he looked embarrassed—which at
once made me feel even more so. What had happened? Bocage told me
that Bute had been out all night and had only come in at cockcrow. The
fellow was as drunk as a fiddler; at Bocage's first words, he had grossly
insulted him and then flown at him and struck him. . . .

"And I've come to ask, Sir," said Bocage, "whether you authorize
me" (he accented the word a little), "whether you *authorize* me to
dismiss him?"

"I'll think about it, Bocage. I'm extremely sorry he should have been
disrespectful. I'll see. . . . Let me reflect a little, and come again in two
hours' time."

Bocage went out.

To keep Bute was to be painfully lacking in consideration for
Bocage; to dismiss Bute was to ask for trouble. Well! there was nothing
to be done about it. Let come what come might! I had only myself to
blame. . . . And as soon as Bocage came back:

"You can tell Bute we have no further use for him here," I said.

Then I waited. What would Bocage do? What would Bute say? It
was not till evening that I heard rumors of scandal. Bute had spoken. I
guessed it at first from the shrieks I heard coming from Bocage's house; it
was Alcide being beaten. Bocage would soon be coming up to see me;
here he was; I heard his old footstep approaching, and my heart beat even
faster than when I was poaching. It was an intolerable moment. I should
have to trot out a lot of fine sentiments. I should be obliged to take him
seriously. What could I invent to explain things? How badly I should act!
I would have given anything to throw up my part! Bocage came in. I
understood absolutely nothing of what he was saying. It was absurd; I

had to make him begin all over again. In the end, this is what I made out. He thought that Bute was the only guilty party; the inconceivable truth had escaped him—that I could have given Bute ten francs! What for? He was too much of a Normandy peasant to admit the possibility of such a thing. Bute must have stolen those ten francs. Not a doubt of it! When he said I had given them to him, he was merely adding a lie to a theft; it was a mere invention to explain away his theft; Bocage wasn't the man to believe a trumped-up story like that. . . . There was no more talk of poaching. If Bocage had beaten Alcide, it was only because the boy had spent the night out.

So, then, I am saved! In Bocage's eyes, at any rate, everything is all right. What a fool that fellow Bute is! This evening, I must say, I don't feel much inclined to go out poaching.

I thought that everything was all over, when an hour later in came Charles. He looked far from amiable; the bare sight of him was enough; he struck me as even more tedious than his father. To think that last year! . . .

"Well, Charles! I haven't seen you for ever so long!"

"If you had wanted to see me, Sir, you had only to come down to the farm. You won't find *me* gallivanting about the woods at night."

"Oh, your father has told you . . ."

"My father has told me nothing, because my father knows nothing. What's the use of telling him at his age that his master is making a fool of him?"

"Take care, Charles, you're going too far. . . ."

"Oh, all right! You're the master—you can do as you please."

"Charles, you know perfectly well I've made a fool of no one, and if I do as I please, it's because it does no one any harm but myself."

He shrugged his shoulders slightly.

"How can one defend your interests when you attack them yourself? You can't protect both the keeper and the poacher at the same time."

"Why not?"

"Because . . . Oh, you're a bit too clever for me, Sir. I just don't like to see my master joining up with rogues and undoing the work that other people do for him."

Charles spoke with more and more confidence as he went on. He held himself almost with dignity. I noticed he had cut off his whiskers. For that matter, what he said was sensible enough, and as I kept silence (what could I have said?), he went on:

"You taught me last year, Sir, that one has duties to one's possessions. One ought to take one's duties seriously and not play with them . . . or else one doesn't deserve to have possessions."

Silence.

"Is that all you have to say?"

"For this evening, yes, Sir; but if you ask me some other time, Sir, I may perhaps tell you that my father and I are leaving La Morinière."

And he went out, bowing very low. I hardly took time to reflect.

"Charles!" . . . He's right, by Jove! . . . Oh, if that's what's meant by possessions . . . "Charles!" And I ran after him, caught up with him in the dark and called out hastily, as if in a hurry to clinch my sudden determination:

"You can tell your father that I am putting La Morinière up for sale."

Charles bowed again gravely and went away without a word.

The whole thing is absurd! Absurd!

That evening Marceline was not able to come down to dinner and sent word to say she was unwell. Full of anxiety, I hurried up to her room. She reassured me quickly. "It's nothing but a cold," she said. She thought she had caught a chill.

"Couldn't you have put on something warmer?"

"I put my shawl on the first moment I felt a shiver."

"You should have put it on before you felt a shiver, not after."

She looked at me and tried to smile. . . . Oh, perhaps it was because the day had begun so badly that I felt so anguished. If she had said aloud: "Do you really care whether I live or not?" I should not have heard the words more clearly.

Oh, I thought, without a doubt, everything in my life is falling to pieces. Nothing that my hand grasps can my hand hold.

I sprang to Marceline and covered her pale face with kisses. At that, she broke down and fell sobbing on my shoulder. . . .

"Oh, Marceline! Marceline! Let us go away. Anywhere else but here I shall love you as I did at Sorrento. . . . You have thought me changed, perhaps? But anywhere else, you will feel that there is nothing altered in our love."

I had not cured her unhappiness, but how eagerly she clutched at hope! . . .

It was not late in the year, but the weather was cold and damp, and the last rosebuds were rotting unopened on the bushes. Our guests had long since left us. Marceline was not too unwell to see to the shutting up of the house, and five days later we left.

Third Part

AND SO I TRIED, yet once more, to close my hand over my love. But what did I want with peaceful happiness? What Marceline gave me, what she stood for in my eyes, was like rest to a man who is not tired. But as I felt she was weary and needed my love, I showered it upon her and pretended that the need was mine. I felt her sufferings unbearably; it was to cure her that I loved her.

O days and nights of passionate tender care! As others stimulate their faith by exaggerating the observance of its practices, so I fanned my love. And Marceline, as I tell you, began forthwith to recover hope. In her there was still so much youth; in me, she thought, so much promise.

We fled from Paris, as though for another honeymoon. But on the very first day of the journey, she got much worse, and we had to break it at Neuchâtel.

I loved this lake, which has nothing Alpine about it, with its gray-green shores, and its waters mingling for a long space, marsh-like, with the land, and filtering through the rushes. I found a very comfortable hotel, with a room looking onto the lake for Marceline. I stayed with her the whole day.

She was so far from well the next day that I sent for a doctor from Lausanne. He wanted to know, quite uselessly, whether there were any other cases of tuberculosis in my wife's family. I said there were, though, as a matter of fact, I knew of none; but I disliked saying that I myself had been almost given up on account of it, and that Marceline had never been ill before she nursed me. I put the whole thing down to the score of the clot, though the doctor declared that this was merely a contributory cause and that the trouble dated from further back. He strongly recommended the air of the high Alps, which he assured me would cure her; and as just what I myself wished was to spend the whole winter in the Engadine, we started as soon as she was able to bear the journey.

I remember every sensation of that journey as vividly as if they had been events. The weather was limpid and cold; we had taken our warmest furs with us. . . . At Coire, the incessant din in the hotel almost entirely prevented us from sleeping. I myself should have put up cheerfully with a sleepless night and not found it tiring; but Marceline . . . And it was not so much the noise that irritated me as the fact that she was not able to sleep in spite of it. Her need of sleep was so great! The next morning we started before daybreak; we had taken places in the coupé of the Coire diligence; the relays were so arranged that St. Moritz could be reached in one day.

Tiefenkasten, the Julier, Samaden . . . I remember it all, hour by hour; I remember the strange, inclement feeling of the air; the sound of the horses' bells; my hunger; the midday halt at the inn; the raw egg that I broke into my soup; the brown bread and the sour wine that was so cold. This coarse fare did not suit Marceline; she could eat hardly anything but a few dry biscuits, which I had had the forethought to bring with me. I can recall the closing in of the daylight; the swiftness with which the shade climbs up the wooded mountainside; then another halt. And now the air becomes keener, rawer. When the coach stops, we plunge into the heart of darkness, into a silence that is limpid—limpid—there is no other word for it. The quality, the sonority of the slightest sound acquire perfection and fullness in that strange transparency. Another start—in the night, this time. Marceline coughs . . . oh, will she never have done coughing? I think of the Sousse diligence; I feel as if I had coughed better than that. She makes too great an effort. . . . How weak and changed she looks! In the shadow there, I should hardly recognize her. How drawn her features are! Used those two black holes of her nostrils always to be so visible? . . . Oh, how horribly she is coughing! Is that the best she can do? I have a horror of sympathy. It is the lurking-place of every kind of contagion; one ought only to sympathize with the strong. Oh! she seems really at the last gasp. Shall we never arrive? What is she doing now? She takes her handkerchief out, puts it to her lips, turns aside . . . Horror! Is she going to spit blood too? I snatch the handkerchief roughly from her hand, and in the half-light of the lantern look at it. . . . Nothing. But my anxiety has been too visible. Marceline attempts a melancholy smile and murmurs:

"No; not yet."

At last we arrived. It was time, for she could hardly stand. I did not like the rooms that had been prepared for us; we spent the night in them, however, and changed them next day. Nothing seemed fine enough for me nor too expensive. And as the winter season had not yet begun, the vast hotel was almost empty and I was able to choose. I took two spacious rooms, bright, and simply furnished; there was a large sitting-room adjoining, with a big bow-window, from which could be seen the hideous blue lake and a crude mountain, whose name I have forgotten and whose slopes were either too wooded or too bare. We had our meals served separately. The rooms were extravagantly dear. But what do I care? I thought. It is true I no longer have my lectures, but I am selling La Morinière. And then we shall see. . . . Besides, what need have I of money? What need have I of all this? . . . I am strong now. . . . A complete change of fortune, I think, must be as instructive as a complete change of health. . . . Marceline, of course, requires luxury; she is weak . . . oh, for her sake I will spend so much, so much that . . . And I felt at one and the same time a horror of luxury and a craving for it. I bathed, I steeped my sensuality in it, and then again it was a vagabond joy that I longed for.

In the meanwhile Marceline was getting better and my constant care was having good results. As she had a difficulty in eating, I ordered the most dainty and delicious food to stimulate her appetite; we drank the best wines. The foreign brands we experimented on every day amused me so much that I persuaded myself she had a great fancy for them; sharp Rhine wines, almost syrupy Tokays that filled me with their heady virtue. I remember too an extraordinary Barba-grisca, of which only one bottle was left, so that I never knew whether the others would have had the same bizarre taste.

Every day we went for a drive, first in a carriage, and later on, when the snow had fallen, in a sledge, wrapped up to our eyes in fur. I came in with glowing cheeks, hungry and then sleepy. I had not, however, given up all idea of work, and every day I found an hour or so in which to meditate on the things I felt it was my duty to say. There was no question of history now; I had long since ceased to take any interest in historical studies except as a means of psychological investigation. I have told you how I had been attracted afresh to the past when I thought I could see in it a disquieting resemblance to the present; I had actually dared to think that by questioning the dead I should be able to extort from them some secret information about life. . . . But now if the youthful Athalaric himself had risen from the grave to speak to me, I should not have listened to him. How could the ancient past have answered my present question? . . . What can man do more? That is what seemed to me important to know. Is what man has hitherto said all that he *could* say? Is there nothing in himself he has overlooked? Can he do nothing but repeat himself? . . . And every day there grew stronger in me a confused consciousness of untouched treasures somewhere lying covered up, hidden, smothered by culture and decency and morality.

It seemed to me then that I had been born to make discoveries of a kind hitherto undreamed of; and I grew strangely and passionately eager in the pursuit of my dark and mysterious researches, for the sake of which, I well knew, the searcher must abjure and repudiate culture and decency and morality.

I soon went to the length of sympathizing only with the wildest outbreaks of conduct in other people, and of regretting that such manifestations were subject to any control whatever. I came very near thinking that honesty was merely the result of restrictions or conventions or fear. I should have liked to cherish it as something rare and difficult; but our manners had turned it into a form of mutual advantage and commonplace contract. In Switzerland it is just a part of one's comfort. I understood that Marceline required it; but I did not conceal from her the new trend of my thoughts; as early as Neuchâtel, when she was praising the honesty that is so visible in the faces of the people and the walls of the houses.

"I prefer my own," I retorted. "I have a horror of honest folk. I may have nothing to fear from them, but I have nothing to learn either. And besides, they have nothing to say. . . . Honest Swiss nation! What does their health do for them? They have neither crimes, nor history, nor literature, nor arts . . . a hardy rose-tree, without thorns or flowers."

That I should be bored by this honest country was a foregone conclusion, but at the end of two months my boredom became a kind of frenzy and my one thought was to fly.

We were in the middle of January. Marceline was better—much better; the continual low fever that was undermining her had disappeared; a brighter color had returned to her cheeks; she once more enjoyed walking, though not for long, and was not continually tired as she used to be. I did not have much difficulty in persuading her that the bracing air had done her all the good that could be expected and that the best thing for her now would be to go down into Italy, where the kindly warmth of spring would completely restore her . . . and above all, I had not much difficulty in persuading myself—so utterly sick was I of those mountain heights.

And yet now, when in my idleness the detested past once more asserts its strength, those are the very memories that haunt me. Swift sledge drives; joy of the dry and stinging air, spattering of the snow, appetite; walks in the baffling fog, curious sonority of voices, abrupt appearance of objects; readings in the snug warmth of the sitting-room, view of the landscape through the windows, view of the icy landscape; tragic waiting for the snow; vanishing of the outer world, soft brooding of one's thoughts. . . . Oh, to skate with her alone once more on the little lake, lying lost among the larches, pure and peaceful—oh, to come home with her once more at night! . . .

That descent into Italy gave me all the dizzy sensations of a fall. The weather was fine. As we dropped into a warmer and denser air, the rigid trees of the highlands—the larches and symmetrical fir-trees—gave way to the softness, the grace and ease of a luxuriant vegetation. I felt I was leaving abstraction for life, and though it was winter, I imagined per-fumes in every breath. Oh, for long—too long—our only smiles had been for shadows! My abstemiousness had gone to my head and I was drunk with thirst as others are with wine. My thrift of life had been admirable; on the threshold of this land of tolerance and promise, all my appetites broke out with sudden vehemence. I was full to bursting with an im-mense reserve of love; sometimes it surged from the obscure depths of my senses up into my head and turned my thoughts to shamelessness.

This illusion of spring did not last long. The sudden change of alti-tude may have deceived me for a moment, but as soon as we left the sheltered shores of the lakes, Bellagio and Como, where we lingered for a day or two, we came into winter and rain. We now suffered from the cold, which we had borne well enough in the Engadine; it was not dry and exhilarating here as it had been in the mountains, but damp and heavy, and Marceline began to cough again. In order to escape it, we pursued our way still farther south; we left Milan for Florence, Florence for Rome, Rome for Naples, which in the winter rain is really the most lugubrious town I know. I dragged along in unspeakable ennui. We went back to Rome in the hopes of finding, if not warmth, at least a semblance of comfort. We rented an apartment on the Pincio, much too vast, but marvelously situated. Already, at Florence, disgusted with hotels, we had rented a lovely villa on the Viale dei Colli, for three months. Anybody else would have wished to spend a lifetime in it. . . . We stayed barely three weeks. And yet at every fresh stage I made a point of arranging everything as if we were never going to leave. . . . Some irresistible demon goaded me on. . . . And add to this that we traveled with no fewer than eight trunks. There was one I never opened during the whole jour-ney, entirely filled with books.

I did not allow Marceline to have any say in our expenses or attempt to moderate them. I knew of course that they were excessive and that they could not last. I could no longer count on any money from La Morinière. It had ceased to bring in anything, and Bocage wrote that he could not find a purchaser. But all thoughts of the future ended only in making me spend the more. What need should I have of so much money, once I was alone, I thought; and sick at heart, I watched Marceline's frail life as it ebbed away more quickly still than my fortune.

Although she depended on me for all the arrangements, these perpetual and hurried moves tired her; but what tired her still more (I do not hesitate now to acknowledge it) was the fear of what was in my mind.

"I understand," she said to me one day, "I quite understand your doctrine—for now it has become a doctrine. A fine one, perhaps," and then she added sadly, dropping her voice: "but it does away with the weak."

"And so it should!" was the answer that burst from me in spite of myself.

In my heart then I felt the sensitive creature shiver and shrivel up at the shock of my dreadful words. . . . Oh, perhaps you will think I did not love Marceline. I swear I loved her passionately. She had never been—I had never thought her—so beautiful. Illness had refined—etherealized her features. I hardly ever left her, surrounded her with every care, watched over her every moment of the night and day. If she slept lightly, I trained myself to sleep more lightly still; I watched her as she fell asleep, and I was the first to wake. When sometimes I left her for an hour to take a solitary walk in the country or streets, a kind of loving anxiety, a fear of her feeling the time long, made me hurry back to her; and sometimes I rebelled against this obsession, called upon my will to help me against it, said to myself: "Are you worth no more than this, you make-believe great man?" And I forced myself to prolong my absence; but then I would come in, my arms laden with flowers, early garden flowers, or hothouse blooms. . . . Yes, I say; I cared for her tenderly. But how can I express this—that in proportion as I respected myself less, I revered her more? And who shall say how many passions and how many hostile thoughts may live together in the mind of man? . . .

The bad weather had long since ceased; the season was advancing; and suddenly the almond trees were in bloom. The day was the first of March. I went down in the morning to the Piazza di Spagna. The peasants had stripped the Campagna of its white branches, and the flower-sellers' baskets were full of almond blossom. I was so enchanted that I bought a whole grove of it. Three men carried it for me. I went home with all this flowering spring. The branches caught in the doorways, and petals snowed upon the carpet. I put the blossoms everywhere, filled all the vases, and, while Marceline was absent from the drawing-room for a moment, made it a bower of whiteness. I was already picturing her delight, when I heard her step . . . ! She opened the door. Oh, what was wrong with her? . . . She tottered. . . . She burst out sobbing.

"What is it, my poor Marceline?"

I ran up to her, showered the tenderest caresses upon her. Then and as if to excuse her tears:

"The flowers smell too strong," she said.

And it was a faint, faint, exquisite scent of honey. . . . Without a word, I seized the innocent fragile branches, broke them to pieces, carried them out of the room and flung them away, my temples throbbing with exasperation, my nerves ajar. Oh, if she finds this little bit of spring too much for her! . . .

I have often thought over those tears of hers and I believe now that she already felt herself condemned and was crying for the loss of other springs. . . . I think too that there are strong joys for the strong and weak joys for the weak who would be hurt by strong joys. She was sated by the merest trifle of pleasure; one shade brighter and it was more than she could bear. What she called happiness, I called rest, and I was unwilling, unable to rest.

Four days later we left again for Sorrento. I was disappointed not to find it warmer The whole country seemed shivering with cold. The wind, which never ceased blowing, was a severe trial to Marceline. Our plan was to go to the same hotel we had been to at the time of our first journey, and we were given the same room. . . . But how astonished we were to see that the gray sky had robbed the whole scene of its magic, and that the place we had thought so charming when we had walked in it as lovers was nothing but a dreary hotel garden!

We settled then to go by sea to Palermo, whose climate we had heard praised; we returned therefore to Naples, where we were to take the boat and where we stayed on for a few days longer. But at any rate, I was not dull at Naples. Naples is alive—a town that is not overshadowed by the past.

I spent nearly every moment of the day with Marceline. At night she was tired and went to bed early; I watched by her until she went to sleep and sometimes went to bed myself; then, when her more regular breathing told me she was asleep, I got up again noiselessly, dressed in the dark, slipped out of doors like a thief.

Out of doors! Oh, I could have shouted with joy! What was I bent on? I cannot tell. The sky, which had been dark all day, was cleared of its clouds; the moon was nearly full. I walked at random, without object, without desire, without constraint. I looked at everything with a fresh eye; I listened to every noise with an attentive ear; I breathed the dampness of the night; I touched things with my hand; I went prowling.

The last night we spent at Naples I stayed out later than usual on this vagabond debauch. When I came in, I found Marceline in tears. She had waked up suddenly, she said, and been frightened at not feeling me there. I calmed her, explained my absence as well as I could, and resolved not to leave her again. But the first night we spent at Palermo was too much for me—I went out. The orange-trees were in flower; the slightest breath of air came laden with their scent. . . .

We only stayed five days at Palermo; then, by a long detour, we made our way to Taormina, which we both wanted to see again. I think I have told you that the village is perched high on the mountainside; the station is on the seashore. The carriage that drove us to the hotel took me back again to the station for me to get our trunks. I stood up in the carriage in order to talk to the driver. He was a Sicilian boy from Catania, as beautiful as a line of Theocritus, full of color and odor and savor, like a fruit.

"*Com'è bella, la signora!*" said he, in a charming voice, as he watched Marceline go into the hotel.

"*Anche tu sei bello, ragazzo,*" I replied; then, as I was standing so near him, I could not resist, but drew him to me and kissed him. He allowed it laughingly.

"*I francesi sono tutti amanti,*" he said.

"*Ma non tutti gli italiani amati,*" I answered, laughing too. . . . I looked for him on the following days, but never succeeded in finding him.

We left Taormina for Syracuse. Step by step we went over the ground we had covered in our first journey, making our way back to the starting point of our love. And as during our first journey I had week by week progressed toward recovery, so week by week as we went southwards, Marceline's health grew worse.

By what aberration, what obstinate blindness, what deliberate folly did I persuade myself, did I above all try and persuade her that what she wanted was still more light and warmth? Why did I remind her of my convalescence at Biskra? . . . And yet the air had become warmer; the climate of Palermo is mild and pleasant; Marceline liked it. There, perhaps, she might have . . . But had I the power to choose what I should determine—to decide what I should desire? The state of the sea and the irregular boat-service delayed us a week at Syracuse. All the time I did not spend with Marceline I spent in the old port. O little port of Syracuse! Smells of sour wine, muddy alleys, stinking booths, where dockers and vagabonds and wine-bibbing sailors loaf and jostle! The society of the lowest dregs of humanity was delectable company to me. And what need had I to understand their language, when I felt it in my whole body? Even the brutality of their passion assumed in my eyes a hypocritical appearance of health and vigor. In vain I told myself that their wretched life could not have the same flavor for them that it had for me. . . . Oh, I wished I could have rolled under the table with them to wake up only with the first gray shiver of dawn. And their company whetted my growing horror of luxury, of comfort, of all the things I was wrapped round with, of the protection that my newly restored health had made unnecessary, of all the precautions one takes to preserve one's body from

the perilous contact of life. I imagined their existence in other surroundings. I should have liked to follow them elsewhere, to probe deeper into
their drunken life. . . . Then suddenly I thought of Marceline. What was
she doing at this very moment? Suffering, crying, perhaps. . . . I got up
hastily and hurried back to the hotel; there, over the door, seemed written
the words: No poor admitted here.

Marceline always received me in the same way, without a word of
reproach or suspicion, and struggling, in spite of everything, to smile. We
took our meals in private; I ordered for her the best our very second-rate
hotel could provide. And all through the meal I kept thinking: A piece of
bread, a bit of cheese, a head of fennel is enough for *them* and would be
enough for *me* too. And perhaps out there, close by, some of them are
hungry and have not even that wretched pittance. And here on my table
is enough to fill them for three days. . . . I should have liked to break
down the walls and let the guests flock in. For to feel there were people
suffering from hunger was dreadful. And I went back again to the port
and scattered about at random the small coins with which my pockets
were filled.

Poverty is a slave-driver; in return for food, men give their grudging
labor; all work that is not joyous is wretched, I thought, and I paid many
of them to rest. "Don't work," I said, "you hate it." In imagination, I
bestowed on each of them that leisure without which nothing can
blossom—neither vice nor art.

Marceline did not mistake my thoughts; when I came back from the
port, I did not conceal from her what sort of wretches I had been frequenting. Every kind of thing goes to the making of man. Marceline
knew well enough what I was trying so furiously to discover; and as I
reproached her for being too apt to credit everyone she knew with special virtues of her own invention, "You," said she, "are never satisfied
until you have made people exhibit some vice. Don't you understand that
by looking at any particular trait, we develop and exaggerate it? And that
we make a man become what we think him?"

I could have wished she were wrong, but I had to admit that the
worst instinct of every human being appeared to me the sincerest. But
then what did I mean by sincere?

We left Syracuse at last. I was haunted by the desire and the memory
of the past. At sea, Marceline's health improved. . . . I can still see the color
of the sea. It is so calm that the ship's track in it seems permanent. I can
still hear the noises of dripping and dropping water—liquid noises; the
swabbing of the deck and the slapping of the sailors' bare feet on the
boards. I can see Malta shining white in the sun—the approach to Tunis.
. . . How changed I am!

It was hot; it was fine; everything was glorious. Oh, how I wish that
every one of my sentences here could distill a quintessence of voluptuous
delight! . . . I cannot hope to tell my story now with more order than I
lived my life. I have been long enough trying to explain how I became

what I am. Oh, if only I could rid my mind of all this intolerable logic!
. . . I feel I have nothing in me that is not noble.

Tunis! The quality of the light here is not strength but abundance.
The shade is still full of it. The air itself is like a luminous fluid in which
everything is steeped; one bathes, one swims in it. This land of pleasure
satisfies desire without appeasing it, and desire is sharpened by satisfaction.

A land free from works of art; I despise those who cannot recognize
beauty until it has been transcribed and interpreted. The Arabs have this
admirable quality, that they live their art, sing it, dissipate it from day to
day; it is not fixed, not embalmed in any work. This is the cause and
effect of the absence of great artists. . . . I have always thought that great
artists were those who dared to confer the right of beauty on things so
natural that people say on seeing them: "Why did I never realize before
that that was beautiful too?"

At Kairouan, which I had not seen before, and which I visited without Marceline, the night was very fine. As I was going back to sleep at the
hotel, I remember a group of Arabs I had seen lying out of doors on mats,
outside a little café. I went and lay down to sleep beside them. I came
away covered with vermin.

Marceline found the damp of the coast very enfeebling, and I persuaded her that we ought to go on to Biskra as quickly as possible. We
were now at the beginning of April.

The journey to Biskra is a very long one. The first day we went to
Constantine without a break; the second day Marceline was very tired
and we only got as far as El Kantara. I remember seeking there, and
toward evening finding, shade that was more delicious and cool than
moonshine at night. It flowed about us like a stream of inexhaustible
refreshment. And from the bank where we were sitting we could see the
plain aflame in the setting sun. That night Marceline could not sleep,
disturbed as she was by the strange silence or the tiniest of noises. I was
afraid she was feverish. I heard her tossing in the night. Next morning I
thought she looked paler. We went on again.

Biskra! That then was my goal. . . . Yes; there are the public gardens;
the bench . . . I recognize the bench on which I used to sit in the first
days of my convalescence. What was it I read there? . . . Homer; I have
not opened the book since. There is the tree with the curious bark I got
up to go and feel. How weak I was then! Look! there come some children! . . . No; I recognize none of them. How grave Marceline is! She is
as changed as I. Why does she cough so in this fine weather? There is the
hotel! There are our rooms, our terrace! What is Marceline thinking? She
has not said a word. As soon as she gets to her room she lies down on the
bed; she is tired and says she wants to sleep a little. I go out.

I do not recognize the children, but the children recognize me. They
have heard of my arrival and come running to meet me. Can it really be
they? What a shock! What has happened? They have grown out of all
knowledge—hideously. In barely two years! It seems impossible. . . .

What fatigues, what vices, what sloth have put their ugly mark on faces that were once so bright with youth? What vile labors can so soon have stunted those beautiful young limbs? What a bankruptcy of hope! . . . I ask a few questions. Bachir is scullion in a café; Ashour is laboriously earning a few pennies by breaking stones on the roads; Hammatar has lost an eye. And who would believe it? Sadek has settled down! He helps an elder brother sell loaves in the market; he looks idiotic. Agib has set up as a butcher with his father; he is getting fat; he is ugly; he is rich; he refuses to speak to his low-class companions. . . . How stupid honorable careers make people! What! Am I going to find here the same things I hated so at home? Boubakir? Married. He is not fifteen yet. It is grotesque. Not altogether, though. When I see him that evening he explains that his marriage is a mere farce. He is, I expect, an utter waster; he has taken to drink and lost his looks. . . . So that is all that remains, is it? That is what life has made of them? My intolerable depression makes me feel it was largely to see them that I came here. Ménalque was right. Memory is an accursed invention.

And Moktir? Ah! Moktir has just come out of prison. He is lying low. The others will have nothing to do with him. I want to see him. He used to be the handsomest of them all. Is he to be a disappointment too? . . . Someone finds him out and brings him to me. No; Moktir has not failed. Even my memory had not painted him as superb as he now is. His strength, his beauty are flawless. . . . He smiles as he recognizes me.

"And what did you do before you went to prison?"

"Nothing."

"Did you steal?"

He protests.

"And what are you doing now?"

He smiles.

"Well, Moktir, if you have nothing to do, you must come with us to Touggourt." And I suddenly feel seized with a desire to go to Touggourt.

Marceline is not well; I do not know what is going on in her mind. When I go back to the hotel that evening, she presses up against me without saying a word and without opening her eyes. Her wide sleeve has slipped up and shows how thin she has grown. I take her in my arms, as if she were a sleepy child, and rock and soothe her. Is it love or anguish or fever that makes her tremble so? . . . Oh! perhaps there might still be time. . . . Will nothing make me stop? . . . I know now—I have found out at last what gives me my special value. It is a kind of stubborn perseverance in evil. But how do I bring myself to tell Marceline that next day we are to leave again for Touggourt? . . .

She is asleep now in the room next mine. The moon has been up some time and is flooding the terrace. The brightness is almost terrifying. There is no hiding from it. The floor of my room is tiled with white, and there the light is brightest. It streams through the wide-open window. I recognize the way it shines into the room and the shadow made by the door. Two years ago, it came in still farther. . . . Yes; it is almost at the same spot it had reached that night I got up because I could not sleep. . . . It was against that very door-jamb I leaned my shoulder. I recognize the stillness of the palm-trees. What was the sentence I read that night? . . . Oh, yes; Christ's words to Peter: "Now thou girdest thyself and goest where thou wouldest . . ." Where am I going? Where would I go? . . . I did not tell you that the last time I was at Naples, I went to Pæstum one day by myself. Oh, I could have wept at the sight of those ruined stones. The ancient beauty shone out from them, simple, perfect, smiling— deserted. Art is leaving me, I feel it. To make room for what else? The smiling harmony once mine is mine no longer. . . . No longer do I know what dark mysterious God I serve. O great new God! grant me the knowledge of other newer races, unimagined types of beauty.

The next morning at daybreak we left in the diligence, and Moktir came with us. Moktir was as happy as a king.

Chegga; Kefeldorh'; M'reyer . . . dreary stages of a still more dreary road—an interminable road. I confess I had expected these oases to be more smiling. But there is nothing here but stone and sand; at times a few shrubs with queer flowers; at times an attempt at palm-trees, watered by some hidden spring. . . . Now, to any oasis, I prefer the desert—land of mortal glory and intolerable splendor! Man's effort here seems ugly and miserable. All other lands now are weariness to me.

"You like what is inhuman," says Marceline.

But she herself, how greedily she looks!

Next day it was not so fine; that is, a wind sprang up and the horizon became dull and gray.

Marceline is suffering; the sand in the air burns and irritates her throat; the overabundance of light tires her eyes; the hostile landscape crushes her. But it is too late now to turn back. In a few hours we shall be at Touggourt.

It is this last part of the journey, though it is still so near me, that I remember least. I find it impossible to recall the scenery of the second day or what I did when we first got to Touggourt. But what I do still remember are my impatience and my haste.

It had been very cold that morning. Toward evening a burning simoon sprang up. Marceline, exhausted by the journey, went to bed as soon as we arrived. I had hoped to find a rather more comfortable hotel, but our room is hideous; the sand, the sun, the flies have tarnished, dirt-ied, discolored everything. As we have eaten scarcely anything since daybreak, I order a meal to be served at once; but Marceline finds every-thing uneatable and I cannot persuade her to touch a morsel. We have with us paraphernalia for making our own tea. I attend to this trifling business, and for dinner we content ourselves with a few biscuits and the tea, made with the brackish water of the country and tasting horrible in consequence.

By a last semblance of virtue, I stay with her till evening. And all of a sudden I feel that I myself have come to the end of my strength. O taste of ashes! O deadly lassitude! O the sadness of superhuman effort! I hardly dare look at her; I am too certain that my eyes, instead of seeking hers, will fasten horribly on the black holes of her nostrils; the suffering expression of her face is agonizing. Nor does she look at me either. I feel her anguish as if I could touch it. She coughs a great deal and then falls asleep. From time to time she is shaken by a sudden shudder.

Perhaps the night will be bad, and before it is too late I must find out where I can get help. I go out.

Outside the hotel, the Touggourt square, the streets, the very atmosphere, are so strange that I can hardly believe it is I who see them. After a little I go in again. Marceline is sleeping quietly. I need not have been so frightened; in this peculiar country, one suspects peril everywhere. Absurd! And more or less reassured, I again go out.

There is a strange nocturnal animation in the square—a silent flitting to and fro—a stealthy gliding of white burnouses. The wind at times tears off a shred of strange music and brings it from I know not where. Someone comes up to me. . . . Moktir! He was waiting for me, he says—expected me to come out again. He laughs. He knows Touggourt, comes here often, knows where to take me. I let myself be guided by him.

We walk along in the dark and go into a Moorish café; this is where the music came from. Some Arab women are dancing—if such a monotonous glide can be called dancing. One of them takes me by the hand; I follow her; she is Moktir's mistress; he comes too. . . . We all three go into the deep, narrow room where the only piece of furniture is a bed. . . . A very low bed on which we sit down. A white rabbit which has been shut up in the room is scared at first but afterwards grows tamer and comes to feed out of Moktir's hand. Coffee is brought. Then, while Moktir is playing with the rabbit, the woman draws me toward her, and I let myself go to her as one lets oneself sink into sleep. . . .

Oh, here I might deceive you or be silent—but what use can this story be to me if it ceases to be truthful?

I go back alone to the hotel, for Moktir remains behind in the café. It is late. A parching sirocco is blowing; the wind is laden with sand, and, in spite of the night, torrid. After three or four steps I am bathed in sweat; but I suddenly feel I must hurry and I reach the hotel almost at a run. She is awake perhaps. . . . Perhaps she wants me? . . . No; the window of her room is dark. I wait for a short lull in the wind before opening the door; I go into the room very softly in the dark. What is that noise? . . . I do not recognize her cough. . . . Is it really Marceline? . . . I light the light.

She is half sitting on the bed, one of her thin arms clutching the bars and supporting her in an upright position; her sheets, her hands, her nightdress are flooded with a stream of blood; her face is soiled with it; her eyes have grown hideously big; and no cry of agony could be more appalling than her silence Her face is bathed in sweat; I try to find a little place on it where I can put a horrible kiss; I feel the taste of her sweat on my lips. I wash and refresh her forehead and cheeks. . . . What is that hard thing I feel under my foot near the bed? I stoop down and pick up the little rosary that she once asked for in Paris and which she has dropped on the ground. I slip it over her open hand, but immediately she lowers her hand and drops the rosary again. . . . What am I to do? I wish I could get help. . . . Her hand clutches me desperately, holds me tight; oh, can she think I want to leave her? She says:

"Oh, you can wait a little longer, can't you?" Then, as she sees I want to say something,

"Don't speak," she adds; "everything is all right."

I pick up the rosary again and put it back on her hand, but again she lets it drop—yes, deliberately—lets it drop. I kneel down beside her, take her hand and press it to me.

She lets herself go, partly against the pillow, partly against my shoulder, seems to sleep a little but her eyes are still wide open.

An hour later she raises herself, disengages her hand from mine, clutches at her nightdress and tears the lace. She is choking.

Toward morning she has another hemorrhage. . . .

I have finished telling you my story. What more should I say?

The French cemetery at Touggourt is a hideous place, half devoured by the sand. . . . What little energy I had left I spent in carrying her away from that miserable spot. She rests at El Kantara, in the shade of a private garden she liked. It all happened barely three months ago. Those three months have put a distance of ten years between that time and this.

*   *   *

MICHEL REMAINED SILENT for a long time. We did not speak either, for we each of us had a strange feeling of uneasiness. We felt, alas, that by telling his story Michel had made his action more legitimate. Our not having known at what point to condemn it in the course of his long explanation seemed almost to make us his accomplices. We felt, as it were, involved. He finished his story without a quaver in his voice, without an inflection or a gesture to show that he was feeling any emotion whatever; he might have had a cynical pride in not appearing moved, or a kind of shyness that made him afraid of arousing emotion in us by his tears, or he might not in fact have been moved. Even now I cannot guess in what proportions pride, strength, reserve, and want of feeling were combined in him. After a pause he went on:

"What frightens me, I admit, is that I am still very young. It seems to me sometimes that my real life has not begun. Take me away from here and give me some reason for living. I have none left. I have freed myself. That may be. But what does it signify? This objectless liberty is a burden to me. It is not, believe me, that I am tired of my crime—if you choose to call it that—but I must prove to myself that I have not overstepped my rights.

"When you knew me first, I had great stability of thought, and I know that that is what makes real men. I have it no longer. But I think it is the fault of this climate. Nothing is more discouraging to thought than this persistent azure. Enjoyment here follows so closely upon desire that effort is impossible. Here, in the midst of splendor and death, I feel the presence of happiness too close, the yielding to it too uniform. In the middle of the day I go and lie down on my bed to while away the long dreary hours and their intolerable leisure.

"Look! I have here a number of white pebbles. I let them soak in the shade, then hold them in the hollow of my hand and wait until their soothing coolness is exhausted. Then I begin once more, changing the pebbles and putting back those that have lost their coolness to soak in the shade again. . . . Time passes and the evening comes on. . . . Take me away; I cannot move of myself. Something in my will is broken; I don't even know how I had the strength to leave El Kantara. Sometimes I am afraid that what I have suppressed will take vengeance on me. I should like to begin over again. I should like to get rid of the remains of my fortune; you see the walls here are still covered with it. . . . I live for next to nothing in this place. A half-caste innkeeper prepares what little food I need. The boy who ran away at your approach brings it to me in the evening and morning, in exchange for a few sous and a caress or two. He turns shy with strangers, but with me he is as affectionate and faithful as a dog. His sister is an Ouled-Naïl and in the winter goes back to Constantine to sell her body to the passers-by. She is very beautiful, and in the first weeks I sometimes allowed her to pass the night with me. But one morning her brother, little Ali, surprised us together. He showed great annoyance and refused to come back for five days. And yet he knows perfectly well how and on what his sister lives; he used to speak of it before without the slightest embarrassment. . . . Can he be jealous? Be that as it may, the little rascal has succeeded in his object; for, partly from distaste, partly because I was afraid of losing Ali, I have given the woman up since this incident. She has not taken offense; but every time I meet her, she laughs and declares that I prefer the boy to her. She makes out that it is he who keeps me here. Perhaps she is not altogether wrong. . . ."

Thomas Mann

DEATH IN VENICE

I

ON A SPRING AFTERNOON of the year 19—, when our continent lay under such threatening weather for whole months, Gustav Aschenbach, or von Aschenbach as his name read officially after his fiftieth birthday, had left his apartment on the Prinzregentenstrasse in Munich and had gone for a long walk. Overwrought by the trying and precarious work of the forenoon—which had demanded a maximum wariness, prudence, penetration, and rigor of the will—the writer had not been able even after the noon meal to break the impetus of the productive mechanism within him, that *motus animi continuus* which constitutes, according to Cicero, the foundation of eloquence; and he had not attained the healing sleep which—what with the increasing exhaustion of his strength —he needed in the middle of each day. So he had gone outdoors soon after tea, in the hopes that air and movement would restore him and prepare him for a profitable evening.

It was the beginning of May, and after cold, damp weeks a false midsummer had set in. The English Gardens, although the foliage was still fresh and sparse, were as pungent as in August, and in the parts nearer the city had been full of conveyances and promenaders. At the Aumeister, which he had reached by quieter and quieter paths, Aschenbach had surveyed for a short time the Wirtsgarten with its lively crowds and its border of cabs and carriages. From here, as the sun was sinking, he had started home, outside the park, across the open fields; and since he felt tired and a storm was threatening from the direction of Föhring, he waited at the North Cemetery for the tram which would take him directly back to the city.

It happened that he found no one in the station or its vicinity. There

Published 1925. Translated from the German by Kenneth Burke. Copyright 1924 by the Dial Publishing Company, Inc. Copyright 1925 by Alfred A. Knopf, Inc. Originally published as *Der Tod in Venedig*. Copyright 1913 by S. Fischer Verlag, Berlin.

was not a vehicle to be seen, either on the paved Ungererstrasse, with its solitary glistening rails stretching out toward Schwabing, or on the Föhringer Chaussee. Behind the fences of the stonemasons' establishments, where the crosses, memorial tablets, and monuments standing for sale formed a second, uninhabited burial ground, there was no sign of life; and opposite him the Byzantine structure of the Funeral Hall lay silent in the reflection of the departing day, its façade ornamented in luminous colors with Greek crosses and hieratic paintings, above which were displayed inscriptions symmetrically arranged in gold letters, and texts chosen to bear on the life beyond, such as "They enter into the dwelling of the Lord" or "The light of eternity shall shine upon them." And for some time, as he stood waiting, he found a grave diversion in spelling out the formulas and letting his mind's eye lose itself in their transparent mysticism, when, returning from his reveries, he noticed in the portico, above the two apocalyptic animals guarding the steps, a man whose somewhat unusual appearance gave his thoughts an entirely new direction.

Whether he had just now come out from the inside through the bronze door, or had approached and mounted from the outside unobserved, remained uncertain. Aschenbach, without applying himself especially to the matter, was inclined to believe the former. Of medium height, thin, smooth-shaven, and noticeably pug-nosed, the man belonged to the red-haired type and possessed the appropriate fresh milky complexion. Obviously, he was not of Bavarian extraction, since at least the white and straight-brimmed straw hat that covered his head gave his appearance the stamp of a foreigner, of someone who had come from a long distance. To be sure, he was wearing the customary knapsack strapped across his shoulders, and a belted suit of rough yellow wool; his left arm was resting on his thigh, and his gray storm cape was thrown across it. In his right hand he held a cane with an iron ferrule, which he had stuck diagonally into the ground, while, with his feet crossed, he was leaning his hip against the crook. His head was raised so that the Adam's apple protruded hard and bare on a scrawny neck emerging from a loose sport shirt. And he was staring sharply off into the distance, with colorless, red-lidded eyes between which stood two strong, vertical wrinkles peculiarly suited to his short, turned-up nose. Thus—and perhaps his elevated position helped to give the impression—his bearing had something majestic and commanding about it, something bold, or even savage. For whether he was grimacing because he was blinded by the setting sun, or whether it was a case of a permanent distortion of the physiognomy, his lips seemed too short, they were so completely pulled back from his teeth that these were exposed even to the gums, and stood out white and long.

It is quite possible that Aschenbach, in his half-distracted, half-inquisitive examination of the stranger, had been somewhat inconsiderate, for he suddenly became aware that his look was being answered, and indeed so militantly, so straight in the eye, so plainly with the intention of driving the thing through to the very end and compelling him to capitulate, that he turned away uncomfortably and began walking along by the fences, deciding casually that he would pay no further attention to the man. The next minute he had forgotten him. But perhaps the exotic element in the stranger's appearance had worked on his imagination; or a new physical or spiritual influence of some sort had come into play. He was quite astonished to note a peculiar inner expansion, a kind of roving unrest, a youthful longing after far-off places: a feeling so vivid, so new, or so long dormant and neglected, that, with his hands behind his back and his eyes on the ground, he came to a sudden stop, and examined into the nature and purport of this emotion.

It was the desire for travel, nothing more; although, to be sure, it had attacked him violently, and was heightened to a passion, even to the point of a hallucination. His yearnings crystallized; his imagination, still in ferment from his hours of work, actually pictured all the marvels and terrors of a manifold world which it was suddenly struggling to conceive. He saw a landscape, a tropical swampland under a heavy, murky sky, damp, luxuriant and enormous, a kind of prehistoric wilderness of islands, bogs, and arms of water, sluggish with mud; he saw, near him and in the distance, the hairy shafts of palms rising out of a rank lecherous thicket, out of places where the plant life was fat, swollen, and blossoming exorbitantly; he saw strangely misshapen trees lowering their roots into the ground, into stagnant pools with greenish reflections; and here, between floating flowers which were milk-white and large as dishes, birds of a strange nature, high-shouldered, with crooked bills, were standing in the muck, and looking motionlessly to one side; between dense, knotted stalks of bamboo he saw the glint from the eyes of a crouching tiger—and he felt his heart knocking with fear and with puzzling desires. Then the image disappeared; and with a shake of his head Aschenbach resumed his walk along past the fences of the stonemasons' establishments.

Since the time, at least, when he could command the means to enjoy the advantages of moving about the world as he pleased, he had considered traveling simply as a hygienic precaution which must be complied with now and then despite one's feelings and one's preferences. Too busy with the tasks arranged for him by his interest in his own ego and in the problems of Europe, too burdened with the onus of production, too little prone to diversion, and in no sense an amateur of the varied amusements of the great world, he had been thoroughly satisfied with such knowledge of the earth's surface as anyone can get without moving far out of his own circle; and he had never even been tempted to leave Europe. Especially now that his life was slowly on the decline, and that the artist's fear of not having finished—this uneasiness lest the clock run down before he had done his part and given himself completely—could no longer be waved aside as a mere whim, he had confined his outer existence almost exclusively to the beautiful city which had become his home and to the rough country house which he had built in the mountains and where he spent the rainy summers.

Further, this thing which had laid hold of him so belatedly, but with such suddenness, was very readily moderated and adjusted by the force of his reason and of a discipline which he had practiced since youth. He had intended carrying his life work forward to a certain point before removing to the country. And the thought of knocking about the world for months and neglecting his work during this time, seemed much too lax and contrary to his plans; it really could not be considered seriously. Yet he knew only too well what the reasons were for this unexpected temptation. It was the urge to escape—he admitted to himself—this yearning for the new and the remote, this appetite for freedom, for unburdening, for forgetfulness; it was a pressure away from his work, from the steady drudgery of a coldly passionate service. To be sure, he loved this work and almost loved the enervating battle that was fought daily between a proud tenacious will—so often tested—and this growing weariness which no one was to suspect and which must not betray itself in his productions by any sign of weakness or negligence. But it seemed wise not to draw the bow overtightly, and not to strangle by sheer obstinacy so strongly persistent an appetite. He thought of his work, thought of the place at which yesterday and now again today he had been forced to leave off, and which, it seemed, would yield neither to patience and coaxing nor to a definite attack. He examined it again, trying to break through or to circumvent the deadlock, but he gave up with a shudder of repugnance. There was no unusual difficulty here; what balked him was the scruples of aversion, which took the form of a fastidious insatiability. Even as a young man this insatiability had meant to him the very nature, the fullest essence, of talent; and for that reason he had restrained and chilled his emotions, since he was aware that they incline to content themselves with a happy approximate, a state of semi-completion. Were these enslaved emotions now taking their vengeance on him, by leaving him in the lurch, by refusing to forward and lubricate his art; and were they bearing off with them every enjoyment, every live interest in form and expression?

Not that he was producing anything bad; his years gave him at least this advantage, that he felt himself at all times in full and easy possession of his craftsmanship. But while the nation honored him for this, he himself was not content; and it seemed to him that his work lacked the marks of that fiery and fluctuating emotionalism which is an enormous thing in one's favor, and which, while it argues an enjoyment on the part of the author, also constitutes, more than any depth of content, the enjoyment of the amateur. He feared the summer in the country, alone in the little house with the maid who prepared his meals, and the servant who brought them to him. He feared the familiar view of the mountain peaks and the slopes which would stand about him in his boredom and his discontent. Consequently there was need of a break in some new direction. If the summer was to be endurable and productive, he must attempt something out of his usual orbit; he must relax, get a change of air, bring an element of freshness into the blood. To travel, then—that much was settled. Not far, not all the way to the tigers. But one night on the sleeper, and a rest of three or four weeks at some pleasant popular resort in the South. . . .

He thought this out while the noise of the electric tram came nearer along the Ungererstrasse; and as he boarded it, he decided to devote the evening to the study of maps and timetables. On the platform it occurred to him to look around for the man in the straw hat, his companion during that most significant time spent waiting at the station. But his whereabouts remained uncertain, as he was not to be seen either at the place where he was formerly standing, or anywhere else in the vicinity of the station, or on the car itself.

II

THE AUTHOR of that lucid and powerful prose epic built around the life of Frederick of Prussia; the tenacious artist who, after long application, wove rich, varied strands of human destiny together under one single predominating theme in the fictional tapestry known as *Maya;* the creator of that stark tale which is called *The Wretch* and which pointed out for an entire oncoming generation the possibility of some moral certainty beyond pure knowledge; finally, the writer (and this sums up briefly the works of his mature period) of the impassioned treatise on "Art and the Spirit," whose capacity for mustering facts, and, further, whose fluency in their presentation, led cautious judges to place this treatise alongside Schiller's conclusions on naïve and sentimental poetry —Gustav Aschenbach, then, was the son of a higher law official, and was born in L——, a leading city in the province of Silesia. His forebears had been officers, magistrates, government functionaries, men who had led severe, steady lives serving their king, their state. A deeper strain of spirituality had been manifest in them once, in the person of a preacher; the preceding generation had brought a brisker, more sensuous blood into the family through the author's mother, daughter of a Bohemian bandmaster. The traces of foreignness in his features came from her. A marriage of sober painstaking conscientiousness with impulses of a darker, more fiery nature had had an artist as its result, and this particular artist.

Since his whole nature was centered on acquiring a reputation, he showed himself, if not exactly precocious, at least (thanks to the firmness and pithiness of his personality, his accent) ripened and adjusted to the public at an early age. Almost as a schoolboy he had made a name for himself. Within ten years he had learned to face the world through the medium of his writing table, to discharge the obligations of his fame in a correspondence which (since many claims are pressed on the successful, the trustworthy) had to be brief as well as pleasant and to the point. At forty, wearied by the vicissitudes and the exertion of his own work, he

THOMAS MANN

photograph by Alfred A. Knopf

MAX BEERBOHM

Wide World Photos

had to manage a daily mail which bore the postmarks of countries in all parts of the world.

Equally removed from the banal and the eccentric, his talents were so constituted as to gain both the confidence of the general public and the stable admiration and sympathy of the critical. Thus even as a young man continually devoted to the pursuit of craftsmanship—and that of no ordinary kind—he had never known the careless freedom of youth. When, around thirty-five years of age, he had been taken ill in Vienna, one sharp observer said of him in company: "You see, Aschenbach has always lived like this," and the speaker contracted the fingers of his left hand into a fist; "never like this," and he let his open hand droop comfortably from the arm of his chair. That hit the mark; and the heroic, the ethical about it all was that he was not of a strong constitution, and though he was pledged by his nature to these steady efforts, he was not really born to them.

Considerations of ill health had kept him from attending school as a boy, and had compelled him to receive instruction at home. He had grown up alone, without comrades—and he was forced to realize soon enough that he belonged to a race which often lacked, not talent, but that physical substructure which talent relies on for its fullest fruition: a race accustomed to giving its best early, and seldom extending its faculties over the years. But his favorite phrase was "carrying through"; in his novel on Frederick he saw the pure apotheosis of this command, which struck him as the essential concept of the virtuous in action and passion. Also, he wished earnestly to grow old, since he had always maintained that the only artistry which can be called truly great, comprehensive— yes, even truly admirable—is that which is permitted to bear fruits characteristic of each stage in human development.

Since he must carry the responsibilities of his talent on frail shoulders, and wanted to go a long way, the primary requirement was discipline—and fortunately discipline was his direct inheritance from his father's side. By forty, fifty, or at an earlier age when others are still slashing about with enthusiasm, and are contentedly putting off to some later date the execution of plans on a large scale, he would start the day early, dashing cold water over his chest and back, and then, with a couple of tall wax candles in silver candlesticks at the head of his manuscript, he would pay out to his art, in two or three eager, scrupulous morning hours, the strength which he had accumulated in sleep. It was pardonable, indeed it was a direct tribute to the effectiveness of his moral scheme, that the uninitiated took his *Maya* world, and the massive epic machinery upon which the life of the hero Frederick was unrolled, as evidence of long breath and sustaining power. While actually they had been built up layer by layer, in small daily allotments, through hundreds and hundreds of single inspirations. And if they were so excellent in both composition and texture, it was solely because their creator had held out for years under the strain of one single work, with a steadiness of will and a tenacity comparable to that which conquered his native province; and because, finally, he had turned over his most vital and valuable hours to the problem of minute revision.

In order that a significant work of the mind may exert immediately some broad and deep effect, a secret relationship, or even conformity, must exist between the personal destiny of the author and the common destiny of his contemporaries. People do not know why they raise a work of art to fame. Far from being connoisseurs, they believe that they see in it hundreds of virtues which justify so much interest; but the true reason for their applause is an unconscious sympathy. Aschenbach had once stated quite plainly in some remote place that nearly everything great which comes into being does so in spite of something—in spite of sorrow or suffering, poverty, destitution, physical weakness, depravity, passion, or a thousand other handicaps. But that was not merely an observation; it was a discovery, the formula of his life and reputation, the key to his work. And what wonder, then, that it was also the distinguishing moral trait, the dominating gesture, of his most characteristic figures?

Years before, one shrewd analyst had written of the new hero type to which this author gave preference, and which kept turning up in variations of one sort or another: he called it the conception of "an intellectual and youthful masculinity" which "stands motionless, haughty, ashamed, with jaw set, while swords and spear points beset the body." That was beautiful and ingenious; and it was exact, although it may have seemed to suggest too much passivity. For to be poised against fatality, to meet adverse conditions gracefully, is more than simple endurance; it is an act of aggression, a positive triumph—and the figure of Sebastian is the most beautiful figure, if not of art as a whole, at least of the art of literature. Looking into this fictional world, one saw: a delicate self-mastery by which any inner deterioration, any biological decay was kept concealed from the eyes of the world; a crude, vicious sensuality capable of fanning its rising passions into pure flame, yes, even of mounting to dominance in the realm of beauty; a pallid weakness which draws from the glowing depths of the soul the strength to bow whole arrogant peoples before the foot of the cross, or before the feet of weakness itself; a charming manner maintained in his cold, strict service to form; a false, precarious mode of living, and the keenly enervating melancholy and artifice of the born deceiver—to observe such trials as this was enough to make one question whether there really was any heroism other than weakness. And, in any case, what heroism could be more in keeping with the times? Gustav Aschenbach was the one poet among the many workers on the verge of exhaustion: the over-burdened, the used-up, the clingers-on, in short all those moralists of production who, delicately built and destitute of means, can rely for a time at least on will power and the shrewd husbandry of their resources to secure the effects of greatness. There are many such: they are the heroes of the period. And they all found themselves in his work; here they were indeed, upheld, intensified, applauded; they were grateful to him, they acclaimed him.

In his time he had been young and raw; and, misled by his age, he had blundered in public. He had stumbled, had exposed himself; both in writing and in talk he had offended against caution and tact. But he had acquired the dignity which, as he insisted, is the innate goad and craving of every great talent; in fact, it could be said that his entire development had been a conscious undeviating progression away from the embarrassments of skepticism and irony, and toward dignity.

The general masses are satisfied by vigor and tangibility of treatment rather than by any close intellectual processes; but youth, with its passion for the absolute, can be arrested only by the problematical. And Aschenbach had been absolute, problematical, as only a youth could be. He had been a slave to the intellect, had played havoc with knowledge, had ground up his seed crops, had divulged secrets, had discredited talent, had betrayed art—yes, while his modelings were entertaining the faithful votaries, filling them with enthusiasm, making their lives more keen, this youthful artist was taking the breath away from the generation then in its twenties by his cynicisms on the questionable nature of art, and of artistry itself.

But it seems that nothing blunts the edge of a noble, robust mind more quickly and more thoroughly than the sharp and bitter corrosion of knowledge; and certainly the moody radicalism of the youth, no matter how conscientious, was shallow in comparison with his firm determination as an older man and a master to deny knowledge, to reject it, to pass it with raised head, insofar as it is capable of crippling, discouraging, or degrading to the slightest degree, our will, acts, feelings, or even passions. How else could the famous story *The Wretch* be understood than as an outburst of repugnance against the disreputable psychologism of the times: embodied in the figure of that soft and stupid half-clown who pilfers a destiny for himself by guiding his wife (from powerlessness, from lasciviousness, from ethical frailty) into the arms of an adolescent, and believes that he may through profundity commit vileness? The verbal pressure with which he here cast out the outcast announced the return from every moral skepticism, from all fellow-feeling with the engulfed: it was the counter-move to the laxity of the sympathetic principle that to understand all is to forgive all—and the thing that was here well begun, even nearly completed, was that "miracle of reborn ingenuousness" which was taken up a little later in one of the author's dialogues expressly and not without a certain discreet emphasis. Strange coincidences! Was it as a result of this rebirth, this new dignity and sternness, that his feeling for beauty—a discriminating purity, simplicity, and evenness of attack which henceforth gave his productions such an obvious, even such a deliberate stamp of mastery and classicism—showed an almost excessive strengthening about this time? But ethical resoluteness in the exclusion of science, of emancipatory and restrictive knowledge—does this not in turn signify a simplification, a reduction morally of the world to too limited terms, and thus also a strengthened capacity for the forbidden, the evil, the morally impossible? And does not form have two aspects? Is it not moral and unmoral at once—moral in that it is the result and expression of discipline, but unmoral, and even immoral, in that by nature it contains an indifference to morality, is calculated, in fact, to make morality bend beneath its proud and unencumbered scepter?

Be that as it may. An evolution is a destiny; and why should his evolution, which had been upheld by the general confidence of a vast public, not run through a different course from one accomplished outside the luster and the entanglements of fame? Only chronic vagabondage will find it tedious and be inclined to scoff when a great talent outgrows the libertine chrysalis stage, learns to seize upon and express the dignity of the mind, and superimposes a formal etiquette upon a solitude which had been filled with unchastened and rigidly isolated sufferings and struggles and had brought all this to a point of power and honor among men. Further, how much sport, defiance, indulgence there is in the self-formation of a talent! Gradually something official, didactic, crept into Gustav Aschenbach's productions, his style in later life fought shy of any abruptness and boldness, any subtle and unexpected contrasts; he inclined toward the fixed and standardized, the conventionally elegant, the conservative, the formal, the formulated, nearly. And, as is traditionally said of Louis XIV, with the advancing years he came to omit every common word from his vocabulary. At about this time it happened that the educational authorities included selected pages by him in their prescribed school readers. This was deeply sympathetic to his nature, and he did not decline when a German prince who had just mounted the throne raised the author of the "Frederick" to knighthood on the occasion of his fiftieth birthday. After a few years of unrest, a few tentative stopping places here and there, he soon chose Munich as his permanent home, and lived there in a state of middle-class respectability such as fits in with the life of the mind in certain individual instances. The marriage which, when still young, he had contracted with a girl of an educated family came to an end with her death after a short period of happiness. He was left with a daughter, now married. He had never had a son.

Gustav von Aschenbach was somewhat below average height, dark, and smooth-shaven. His head seemed a bit too large in comparison with his almost dapper figure. His hair was brushed straight back, thinning out toward the crown, but very full about the temples, and strongly marked with gray; it framed a high, ridged forehead. Gold spectacles with rimless lenses cut into the bridge of his bold, heavy nose. The mouth was big, sometimes drooping, sometimes suddenly pinched and firm. His cheeks were thin and wrinkled, his well-formed chin had a slight cleft. This head, usually bent patiently to one side, seemed to have gone through momentous experiences, and yet it was his art which had produced those effects in his face, effects which are elsewhere the result of hard and agitated living. Behind this brow the brilliant repartee of the dialogue on war between Voltaire and the king had been born; these eyes, peering steadily and wearily from behind their glasses, had seen the bloody inferno of the lazaret in the Seven Years' War. Even as it applies to the individual, art is a heightened mode of existence. It gives deeper pleasures, it consumes more quickly. It carves into its servants' faces the marks of imaginary and spiritual adventures, and though their external activities may be as quiet as a cloister, it produces a lasting voluptuousness, overrefinement, fatigue, and curiosity of the nerves such as can barely result from a life filled with illicit passions and enjoyments.

III

VARIOUS MATTERS of a literary and social nature delayed his departure until about two weeks after that walk in Munich. Finally he gave orders to have his country house ready for occupancy within a month; and one day between the middle and the end of May he took the night train for Trieste, where he made a stopover of only twenty-four hours, and embarked the following morning for Pola.

What he was hunting was something foreign and unrelated to himself which would at the same time be quickly within reach; and so he stopped at an island in the Adriatic which had become well known in recent years. It lay not far off the Istrian coast, with beautifully rugged cliffs fronting the open sea, and natives who dressed in variegated tatters and made strange sounds when they spoke. But rain and a heavy atmosphere, a provincial and exclusively Austrian patronage at the hotel, and the lack of that restfully intimate association with the sea which can be gotten only by a soft, sandy beach, irritated him, and prevented him from feeling that he had found the place he was looking for. Something within was disturbing him, and drawing him he was not sure where. He studied sailing dates, he looked about him questioningly, and of a sudden, as a thing both astounding and self-evident, his goal was before him. If you wanted to reach overnight the unique, the fabulously different, where did you go? But that was plain. What was he doing here? He had lost the trail. He had wanted to go there. He did not delay in giving notice of his mistake in stopping here. In the early morning mist, a week and a half after his arrival on the island, a fast motorboat was carrying him and his luggage back over the water to the naval port, and he landed there just long enough to cross the gangplank to the damp deck of a ship which was lying under steam ready for the voyage to Venice.

It was an old hulk flying the Italian flag, decrepit, sooty, and mournful. In a cavelike, artificially lighted inside cabin where Aschenbach, immediately upon boarding the ship, was conducted by a dirty hunchbacked sailor, who smirked politely, there was sitting behind a table, his hat cocked over his forehead and a cigarette stump in the corner of his mouth, a man with a goatee, and with the face of an old-style circus director, who was taking down the particulars of the passengers with professional grimaces and distributing the tickets. "To Venice!" He repeated Aschenbach's request, as he extended his arm and plunged his pen into the pasty dregs of a precariously tilted inkwell. "To Venice, first class! At your service, sir." And he wrote a generous scrawl, sprinkled it with blue sand out of a box, let the sand run off into a clay bowl, folded the paper with sallow, bony fingers, and began writing again. "A happily chosen destination!" he chatted on. "Ah, Venice! A splendid city! A city of irresistible attractiveness for the educated on account of its history as well as its present-day charms." The smooth rapidity of his movements and the empty words accompanying them had something anaesthetic and reassuring about them, much as though he feared lest the traveler might still be vacillating in his decision to go to Venice. He handled the cash briskly, and let the change fall on the spotted table cover with the skill of a croupier. "A pleasant journey, sir!" he said with a theatrical bow. "Gentlemen, I have the honor of serving you!" he called out immediately after, with his arm upraised, and he acted as if business were in full swing, although no one else was there to require his attention. Aschenbach returned to the deck.

With one arm on the railing, he watched the passengers on board and the idlers who loitered around the dock waiting for the ship to sail. The second-class passengers, men and women, were huddled together on the foredeck, using boxes and bundles as seats. A group of young people made up the travelers on the first deck, clerks from Pola, it seemed, who had gathered in the greatest excitement for an excursion to Italy. They made a considerable fuss about themselves and their enterprise, chattered, laughed, enjoyed their own antics self-contentedly, and, leaning over the hand rails, shouted flippantly and mockingly at their comrades who, with portfolios under their arms, were going up and down the waterfront on business and kept threatening the picnickers with their canes. One, in a bright yellow summer suit of ultra-fashionable cut, with a red necktie, and a rakishly tilted Panama, surpassed all the others in his crowning good humor. But as soon as Aschenbach looked at him a bit more carefully, he discovered with a kind of horror that the youth was a cheat. He was old, that was unquestionable. There were wrinkles around his eyes and mouth. The faint crimson of the cheeks was paint, the hair under his brilliantly decorated straw hat was a wig; his neck was hollow and stringy, his turned-up mustache and the imperial on his chin were dyed; the full set of yellow teeth which he displayed when he laughed, a cheap artificial plate; and his hands, with signet rings on both index fingers, were those of an old man. Fascinated with loathing, Aschenbach watched him in his intercourse with his friends. Did they not know, did they not observe that he was old, that he was not entitled to wear their bright, foppish clothing, that he was not entitled to play at being one of them? Unquestioningly, and as quite the usual thing, it seemed, they allowed him among them, treating him as one of their own kind and returning his jovial nudges in the ribs without repugnance. How could that be? Aschenbach laid his hand on his forehead and closed his eyes; they were hot, since he had had too little sleep. He felt as though everything were not quite the same as usual, as though some dreamlike estrangement, some peculiar distortion of the world, were beginning to take possession of him, and perhaps this could be stopped if he hid his face for a time and then looked around him again. Yet at this moment he felt as though he were swimming; and, looking up with an unreasoned fear, he discovered that the heavy, lugubrious body of the ship was separating slowly from the walled bank. Inch by inch, with the driving and reversing of the engine, the strip of dirty glistening water widened between the dock and the side of the ship; and, after cumbersome maneuvering, the steamer finally turned its nose toward the open sea. Aschenbach crossed to the starboard side, where the hunchback had set up a deck chair for him, and a steward in a spotted dress coat asked after his wants.

The sky was gray, the wind damp. Harbor and islands had been left behind, and soon all land was lost in the haze. Flakes of coal dust, bloated with moisture, fell over the washed deck, which would not dry. After the first hour an awning was spread, since it had begun to rain.

Bundled up in his coat, a book in his lap, the traveler rested, and the hours passed unnoticed. It stopped raining; the canvas awning was removed. The horizon was unbroken. The sea, empty, like an enormous disk, lay stretched under the curve of the sky. But in empty inarticulate space our senses lose also the dimensions of time, and we slip into the incommensurate. As he rested, strange shadowy figures, the old dandy, the goatee from the inside cabin, passed through his mind, with vague gestures, muddled dream words—and he was asleep.

About noon he was called to a meal down in the corridorlike dining hall into which the doors opened from the sleeping cabins; he ate near the head of a long table, at the other end of which the clerks, including the old man, had been drinking with the boisterous captain since ten o'clock. The food was poor, and he finished rapidly. He felt driven outside to look at the sky, to see if it showed signs of being brighter above Venice.

He had kept thinking that this had to occur, since the city had always received him in full blaze. But sky and sea remained dreary and leaden, at times a misty rain fell, and here he was reaching by water a different Venice than he had ever found when approaching on land. He stood by the forestays, looking in the distance, waiting for land. He thought of the heavy-hearted, enthusiastic poet for whom the domes and bell towers of his dreams had once risen out of these waters; he relived in silence some of that reverence, happiness, and sorrow which had been turned then into cautious song; and easily susceptible to sensations already molded, he asked himself wearily and earnestly whether some new enchantment and distraction, some belated adventure of the emotions, might still be held in store for this idle traveler.

Then the flat coast emerged on the right; the sea was alive with fishing smacks; the bathers' island appeared; it dropped behind to the left, the steamer slowly entered the narrow port which is named after it; and on the lagoon, facing gay ramshackle houses, it stopped completely, since it had to wait for the barque of the health department.

An hour passed before it appeared. He had arrived, and yet he had not; no one was in any hurry, no one was driven by impatience. The young men from Pola, patriotically attracted by the military bugle calls which rang over the water from the vicinity of the public gardens, had come on deck and, warmed by their Asti, they burst out with cheers for the drilling *bersaglieri*. But it was repulsive to see what a state the primped-up old man had been brought to by his comradeship with youth. His old head was not able to resist its wine like the young and robust: he was painfully drunk. With glazed eyes, a cigarette between his trembling fingers, he stood in one place, swaying backward and forward from giddiness, and balancing himself laboriously. Since he would have fallen at the first step, he did not trust himself from the spot—yet he showed a deplorable insolence, buttonholed everyone who came near him, stammered, winked and tittered, lifted his wrinkled, ornamented index finger in a stupid attempt at bantering, while he licked the corners of his mouth with his tongue in the most abominably suggestive manner. Aschenbach observed him darkly, and a feeling of numbness came over him again, as though the world were displaying a faint but irresistible tendency to distort itself into the peculiar and the grotesque: a feeling which circumstances prevented him from surrendering himself to completely, for just then the pounding activity of the engines commenced again, and the ship, resuming a voyage which had been interrupted so near its completion, passed through the San Marco canal.

So he saw it again, the most remarkable of landing places, that blinding composition of fantastic buildings which the Republic lays out before the eyes of approaching seafarers: the soft splendor of the palace, the Bridge of Sighs, on the bank the columns with lion and saint, the advancing, showy flank of the enchanted temple, the glimpse through to the archway, and the giant clock. And as he looked on he thought that to reach Venice by land, on the railroad, was like entering a palace from the rear, and that this most unreal of cities should not be approached except as he was now doing, by ship, over the high seas.

The engine stopped, gondolas pressed in, the gangway was let down, customs officials climbed on board and discharged their duties perfunctorily; the disembarking could begin. Aschenbach made it understood that he wanted a gondola to take him and his luggage to the dock of those little steamers which ply between the city and the Lido, since he intended to locate near the sea. His plans were complied with, his wants were shouted down to the water, where the gondoliers were wrangling with one another in dialect. He was still hindered from descending; he was hindered by his trunk, which was being pulled and dragged with difficulty down the ladderlike steps—so that for some minutes he was not able to avoid the importunities of the atrocious old man, whose drunkenness gave him a sinister desire to do the foreigner parting honors. "We wish you a very agreeable visit," he bleated as he made an awkward bow. "We leave with pleasant recollections! *Au revoir, excusez, et bon jour,* Your Excellency!" His mouth watered, he pressed his eyes shut, he licked the corners of his mouth, and the dyed imperial turned up about his senile lips. "Our compliments," he mumbled, with two fingertips on his mouth, "our compliments to our sweetheart, the dearest prettiest sweetheart . . ." And suddenly his false upper teeth fell down on his lower lip. Aschenbach was able to escape. "To our sweetheart, our handsome sweetheart," he heard the cooing, hollow, stuttering voice behind him while, supporting himself against the hand rail, he went down the gangway.

Who would not have to suppress a fleeing shudder, a vague timidity and uneasiness, if it were a matter of boarding a Venetian gondola for the first time or after several years? The strange craft, an entirely unaltered survival from the times of balladry, with that peculiar blackness which is found elsewhere only in coffins—it suggests silent, criminal adventures in the rippling night, it suggests even more strongly death itself, the bier and the mournful funeral, and the last silent journey. And has it been observed that the seat of such a barque, this armchair of coffin-black veneer and dull black upholstery, is the softest, most luxuriant, most lulling seat in the world? Aschenbach noted this when he had relaxed at the feet of the gondolier, opposite his luggage, which lay neatly assembled on the prow. The rowers were still wrangling, harshly, incomprehensibly, with threatening gestures. But the strange silence of this canal city seemed to soften their voices, to disembody them, and dissipate them over the water. It was warm here in the harbor. Touched faintly by the warm breeze of the sirocco, leaning back against the limber portions of the cushions, the traveler closed his eyes in the enjoyment of a lassitude which was as unusual with him as it was sweet. The trip would be short, he thought; if only it went on forever! He felt himself glide with a gentle motion away from the crowd and the confusion of voices.

It became quieter and quieter around him! There was nothing to be heard but the splashing of the oar, the hollow slapping of the waves against the prow of the boat as it stood above the water black and bold and armed with its halberdlike tip, and a third sound, of speaking, of whispering—the whispering of the gondolier, who was talking to himself between his teeth, fitfully, in words that were pressed out by the exertion of his arms. Aschenbach looked up, and was slightly astonished to discover that the lagoon was widening, and he was headed for the open sea. This seemed to indicate that he ought not to rest too much, but should see to it that his wishes were carried out.

"To the steamer dock!" he repeated, turning around completely and looking into the face of the gondolier who stood behind on a raised platform and towered up between him and the dun-colored sky. He was a man of unpleasant, even brutal appearance, dressed in sailor blue, with a yellow sash; a formless straw hat, its weave partially unraveled, was tilted insolently on his head. The set of his face, the blond curly mustache beneath a curtly turned-up nose, undoubtedly meant that he was not Italian. Although of somewhat frail build, so that one would not have thought him especially well suited to his trade, he handled the oar with great energy, throwing his entire body into each stroke. Occasionally he drew back his lips from the exertion, and disclosed his white teeth. Wrinkling his reddish brows, he gazed on past his passenger, as he answered deliberately, almost gruffly: "You are going to the Lido." Aschenbach replied: "Of course. But I have just taken the gondola to get me across to San Marco. I want to use the *vaporetto*."

"You cannot use the *vaporetto*, sir."

"And why not?"

"Because the *vaporetto* will not haul luggage."

That was so; Aschenbach remembered. He was silent. But the fellow's harsh, presumptuous manner, so unusual toward a foreigner here, seemed unbearable. He said: "That is my affair. Perhaps I want to put my things in storage. You will turn back."

There was silence. The oar splashed, the water thudded against the bow. And the talking and whispering began again. The gondolier was talking to himself between his teeth.

What was to be done? This man was strangely insolent, and had an uncanny decisiveness; the traveler, alone with him on the water, saw no way of getting what he wanted. And besides, how softly he could rest, if only he did not become excited! Hadn't he wanted the trip to go on and on forever? It was wisest to let things take their course, and the main thing was that he was comfortable. The poison of inertia seemed to be issuing from the seat, from this low, black-upholstered armchair, so gently cradled by the oar strokes of the imperious gondolier behind him. The notion that he had fallen into the hands of a criminal passed dreamily across Aschenbach's mind—without the ability to summon his thoughts to an active defense. The possibility that it was all simply a plan for cheating him seemed more abhorrent. A feeling of duty or pride, a kind of recollection that one should prevent such things, gave him the strength to arouse himself once more. He asked: "What are you asking for the trip?"

Looking down upon him, the gondolier answered: "You will pay."

It was plain how this should be answered. Aschenbach said mechanically: "I shall pay nothing, absolutely nothing, if you don't take me where I want to go."

"You want to go to the Lido."

"But not with you."

"I am rowing you well."

That is so, Aschenbach thought, and relaxed. That is so; you are rowing me well. Even if you do have designs on my cash, and send me down to Pluto with a blow of your oar from behind, you will have rowed me well.

But nothing like that happened. They were even joined by others: a boatload of musical brigands, men and women, who sang to guitar and mandolin, riding persistently side by side with the gondola and filling the silence over the water with their covetous foreign poetry. A hat was held out, and Aschenbach threw in money. Then they stopped singing, and rowed away. And again the muttering of the gondolier could be heard as he talked fitfully and jerkily to himself.

So they arrived, tossed in the wake of a steamer plying toward the city. Two municipal officers, their hands behind their backs, their faces turned in the direction of the lagoon, were walking back and forth on the bank. Aschenbach left the gondola at the dock, supported by that old man who is stationed with his grappling hook at each one of Venice's landing places. And since he had no small money, he crossed over to the hotel by the steamer wharf to get change and pay the rower what was due him. He got what he wanted in the lobby, he returned and found his traveling bags in a cart on the dock, and gondola and gondolier had vanished.

"He got out in a hurry," said the old man with the grappling hook. "A bad man, a man without a license, sir. He is the only gondolier who doesn't have a license. The others telephoned here."

Aschenbach shrugged his shoulders.

"The gentleman rode for nothing," the old man said, and held out his hat. Aschenbach tossed in a coin. He gave instructions to have his luggage taken to the beach hotel, and followed the cart through the avenue, the white-blossomed avenue which, lined on both sides with taverns, shops, and boarding houses, runs across the island to the shore.

He entered the spacious hotel from the rear, by the terraced garden, and passed through the vestibule and the lobby until he reached the desk. Since he had been announced, he was received with obliging promptness. A manager, a small, frail, flatteringly polite man with a black mustache and a French-style frock coat, accompanied him to the third floor in the lift, and showed him his room, an agreeable place furnished in cherry wood. It was decorated with strong-smelling flowers, and its high windows afforded a view out across the open sea. He stepped up to one of them after the employee had left; and while his luggage was being brought up and placed in the room behind him, he looked down on the beach (it was comparatively deserted in the afternoon) and on the sunless ocean which was at flood tide and was sending long low waves against the bank in a calm regular rhythm.

The experiences of a man who lives alone and in silence are both vaguer and more penetrating than those of people in society; his thoughts are heavier, more odd, and touched always with melancholy. Images and observations which could easily be disposed of by a glance, a smile, an exchange of opinion, will occupy him unbearably, sink deep into the silence, become full of meaning, become life, adventure, emotion. Loneliness ripens the eccentric, the daringly and estrangingly beautiful, the poetic. But loneliness also ripens the perverse, the disproportionate, the absurd, and the illicit. So, the things he had met with on the trip, the

ugly old fop with his twaddle about sweethearts, the lawbreaking gondolier who was cheated of his pay, still left the traveler uneasy. Without
really providing any resistance to the mind, without offering any solid
stuff to think over, they were nevertheless profoundly strange, as it
seemed to him, and disturbing precisely because of this contradiction. In
the meanwhile, he greeted the sea with his eyes, and felt pleasure at the
knowledge that Venice was so conveniently near. Finally he turned away,
bathed his face, left orders to the chambermaid for a few things he still
needed done to make his comfort complete, and let himself be taken to
the ground floor by the green-uniformed Swiss who operated the lift.

He took his tea on the terrace facing the ocean, then descended and
followed the boardwalk for quite a way in the direction of the Hotel
Excelsior. When he returned it seemed time to dress for dinner. He did
this with his usual care and slowness, since he was accustomed to working
over his toilet. And yet he came down a little early to the lobby, where
he found a great many of the hotel guests assembled, mixing distantly and
with a show of mutual indifference to one another, but all waiting for
mealtime. He took a paper from the table, dropped into a leather chair,
and observed the company; they differed agreeably from the guests
where he had first stopped.

A wide and tolerantly inclusive horizon was spread out before him.
Sounds of all the principal languages formed a subdued murmur. The
accepted evening dress, a uniform of good manners, brought all human
varieties into a fitting unity. There were Americans with their long wry
features, large Russian families, English ladies, German children with
French nurses. The Slavic element seemed to predominate. Polish was
being spoken nearby.

It was a group of children gathered around a little wicker table,
under the protection of a teacher or governess: three young girls, apparently fifteen to seventeen, and a long-haired boy about fourteen years old.
With astonishment Aschenbach noted that the boy was absolutely beautiful. His face, pale and reserved, framed with honey-colored hair, the
straight sloping nose, the lovely mouth, the expression of sweet and godlike seriousness, recalled Greek sculpture of the noblest period; and the
complete purity of the forms was accompanied by such a rare personal
charm that, as he watched, he felt that he had never met with anything
equally felicitous in nature or the plastic arts. He was further struck by
the obviously intentional contrast with the principles of upbringing
which showed in the sisters' attire and bearing. The three girls, the eldest
of whom could be considered grown up, were dressed with a chasteness
and severity bordering on disfigurement. Uniformly cloisterlike costumes, of medium length, slate-colored, sober, and deliberately unbecom-
ing in cut, with white turned-down collars as the only relief, suppressed
every possible appeal of shapeliness. Their hair, brushed down flat and
tight against the head, gave their faces a nunlike emptiness and lack of
character. Surely this was a mother's influence, and it had not even oc-

curred to her to apply the pedagogical strictness to the boy which she seemed to find necessary for her girls. It was clear that in his existence the first factors were gentleness and tenderness. The shears had been resolutely kept from his beautiful hair; like a Prince Charming's, it fell in curls over his forehead, his ears, and still deeper, across his neck. The English sailor suit, with its braids, stitchings, and embroideries, its puffy sleeves narrowing at the ends and fitting snugly about the fine wrists of his still childish but slender hands, gave the delicate figure something rich and luxurious. He was sitting, half-profile to the observer, one foot in its black patent-leather shoe placed before the other, an elbow resting on the arm of his wicker chair, a cheek pressed against his fist, in a position of negligent good manners, entirely free of the almost subservient stiffness to which his sisters seemed accustomed. Did he have some illness? For his skin stood out as white as ivory against the golden darkness of the surrounding curls. Or was he simply a pampered favorite child, made this way by a doting and moody love? Aschenbach inclined to believe the latter. Almost every artist is born with a rich and treacherous tendency to recognize injustices which have created beauty, and to meet aristocratic distinction with sympathy and reverence.

A waiter passed through and announced in English that the meal was ready. Gradually the guests disappeared through the glass door into the dining hall. Stragglers crossed, coming from the entrance, or the lifts. Inside, they had already begun serving, but the young Poles were still waiting around the little wicker table; and Aschenbach, comfortably propped in his deep chair, and with this beauty before his eyes, stayed with them.

The governess, a small corpulent middle-class woman with a red face, finally gave the sign to rise. With lifted brows, she pushed back her chair and bowed, as a large woman dressed in gray and richly jeweled with pearls entered the lobby. This woman was advancing with coolness and precision; her lightly powdered hair and the lines of her dress were arranged with the simplicity which always signifies taste in those quarters where devoutness is taken as one element of dignity. She might have been the wife of some high German official. Except that her jewelry added something fantastically lavish to her appearance; indeed, it was almost priceless, and consisted of ear pendants and a very long triple chain of softly glowing pearls, as large as cherries.

The children had risen promptly. They bent over to kiss the hand of their mother, who, with a distant smile on her well-preserved though somewhat tired and peaked features, looked over their heads and directed a few words to the governess in French. Then she walked to the glass door. The children followed her: the girls in the order of their age, after them the governess, the boy last. For some reason or other he turned around before crossing the sill, and since no one else was in the lobby his strange dusky eyes met those of Aschenbach, who, his newspaper on his knees, lost in thought, was gazing after the group.

What he saw had not been unusual in the slightest detail. They had not preceded the mother to the table; they had waited, greeted her with respect, and observed the customary forms on entering the room. But it had taken place so pointedly, with such an accent of training, duty, and self-respect, that Aschenbach felt peculiarly touched by it all. He delayed for a few moments, then he too crossed into the dining room, and was assigned to his table, which, as he noted with a brief touch of regret, was very far removed from that of the Polish family.

Weary, and yet intellectually active, he entertained himself during the lengthy meal with abstract, or even transcendental things; he thought over the secret union which the lawful must enter upon with the individual for human beauty to result, from this he passed into general problems of form and art, and at the end he found that his thoughts and discoveries were like the seemingly felicitous promptings of a dream which, when the mind is sobered, are seen to be completely empty and unfit. After the meal, smoking, sitting, taking an occasional turn in the park with its smell of nightfall, he went to bed early and spent the night in a sleep deep and unbroken, but often enlivened with the apparitions of dreams.

The weather did not improve any the following day. A land breeze was blowing. Under a cloudy ashen sky, the sea lay in dull peacefulness; it seemed shriveled up, with a close dreary horizon, and it had retreated from the beach, baring the long ribs of several sandbanks. As Aschenbach opened his window, he thought that he could detect the foul smell of the lagoon.

He felt depressed. He thought already of leaving. Once, years ago, after several weeks of spring here, this same weather had afflicted him, and impaired his health so seriously that he had to abandon Venice like a fugitive. Was not this old feverish unrest again setting in, the pressure in the temples, the heaviness of the eyelids? It would be annoying to change his residence still another time; but if the wind did not turn, he could not stay here. To be safe, he did not unpack completely. He breakfasted at nine in the buffet room provided for this purpose between the lobby and the dining room.

That formal silence reigned here which is the ambition of large hotels. The waiters who were serving walked about on soft soles. Nothing was audible but the tinkling of the tea things, a word half whispered. In one corner, obliquely across from the door, and two tables removed from his own, Aschenbach observed the Polish girls with their governess. Erect and red-eyed, their ash-blond hair freshly smoothed down, dressed in stiff blue linen with little white cuffs and turned-down collars—they were sitting there, handing around a glass of marmalade. They had almost finished their breakfast. The boy was missing.

Aschenbach smiled. "Well, little Phaeacian!" he thought. "You seem to be enjoying the pleasant privilege of having your sleep out." And, suddenly exhilarated, he recited to himself the line: "A frequent change of dress; warm baths, and rest."

He breakfasted without haste. From the porter, who entered the hall holding his braided cap in his hand, he received some forwarded mail; and while he smoked a cigarette he opened a few letters. In this way it happened that he was present at the entrance of the late sleeper who was being waited for over yonder.

He came through the glass door and crossed the room in silence to his sisters' table. His approach—the way he held the upper part of his body, and bent his knees, the movement of his white-shod feet—had an extraordinary charm; he walked very lightly, at once timid and proud, and this became still more lovely through the childish embarrassment with which, twice as he proceeded, he turned his face toward the center of the room, raising and lowering his eyes. Smiling, with something half muttered in his soft vague tongue, he took his place; and now, as he turned his full profile to the observer, Aschenbach was again astonished, terrified even, by the really godlike beauty of this human child. Today the boy was wearing a light blouse of blue-and-white-striped cotton goods, with a red silk tie in front, and closed at the neck by a plain white high collar. This collar lacked the distinctiveness of the blouse, but above it the flowering head was poised with an incomparable seductiveness—the head of an Eros, in blended yellows of Parian marble, with fine serious brows, the temples and ears covered softly by the abrupt encroachment of his curls.

"Good, good!" Aschenbach thought, with that deliberate expert appraisal which artists sometimes employ as a subterfuge when they have been carried away with delight before a masterwork. And he thought further: "Really, if the sea and the beach weren't waiting for me, I should stay here as long as you stayed!" But he went then, passed through the lobby under the inspection of the servants, down the wide terrace, and straight across the boardwalk to the section of the beach reserved for the hotel guests. The barefoot old man in dungarees and straw hat who was functioning here as bathing master assigned him to the bathing house he had rented; a table and a seat were placed on the sandy board platform, and he made himself comfortable in the lounge chair which he had drawn closer to the sea, out into the waxen yellow sand.

More than ever before, he was entertained and amused by the sights on the beach, this spectacle of carefree, civilized people getting sensuous enjoyment at the very edge of the elements. The gray flat sea was already alive with wading children, swimmers, a motley of figures lying on the sandbanks with arms bent behind their heads. Others were rowing about in little red-and-blue-striped boats without keels; they were continually upsetting, amid laughter. Before the long stretches of bathing houses, where people were sitting on the platforms as though on small verandas, there was a play of movement against the line of rest and inertness behind —visits and chatter, fastidious morning elegance alongside the nakedness which, boldly at ease, was enjoying the freedom which the place afforded. Farther in front, on the damp firm sand, people were parading about in white bathing cloaks, in ample, brilliantly colored wrappers. An elaborate sand pile to the right, erected by children, had flags in the colors of all nations planted around it. Venders of shells, cakes, and fruit spread out their wares, kneeling. To the left, before one of the bathing houses which stood at right angles to the others and to the sea, a Russian family was encamped: men with beards and large teeth, slow delicate women, a Baltic girl sitting by an easel and painting the sea amidst exclamations of despair, two ugly good-natured children, an old maidservant who wore a kerchief on her head and had the alert scraping manners of a slave. Delighted and appreciative, they were living there, patiently calling the names of the two rowdy disobedient children, using their scanty Italian to joke with the humorous old man from whom they were buying candy, kissing one another on the cheek, and not in the least concerned with anyone who might be observing their community.

"Yes, I shall stay," Aschenbach thought. "Where would things be better?" And, his hands folded in his lap, he let his eyes lose themselves in the expanses of the sea, his gaze gliding, swimming, and failing in the monotone mist of the wilderness of space. He loved the ocean for deep-seated reasons: because of that yearning for rest, when the hard-pressed artist hungers to shut out the exacting multiplicities of experience and hide himself on the breast of the simple, the vast; and because of a forbidden hankering—seductive, by virtue of its being directly opposed to his obligations—after the incommunicable, the incommensurate, the eternal, the nonexistent. To be at rest in the face of perfection is the hunger of everyone who is aiming at excellence; and what is the nonexistent but a form of perfection? But now, just as his dreams were so far out in vacancy, suddenly the horizontal fringe of the sea was broken by a human figure; and as he brought his eyes back from the unbounded, and focused them, it was the lovely boy who was there, coming from the left and passing him on the sand. He was barefooted, ready for wading, his slender legs exposed above the knees; he walked slowly, but as lightly and proudly as though it were the customary thing for him to move about without shoes; and he was looking around him toward the line of bathing houses opposite. But as soon as he had noticed the Russian family, occupied with their own harmony and contentment, a cloud of scorn and detestation passed over his face. His brow darkened, his mouth was compressed, he gave his lips an embittered twist to one side, so that the cheek was distorted and the forehead became so heavily furrowed that the eyes seemed sunken beneath its pressure: malicious and glowering, they spoke the language of hate. He looked down, looked back once more threateningly, then with his shoulder made an abrupt gesture of disdain and dismissal, and left the enemy behind him.

A kind of pudency or confusion, something like respect and shyness, caused Aschenbach to turn away as though he had seen nothing. For the earnest-minded who have been casual observers of some passion, struggle against making use, even to themselves, of what they have seen. But he was both cheered and unstrung—which is to say, he was happy. This childish fanaticism, directed against the most good-natured possible aspect of life—it brought the divinely arbitrary into human relationships; it made a delightful natural picture which had appealed only to the eye now seem worthy of a deeper sympathy; and it gave the figure of this half-grown boy, who had already been important enough by his sheer beauty, something to offset him still further, and to make one take him more seriously than his years justified. Still looking away, Aschenbach could hear the boy's voice, the shrill, somewhat weak voice with which, in the distance now, he was trying to call hello to his playfellows busied around the sand pile. They answered him, shouting back his name, or some affectionate nickname; and Aschenbach listened with a certain curiosity, without being able to catch anything more definite than two melodic syllables like "Adgio," or still more frequently "Adgiu," with a ringing *u*-sound prolonged at the end. He was pleased with the resonance of this; he found it adequate to the subject. He repeated it silently and, satisfied, turned to his letters and manuscripts.

His small portable writing desk on his knees, he began writing with his fountain pen an answer to this or that bit of correspondence. But after the first fifteen minutes he found it a pity to abandon the situation—the most enjoyable he could think of—in this manner and waste it in activities which did not interest him. He tossed the writing materials to one side, and he faced the ocean again; soon afterward, diverted by the childish voices around the sand heap, he revolved his head comfortably along the back of the chair toward the right, to discover where that excellent little Adgio might be and what he was doing.

He was found at a glance; the red tie on his breast was not to be overlooked. Busied with the others in laying an old plank across the damp moat of the sand castle, he was nodding, and shouting instructions for this work. There were about ten companions with him, boys and girls of his age, and a few younger ones who were chattering with one another in Polish, French, and several Balkan tongues. But it was his name which rang out most often. He was openly in demand, sought after, admired. One boy especially, like him a Pole, a stocky fellow who was called something like "Jaschu," with sleek black hair and a belted linen coat, seemed to be his closest vassal and friend. When the work on the sand structure was finished for the time being, they walked arm in arm along the beach, and the boy who was called "Jaschu" kissed the beauty.

Aschenbach was half minded to raise a warning finger. "I advise you, Critobulus," he thought, smiling, "to travel for a year! For you need that much time at least to get over it." And then he breakfasted on large ripe strawberries which he got from a peddler. It had become very warm, although the sun could no longer penetrate the blanket of mist in the sky. Laziness clogged his brain, even while his senses delighted in the numbing, drugging distractions of the ocean's stillness. To guess, to puzzle out just what name it was that sounded something like "Adgio," seemed to the sober man an appropriate ambition, a thoroughly comprehensive pur-

suit. And with the aid of a few scrappy recollections of Polish he decided
that they must mean "Tadzio," the shortened form of "Tadeusz," and
sounding like "Tadziu" when it is called.

Tadzio was bathing. Aschenbach, who had lost sight of him, spied his
head and the arm with which he was propelling himself, far out in the
water; for the sea must have been smooth for a long distance out. But
already people seemed worried about him; women's voices were calling
after him from the bathing houses, uttering this name again and again. It
almost dominated the beach like a battle cry, and with its soft consonants,
its long-drawn *u*-note at the end, it had something at once sweet and wild
about it: "Tadziu! Tadziu!" He turned back; beating the resistant water
into a foam with his legs, he hurried, his head bent down over the waves.
And to see how this living figure, graceful and clean-cut in its advance,
with dripping curls, and lovely as some frail god, came up out of the
depths of sky and sea, rose and separated from the elements—this spectacle aroused a sense of myth, it was like some poet's recovery of time at its
beginning, of the origin of forms and the birth of gods. Aschenbach
listened with closed eyes to this song ringing within him, and he thought
again that it was pleasant here, and that he would like to remain.

Later Tadzio was resting from his bath; he lay in the sand, wrapped
in his white robe, which was drawn under the right shoulder, his head
supported on his bare arm. And even when Aschenbach was not observing him, but was reading a few pages in his book, he hardly ever forgot
that this boy was lying there and that it would cost him only a slight turn
of his head to the right to behold the mystery. It seemed that he was
sitting here just to keep watch over his repose—busied with his own
concerns, and yet constantly aware of this noble picture at his right, not
far in the distance. And he was stirred by a paternal affection, the profound leaning which those who have devoted their thoughts to the creation of beauty feel toward those who possess beauty itself.

A little past noon he left the beach, returned to the hotel, and was
taken up to his room. He stayed there for some time in front of the
mirror, looking at his gray hair, his tired sharp features. At this moment
he thought of his reputation, and of the fact that he was often recognized
on the streets and observed with respect, thanks to the sure aim and the
appealing finish of his words. He called up all the exterior successes of his
talent which he could think of, remembering also his elevation to the
knighthood. Then he went down to the dining hall for lunch, and ate at
his little table. As he was riding up in the lift, after the meal was ended, a
group of young people just coming from breakfast pressed into the swaying cage after him, and Tadzio entered too. He stood quite near to Aschenbach, for the first time so near that Aschenbach could see him, not with
the aloofness of a picture, but in minute detail, in all his human particu-
larities. The boy was addressed by someone or other, and as he was
answering with an indescribably agreeable smile he stepped out again, on
the second floor, walking backward, and with his eyes lowered. "Beauty

makes modest," Aschenbach thought, and he tried insistently to explain why this was so. But he had noticed that Tadzio's teeth were not all they should be; they were somewhat jagged and pale. The enamel did not look healthy; it had a peculiar brittleness and transparency, as is often the case with anemics. "He is very frail, he is sickly," Aschenbach thought. "In all probability he will not grow old." And he refused to reckon with the feeling of gratification or reassurance which accompanied this notion.

He spent two hours in his room, and in the afternoon he rode in the *vaporetto* across the foul-smelling lagoon to Venice. He got off at San Marco, took tea on the Piazza, and then, in accord with his schedule for the day, he went for a walk through the streets. Yet it was this walk which produced a complete reversal in his attitudes and his plans.

An offensive sultriness lay over the streets. The air was so heavy that the smells pouring out of homes, stores, and eating houses became mixed with oil, vapors, clouds of perfumes, and still other odors—and these would not blow away, but hung in layers. Cigarette smoke remained suspended, disappearing very slowly. The crush of people along the narrow streets irritated rather than entertained the walker. The farther he went, the more he was depressed by the repulsive condition resulting from the combination of sea air and sirocco, which was at the same time both stimulating and enervating. He broke into an uncomfortable sweat. His eyes failed him, his chest became tight, he had a fever, the blood was pounding in his head. He fled from the crowded business streets across a bridge into the walks of the poor. On a quiet square, one of those forgotten and enchanting places which lie in the interior of Venice, he rested at the brink of a well, dried his forehead, and realized that he would have to leave here.

For the second and last time it had been demonstrated that this city in this kind of weather was decidedly unhealthy for him. It seemed foolish to attempt a stubborn resistance, while the prospects for a change of wind were completely uncertain. A quick decision was called for. It was not possible to go home this soon. Neither summer nor winter quarters were prepared to receive him. But this was not the only place where there were sea and beach; and elsewhere these could be found without the lagoon and its malarial mists. He remembered a little watering place not far from Trieste which had been praised to him. Why not there? And without delay, so that this new change of location would still have time to do him some good. He pronounced this as good as settled, and stood up. At the next gondola station he took a boat back to San Marco, and was led through the dreary labyrinth of canals, under fancy marble balconies flanked with lions, around the corners of smooth walls, past the sorrowing façade of palaces which mirrored large dilapidated business signs in the pulsing water. He had trouble arriving there, for the gondolier, who was in league with lace-makers and glass-blowers, was always trying to land him for inspections and purchases; and just as the bizarre trip through Venice would begin to cast its spell, the greedy business sense the sunken Queen did all it could to destroy the illusion.

When he had returned to the hotel, he announced at the office before dinner that unforeseen developments necessitated his departure the following morning. He was assured of their regrets. He settled his accounts. He dined, and spent the warm evening reading the newspapers in a rocking chair on the rear terrace. Before going to bed he got his luggage all ready for departure.

He did not sleep so well as he might, since the impending break-up made him restless. When he opened the window in the morning, the sky was as overcast as ever, but the air seemed fresher, and he was already beginning to repent. Hadn't his decision been somewhat hasty and uncalled for, the result of a passing diffidence and indisposition? If he had delayed a little, if, instead of surrendering so easily, he had made some attempt to adjust himself to the air of Venice or to wait for an improvement in the weather, he would not be so rushed and inconvenienced, but could anticipate another forenoon on the beach like yesterday's. Too late. Now he would have to go on wanting what he had wanted yesterday. He dressed, and at about eight o'clock rode down to the ground floor for breakfast.

As he entered, the buffet room was still empty of guests. A few came in while he sat waiting for his order. With his teacup to his lips, he saw the Polish girls and their governess appear: rigid, with morning freshness, their eyes still red, they walked across to their table in the corner by the window. Immediately afterward, the porter approached him, cap in hand, and warned him that it was time to go. The automobile is ready to take him and the other passengers to the Hotel Excelsior, and from here the motorboat will bring the ladies and gentlemen to the station through the company's private canal. Time is pressing. Aschenbach found that it was doing nothing of the sort. It was still over an hour before his train left. He was irritated by this hotel custom of hustling departing guests out of the house, and indicated to the porter that he wished to finish his breakfast in peace. The man retired hesitatingly, to appear again five minutes later. It is impossible for the car to wait any longer. Then he would take a cab, and carry his trunk with him, Aschenbach replied in anger. He would use the public steamboat at the proper time, and he requested that it be left to him personally to worry about his departure. The employee bowed himself away. Pleased with the way he warded off these importunate warnings, Aschenbach finished his meal at leisure; in fact, he even had the waiter bring him a newspaper. The time had become quite short when he finally arose. It was fitting that at the same moment Tadzio should come through the glass door.

On the way to his table he walked in the opposite direction to Aschenbach, lowering his eyes modestly before the man with the gray hair and high forehead, only to raise them again, in his delicious manner, soft and full upon him—and he had passed. "Good-bye, Tadzio!" Aschenbach thought. "I did not see much of you." He did what was unusual with him, really formed the words on his lips and spoke them to himself; then

he added: "God bless you!" After this he left, distributed tips, was ushered out by the small gentle manager in the French frock coat, and made
off from the hotel on foot, as he had come, going along the white-
blossoming avenue which crossed the island to the steamer bridge, accompanied by the house servant carrying his hand luggage. He arrived,
took his place—and then followed a painful journey through all the
depths of regret.

It was the familiar trip across the lagoon, past San Marco, up the
Grand Canal. Aschenbach sat on the circular bench at the bow, his arm
supported against the railing, shading his eyes with his hand. The public
gardens were left behind, the Piazzetta opened up once more in princely
splendor and was gone, then came the great flock of palaces, and as the
channel made a turn the magnificently slung marble arch of the Rialto
came into view. The traveler was watching; his emotions were in conflict.
The atmosphere of the city, this slightly foul smell of sea and swamp
which he had been so anxious to avoid—he breathed it now in deep,
exquisitely painful draughts. Was it possible that he had not known, had
not considered, just how much he was attached to all this? What had
been a partial misgiving this morning, a faint doubt as to the advisability
of his move, now became a distress, a positive misery, a spiritual hunger,
and so bitter that it frequently brought tears to his eyes, while he told
himself that he could not possibly have foreseen it. Hardest of all to bear,
at times completely insufferable, was the thought that he would never see
Venice again, that this was a leave-taking forever. Since it had been
shown for the second time that the city affected his health, since he was
compelled for the second time to get away in all haste, from now on he
would have to consider it a place impossible and forbidden to him, a place
which he was not equal to, and which it would be foolish for him to visit
again. Yes, he felt that if he left now, he would be shamefaced and
defiant enough never to see again the beloved city which had twice
caused him a physical breakdown. And of a sudden this struggle between
his desires and his physical strength seemed to the aging man so grave and
important, his physical defeat seemed so dishonorable, so much a challenge to hold out at any cost, that he could not understand the ready
submissiveness of the day before, when he had decided to give in without
attempting any serious resistance.

Meanwhile the steamboat was nearing the station; pain and perplexity increased, he became distracted. In his affliction, he felt that it was
impossible to leave, and just as impossible to turn back. The conflict was
intense as he entered the station. It was very late; there was not a moment
to lose if he was to catch the train. He wanted to, and he did not want to.
But time was pressing; it drove him on. He hurried to get his ticket, and
looked about in the tumult of the hall for the officer on duty here from
the hotel. The man appeared and announced that the large trunk had been
transferred. Transferred already? Yes, thank you—to Como. To Como?
And in the midst of hasty running back and forth, angry questions and

confused answers, it came to light that the trunk had already been sent with other foreign baggage from the express office of the Hotel Excelsior in a completely wrong direction.

Aschenbach had difficulty in preserving the expression which was required under these circumstances. He was almost convulsed with an adventurous delight, an unbelievable hilarity. The employee rushed off to see if it were still possible to stop the trunk, and, as was to be expected, he returned with nothing accomplished. Aschenbach declared that he did not want to travel without his trunk, but had decided to go back and wait at the beach hotel for its return. Was the company's motorboat still at the station? The man assured him that it was lying at the door. With Italian volubility he persuaded the clerk at the ticket window to redeem the canceled ticket, he swore that they would act speedily, that no time or money would be spared in recovering the trunk promptly, and—so the strange thing happened that, twenty minutes after his arrival at the station, the traveler found himself again on the Grand Canal, returning to the Lido.

Here was an adventure, wonderful, abashing, and comically dreamlike beyond belief: places which he had just bid farewell to forever in the most abject misery—yet he had been turned and driven back by fate, and was seeing them again in the same hour! The spray from the prow, washing between gondolas and steamers with an absurd agility, shot the speedy little craft ahead to its goal, while the lone passenger was hiding the nervousness and ebullience of a truant boy under a mask of resigned anger. From time to time he shook with laughter at this mishap which, as he told himself, could not have turned out better for a child of destiny. There were explanations to be given, expressions of astonishment to be faced—and then, he told himself, everything would be all right; then a misfortune would be avoided, a grave error rectified. And all that he had thought he was leaving behind him would be open to him again, there at his disposal. . . . And, to cap it all, was the rapidity of the ride deceiving him, or was the wind really coming from the sea?

The waves beat against the walls of the narrow canal which runs through the island to the Hotel Excelsior. An automobile omnibus was awaiting his return there, and took him above the rippling sea straight to the beach hotel. The little manager with mustache and long-tailed frock coat came down the stairs to meet him.

He ingratiatingly regretted the episode, spoke of it as highly painful to him and the establishment, but firmly approved of Aschenbach's decision to wait here for the baggage. Of course his room had been given up, but there was another one, just as good, which he could occupy immediately. *"Pas de chance, monsieur,"* the Swiss elevator boy smiled as they were ascending. And so the fugitive was established again, in a room almost identical with the other in its location and furnishings.

Tired out by the confusion of this strange forenoon, he distributed the contents of his hand bag about the room and dropped into an armchair by the open window. The sea had become a pale green, the air seemed thinner and purer; the beach, with its cabins and boats, seemed to have color, although the sky was still gray. Aschenbach looked out, his hands folded in his lap; he was content to be back, but shook his head disapprovingly at his irresolution, his failure to know his own mind. He sat here for the better part of an hour, resting and dreaming vaguely. About noon he saw Tadzio in a striped linen suit with a red tie, coming back from the sea across the private beach and along the boardwalk to the hotel. Aschenbach recognized him from this altitude before he had actually set eyes on him; he was about to think some such words as "Well, Tadzio, there you are again!" but at the same moment he felt this careless greeting go dumb before the truth in his heart. He felt the exhilaration of his blood, a conflict of pain and pleasure, and he realized that it was Tadzio who had made it so difficult for him to leave.

He sat very still, entirely unobserved from this height, and looked within himself. His features were alert, his eyebrows raised, and an attentive, keenly inquisitive smile distended his mouth. Then he raised his head, lifted both hands, which had hung relaxed over the arms of the chair, and in a slow twisting movement turned the palms upward—as though to suggest an opening and spreading outward of his arms. It was a spontaneous act of welcome, of calm acceptance.

IV

DAY AFTER DAY NOW the naked god with the hot cheeks drove his fire-breathing quadriga across the expanses of the sky, and his yellow locks fluttered in the assault of the east wind. A white silk sheen stretched over the slowly simmering Ponto. The sand glowed. Beneath the quaking silver blue of the ether, rust-colored canvases were spread in front of the bathing houses, and the afternoons were spent in the sharply demarcated spots of shade which they cast. But it was also delightful in the evening, when the vegetation in the park had the smell of balsam, and the stars were working through their courses above, and the soft persistent murmur of the sea came up enchantingly through the night. Such evenings contained the cheering promise that more sunny days of casual idleness would follow, dotted with countless closely interspersed possibilities of well-timed accidents.

The guest who was detained here by such an accommodating mishap did not consider the return of his property as sufficient grounds for another departure. He suffered some inconvenience for two days, and had to appear for meals in the large dining room in his traveling clothes. When the strayed luggage was finally deposited in his room again, he unpacked completely and filled the closet and drawers with his belongings; he had decided to remain here indefinitely, content now that he could pass the hours on the beach in a silk suit and appear for dinner at his little table again in appropriate evening dress.

The comfortable rhythm of this life had already cast its spell over him; he was soon enticed by the ease, the mild splendor, of his program. Indeed, what a place to be in, when the usual allurement of living in watering places on southern shores was coupled with the immediate nearness of the most wonderful of all cities! Aschenbach was not a lover of pleasure. Whenever there was some call for him to take a holiday, to indulge himself, to have a good time—and this was especially true at an earlier age—restlessness and repugnance soon drove him back to his rigorous toil, the faithful sober efforts of his daily routine. Except that this place was bewitching him, relaxing his will, making him happy. In the mornings, under the shelter of his bathing house, letting his eyes roam dreamily in the blue of the southern sea; or on a warm night as he leaned back against the cushions of the gondola carrying him under the broad starry sky home to the Lido from the Piazza di San Marco after long hours of idleness—and the brilliant lights, the melting notes of the serenade were being left behind—he often recalled his place in the mountains, the scene of his battles in the summer, where the clouds blew low across his garden, and terrifying storms put out the lamps at night, and the crows which he fed were swinging in the tops of the pine trees. Then everything seemed just right to him, as though he were lifted into the Elysian fields, on the borders of the earth, where man enjoys the easiest life, where there is no snow or winter, nor storms and pouring rains, but where Oceanus continually sends forth gentle cooling breezes, and the days pass in a blessed inactivity, without work, without effort, devoted wholly to the sun and to the feast days of the sun.

Aschenbach saw the boy Tadzio frequently, almost constantly. Owing to the limited range of territory and the regularity of their lives, the beauty was near him at short intervals throughout the day. He saw him, met him, everywhere: in the lower rooms of the hotel, on the cooling water trips to the city and back, in the arcades of the square, and at times when he was especially lucky ran across him on the streets. But principally, and with the most gratifying regularity, the forenoon on the beach allowed him to admire and study this rare spectacle at his leisure. Yes, it was this guaranty of happiness, this daily recurrence of good fortune, which made his stay here so precious, and gave him such pleasure in the constant procession of sunny days.

He was up as early as he used to be when under the driving pressure of work, and was on the beach before most people, when the sun was still mild and the sea lay blinding white in the dreaminess of morning. He spoke amiably to the guard of the private beach, and also spoke familiarly to the barefoot, white-bearded old man who had prepared his place for him, stretching the brown canopy and bringing the furniture of the cabin out on the platform. Then he took his seat. There would now be three or four hours in which the sun mounted and gained terrific strength, the sea a deeper and deeper blue, and he might look at Tadzio.

He saw him approaching from the left, along the edge of the sea; he

saw him as he stepped out backward from among the cabins; or he would
suddenly find, with a shock of pleasure, that he had missed his coming,
that he was already here in the blue-and-white bathing suit which was his
only garment now while on the beach, that he had already commenced
his usual activities in the sun and the sand—a pleasantly trifling, idle, and
unstable manner of living, a mixture of rest and play. Tadzio would
saunter about, wade, dig, catch things, lie down, go for a swim, all the
while being kept under surveillance by the women on the platform who
made his name ring out in their falsetto voices: "Tadziu! Tadziu!" Then
he would come running to them with a look of eagerness, to tell them
what he had seen, what he had experienced, or to show them what he had
found or caught: mussels, sea horses, jellyfish, and crabs that ran sideways. Aschenbach did not understand a word he said, and though it
might have been the most ordinary thing in the world, it was a vague
harmony in his ear. So the foreignness of the boy's speech turned it into
music, a wanton sun poured its prodigal splendor down over him, and his
figure was always set off against the background of an intense sea blue.

This piquant body was so freely exhibited that his eyes soon knew
every line and posture. He was continually rediscovering with new pleasure all this familiar beauty, and his astonishment at its delicate appeal to
his senses was unending. The boy was called to greet a guest who was
paying his respects to the ladies at the bathing house. He came running,
running wet perhaps out of the water, tossed back his curls, and as he
held out his hand, resting on one leg and raising his other foot on the toes,
the set of his body was delightful; it had a charming expectancy about it,
a well-meaning shyness, a winsomeness which showed his aristocratic
training. . . . He lay stretched full-length, his bath towel slung across his
shoulders, his delicately chiseled arm supported in the sand, his chin in his
palm; the boy called Jaschu was squatting near him and making up to
him—and nothing could be more enchanting than the smile of his eyes
and lips when the leader glanced up at his inferior, his servant. . . . He
stood on the edge of the sea, alone, apart from his people, quite near to
Aschenbach—erect, his hands locked across the back of his neck, he
swayed slowly on the balls of his feet, looked dreamily into the blueness
of sea and sky, while tiny waves rolled up and bathed his feet. His honey-
colored hair clung in rings about his neck and temples. The sun made the
down on his back glitter; the fine etching of the ribs, the symmetry of
the chest, were emphasized by the tightness of the suit across the buttocks. His armpits were still as smooth as those of a statue; the hollows of
his knees glistened, and their bluish veins made his body seem built of
some clearer stuff. What rigor, what precision of thought were expressed
in this erect, youthfully perfect body! Yet the pure and strenuous will
which, darkly at work, could bring such godlike sculpture to the light—
was not he, the artist, familiar with this? Did it not operate in him too
when he, under the press of frugal passions, would free from the marble
mass of speech some slender form which he had seen in the mind and

which he put before his fellows as a statue and a mirror of intellectual beauty?

Statue and mirror! His eyes took in the noble form there bordered with blue; and with a rush of enthusiasm he felt that in this spectacle he was catching the beautiful itself, form as the thought of God, the one pure perfection which lives in the mind, and which, in this symbol and likeness, had been placed here quietly and simply as an object of devotion. That was drunkenness; and eagerly, without thinking, the aging artist welcomed it. His mind was in travail; all that he had learned dropped back into flux; his understanding threw up age-old thoughts which he had inherited with youth though they had never before lived with their own fire. Is it not written that the sun diverts our attention from intellectual to sensual things? Reason and understanding, it is said, become so numbed and enchanted that the soul forgets everything out of delight with its immediate circumstances, and in astonishment becomes attached to the most beautiful object shined on by the sun; indeed, only with the aid of a body is it capable then of raising itself to higher considerations. To be sure, Amor did as the instructors of mathematics who show backward children tangible representations of the pure forms—similarly the god, in order to make the spiritual visible for us, readily utilized the form and color of man's youth, and as a reminder he adorned these with the re-flected splendor of beauty which, when we behold it, makes us flare up in pain and hope.

His enthusiasm suggested these things, put him in the mood for them. And from the noise of the sea and the luster of the sun he wove himself a charming picture. Here was the old plane tree, not far from the walls of Athens—a holy, shadowy place filled with the smell of agnus castus blossoms and decorated with ornaments and images sacred to Achelous and the Nymphs. Clear and pure, the brook at the foot of the spreading tree fell across the smooth pebbles; the cicadas were fiddling. But on the grass, which was like a pillow gently sloping to the head, two people were stretched out, in hiding from the heat of the day: an older man and a youth, one ugly and one beautiful, wisdom next to loveliness. And amid gallantries and skillfully engaging banter, Socrates was instruct-ing Phaedrus in matters of desire and virtue. He spoke to him of the hot terror which the initiates suffer when their eyes light on an image of the eternal beauty; spoke of the greed of the impious and the wicked who cannot think beauty when they see its likeness, and who are incapable of reverence; spoke of the holy distress which befalls the noble-minded when a godlike countenance, a perfect body, appears before them; they tremble and grow distracted, and hardly dare to raise their eyes, and they honor the man who possesses this beauty, yes, if they were not afraid of being thought downright madmen they would sacrifice to the beloved as to the image of a god. For beauty, my Phaedrus, beauty alone is both lovely and visible at once; it is, mark me, the only form of the spiritual which we can receive through the senses. Else what would become of us if the divine, if reason and virtue and truth, should appear to us through the senses? Should we not perish and be consumed with love, as Semele once was with Zeus? Thus, beauty is the sensitive man's access to the spirit—but only a road, a means simply, little Phaedrus. . . . And then this crafty suitor made the neatest remark of all; it was this, that the lover is more divine than the beloved, since the god is in the one, but not in the other—perhaps the most delicate, the most derisive thought which has ever been framed, and the one from which spring all the cunning and the profoundest pleasures of desire.

Writers are happiest with an idea which can become all emotion, and an emotion all idea. Just such a pulsating idea, such a precise emotion, belonged to the lonely man at this moment, was at his call. Nature, it ran, shivers with ecstasy when the spirit bows in homage before beauty. Suddenly he wanted to write. Eros loves idleness, they say, and he is suited only to idleness. But at this point in the crisis the affliction became a stimulus toward productivity.The incentive hardly mattered. A request, an agitation for an open statement on a certain large burning issue of culture and taste, was going about the intellectual world, and had finally caught up with the traveler here. He was familiar with the subject, it had touched his own experience; and suddenly he felt an irresistible desire to display it in the light of his own version. And he even went so far as to prefer working in Tadzio's presence, taking the scope of the boy as a standard for his writing, making his style follow the lines of this body which seemed godlike to him, and carrying his beauty over into the spiritual just as the eagle once carried the Trojan stag up into the ether. Never had his joy in words been more sweet. He had never been so aware that Eros is in the word as during those perilously precious hours when, at his crude table under the canopy, facing the idol and listening to the music of his voice, he followed Tadzio's beauty in the forming of his little tract, a page and a half of choice prose which was soon to excite the admiration of many through its clarity, its poise, and the vigorous curve of its emotion. Certainly it is better for people to know only the beautiful product as finished, and not in its conception, its conditions of origin. For knowledge of the sources from which the artist derives his inspiration would often confuse and alienate, and in this way detract from the effects of his mastery. Strange hours! Strange enervating efforts! Rare creative intercourse between the spirit and body! When Aschenbach put away his work and started back from the beach, he felt exhausted, or in dispersion even; and it was as though his conscience were complaining after some transgression.

The following morning, as he was about to leave the hotel, he looked off from the steps and noticed that Tadzio, who was alone and was already on his way toward the sea, was just approaching the private beach. He was half tempted by the simple notion of seizing this opportunity to strike up a casual friendly acquaintanceship with the boy who had been the unconscious source of so much agitation and upheaval; he

wanted to address him, and enjoy the answering look in his eyes. The boy
was sauntering along, he could be overtaken; and Aschenbach quickened
his pace. He reached him on the boardwalk behind the bathing houses;
was about to lay a hand on his head and shoulders; and some word or
other, an amiable phrase in French, was on the tip of his tongue. But he
felt that his heart, perhaps also because of his rapid stride, was beating like
a hammer; and he was so short of breath that his voice would have been
tight and trembling. He hesitated, he tried to get himself under control.
Suddenly he became afraid that he had been walking too long so close
behind the boy. He was afraid of arousing his curiosity and causing him
to look back questioningly. He made one more spurt, failed, surrendered,
and passed with bowed head.

"Too late!" he thought immediately. "Too late!" Yet was it too late?
This step which he had just been on the verge of taking would very
possibly have put things on a sound, free and easy basis, and would have
restored him to wholesome soberness. But the fact was that Aschenbach
did not want soberness: his intoxication was too precious. Who can explain the stamp and the nature of the artist? Who can understand this
deep instinctive welding of discipline and license? For to be unable to
want wholesome soberness is license. Aschenbach was no longer given to
self-criticism. His tastes, the mental caliber of his years, his self-respect,
ripeness, and a belated simplicity made him unwilling to dismember his
motives and to debate whether his impulses were the result of conscientiousness or of dissolution and weakness. He was embarrassed, as he
feared that someone or other, if only the guard on the beach, must have
observed his pursuit and defeat. He was very much afraid of the ridiculous. Further, he joked with himself about his comically pious distress.
"Downed," he thought, "downed like a rooster, with his wings hanging
miserably in the battle. It really is a god who can, at one sight of his
loveliness, break our courage this way and force down our pride so
thoroughly. . . ." He toyed and skirmished with his emotions, and was far
too haughty to be afraid of them.

He had already ceased thinking about the time when the vacation
period which he had fixed for himself would expire; the thought of going
home never even suggested itself. He had sent for an ample supply of
money. His only concern was with the possible departure of the Polish
family; by a casual questioning of the hotel barber he had contrived to
learn that these people had come here only a short time before his own
arrival. The sun browned his face and hands, the invigorating salt breezes
made him feel fresher. Once he had been in the habit of expending on his
work every bit of nourishment which food, sleep, or nature could provide him; and similarly now he was generous and uneconomical, letting
pass off as elation and emotion all the daily strengthening derived from
the sun, idleness, and sea air.

His sleep was fitful; the preciously uniform days were separated by
short nights of happy unrest. He did retire early, for at nine o'clock,

when Tadzio had disappeared from the scene, the day seemed over. But at the first gray of dawn he was awakened by a gently insistent shock; he suddenly remembered his adventure, he could no longer remain in bed; he arose and, clad lightly against the chill of morning, he sat down by the open window to await the rising of the sun. Toned by his sleep, he watched this miraculous event with reverence. Sky, earth, and sea still lay in glassy, ghostlike twilight; a dying star still floated in the emptiness of space. But a breeze started up, a winged message from habitations beyond reach, telling that Eos was rising from beside her husband. And that first sweet reddening in the farthest stretches of sky and sea took place by which the sentiency of creation is announced. The goddess was approaching, the seductress of youth who stole Cleitus and Cephalus, and despite the envy of all the Olympians enjoyed the love of handsome Orion. A strewing of roses began there on the edge of the world, an unutterably pure glowing and blooming. Childish clouds, lighted and shined through, floated like busy little Cupids in the rosy, bluish mist. Purple fell upon the sea, which seemed to be simmering, and washing the color toward him. Golden spears shot up into the sky from behind. The splendor caught fire, silently; with godlike power an intense flame of licking tongues broke out—and with rattling hoofs the brother's sacred chargers mounted the horizon. Lighted by the god's brilliance, he sat there, keeping watch alone. He closed his eyes, letting this glory play against the lids. Past emotions, precious early afflictions and yearnings which had been stifled by his rigorous program of living, were now returning in such strange new forms. With an embarrassed, astonished smile, he recognized them. He was thinking, dreaming; slowly his lips formed a name. And still smiling, with his face turned upward, hands folded in his lap, he fell asleep again in his chair.

But the day which began with such fiery solemnity underwent a strange mythical transformation. Where did the breeze originate which suddenly began playing so gently and insinuatingly, like some whispered suggestion, about his ears and temples? Little white choppy clouds stood in the sky in scattered clumps, like the pasturing herds of the gods. A stronger wind arose, and the steeds of Poseidon came prancing up, and along with them the steers which belonged to the blue-locked god, bellowing and lowering their horns as they ran. Yet among the detritus of the more distant beach, waves were hopping forward like agile goats. He was caught in the enchantment of a sacredly distorted world full of Panic life—and he dreamed delicate legends. Often, when the sun was sinking behind Venice, he would sit on a bench in the park observing Tadzio, who was dressed in a white suit with a colored sash and was playing ball on the smooth gravel—and it was Hyacinth that he seemed to be watching, Hyacinth who was to die because two gods loved him. Yes, he felt Zephyr's aching jealousy of the rival who forgot the oracle, the bow, and the lyre, in order to play forever with this beauty. He saw the discus, guided by a pitiless envy, strike the lovely head; he too, growing pale, caught the drooping body—and the flower, sprung from this sweet blood, bore the inscription of his unending grief.

Nothing is more unusual and strained than the relationship between people who know each other only with their eyes, who meet daily, even hourly, and yet are compelled, by force of custom or their own caprices, to say no word or make no move of acknowledgment, but to maintain the appearance of an aloof unconcern. There is a restlessness and a surcharged curiosity existing between them, the hysteria of an unsatisfied, unnaturally repressed desire for acquaintanceship and intercourse; and especially there is a kind of tense respect. For one person loves and honors another so long as he cannot judge him, and desire is an evidence of incomplete knowledge.

Some kind of familiarity had necessarily to form itself between Aschenbach and young Tadzio; and it gave the elderly man keen pleasure to see that his sympathies and interests were not left completely unanswered. For example, when the boy appeared on the beach in the morning and was going toward his family's bathing house, what had induced him never to use the boardwalk on the far side of it any more, but to stroll along the front path, through the sand, past Aschenbach's habitual place, and often unnecessarily close to him, almost touching his table, or his chair even? Did the attraction, the fascination of an overpowering emotion have such an effect upon the frail unthinking object of it? Aschenbach watched daily for Tadzio to approach; and sometimes he acted as though he were occupied when this event was taking place, and he let the boy pass unobserved. But at other times he would look up, and their glances met. They were both in deep earnest when this occurred. Nothing in the elderly man's cultivated and dignified expression betrayed any inner movement; but there was a searching look in Tadzio's eyes, a thoughtful questioning—he began to falter, looked down, then looked up again charmingly, and, when he had passed, something in his bearing seemed to indicate that it was only his breeding which kept him from turning around.

Once, however, one evening, things turned out differently. The Polish children and their governess had been missing at dinner in the large hall; Aschenbach had noted this uneasily. After the meal, disturbed by their absence, Aschenbach was walking in evening dress and straw hat in front of the hotel at the foot of the terrace, when suddenly he saw the nunlike sisters appear in the light of the arc lamp, accompanied by their governess and with Tadzio a few steps behind. Evidently they were coming from the steamer pier after having dined for some reason in the city. It must have been cool on the water; Tadzio was wearing a dark blue sailor overcoat with gold buttons, and on his head he had a cap to match. The sun and sea air had not browned him; his skin still had the same yellow marble color as at first. It even seemed paler today than usual, whether from the coolness or from the blanching moonlight of the lamps. His regular eyebrows showed up more sharply, the darkness of his eyes was deeper. It is hard to say how beautiful he was; and Aschenbach was distressed, as he had often been before, by the thought that words can only evaluate sensuous beauty, but not regive it.

He had not been prepared for this rich spectacle; it came unhoped for. He had no time to entrench himself behind an expression of repose and dignity. Pleasure, surprise, admiration must have shown on his face as his eyes met those of the boy—and at this moment it happened that Tadzio smiled, smiled to him, eloquently, familiarly, charmingly, without concealment; and during the smile his lips slowly opened. It was the smile of Narcissus bent over the reflecting water, that deep, fascinated, magnetic smile with which he stretches out his arms to the image of his own beauty—a smile distorted ever so little, distorted at the hopelessness of his efforts to kiss the pure lips of the shadow. It was coquettish, inquisitive, and slightly tortured. It was infatuated, and infatuating.

He had received this smile, and he hurried away as though he carried a fatal gift. He was so broken up that he was compelled to escape the light of the terrace and the front garden; he hastily hunted out the darkness of the park in the rear. Strangely indignant and tender admonitions wrung themselves out of him: "You dare not smile like that! Listen, no one dare smile like that to another!" He threw himself down on a bench; in a frenzy he breathed the night smell of the vegetation. And leaning back, his arms loose, overwhelmed, with frequent chills running through him, he whispered the fixed formula of desire—impossible in this case, absurd, abject, ridiculous, and yet holy, even in this case venerable: "I love you!"

V

During his fourth week at the Lido, Gustav von Aschenbach made several sinister observations touching on the world about him. First, it seemed to him that as the season progressed the number of guests at the hotel was diminishing rather than increasing; and German especially seemed to be dropping away, so that finally he heard nothing but foreign sounds at table and on the beach. Then one day in conversation with the barber, whom he visited often, he caught a word which startled him. The man had mentioned a German family that left soon after their arrival; he added glibly and flatteringly: "But you are staying, sir. You have no fear of the plague." Aschenbach looked at him. "The plague?" he repeated. The gossiper was silent, made out as though busy with other things, ignored the question. When it was put more insistently, he declared that he knew nothing, and with embarrassing volubility he tried to change the subject.

That was about noon. In the afternoon there was a calm, and Aschenbach rode to Venice under an intense sun. For he was driven by a mania to follow the Polish children, whom he had seen with their governess taking the road to the steamer pier. He did not find the idol at San Marco. But while sitting over his tea at his little round iron table on the shady side of the square, he suddenly detected a peculiar odor in the air which, it seemed to him now, he had noticed for days without being consciously aware of it. The smell was sweetish and druglike, suggesting sickness, and wounds, and a suspicious cleanliness. He tested and examined it thoughtfully, finished his luncheon, and left the square on the side opposite the church. The smell was stronger where the street narrowed. On the corners printed posters were hung, giving municipal warnings against certain diseases of the gastric system liable to occur at this season, against the eating of oysters and clams, and also against the water of the canals. The euphemistic nature of the announcement was palpable. Groups of people had collected in silence on the bridge and squares; and the foreigner stood among them, scenting and investigating.

At a little shop he inquired about the fatal smell, asking the proprietor, who was leaning against his door surrounded by coral chains and imitation amethyst jewelry. The man measured him with heavy eyes, and brightened up hastily. "A matter of precaution, sir!" he answered with a gesture. "A regulation of the police which must be taken for what it is worth. This weather is oppressive, the sirocco is not good for the health. In short, you understand—an exaggerated prudence perhaps." Aschenbach thanked him and went on. Also on the steamer back to the Lido he caught the smell of the disinfectant.

Returning to the hotel, he went immediately to the periodical stand in the lobby and ran through the papers. He found nothing in the foreign-language press. The domestic press spoke of rumors, produced hazy statistics, repeated official denials and questioned their truthfulness. This explained the departure of the German and Austrian guests. Obviously, the subjects of the other nations knew nothing, suspected nothing, were not yet uneasy. "To keep it quiet!" Aschenbach thought angrily, as he threw the papers back on the table. "To keep that quiet!" But at the same moment he was filled with satisfaction over the adventure that was to befall the world about him. For passion, like crime, is not suited to the secure daily rounds of order and well-being; and every slackening in the bourgeois structure, every disorder and affliction of the world, must be held welcome, since they bring with them a vague promise of advantage. So Aschenbach felt a dark contentment with what was taking place, under cover of the authorities, in the dirty alleys of Venice. This wicked secret of the city was welded with his own secret, and he too was involved in keeping it hidden. For in his infatuation he cared about nothing but the possibility of Tadzio's leaving, and he realized with something like terror that he would not know how to go on living if this occurred.

Lately he had not been relying simply on good luck and the daily routine for his chances to be near the boy and look at him. He pursued him, stalked him. On Sundays, for instance, the Poles never appeared on the beach. He guessed that they must be attending mass at San Marco. He hurried there; and, stepping from the heat of the square into the golden twilight of the church, he found the boy he was hunting, bowed over a prie-dieu, praying. Then he stood in the background, on the cracked mosaic floor, with people on all sides kneeling, murmuring, and making the sign of the cross. And the compact grandeur of this Oriental temple weighed heavily on his senses. In front, the richly ornamented priest was conducting the office, moving about and singing; incense poured forth, clouding the weak little flame of the candle on the altar—and with the sweet, stuffy sacrificial odor another seemed to commingle faintly: the smell of the infested city. But through the smoke and the sparkle Aschenbach saw how the boy there in front turned his head, hunted him out, and looked at him.

When the crowd was streaming out through the opened portals into the brilliant square with its swarms of pigeons, the lover hid in the vestibule; he kept under cover, he lay in wait. He saw the Poles quit the church, saw how the children took ceremonious leave of their mother, and how she turned toward the Piazzetta on her way home. He made sure that the boy, the nunlike sisters, and the governess took the road to the right through the gateway of the clock tower and into the Merceria. And after giving them a slight start, he followed, followed them furtively on their walk through Venice. He had to stand still when they stopped, had to take flight in shops and courts to let them pass when they turned back. He lost them; hot and exhausted, he hunted them over bridges and down dirty blind alleys—and he underwent minutes of deadly agony when suddenly he saw them coming toward him in a narrow passage where escape was impossible. Yet it could not be said that he suffered. He was drunk, and his steps followed the promptings of the demon who delights in treading human reason and dignity underfoot.

In one place Tadzio and his companions took a gondola; and shortly after they had pushed off from the shore, Aschenbach, who had hidden behind some structure, a well, while they were climbing in, now did the same. He spoke in a hurried undertone as he directed the rower, with the promise of a generous tip, to follow unnoticed and at a distance that gondola which was just rounding the corner. And he thrilled when the man, with the roguish willingness of an accomplice, assured him in the same tone that his wishes would be carried out, carried out faithfully.

Leaning back against the soft black cushions, he rocked and glided toward the other black-beaked craft where his passion was drawing him. At times it escaped; then he felt worried and uneasy. But his pilot, as though skilled in such commissions, was always able through sly maneuvers, speedy diagonals and shortcuts, to bring the quest into view again. The air was quiet and smelly, the sun burned down strong through the slate-colored mist. Water slapped against the wood and stone. The call of the gondolier, half warning, half greeting, was answered with a strange obedience far away in the silence of the labyrinth. White and purple umbels with the scent of almonds hung down from little elevated gardens over crumbling walls. Arabian window casings were outlined through the murkiness. The marble steps of a church descended into the water; a beggar squatted there, protesting his misery, holding out his hat, and showing the whites of his eyes as though he were blind. An antiquarian in front of his den fawned on the passer-by and invited him to stop in the hopes of swindling him. That was Venice, the flatteringly and suspiciously beautiful—this city, half legend, half snare for strangers; in its foul air art once flourished gluttonously, and had suggested to its musicians seductive notes which cradle and lull. The adventurer felt as though his eyes were taking in this same luxury, as though his ears were being won by just such melodies. He recalled too that the city was diseased and was concealing this through greed—and he peered more eagerly after the retreating gondola.

Thus, in his infatuation, he wanted simply to pursue uninterrupted the object that aroused him, to dream of it when it was not there, and, after the fashion of lovers, to speak softly to its mere outline. Loneliness, strangeness, and the joy of a deep belated intoxication encouraged him and prompted him to accept even the remotest things without reserve or shame—with the result that as he returned late in the evening from Venice, he stopped on the second floor of the hotel before the door of the boy's room, laid his head in utter drunkenness against the hinge of the door, and for a long time could not drag himself away despite the danger of being caught and embarrassed in such a mad situation.

Yet there were still moments of relief when he came partly to his senses. "Where to?" he would think, alarmed. "Where to?" Like every man whose natural abilities stimulate an aristocratic interest in his ancestry, he was accustomed to think of his forebears in connection with the accomplishments and successes of his life, to assure himself of their approval, their satisfaction, their undeniable respect. He thought of them now, entangled as he was in such an illicit experience, caught in such exotic transgressions. He thought of their characteristic rigidity of principle, their scrupulous masculinity—and he smiled dejectedly. What would they say? But then, what would they have said to his whole life, which was almost degenerate in its departure from theirs, this life under the bane of art—a life against which he himself had once issued such youthful mockeries out of loyalty to his fathers, but which at bottom had been so much like theirs! He too had served, he too had been a soldier and a warrior like many of them—for art was a war, a destructive battle, and one was not equal to it for long, these days. A life of self-conquest and of in-spite-of's, a rigid, sober, and unyielding life which he had formed into the symbol of a delicate and timely heroism. He might well call it masculine, or brave; and it almost seemed as though the Eros mastering him were somehow peculiarly adapted and inclined to such a life. Had not this Eros stood in high repute among the bravest of peoples; was it not true that precisely through bravery he had flourished in their cities? Numerous war heroes of antiquity had willingly borne his yoke, for nothing was deemed a disgrace which the god imposed; and acts which would have been rebuked as the sign of cowardice if they had been done for other purposes—prostrations, oaths, entreaties, abjectness—such things did not bring shame upon the lover, but rather he reaped praise for them.

In this way his infatuation determined the course of his thoughts, in this way he tried to uphold himself, to preserve his respect. But at the same time, selfish and calculating, he turned his attention to the unclean transactions here in Venice, this adventure of the outer world which conspired darkly with his own and which fed his passion with vague lawless hopes.

Bent on getting reliable news of the condition and progress of the pestilence, he ransacked the local papers in the city cafés, as they had been missing from the reading table of the hotel lobby for several days now. Statements alternated with disavowals. The number of the sick and dead was supposed to reach twenty, forty, or even a hundred and more—and immediately afterward every instance of the plague would be either flatly denied or attributed to completely isolated cases which had crept in from the outside. There were scattered admonitions, protests against the dangerous conduct of foreign authorities. Certainty was impossible. Nevertheless, the lone man felt especially entitled to participate in the secret; and although he was excluded, he derived a grotesque satisfaction from putting embarrassing questions to those who did know, and, as they were pledged to silence, forcing them into deliberate lies. One day at breakfast in the large dining hall he entered into a conversation with the manager, that softly treading little man in the French frock coat who was moving amiably and solicitously about among the diners and had stopped at Aschenbach's table for a few passing words. Just why, the guest asked negligently and casually, had disinfectants become so prevalent in Venice recently? "It has to do," was the evasive answer, "with a police regulation, and is intended to prevent any inconveniences or disturbances to the public health which might result from the exceptionally warm and threatening weather." . . . "The police are to be congratulated," Aschenbach answered; and after the exchange of a few remarks on the weather, the manager left.

Yet that same day, in the evening, after dinner, it happened that a little band of strolling singers from the city gave a performance in the front garden of the hotel. Two men and two women, they stood by the iron post of an arc lamp and turned their whitened faces up toward the large terrace where the guests were enjoying this folk recital over their coffee and cooling drinks. The hotel personnel, bellboys, waiters, and clerks from the office, could be seen listening by the doors of the vestibule. The Russian family, eager and precise in their amusements, had had wicker chairs placed in the garden in order to be nearer the performers; and they were sitting there in an appreciative semicircle. Behind the ladies and gentlemen, in her turbanlike kerchief, stood the old slave.

Mandolin, guitar, harmonica, and a squeaky violin were responding to the touch of the virtuoso beggars. Instrumental numbers alternated with songs, as when the younger of the women, with a sharp trembling voice, joined with the sweetly falsetto tenor in a languishing love duet. But the real talent and leader of the group was undoubtedly the other of the two men, the one with the guitar. He was a kind of *buffo* baritone, with not much of a voice, although he did have a gift for pantomime, and a remarkable comic energy. Often, with his large instrument under his arm, he would leave the rest of the group and, still acting, would intrude on the platform, where his antics were rewarded with encouraging laughter. The Russians in their seats down front seemed to be especially enchanted with so much southern mobility, and their applause incited him to let himself out more and more boldly and assertively.

Aschenbach sat on the balustrade, cooling his lips now and then with a mixture of pomegranate juice and soda which glowed ruby-red in his glass in front of him. His nerves took in the miserable notes, the vulgar crooning melodies; for passion lames the sense of discrimination, and surrenders in all seriousness to appeals which, in sober moments, are either humorously allowed for or rejected with annoyance. At the clown's antics his features had twisted into a set painful smile. He sat there relaxed, although inwardly he was intensely awake; for six paces from him Tadzio was leaning against the stone hand rail.

In the white belted coat which he often wore at mealtime, he was standing in a position of spontaneous and inborn gracefulness, his left forearm on the railing, feet crossed, the right hand on a supporting hip; and he looked down at the street singers with an expression which was hardly a smile, but only an aloof curiosity, a polite amiability. Often he would stand erect and, expanding his chest, would draw the white smock down under his leather belt with a beautiful gesture. And then, too, the aging man observed with a tumult of fright and triumph how he would often turn his head over the left shoulder in the direction of his admirer, carefully and hesitatingly, or even with abruptness as though to attack by surprise. He did not meet Aschenbach's eyes, for a mean precaution compelled the transgressor to keep from staring at him: in the background of the terrace the women who guarded Tadzio were sitting, and things had reached a point where the lover had to fear he might be noticed and suspected. Yes, he had often observed with a kind of numbness how, when Tadzio was near him, on the beach, in the hotel lobby, in the Piazza San Marco, they called him back, they were set on keeping him at a distance—and this wounded him frightfully, causing his pride unknown tortures which his conscience would not permit him to evade.

Meanwhile the guitar player had begun a solo to his own accompaniment, a street ballad popular throughout Italy. It had several strophes, and the entire company joined each time in the refrain, all singing and playing, while he managed to give a plastic and dramatic twist to the performance. Of slight build, with thin and impoverished features, he stood on the gravel, apart from his companions, in an attitude of insolent bravado, his shabby felt hat on the back of his head so that a bunch of his red hair jutted out from under the brim. And to the thrumming of the strings he flung his jokes up at the terrace in a penetrating recitative; while the veins were swelling on his forehead from the exertion of his performance. He did not seem of Venetian stock, but rather of the race of Neapolitan comedians, half pimp, half entertainer, brutal and audacious, dangerous and amusing. His song was stupid enough so far as the words went; but in his mouth, by his gestures, the movements of his body, his way of blinking significantly and letting the tongue play across his lips, it acquired something ambiguous, something vaguely repulsive. In addition to the customary civilian dress, he was wearing a sport shirt; and his skinny neck protruded above the soft collar, baring a noticeably large and active Adam's apple. He was pale and snub-nosed. It was hard to fix an age to his beardless features, which seemed furrowed with grimaces and depravity; and the two wrinkles standing arrogantly, harshly, almost savagely between his reddish eyebrows were strangely suited to the smirk on his mobile lips. Yet what really prompted the lonely man to pay him keen attention was the observation that the questionable figure seemed also to provide its own questionable atmosphere. For each time they came to the refrain the singer, amid buffoonery and familiar handshakes, began a grotesque circular march which brought him immediately beneath Aschenbach's place; and each time this happened, there blew up to the terrace from his clothes and body a strong carbolic smell.

After the song was ended, he began collecting money. He started with the Russians, who were evidently willing to spend, and then came up the stairs. Up here he showed himself just as humble as he had been bold during the performance. Cringing and bowing, he stole about among the tables, and a smile of obsequious cunning exposed his strong teeth, while the two wrinkles still stood ominously between his red eyebrows. This singular character collecting money to live on—they eyed him with a curiosity and a kind of repugnance, they tossed coins into his felt hat with the tips of their fingers, and were careful not to touch him. The elimination of the physical distance between the comedian and the audience, no matter how great the enjoyment may have been, always causes a certain uneasiness. He felt it, and tried to excuse it by groveling. He came up to Aschenbach, and along with him the smell, which no one else seemed concerned about.

"Listen!" the recluse said in an undertone, almost mechanically. "They are disinfecting Venice. Why?" The jester answered hoarsely: "On account of the police. That is a precaution, sir, with such heat, and the sirocco. The sirocco is oppressive. It is not good for the health." He spoke as though astonished that anyone could ask such things, and demonstrated with his open hand how oppressive the sirocco was. "Then there is no plague in Venice?" Aschenbach asked quietly, between his teeth. The clown's muscular features fell into a grimace of comical embarrassment. "A plague? What kind of plague? Perhaps our police are a plague? You like to joke! A plague! Of all things! A precautionary measure, you understand! A police regulation against the effects of the oppressive weather." He gesticulated. "Very well," Aschenbach said several times curtly and quietly; and he quickly dropped an unduly large coin into the hat. Then with his eyes he signaled the man to leave. He obeyed, smirking and bowing. But he had not reached the stairs before two hotel employees threw themselves upon him, and with their faces close to his began a whispered cross-examination. He shrugged his shoulders; he gave assurances, he swore that he had kept quiet—that was evident. He was released, and he returned to the garden; then, after a short conference with his companions, he stepped out once more for a final song of thanks and leave-taking.

It was a rousing song which the recluse never recalled having heard before, a "big number" in incomprehensible dialect, with a laugh refrain in which the troupe joined regularly at the top of their voices. At this point both the words and the accompaniment of the instruments stopped, with nothing left but a laugh which was somehow arranged rhythmically although very naturally done—and the soloist especially showed great talent in giving it a most deceptive vitality. At the renewal of his professional distance from the audience, he recovered all his boldness again, and the artificial laugh that he directed up toward the terrace was derisive. Even before the end of the articulate portion of the strophe, he seemed to struggle against an irresistible tickling. He gulped, his voice trembled, he pressed his hand over his mouth, he contorted his shoulders; and at the proper moment the ungovernable laugh broke out of him, burst into such real cackles that it was infectious and communicated itself to the audience, so that on the terrace also an unfounded hilarity, living off itself alone, started up. But this seemed to double the singer's exuberance. He bent his knees, he slapped his thighs, he nearly split himself; he no longer laughed, he shrieked. He pointed up with his finger, as though nothing were more comic than the laughing guests there, and finally everyone in the garden and on the veranda was laughing, even to the waiters, bellboys, and house servants in the doorways.

Aschenbach was no longer resting in his chair; he sat upright, as if attempting to defend himself, or to escape. But the laughter, the whiffs of the hospital smell, and the boy's nearness combined to put him into a trance that held his mind and his senses hopelessly captive. In the general movement and distraction he ventured to glance across at Tadzio, and as he did so he dared observe that the boy, in reply to his glance, was equally serious, much as though he had modeled his conduct and expression after those of one man, and the prevalent mood had no effect on him since this one man was not part of it. This portentous childish obedience had something so disarming and overpowering about it that the gray-haired man could hardly restrain himself from burying his face in his hands. It had also seemed to him that Tadzio's occasional stretching and quick breathing indicated a complaint, a congestion, of the lungs. "He is sickly, he will probably not grow old," he thought repeatedly with that positiveness which is often a peculiar relief to desire and passion.

And along with pure solicitude he had a feeling of rakish gratification.

Meanwhile the Venetians had ended and were leaving. Applause accompanied them, and their leader did not miss the opportunity to cover his retreat with further jests. His bows, the kisses he blew, were laughed at—and so he doubled them. When his companions were already gone, he acted as though he had hurt himself by backing into a lamppost, and he crept through the gate seemingly crippled with pain. Then he suddenly threw off the mask of comic hard luck, stood upright, hurried away jauntily, stuck out his tongue insolently at the guests on the terrace, and slipped into the darkness. The company was breaking up; Tadzio had been missing from the balustrade for some time. But, to the displeasure of the waiters, the lonely man sat for a long while over the remains of his pomegranate drink. Night advanced. Time was crumbling. In the house of his parents many years back, there had been an hourglass—of a sudden he saw the fragile and expressive instrument again, as though it were standing in front of him. Fine and noiseless, the rust-red sand was running through the glass neck; and since it was getting low in the upper half, a speedy little vortex had been formed there.

As early as the following day, in the afternoon, he had made new progress in his obstinate baiting of the people he met—and this time he had all possible success. He walked from the Piazza San Marco into the English travel bureau located there; and after changing some money at the cash desk, he put on the expression of a distrustful foreigner and launched his fatal question at the attendant clerk. He was a Britisher; he wore a woollen suit, and was still young, with close-set eyes, and had that characteristic stolid reliability which is so peculiarly and strikingly appealing in the tricky, nimble-witted South. He began: "No reason for alarm, sir. A regulation without any serious significance. Such measures are often taken to anticipate the unhealthy effects of the heat and the sirocco. . . ." But as he raised his blue eyes, he met the stare of the foreigner, a tired and somewhat unhappy stare focused on his lips with a touch of scorn. Then the Englishman blushed. "At least," he continued in an emotional undertone, "that is the official explanation which people here are content to accept. I will admit that there is something more behind it." And then in his frank and leisurely manner he told the truth.

For several years now Asiatic cholera had shown a heightened tendency to spread and migrate. Hatched in the warm swamps of the Ganges delta, rising with the noxious breath of that luxuriant, unfit primitive world and island wilderness which is shunned by humans and where the tiger crouches in the bamboo thickets, the plague had raged continuously and with unusual strength in Hindustan, had reached eastward to China, westward to Afghanistan and Persia, and, following the chief caravan routes, had carried its terrors to Astrakhan, and even to Moscow. But while Europe was trembling lest the specter continue its advance from there across the country, it had been transported over the sea by Syrian merchantmen, and had turned up almost simultaneously in several Medi-

terranean ports, had raised its head in Toulon and Málaga, had showed its
mask several times in Palermo and Naples, and seemed permanently en-
trenched through Calabria and Apulia. The north of the peninsula had
been spared. Yet in the middle of this May in Venice the frightful
vibrions were found on one and the same day in the blackish wasted
bodies of a cabin boy and a woman who sold greengroceries. The cases
were kept secret. But within a week there were ten, twenty, thirty more,
and in various sections. A man from the Austrian provinces who had
made a pleasure trip to Venice for a few days, returned to his home town
and died with unmistakable symptoms—and that is how the first reports
of the pestilence in the lagoon city got into the German newspapers. The
Venetian authorities answered that the city's health conditions had never
been better, and took the most necessary preventive measures. But probably the food supply had been infected. Denied and glossed over, death
was eating its way along the narrow streets, and its dissemination was
especially favored by the premature summer heat which made the water
of the canals lukewarm. Yes, it seemed as though the plague had got
renewed strength, as though the tenacity and fruitfulness of its stimuli had
doubled. Cases of recovery were rare. Out of a hundred attacks, eighty
were fatal, and in the most horrible manner. For the plague moved with
utter savagery, and often showed that most dangerous form which is
called "the drying." Water from the blood vessels collected in pockets,
and the blood was unable to carry this off. Within a few hours the victim
was parched, his blood became as thick as glue, and he stifled amid cramps
and hoarse groans. Lucky for him if, as sometimes happened, the attack
took the form of a light discomfiture followed by a profound coma from
which he seldom or never awakened. At the beginning of June the pest-
house of the Ospedale Civico had quietly filled; there was not much room
left in the two orphan asylums, and a frightfully active commerce was
kept up between the wharf of the Fondamente Nuove and San Michele,
the burial island. But there was the fear of a general drop in prosperity.
The recently opened art exhibit in the public gardens was to be considered, along with the heavy losses which, in case of panic or unfavorable
rumors, would threaten business, the hotels, the entire elaborate system
for exploiting foreigners—and as these considerations evidently carried
more weight than love of truth or respect for international agreements,
the city authorities upheld obstinately their policy of silence, and denial.
The chief health officer had resigned from his post in indignation, and
had been promptly replaced by a more tractable personality. The people
knew this; and the corruption of their superiors, together with the predominating insecurity, the exceptional condition into which the preva-
lence of death had plunged the city, induced a certain demoralization of
the lower classes, encouraging shady and antisocial impulses which manifested themselves in license, profligacy, and a rising crime wave. Contrary
to custom, many drunkards were seen in the evenings; it was said that at
night nasty mobs made the streets unsafe. Burglaries and even murders

became frequent, for it had already been proved on two occasions that persons who had presumably fallen victim to the plague had in reality been dispatched with poison by their own relatives. And professional debauchery assumed abnormal obtrusive proportions such as had never been known here before, and to an extent which is usually found only in the southern parts of the country and in the Orient.

The Englishman pronounced the final verdict on these facts. "You would do well," he concluded, "to leave today rather than tomorrow. It cannot be much more than a couple of days before a quarantine zone is declared."

"Thank you," Aschenbach said, and left the office.

The square lay sunless and stifling. Unsuspecting foreigners sat in front of the cafés or stood among the pigeons in front of the church and watched the swarms of birds flapping their wings, crowding one another, and pecking at grains of corn offered them in open palms. The recluse was feverishly excited, triumphant in his possession of the truth. But it had left him with a bad taste in his mouth, and a weird horror in his heart. As he walked up and down the flagstones of the gorgeous court, he was weighing an action which would meet the situation and would absolve him. This evening after dinner he could approach the woman with the pearls and make her a speech; he had figured it out word for word: "Permit a foreigner, madam, to give you some useful advice, a warning, which is being withheld from you through self-interest. Leave immediately with Tadzio and your daughters! Venice is full of the plague." Then he could lay a farewell hand on the head of this tool of a mocking divinity, turn away, and flee this morass. But he felt at the same time that he was very far from seriously desiring such a move. He would retract it, would disengage himself from it. . . . But when we are distracted we loathe most the thought of retracing our steps. He recalled a white building, ornamented with inscriptions which glistened in the evening and in whose transparent mysticism his mind's eye had lost itself—and then that strange wanderer's form which had awakened in the aging man the roving hankerings of youth after the foreign and the remote. And the thought of return, the thought of prudence and soberness, effort, mastery, disgusted him to such an extent that his face was distorted with an expression of physical nausea. "It must be kept quiet!" he whispered heavily. And: "I will keep quiet!" The consciousness of his share in the facts and the guilt intoxicated him, much as a little wine intoxicates a tired brain. The picture of the diseased and neglected city hovering desolately before him aroused vague hopes beyond the bounds of reason, but with an egregious sweetness. What was the scant happiness he had dreamed of a moment ago compared with these expectations? What were art and virtue worth to him over against the advantages of chaos? He kept quiet, and remained in Venice.

This same night he had a frightful dream, if one can designate as a dream a bodily and mental experience which occurred to him in the

deepest sleep, completely independent of him, and with a physical realness, although he never saw himself present or moving about among the
incidents; but their stage rather was his soul itself, and they broke in from
without, trampling down his resistance—a profound and spiritual resistance—by sheer force; and when they had passed through, they left his
substance, the culture of his lifetime, crushed and annihilated behind them.

It began with anguish, anguish and desire, and a frightened curiosity as to what was coming. It was night, and his senses were on the
watch. From far off a grumble, an uproar, was approaching, a jumble of
noises. Clanking, blaring, and dull thunder, with shrill shouts and a definite whine in a long-drawn-out *u*-sound—all this was sweetly, ominously
interspersed with and dominated by the deep cooing of wickedly persistent flutes which charmed the bowels in a shamelessly penetrative manner.
But he knew one phrase; it was veiled, and yet would name what was
approaching: "The foreign god!" Vaporous fire began to glow; then he
recognized mountains like those about his summer house. And in the
scattered light, from high up in the woods, among tree trunks and crumbling moss-grown rocks—people, beasts, a throng, a raging mob plunged
twisting and whirling downward, and made the hill swarm with bodies,
flames, tumult, and a riotous round dance. Women, tripped by overlong
fur draperies which hung from their waists, were holding up tambourines
and beating on them, their groaning heads flung back. Others swung
sparking firebrands and bare daggers, or wore hissing snakes about the
middle of their bodies, or, shrieking, held their breasts in their two hands.
Men with horns on their foreheads, shaggy-haired, girded with hides,
bent back their necks and raised their arms and thighs, clashed brass
cymbals and beat furiously at kettledrums, while smooth boys prodded he-
goats with wreathed sticks, climbing on their horns and falling off with
shouts when they bounded. And the bacchantes wailed the word with the
soft consonants and the drawn-out *u*-sound, at once sweet and savage, like
nothing ever heard before. In one place it rang out as though piped into
the air by stags, and it was echoed in another by many voices, in wild
triumph—with it they incited one another to dance and to fling out their
arms and legs, and it was never silent. But everything was pierced and
dominated by the deep coaxing flute. He who was fighting against this
experience—did it not coax him too, with its shameless penetration, into
the feast and the excesses of the extreme sacrifice? His repugnance, his
fear, were keen—he was honorably set on defending himself to the very
last against the barbarian, the foe to intellectual poise and dignity. But the
noise, the howling, multiplied by the resonant walls of the hills, grew,
took the upper hand, swelled to a fury of rapture. Odors oppressed the
senses, the pungent smell of the bucks, the scent of moist bodies, and a
waft of stagnant water, with another smell, something familiar, the smell
of wounds and prevalent disease. At the beating of the drum his heart
fluttered, his head was spinning, he was caught in a frenzy, in a blinding
deafening lewdness—and he yearned to join the ranks of the god. The

obscene symbol, huge, wooden was uncovered and raised up; then they howled the magic word with more abandon. Foaming at the mouth, they raged, teased one another with ruttish gestures and caressing hands; laughing and groaning, they stuck the goads into one another's flesh and licked the blood from their limbs. But the dreamer now was with them, in them, and he belonged to the foreign god. Yes, they were he himself, as they hurled themselves biting and tearing upon the animals, got entangled in steaming rags, and fell in promiscuous unions on the torn moss, in sacrifice to their god. And his soul tasted the unchastity and fury of decay.

When he awakened from the affliction of this dream he was unnerved, shattered, and hopelessly under the power of the demon. He no longer avoided the inquisitive glances of other people; he did not care if he was exciting their suspicions. And as a matter of fact they were fleeing, traveling elsewhere. Numerous bathing houses stood empty, the occupants of the dining hall became more and more scattered, and in the city now one rarely saw a foreigner. The truth seemed to have leaked out; the panic, despite the reticence of those whose interests were involved, seemed no longer avoidable. But the woman with the pearls remained with her family, either because the rumors had not yet reached her or because she was too proud and fearless to heed them. Tadzio remained. And to Aschenbach, in his infatuation, it seemed at times as though flight and death might remove all the disturbing elements of life around them and leave him here alone with the boy. Yes, by the sea in the forenoon when his eyes rested heavily, irresponsibly, unwaveringly on the thing he coveted, or when, as the day was ending, he followed shamelessly after him through streets where the hideous death lurked in secret—at such times the attrocious seemed to him rich in possibilities, and laws of morality had dropped away.

Like any lover, he wanted to please; and he felt a bitter anguish lest it might not be possible. He added bright youthful details to his dress, he put on jewels, and used perfumes. During the day he often spent much time over his toilet, and came to the table strikingly dressed, excited, and in suspense. In the light of the sweet youthfulness which had done this to him, he detested his aging body. The sight of his gray hair, his sharp features, plunged him into shame and hopelessness. It induced him to attempt rejuvenating his body and appearance. He often visited the hotel barber.

Beneath the barber's apron, leaning back on the chair under the gossiper's expert hands, he winced to observe his reflection in the mirror.

"Gray," he said, making a wry face.

"A little," the man answered. "Due entirely to a slight neglect, an indifference to outward things, which is conceivable in people of importance, but it is not exactly praiseworthy. And all the less so since such persons are above prejudice in matters of nature or art. If the moral objections of certain people to the art of cosmetics were to be logically extended to the care of the teeth, they would give no slight offense. And after all, we are just as old as we feel, and under some circumstances gray

hair would actually stand for more of an untruth than the despised cor-
rection. In your case, sir, you are entitled to the natural color of your
hair. Will you permit me simply to return what belongs to you?"

"How is that?" Aschenbach asked.

Then the orator washed his client's hair with two kinds of water, one
clear and one dark, and it was as black as in youth. Following this, he
curled it with irons into soft waves, stepped back, and eyed his work.

"All that is left now," he said, "would be to freshen up the skin a
little."

And like someone who cannot finish, cannot satisfy himself, he
passed with quickening energy from one manipulation to another. Aschenbach rested comfortably, incapable of resistance, or rather his hopes
were aroused by what was taking place. In the glass he saw his brows arch
more evenly and decisively. His eyes became longer; their brilliance was
heightened by a light touching up of the lids. A little lower, where the
skin had been a leatherish brown, he saw a delicate crimson tint grow
beneath a deft application of color. His lips, bloodless a little while past,
became full, and as red as raspberries. The furrows in the cheeks and
about the mouth, the wrinkles of the eyes, disappeared beneath lotions
and cream. With a knocking heart he beheld a blossoming youth. Finally
the beauty specialist declared himself content, after the manner of such
people, by obsequiously thanking the man he had been serving. "A trifling assistance," he said, as he applied one parting touch. "Now the gentleman can fall in love unhesitatingly." He walked away, fascinated; he
was happy as in a dream, timid and bewildered. His necktie was red, his
broad-brimmed straw hat was trimmed with a variegated band.

A tepid storm wind had risen. It was raining sparsely and at intervals,
but the air was damp, thick, and filled with the smell of things rotting. All
around him he heard a fluttering, pattering, and swishing; and under the
fever of his cosmetics it seemed to him as though evil wind-spirits were
haunting the place, impure sea birds which rooted and gnawed at the
food of the condemned and befouled it with their droppings. For the sultriness destroyed his appetite, and the fancy suggested itself that the
foods were poisoned with contaminating substances. Tracking the boy
one afternoon, Aschenbach had plunged deep into the tangled center of
the diseased city. He was becoming uncertain of where he was, since the
alleys, waterways, bridges, and little squares of the labyrinth were all so
much alike, and he was no longer even sure of directions. He was absorbed with the problem of keeping the pursued figure in sight. And,
driven to disgraceful subterfuges, flattening himself against walls, hiding
behind the backs of other people, for a long time he did not notice the
weariness, the exhaustion, with which emotion and the continual suspense
had taxed his mind and his body. Tadzio walked behind his companions.
He always allowed the governess and the nunlike sisters to precede him in
the narrow places; and, loitering behind alone, he would turn his head
occasionally to look over his shoulder and make sure by a glance of his

peculiarly dark-gray eyes that his admirer was following. He saw him, and did not betray him. Drunk with the knowledge of this, lured forward by those eyes, led meekly by his passion, the lover stole after his unseemly hope—but finally he was cheated and lost sight of him. The Poles had crossed a short arching bridge; the height of the curve hid them from the pursuer, and when he himself had arrived there he no longer saw them. He hunted for them vainly in three directions, straight ahead and to either side along the narrow dirty wharf. In the end he was so tired and unnerved that he had to give up the search.

His head was on fire, his body was covered with a sticky sweat, his knees trembled. He could no longer endure the thirst that was torturing him, and he looked around for some immediate relief. From a little vegetable store he bought some fruit—strawberries, soft and overly ripe—and he ate them as he walked. A very charming, forsaken little square opened up before him. He recognized it; here he had made his frustrated plans for flight weeks ago. He let himself sink down on the steps of the cistern in the middle of the square, and laid his head against the stone cylinder. It was quiet; grass was growing up through the pavement; refuse was scattered about. Among the weather-beaten, unusually tall houses surrounding him there was one like a palace, with little lion-covered balconies and Gothic windows with blank emptiness behind them. On the ground floor of another house was a drugstore. Warm gusts of wind occasionally carried the smell of carbolic acid.

He sat there, he, the master, the artist of dignity, the author of *The Wretch*, a work which had, in such accurate symbols, renounced vagabondage and the depths of misery, had denied all sympathy with the engulfed, and had cast out the outcast; the man who had arrived and, victor over his own knowledge, had outgrown all irony and acclimatized himself to the obligations of public confidence; whose reputation was official, whose name had been knighted, and on whose style boys were urged to pattern themselves—he sat there. His eyelids were shut; only now and then a mocking uneasy side glance slipped out from beneath them. And his loose lips, set off by the cosmetics, formed isolated words of the strange dream logic created by his half-slumbering brain.

"For beauty, Phaedrus, mark me, beauty alone is both divine and visible at once; and thus it is the road of the sensuous; it is, little Phaedrus, the road of the artist to the spiritual. But do you now believe, my dear, that they can ever attain wisdom and true human dignity for whom the road to the spiritual leads through the senses? Or do you believe rather (I leave the choice to you) that this is a pleasant but perilous road, a really wrong and sinful road, which necessarily leads astray? For you must know that we poets cannot take the road of beauty without having Eros join us and set himself up as our leader. Indeed, we may even be heroes after our fashion, and hardened warriors, though we be like women, for passion is our exaltation, and our desire must remain love—that is our pleasure and our disgrace. You now see, do you not, that we poets cannot be wise and dignified? That we necessarily go astray, necessarily remain lascivious, and adventurers in emotion? The mastery of our style is all lies and foolishness, our renown and honor are a farce, the confidence of the masses in us is highly ridiculous, and the training of the public and of youth through art is a precarious undertaking which should be forbidden. For how, indeed, could he be a fit instructor who is born with a natural leaning toward the precipice? We might well disavow it and reach after dignity, but wherever we turn it attracts us. Let us, say, renounce the dissolvent of knowledge, since knowledge, Phaedrus, has no dignity or strength. It is aware, it understands and pardons, but without reserve and form. It feels sympathy with the precipice, it *is* the precipice. This, then, we abandon with firmness, and from now on our efforts matter only by their yield of beauty, or, in other words, simplicity, greatness, and new rigor, form, and a second type of openness. But form and openness, Phaedrus, lead to intoxication and to desire, lead the noble perhaps into sinister revels of emotion which his own beautiful rigor rejects as infamous, lead to the precipice—yes, they too lead to the precipice. They lead us poets there, I say, since we cannot force ourselves, since we can merely let ourselves out. And now I am going, Phaedrus. You stay here; and when you no longer see me, then you go too."

A few days later, as Gustav von Aschenbach was not feeling well, he left the beach hotel at a later hour in the morning than usual. He had to fight against certain attacks of vertigo which were only partially physical and were accompanied by a pronounced malaise, a feeling of bafflement and hopelessness—while he was not certain whether this had to do with conditions outside him or with his own nature. In the lobby he noticed a large pile of luggage ready for shipment; he asked the doorkeeper who it was that was leaving, and heard in answer the Polish title which he had learned secretly. He accepted this without any alteration of his sunken features, with that curt elevation of the head by which one acknowledges something he does not need to know. Then he asked: "When?" The answer was: "After lunch." He nodded, and went to the beach.

It was not very inviting. Rippling patches of rain retreated across the wide flat water separating the beach from the first long sandbank. An air of autumn, of things past their prime, seemed to lie over the pleasure spot which had once been so alive with color and was now almost abandoned. The sand was no longer kept clean. A camera, seemingly without an owner, stood on its tripod by the edge of the sea; and a black cloth thrown over it was flapping noisily in the wind.

Tadzio, with the three or four companions still left, was moving about to the right in front of his family's cabin. And midway between the sea and the row of bathing houses, lying back in his chair with a robe over his knees, Aschenbach looked at him once more. The game, which was not being supervised since the women were probably occupied with preparations for the journey, seemed to have no rules, and it was degenerating. The stocky boy with the sleek black hair who was called Jaschu had been angered and blinded by sand flung in his face. He forced Tadzio into a wrestling match which quickly ended in the fall of the beauty, who was weaker. But as though, in the hour of parting, the servile feelings of the inferior had turned to merciless brutality and were trying to get vengeance for a long period of slavery, the victor did not let go of the boy underneath, but knelt on his back and pressed his face so persistently into the sand that Tadzio, already breathless from the struggle, was in danger of strangling. His attempts to shake off the weight were fitful; for moments they stopped entirely and were resumed again as mere twitchings. Enraged, Aschenbach was about to spring to the rescue, when the torturer finally released his victim. Tadzio, very pale, raised himself halfway and sat motionless for several minutes, resting on one arm, with rumpled hair and glowering eyes. Then he stood up completely, and moved slowly away. They called him, cheerfully at first, then anxiously and imploringly; he did not listen. The swarthy boy, who seemed to regret his excesses immediately afterward, caught up with him and tried to placate him. A movement of the shoulder put him at his distance. Tadzio went down obliquely to the water. He was barefoot, and wore his striped linen suit with the red bow.

He lingered on the edge of the water with his head down, drawing figures in the wet sand with one toe; then he went into the shallows, which did not cover his knees in the deepest place, crossed them leisurely, and arrived at the sandbank. He stood there a moment, his face turned to the open sea; soon after, he began stepping slowly to the left along the narrow stretch of exposed ground. Separated from the mainland by the expanse of water, separated from his companions by a proud moodiness, he moved along, a strongly isolated and unrelated figure with fluttering hair—placed out there in the sea, the wind, against the vague mists. He stopped once more to look around. And suddenly, as though at some recollection, some impulse, with one hand on his hip he turned the upper part of his body in a beautiful twist which began from the base—and he looked over his shoulder toward the shore. The watcher sat there, as he had sat once before when for the first time these twilight-gray eyes had turned at the doorway and met his own. His head, against the back of the chair, had slowly followed the movements of the boy walking yonder. Now, simultaneously with this glance, it rose and sank on his breast, so that his eyes looked out from underneath, while his face took on the loose, inwardly relaxed expression of deep sleep. But it seemed to him as though the pale and lovely lure out there were smiling to him, nodding to him; as though, removing his hand from his hip, he were signaling to come out, were vaguely guiding toward egregious promises. And, as often before, he stood up to follow him.

Some minutes passed before anyone hurried to the aid of the man who had collapsed into one corner of his chair. He was brought to his room. And on the same day a respectfully shocked world received the news of his death.

Thomas Mann

MARIO AND THE MAGICIAN

THE ATMOSPHERE OF Torre di Venere remains unpleasant in the memory. From the first moment the air of the place made us uneasy, we felt irritable, on edge; then at the end came the shocking business of Cipolla, that dreadful being who seemed to incorporate, in so fateful and so humanly impressive a way, all the peculiar evilness of the situation as a whole. Looking back, we had the feeling that the horrible end of the affair had been preordained and lay in the nature of things; that the children had to be present at it was an added impropriety, due to the false colours in which the weird creature presented himself. Luckily for them, they did not know where the comedy left off and the tragedy began; and we let them remain in their happy belief that the whole thing had been a play up till the end.

Torre di Venere lies some fifteen kilometers from Portoclemente, one of the most popular summer resorts on the Tyrrhenian Sea. Portoclemente is urban and elegant and full to overflowing for months on end. Its gay and busy main street of shops and hotels runs down to a wide sandy beach covered with tents and pennanted sand-castles and sunburnt humanity, where at all times a lively social bustle reigns, and much noise. But this same spacious and inviting fine-sanded beach, this same border of pine grove and near, presiding mountains, continues all the way along the coast. No wonder then that some competition of a quiet kind should have sprung up further on. Torre di Venere—the tower that gave the town its name is gone long since, one looks for it in vain—is an offshoot of the larger resort, and for some years remained an idyll for the few, a refuge for more unworldly spirits. But the usual history of such places repeated itself: peace has had to retire further along the coast, to Marina

Petriera and dear knows where else. We all know how the world at once seeks peace and puts her to flight—rushing upon her in the fond idea that they two will wed, and where she is, there it can be at home. It will even set up its Vanity Fair in a spot and be capable of thinking that peace is still by its side. Thus Torre—though its atmosphere so far is more modest and contemplative than that of Portoclemente—has been quite taken up, by both Italians and foreigners. It is no longer the thing to go to Portoclemente—though still so much the thing that it is as noisy and crowded as ever. One goes next door, so to speak: to Torre. So much more refined, even, and cheaper to boot. And the attractiveness of these qualities persists, though the qualities themselves long ago ceased to be evident. Torre has got a Grand Hotel. Numerous pensions have sprung up, some modest, some pretentious. The people who own or rent the villas and pinetas overlooking the sea no longer have it all their own way on the beach. In July and August it looks just like the beach at Porto-clemente: it swarms with a screaming, squabbling, merrymaking crowd, and the sun, blazing down like mad, peels the skin off their necks. Garish little flat-bottomed boats rock on the glittering blue, manned by children, whose mothers hover afar and fill the air with anxious cries of Nino! and Sandro! and Bice! and Maria! Pedlars step across the legs of recumbent sun-bathers, selling flowers and corals, oysters, lemonade, and *cornetti al burro,* and crying their wares in the breathy, full-throated southern voice.

Such was the scene that greeted our arrival in Torre: pleasant enough, but after all, we thought, we had come too soon. It was the middle of August, the Italian season was still at its height, scarcely the moment for strangers to learn to love the special charms of the place. What an afternoon crowd in the cafés on the front! For instance, in the Esquisito, where we sometimes sat and were served by Mario, that very Mario of whom I shall have presently to tell. It is well-nigh impossible to find a table; and the various orchestras contend together in the midst of one's conversation with bewildering effect. Of course, it is in the after-noon that people come over from Portoclemente. The excursion is a favourite one for the restless denizens of that pleasure resort, and a Fiat motor-bus plies to and fro, coating inch-thick with dust the oleander and laurel hedges along the highroad—a notable if repulsive sight.

Yes, decidedly one should go to Torre in September, when the great public has left. Or else in May, before the water is warm enough to tempt the southerner to bathe. Even in the before and after seasons Torre is not empty, but life is less national and more subdued. English, French, and German prevail under the tent-awnings and in the pension dining-rooms; whereas in August—in the Grand Hotel, at least, where, in default of private addresses, we had engaged rooms—the stranger finds the field so occupied by Florentine and Roman society that he feels quite isolated and even temporarily *déclassé.*

We had, rather to our annoyance, this experience on the evening we arrived, when we went in to dinner and were shown to our table by the waiter in charge. As a table, it had nothing against it, save that we had already fixed our eyes upon those on the veranda beyond, built out over the water, where little red-shaded lamps glowed—and there were still some tables empty, though it was as full as the dining-room within. The children went into raptures at the festive sight, and without more ado we announced our intention to take our meals by preference in the veranda. Our words, it appeared, were prompted by ignorance; for we were informed, with somewhat embarrassed politeness, that the cosy nook outside was reserved for the clients of the hotel: *ai nostri clienti.* Their clients? But we were their clients. We were not tourists or trippers, but boarders for a stay of some three or four weeks. However, we forbore to press for an explanation of the difference between the likes of us and that clientèle to whom it was vouchsafed to eat out there in the glow of the red lamps, and took our dinner by the prosaic common light of the dining-room chandelier—a thoroughly ordinary and monotonous hotel bill of fare, be it said. In Pensione Eleonora, a few steps landward, the table, as we were to discover, was much better.

And thither it was that we moved, three or four days later, before we had had time to settle in properly at the Grand Hotel. Not on account of the veranda and the lamps. The children, straightway on the best of terms with waiters and pages, absorbed in the joys of life on the beach, promptly forgot those colourful seductions. But now there arose, between ourselves and the veranda clientèle—or perhaps more correctly with the compliant management—one of those little unpleasantnesses which can quite spoil the pleasure of a holiday. Among the guests were some high Roman aristocracy, a Principe X and his family. These grand folk occupied rooms close to our own, and the Principessa, a great and a passionately maternal lady, was thrown into a panic by the vestiges of a whooping-cough which our little ones had lately got over, but which now and then still faintly troubled the unshatterable slumbers of our youngest-born. The nature of this illness is not clear, leaving some play for the imagination. So we took no offence at our elegant neighbour for clinging to the widely held view that whooping-cough is acoustically contagious and quite simply fearing lest her children yield to the bad example set by ours. In the fullness of her feminine self-confidence she protested to the management, which then, in the person of the proverbial frock-coated manager, hastened to represent to us, with many expressions of regret, that under the circumstances they were obliged to transfer us to the annexe. We did our best to assure him that the disease was in its very last stages, that it was actually over, and presented no danger of infection to anybody. All that we gained was permission to bring the case before the hotel physician—not one chosen by us—by whose verdict we must then abide. We agreed, convinced that thus we should at once pacify the Princess and escape the trouble of moving. The doctor appeared, and behaved like a faithful and honest servant of science. He examined the child and gave his opinion: the disease was quite over, no danger of contagion was present. We drew a long breath and considered the incident closed—until the manager announced that despite the doctor's verdict it would still be necessary for us to give up our rooms and retire to the *dépendance*. Byzantinism like this outraged us. It is not likely that the Principessa was responsible for the wilful breach of faith. Very likely the fawning management had not even dared to tell her what the physician said. Anyhow, we made it clear to his understanding that we preferred to leave the hotel altogether and at once—and packed our trunks. We could do so with a light heart, having already set up casual friendly relations with Casa Eleonora. We had noticed its pleasant exterior and formed the acquaintance of its proprietor, Signora Angiolieri, and her husband: she slender and black-haired, Tuscan in type, probably at the beginning of the thirties, with the dead ivory complexion of the southern woman, he quiet and bald and carefully dressed. They owned a larger establishment in Florence and presided only in summer and early autumn over the branch in Torre di Venere. But earlier, before her marriage, our new landlady had been companion, fellow-traveller, wardrobe mistress, yes, friend, of Eleonora Duse and manifestly regarded that period as the crown of her career. Even at our first visit she spoke of it with animation. Numerous photographs of the great actress, with affectionate inscriptions, were displayed about the drawing-room, and other souvenirs of their life together adorned the little tables and étagères. This cult of a so interesting past was calculated, of course, to heighten the advantages of the signora's present business. Nevertheless our pleasure and interest were quite genuine as we were conducted through the house by its owner and listened to her sonorous and staccato Tuscan voice relating anecdotes of that immortal mistress, depicting her suffering saintliness, her genius, her profound delicacy of feeling.

Thither, then, we moved our effects, to the dismay of the staff of the Grand Hotel, who, like all Italians, were very good to children. Our new quarters were retired and pleasant, we were within easy reach of the sea through the avenue of young plane trees that ran down to the esplanade. In the clean, cool dining-room Signora Angiolieri daily served the soup with her own hands, the service was attentive and good, the table capital. We even discovered some Viennese acquaintances, and enjoyed chatting with them after luncheon, in front of the house. They, in their turn, were the means of our finding others—in short, all seemed for the best, and we were heartily glad of the change we had made. Nothing was now wanting to a holiday of the most gratifying kind.

And yet no proper gratification ensued. Perhaps the stupid occasion of our change of quarters pursued us to the new ones we had found. Personally, I admit that I do not easily forget these collisions with ordinary humanity, the naïve misuse of power, the injustice, the sycophantic corruption. I dwelt upon the incident too much, it irritated me in retrospect—quite futilely, of course, since such phenomena are only all too natural and all too much the rule. And we had not broken off relations with the Grand Hotel. The children were as friendly as ever there, the porter mended their toys, and we sometimes took tea in the garden. We even saw the Principessa. She would come out, with her firm and delicate tread, her lips emphatically corallined, to look after her children, playing under the supervision of their English governess. She did not dream that we were anywhere near, for so soon as she appeared in the offing we sternly forbade our little one even to clear his throat.

The heat—if I may bring it in evidence—was extreme. It was African. The power of the sun, directly one left the border of the indigo-blue wave, was so frightful, so relentless, that the mere thought of the few steps between the beach and luncheon was a burden, clad though one might be only in pyjamas. Do you care for that sort of thing? Weeks on end? Yes, of course, it is proper to the south, it is classic weather, the sun of Homer, the climate wherein human culture came to flower—and all the rest of it. But after a while it is too much for me, I reach a point where I begin to find it dull. The burning void of the sky, day after day, weighs one down; the high coloration, the enormous naïveté of the unrefracted light—they do, I dare say, induce light-heartedness, a carefree mood born of immunity from downpours and other meteorological caprices. But slowly, slowly, there makes itself felt a lack: the deeper, more complex needs of the northern soul remain unsatisfied. You are left barren—even it may be, in time, a little contemptuous. True without that stupid business of the whooping-cough I might not have been feeling these things. I was annoyed, very likely I wanted to feel them and so half-unconsciously seized upon an idea lying ready to hand to induce, or if not to induce, at least to justify and strengthen, my attitude. Up to this point, then, if you like, let us grant some ill will on our part. But the sea; and the morning spent extended upon the fine sand in face of its eternal splendours—no, the sea could not conceivably induce such feelings. Yet it was none the less true that, despite all previous experience, we were not at home on the beach, we were not happy.

It was too soon, too soon. The beach, as I have said, was still in the hands of the middle-class native. It is a pleasing breed to look at, and among the young we saw much shapeliness and charm. Still, we were necessarily surrounded by a great deal of very average humanity—a middle-class mob, which, you will admit, is not more charming under this sun than under one's own native sky. The voices these women have! It was sometimes hard to believe that we were in the land which is the western cradle of the art of song. "*Fuggièro!*" I can still hear that cry, as for twenty mornings long I heard it close behind me, breathy, full-throated, hideously stressed, with a harsh open *e*, uttered in accents of mechanical despair. "*Fuggièro! Rispondi almeno!*" Answer when I call you! The *sp* in *rispondi* was pronounced like *shp*, as Germans pronounce it; and this, on top of what I felt already, vexed my sensitive soul. The cry was addressed to a repulsive youngster whose sunburn had made disgusting raw sores on his shoulders. He outdid anything I have ever seen for ill-breeding, refractoriness, and temper and was a great coward to boot, putting the whole beach in an uproar, one day, because of his outrageous sensitiveness to the slightest pain. A sand-crab had pinched his toe in the water, and the minute injury made him set up a cry of heroic proportions—the shout of an antique hero in his agony—that pierced one to the marrow and called up visions of some frightful tragedy. Evidently he considered himself not only wounded, but poisoned as well; he crawled out on the sand and lay in apparently intolerable anguish, groaning "*Ohi!*" and "*Ohimè!*" and threshing about with arms and legs to ward off his mother's tragic appeals and the questions of the bystanders. An audience gathered round. A doctor was fetched—the same who had pronounced objective judgment on our whooping-cough—and here again acquitted himself like a man of science. Good-naturedly he reassured the boy, telling him that he was not hurt at all, he should simply go into the water again to relieve the smart. Instead of which, Fuggièro was borne off the beach, followed by a concourse of people. But he did not fail to appear next morning, nor did he leave off spoiling our children's sand-castles. Of course, always by accident. In short, a perfect terror.

And this twelve-year-old lad was prominent among the influences that, imperceptibly at first, combined to spoil our holiday and render it unwholesome. Somehow or other, there was a stiffness, a lack of innocent enjoyment. These people stood on their dignity—just why, and in what spirit, it was not easy at first to tell. They displayed much self-respecting-ness; towards each other and towards the foreigner their bearing was that of a person newly conscious of a sense of honour. And wherefore? Gradually we realized the political implications and understood that we were in the presence of a national ideal. The beach, in fact, was alive with patriotic children—a phenomenon as unnatural as it was depressing. Children are a human species and a society apart, a nation of their own, so to speak. On the basis of their common form of life, they find each other out with the greatest ease, no matter how different their small vocabularies. Ours soon played with natives and foreigners alike. Yet they were plainly both puzzled and disappointed at times. There were wounded sensibilities, displays of assertiveness—or rather hardly assertiveness, for it was too self-conscious and too didactic to deserve the name. There were quarrels over flags, disputes about authority and precedence. Grownups joined in, not so much to pacify as to render judgment and enunciate principles. Phrases were dropped about the greatness and dignity of Italy, solemn phrases that spoilt the fun. We saw our two little ones retreat, puzzled and hurt, and were put to it to explain the situation. These people, we told them, were just passing through a certain stage, something rather like an illness, perhaps; not very pleasant, but probably unavoidable.

We had only our own carelessness to thank that we came to blows in the end with this "stage"—which, after all, we had seen and sized up long

before now. Yes, it came to another "cross-purposes," so evidently the
earlier ones had not been sheer accident. In a word, we became an offence
to the public morals. Our small daughter—eight years old, but in physical
development a good year younger and thin as a chicken—had had a good
long bathe and gone playing in the warm sun in her wet costume. We
told her that she might take off her bathing-suit, which was stiff with
sand, rinse it in the sea, and put it on again, after which she must take
care to keep it cleaner. Off goes the costume and she runs down naked to
the sea, rinses her little jersey, and comes back. Ought we to have foreseen the outburst of anger and resentment which her conduct, and thus
our conduct, called forth? Without delivering a homily on the subject, I
may say that in the last decade our attitude towards the nude body and
our feelings regarding it have undergone, all over the world, a fundamental change. There are things we "never think about" any more, and
among them is the freedom we had permitted to this by no means provo-
vocative little childish body. But in these parts it was taken as a challenge.
The patriotic children hooted. Fuggièro whistled on his fingers. The
sudden buzz of conversation among the grown people in our neighbourhood boded no good. A gentleman in city togs, with a not very apropos
bowler hat on the back of his head, was assuring his outraged womenfolk
that he proposed to take punitive measures; he stepped up to us, and a
philippic descended on our unworthy heads, in which all the emotionalism of the sense-loving south spoke in the service of morality and discipline. The offence against decency of which we had been guilty was, he
said, the more to be condemned because it was also a gross ingratitude and
an insulting breach of his country's hospitality. We had criminally injured not only the letter and spirit of the public bathing regulations, but
also the honour of Italy; he, the gentleman in the city togs, knew how to
defend that honour and proposed to see to it that our offence against the
national dignity should not go unpunished.

We did our best, bowing respectfully, to give ear to this eloquence.
To contradict the man, overheated as he was, would probably be to fall
from one error into another. On the tips of our tongues we had various
answers: as, that the word "hospitality," in its strictest sense, was not
quite the right one, taking all the circumstances into consideration. We
were not literally the guests of Italy, but of Signora Angiolieri, who had
assumed the rôle of dispenser of hospitality some years ago on laying
down that of familiar friend to Eleonora Duse. We longed to say that
surely this beautiful country had not sunk so low as to be reduced to a
state of hypersensitive prudishness. But we confined ourselves to assuring
the gentleman that any lack of respect, any provocation on our parts,
had been the furthest from our thoughts. And as a mitigating circumstance we pointed out the tender age and physical slightness of the little
culprit. In vain. Our protests were waved away, he did not believe in
them; our defence would not hold water. We must be made an example
of. The authorities were notified, by telephone, I believe, and their repre-

sentatives appeared on the beach. He said the case was *"molto grave."* We had to go with him to the Municipio up in the Piazza, where a higher official confirmed the previous verdict of *"molto grave,"* launched into a stream of the usual didactic phrases—the selfsame tune and words as the man in the bowler hat—and levied a fine and ransom of fifty lire. We felt that the adventure must willy-nilly be worth to us this much of a contribution to the economy of the Italian government; paid, and left. Ought we not at this point to have left Torre as well?

If we only had! We should thus have escaped that fatal Cipolla. But circumstances combined to prevent us from making up our minds to a change. A certain poet says that it is indolence that makes us endure uncomfortable situations. The *aperçu* may serve as an explanation for our inaction. Anyhow, one dislikes voiding the field immediately upon such an event. Especially if sympathy from other quarters encourages one to defy it. And in the Villa Eleonora they pronounced as with one voice upon the injustice of our punishment. Some Italian after-dinner acquaintances found that the episode put their country in a very bad light, and proposed taking the man in the bowler hat to task, as one fellow-citizen to another. But the next day he and his party had vanished from the beach. Not on our account, of course. Though it might be that the consciousness of his impending departure had added energy to his rebuke; in any case his going was a relief. And, furthermore, we stayed because our stay had by now become remarkable in our own eyes, which is worth something in itself, quite apart from the comfort or discomfort involved. Shall we strike sail, avoid a certain experience so soon as it seems not expressly calculated to increase our enjoyment or our self-esteem? Shall we go away whenever life looks like turning in the slightest uncanny, or not quite normal, or even rather painful and mortifying? No, surely not. Rather stay and look matters in the face, brave them out; perhaps precisely in so doing lies a lesson for us to learn. We stayed on and reaped as the awful reward of our constancy the unholy and staggering experience with Cipolla.

I have not mentioned that the after season had begun, almost on the very day we were disciplined by the city authorities. The worshipful gentleman in the bowler hat, our denouncer, was not the only person to leave the resort. There was a regular exodus, on every hand you saw luggage-carts on their way to the station. The beach denationalized itself. Life in Torre, in the cafés and the pinetas, became more homelike and more European. Very likely we might even have eaten at a table in the glass veranda, but we refrained, being content at Signora Angiolieri's—as content, that is, as our evil star would let us be. But at the same time with this turn for the better came a change in the weather: almost to an hour it showed itself in harmony with the holiday calendar of the general public. The sky was overcast; not that it grew any cooler, but the unclouded heat of the entire eighteen days since our arrival, and probably long before that, gave place to a stifling sirocco air, while from time to time a little ineffectual rain sprinkled the velvety surface of the beach. Add to which, that two-thirds of our intended stay at Torre had passed. The colourless, lazy sea, with sluggish jellyfish floating in its shallows, was at least a change. And it would have been silly to feel retrospective longings after a sun that had caused us so many sighs when it burned down in all its arrogant power.

At this juncture, then, it was that Cipolla announced himself. Cavaliere Cipolla he was called on the posters that appeared one day stuck up everywhere, even in the dining-room of Pensione Eleonora. A travelling virtuoso, an entertainer, "*forzatore, illusionista, prestidigatore,*" as he called himself, who proposed to wait upon the highly respectable population of Torre di Venere with a display of extraordinary phenomena of a mysterious and staggering kind. A conjuror! The bare announcement was enough to turn our children's heads. They had never seen anything of the sort, and now our present holiday was to afford them this new excitement. From that moment on they besieged us with prayers to take tickets for the performance. We had doubts, from the first, on the score of the lateness of the hour, nine o'clock; but gave way, in the idea that we might see a little of what Cipolla had to offer, probably no great matter, and then go home. Besides, of course, the children could sleep late next day. We bought four tickets of Signora Angiolieri herself, she having taken a number of the stalls on commission to sell them to her guests. She could not vouch for the man's performance, and we had no great expectations. But we were conscious of a need for diversion, and the children's violent curiosity proved catching.

The Cavaliere's performance was to take place in a hall where during the season there had been a cinema with a weekly programme. We had never been there. You reached it by following the main street under the wall of the "*palazzo,*" a ruin with a "For sale" sign, that suggested a castle and had obviously been built in lordlier days. In the same street were the chemist, the hairdresser, and all the better shops; it led, so to speak, from the feudal past the bourgeois into the proletarian, for it ended off between two rows of poor fishing-huts, where old women sat mending nets before the doors. And here, among the proletariat, was the hall, not much more, actually, than a wooden shed, though a large one, with a turreted entrance, plastered on either side with layers of gay placards. Some while after dinner, then, on the appointed evening, we wended our way thither in the dark, the children dressed in their best and blissful with the sense of so much irregularity. It was sultry, as it had been for days; there was heat lightning now and then, and a little rain; we proceeded under umbrellas. It took us a quarter of an hour.

Our tickets were collected at the entrance, our places we had to find ourselves. They were in the third row left, and as we sat down we saw that, late though the hour was for the performance, it was to be interpreted with even more laxity. Only very slowly did an audience—who seemed to be relied upon to come late—begin to fill the stalls. These comprised the whole auditorium; there were no boxes. This tardiness gave us some concern. The children's cheeks were already flushed as much with fatigue as with excitement. But even when we entered, the standing-room at the back and in the side aisles was already well occupied. There stood the manhood of Torre di Venere, all and sundry, fisherfolk, rough-and-ready youths with bare forearms crossed over their striped jerseys. We were well pleased with the presence of this native assemblage, which always adds colour and animation to occasions like the present; and the children were frankly delighted. For they had friends among these people—acquaintances picked up on afternoon strolls to the further ends of the beach. We would be turning homeward, at the hour when the sun dropped into the sea, spent with the huge effort it had made and gilding with reddish gold the oncoming surf; and we would come upon bare-legged fisherfolk standing in rows, bracing and hauling with long-drawn cries as they drew in the nets and harvested in dripping baskets their catch, often so scanty of *frutto di mare*. The children looked on, helped to pull, brought out their little stock of Italian words, made friends. So now they exchanged nods with the "standing-room" clientèle; there was Guiscardo, there Antonio, they knew them by name and waved and called across in half-whispers, getting answering nods and smiles that displayed rows of healthy white teeth. Look, there is even Mario, Mario from the Esquisito, who brings us the chocolate. He wants to see the conjuror, too, and he must have come early, for he is almost in front; but he does not see us, he is not paying attention; that is a way he has, even though he is a waiter. So we wave instead to the man who lets out the little boats on the beach; he is there too, standing at the back.

It had got to a quarter past nine, it got to almost half past. It was natural that we should be nervous. When would the children get to bed? It had been a mistake to bring them, for now it would be very hard to suggest breaking off their enjoyment before it had got well under way. The stalls had filled in time; all Torre, apparently, was there: the guests of the Grand Hotel, the guests of Villa Eleonora, familiar faces from the beach. We heard English and German and the sort of French that Rumanians speak with Italians. Madame Angiolieri herself sat two rows behind us, with her quiet, bald-headed spouse, who kept stroking his moustache with the two middle fingers of his right hand. Everybody had come late, but nobody too late. Cipolla made us wait for him.

He made us wait. That is probably the way to put it. He heightened the suspense by his delay in appearing. And we could see the point of this, too—only not when it was carried to extremes. Towards half past nine the audience began to clap—an amiable way of expressing justifiable impatience, evincing as it does an eagerness to applaud. For the little ones, this was a joy in itself—all children love to clap. From the popular sphere came loud cries of *"Pronti!" "Cominciamo!"* And lo, it seemed now as easy to begin as before it had been hard. A gong sounded, greeted by the standing rows with a many-voiced "Ah-h!" and the curtains parted. They revealed a platform furnished more like a schoolroom than like the theatre of a conjuring performance—largely because of the blackboard in the left foreground. There was a common yellow hat-stand, a few ordinary straw-bottomed chairs, and further back a little round table holding a water carafe and glass, also a tray with a liqueur glass and a flask of pale yellow liquid. We had still a few seconds of time to let these things sink in. Then, with no darkening of the house, Cavaliere Cipolla made his entry.

He came forward with a rapid step that expressed his eagerness to appear before his public and gave rise to the illusion that he had already come a long way to put himself at their service—whereas, of course, he had only been standing in the wings. His costume supported the fiction. A man of an age hard to determine, but by no means young; with a sharp, ravaged face, piercing eyes, compressed lips, small black waxed moustache, and a so-called imperial in the curve between mouth and chin. He was dressed for the street with a sort of complicated evening elegance, in a wide black pelerine with velvet collar and satin lining; which, in the hampered state of his arms, he held together in front with his white-gloved hands. He had a white scarf round his neck; a top hat with a curving brim sat far back on his head. Perhaps more than anywhere else the eighteenth century is still alive in Italy, and with it the charlatan and mountebank type so characteristic of the period. Only there, at any rate, does one still encounter really well-preserved specimens. Cipolla had in his whole appearance much of the historic type; his very clothes helped to conjure up the traditional figure with its blatantly, fantastically foppish air. His pretentious costume sat upon him, or rather hung upon him, most curiously, being in one place drawn too tight, in another a mass of awkward folds. There was something not quite in order about his figure, both front and back—that was plain later on. But I must emphasize the fact that there was not a trace of personal jocularity or clownishness in his pose, manner, or behaviour. On the contrary, there was complete seriousness, an absence of any humorous appeal; occasionally even a cross-grained pride, along with that curious, self-satisfied air so characteristic of the deformed. None of all this, however, prevented his appearance from being greeted with laughter from more than one quarter of the hall.

All the eagerness had left his manner. The swift entry had been merely an expression of energy, not of zeal. Standing at the footlights he negligently drew off his gloves, to display long yellow hands, one of them adorned with a seal ring with a lapis-lazuli in a high setting. As he stood there, his small hard eyes, with flabby pouches beneath them, roved appraisingly about the hall, not quickly, rather in a considered examination, pausing here and there upon a face with his lips clipped together, not speaking a word. Then with a display of skill as surprising as it was casual, he rolled his gloves into a ball and tossed them across a considerable distance into the glass on the table. Next from an inner pocket he drew forth a packet of cigarettes; you could see by the wrapper that they were the cheapest sort the government sells. With his fingertips he pulled out a cigarette and lighted it, without looking, from a quick-firing benzine lighter. He drew the smoke deep into his lungs and let it out again, tapping his foot, with both lips drawn in an arrogant grimace and the grey smoke streaming out between broken and saw-edged teeth.

With a keenness equal to his own his audience eyed him. The youths at the rear scowled as they peered at this cocksure creature to search out his secret weaknesses. He betrayed none. In fetching out and putting back the cigarettes his clothes got in his way. He had to turn back his pelerine, and in so doing revealed a riding-whip with a silver claw-handle that hung by a leather thong from his left forearm and looked decidedly out of place. You could see that he had on not evening clothes but a frock-coat, and under this, as he lifted it to get at his pocket, could be seen a striped sash worn about the body. Somebody behind me whispered that this sash went with his title of Cavaliere. I give the information for what it may be worth—personally, I never heard that the title carried such insignia with it. Perhaps the sash was sheer pose, like the way he stood there, without a word, casually and arrogantly puffing smoke into his audience's face.

People laughed, as I said. The merriment had become almost general when somebody in the "standing seats," in a loud, dry voice, remarked: *"Buona sera."*

Cipolla cocked his head. "Who was that?" asked he, as though he had been dared. "Who was that just spoke? Well? First so bold and now so modest? *Paura,* eh?" He spoke with a rather high, asthmatic voice, which yet had a metallic quality. He waited.

"That was me," a youth at the rear broke into the stillness, seeing himself thus challenged. He was not far from us, a handsome fellow in a woollen shirt, with his coat hanging over one shoulder. He wore his surly, wiry hair in a high, dishevelled mop, the style affected by the youth of the awakened Fatherland; it gave him an African appearance that rather spoiled his looks. *"Bè!* That was me. It was your business to say it first, but I was trying to be friendly."

More laughter. The chap had a tongue in his head. *"Ha sciolto la scilinguágnolo,"* I heard near me. After all, the retort was deserved.

"Ah, bravo!" answered Cipolla. "I like you, *giovanotto.* Trust me, I've had my eye on you for some time. People like you are just in my line. I can use them. And you are the pick of the lot, that's plain to see. You do what you like. Or is it possible you have ever not done what you liked—or even, maybe, what you didn't like? What somebody else liked, in short? Hark ye, my friend, that might be a pleasant change for you, to divide up the willing and the doing and stop tackling both jobs at once. Division of labour, *sistema americano, sa!* For instance, suppose you were to show your tongue to this select and honourable audience here—your whole tongue, right down to the roots?"

"No, I won't," said the youth, hostilely. "Sticking out your tongue shows a bad bringing-up."

"Nothing of the sort," retorted Cipolla. "You would only be *doing* it. With all due respect to your bringing-up, I suggest that before I count ten, you will perform a right turn and stick out your tongue at the company here further than you knew yourself that you could stick it out."

He gazed at the youth, and his piercing eyes seemed to sink deeper into their sockets. "*Uno!*" said he. He had let his riding-whip slide down his arm and made it whistle once through the air. The boy faced about and put out his tongue, so long, so extendedly, that you could see it was the very uttermost in tongue which he had to offer. Then turned back, stony-faced, to his former position.

"That was me," mocked Cipolla, with a jerk of his head towards the youth. "*Bè!* That was me." Leaving the audience to enjoy its sensations, he turned towards the little round table, lifted the bottle, poured out a small glass of what was obviously cognac, and tipped it up with a practised hand.

The children laughed with all their hearts. They had understood practically nothing of what had been said, but it pleased them hugely that something so funny should happen, straightaway, between that queer man up there and somebody out of the audience. They had no preconception of what an "evening" would be like and were quite ready to find this a priceless beginning. As for us, we exchanged a glance and I remember that involuntarily I made with my lips the sound that Cipolla's whip had made when it cut the air. For the rest, it was plain that people did not know what to make of a preposterous beginning like this to a sleight-of-hand performance. They could not see why the *giovanotto*, who after all in a way had been their spokesman, should suddenly have turned on them to vent his incivility. They felt that he had behaved like a silly ass and withdrew their countenances from him in favour of the artist, who now came back from his refreshment table and addressed them as follows:

"Ladies and gentlemen," said he, in his wheezing, metallic voice, "you saw just now that I was rather sensitive on the score of the rebuke this hopeful young linguist saw fit to give me"—"*questo linguista di belle speranze*" was what he said, and we all laughed at the pun. "I am a man who sets some store by himself, you may take it from me. And I see no point in being wished a good-evening unless it is done courteously and in all seriousness. For anything else there is no occasion. When a man wishes me a good-evening he wishes himself one, for the audience will have one only if I do. So this lady-killer of Torre di Venere" (another thrust) "did well to testify that I have one tonight and that I can dispense with any wishes of his in the matter. I can boast of having good evenings almost without exception. One not so good does come my way now and again, but very seldom. My calling is hard and my health not of the best. I have a little physical defect which prevented me from doing my bit in the war for the greater glory of the Fatherland. It is perforce with my mental and spiritual parts that I conquer life—which after all only means conquering oneself. And I flatter myself that my achievements have aroused interest and respect among the educated public. The leading newspapers have lauded me, the *Corriere della Sera* did me the courtesy of calling me a phenomenon, and in Rome the brother of the *Duce* honoured me by his presence at one of my evenings. I should not have thought that in a relatively less important place" (laughter here, at the expense of poor little Torre) "I should have to give up the small personal habits which brilliant and elevated audiences had been ready to overlook. Nor did I think I had to stand being heckled by a person who seems to have been rather spoilt by the favours of the fair sex." All this of course at the expense of the youth whom Cipolla never tired of presenting in the guise of *donnaiuolo* and rustic Don Juan. His persistent thin-skinnedness and animosity were in striking contrast to the self-confidence and the worldly success he boasted of. One might have assumed that the *giovanotto* was merely the chosen butt of Cipolla's customary professional sallies, had not the very pointed witticisms betrayed a genuine antagonism. No one looking at the physical parts of the two men need have been at a loss for the explanation, even if the deformed man had not constantly played on the other's supposed success with the fair sex. "Well," Cipolla went on, "before beginning our entertainment this evening, perhaps you will permit me to make myself comfortable."

And he went towards the hat-stand to take off his things.

"*Parla benissimo,*" asserted somebody in our neighbourhood. So far, the man had done nothing; but what he had said was accepted as an achievement, by means of that he had made an impression. Among southern peoples speech is a constituent part of the pleasure of living, it enjoys far livelier social esteem than in the north. That national cement, the mother tongue, is paid symbolic honours down here, and there is something blithely symbolical in the pleasure people take in their respect for its forms and phonetics. They enjoy speaking, they enjoy listening; and they listen with discrimination. For the way a man speaks serves as a measure of his personal rank; carelessness and clumsiness are greeted with scorn, elegance and mastery are rewarded with social éclat. Wherefore the small man too, where it is a question of getting his effect, chooses his phrase nicely and turns it with care. On this count, then, at least, Cipolla had won his audience; though he by no means belonged to the class of men which the Italian, in a singular mixture of moral and æsthetic judgments, labels "*simpatico.*"

After removing his hat, scarf, and mantle he came to the front of the stage, settling his coat, pulling down his cuffs with their large cuff-buttons, adjusting his absurd sash. He had very ugly hair; the top of his head, that is, was almost bald, while a narrow, black-varnished frizz of curls ran from front to back as though stuck on; the side hair, likewise blackened, was brushed forward to the corners of the eyes—it was, in short, the hairdressing of an old-fashioned circus-director, fantastic, but entirely suited to his outmoded personal type and worn with so much assurance as to take the edge off the public's sense of humour. The little physical defect of which he had warned us was now all too visible, though the nature of it was even now not very clear; the chest was too high, as is usual in such cases, but the corresponding malformation of the back did not sit between the shoulders, it took the form of a sort of hips or buttocks hump, which did not indeed hinder his movements but gave him a grotesque and dipping stride at every step he took. However, by mentioning his deformity beforehand he had broken the shock of it, and a delicate propriety of feeling appeared to reign throughout the hall.

"At your service," said Cipolla. "With your kind permission, we will begin the evening with some arithmetical tests."

Arithmetic? That did not sound much like sleight-of-hand. We began to have our suspicions that the man was sailing under a false flag, only we did not yet know which was the right one. I felt sorry on the children's account; but for the moment they were content simply to be there.

The numerical test which Cipolla now introduced was as simple as it was baffling. He began by fastening a piece of paper to the upper right-hand corner of the blackboard; then lifting it up, he wrote something underneath. He talked all the while, relieving the dryness of his offering by a constant flow of words, and showed himself a practised speaker, never at a loss for conversational turns of phrase. It was in keeping with the nature of his performance, and at the same time vastly entertained the children, that he went on to eliminate the gap between stage and audience, which had already been bridged over by the curious skirmish with the fisher lad; he had representatives from the audience mount the stage, and himself descended the wooden steps to seek personal contact with his public. And again, with individuals, he fell into his former taunting tone. I do not know how far that was a deliberate feature of his system; he preserved a serious, even a peevish air, but his audience, at least the more popular section, seemed convinced that that was all part of the game. So then, after he had written something and covered the writing by the paper, he desired that two persons should come up on the platform and help to perform the calculations. They would not be difficult, even for people not clever at figures. As usual, nobody volunteered, and Cipolla took care not to molest the more select portion of his audience. He kept to the populace. Turning to two sturdy young louts standing behind us, he beckoned them to the front, encouraging and scolding by turns. They should not stand there gaping, he said, unwilling to oblige the company. Actually he got them in motion; with clumsy tread they came down the middle aisle, climbed the steps, and stood in front of the blackboard, grinning sheepishly at their comrades' shouts and applause. Cipolla joked with them for a few minutes, praised their heroic firmness of limb and the size of their hands, so well calculated to do this service for the public. Then he handed one of them the chalk and told him to write down the numbers as they were called out. But now the creature declared that he could not write! *"Non so scrivere,"* said he in his gruff voice, and his companion added that neither did he.

God knows whether they told the truth or whether they wanted to make game of Cipolla. Anyhow, the latter was far from sharing the general merriment which their confession aroused. He was insulted and disgusted. He sat there on a straw-bottomed chair in the centre of the stage with his legs crossed, smoking a fresh cigarette out of his cheap packet; obviously it tasted the better for the cognac he had indulged in while the yokels were stumping up the steps. Again he inhaled the smoke and let it stream out between curling lips. Swinging his leg, with his gaze sternly averted from the two shamelessly chuckling creatures and from the audience as well, he stared into space as one who withdraws himself and his dignity from the contemplation of an utterly despicable phenomenon.

"Scandalous," said he, in a sort of icy snarl. "Go back to your places! In Italy everybody can write—in all her greatness there is no room for ignorance and unenlightenment. To accuse her of them, in the hearing of this international company, is a cheap joke, in which you yourselves cut a very poor figure and humiliate the government and the whole country as well. If it is true that Torre di Venere is indeed the last refuge of such ignorance, then I must blush to have visited the place—being, as I already was, aware of its inferiority to Rome in more than one respect—"

Here Cipolla was interrupted by the youth with the Nubian coiffure and his jacket across his shoulder. His fighting spirit, as we now saw, had only abdicated temporarily, and he now flung himself into the breach in defence of his native heath. "That will do," said he loudly. "That's enough jokes about Torre. We all come from the place and we won't stand strangers making fun of it. These two chaps are our friends. Maybe they are no scholars, but even so they may be straighter than some folks in the room who are so free with their boasts about Rome, though they did not build it either."

That was capital. The young man had certainly cut his eye-teeth. And this sort of spectacle was good fun, even though it still further delayed the regular performance. It is always fascinating to listen to an altercation. Some people it simply amuses, they take a sort of kill-joy pleasure in not being principals. Others feel upset and uneasy, and my sympathies are with these latter, although on the present occasion I was under the impression that all this was part of the show—the analphabetic yokels no less than the *giovanotto* with the jacket. The children listened well pleased. They understood not at all, but the sound of the voices made them hold their breath. So this was a "magic evening"—at least it was the kind they have in Italy. They expressly found it "lovely." Cipolla had stood up and with two of his scooping strides was at the footlights.

"Well, well, see who's here!" said he with grim cordiality. "An old acquaintance! A young man with his heart at the end of his tongue" (he used the word *linguaccia*, which means a coated tongue, and gave rise to much hilarity). "That will do, my friends," he turned to the yokels. "I do not need you now, I have business with this deserving young man here, *con questo torregiano di Venere*, this tower of Venus, who no doubt expects the gratitude of the fair as a reward for his prowess—"

"*Ah, non scherziamo!* We're talking earnest," cried out the youth. His eyes flashed, and he actually made as though to pull off his jacket and proceed to direct methods of settlement.

Cipolla did not take him too seriously. We had exchanged apprehensive glances; but he was dealing with a fellow-countryman and had his native soil beneath his feet. He kept quite cool and showed complete mastery of the situation. He looked at his audience, smiled, and made a sideways motion of the head towards the young cockerel as though calling the public to witness how the man's bumptiousness only served to betray the simplicity of his mind. And then, for the second time, something strange happened, which set Cipolla's calm superiority in an uncanny light, and in some mysterious and irritating way turned all the explosiveness latent in the air into matter for laughter.

Cipolla drew still nearer to the fellow, looking him in the eye with a peculiar gaze. He even came half-way down the steps that led into the auditorium on our left, so that he stood directly in front of the troublemaker, on slightly higher ground. The riding-whip hung from his arm.

"My son, you do not feel much like joking," he said. "It is only too natural, for anyone can see that you are not feeling too well. Even your tongue, which leaves something to be desired on the score of cleanliness, indicates acute disorder of the gastric system. An evening entertainment is no place for people in your state; you yourself, I can tell, were of several minds whether you would not do better to put on a flannel bandage and go to bed. It was not good judgment to drink so much of that very sour white wine this afternoon. Now you have such a colic you would like to double up with the pain. Go ahead, don't be embarrassed. There is a distinct relief that comes from bending over, in cases of intestinal cramp."

He spoke thus, word for word, with quiet impressiveness and a kind of stern sympathy, and his eyes, plunged the while deep in the young man's, seemed to grow very tired and at the same time burning above their enlarged tear-ducts—they were the strangest eyes, you could tell that not manly pride alone was preventing the young adversary from withdrawing his gaze. And presently, indeed, all trace of its former arrogance was gone from the bronzed young face. He looked open-mouthed at the Cavaliere and the open mouth was drawn in a rueful smile.

"Double over," repeated Cipolla. "What else can you do? With a colic like that you *must* bend. Surely you will not struggle against the performance of a perfectly natural action just because somebody suggests it to you?"

Slowly the youth lifted his forearms, folded and squeezed them across his body; it turned a little sideways, then bent, lower and lower, the feet shifted, the knees turned inward, until he had become a picture of writhing pain, until he all but grovelled upon the ground. Cipolla let him stand for some seconds thus, then made a short cut through the air with his whip and went with his scooping stride back to the little table, where he poured himself out a cognac.

"*Il boit beaucoup,*" asserted a lady behind us. Was that the only thing that struck her? We could not tell how far the audience grasped the situation. The fellow was standing upright again, with a sheepish grin—he looked as though he scarcely knew how it had all happened. The scene had been followed with tense interest and applauded at the end; there were shouts of "*Bravo, Cipolla!*" and "*Bravo, giovanotto!*" Apparently the issue of the duel was not looked upon as a personal defeat for the young man. Rather the audience encouraged him as one does an actor who succeeds in an unsympathetic rôle. Certainly his way of screwing himself up with cramp had been highly picturesque, its appeal was directly calculated to impress the gallery—in short, a fine dramatic performance. But I am not sure how far the audience were moved by that natural tactfulness in which the south excels, or how far it penetrated into the nature of what was going on.

The Cavaliere, refreshed, had lighted another cigarette. The numerical tests might now proceed. A young man was easily found in the back row who was willing to write down on the blackboard the numbers as they were dictated to him. Him too we knew; the whole entertainment had taken on an intimate character through our acquaintance with so many of the actors. This was the man who worked at the greengrocer's in the main street; he had served us several times, with neatness and dispatch. He wielded the chalk with clerkly confidence, while Cipolla descended to our level and walked with his deformed gait through the audience, collecting numbers as they were given, in two, three, and four places, and calling them out to the grocer's assistant, who wrote them down in a column. In all this, everything on both sides was calculated to amuse, with its jokes and its oratorical asides. The artist could not fail to hit on foreigners, who were not ready with their figures, and with them he was elaborately patient and chivalrous, to the great amusement of the natives, whom he reduced to confusion in their turn, by making them translate numbers that were given in English or French. Some people gave dates concerned with great events in Italian history. Cipolla took them up at once and made patriotic comments. Somebody shouted "Number one!" The Cavaliere, incensed at this as at every attempt to make game of him, retorted over his shoulder that he could not take less than two-place figures. Whereupon another joker cried out "Number two!" and was greeted with the applause and laughter which every reference to natural functions is sure to win among southerners.

When fifteen numbers stood in a long straggling row on the board, Cipolla called for a general adding-match. Ready reckoners might add in their heads, but pencil and paper were not forbidden. Cipolla, while the work went on, sat on his chair near the blackboard, smoked and grimaced, with the complacent, pompous air cripples so often have. The five-place addition was soon done. Somebody announced the answer, somebody else confirmed it, a third had arrived at a slightly different result, but the fourth agreed with the first and second. Cipolla got up, tapped some ash from his coat, and lifted the paper at the upper right-hand corner of the board to display the writing. The correct answer, a sum close on a million, stood there; he had written it down beforehand.

Astonishment, and loud applause. The children were overwhelmed. How had he done that, they wanted to know. We told them it was a trick, not easily explainable offhand. In short, the man was a conjuror. This was what a sleight-of-hand evening was like, so now they knew. First the fisherman had cramp, and then the right answer was written down beforehand—it was all simply glorious, and we saw with dismay that despite the hot eyes and the hand of the clock at almost half past ten, it would be very hard to get them away. There would be tears. And yet it was plain that this magician did not "magick"—at least not in the accepted sense, of manual dexterity—and that the entertainment was not at all suitable for children. Again, I do not know, either, what the audience really thought. Obviously there was grave doubt whether its answers had been given of "free choice"; here and there an individual might have answered of his own motion, but on the whole Cipolla certainly selected his people and thus kept the whole procedure in his own hands and directed it towards the given result. Even so, one had to admire the quickness of his calculations, however much one felt disinclined to admire anything else about the performance. Then his patriotism, his irritable sense of dignity—the Cavaliere's own countrymen might feel in their element with all that and continue in a laughing mood; but the combination certainly gave us outsiders food for thought.

Cipolla himself saw to it—though without giving them a name—that the nature of his powers should be clear beyond a doubt to even the least-instructed person. He alluded to them, of course, in his talk—and he talked without stopping—but only in vague, boastful, self-advertising phrases. He went on awhile with experiments on the same lines as the first, merely making them more complicated by introducing operations in multiplying, subtracting, and dividing; then he simplified them to the last degree in order to bring out the method. He simply had numbers "guessed" which were previously written under the paper; and the guess was nearly always right. One guesser admitted that he had had in mind to give a certain number, when Cipolla's whip went whistling through the air, and a quite different one slipped out, which proved to be the "right" one. Cipolla's shoulders shook. He pretended admiration for the powers of the people he questioned. But in all his compliments there was something fleering and derogatory; the victims could scarcely have relished them much, although they smiled, and although they might easily have

set down some part of the applause to their own credit. Moreover, I had
not the impression that the artist was popular with his public. A certain ill
will and reluctance were in the air, but courtesy kept such feelings in
check, as did Cipolla's competency and his stern self-confidence. Even the
riding-whip, I think, did much to keep rebellion from becoming overt.

From tricks with numbers he passed to tricks with cards. There were
two packs, which he drew out of his pockets, and so much I still remember, that the basis of the tricks he played with them was as follows: from
the first pack he drew three cards and thrust them without looking at
them inside his coat. Another person then drew three out of the second
pack, and these turned out to be the same as the first three—not invariably all the three, for it did happen that only two were the same. But in
the majority of cases Cipolla triumphed, showing his three cards with a
little bow in acknowledgment of the applause with which his audience
conceded his possession of strange powers—strange whether for good or
evil. A young man in the front row, to our right, an Italian, with proud,
finely chiselled features, rose up and said that he intended to assert his
own will in his choice and consciously to resist any influence, of whatever sort. Under these circumstances, what did Cipolla think would be
the result? "You will," answered the Cavaliere, "make my task somewhat
more difficult thereby. As for the result, your resistance will not alter it
in the least. Freedom exists, and also the will exists; but freedom of the
will does not exist, for a will that aims at its own freedom aims at the
unknown. You are free to draw or not to draw. But if you draw, you will
draw the right cards—the more certainly, the more wilfully obstinate
your behaviour."

One must admit that he could not have chosen his words better, to
trouble the waters and confuse the mind. The refractory youth hesitated
before drawing. Then he pulled out a card and at once demanded to see if
it was among the chosen three. "But why?" queried Cipolla. "Why do
things by halves?" Then, as the other defiantly insisted, *"E servito,"* said
the juggler, with a gesture of exaggerated servility; and held out the three
cards fanwise, without looking at them himself. The left-hand card was
the one drawn.

Amid general applause, the apostle of freedom sat down. How far
Cipolla employed small tricks and manual dexterity to help out his natural
talents, the deuce only knew. But even without them the result would
have been the same: the curiosity of the entire audience was unbounded
and universal, everybody both enjoyed the amazing character of the entertainment and unanimously conceded the professional skill of the performer. *"Lavora bene,"* we heard, here and there in our neighbourhood;
it signified the triumph of objective judgment over antipathy and repressed resentment.

After his last, incomplete, yet so much the more telling success,
Cipolla had at once fortified himself with another cognac. Truly he did
"drink a lot," and the fact made a bad impression. But obviously he

needed the liquor and the cigarettes for the replenishment of his energy, upon which, as he himself said, heavy demands were made in all directions. Certainly in the intervals he looked very ill, exhausted and holloweyed. Then the little glassful would redress the balance, and the flow of lively, self-confident chatter run on, while the smoke he inhaled gushed out grey from his lungs. I clearly recall that he passed from the card-tricks to parlour games—the kind based on certain powers which in human nature are higher or else lower than human reason: on intuition and "magnetic" transmission; in short, upon a low type of manifestation. What I do not remember is the precise order things came in. And I will not bore you with a description of these experiments; everybody knows them, everybody has at one time or another taken part in this finding of hidden articles, this blind carrying out of a series of acts, directed by a force that proceeds from organism to organism by unexplored paths. Everybody has had his little glimpse into the equivocal, impure, inexplicable nature of the occult, has been conscious of both curiosity and contempt, has shaken his head over the human tendency of those who deal in it to help themselves out with humbuggery, though, after all, the humbuggery is no disproof whatever of the genuineness of the other elements in the dubious amalgam. I can only say here that each single circumstance gains in weight and the whole greatly in impressiveness when it is a man like Cipolla who is the chief actor and guiding spirit in the sinister business. He sat smoking at the rear of the stage, his back to the audience while they conferred. The object passed from hand to hand which it was his task to find, with which he was to perform some action agreed upon beforehand. Then he would start to move zigzag through the hall, with his head thrown back and one hand outstretched, the other clasped in that of a guide who was in the secret but enjoined to keep himself perfectly passive, with his thoughts directed upon the agreed goal. Cipolla moved with the bearing typical in these experiments: now groping upon a false start, now with a quick forward thrust, now pausing as though to listen and by sudden inspiration correcting his course. The rôles seemed reversed, the stream of influence was moving in the contrary direction, as the artist himself pointed out, in his ceaseless flow of discourse. The suffering, receptive, performing part was now his, the will he had before imposed on others was shut out, he acted in obedience to a voiceless common will which was in the air. But he made it perfectly clear that it all came to the same thing. The capacity for self-surrender, he said, for becoming a tool, for the most unconditional and utter self-abnegation, was but the reverse side of that other power to will and to command. Commanding and obeying formed together one single principle, one indissoluble unity; he who knew how to obey knew also how to command, and conversely; the one idea was comprehended in the other, as people and leader were comprehended in one another. But that which was *done*, the highly exacting and exhausting performance, was in every case his, the leader's and mover's, in whom the will became obedience, the obedience will, whose person was the cradle and womb of both, and who thus suffered enormous hardship. Repeatedly he emphasized the fact that his lot was a hard one—presumably to account for his need of stimulant and his frequent recourse to the little glass.

Thus he groped his way forward, like a blind seer, led and sustained by the mysterious common will. He drew a pin set with a stone out of its hiding-place in an Englishwoman's shoe, carried it, halting and pressing on by turns, to another lady—Signora Angiolieri—and handed it to her on bended knee, with the words it had been agreed he was to utter. "I present you with this in token of my respect," was the sentence. Their sense was obvious, but the words themselves not easy to hit upon, for the reason that they had been agreed on in French; the language complication seemed to us a little malicious, implying as it did a conflict between the audience's natural interest in the success of the miracle, and their desire to witness the humiliation of this presumptuous man. It was a strange sight: Cipolla on his knees before the signora, wrestling, amid efforts at speech, after knowledge of the preordained words. "I must say something," he said, "and I feel clearly what it is I must say. But I also feel that if it passed my lips it would be wrong. Be careful not to help me unintention-ally!" he cried out, though very likely that was precisely what he was hoping for. *"Pensez très fort,"* he cried all at once, in bad French, and then burst out with the required words—in Italian, indeed, but with the final substantive pronounced in the sister tongue, in which he was probably far from fluent: he said *vénération* instead of *venerazione*, with an impossible nasal. And this partial success, after the complete success before it, the finding of the pin, the presentation of it on his knees to the right person— was almost more impressive than if he had got the sentence exactly right, and evoked bursts of admiring applause.

Cipolla got up from his knees and wiped the perspiration from his brow. You understand that this experiment with the pin was a single case, which I describe because it sticks in my memory. But he changed his method several times and improvised a number of variations suggested by his contact with his audience; a good deal of time thus went by. He seemed to get particular inspiration from the person of our landlady; she drew him on to the most extraordinary displays of clairvoyance. "It does not escape me, madame," he said to her, "that there is something unusual about you, some special and honourable distinction. He who has eyes to see descries about your lovely brow an aureola—if I mistake not, it once was stronger than now—a slowly paling radiance . . . hush, not a word! Don't help me. Beside you sits your husband—yes?" He turned towards the silent Signor Angiolieri. "You are the husband of this lady, and your happiness is complete. But in the midst of this happiness memories rise . . . the past, signora, so it seems to me, plays an important part in your present. You knew a king . . . has not a king crossed your path in bygone days?"

"No," breathed the dispenser of our midday soup, her golden-brown eyes gleaming in the noble pallor of her face.

"No? No, not a king; I meant that generally, I did not mean literally a king. Not a king, not a prince, and a prince after all, a king of a loftier realm; it was a great artist, at whose side you once—you would contradict me, and yet I am not wholly wrong. Well, then! It was a woman, a great, a world-renowned woman artist, whose friendship you enjoyed in your tender years, whose sacred memory overshadows and transfigures your whole existence. Her name? Need I utter it, whose fame has long been bound up with the Fatherland's, immortal as its own? Eleonora Duse," he finished, softly and with much solemnity.

The little woman bowed her head, overcome. The applause was like a patriotic demonstration. Nearly everyone there knew about Signora Angiolieri's wonderful past; they were all able to confirm the Cavaliere's intuition—not least the present guests of Casa Eleonora. But we wondered how much of the truth he had learned as the result of professional inquiries made on his arrival. Yet I see no reason at all to cast doubt, on rational grounds, upon powers which, before our very eyes, became fatal to their possessor.

At this point there was an intermission. Our lord and master withdrew. Now I confess that almost ever since the beginning of my tale I have looked forward with dread to this moment in it. The thoughts of men are mostly not hard to read; in this case they are very easy. You are sure to ask why we did not choose this moment to go away—and I must continue to owe you an answer. I do not know why. I cannot defend myself. By this time it was certainly eleven, probably later. The children were asleep. The last series of tests had been too long, nature had had her way. They were sleeping in our laps, the little one on mine, the boy on his mother's. That was, in a way, a consolation; but at the same time it was also ground for compassion and a clear leading to take them home to bed. And I give you my word that we wanted to obey this touching admonition, we seriously wanted to. We roused the poor things and told them it was now high time to go. But they were no sooner conscious than they began to resist and implore—you know how horrified children are at the thought of leaving before the end of a thing. No cajoling has any effect, you have to use force. It was so lovely, they wailed. How did we know what was coming next? Surely we could not leave until after the intermission; they liked a little nap now and again—only not go home, only not go to bed, while the beautiful evening was still going on!

We yielded, but only for the moment, of course—so far as we knew —only for a little while, just a few minutes longer. I cannot excuse our staying, scarcely can I even understand it. Did we think, having once said A, we had to say B—having once brought the children hither we had to let them stay? No, it is not good enough. Were we ourselves so highly entertained? Yes, and no. Our feelings for Cavaliere Cipolla were of a very mixed kind, but so were the feelings of the whole audience, if I mistake not, and nobody left. Were we under the sway of a fascination which emanated from this man who took so strange a way to earn his bread; a fascination which he gave out independently of the programme and even between the tricks and which paralysed our resolve? Again, sheer curiosity may account for something. One was curious to know how such an evening turned out; Cipolla in his remarks having all along hinted that he had tricks in his bag stranger than any he had yet produced.

But all that is not it—or at least it is not all of it. More correct it would be to answer the first question with another. Why had we not left Torre di Venere itself before now? To me the two questions are one and the same, and in order to get out of the impasse I might simply say that I had answered it already. For, as things had been in Torre in general: queer, uncomfortable, troublesome, tense, oppressive, so precisely they were here in this hall tonight. Yes, more than precisely. For it seemed to be the fountainhead of all the uncanniness and all the strained feelings which had oppressed the atmosphere of our holiday. This man whose return to the stage we were awaiting was the personification of all that; and, as we had not gone away in general, so to speak, it would have been inconsistent to do it in the particular case. You may call this an explanation, you may call it inertia, as you see fit. Any argument more to the purpose I simply do not know how to adduce.

Well, there was an interval of ten minutes, which grew into nearly twenty. The children remained awake. They were enchanted by our compliance, and filled the break to their own satisfaction by renewing relations with the popular sphere, with Antonio, Guiscardo, and the canoe man. They put their hands to their mouths and called messages across, appealing to us for the Italian words. "Hope you have a good catch tomorrow, a whole netful!" They called to Mario, Esquisito Mario: "*Mario, una cioccolata e biscotti!*" And this time he heeded and answered with a smile: "*Subito, signorini!*" Later we had reason to recall this kindly, if rather absent and pensive smile.

Thus the interval passed, the gong sounded. The audience, which had scattered in conversation, took their places again, the children sat up straight in their chairs with their hands in their laps. The curtain had not been dropped. Cipolla came forward again, with his dipping stride, and began to introduce the second half of the programme with a lecture.

Let me state once for all that this self-confident cripple was the most powerful hypnotist I have ever seen in my life. It was pretty plain now that he threw dust in the public eye and advertised himself as a prestidigitator on account of police regulations which would have prevented him from making his living by the exercise of his powers. Perhaps this eyewash is the usual thing in Italy; it may be permitted or even connived at by the authorities. Certainly the man had from the beginning made little concealment of the actual nature of his operations; and this second half of the programme was quite frankly and exclusively devoted to one sort of experiment. While he still practised some rhetorical circumlocutions, the tests themselves were one long series of attacks upon the will-power, the loss or compulsion of volition. Comic, exciting, amazing by turns, by midnight they were still in full swing; we ran the gamut of all the phenomena this natural-unnatural field has to show, from the unimpressive at one end of the scale to the monstrous at the other. The audience laughed and applauded as they followed the grotesque details; shook their heads, clapped their knees, fell very frankly under the spell of this stern, self-assured personality. At the same time I saw signs that they were not quite complacent, not quite unconscious of the peculiar ignominy which lay, for the individual and for the general, in Cipolla's triumphs.

Two main features were constant in all the experiments: the liquor glass and the claw-handled riding-whip. The first was always invoked to add fuel to his demoniac fires; without it, apparently, they might have burned out. On this score we might even have felt pity for the man; but the whistle of his scourge, the insulting symbol of his domination, before which we all cowered, drowned out every sensation save a dazed and outbraved submission to his power. Did he then lay claim to our sympathy to boot? I was struck by a remark he made—it suggested no less. At the climax of his experiments, by stroking and breathing upon a certain young man who had offered himself as a subject and already proved himself a particularly susceptible one, he had not only put him into the condition known as deep trance and extended his insensible body by neck and feet across the backs of two chairs, but had actually sat down on the rigid form as on a bench, without making it yield. The sight of this unholy figure in a frock-coat squatted on the stiff body was horrible and incredible; the audience, convinced that the victim of this scientific diversion must be suffering, expressed its sympathy: *"Ah, poveretto!"* Poor soul, poor soul! *"Poor soul!"* Cipolla mocked them, with some bitterness. "Ladies and gentlemen, you are barking up the wrong tree. *Sono io il poveretto.* I am the person who is suffering, I am the one to be pitied." We pocketed the information. Very good. Maybe the experiment was at his expense, maybe it was he who had suffered the cramp when the *giovanotto* over there had made the faces. But appearances were all against it; and one does not feel like saying *poveretto* to a man who is suffering to bring about the humiliation of others.

I have got ahead of my story and lost sight of the sequence of events. To this day my mind is full of the Cavaliere's feats of endurance; only I do not recall them in their order—which does not matter. So much I do know: that the longer and more circumstantial tests, which got the most applause, impressed me less than some of the small ones which passed quickly over. I remember the young man whose body Cipolla converted into a board, only because of the accompanying remarks which I have quoted. An elderly lady in a cane-seated chair was lulled by Cipolla in the delusion that she was on a voyage to India and gave a voluble account of her adventures by land and sea. But I found this phenomenon less impressive than one which followed immediately after the intermission. A tall, well-built, soldierly man was unable to lift his arm, after the hunchback had told him that he could not and given a cut through the air with his whip. I can still see the face of that stately, mustachioed colonel smiling and clenching his teeth as he struggled to regain his lost freedom of action. A staggering performance! He seemed to be exerting his will, and in vain; the trouble, however, was probably simply that he could not will. There was involved here that recoil of the will upon itself which paralyses choice—as our tyrant had previously explained to the Roman gentleman.

Still less can I forget the touching scene, at once comic and horrible, with Signora Angiolieri. The Cavaliere, probably in his first bold survey of the room, had spied out her ethereal lack of resistance to his power. For actually he bewitched her, literally drew her out of her seat, out of her row, and away with him whither he willed. And in order to enhance his effect, he bade Signor Angiolieri call upon his wife by her name, to throw, as it were, all the weight of his existence and his rights in her into the scale, to rouse by the voice of her husband everything in his spouse's soul which could shield her virtue against the evil assaults of magic. And how vain it all was! Cipolla was standing at some distance from the couple, when he made a single cut with his whip through the air. It caused our landlady to shudder violently and turn her face towards him. "Sofronia!" cried Signor Angiolieri—we had not known that Signora Angiolieri's name was Sofronia. And he did well to call, everybody saw that there was no time to lose. His wife kept her face turned in the direction of the diabolical Cavaliere, who with his ten long yellow fingers was making passes at his victim, moving backwards as he did so, step by step. Then Signora Angiolieri, her pale face gleaming, rose up from her seat, turned right round, and began to glide after him. Fatal and forbidding sight! Her face as though moonstruck, stiff-armed, her lovely hands lifted a little at the wrists, the feet as it were together, she seemed to float slowly out of her row and after the tempter. "Call her, sir, keep on calling," prompted the redoubtable man. And Signor Angiolieri, in a weak voice, called: "Sofronia!" Ah, again and again he called; as his wife went further off he even curved one hand round his lips and beckoned with the other as he called. But the poor voice of love and duty echoed unheard, in vain, behind the lost one's back; the signora swayed along, moonstruck, deaf, enslaved; she glided into the middle aisle and down it towards the fingering hunchback, towards the door. We were driven to the conviction, that she would have followed her master, had he so willed it, to the ends of the earth.

"*Accidente!*" cried out Signor Angiolieri, in genuine affright, springing up as the exit was reached. But at the same moment the Cavaliere put aside, as it were, the triumphal crown and broke off. "Enough, signora, I thank you," he said, and offered his arm to lead her back to her husband. "Signor," he greeted the latter, "here is your wife. Unharmed, with my compliments, I give her into your hands. Cherish with all the strength of your manhood a treasure which is so wholly yours, and let your zeal be quickened by knowing that there are powers stronger than reason or virtue, and not always so magnanimously ready to relinquish their prey!"

Poor Signor Angiolieri, so quiet, so bald! He did not look as though he would know how to defend his happiness, even against powers much less demoniac than these which were now adding mockery to frightfulness. Solemnly and pompously the Cavaliere retired to the stage, amid applause to which his eloquence gave double strength. It was this particular episode, I feel sure, that set the seal upon his ascendancy. For now he made them dance, yes, literally; and the dancing lent a dissolute, abandoned, topsy-turvy air to the scene, a drunken abdication of the critical spirit which had so long resisted the spell of this man. Yes, he had had to fight to get the upper hand—for instance against the animosity of the young Roman gentleman, whose rebellious spirit threatened to serve others as a rallying-point. But it was precisely upon the importance of example that the Cavaliere was so strong. He had the wit to make his attack at the weakest point and to choose as his first victim that feeble, ecstatic youth whom he had previously made into a board. The master had but to look at him, when this young man would fling himself back as though struck by lightning, place his hands rigidly at his sides, and fall into a state of military somnambulism, in which it was plain to any eye that he was open to the most absurd suggestion that might be made to him. He seemed quite content in his abject state, quite pleased to be relieved of the burden of voluntary choice. Again and again he offered himself as a subject and gloried in the model facility he had in losing consciousness. So now he mounted the platform, and a single cut of the whip was enough to make him dance to the Cavaliere's orders, in a kind of complacent ecstasy, eyes closed, head nodding, lank limbs flying in all directions.

It looked unmistakably like enjoyment, and other recruits were not long in coming forward: two other young men, one humbly and one well dressed, were soon jigging alongside the first. But now the gentleman from Rome bobbed up again, asking defiantly if the Cavaliere would engage to make him dance too, even against his will.

"Even against your will," answered Cipolla, in unforgettable accents. That frightful *"anche se non vuole"* still rings in my ears. The struggle began. After Cipolla had taken another little glass and lighted a fresh cigarette he stationed the Roman at a point in the middle aisle and himself took up a position some distance behind, making his whip whistle through the air as he gave the order: *"Balla!"* His opponent did not stir. *"Balla!"* repeated the Cavaliere incisively, and snapped his whip. You saw the young man move his neck round in his collar; at the same time one hand lifted slightly at the wrist, one ankle turned outward. But that was all, for the time at least; merely a tendency to twitch, now sternly repressed, now seeming about to get the upper hand. It escaped nobody that here a heroic obstinacy, a fixed resolve to resist, must needs be conquered; we were beholding a gallant effort to strike out and save the honour of the

human race. He twitched but danced not; and the struggle was so prolonged that the Cavaliere had to divide his attention between it and the
stage, turning now and then to make his riding-whip whistle in the direction of the dancers, as it were to keep them in leash. At the same time he
advised the audience that no fatigue was involved in such activities, however long they went on, since it was not the automatons up there who
danced, but himself. Then once more his eye would bore itself into the
back of the Roman's neck and lay siege to the strength of purpose which
defied him.

One saw it waver, that strength of purpose, beneath the repeated
summons and whip-crackings. Saw with an objective interest which yet
was not quite free from traces of sympathetic emotion—from pity, even
from a cruel kind of pleasure. If I understand what was going on, it was
the negative character of the young man's fighting position which was his
undoing. It is likely that not willing is not a practicable state of mind; *not*
to want to do something may be in the long run a mental content
impossible to subsist on. Between not willing a certain thing and not
willing at all—in other words, yielding to another person's will—there
may lie too small a space for the idea of freedom to squeeze into. Again,
there were the Cavaliere's persuasive words, woven in among the whip-
crackings and commands, as he mingled effects that were his own secret
with others of a bewilderingly psychological kind. "*Balla!*" said he.
"Who wants to torture himself like that? Is forcing yourself your idea of
freedom? *Una ballatina!* Why, your arms and legs are aching for it. What
a relief to give way to them—there, you are dancing already! That is no
struggle any more, it is a pleasure!" And so it was. The jerking and
twitching of the refractory youth's limbs had at last got the upper hand;
he lifted his arms, then his knees, his joints quite suddenly relaxed, he
flung his legs and danced, and amid bursts of applause the Cavaliere led
him to join the row of puppets on the stage. Up there we could see his
face as he "enjoyed" himself; it was clothed in a broad grin and the eyes
were half-shut. In a way, it was consoling to see that he was having a
better time than he had had in the hour of his pride.

His "fall" was, I may say, an epoch. The ice was completely broken,
Cipolla's triumph had reached its height. The Circe's wand, that whistling
leather whip with the claw handle, held absolute sway. At one time—it
must have been well after midnight—not only were there eight or ten
persons dancing on the little stage, but in the hall below a varied animation reigned, and a long-toothed Anglo-Saxoness in a pince-nez left her
seat of her own motion to perform a tarantella in the centre aisle. Cipolla
was lounging in a cane-seated chair at the left of the stage, gulping down
the smoke of a cigarette and breathing it impudently out through his bad
teeth. He tapped his foot and shrugged his shoulders, looking down upon
the abandoned scene in the hall; now and then he snapped his whip
backwards at a laggard upon the stage. The children were awake at the
moment. With shame I speak of them. For it was not good to be here,

least of all for them; that we had not taken them away can only be explained by saying that we had caught the general devil-may-careness of the hour. By that time it was all one. Anyhow, thank goodness, they lacked understanding for the disreputable side of the entertainment, and in their innocence were perpetually charmed by the unheard-of indulgence which permitted them to be present at such a thing as a magician's "evening." Whole quarter-hours at a time they drowsed on our laps, waking refreshed and rosy-cheeked, with sleep-drunken eyes, to laugh to bursting at the leaps and jumps the magician made those people up there make. They had not thought it would be so jolly; they joined with their clumsy little hands in every round of applause. And jumped for joy upon their chairs, as was their wont, when Cipolla beckoned to their friend Mario from the Esquisito, beckoned to him just like a picture in a book, holding his hand in front of his nose and bending and straightening the forefinger by turns.

Mario obeyed. I can see him now going up the stairs to Cipolla, who continued to beckon him, in that droll, picture-book sort of way. He hesitated for a moment at first; that, too, I recall quite clearly. During the whole evening he had lounged against a wooden pillar at the side entrance, with his arms folded, or else with his hands thrust into his jacket pockets. He was on our left, near the youth with the militant hair, and had followed the performance attentively, so far as we had seen, if with no particular animation and God knows how much comprehension. He could not much relish being summoned thus, at the end of the evening. But it was only too easy to see why he obeyed. After all, obedience was his calling in life; and then, how should a simple lad like him find it within his human capacity to refuse compliance to a man so throned and crowned as Cipolla at that hour? Willy-nilly he left his column and with a word of thanks to those making way for him he mounted the steps with a doubtful smile on his full lips.

Picture a thickset youth of twenty years, with clipped hair, a low forehead, and heavy-lidded eyes of an indefinite grey, shot with green and yellow. These things I knew from having spoken with him, as we often had. There was a saddle of freckles on the flat nose, the whole upper half of the face retreated behind the lower, and that again was dominated by thick lips that parted to show the salivated teeth. These thick lips and the veiled look of the eyes lent the whole face a primitive melancholy—it was that which had drawn us to him from the first. In it was not the faintest trace of brutality—indeed, his hands would have given the lie to such an idea, being unusually slender and delicate even for a southerner. They were hands by which one liked being served.

We knew him humanly without knowing him personally, if I may make that distinction. We saw him nearly every day, and felt a certain kindness for his dreamy ways, which might at times be actual inattentiveness, suddenly transformed into a redeeming zeal to serve. His mien was serious, only the children could bring a smile to his face. It was not sulky, but uningratiating, without intentional effort to please—or, rather, it seemed to give up being pleasant in the conviction that it could not succeed. We should have remembered Mario in any case, as one of those homely recollections of travel which often stick in the mind better than more important ones. But of his circumstances we knew no more than that his father was a petty clerk in the Municipio and his mother took in washing.

His white waiter's-coat became him better than the faded striped suit he wore, with a gay coloured scarf instead of a collar, the ends tucked into his jacket. He neared Cipolla, who however did not leave off that motion of his finger before his nose, so that Mario had to come still closer, right up to the chair-seat and the master's legs. Whereupon the latter spread out his elbows and seized the lad, turning him so that we had a view of his face. Then gazed at him briskly up and down, with a careless, commanding eye.

"Well, *ragazzo mio*, how comes it we make acquaintance so late in the day? But believe me, I made yours long ago. Yes, yes, I've had you in my eye this long while and known what good stuff you were made of. How could I go and forget you again? Well, I've had a good deal to think about. . . . Now tell me, what is your name? The first name, that's all I want."

"My name is Mario," the young man answered, in a low voice.

"Ah, Mario. Very good. Yes, yes, there is such a name, quite a common name, a classic name too, one of those which preserve the heroic traditions of the Fatherland. *Bravo! Salve!*" And he flung up his arm slantingly above his crooked shoulder, palm outward, in the Roman salute. He may have been slightly tipsy by now, and no wonder; but he spoke as before, clearly, fluently, and with emphasis. Though about this time there had crept into his voice a gross, autocratic note, and a kind of arrogance was in his sprawl.

"Well, now, Mario *mio*," he went on, "it's a good thing you came this evening, and that's a pretty scarf you've got on; it is becoming to your style of beauty. It must stand you in good stead with the girls, the pretty pretty girls of Torre—"

From the row of youths, close by the place where Mario had been standing, sounded a laugh. It came from the youth with the militant hair. He stood there, his jacket over his shoulder, and laughed outright, rudely and scornfully.

Mario gave a start. I think it was a shrug, but he may have started and then hastened to cover the movement by shrugging his shoulders, as much as to say that the neckerchief and the fair sex were matters of equal indifference to him.

The Cavaliere gave a downward glance.

"We needn't trouble about him," he said. "He is jealous, because your scarf is so popular with the girls, maybe partly because you and I are so friendly up here. Perhaps he'd like me to put him in mind of his colic—I could do it free of charge. Tell me, Mario. You've come here this evening for a bit of fun—and in the daytime you work in an iron-monger's shop?"

"In a café," corrected the youth.

"Oh, in a café. That's where Cipolla nearly came a cropper! What you are is a cup-bearer, a Ganymede—I like that, it is another classical allusion—*Salvietta!*" Again the Cavaliere saluted, to the huge gratification of his audience.

Mario smiled too. "But before that," he interpolated, in the interest of accuracy, "I worked for a while in a shop in Portoclemente." He seemed visited by a natural desire to assist the prophecy by dredging out its essential features.

"There, didn't I say so? In an ironmonger's shop?"

"They kept combs and brushes," Mario got round it.

"Didn't I say that you were not always a Ganymede? Not always at the sign of the serviette? Even when Cipolla makes a mistake, it is a kind that makes you believe in him. Now tell me: Do you believe in me?"

An indefinite gesture.

"A half-way answer," commented the Cavaliere. "Probably it is not easy to win your confidence. Even for me, I can see, it is not so easy. I see in your features a reserve, a sadness, *un tratto di malinconia* . . . tell me" (he seized Mario's hand persuasively) "have you troubles?"

"*Nossignore*," answered Mario, promptly and decidedly.

"You *have* troubles," insisted the Cavaliere, bearing down the denial by the weight of his authority. "Can't I see? Trying to pull the wool over Cipolla's eyes, are you? Of course, about the girls—it is a girl, isn't it? You have love troubles?"

Mario gave a vigorous head-shake. And again the *giovanotto's* brutal laugh rang out. The Cavaliere gave heed. His eyes were roving about somewhere in the air: but he cocked an ear to the sound, then swung his whip backwards, as he had once or twice before in his conversation with Mario, that none of his puppets might flag in their zeal. The gesture had nearly cost him his new prey: Mario gave a sudden start in the direction of the steps. But Cipolla had him in his clutch.

"Not so fast," said he. "That would be fine, wouldn't it? So you want to skip, do you, Ganymede, right in the middle of the fun, or, rather, when it is just beginning? Stay with me, I'll show you something nice. I'll convince you. You have no reason to worry, I promise you. This girl—you know her and others know her too—what's her name? Wait! I read the name in your eyes, it is on the tip of my tongue and yours too—"

"Silvestra!" shouted the *giovanotto* from below.

The Cavaliere's face did not change.

"Aren't there the forward people?" he asked, not looking down, more as in undisturbed converse with Mario. "Aren't there the young fighting-cocks that crow in season and out? Takes the word out of your mouth, the conceited fool, and seems to think he has some special right to it. Let him be. But Silvestra, your Silvestra—ah, what a girl that is! What a prize! Brings your heart into your mouth to see her walk or laugh or breathe, she is so lovely. And her round arms when she washes, and tosses her head back to get the hair out of her eyes! An angel from paradise!"

Mario started at him, his head thrust forward. He seemed to have forgotten the audience, forgotten where he was. The red rings round his eyes had got larger, they looked as though they were painted on. His thick lips parted.

"And she makes you suffer, this angel," went on Cipolla, "or, rather, you make yourself suffer for her—there is a difference, my lad, a most important difference, let me tell you. There are misunderstandings in love, maybe nowhere else in the world are there so many. I know what you are thinking: what does this Cipolla, with his little physical defect, know about love? Wrong, all wrong, he knows a lot. He has a wide and powerful understanding of its workings, and it pays to listen to his advice. But let's leave Cipolla out, cut him out altogether and think only of Silvestra, your peerless Silvestra! What! Is she to give any young game-cock the preference, so that he can laugh while you cry? To prefer him to a chap like you, so full of feeling and so sympathetic? Not very likely, is it? It is impossible—we know better, Cipolla and she. If I were to put myself in her place and choose between the two of you, a tarry lout like that—a codfish, a sea-urchin—and a Mario, a knight of the serviette, who moves among gentlefolk and hands round refreshments with an air—my word, but my heart would speak in no uncertain tones—it knows to whom I gave it long ago. It is time that he should see and understand, my chosen one! It is time that you see me and recognize me, Mario, my beloved! Tell me, who am I?"

It was grisly, the way the betrayer made himself irresistible, wreathed and coquetted with his crooked shoulder, languished with the puffy eyes, and showed his splintered teeth in a sickly smile. And alas, at his beguiling words, what was come of our Mario? It is hard for me to tell, hard as it was for me to see; for here was nothing less than an utter abandonment of the inmost soul, a public exposure of timid and deluded passion and rapture. He put his hands across his mouth, his shoulders rose and fell with his pantings. He could not, it was plain, trust his eyes and ears for joy, and the one thing he forgot was precisely that he could not trust them. "Silvestra!" he breathed, from the very depths of his van-quished heart.

"Kiss me!" said the hunchback. "Trust me, I love thee. Kiss me here." And with the tip of his index finger, hand, arm, and little finger outspread, he pointed to his cheek, near the mouth. And Mario bent and kissed him.

It had grown very still in the room. That was a monstrous moment, grotesque and thrilling, the moment of Mario's bliss. In that evil span of time, crowded with a sense of the illusiveness of all joy, one sóund became audible, and that not quite at once, but on the instant of the melancholy and ribald meeting between Mario's lips and the repulsive flesh which thrust itself forward for his caress. It was the sound of a laugh, from the *giovanotto* on our left. It broke into the dramatic suspense of the moment, coarse, mocking, and yet—or I must have been grossly mistaken—with an undertone of compassion for the poor bewildered, victimized creature. It had a faint ring of that *"Poveretto"* which Cipolla had declared was wasted on the wrong person, when he claimed the pity for his own.

The laugh still rang in the air when the recipient of the caress gave his whip a little swish, low down, close to his chair-leg, and Mario started up and flung himself back. He stood in that posture staring, his hands one over the other on those desecrated lips. Then he beat his temples with his clenched fists, over and over; turned and staggered down the steps, while the audience applauded, and Cipolla sat there with his hands in his lap, his shoulders shaking. Once below, and even while in full retreat, Mario hurled himself round with legs flung wide apart; one arm flew up, and two flat shattering detonations crashed through applause and laughter.

There was instant silence. Even the dancers came to a full stop and stared about, struck dumb. Cipolla bounded from his seat. He stood with his arms spread out, slanting as though to ward everybody off, as though next moment he would cry out: "Stop! Keep back! Silence! What was that?" Then, in that instant, he sank back in his seat, his head rolling on his chest; in the next he had fallen sideways to the floor, where he lay motionless, a huddled heap of clothing, with limbs awry.

The commotion was indescribable. Ladies hid their faces, shuddering, on the breasts of their escorts. There were shouts for a doctor, for the police. People flung themselves on Mario in a mob, to disarm him, to take away the weapon that hung from his fingers—that small, dull-metal, scarcely pistol-shaped tool with hardly any barrel—in how strange and unexpected a direction had fate levelled it!

And now—now finally, at last—we took the children and led them towards the exit, past the pair of *carabinieri* just entering. Was that the end, they wanted to know, that they might go in peace? Yes, we assured them, that was the end. An end of horror, a fatal end. And yet a liberation—for I could not, and I cannot, but find it so!

Short Stories

T HE FINEST CARICATURIST of his day, a good though second-order familiar essayist, the greatest parodist in English, a short-story writer of a school which has developed no successful pupils, and in his old age a brilliantly successful broadcaster, Sir Max Beerbohm (1872–1956) will for at least a few generations to come occupy a modest but unfellowed place in the history of English literature and the tradition of English wit. He is the perfect example of how far a man with no pretensions to owning a first-class mind can go provided he knows precisely how to husband, employ, and develop the talents he has. A noted figure during the nineties (whose decadent poses both influenced him and nourished his irony), he succeeded Shaw as critic of the *Saturday Review*, wrote a few books, drew hundreds of inimitable caricatures, retired in middle life to Italy and there lived, with occasional visits to London, quietly and rather unproductively until his death at the age of eighty-four.

"Enoch Soames," drawn from his book of short stories *Seven Men*, has been and will continue to be often reprinted. It has nothing very important to say to us. But the manner of the saying has so far resisted the tooth of time. Its sly mingling of the actual and the fantastic, the perfection of its teasing of the nineties, the neatness with which the whole small trick is performed—all bring us back again to the feeling that Shaw's over-familiar adjective is after all the only right one. Here is the Incomparable Max.

"The Demon Lover" is an inadequate sample of Elizabeth Bowen's art, better displayed in her sensitive novels, especially *The Death of the Heart* (1939), which I feel is her masterpiece. But it is a good story, one of the finest I know in the well-worked genre of the supernatural, and perhaps gains added interest when set against "Enoch Soames." It shows the horrid, as Beerbohm shows the comic, face of fantasy.

Elizabeth Bowen, born in 1899, is of upper-class Anglo-Irish stock, the author of many successful novels, rather in the Henry James vein; of several books of short stories and critical essays; and of a remarkable study of the Bowen family and its family house, *Bowen's Court* (1942).

Willa Cather's "Two Friends" is only by courtesy a story. Call it a sketch, call it a memory, call it—best of all—a delicate drawing. Its only object is to bring back, by suggestion rather than statement, a time, a place, and more especially a class and type of American male now becoming less identifiable in our faceless economic society: "successful, large-minded men who had made their way in the world when business was still a personal adventure." This unpretentious but flawless exercise in recollection not only is beautiful (a worn-out adjective one is forced to apply to much of Willa Cather's work) but exerts on the reader the moral effect for which the author is striving: "in some unaccountable and very personal way" it gives us "courage."

At almost the dead center of the tale is a sentence I have often quoted to young people with writing ambitions. It shows how much can be done, even with prose, so much less economical and precise than poetry, to convey by rhythm alone a whole atmosphere of time and place, and at the same time suggest the key of the entire piece of writing of which it is a small part. A perfect example of T. S. Eliot's "objective correlative," this is the sentence:

> Nothing in the world, not snow mountains or blue seas, is so beautiful in moonlight as the soft, dry summer roads in a farming country, roads where the white dust falls back from the slow wagon-wheel.

The art of A. E. Coppard (1878–1957) is so strange, so limited, and also so uneven that his reputation, at one time very high indeed, may not endure. A pity, for at his best he is as fine a tale-teller as our tongue can show. Born the son of a tailor and a housemaid, Coppard lived an obscure life of semi-poverty, one remote from literary London. He wrote story after story in which are blended imagination, whimsy (sometimes a touch too much), sadness, and a curious quality, almost of legend or folk tale. "It is my feeling," he has written, "that the closer the modern short story conforms to the ancient tradition of being spoken at you, rather than being read at you, the more acceptable it becomes."

Willa Cather once remarked that she began to learn to write only when she began to learn to remember. "Two Friends" bears out the truth of the statement. So does "Dusky Ruth." I have always placed this tale among the most enchanting love stories in the language. Perhaps its magic lies in the fact that it tells of one of those erotic adventures, beautiful yet incomplete, that every man in his hidden heart would like to have had, and to be able, many years afterward, richly to remember.

Roald Dahl, born in 1916 in Wales of Norwegian parentage, was a fighter pilot in the R.A.F., experience which later helped to produce his first collection of stories, *Over to You* (1946). He is best known for his mastery of the eerie, the macabre, and the sardonic (not to say the cruel), displayed in two books of tales, *Someone Like You* (1953) and *Kiss Kiss* (1960). In his special field he is rivaled only by John Collier. Mr. Dahl has also written two odd and excellent books for children. "The Landlady" is not for them.

Offhand the superficial reader might conclude that Mr. Dahl's and Walter de la Mare's talents have something in common; but no. Mr. Dahl is an enormously clever contriver of shivers and shudders, but he himself does not believe in them. Walter de la Mare (1873–1956), on the other hand, never wrote for effect; his stories of the supernatural are natural to him. "I mean," says poor Seaton in this, one of de la Mare's most troubling stories, "I know that what we see and hear is only the smallest fraction of what is."

Most writers, including many of the greatest, believe that this world is the world; and so think most of us. But we have never quite been able to reject or shrug off that small band of writers who, like Coleridge, Blake, and Walter de la Mare, persist in bringing us news, for them quite authentic, of other worlds or perhaps of one of which ours is "the smallest fraction."

In his long, quiet life (part of which was spent working in the offices of the Anglo-American Oil Company) Walter de la Mare wrote at least one unforgettable novel, *Memoirs of a Midget* (1921); several volumes of poems for which the standard adjective is "haunting"; many tales, some merely puzzling, others as powerful as nightmares; poems and stories for and of children, unrivaled in their field; an uncharacterizable series of books of criticism and literary ruminations; and a sheaf of anthologies so creative, so original, that some other noun is needed to characterize them. At the moment the de la Mare sensibility is quite out of fashion. But if the history of mankind is any evidence we will return to it, for the triumph of the rational approach to life never appears to be permanent.

"Seaton's Aunt" is one of many stories I might have chosen. It belongs to a well-known genre: the vampire tale. But the blood-sucking is spiritual, and the horrors lie not in what is said but in what lurks behind the cool and crafty sentences.

At this writing E. M. Forster, born in 1879, is eighty-six. Except for *A Passage to India* (1924) his finest work was completed before World War I. Not only, however, does he not belong to the past but it may safely be said that his influence as personality and writer shows no sign of diminution. His novels, like many of his short stories, deal with the modes in which some fruitful accommodation may be reached between the claims of the imagination and the imperatives of practical life. The theme is found in many other writers, including, as we have seen, Thomas Mann; but Forster has his own way of dealing with it.

E. M. Forster is one of the noblest representatives of England's intellectual middle class. In large part his life has been influenced by the spirit of place: by King's College, Cambridge, which formed him and where he now passes his ultimate years; by the London, not so much of his birthplace, as of the Bloomsbury where he was intimate with the famous circle that gathered around Keynes and the Stephens family; by Italy, which furnished the setting for several of his narratives; by India; by Egypt, out of which came *Pharos and Pharillon* (1923) and his *Alexandria: A History and a Guide* (1922); and by his home in Abinger, Surrey, which seems to have nourished in him that English love of continuity and order sounding as an undertone in many of his books.

Forster is a major novelist and a first-rate second-order critic, but his short stories represent perhaps his least durable work. "The Celestial Omnibus," however, has never ceased to charm. There is nothing puzzling about it; it is a parable of which the imagination is the hero. Many such parables have been written; few, if any, are so sly, so charming, so tremulous with the vibrations by which high art and literature continue almost imperceptibly to stir the whole world.

We think of W. H. Hudson (1841–1922) as an Englishman but in fact he was born in Argentina of New England stock. In 1874 he left South America for England though not until 1900 did he become a naturalized British subject. He loved nature, birds and animals, non-industrial life, and those hours during which he set down his intimations of these matters. Hence he lived for the most part in obscurity, often in poverty, waiting many decades for the world's recognition. In his little Hampshire village, however, is a stone on which appears, carved by the villagers, the words: "W. H. Hudson used to sit here."

I suppose (except for *Green Mansions*) there is no great interest in Hudson today. That is regrettable, for his finest work, especially the autobiographical *Far Away and Long Ago* (1918) and his nature studies, whether of the Argentinian pampas or of the English downlands, is dateless.

I recently read an essay on Hudson's *The Purple Land* by the Argentinian genius Jorge Luis Borges. In it he quotes a sentence from a colleague-critic, Ezequiel Martínez Estrada: "Never has there been a poet, a painter or an interpreter of things Argentinian like Hudson, nor will there ever be again." This is remarkable praise. It means, if deserved, that an Anglo-Saxon, though he wrote in English—and what English!—is the classic figure of the rich Argentinian literary tradition.

"El Ombú" is perhaps the best of his "tales of the pampas." Loosely constructed, built around the spirit of place (a rancho), it has a kind of

Goyaesque graphic power, and is written in a simple, eloquent *oral* prose, with almost a touch of Homer.

The brief happy-unhappy life of D. H. Lawrence (1885–1930) comprises an interlocked series of inner and outer migrations. One of the most interesting of these shifts is posthumous, for in the last ten years or so he has climbed to a level of literary ranking that would not have been thought possible a few years after his death. The circumstance may be due less to his intrinsic genius than to the fact that those who currently make literary reputations are generally at violent odds with their own age, an age of which Lawrence, prophetically, was one of the most eloquent enemies.

Schoolteacher, novelist, poet, essayist, short-story writer, remarkable letter writer, dramatist, painter, traveler, controversialist, defender of his highly idiosyncratic notion of the natural man, Lawrence lived a life of burning intensity, stupefying productivity, and pathetic adversity. Often in trouble with censors, bureaucrats, and ex-friends, he lived at various times in England, Italy, Germany, Australia, the French Riviera, Mexico, and New Mexico. He died of tuberculosis in Vence, France, and has become since his death the object of much sincere admiration and much solemn cult-worship.

Some of his novels (*Sons and Lovers*, *Women in Love*, *The Rainbow*, but not the high-pitched, almost falsetto *Lady Chatterley's Lover*) will long retain their power to move readers toward a new and deeper sensibility. But it may be argued that his least faulty work is to be found in his wonderful long short stories. Of these I have chosen one of the less familiar. "The Man Who Loved Islands" is a fable penetrating to the core of the mysterious Yin and Yang relation between the human drive toward utter and independent individuality and the necessity to establish contact with other human beings. It is *Robinson Crusoe* rethought and refelt by a contemporary man of great complexity of mind and spirit. A disturbing story. Lawrence, even at his most ridiculous, is a disturbing man.

At one time Katherine Mansfield, with her husband, J. Middleton Murry, was very much a part of Lawrence's constantly shifting social world. It is said that Gudrun in *Women in Love* was suggested by her intense personality. Born in New Zealand in 1888, she removed to England, married Murry in 1912, and from 1911 to her death in 1923 continued to produce the strange, fugitive, but often enduringly poignant short stories on which her reputation rests. In 1923 she died of tuberculosis, perhaps needlessly, in the phony cultist community at Fontainebleau presided over by the dubious Gurdjieff. Had her difficult, poverty-filled life not been cut short she might very well have developed her special genius as did Virginia Woolf, and achieved as high a place in English letters.

"The Fly" is, I think, one of her last or surely later stories. No one tale can represent Katherine Mansfield, for her work was not of a piece.

"The Fly" does not, for instance, at all suggest the delightful tenderness of her many sketches of child life. It is hard, as much of her work, often misdescribed as vague and dreamy, is—even brutal. An allegory, one supposes, of the terrible helplessness of human nature, which, constantly suffering pain, constantly is compelled to inflict it. Katherine Mansfield is often listed as a disciple of Chekhov, and it is true that much of her work recalls his. This one does not; it is almost inhuman. But powerful.

With Alan Sillitoe and John Updike we are jolted into our day. While Beerbohm, Willa Cather, A. E. Coppard, de la Mare, Forster, Hudson, Lawrence, and Katherine Mansfield will endure, they are all touched, though differently, with a certain elusive *pastness*. They wrote for and could not have helped being influenced by men and women most of whom are dead or old. That is manifestly true also of Shakespeare and Homer. But it is possible, if a writer is good enough, to be past and present simultaneously. Sillitoe and Updike are quite flagrantly present, fastened, perhaps even pinioned, to their own time.

Alan Sillitoe (1928–), born in Nottingham, England, the son of a tannery worker, left school at fourteen. His work, drawing on his own experience, deals mainly with the industrial workers in drab English towns. Its undertone is one of indignation and rebellion, mitigated by a notable humor and zest for life. He has still to find himself as a writer, but it is impossible to fault this particular specimen of his talent, the wonderfully titled "The Loneliness of the Long-Distance Runner." It uses the working-class town vernacular with clean precision, but without ostentation. It has speed, comic force, and tremendous gusto.

John Updike's qualities are quite other. His forte (in his short stories only) lies in delicacy—sometimes an excess of it, if that is possible—a fragile humor, unexpectedness, oddity, precise observation. His characters belong to a small world, probably a transient one, like that of O'Hara or Fitzgerald. They are very closely looked at, very carefully overheard. The notations will have historical value when they give way, as they will, to other big-city types. "Snowing in Greenwich Village" is a most creditable example of his art. It is interesting to compare it with "Dusky Ruth," as both stories deal with an unfinished erotic experience. The difference between Coppard's figures and Mr. Updike's possibly illuminates in part the distance we have traveled in half a century.

John Updike was born in 1932 in a small Pennsylvania town (the scene of many of his tales), attended Harvard, and studied at the Ruskin School of Drawing and Fine Art (Oxford) on a fellowship. Much of his shorter work, including poems brilliantly witty, has been published in *The New Yorker,* of whose spirit he is typical. His novels, *The Poorhouse Fair* (1959), *Rabbit, Run* (1960), and *The Centaur* (1963), have been highly praised. He is by many considered one of the most promising writers of his generation.

Max Beerbohm

ENOCH SOAMES

WHEN A BOOK ABOUT the literature of the eighteen-nineties was given by Mr. Holbrook Jackson to the world, I looked eagerly in the index for SOAMES, ENOCH. I had feared he would not be there. He was not there. But everybody else was. Many writers whom I had quite forgotten, or remembered but faintly, lived again for me, they and their work, in Mr. Holbrook Jackson's pages. The book was as thorough as it was brilliantly written. And thus the omission found by me was an all the deadlier record of poor Soames' failure to impress himself on his decade.

I daresay I am the only person who noticed the omission. Soames had failed so piteously as all that! Nor is there a counterpoise in the thought that if he had had some measure of success he might have passed, like those others, out of my mind, to return only at the historian's beck. It is true that had his gifts, such as they were, been acknowledged in his lifetime, he would never have made the bargain I saw him make—that strange bargain whose results have kept him always in the foreground of my memory. But it is from those very results that the full piteousness of him glares out.

Not my compassion, however, impels me to write of him. For his sake, poor fellow, I should be inclined to keep my pen out of the ink. It is ill to deride the dead. And how can I write about Enoch Soames without making him ridiculous? Or rather, how am I to hush up the horrid fact that he *was* ridiculous? I shall not be able to do that. Yet, sooner or later, write about him I must. You will see, in due course, that I have no option. And I may as well get the thing done now.

In the Summer Term of '93 a bolt from the blue flashed down on Oxford. It drove deep, it hurtlingly embedded itself in the soil. Dons and undergraduates stood around, rather pale, discussing nothing but it. Whence came it, this meteorite? From Paris. Its name? Will Rothenstein. Its aim? To do a series of twenty-four portraits in lithograph. These were to be published from the Bodley Head, London. The matter was urgent. Already the Warden of A, and the Master of B, and the Regius Professor of C, had meekly "sat." Dignified and doddering old men, who had never consented to sit to any one, could not withstand this dynamic little stranger. He did not sue: he invited; he did not invite: he commanded. He was twenty-one years old. He wore spectacles that flashed more than any other pair ever seen. He was a wit. He was brimful of ideas. He knew Whistler. He knew Edmond de Goncourt. He knew every one in Paris. He knew them all by heart. He was Paris in Oxford. It was whispered that, so soon as he had polished off his selection of dons, he was going to include a few undergraduates. It was a proud day for me when I—I—was included. I liked Rothenstein not less than I feared him; and there arose between us a friendship that has grown ever warmer, and been more and more valued by me, with every passing year.

At the end of Term he settled in—or rather, meteoritically into— London. It was to him I owed my first knowledge of that forever enchanting little world-in-itself, Chelsea, and my first acquaintance with Walter Sickert and other august elders who dwelt there. It was Rothenstein that took me to see, in Cambridge Street, Pimlico, a young man whose drawings were already famous among the few—Aubrey Beardsley, by name. With Rothenstein I paid my first visit to the Bodley Head. By him I was inducted into another haunt of intellect and daring, the domino room of the Café Royal.

There, on that October evening—there, in that exuberant vista of gilding and crimson velvet set amidst all those opposing mirrors and upholding caryatids, with fumes of tobacco ever rising to the painted and pagan ceiling, and with the hum of presumably cynical conversation broken into so sharply now and again by the clatter of dominoes shuffled on marble tables, I drew a deep breath, and "This indeed," said I to myself, "is life!"

It was the hour before dinner. We drank vermouth. Those who knew Rothenstein were pointing him out to those who knew him only by name. Men were constantly coming in through the swing-doors and wandering slowly up and down in search of vacant tables, or of tables occupied by friends. One of these rovers interested me because I was sure he wanted to catch Rothenstein's eye. He had twice passed our table, with a hesitating look; but Rothenstein, in the thick of a disquisition on Puvis de Chavannes, had not seen him. He was a stooping, shambling person, rather tall, very pale, with longish and brownish hair. He had a thin vague beard—or rather, he had a chin on which a large number of hairs weakly curled and clustered to cover its retreat. He was an odd-looking person; but in the 'nineties odd apparitions were more frequent, I think, than they are now. The young writers of that era—and I was sure this man was a writer—strove earnestly to be distinct in aspect. This man had striven unsuccessfully. He wore a soft black hat of clerical kind but of Bohemian intention, and a grey waterproof cape which, perhaps because it was waterproof, failed to be romantic. I decided that "dim" was the *mot juste* for him. I had already essayed to write, and was immensely keen on the *mot juste*, that Holy Grail of the period.

The dim man was now again approaching our table, and this time he made up his mind to pause in front of it. "You don't remember me," he said in a toneless voice.

Rothenstein brightly focussed him. "Yes, I do," he replied after a moment, with pride rather than effusion—pride in a retentive memory. "Edwin Soames."

"Enoch Soames," said Enoch.

"Enoch Soames," repeated Rothenstein in a tone implying that it was enough to have hit on the surname. "We met in Paris two or three times when you were living there. We met at the Café Groche."

"And I came to your studio once."

"Oh yes; I was sorry I was out."

"But you were in. You showed me some of your paintings you know. . . . I hear you're in Chelsea now."

"Yes."

I almost wondered that Mr. Soames did not, after this monosyllable, pass along. He stood patiently there, rather like a dumb animal, rather like a donkey looking over a gate. A sad figure, his. It occurred to me that "hungry" was perhaps the *mot juste* for him; but—hungry for what? He looked as if he had little appetite for anything. I was sorry for him; and Rothenstein, though he had not invited him to Chelsea, did ask him to sit down and have something to drink.

Seated, he was more self-assertive. He flung back the wings of his cape with a gesture which—had not those wings been waterproof—might have seemed to hurl defiance at things in general. And he ordered an absinthe. "*Je me tiens toujours fidèle,*" he told Rothenstein, "*à la sorcière glauque.*"

"It is bad for you," said Rothenstein drily.

"Nothing is bad for one," answered Soames. "*Dans ce monde il n'y a ni de bien ni de mal.*"

"Nothing good and nothing bad? How do you mean?"

"I explained it all in the preface to 'Negations.'"

" 'Negations'?"

"Yes; I gave you a copy of it."

"Oh yes, of course. But did you explain—for instance—that there was no such thing as bad or good grammar?"

"N-no," said Soames. "Of course in Art there is the good and the evil. But in Life—no." He was rolling a cigarette. He had weak white hands, not well washed, and with finger-tips much stained by nicotine. "In Life there are illusions of good and evil, but"—his voice trailed away to a murmur in which the words "vieux jeu" and "rococo" were faintly audible. I think he felt he was not doing himself justice, and feared that Rothenstein was going to point out fallacies. Anyway, he cleared his throat and said *"Parlons d'autre chose."*

It occurs to you that he was a fool? It didn't to me. I was young, and had not the clarity of judgment that Rothenstein already had. Soames was quite five or six years older than either of us. Also, he had written a book.

It was wonderful to have written a book.

If Rothenstein had not been there, I should have revered Soames. Even as it was, I respected him. And I was very near indeed to reverence when he said he had another book coming out soon. I asked if I might ask what kind of book it was to be.

"My poems," he answered. Rothenstein asked if this was to be the title of the book. The poet meditated on this suggestion, but said he rather thought of giving the book no title at all. "If a book is good in itself—" he murmured, waving his cigarette.

Rothenstein objected that absence of title might be bad for the sale of a book. "If," he urged, "I went into a bookseller's and said simply 'Have you got?' or 'Have you a copy of?' how would they know what I wanted?"

"Oh, of course I should have my name on the cover," Soames answered earnestly. "And I rather want," he added, looking hard at Rothenstein, "to have a drawing of myself as frontispiece." Rothenstein admitted that this was a capital idea, and mentioned that he was going into the country and would be there for some time. He then looked at his watch, exclaimed at the hour, paid the waiter, and went away with me to dinner. Soames remained at his post of fidelity to the glaucous witch.

"Why were you so determined not to draw him?" I asked.

"Draw him? Him? How can one draw a man who doesn't exist?"

"He is dim," I admitted. But my *mot juste* fell flat. Rothenstein repeated that Soames was non-existent.

Still, Soames had written a book. I asked if Rothenstein had read "Negations." He said he had looked into it, "but," he added crisply, "I don't profess to know anything about writing." A reservation very characteristic of the period! Painters would not then allow that any one outside their own order had a right to any opinion about painting. This law (graven on the tablets brought down by Whistler from the summit of Fujiyama) imposed certain limitations. If other arts than painting were not utterly unintelligible to all but the men who practised them, the law tottered—the Monroe Doctrine, as it were, did not hold good. Therefore no painter would offer an opinion of a book without warning you at any rate that his opinion was worthless. No one is a better judge of literature than Rothenstein; but it wouldn't have done to tell him so in those days; and I knew that I must form an unaided judgment on "Negations."

Not to buy a book of which I had met the author face to face would have been for me in those days an impossible act of self-denial. When I returned to Oxford for the Christmas Term I had duly secured "Negations." I used to keep it lying carelessly on the table in my room, and whenever a friend took it up and asked what it was about I would say "Oh, it's rather a remarkable book. It's by a man whom I know." Just "what it was about" I never was able to say. Head or tail was just what I hadn't made of that slim green volume. I found in the preface no clue to the exiguous labyrinth of contents, and in that labyrinth nothing to explain the preface.

> *Lean near to life. Lean very near—nearer.*
> *Life is web, and therein nor warp nor woof is, but web only.*
> *It is for this I am Catholick in church and in thought, yet do let*
> *swift Mood weave there what the shuttle of Mood wills.*

These were the opening phrases of the preface, but those which followed were less easy to understand. Then came "Stark: A *Conte*," about a midinette who, so far as I could gather, murdered, or was about to murder, a mannequin. It seemed to me like a story by Catulle Mendès in which the translator had either skipped or cut out every alternate sentence. Next, a dialogue between Pan and St. Ursula—lacking, I rather felt, in "snap." Next, some aphorisms (entitled ἀφορίσματα). Throughout, in fact, there was a great variety of form; and the forms had evidently been wrought with much care. It was rather the substance that eluded me. Was there, I wondered, any substance at all? It did now occur to me: suppose Enoch Soames was a fool! Up cropped a rival hypothesis: suppose *I* was! I inclined to give Soames the benefit of the doubt. I had read "L'Après-midi d'un Faune" without extracting a glimmer of meaning. Yet Mallarmé—of course—was a Master. How was I to know that Soames wasn't another? There was a sort of music in his prose, not indeed arresting, but perhaps, I thought, haunting, and laden perhaps with meanings as deep as Mallarmé's own. I awaited his poems with an open mind.

And I looked forward to them with positive impatience after I had had a second meeting with him. This was on an evening in January. Going into the aforesaid domino room, I passed a table at which sat a pale man with an open book before him. He looked from his book to me, and I looked back over my shoulder with a vague sense that I ought to have recognised him. I returned to pay my respects. After exchanging a few words, I said with a glance to the open book, "I see I am interrupting you," and was about to pass on, but "I prefer," Soames replied in his toneless voice, "to be interrupted," and I obeyed his gesture that I should sit down.

I asked him if he often read here. "Yes; things of this kind I read here," he answered, indicating the title of his book—"The Poems of Shelley."

"Anything that you really"—and I was going to say "admire?" But I cautiously left my sentence unfinished, and was glad that I had done so, for he said, with unwonted emphasis, "Anything second-rate."

I had read little of Shelley, but "Of course," I murmured, "he's very uneven."

"I should have thought evenness was just what was wrong with him. A deadly evenness. That's why I read him here. The noise of this place breaks the rhythm. He's tolerable here." Soames took up the book and glanced through the pages. He laughed. Soames' laugh was a short, single and mirthless sound from the throat, unaccompanied by any movement of the face or brightening of the eyes. "What a period!" he uttered, laying the book down. And "What a country!" he added.

I asked rather nervously if he didn't think Keats had more or less held his own against the drawbacks of time and place. He admitted that there were "passages in Keats," but did not specify them. Of "the older men," as he called them, he seemed to like only Milton. "Milton," he said, "wasn't sentimental." Also, "Milton had a dark insight." And again, "I can always read Milton in the reading-room."

"The reading-room?"

"Of the British Museum. I go there every day."

"You do? I've only been there once. I'm afraid I found it rather a depressing place. It—it seemed to sap one's vitality."

"It does. That's why I go there. The lower one's vitality, the more sensitive one is to great art. I live near the Museum. I have rooms in Dyott Street."

"And you go round to the reading-room to read Milton?"

"Usually Milton." He looked at me. "It was Milton," he certificatively added, "who converted me to Diabolism."

"Diabolism? Oh yes? Really?" said I, with that vague discomfort and that intense desire to be polite which one feels when a man speaks of his own religion. "You—worship the Devil?"

Soames shook his head. "It's not exactly worship," he qualified, sipping his absinthe. "It's more a matter of trusting and encouraging."

"Ah, yes. . . . But I had rather gathered from the preface to 'Negations' that you were a—a Catholic."

"*Je l'étais à cette époque.* Perhaps I still am. Yes, I'm a Catholic Diabolist."

This profession he made in an almost cursory tone. I could see that what was upmost in his mind was the fact that I had read "Negations." His pale eyes had for the first time gleamed. I felt as one who is about to be examined, *viva voce*, on the very subject in which he is shakiest. I hastily asked him how soon his poems were to be published. "Next week," he told me.

"And are they to be published without a title?"

"No. I found a title, at last. But I shan't tell you what it is," as though I had been so impertinent as to inquire. "I am not sure that it wholly satisfies me. But it is the best I can find. It does suggest something of the quality of the poems. . . . Strange growths, natural and wild; yet exquisite," he added, "and many-hued, and full of poisons."

I asked him what he thought of Baudelaire. He uttered the snort that was his laugh, and "Baudelaire," he said, "was a *bourgeois malgré lui*." France had had only one poet: Villon; "and two-thirds of Villon were sheer journalism." Verlaine was "an *épicier malgré lui*." Altogether, rather to my surprise, he rated French literature lower than English. There were "passages" in Villiers de l'Isle-Adam. But "I," he summed up, "owe nothing to France." He nodded at me. "You'll see," he predicted.

I did not, when the time came, quite see that. I thought the author of "Fungoids" did—unconsciously, no doubt—owe something to the young Parisian décadents, or to the young English ones who owed something to *them*. I still think so. The little book—bought by me in Oxford—lies before me as I write. Its pale grey buckram cover and silver lettering have not worn well. Nor have its contents. Through these, with a melancholy interest, I have again been looking. They are not much. But at the time of their publication I had a vague suspicion that they *might* be. I suppose it is my capacity for faith, not poor Soames' work, that is weaker than it once was . . .

TO A YOUNG WOMAN

Thou art, who hast not been!
    Pale tunes irresolute
    And traceries of old sounds
    Blown from a rotted flute
Mingle with noise of cymbals rouged with rust,
Nor not strange forms and epicene
    Lie bleeding in the dust,
      Being wounded with wounds.
      For this it is
    That is thy counterpart
      Of age-long mockeries
Thou hast not been nor art!

There seemed to me a certain inconsistency as between the first and last lines of this. I tried, with bent brows, to resolve the discord. But I did not take my failure as wholly incompatible with a meaning in Soames' mind. Might it not rather indicate the depth of his meaning? As for the craftsmanship, "rouged with rust" seemed to me a fine stroke, and "nor not" instead of "and" had a curious felicity. I wondered who the Young Woman was, and what she had made of it all. I sadly suspect that Soames could not have made more of it than she. Yet, even now, if one doesn't try to make any sense at all of the poem, and reads it just for the sound, there is a certain grace of cadence. Soames was an artist—in so far as he was anything, poor fellow!

It seemed to me, when first I read "Fungoids," that, oddly enough, the Diabolistic side of him was the best. Diabolism seemed to be a cheerful, even a wholesome, influence in his life.

NOCTURNE

Round and round the shutter'd Square
I stroll'd with the Devil's arm in mine.
No sound but the scrape of his hoofs was there
And the ring of his laughter and mine.
　　We had drunk black wine.

I scream'd "I will race you, Master!"
"What matter," he shriek'd, "to-night
Which of us runs the faster?
There is nothing to fear to-night
*　　In the foul moon's light!"*

Then I look'd him in the eyes,
And I laugh'd full shrill at the lie he told
And the gnawing fear he would fain disguise.
It was true, what I'd time and again been told:
　　He was old—old.

There was, I felt, quite a swing about that first stanza—a joyous and
rollicking note of comradeship. The second was slightly hysterical perhaps. But I liked the third: it was so bracingly unorthodox, even according to the tenets of Soames' peculiar sect in the faith. Not much "trusting
and encouraging" here! Soames triumphantly exposing the Devil as a liar,
and laughing "full shrill," cut a quite heartening figure, I thought—then!
Now, in the light of what befell, none of his poems depresses me so much
as "Nocturne."

I looked out for what the metropolitan reviewers would have to say.
They seemed to fall into two classes: those who had little to say and those
who had nothing. The second class was the larger, and the words of the
first were cold; insomuch that

> Strikes a note of modernity throughout. . . . These tripping num-
> bers.—*Preston Telegraph.*

was the sole lure offered in advertisements by Soames' publisher. I had
hoped that when next I met the poet I could congratulate him on having
made a stir; for I fancied he was not so sure of his intrinsic greatness as he
seemed. I was but able to say, rather coarsely, when next I did see him,
that I hoped "Fungoids" was "selling splendidly." He looked at me across
his glass of absinthe and asked if I had bought a copy. His publisher had
told him that three had been sold. I laughed, as at a jest.

"You don't suppose I *care,* do you?" he said, with something like a
snarl. I disclaimed the notion. He added that he was not a tradesman. I
said mildly that I wasn't, either, and murmured that an artist who gave
truly new and great things to the world had always to wait long for
recognition. He said he cared not a sou for recognition. I agreed that the
act of creation was its own reward.

His moroseness might have alienated me if I had regarded myself as a nobody. But ah! hadn't both John Lane and Aubrey Beardsley suggested that I should write an essay for the great new venture that was afoot— "The Yellow Book"? And hadn't Henry Harland, as editor, accepted my essay? And wasn't it to be in the very first number? At Oxford I was still *in statu pupillari*. In London I regarded myself as very much indeed a graduate now—one whom no Soames could ruffle. Partly to show off, partly in sheer good-will, I told Soames he ought to contribute to "The Yellow Book." He uttered from the throat a sound of scorn for that publication.

Nevertheless, I did, a day or two later, tentatively ask Harland if he knew anything of the work of a man called Enoch Soames. Harland paused in the midst of his characteristic stride around the room, threw up his hands towards the ceiling, and groaned aloud: he had often met "that absurd creature" in Paris, and this very morning had received some poems in manuscript from him.

"Has he *no* talent?" I asked.

"He has an income. He's all right." Harland was the most joyous of men and most generous of critics, and he hated to talk of anything about which he couldn't be enthusiastic. So I dropped the subject of Soames. The news that Soames had an income did take the edge off solicitude. I learned afterwards that he was the son of an unsuccessful and deceased bookseller in Preston, but had inherited an annuity of £300 from a married aunt, and had no surviving relatives of any kind. Materially, then, he was "all right." But there was still a spiritual pathos about him, sharpened for me now by the possibility that even the praises of "The Preston Telegraph" might not have been forthcoming had he not been the son of a Preston man. He had a sort of weak doggedness which I could not but admire. Neither he nor his work received the slightest encouragement; but he persisted in behaving as a personage: always he kept his dingy little flag flying. Wherever congregated the *jeunes féroces* of the arts, in whatever Soho restaurant they had just discovered, in whatever music-hall they were most frequenting, there was Soames in the midst of them, or rather on the fringe of them, a dim but inevitable figure. He never sought to propitiate his fellow-writers, never bated a jot of his arrogance about his own work or of his contempt for theirs. To the painters he was respectful, even humble; but for the poets and prosaists of "The Yellow Book," and later of "The Savy," he had never a word but of scorn. He wasn't resented. It didn't occur to anybody that he or his Catholic Diabolism mattered. When, in the autumn of '96, he brought out (at his own expense, this time) a third book, his last book, nobody said a word for or against it. I meant, but forgot, to buy it. I never saw it, and am ashamed to say I don't even remember what it was called. But I did, at the time of its publication, say to Rothenstein that I thought poor old Soames was really a rather tragic figure, and that I believed he would literally die for want of recognition. Rothenstein scoffed. He said I was trying to get credit for a kind heart which I didn't possess; and perhaps this was so. But at the private view of the New English Art Club, a few weeks later, I beheld a pastel portrait of "Enoch Soames, Esq." It was very like him, and very like Rothenstein to have done it. Soames was standing near it, in his soft hat and his waterproof cape, all through the afternoon. Anybody who knew him would have recognised the portrait at a glance, but nobody who didn't know him would have recognised the portrait from its bystander: it "existed" so much more than he; it was bound to. Also, it had not that expression of faint happiness which on this day was discernible, yes, in Soames' countenance. Fame had breathed on him. Twice again in the course of the month I went to the New English, and on both occasions Soames himself was on view there. Looking back, I regard the close of that exhibition as having been virtually the close of his career. He felt the breath of Fame against his cheek—so late, for such a little while; and at its withdrawal he gave in, gave up, gave out. He, who had never looked strong or well, looked ghastly now—a shadow of the shade he had once been. He still frequented the domino room, but, having lost all wish to excite curiosity, he no longer read books there. "You read only at the Museum now?" asked I, with attempted cheerfulness. He said he never went there now. "No absinthe there," he muttered. It was the sort of thing that in the old days he would have said for effect; but it carried conviction now. Absinthe, erst but a point in the "personality" he had striven so hard to build up, was solace and necessity now. He no longer called it "la sorcière glauque." He had shed away all his French phrases. He had become a plain, unvarnished, Preston man.

Failure, if it be a plain, unvarnished, complete failure, and even though it be a squalid failure, has always a certain dignity. I avoided Soames because he made me feel rather vulgar. John Lane had published, by this time, two little books of mine, and they had had a pleasant little success of esteem. I was a—slight but definite—"personality." Frank Harris had engaged me to kick up my heels in *The Saturday Review.* Alfred Harmsworth was letting me do likewise in *The Daily Mail.* I was just what Soames wasn't. And he shamed my gloss. Had I known that he really and firmly believed in the greatness of what he as an artist had achieved, I might not have shunned him. No man who hasn't lost his vanity can be held to have altogether failed. Soames' dignity was an illusion of mine. One day in the first week of June, 1897, that illusion went. But on the evening of that day Soames went too.

I had been out most of the morning, and, as it was too late to reach home in time for luncheon, I sought "the Vingtième." This little place —Restaurant du Vingtième Siècle, to give it its full title—had been discovered in '96 by the poets and prosaists, but had now been more or less abandoned in favour of some later find. I don't think it lived long enough to justify its name; but at that time there it still was, in Greek Street, a few doors from Soho Square, and almost opposite to that house where, in the first years of the century, a little girl, and with her a boy named De

A page torn from a sketch-book of which I filled several pages with efforts to adumbrate Enoch Soames soon after my first meeting with that "dim" personage in '93. The face in the right-hand corner at the top is that of Professor Rothenstein as he appeared in his pre-professorial days. [M.B.]

Quincey, made nightly encampment in darkness and hunger among dust and rats and old legal parchments. The Vingtième was but a small white-washed room, leading out into the street at one end and into a kitchen at the other. The proprietor and cook was a Frenchman, known to us as Monsieur Vingtième; the waiters were his two daughters, Rose and Berthe; and the food, according to faith, was good. The tables were so narrow, and were set so close together, that there was space for twelve of them, six jutting from either wall.

Only the two nearest to the door, as I went in, were occupied. On one side sat a tall, flashy, rather Mephistophelian man whom I had seen from time to time in the domino room and elsewhere. On the other side sat Soames. They made a queer contrast in that sunlit room—Soames sitting haggard in that hat and cape which nowhere at any season had I seen him doff, and this other, this keenly vital man, at sight of whom I more than ever wondered whether he were a diamond merchant, a con-jurer, or the head of a private detective agency. I was sure Soames didn't want my company; but I asked, as it would have seemed brutal not to, whether I might join him, and took the chair opposite to his. He was smoking a cigarette, with an untasted salmi of something on his plate and a half-empty bottle of Sauterne before him; and he was quite silent. I said that the preparations for the Jubilee made London impossible. (I rather liked him, really.) I professed a wish to go right away till the whole thing was over. In vain did I attune myself to his gloom. He seemed not to hear me nor even to see me. I felt that his behaviour made me ridiculous in the eyes of the other man. The gangway between the two rows of tables at the Vingtième was hardly more than two feet wide (Rose and Berthe, in their ministrations, had always to edge past each other, quarrelling in whispers as they did so), and any one at the table abreast of yours was practically at yours. I thought our neighbour was amused at my failure to interest Soames, and so, as I could not explain to him that my insistence was merely charitable, I became silent. Without turning my head, I had him well within my range of vision. I hoped I looked less vulgar than he in contrast with Soames. I was sure he was not an Englishman, but what *was* his nationality? Though his jet-black hair was *en brosse*, I did not think he was French. To Berthe, who waited on him, he spoke French fluently, but with a hardly native idiom and accent. I gathered that this was his first visit to the Vingtième; but Berthe was off-hand in her manner to him: he had not made a good impression. His eyes were handsome, but—like the Vingtième's tables—too narrow and set too close together. His nose was predatory, and the points of his moustache, waxed up beyond his nostrils, gave a fixity to his smile. Decidedly, he was sinister. And my sense of discomfort in his presence was intensified by the scarlet waistcoat which tightly, and so unseasonably in June, sheathed his ample chest. This waistcoat wasn't wrong merely because of the heat, either. It was somehow all wrong in itself. It wouldn't have done on Christmas morning. It would have struck a jarring note at the first night of "Hernani." I was trying to account for its wrongness when Soames suddenly and strangely broke silence. "A hundred years hence!" he murmured, as in a trance.

"We shall not be here!" I briskly but fatuously added.

"We shall not be here. No," he droned, "but the Museum will still be just where it is. And the reading-room, just where it is. And people will be able to go and read there." He inhaled sharply, and a spasm as of actual pain contorted his features.

I wondered what train of thought poor Soames had been following. He did not enlighten me when he said, after a long pause, "You think I haven't minded."

"Minded what, Soames?"

"Neglect. Failure."

"*Failure?*" I said heartily. "Failure?" I repeated vaguely. "Neglect— yes, perhaps; but that's quite another matter. Of course you haven't been—appreciated. But what then? Any artist who—who gives—" What I wanted to say was, "Any artist who gives truly new and great things to the world has always to wait long for recognition"; but the flattery would not out: in the face of his misery, a misery so genuine and so unmasked, my lips would not say the words.

And then—he said them for me. I flushed. "That's what you were going to say, isn't it?" he asked.

"How did you know?"

"It's what you said to me three years ago, when 'Fungoids' was published." I flushed the more. I need not have done so at all, for "It's the only important thing I ever heard you say," he continued. "And I've never forgotten it. It's a true thing. It's a horrible truth. But—d'you remember what I answered? I said 'I don't care a sou for recognition.' And you believed me. You've gone on believing I'm above that sort of thing. You're shallow. What should *you* know of the feelings of a man like me? You imagine that a great artist's faith in himself and in the verdict of posterity is enough to keep him happy . . . You've never guessed at the bitterness and loneliness, the"—his voice broke; but presently he resumed, speaking with a force that I had never known in him. "Posterity! What use is it to *me?* A dead man doesn't know that people are visiting his grave—visiting his birthplace—putting up tablets to him— unveiling statues of him. A dead man can't read the books that are written about him. A hundred years hence! Think of it! If I could come back to life *then*—just for a few hours—and go to the reading-room, and *read!* Or better still: if I could be projected, now, at this moment, into that future, into that reading-room, just for this one afternoon! I'd sell myself body and soul to the devil, for that! Think of the pages and pages in the catalogue: 'SOAMES, ENOCH' endlessly—endless editions, commentaries, prolegomena, biographies"—but here he was interrupted by a sudden loud creak of the chair at the next table. Our neighbour had half risen from his place. He was leaning towards us, apologetically intrusive.

"Excuse—permit me," he said softly. "I have been unable not to hear. Might I take a liberty? In this little restaurant-sans-façon"—he spread wide his hands—"might I, as the phrase is, 'cut in'?"

I could but signify our acquiescence. Berthe had appeared at the kitchen door, thinking the stranger wanted his bill. He waved her away with his cigar, and in another moment had seated himself beside me, commanding a full view of Soames.

"Though not an Englishman," he explained, "I know my London well, Mr. Soames. Your name and fame—Mr. Beerbohm's too—very known to me. Your point is: who am *I?*" He glanced quickly over his shoulder, and in a lowered voice said "I am the Devil."

I couldn't help it: I laughed. I tried not to, I knew there was nothing to laugh at, my rudeness shamed me, but—I laughed with increasing volume. The Devil's quiet dignity, the surprise and disgust of his raised eyebrows, did but the more dissolve me. I rocked to and fro, I lay back aching. I behaved deplorably.

"I am a gentleman, and," he said with intense emphasis, "I thought I was in the company of *gentlemen.*"

"Don't!" I gasped faintly. "Oh, don't!"

"Curious, *nicht wahr?*" I heard him say to Soames. "There is a type of person to whom the very mention of my name is—oh-so-awfully-funny! In your theatres the dullest comédien needs only to say 'The Devil!' and right away they give him 'the loud laugh that speaks the vacant mind.' Is it not so?"

I had now just breath enough to offer my apologies. He accepted them, but coldly, and re-addressed himself to Soames.

"I am a man of business," he said, "and always I would put things through 'right now,' as they say in the States. You are a poet. *Les affaires* —you detest them. So be it. But with me you will deal, eh? What you have said just now gives me furiously to hope."

Soames had not moved, except to light a fresh cigarette. He sat crouched forward, with his elbows squared on the table, and his head just above the level of his hands, staring up at the Devil. "Go on," he nodded. I had no remnant of laughter in me now.

"It will be the more pleasant, our little deal," the Devil went on, "because you are—I mistake not?—a Diabolist."

"A Catholic Diabolist," said Soames.

The Devil accepted the reservation genially. "You wish," he resumed, "to visit now—this afternoon as-ever-is—the reading-room of the British Museum, yes? but of a hundred years hence, yes? *Parfaitement.* Time—an illusion. Past and future—they are as ever-present as the present, or at any rate only what you call 'just-round-the-corner.' I switch you on to any date. I project you—pouf! You wish to be in the reading-room just as it will be on the afternoon of June 3rd, 1997? You wish to find yourself standing in that room, just past the swing-doors, this very minute, yes? and to stay there till closing time? Am I right?"

Soames nodded.

The Devil looked at his watch. "Ten past two," he said. "Closing time in summer same then as now: seven o'clock. That will give you almost five hours. At seven o'clock—pouf!—you find yourself again here, sitting at this table. I am dining to-night *dans le monde—dans le higlif*. That concludes my present visit to your great city. I come and fetch you here, Mr. Soames, on my way home."

"Home?" I echoed.

"Be it never so humble!" said the Devil lightly.

"All right," said Soames.

"Soames!" I entreated. But my friend moved not a muscle.

The Devil had made as though to stretch forth his hand across the table and touch Soames' forearm; but he paused in his gesture.

"A hundred years hence, as now," he smiled, "no smoking allowed in the reading-room. You would better therefore—"

Soames removed the cigarette from his mouth and dropped it into his glass of Sauterne.

"Soames!" again I cried. "Can't you"—but the Devil had now stretched forth his hand across the table. He brought it slowly down on—the tablecloth. Soames' chair was empty. His cigarette floated sodden in his wine-glass. There was no other trace of him.

For a few moments the Devil let his hand rest where it lay, gazing at me out of the corners of his eyes, vulgarly triumphant.

A shudder shook me. With an effort I controlled myself and rose from my chair. "Very clever," I said condescendingly. "But—'The Time Machine' is a delightful book, don't you think? So entirely original!"

"You are pleased to sneer," said the Devil, who had also risen, "but it is one thing to write about a not possible machine; it is a quite other thing to be a Supernatural Power." All the same, I had scored.

Berthe had come forth at the sound of our rising. I explained to her that Mr. Soames had been called away, and that both he and I would be dining here. It was not until I was out in the open air that I began to feel giddy. I have but the haziest recollection of what I did, where I wandered, in the glaring sunshine of that endless afternoon. I remember the sound of carpenters' hammers all along Piccadilly, and the bare chaotic look of the half-erected "stands." Was it in the Green Park, or in Kensington Gardens, or *where* was it that I sat on a chair beneath a tree, trying to read an evening paper? There was a phrase in the leading article that went on repeating itself in my fagged mind—"Little is hidden from this august Lady full of the garnered wisdom of sixty years of Sovereignty." I remember wildly conceiving a letter (to reach Windsor by express messenger told to await answer):

> MADAM,—Well knowing that your Majesty is full of the garnered wisdom of sixty years of Sovereignty, I venture to ask your advice in the following delicate matter. Mr. Enoch Soames, whose poems you may or may not know, . . .

Was there *no* way of helping him—saving him? A bargain was a bargain, and I was the last man to aid or abet any one in wriggling out of a reasonable obligation. I wouldn't have lifted a little finger to save Faust. But poor Soames!—doomed to pay without respite an eternal price for nothing but a fruitless search and a bitter disillusioning . . .

Odd and uncanny it seemed to me that he, Soames, in the flesh, in the waterproof cape, was at this moment living in the last decade of the next century, poring over books not yet written, and seeing and seen by men not yet born. Uncannier and odder still, that to-night and evermore he would be in Hell. Assuredly, truth was stranger than fiction.

Endless that afternoon was. Almost I wished I had gone with Soames —not indeed to stay in the reading-room, but to sally forth for a brisk sight-seeing walk around a new London. I wandered restlessly out of the Park I had sat in. Vainly I tried to imagine myself an ardent tourist from the eighteenth century. Intolerable was the strain of the slow-passing and empty minutes. Long before seven o'clock I was back at the Vingtième.

I sat there just where I had sat for luncheon. Air came in listlessly through the open door behind me. Now and again Rose or Berthe appeared for a moment. I had told them I would not order any dinner till Mr. Soames came. A hurdy-gurdy began to play, abruptly drowning the noise of a quarrel between some Frenchmen further up the street. Whenever the tune was changed I heard the quarrel still raging. I had bought another evening paper on my way. I unfolded it. My eyes gazed ever away from it to the clock over the kitchen door . . .

Five minutes, now, to the hour! I remembered that clocks in restaurants are kept five minutes fast. I concentrated my eyes on the paper. I vowed I would not look away from it again. I held it upright, at its full width, close to my face, so that I had no view of anything but it . . . Rather a tremulous sheet? Only because of the draught, I told myself.

My arms gradually became stiff; they ached; but I could not drop them—now. I had a suspicion, I had a certainty. Well, what then? . . . What else had I come for? Yet I held tight that barrier of newspaper. Only the sound of Berthe's brisk footstep from the kitchen enabled me, forced me, to drop it, and to utter:

"What shall we have to eat, Soames?"

"*Il est souffrant, ce pauvre Monsieur Soames?*" asked Berthe.

"He's only—tired." I asked her to get some wine—Burgundy—and whatever food might be ready. Soames sat crouched forward against the table, exactly as when last I had seen him. It was as though he had never moved—he who had moved so unimaginably far. Once or twice in the afternoon it had for an instant occurred to me that perhaps his journey was not to be fruitless—that perhaps we had all been wrong in our estimate of the works of Enoch Soames. That we had been horribly right was horribly clear from the look of him. But "Don't be discouraged," I falteringly said. "Perhaps it's only that you—didn't leave enough time. Two, three centuries hence, perhaps—"

"Yes," his voice came. "I've thought of that."

"And now—now for the more immediate future! Where are you going to hide? How would it be if you caught the Paris express from Charing Cross? Almost an hour to spare. Don't go on to Paris. Stop at Calais. Live in Calais. He'd never think of looking for you in Calais."

"It's like my luck," he said, "to spend my last hours on earth with an ass." But I was not offended. "And a treacherous ass," he strangely added, tossing across to me a crumpled bit of paper which he had been holding in his hand. I glanced at the writing on it—some sort of gibberish, apparently. I laid it impatiently aside.

"Come, Soames! pull yourself together! This isn't a mere matter of life and death. It's a question of eternal torment, mind you! You don't mean to say you're going to wait limply here till the Devil comes to fetch you?"

"I can't do anything else. I've no choice."

"Come! This is 'trusting and encouraging' with a vengeance! This is Diabolism run mad!" I filled his glass with wine. "Surely, now that you've *seen* the brute—"

"It's no good abusing him."

"You must admit there's nothing Miltonic about him, Soames."

"I don't say he's not rather different from what I expected."

"He's a vulgarian, he's a swell-mobsman, he's the sort of man who hangs about the corridors of trains going to the Riviera and steals ladies' jewel-cases. Imagine eternal torment presided over by *him!*"

"You don't suppose I look forward to it, do you?"

"Then why not slip quietly out of the way?"

Again and again I filled his glass, and always, mechanically, he emptied it; but the wine kindled no spark of enterprise in him. He did not eat, and I myself ate hardly at all. I did not in my heart believe that any dash for freedom could save him. The chase would be swift, the capture certain. But better anything than this passive, meek, miserable waiting. I told Soames that for the honour of the human race he ought to make some show of resistance. He asked what the human race had ever done for him. "Besides," he said, "can't you understand that I'm in his power? You saw him touch me, didn't you? There's an end of it. I've no will. I'm sealed."

I made a gesture of despair. He went on repeating the word "sealed." I began to realise that the wine had clouded his brain. No wonder! Foodless he had gone into futurity, foodless he still was. I urged him to eat at any rate some bread. It was maddening to think that he, who had so much to tell, might tell nothing. "How was it all," I asked, "yonder? Come! Tell me your adventures."

"They'd make first-rate 'copy,' wouldn't they?"

"I'm awfully sorry for you, Soames, and I make all possible allowances; but what earthly right have you to insinuate that I should make 'copy,' as you call it, out of you?"

The poor fellow pressed his hands to his forehead. "I don't know," he said. "I had some reason, I'm sure . . . I'll try to remember."

"That's right. Try to remember everything. Eat a little more bread. What did the reading-room look like?"

"Much as usual," he at length muttered.

"Many people there?"

"Usual sort of number."

"What did they look like?"

Soames tried to visualise them. "They all," he presently remembered, "looked very like one another."

My mind took a fearsome leap. "All dressed in Jaeger?"

"Yes. I think so. Greyish-yellowish stuff."

"A sort of uniform?" He nodded. "With a number on it, perhaps? —a number on a large disc of metal sewn on to the left sleeve? DKF 78,910—that sort of thing?" It was even so. "And all of them—men and women alike—looking very well-cared-for? very Utopian? and smelling rather strongly of carbolic? and all of them quite hairless?" I was right every time. Soames was only not sure whether the men and women were hairless or shorn. "I hadn't time to look at them very closely," he explained.

"No, of course not. But—"

"They stared at *me*, I can tell you. I attracted a great deal of attention." At last he had done that! "I think I rather scared them. They moved away whenever I came near. They followed me about at a distance, wherever I went. The men at the round desk in the middle seemed to have a sort of panic whenever I went to make inquiries."

"What did you do when you arrived?"

Well, he had gone straight to the catalogue, of course—to the S volumes, and had stood long before SN–SOF, unable to take this volume out of the shelf, because his heart was beating so . . . At first, he said, he wasn't disappointed—he only thought there was some new arrangement. He went to the middle desk and asked where the catalogue of *twentieth*-century books was kept. He gathered that there was still only one catalogue. Again he looked up his name, stared at the three little pasted slips he had known so well. Then he went and sat down for a long time . . .

"And then," he droned, "I looked up the 'Dictionary of National Biography' and some encyclopædias . . . I went back to the middle desk and asked what was the best modern book on late nineteenth-century literature. They told me Mr. T. K. Nupton's book was considered the best. I looked it up in the catalogue and filled in a form for it. It was brought to me. My name wasn't in the index, but—Yes!" he said with a sudden change of tone. "That's what I'd forgotten. Where's that bit of paper? Give it me back."

I, too, had forgotten that cryptic screed. I found it fallen on the floor, and handed it to him.

He smoothed it out, nodding and smiling at me disagreeably. "I found myself glancing through Nupton's book," he resumed. "Not very easy reading. Some sort of phonetic spelling . . . All the modern books I saw were phonetic."

"Then I don't want to hear any more, Soames, please."

"The proper names seemed all to be spelt in the old way. But for that, I mightn't have noticed my own name."

"Your own name? Really? Soames, I'm *very* glad."

"And yours."

"No!"

"I thought I should find you waiting here tonight. So I took the trouble to copy out the passage. Read it."

I snatched the paper. Soames' handwriting was characteristically dim. It, and the noisome spelling, and my excitement, made me all the slower to grasp what T. K. Nupton was driving at.

The document lies before me at this moment. Strange that the words I here copy out for you were copied out for me by poor Soames just seventy-eight years hence . . .

From p. 234 of "Inglish Littracher 1890-1900," bi T. K. Nupton, publishd bi th Stait, 1992:

"Fr egzarmpl, a riter ov th time, naimd Max Beerbohm, hoo woz stil alive in th twentieth senchri, rote a stauri in wich e pautraid an immajnari karrakter kauld 'Enoch Soames'—a thurd-rait poit hoo beleevz imself a grate jeneus an maix a bargin with th Devvl in auder ter no wot posterriti thinx ov im! It iz a sumwot labud sattire but not without vallu az showing hou seriusli th yung men ov th aiteen-ninetiz took themselvz. Nou that th littreri profeshn haz bin auganizd az a departmnt of publik servis, our riters hav found their levvl an hav lernt ter doo their duti without thort ov th morro. 'Th laibrer iz werthi ov hiz hire,' an that iz aul. Thank hevvn we hav no Enoch Soameses amung us to-dai!"

I found that by murmuring the words aloud (a device which I commend to my reader) I was able to master them, little by little. The clearer they became, the greater was my bewilderment, my distress and horror. The whole thing was a nightmare. Afar, the great grisly background of what was in store for the poor dear art of letters; here, at the table, fixing on me a gaze that made me hot all over, the poor fellow whom—whom evidently . . . but no: whatever down-grade my character might take in coming years, I should never be such a brute as to—

Again I examined the screed. "Immajnari"—but here Soames was, no more imaginary, alas! than I. And "labud"—what on earth was that? (To this day, I have never made out that word.) "It's all very—baffling," I at length stammered.

Soames said nothing, but cruelly did not cease to look at me.

"Are you sure," I temporised, "quite sure you copied the thing out correctly?"

"Quite."

"Well, then it's this wretched Nupton who must have made—must be going to make—some idiotic mistake . . . Look here, Soames! you know me better than to suppose that I . . . After all, the name 'Max Beerbohm' is not at all an uncommon one, and there must be several Enoch Soameses running around—or rather, 'Enoch Soames' is a name that might occur to any one writing a story. And I don't write stories: I'm an essayist, an observer, a recorder . . . I admit that it's an extraordinary coincidence. But you must see—"

"I see the whole thing," said Soames quietly. And he added, with a touch of his old manner, but with more dignity than I had ever known in him, "*Parlons d'autre chose.*"

I accepted that suggestion very promptly. I returned straight to the more immediate future. I spent most of the long evening in renewed appeals to Soames to slip away and seek refuge somewhere. I remember saying at last that if indeed I was destined to write about him, the supposed "stauri" had better have at least a happy ending. Soames repeated those last three words in a tone of intense scorn. "In Life and in Art," he said, "all that matters is an *inevitable* ending."

"But," I urged, more hopefully than I felt, "an ending that can be avoided *isn't* inevitable."

"You aren't an artist," he rasped. "And you're so hopelessly not an artist that, so far from being able to imagine a thing and make it seem true, you're going to make even a true thing seem as if you'd made it up. You're a miserable bungler. And it's like my luck."

I protested that the miserable bungler was not I—was not going to be I—but T. K. Nupton; and we had a rather heated argument, in the thick of which it suddenly seemed to me that Soames saw he was in the wrong: he had quite physically cowered. But I wondered why—and now I guessed with a cold throb just why—he stared so, past me. The bringer of that "inevitable ending" filled the doorway.

I managed to turn in my chair and to say, not without a semblance of lightness, "Aha, come in!" Dread was indeed rather blunted in me by his looking so absurdly like a villain in a melodrama. The sheen of his tilted hat and of his shirtfront, the repeated twists he was giving to his moustache, and most of all the magnificence of his sneer, gave token that he was there only to be foiled.

He was at our table in a stride. "I am sorry," he sneered witheringly, "to break up your pleasant party, but—"

"You don't: you complete it," I assured him. "Mr. Soames and I want to have a little talk with you. Won't you sit? Mr. Soames got nothing—frankly nothing—by his journey this afternoon. We don't wish to say that the whole thing was a swindle—a common swindle. On the contrary, we believe you meant well. But of course the bargain, such as it was, is off."

The Devil gave no verbal answer. He merely looked at Soames and pointed with rigid forefinger to the door. Soames was wretchedly rising from his chair when, a desperate quick gesture, I swept together two dinner-knives that were on the table, and laid their blades across each other. The Devil stepped sharp back against the table behind him, averting his face and shuddering.

"You are not superstitious!" he hissed.

"Not at all," I smiled.

"Soames!" he said as to an underling, but without turning his face, "put those knives straight!"

With an inhibitive gesture to my friend, "Mr. Soames," I said emphatically to the Devil, "is a *Catholic* Diabolist"; but my poor friend did the Devil's bidding, not mine; and now, with his master's eyes again fixed on him, he arose, he shuffled past me. I tried to speak. It was he that spoke. "Try," was the prayer he threw back at me as the Devil pushed him roughly out through the door, "*try* to make them know that I did exist!"

In another instant I too was through that door. I stood staring all ways—up the street, across it, down it. There was moonlight and lamplight, but there was not Soames nor that other.

Dazed, I stood there. Dazed, I turned back, at length, into the little room; and I suppose I paid Berthe or Rose for my dinner and luncheon, and for Soames': I hope so, for I never went to the Vingtième again. Ever since that night I have avoided Greek Street altogether. And for years I did not set foot even in Soho Square, because on that same night it was there that I paced and loitered, long and long, with some dull sense of hope as a man has in not straying far from the place where he has lost something . . . "Round and round the shutter'd Square"—that line came back to me on my lonely beat, and with it the whole stanza, ringing in my brain and bearing in on me how tragically different from the happy scene imagined by him was the poet's actual experience of that prince in whom of all princes we should put not our trust.

But—strange how the mind of an essayist, be it never so stricken, roves and ranges!—I remember pausing before a wide doorstep and wondering if perchance it was on this very one that the young De Quincey lay ill and faint while poor Ann flew as fast as her feet would carry her to Oxford Street, the "stony-hearted stepmother" of them both, and came back bearing that "glass of port wine and spices" but for which he might, so he thought, actually have died. Was this the very doorstep that the old De Quincey used to revisit in homage? I pondered Ann's fate, the cause of her sudden vanishing from the ken of her boy-friend; and presently I blamed myself for letting the past override the present. Poor vanished Soames!

And for myself, too, I began to be troubled. What had I better do? Would there be a hue and cry—Mysterious Disappearance of an Author and all that? He had last been seen lunching and dining in my company. Hadn't I better get a hansom and drive straight to Scotland Yard? . . .

They would think I was a lunatic. After all, I reassured myself, London was a very large place, and one very dim figure might easily drop out of it unobserved—now especially, in the blinding glare of the near Jubilee. Better say nothing at all, I thought.

And I was right. Soames' disappearance made no stir at all. He was utterly forgotten before any one, so far as I am aware, noticed that he was no longer hanging around. Now and again some poet or prosaist may have said to another, "What has become of that man Soames?" but I never heard any such question asked. The solicitor through whom he was paid his annuity may be presumed to have made inquiries, but no echo of these resounded. There was something rather ghastly to me in the general unconsciousness that Soames had existed, and more than once I caught myself wondering whether Nupton, that babe unborn, were going to be right in thinking him a figment of my brain.

In that extract from Nupton's repulsive book there is one point which perhaps puzzles you. How is it that the author, though I have here mentioned him by name and have quoted the exact words he is going to write, is not going to grasp the obvious corollary that I have invented nothing? The answer can but be this: Nupton will not have read the later passages of this memoir. Such lack of thoroughness is a serious fault in any one who undertakes to do scholar's work. And I hope these words will meet the eye of some contemporary rival to Nupton and be the undoing of Nupton.

I like to think that some time between 1992 and 1997 somebody will have looked up this memoir, and will have forced on the world his inevitable and startling conclusions. And I have reasons for believing that this will be so. You realise that the reading-room into which Soames was projected by the Devil was in all respects precisely as it will be on the afternoon of June 3rd, 1997. You realise, therefore, that on that afternoon, when it comes round, there the self-same crowd will be, and there Soames too will be, punctually, he and they doing precisely what they did before. Recall now Soames' account of the sensation he made. You may say that the mere difference of his costume was enough to make him sensational in that uniformed crowd. You wouldn't say so if you had ever seen him. I assure you that in no period could Soames be anything but dim. The fact that people are going to stare at him, and follow him around, and seem afraid of him, can be explained only on the hypothesis that they will somehow have been prepared for his ghostly visitation. They will have been awfully waiting to see whether he really would come. And when he does come the effect will of course be—awful.

An authentic, guaranteed, proven ghost, but—only a ghost, alas! Only that. In his first visit, Soames was a creature of flesh and blood, whereas the creatures into whose midst he was projected were but ghosts, I take it—solid, palpable, vocal, but unconscious and automatic ghosts, in a building that was itself an illusion. Next time, that building and those creatures will be real. It is of Soames that there will be but the semblance.

I wish I could think him destined to re-visit the world actually, physically, consciously. I wish he had this one brief escape, this one small treat, to look forward to. I never forget him for long. He is where he is, and forever. The more rigid moralists among you may say he has only himself to blame. For my part, I think he has been very hardly used. It is well that vanity should be chastened; and Enoch Soames' vanity was, I admit, above the average, and called for special treatment. But there was no need for vindictiveness. You say he contracted to pay the price he is paying; yes; but I maintain that he was induced to do so by fraud. Well-informed in all things, the Devil must have known that my friend would gain nothing by his visit to futurity. The whole thing was a very shabby trick. The more I think of it, the more detestable the Devil seems to me.

Of him I have caught sight several times, here and there, since that day at the Vingtième. Only once, however, have I seen him at close quarters. This was in Paris. I was walking, one afternoon, along the Rue d'Antin, when I saw him advancing from the opposite direction—overdressed as ever, and swinging an ebony cane, and altogether behaving as though the whole pavement belonged to him. At thought of Enoch Soames and the myriads of other sufferers eternally in this brute's dominion, a great cold wrath filled me, and I drew myself up to my full height. But—well, one is so used to nodding and smiling in the street to anybody whom one knows, that the action becomes almost independent of oneself: to prevent it requires a very sharp effort and great presence of mind. I was miserably aware, as I passed the Devil, that I nodded and smiled to him. And my shame was the deeper and hotter because he, if you please, stared straight at me with the utmost haughtiness.

To be cut—deliberately cut—by *him!* I was, I still am, furious at having had that happen to me.

Elizabeth Bowen

THE DEMON LOVER

OWARDS THE END OF HER DAY in London Mrs. Drover went round to her shut-up house to look for several things she wanted to take away. Some belonged to herself, some to her family, who were by now used to their country life. It was late August; it had been a steamy, showery day: at the moment the trees down the pavement glittered in an escape of humid yellow afternoon sun. Against the next batch of clouds, already piling up ink-dark, broken chimneys and parapets stood out. In her once familiar street, as in any unused channel, an unfamiliar queerness had silted up; a cat wove itself in and out of railings, but no human eye watched Mrs. Drover's return. Shifting some parcels under her arm, she slowly forced round her latchkey in an unwilling lock, then gave the door, which had warped, a push with her knee. Dead air came out to meet her as she went in.

The staircase window having been boarded up, no light came down into the hall. But one door, she could just see, stood ajar, so she went quickly through into the room and unshuttered the big window in there. Now the prosaic woman, looking about her, was more perplexed than she knew by everything that she saw, by traces of her long former habit of life—the yellow smoke-stain up the white marble mantelpiece, the ring left by a vase on the top of the escritoire; the bruise in the wallpaper where, on the door being thrown open widely, the china handle had always hit the wall. The piano, having gone away to be stored, had left what looked like claw-marks on its part of the parquet. Though not much dust had seeped in, each object wore a film of another kind; and, the only ventilation being the chimney, the whole drawing-room smelled of the cold hearth. Mrs. Drover put down her parcels on the escritoire and left the room to proceed upstairs; the things she wanted were in a bedroom chest.

She had been anxious to see how the house was—the part-time care-taker she shared with some neighbours was away this week on his holi-day, known to be not yet back. At the best of times he did not look in often, and she was never sure that she trusted him. There were some cracks in the structure, left by the last bombing, on which she was anxious to keep an eye. Not that one could do anything—

A shaft of refracted daylight now lay across the hall. She stopped dead and stared at the hall table—on this lay a letter addressed to her.

She thought first—then the caretaker *must* be back. All the same, who, seeing the house shuttered, would have dropped a letter in at the box? It was not a circular, it was not a bill. And the post office redirected, to the address in the country, everything for her that came through the post. The caretaker (even if he *were* back) did not know she was due in London to-day—her call here had been planned to be a surprise—so his negligence in the manner of this letter, leaving it to wait in the dusk and the dust, annoyed her. Annoyed, she picked up the letter, which bore no stamp. But it cannot be important, or they would know . . . She took the letter rapidly upstairs with her, without a stop to look at the writing till she reached what had been her bedroom, where she let in light. The room looked over the garden and other gardens: the sun had gone in; as the clouds sharpened and lowered, the trees and rank lawns seemed already to smoke with dark. Her reluctance to look again at the letter came from the fact that she felt intruded upon—and by someone contemptuous of her ways. However, in the tenseness preceding the fall of rain she read it: it was a few lines.

> DEAR KATHLEEN,
> You will not have forgotten that to-day is our anniversary, and the day we said. The years have gone by at once slowly and fast. In view of the fact that nothing has changed, I shall rely upon you to keep your promise. I was sorry to see you leave London, but was satisfied that you would be back in time. You may expect me, there-fore, at the hour arranged.
>   Until then . . .
>   K.

Mrs. Drover looked for the date: it was to-day's. She dropped the letter on to the bed-springs, then picked it up to see the writing again—her lips, beneath the remains of lipstick, beginning to go white. She felt so much the change in her own face that she went to the mirror, polished a clear patch in it and looked at once urgently and stealthily in. She was con-fronted by a woman of forty-four, with eyes starting out under a hat-brim that had been rather carelessly pulled down. She had not put on any more powder since she left the shop where she ate her solitary tea. The pearls her husband had given her on their marriage hung loose round her now rather thinner throat, slipping into the V of the pink wool jumper her sister knitted last autumn as they sat round the fire. Mrs. Drover's most normal expression was one of controlled worry, but of assent. Since the birth of the third of her little boys, attended by a quite serious illness, she had had an intermittent muscular flicker to the left of her mouth, but in spite of this she could always sustain a manner that was at once energetic and calm.

Turning from her own face as precipitately as she had gone to meet it, she went to the chest where the things were, unlocked it, threw up the lid and knelt to search. But as rain began to come crashing down she could not keep from looking over her shoulder at the stripped bed on which the letter lay. Behind the blanket of rain the clock of the church that still stood struck six—with rapidly heightening apprehension she counted each of the slow strokes. "The hour arranged . . . My God," she said, "*what* hour? How should I . . . ? After twenty-five years. . . ."

The young girl talking to the soldier in the garden had not ever completely seen his face. It was dark; they were saying good-bye under a tree. Now and then—for it felt, from not seeing him at this intense moment, as though she had never seen him at all—she verified his presence for these few moments longer by putting out a hand, which he each time pressed, without very much kindness, and painfully, on to one of the breast buttons of his uniform. That cut of the button on the palm of her hand was, principally, what she was to carry away. This was so near the end of a leave from France that she could only wish him already gone. It was August 1916. Being not kissed, being drawn away from and looked at intimidated Kathleen till she imagined spectral glitters in the place of his eyes. Turning away and looking back up the lawn she saw, through branches of trees, the drawing-room window alight: she caught a breath for the moment when she could go running back there into the safe arms of her mother and sister, and cry: "What shall I do, what shall I do? He has gone."

Hearing her catch her breath, her fiancé said, without feeling: "Cold?"

"You're going away such a long way."

"Not so far as you think."

"I don't understand?"

"You don't have to," he said. "You will. You know what we said."

"But that was—suppose you—I mean, suppose."

"I shall be with you," he said, "sooner or later. You won't forget that. You need do nothing but wait."

Only a little more than a minute later she was free to run up the silent lawn. Looking in through the window at her mother and sister, who did not for the moment perceive her, she already felt that unnatural promise drive down between her and the rest of all human kind. No other way of having given herself could have made her feel so apart, lost and forsworn. She could not have plighted a more sinister troth.

Kathleen behaved well when, some months later, her fiancé was reported missing, presumed killed. Her family not only supported her but were able to praise her courage without stint because they could not regret, as a husband for her, the man they knew almost nothing about.

They hoped she would, in a year or two, console herself—and had it been only a question of consolation things might have gone much straighter ahead. But her trouble, behind just a little grief, was a complete dislocation from everything. She did not reject other lovers, for these failed to appear: for years she failed to attract men—and with the approach of her 'thirties she became natural enough to share her family's anxiousness on this score. She began to put herself out, to wonder; and at thirty-two she was very greatly relieved to find herself being courted by William Drover. She married him, and the two of them settled down in this quiet, arboreal part of Kensington: in this house the years piled up, her children were born and they all lived till they were driven out by the bombs of the next war. Her movements as Mrs. Drover were circumscribed, and she dismissed any idea that they were still watched.

As things were—dead or living the letter-writer sent her only a threat. Unable, for some minutes, to go on kneeling with her back exposed to the empty room, Mrs. Drover rose from the chest to sit on an upright chair whose back was firmly against the wall. The desuetude of her former bedroom, her married London home's whole air of being a cracked cup from which memory, with its reassuring power, had either evaporated or leaked away, made a crisis—and at just this crisis the letter-writer had, knowledgeably, struck. The hollowness of the house this evening cancelled years on years of voices, habits and steps. Through the shut windows she only heard rain fall on the roofs around. To rally herself, she said she was in a mood—and, for two or three seconds shutting her eyes, told herself that she had imagined the letter. But she opened them—there it lay on the bed.

On the supernatural side of the letter's entrance she was not permitting her mind to dwell. Who, in London, knew she meant to call at the house to-day? Evidently, however, this had been known. The caretaker, *had* he come back, had had no cause to expect her: he would have taken the letter in his pocket, to forward it, at his own time, through the post. There was no other sign that the caretaker had been in—but, if not? Letters dropped in at doors of deserted houses do not fly or walk to tables in halls. They do not sit on the dust of empty tables with the air of certainty that they will be found. There is needed some human hand— but nobody but the caretaker had a key. Under circumstances she did not care to consider, a house can be entered without a key. It was possible that she was not alone now. She might be being waited for, downstairs. Waited for—until when? Until "the hour arranged." At least that was not six o'clock: six has struck.

She rose from the chair and went over and locked the door.

The thing was, to get out. To fly? No, not that: she had to catch her train. As a woman whose utter dependability was the keystone of her family life she was not willing to return to the country, to her husband, her little boys and her sister, without the objects she had come up to fetch. Resuming work at the chest she set about making up a number of parcels in a rapid, fumbling-decisive way. These, with her shopping parcels, would be too much to carry; these meant a taxi—at the thought of the taxi her heart went up and her normal breathing resumed. I will ring up the taxi now; the taxi cannot come too soon: I shall hear the taxi out there running its engine, till I walk calmly down to it through the hall. I'll ring up—But no: the telephone is cut off . . . She tugged at a knot she had tied wrong.

The idea of flight . . . He was never kind to me, not really. I don't remember him kind at all. Mother said he never considered me. He was set on me, that was what it was—not love. Not love, not meaning a person well. What did he do, to make me promise like that? I can't remember— But she found that she could.

She remembered with such dreadful acuteness that the twenty-five years since then dissolved like smoke and she instinctively looked for the weal left by the button on the palm of her hand. She remembered not only all that he said and did but the complete suspension of *her* existence during that August week. I was not myself—they all told me so at the time. She remembered—but with one white burning blank as where acid has dropped on a photograph: *under no conditions* could she remember his face.

So, wherever he may be waiting, I shall not know him. You have no time to run from a face you do not expect.

The thing was to get to the taxi before any clock struck what could be the hour. She would slip down the street and round the side of the square to where the square gave on the main road. She would return in the taxi, safe, to her own door, and bring the solid driver into the house with her to pick up the parcels from room to room. The idea of the taxi driver made her decisive, bold: she unlocked her door, went to the top of the staircase and listened down.

She heard nothing—but while she was hearing nothing the *passé* air of the staircase was disturbed by a draught that travelled up to her face. It emanated from the basement: down there a door or window was being opened by someone who chose this moment to leave the house.

The rain had stopped; the pavements steamily shone as Mrs. Drover let herself out by inches from her own front door into the empty street. The unoccupied houses opposite continued to meet her look with their damaged stare. Making towards the thoroughfare and the taxi, she tried not to keep looking behind. Indeed, the silence was so intense—one of those creeks of London silence exaggerated this summer by the damage of war—that no tread could have gained on hers unheard. Where her street debouched on the square where people went on living she grew conscious of and checked her unnatural pace. Across the open end of the square two buses impassively passed each other; women, a perambulator, cyclists, a man wheeling a barrow signalized, once again, the ordinary flow of life. At the square's most populous corner should be—and was—the short taxi rank. This evening, only one taxi—but this, although it presented its blank rump, appeared already to be alertly waiting for her. Indeed, without looking round the driver started his engine as she panted up from behind and put her hand on the door. As she did so, the clock struck seven. The taxi faced the main road: to make the trip back to her house it would have to turn—she had settled back on the seat and the taxi *had* turned before she, surprised by its knowing movement, recollected that she had not "said where." She leaned forward to scratch at the glass panel that divided the driver's head from her own.

The driver braked to what was almost a stop, turned round and slid the glass panel back: the jolt of this flung Mrs. Drover forward till her face was almost into the glass. Through the aperture driver and passenger, not six inches between them, remained for an eternity eye to eye. Mrs. Drover's mouth hung open for some seconds before she could issue her first scream. After that she continued to scream freely and to beat with her gloved hands on the glass all round as the taxi, accelerating without mercy, made off with her into the hinterland of deserted streets.

Willa Cather

TWO FRIENDS

I

EVEN IN EARLY YOUTH, when the mind is so eager for the new and un-tried, while it is still a stranger to faltering and fear, we yet like to think that there are certain unalterable realities, somewhere at the bottom of things. These anchors may be ideas; but more often they are merely pictures, vivid memories, which in some unaccountable and very personal way give us courage. The sea-gulls, that seem so much creatures of the free wind and waves, that are as homeless as the sea (able to rest upon the tides and ride the storm, needing nothing but water and sky), at certain seasons even they go back to something they have known before; to remote islands and lonely ledges that are their breeding-grounds. The restlessness of youth has such retreats, even though it may be ashamed of them.

Long ago, before the invention of the motorcar (which has made more changes in the world than the War, which indeed produced the particular kind of war that happened just a hundred years after Water-loo), in a little wooden town in a shallow Kansas river valley, there lived two friends. They were "business men," the two most prosperous and influential men in our community, the two men whose affairs took them out into the world to big cities, who had "connections" in St. Joseph and Chicago. In my childhood they represented to me success and power.

R. E. Dillon was of Irish extraction, one of the dark Irish, with glistening jet-black hair and moustache, and thick eyebrows. His skin was very white, bluish on his shaven cheeks and chin. Shaving must have been a difficult process for him, because there were no smooth expanses for the

From *Obscure Destinies*, 1932. Copyright 1932 by Willa Cather. Renewal copyright 1959 by Edith Lewis and City Bank Farmers Trust Co.

razor to glide over. The bony structure of his face was prominent and unusual; high cheek-bones, a bold Roman nose, a chin cut by deep lines, with a hard dimple at the tip, a jutting ridge over his eyes where his curly black eyebrows grew and met. It was a face in many planes, as if the carver had whittled and modelled and indented to see how far he could go. Yet on meeting him what you saw was an imperious head on a rather small, wiry man, a head held conspicuously and proudly erect, with a carriage unmistakably arrogant and consciously superior. Dillon had a musical, vibrating voice, and the changeable grey eye that is peculiarly Irish. His full name, which he never used, was Robert Emmet Dillon, so there must have been a certain feeling somewhere back in his family.

He was the principal banker in our town, and proprietor of the large general store next the bank; he owned farms up in the grass country, and a fine ranch in the green timbered valley of the Caw. He was, according to our standards, a rich man.

His friend, J. H. Trueman, was what we called a big cattleman. Trueman was from Buffalo; his family were old residents there, and he had come West as a young man because he was restless and unconventional in his tastes. He was fully ten years older than Dillon,—in his early fifties, when I knew him; large, heavy, very slow in his movements, not given to exercise. His countenance was as unmistakably American as Dillon's was not,—but American of that period, not of this. He did not belong to the time of efficiency and advertising and progressive methods. For any form of pushing or boosting he had a cold, unqualified contempt. All this was in his face,—heavy, immobile, rather melancholy, not remarkable in any particular. But the moment one looked at him one felt solidity, an entire absence of anything mean or small, easy carelessness, courage, a high sense of honour.

These two men had been friends for ten years before I knew them, and I knew them from the time I was ten until I was thirteen. I saw them as often as I could, because they led more varied lives than the other men in our town; one could look up to them. Dillon, I believe, was the more intelligent. Trueman had, perhaps, a better tradition, more background.

Dillon's bank and general store stood at the corner of Main Street and a cross-street, and on this cross-street, two short blocks away, my family lived. On my way to and from school, and going on the countless errands that I was sent upon day and night, I always passed Dillon's store. Its long, red brick wall, with no windows except high overhead, ran possibly a hundred feet along the sidewalk of the cross-street. The front door and show windows were on Main Street, and the bank was next door. The board sidewalk along that red brick wall was wider than any other piece of walk in town, smoother, better laid, kept in perfect repair; very good to walk on in a community where most things were flimsy. I liked the store and the brick wall and the sidewalk because they were solid and well built, and possibly I admired Dillon and Trueman for much the same reason. They were secure and established. So many of our citizens were nervous little hopper men, trying to get on. Dillon and Trueman had got on; they stood with easy assurance on a deck that was their own.

In the daytime one did not often see them together—each went about his own affairs. But every evening they were both to be found at Dillon's store. The bank, of course, was locked and dark before the sun went down, but the store was always open until ten o'clock; the clerks put in a long day. So did Dillon. He and his store were one. He never acted as salesman, and he kept a cashier in the wire-screened office at the back end of the store; but he was there to be called on. The thrifty Swedes to the north, who were his best customers, usually came to town and did their shopping after dark—they didn't squander daylight hours in farming season. In these evening visits with his customers, and on his drives in his buckboard among the farms, Dillon learned all he needed to know about how much money it was safe to advance a farmer who wanted to feed cattle, or to buy a steam thrasher or build a new barn.

Every evening in winter, when I went to the post-office after supper, I passed through Dillon's store instead of going round it,—for the warmth and cheerfulness, and to catch sight of Mr. Dillon and Mr. Trueman playing checkers in the office behind the wire screening; both seated on high accountant's stools, with the checker-board on the cashier's desk before them. I knew all Dillon's clerks, and if they were not busy, I often lingered about to talk to them; sat on one of the grocery counters and watched the checker-players from a distance. I remember Mr. Dillon's hand used to linger in the air above the board before he made a move; a well-kept hand, white, marked with blue veins and streaks of strong black hair. Trueman's hands rested on his knees under the desk while he considered; he took a checker, set it down, then dropped his hand on his knee again. He seldom made an unnecessary movement with his hands or feet. Each of the men wore a ring on his little finger. Mr. Dillon's was a large diamond solitaire set in a gold claw, Trueman's the head of a Roman soldier cut in onyx and set in pale twisted gold; it had been his father's, I believe.

Exactly at ten o'clock the store closed. Mr. Dillon went home to his wife and family, to his roomy, comfortable house with a garden and orchard and big stables. Mr. Trueman, who had long been a widower, went to his office to begin the day over. He led a double life, and until one or two o'clock in the morning entertained the poker-players of our town. After everything was shut for the night, a queer crowd drifted into Trueman's back office. The company was seldom the same on two successive evenings, but there were three tireless poker-players who always came: the billiard-hall proprietor, with green-gold moustache and eyebrows, and big white teeth; the horse-trader, who smelled of horses; the dandified cashier of the bank that rivalled Dillon's. The gamblers met in Trueman's place because a game that went on there was respectable, was a social game, no matter how much money changed hands. If the horse-trader or

the crooked money-lender got over-heated and broke loose a little, a look
or a remark from Mr. Trueman would freeze them up. And his remark
was always the same:

"Careful of the language around here."

It was never "your" language, but "the" language,—though he certainly intended no pleasantry. Trueman himself was not a lucky poker
man; he was never ahead of the game on the whole. He played because he
liked it, and he was willing to pay for his amusement. In general he was
large and indifferent about money matters,—always carried a few
hundred-dollar bills in his inside coat-pocket, and left his coat hanging
anywhere,—in his office, in the bank, in the barber shop, in the cattle-
sheds behind the freight yard.

Now, R. E. Dillon detested gambling, often dropped a contemptuous
word about "poker bugs" before the horse-trader and the billiard-hall
man and the cashier of the other bank. But he never made remarks of that
sort in Trueman's presence. He was a man who voiced his prejudices
fearlessly and cuttingly, but on this and other matters he held his peace
before Trueman. His regard for him must have been very strong.

During the winter, usually in March, the two friends always took a
trip together, to Kansas City and St. Joseph. When they got ready, they
packed their bags and stepped aboard a fast Santa Fé train and went: the
Limited was often signalled to stop for them. Their excursions made some
of the rest of us feel less shut away and small-townish, just as their fur
overcoats and silk shirts did. They were the only men in Singleton who
wore silk shirts. The other business men wore white shirts with detach-
able collars, high and stiff or low and sprawling, which were changed
much oftener than the shirts. Neither of my heroes was afraid of laundry
bills. They did not wear waistcoats, but went about in their shirt-sleeves
in hot weather; their suspenders were chosen with as much care as their
neckties and handkerchiefs. Once when a bee stung my hand in the store
(a few of them had got into the brown-sugar barrel), Mr. Dillon himself
moistened the sting, put baking soda on it, and bound my hand up with
his pocket handkerchief. It was of the smoothest linen, and in one corner
was a violet square bearing his initials, R. E. D., in white. There were
never any handkerchiefs like that in my family. I cherished it until it was
laundered, and I returned it with regret.

It was in the spring and summer that one saw Mr. Dillon and Mr.
Trueman at their best. Spring began early with us,—often the first week
of April was hot. Every evening when he came back to the store after
supper, Dillon had one of his clerks bring two arm-chairs out to the wide
sidewalk that ran beside the red brick wall,—office chairs of the old-
fashioned sort, with a low round back which formed a half-circle to
enclose the sitter, and spreading legs, the front ones slightly higher. In
those chairs the two friends would spend the evening. Dillon would sit
down and light a good cigar. In a few moments Mr. Trueman would
come across from Main Street, walking slowly, spaciously, as if he were

used to a great deal of room. As he approached, Mr. Dillon would call out to him:

"Good evening, J. H. Fine weather."

J. H. would take his place in the empty chair.

"Spring in the air," he might remark, if it were April. Then he would relight a dead cigar which was always in his hand,—seemed to belong there, like a thumb or finger.

"I drove up north today to see what the Swedes are doing," Mr. Dillon might begin. "They're the boys to get the early worm. They never let the ground go to sleep. Whatever moisture there is, they get the benefit of it."

"The Swedes are good farmers. I don't sympathize with the way they work their women."

"The women like it, J. H. It's the old-country way; they're accustomed to it, and they like it."

"Maybe. I don't like it," Trueman would reply with something like a grunt.

They talked very much like this all evening; or, rather, Mr. Dillon talked, and Mr. Trueman made an occasional observation. No one could tell just how much Mr. Trueman knew about anything, because he was so consistently silent. Not from diffidence, but from superiority; from a contempt for chatter, and a liking for silence, a taste for it. After they had exchanged a few remarks, he and Dillon often sat in an easy quiet for a long time, watching the passers-by, watching the wagons on the road, watching the stars. Sometimes, very rarely, Mr. Trueman told a long story, and it was sure to be an interesting and unusual one.

But on the whole it was Mr. Dillon who did the talking; he had a wide-awake voice with much variety in it. Trueman's was thick and low,—his speech was rather indistinct and never changed in pitch or tempo. Even when he swore wickedly at the hands who were loading his cattle into freight cars, it was a mutter, a low, even growl. There was a curious attitude in men of his class and time, that of being rather above speech, as they were above any kind of fussiness or eagerness. But I knew he liked to hear Mr. Dillon talk,—anyone did. Dillon had such a crisp, clear enunciation, and he could say things so neatly. People would take a reprimand from him they wouldn't have taken from anyone else, because he put it so well. His voice was never warm or soft—it had a cool, sparkling quality; but it could be very humorous, very kind and considerate, very teasing and stimulating. Every sentence he uttered was alive, never languid, perfunctory, slovenly, unaccented. When he made a remark, it not only meant something, but sounded like something,—sounded like the thing he meant.

When Mr. Dillon was closeted with a depositor in his private room in the bank, and you could not hear his words through the closed door, his voice told you exactly the degree of esteem in which he held that customer. It was interested, encouraging, deliberative, humorous, satisfied, admiring, cold, critical, haughty, contemptuous, according to the deserts and pretensions of his listener. And one could tell when the person closeted with him was a woman; a farmer's wife, or a woman who was trying to run a little business, or a country girl hunting a situation. There was a difference; something peculiarly kind and encouraging. But if it were a foolish, extravagant woman, or a girl he didn't approve of, oh, then one knew it well enough! The tone was courteous, but cold; relentless as the multiplication table.

All these possibilities of voice made his evening talk in the spring dusk very interesting; interesting for Trueman and for me. I found many pretexts for lingering near them, and they never seemed to mind my hanging about. I was very quiet. I often sat on the edge of the sidewalk with my feet hanging down and played jacks by the hour when there was moonlight. On dark nights I sometimes perched on top of one of the big goods-boxes—we called them "store boxes,"—there were usually several of these standing empty on the sidewalk against the red brick wall.

I liked to listen to those two because theirs was the only "conversation" one could hear about the streets. The older men talked of nothing but politics and their business, and the very young men's talk was entirely what they called "josh"; very personal, supposed to be funny, and really not funny at all. It was scarcely speech, but noises, snorts, giggles, yawns, sneezes, with a few abbreviated words and slang expressions which stood for a hundred things. The original Indians of the Kansas plains had more to do with articulate speech than had our promising young men.

To be sure my two aristocrats sometimes discussed politics, and joked each other about the policies and pretensions of their respective parties. Mr. Dillon, of course, was a Democrat,—it was in the very frosty sparkle of his speech,—and Mr. Trueman was a Republican; his rear, as he walked about the town, looked a little like the walking elephant labelled "G. O. P." in *Puck*. But each man seemed to enjoy hearing his party ridiculed, took it as a compliment.

In the spring their talk was usually about weather and planting and pasture and cattle. Mr. Dillon went about the country in his light buckboard a great deal at that season, and he knew what every farmer was doing and what his chances were, just how much he was falling behind or getting ahead.

"I happened to drive by Oscar Ericson's place today, and I saw as nice a lot of calves as you could find anywhere," he would begin, and Ericson's history and his family would be pretty thoroughly discussed before they changed the subject.

Or he might come out with something sharp: "By the way, J. H., I saw an amusing sight today. I turned in at Sandy Bright's place to get water for my horse, and he had a photographer out there taking pictures of his house and barn. It would be more to the point if he had a picture taken of the mortgages he's put on that farm."

Trueman would give a short, mirthless response, more like a cough than a laugh.

Those April nights, when the darkness itself tasted dusty (or, by the special mercy of God, cool and damp), when the smell of burning grass was in the air, and a sudden breeze brought the scent of wild plum blossoms,—those evenings were only a restless preparation for the summer nights,—nights of full liberty and perfect idleness. Then there was no school, and one's family never bothered about where one was. My parents were young and full of life, glad to have the children out of the way. All day long there had been the excitement that intense heat produces in some people,—a mild drunkenness made of sharp contrasts; thirst and cold water, the blazing stretch of Main Street and the cool of the brick stores when one dived into them. By nightfall one was ready to be quiet. My two friends were always in their best form on those moonlit summer nights, and their talk covered a wide range.

I suppose there were moonless nights, and dark ones with but a silver shaving and pale stars in the sky, just as in the spring. But I remember them all as flooded by the rich indolence of a full moon, or a half-moon set in uncertain blue. Then Trueman and Dillon would sit with their coats off and have a supply of fresh handkerchiefs to mop their faces; they were more largely and positively themselves. One could distinguish their features, the stripes on their shirts, the flash of Mr. Dillon's diamond; but their shadows made two dark masses on the white sidewalk. The brick wall behind them, faded almost pink by the burning of successive summers, took on a carnelian hue at night. Across the street, which was merely a dusty road, lay an open space, with a few stunted box-elder trees, where the farmers left their wagons and teams when they came to town. Beyond this space stood a row of frail wooden buildings, due to be pulled down any day; tilted, crazy, with outside stairs going up to rickety second-storey porches that sagged in the middle. They had once been white, but were now grey, with faded blue doors along the wavy upper porches. These abandoned buildings, an eyesore by day, melted together into a curious pile in the moonlight, became an immaterial structure of velvet-white and glossy blackness, with here and there a faint smear of blue door, or a tilted patch of sage-green that had once been a shutter.

The road, just in front of the sidewalk where I sat and played jacks, would be ankle-deep in dust, and seemed to drink up the moonlight like folds of velvet. It drank up sound, too; muffled the wagon-wheels and hoof-beats; lay soft and meek like the last residuum of material things, —the soft bottom resting-place. Nothing in the world, not snow mountains or blue seas, is so beautiful in moonlight as the soft, dry summer roads in a farming country, roads where the white dust falls back from the slow wagon-wheel.

Wonderful things do happen even in the dullest places—in the cornfields and the wheat-fields. Sitting there on the edge of the sidewalk one

summer night, my feet hanging in the warm dust, I saw an occultation of
Venus. Only the three of us were there. It was a hot night, and the clerks
had closed the store and gone home. Mr. Dillon and Mr. Trueman waited
on a little while to watch. It was a very blue night, breathless and clear,
not the smallest cloud from horizon to horizon. Everything up there
overhead seemed as usual, it was the familiar face of a summer-night sky.
But presently we saw one bright star moving. Mr. Dillon called to me;
told me to watch what was going to happen, as I might never chance to
see it again in my lifetime.

That big star certainly got nearer and nearer the moon,—very
rapidly, too, until there was not the width of your hand between them—
now the width of two fingers—then it passed directly into the moon at
about the middle of its girth; absolutely disappeared. The star we had
been watching was gone. We waited, I do not know how long, but it
seemed to me about fifteen minutes. Then we saw a bright wart on the
other edge of the moon, but for a second only,—the machinery up there
worked fast. While the two men were exclaiming and telling me to look, the
planet swung clear of the golden disk, a rift of blue came between them
and widened very fast. The planet did not seem to move, but that inky
blue space between it and the moon seemed to spread. The thing was over.

My friends stayed on long past their usual time and talked about
eclipses and such matters.

"Let me see," Mr. Trueman remarked slowly, "they reckon the
moon's about two hundred and fifty thousand miles away from us. I
wonder how far that star is."

"I don't know, J. H., and I really don't much care. When we can get
the tramps off the railroad, and manage to run this town with one fancy
house instead of two, and have a Federal Government that is as honest as
a good banking business, then it will be plenty of time to turn our
attention to the stars."

Mr. Trueman chuckled and took his cigar from between his teeth.
"Maybe the stars will throw some light on all that, if we get the run of
them," he said humorously. Then he added: "Mustn't be a reformer, R. E.
Nothing in it. That's the only time you ever get off on the wrong foot.
Life is what it always has been, always will be. No use to make a fuss."
He got up, said: "Good-night, R. E.," said good-night to me, too, because
this had been an unusual occasion, and went down the sidewalk with his
wide, sailor-like tread, as if he were walking the deck of his own ship.

When Dillon and Trueman went to St. Joseph, or, as we called it, St.
Joe, they stopped at the same hotel, but their diversions were very dissimilar. Mr. Dillon was a family man and a good Catholic; he behaved in St.
Joe very much as if he were at home. His sister was Mother Superior of a
convent there, and he went to see her often. The nuns made much of
him, and he enjoyed their admiration and all the ceremony with which
they entertained him. When his two daughters were going to the convent
school, he used to give theatre parties for them, inviting all their friends.

Mr. Trueman's way of amusing himself must have tried his friend's patience—Dillon liked to regulate other people's affairs if they needed it. Mr. Trueman had a lot of poker-playing friends among the commission men in St. Joe, and he sometimes dropped a good deal of money. He was supposed to have rather questionable women friends there, too. The grasshopper men of our town used to say that Trueman was financial adviser to a woman who ran a celebrated sporting house. Mary Trent, her name was. She must have been a very unusual woman; she had credit with all the banks, and never got into any sort of trouble. She had formerly been head mistress of a girls' finishing school and knew how to manage young women. It was probably a fact that Trueman knew her and found her interesting, as did many another sound business man of that time. Mr. Dillon must have shut his ears to these rumours,—a measure of the great value he put on Trueman's companionship.

Though they did not see much of each other on these trips, they immensely enjoyed taking them together. They often dined together at the end of the day, and afterwards went to the theatre. They both loved the theatre; not this play or that actor, but the theatre,—whether they saw *Hamlet* or *Pinafore*. It was an age of good acting, and the drama held a more dignified position in the world than it holds today.

After Dillon and Trueman had come home from the city, they used sometimes to talk over the plays they had seen, recalling the great scenes and fine effects. Occasionally an item in the Kansas City *Star* would turn their talk to the stage.

"J. H., I see by the paper that Edwin Booth is very sick," Mr. Dillon announced one evening as Trueman came up to take the empty chair.

"Yes, I noticed." Trueman sat down and lit his dead cigar. "He's not a young man any more." A long pause. Dillon always seemed to know when the pause would be followed by a remark, and waited for it. "The first time I saw Edwin Booth was in Buffalo. It was in *Richard the Second*, and it made a great impression on me at the time." Another pause. "I don't know that I'd care to see him in that play again. I like tragedy, but that play's a little too tragic. Something very black about it. I think I prefer *Hamlet*."

They had seen Mary Anderson in St. Louis once, and talked of it for years afterwards. Mr. Dillon was very proud of her because she was a Catholic girl, and called her "our Mary." It was curious that a third person, who had never seen these actors or read the plays, could get so much of the essence of both from the comments of two business men who used none of the language in which such things are usually discussed, who merely reminded each other of moments here and there in the action. But they saw the play over again as they talked of it, and perhaps whatever is seen by the narrator as he speaks is sensed by the listener, quite irrespective of words. This transference of experience went further: in some way the lives of those two men came across to me as they talked, the strong, bracing reality of successful, large-minded men who

had made their way in the world when business was still a personal
adventure.

II

Mr. Dillon went to Chicago once a year to buy goods for his store.
Trueman would usually accompany him as far as St. Joe, but no farther.
He dismissed Chicago as "too big." He didn't like to be one of the crowd,
didn't feel at home in a city where he wasn't recognized as J. H. Trueman.

It was one of these trips to Chicago that brought about the end—for
me and for them; a stupid, senseless, commonplace end.

Being a Democrat, already somewhat "tainted" by the free-silver
agitation, one spring Dillon delayed his visit to Chicago in order to be
there for the Democratic Convention—it was the Convention that first
nominated Bryan.

On the night after his return from Chicago, Mr. Dillon was seated in
his chair on the sidewalk, surrounded by a group of men who wanted to
hear all about the nomination of a man from a neighbour State. Mr.
Trueman came across the street in his leisurely way, greeted Dillon, and
asked him how he had found Chicago,—whether he had had a good trip.

Mr. Dillon must have been annoyed because Trueman didn't mention
the Convention. He threw back his head rather haughtily. "Well, J. H.,
since I saw you last, we've found a great leader in this country, and a
great orator." There was a frosty sparkle in his voice that presupposed
opposition,—like the feint of a boxer getting ready.

"Great windbag!" muttered Trueman. He sat down in his chair, but
I noticed that he did not settle himself and cross his legs as usual.

Mr. Dillon gave an artificial laugh. "It's nothing against a man to be a
fine orator. All the great leaders have been eloquent. This Convention
was a memorable occasion; it gave the Democratic party a rebirth."

"Gave it a black eye, and a blind spot, I'd say!" commented Trueman. He didn't raise his voice, but he spoke with more heat than I had
ever heard from him. After a moment he added: "I guess Grover Cleveland must be a sick man; must feel like he'd taken a lot of trouble for
nothing."

Mr. Dillon ignored these thrusts and went on telling the group
around him about the Convention, but there was a special nimbleness and exactness in his tongue, a chill politeness in his voice that meant anger. Presently he turned again to Mr. Trueman, as if he could not trust himself:

"It was one of the great speeches of history, J. H.; our grandchildren
will have to study it in school, as we did Patrick Henry's."

"Glad I haven't got any grandchildren, if they'd be brought up on
that sort of tall talk," said Mr. Trueman. "Sounds like a schoolboy had
written it. Absolutely nothing back of it but an unsound theory."

Mr. Dillon's laugh made me shiver; it was like a thin glitter of danger. He arched his curly eyebrows provokingly.

"We'll have four years of currency reform, anyhow. By the end of that time, you old dyed-in-the-wool Republicans will be thinking differently. The under dog is going to have a chance."

Mr. Trueman shifted in his chair. "That's no way for a banker to talk." He spoke very low. "The Democrats will have a long time to be sorry they ever turned Pops. No use talking to you while your Irish is up. I'll wait till you cool off." He rose and walked away, less deliberately than usual, and Mr. Dillon, watching his retreating figure, laughed haughtily and disagreeably. He asked the grain-elevator man to take the vacated chair. The group about him grew, and he sat expounding the reforms proposed by the Democratic candidate until a late hour.

For the first time in my life I listened with breathless interest to a political discussion. Whoever Mr. Dillon failed to convince, he convinced me. I grasped it at once: that gold had been responsible for most of the miseries and inequalities of the world; that it had always been the club the rich and cunning held over the poor; and that "the free and unlimited coinage of silver" would remedy all this. Dillon declared that young Mr. Bryan had looked like the patriots of old when he faced and challenged high finance with: "You shall not press this crown of thorns upon the brow of labour; you shall not crucify mankind upon a cross of gold." I thought that magnificent; I thought the corn-fields would show them a thing or two, back there!

R. E. Dillon had never taken an aggressive part in politics. But from that night on, the Democratic candidate and the free-silver plank were the subject of his talks with his customers and depositors. He drove about the country convincing the farmers, went to the neighbouring towns to use his influence with the merchants, organized the Bryan Club and the Bryan Ladies' Quartette in our county, contributed largely to the campaign fund. This was all a new line of conduct for Mr. Dillon, and it sat unsteadily on him. Even his voice became unnatural; there was a sting of comeback in it. His new character made him more like other people and took away from his special personal quality. I wonder whether it was not Trueman, more than Bryan, who put such an edge on him.

While all these things were going on, Trueman kept to his own office. He came to Dillon's bank on business, but he did not "come back to the sidewalk," as I put it to myself. He waited and said nothing, but he looked grim. After a month or so, when he saw that this thing was not going to blow over, when he heard how Dillon had been talking to representative men all over the county, and saw the figure he had put down for the campaign fund, then Trueman remarked to some of his friends that a banker had no business to commit himself to a scatter-brained financial policy which would destroy credit.

The next morning Mr. Trueman went to the bank across the street, the rival of Dillon's, and wrote a check on Dillon's bank "for the amount of my balance." He wasn't the sort of man who would ever know what his balance was, he merely kept it big enough to cover emergencies. That afternoon the Merchants' National took the check over to Dillon on its collecting rounds, and by night the word was all over town that Trueman had changed his bank. After this there would be no going back, people said. To change your bank was one of the most final things you could do. The little, unsuccessful men were pleased, as they always are at the destruction of anything strong and fine.

All through the summer and the autumn of that campaign Mr. Dillon was away a great deal. When he was at home, he took his evening airing on the sidewalk, and there was always a group of men about him, talking of the coming election; that was the most exciting presidential campaign people could remember. I often passed this group on my way to the post-office, but there was no temptation to linger now. Mr. Dillon seemed like another man, and my zeal to free humanity from the cross of gold had cooled. Mr. Trueman I seldom saw. When he passed me on the street, he nodded kindly.

The election and Bryan's defeat did nothing to soften Dillon. He had been sure of a Democratic victory. I believe he felt almost as if Trueman were responsible for the triumph of Hanna and McKinley. At least he knew that Trueman was exceedingly well satisfied, and that was bitter to him. He seemed to me sarcastic and sharp all the time now.

I don't believe self-interest would ever have made a breach between Dillon and Trueman. Neither would have taken advantage of the other. If a combination of circumstances had made it necessary that one or the other should take a loss in money or prestige, I think Trueman would have pocketed the loss. That was his way. It was his code, moreover. A gentleman pocketed his gains mechanically, in the day's routine; but he pocketed losses punctiliously, with a sharp, if bitter, relish. I believe now, as I believed then, that this was a quarrel of "principle." Trueman looked down on anyone who could take the reasoning of the Populist party seriously. He was a perfectly direct man, and he showed his contempt. That was enough. It lost me my special pleasure of summer nights: the old stories of the early West that sometimes came to the surface; the minute biographies of the farming people; the clear, detailed, illuminating accounts of all that went on in the great crop-growing, cattle-feeding world; and the silence,—the strong, rich, outflowing silence between two friends, that was as full and satisfying as the moonlight. I was never to know its like again.

After that rupture nothing went well with either of my two great men. Things were out of true, the equilibrium was gone. Formerly, when they used to sit in their old places on the sidewalk, two black figures with patches of shadow below, they seemed like two bodies held steady by some law of balance, an unconscious relation like that between the earth and the moon. It was this mathematical harmony which gave a third person pleasure.

Before the next presidential campaign came round, Mr. Dillon died (a young man still) very suddenly, of pneumonia. We didn't know that he was seriously ill until one of his clerks came running to our house to tell us he was dead. The same clerk, half out of his wits—it looked like the end of the world to him—ran on to tell Mr. Trueman.

Mr. Trueman thanked him. He called his confidential man, and told him to order flowers from Kansas City. Then he went to his house, informed his housekeeper that he was going away on business, and packed his bag. That same night he boarded the Santa Fé Limited and didn't stop until he was in San Francisco. He was gone all spring. His confidential clerk wrote him letters every week about the business and the new calves, and got telegrams in reply. Trueman never wrote letters.

When Mr. Trueman at last came home, he stayed only a few months. He sold out everything he owned to a stranger from Kansas City; his feeding ranch, his barns and sheds, his house and town lots. It was a terrible blow to me; now only the common, everyday people would be left. I used to walk mournfully up and down before his office while all these deeds were being signed,—there were usually lawyers and notaries inside. But once, when he happened to be alone, he called me in, asked me how old I was now, and how far along I had got in school. His face and voice were more than kind, but he seemed absent-minded, as if he were trying to recall something. Presently he took from his watch-chain a red seal I had always admired, reached for my hand, and dropped the piece of carnelian into my palm.

"For a keepsake," he said evasively.

When the transfer of his property was completed, Mr. Trueman left us for good. He spent the rest of his life among the golden hills of San Francisco. He moved into the Saint Francis Hotel when it was first built, and had an office in a high building at the top of what is now Powell Street. There he read his letters in the morning and played poker at night. I've heard a man whose offices were next his tell how Trueman used to sit tilted back in his desk chair, a half-consumed cigar in his mouth, morning after morning, apparently doing nothing, watching the Bay and the ferry-boats, across a line of wind-racked eucalyptus trees. He died at the Saint Francis about nine years after he left our part of the world.

The breaking-up of that friendship between two men who scarcely noticed my existence was a real loss to me, and has ever since been a regret. More than once, in Southern countries where there is a smell of dust and dryness in the air and the nights are intense, I have come upon a stretch of dusty white road drinking up the moonlight beside a blind wall, and have felt a sudden sadness. Perhaps it was not until the next morning that I knew why,—and then only because I had dreamed of Mr. Dillon or Mr. Trueman in my sleep. When that old scar is occasionally touched by chance, it rouses the old uneasiness; the feeling of something broken that could so easily have been mended; of something delightful that was senselessly wasted, of a truth that was accidentally distorted—one of the truths we want to keep.

A. E. Coppard

DUSKY RUTH

AT THE CLOSE OF AN APRIL DAY, chilly and wet, the traveller came to a country town. In the Cotswolds, though the towns are small and sweet and the inns snug, the general habit of the land is bleak and bare. He had newly come upon upland roads so void of human affairs, so lonely, that they might have been made for some forgotten uses by departed men, and left to the unwitting passage of such strangers as himself. Even the unending walls, built of old rough laminated rock, that detailed the far-spreading fields, had grown very old again in their courses; there were dabs of darkness, buttons of moss, and fossils on every stone. He had passed a few neighbourhoods, sometimes at the crook of a stream, or at the cross of debouching roads, where old habitations, their gangrenated thatch riddled with bird holes, had been not so much erected as just spattered about the places. Beyond these signs an odd lark or blackbird, the ruckle of partridges, or the nifty gallop of a hare had been the only mitigation of the living loneliness that was almost as profound by day as by night. But the traveller had a care for such times and places. There are men who love to gaze with the mind at things that can never be seen, feel at least the throb of a beauty that will never be known, and hear over immense bleak reaches the echo of that which is no celestial music, but only their own hearts' vain cries; and though his garments clung to him like clay it was with deliberate questing step that the traveller trod the single street of the town, and at last entered the inn, shuffling his shoes in the doorway for a moment and striking the raindrops from his hat. Then he turned into a small smoking-room. Leather-lined benches, much worn, were fixed to the wall under the window and in other odd corners and nooks behind mahogany tables. One wall was furnished with all the congenial gear of a bar, but without any intervening counter. Opposite, a bright fire was burning, and a neatly dressed young woman sat before it in a Windsor chair, staring at the flames. There was no other inmate of the room, and as he entered, the girl rose up and greeted him. He found that he could be accommodated for the night, and in a few moments his hat and scarf were removed and placed inside the fender, his wet overcoat was taken to the kitchen, the landlord, an old fellow, was lending him a roomy pair of slippers, and a maid was setting supper in an adjoining room.

He sat while this was doing and talked to the barmaid. She had a beautiful but rather mournful face as it was lit by the firelight, and when her glance was turned away from it her eyes had a piercing brightness. Friendly and well spoken as she was, the melancholy in her aspect was noticeable—perhaps it was the dim room, or the wet day, or the long hours ministering a multitude of cocktails to thirsty gallantry.

When he went to his supper he found cheering food and drink, with pleasant garniture of silver and mahogany. There were no other visitors, he was to be alone; blinds were drawn, lamps lit, and the fire at his back was comforting. So he sat long about his meal until a white-faced maid came to clear the table, discoursing to him about country things as she busied about the room. It was a long, narrow room, with a sideboard and the door at one end and the fireplace at the other. A bookshelf, almost devoid of books, contained a number of plates; the long wall that faced the windows was almost destitute of pictures, but there were hung upon it, for some inscrutable but doubtless sufficient reason, many dish-covers, solidly shaped, of the kind held in such mysterious regard and known as "willow pattern"; one was even hung upon the face of a map. Two musty prints were mixed with them, presentments of horses having a stilted extravagant physique and bestridden by images of inhuman and incommunicable dignity, clothed in whiskers, coloured jackets, and tight white breeches.

He took down the books from the shelf, but his interest was speedily exhausted, and the almanacs, the county directory, and various guidebooks were exchanged for the *Cotswold Chronicle*. With this, having drawn the deep chair to the hearth, he whiled away the time. The newspaper amused him with its advertisements of stock shows, farm auctions, travelling quacks and conjurers, and there was a lengthy account of the execution of a local felon, one Timothy Bridger, who had murdered an infant in some shameful circumstances. This dazzling crescendo proved rather trying to the traveller; he threw down the paper.

The town was all as quiet as the hills, and he could hear no sounds in the house. He got up and went across the hall to the smoke-room. The door was shut, but there was light within, and he entered. The girl sat there much as he had seen her on his arrival, still alone, with feet on fender. He shut the door behind him, sat down, and crossing his legs puffed at his pipe, admired the snug little room and the pretty figure of the girl, which he could do without embarrassment, as her meditative head, slightly bowed, was turned away from him. He could see something of her, too, in the mirror at the bar, which repeated also the agreeable contours of bottles of coloured wines and rich liqueurs—so entrancing in form and aspect that they seemed destined to charming histories, even in disuse—and those of familiar outline containing mere spirits or small beer, for which are reserved the harsher destinies of base oils, horse medicines, disinfectants, and cold tea. There were coloured glasses for bitter wines, white glasses for sweet, a tiny leaden sink beneath them, and the four black handles of the beer engines.

The girl wore a light blouse of silk, a short skirt of black velvet, and a pair of very thin silk stockings that showed the flesh of instep and shin so plainly that he could see they were reddened by the warmth of the fire. She had on a pair of dainty cloth shoes with high heels, but what was wonderful about her was the heap of rich black hair piled at the back of her head and shadowing the dusky neck. He sat puffing his pipe and letting the loud tick of the clock fill the quiet room. She did not stir and he could move no muscle. It was as if he had been willed to come there and wait silently. That, he felt now, had been his desire all the evening; and here, in her presence, he was more strangely stirred in a few short minutes than by any event he could remember.

In youth he had viewed women as futile, pitiable things that grew long hair, wore stays and garters, and prayed incomprehensible prayers. Viewing them in the stalls of the theatre from his vantage-point in the gallery, he always disliked the articulation of their naked shoulders. But still, there was a god in the sky, a god with flowing hair and exquisite eyes, whose one stride with an ardour grandly rendered took him across the whole round hemisphere to which his buoyant limbs were bound like spokes to the eternal rim and axle, his bright hair burning in the pity of the sunsets and tossing in the anger of the dawns.

Master traveller had indeed come into this room to be with this woman, and she as surely desired him, and for all its accidental occasion it was as if he, walking the ways of the world, had suddenly come upon what, what so imaginable with all permitted reverence as, well, just a shrine; and he, admirably humble, bowed the instant head.

Were there no other people within? The clock indicated a few minutes to nine. He sat on, still as stone, and the woman might have been of wax for all the movement or sound she made. There was allurement in the air between them; he had forborne his smoking, the pipe grew cold between his teeth. He waited for a look from her, a movement to break the trance of silence. No footfall in street or house, no voice in the inn but the clock, beating away as if pronouncing a doom. Suddenly it rasped out nine large notes, a bell in the town repeated them dolefully, and a cuckoo no farther than the kitchen mocked them with three times three. After that came the weak steps of the old landlord along the hall, the slam of doors, the clatter of lock and bolt, and then the silence returning unendurably upon them.

He rose and stood behind her; he touched the black hair. She made
no movement or sign. He pulled out two or three combs and, dropping
them into her lap, let the whole mass tumble about his hands. It had a
curious harsh touch in the unravelling, but was so full and shining; black
as a rook's wings it was. He slid his palms through it. His fingers searched
it and fought with its fine strangeness; into his mind there travelled a
serious thought, stilling his wayward fancy—this was no wayward fancy,
but a rite accomplishing itself! (*Run, run, silly man, y'are lost!*) But
having got so far, he burnt his boats, leaned over, and drew her face back
to him. And at that, seizing his wrists, she gave him back ardour for
ardour, pressing his hands to her bosom, while the kiss was sealed and
sealed again. Then she sprang up and picking his scarf and hat from the
fender said:

"I have been drying them for you, but the hat has shrunk a bit, I'm
sure—I tried it on."

He took them from her and put them behind him; he leaned lightly
back upon the table, holding it with both his hands behind him; he could
not speak.

"Aren't you going to thank me for drying them?" she asked, picking
her combs from the rug and repinning her hair.

"I wonder why we did that?" he asked, shamedly.

"It is what I'm thinking too," she said.

"You were so beautiful about—about it, you know."

She made no rejoinder, but continued to bind her hair, looking
brightly at him under her brows. When she had finished she went close to
him.

"Will that do?"

"I'll take it down again."

"No, no, the old man or the old woman will be coming in."

"What of that?" he said, taking her into his arms. "Tell me your
name."

She shook her head, but she returned his kisses and stroked his hair
and shoulders with beautifully melting gestures.

"What is your name? I want to call you by your name," he said. "I
can't keep calling you Lovely Woman, Lovely Woman."

Again she shook her head and was dumb.

"I'll call you Ruth, then, Dusky Ruth, Ruth of the black, beautiful
hair."

"That is a nice-sounding name—I knew a deaf and dumb girl named
Ruth; she went to Nottingham and married an organ-grinder—but I
should like it for my name."

"Then I give it to you."

"Mine is so ugly."

"What is it?"

Again the shaken head and the burning caress.

"Then you shall be Ruth; will you keep that name?"

"Yes, if you give me the name I will keep it for you."

Time had indeed taken them by the forelock, and they looked upon a ruddled world.

"I stake my one talent," he said jestingly, "and behold it returns me fortyfold; I feel like the boy who catches three mice with one piece of cheese."

At ten o'clock the girl said:

"I must go and see how *they* are getting on," and she went to the door.

"Are we keeping them up?"

She nodded.

"Are you tired?"

"No, I am not tired." She looked at him doubtfully.

"We ought not to stay in here; go into the coffee room and I'll come there in a few minutes."

"Right," he whispered gaily, "we'll sit up all night."

She stood at the door for him to pass out, and he crossed the hall to the other room. It was in darkness except for the flash of the fire. Standing at the hearth he lit a match for the lamp, but paused at the globe; then he extinguished the match.

"No, it's better to sit in the firelight."

He heard voices at the other end of the house that seemed to have a chiding note in them.

"Lord," he thought, "is she getting into a row?"

Then her steps came echoing over the stone floor of the hall; she opened the door and stood there with a lighted candle in her hand; he stood at the other end of the room, smiling.

"Good night," she said.

"Oh no, no! come along," he protested, but not moving from the hearth.

"Got to go to bed," she answered.

"Are they angry with you?"

"No."

"Well, then, come over here and sit down."

"Got to go to bed," she said again, but she had meanwhile put her candlestick upon the little sideboard and was trimming the wick with a burnt match.

"Oh, come along, just half an hour," he protested. She did not answer, but went on prodding the wick of the candle.

"Ten minutes, then," he said, still not going towards her.

"Five minutes," he begged.

She shook her head and, picking up the candlestick, turned to the door. He did not move, he just called her name: "Ruth!"

She came back then, put down the candlestick, and tiptoed across the room until he met her. The bliss of the embrace was so poignant that he was almost glad when she stood up again and said with affected steadiness, though he heard the tremor in her voice:

"I must get you your candle."

She brought one from the hall, set it on the table in front of him, and struck the match.

"What is my number?" he asked.

"Number-six room," she answered, prodding the wick vaguely with her match, while a slip of white wax dropped over the shoulder of the new candle. "Number six . . . next to mine."

The match burnt out; she said abruptly: "Good night," took up her own candle, and left him there.

In a few moments he ascended the stairs and went into his room. He fastened the door, removed his coat, collar, and slippers, but the rack of passion had seized him and he moved about with no inclination to sleep. He sat down, but there was no medium of distraction. He tried to read the newspaper that he had carried up with him, and without realizing a single phrase he forced himself to read again the whole account of the execution of the miscreant Bridger. When he had finished this he carefully folded the paper and stood up, listening. He went to the parting wall and tapped thereon with his fingertips. He waited half a minute, one minute, two minutes; there was no answering sign. He tapped again, more loudly, with his knuckles, but there was no response, and he tapped many times. He opened his door as noiselessly as possible; along the dark passage there were slips of light under the other doors, the one next his own, and the one beyond that. He stood in the corridor listening to the rumble of old voices in the farther room, the old man and his wife going to their rest. Holding his breath fearfully, he stepped to *her* door and tapped gently upon it. There was no answer, but he could somehow divine her awareness of him; he tapped again; she moved to the door and whispered: "No, no, go away." He turned the handle, the door was locked.

"Let me in," he pleaded. He knew she was standing there an inch or two beyond him.

"Hush," she called softly. "Go away, the old woman has ears like a fox."

He stood silent for a moment.

"Unlock it," he urged; but he got no further reply, and feeling foolish and baffled he moved back to his own room, cast his clothes from him, doused the candle and crept into the bed with soul as wild as a storm-swept forest, his heart beating a vagrant summons. The room filled with strange heat, there was no composure for mind or limb, nothing but flaming visions and furious embraces.

"Morality . . . what is it but agreement with your own soul?"

So he lay for two hours—the clocks chimed twelve—listening with foolish persistency for *her* step along the corridor, fancying every light sound—and the night was full of them—was her hand upon the door.

Suddenly, then—and it seemed as if his very heart would abash the house with its thunder—he could hear distinctly someone knocking on the wall. He got quickly from his bed and stood at his door, listening. Again the knocking was heard, and having half-clothed himself he crept into the passage, which was now in utter darkness, trailing his hand along the wall until he felt her door; it was standing open. He entered her room and closed the door behind him. There was not the faintest gleam of light, he could see nothing. He whispered: "Ruth!" and she was standing there. She touched him, but not speaking. He put out his hands, and they met round her neck; her hair was flowing in its great wave about her; he put his lips to her face and found that her eyes were streaming with tears, salt and strange and disturbing. In the close darkness he put his arms about her with no thought but to comfort her; one hand had plunged through the long harsh tresses and the other across her hips before he realized that she was ungowned; then he was aware of the softness of her breasts and the cold naked sleekness of her shoulders. But she was crying there, crying silently with great tears, her strange sorrow stifling his desire.

"Ruth, Ruth, my beautiful dear!" he murmured soothingly. He felt for the bed with one hand, and turning back the quilt and sheets, he lifted her in as easily as a mother does her child, replaced the bedding, and, in his clothes, he lay stretched beside her, comforting her. They lay so, innocent as children, for an hour, when she seemed to have gone to sleep. He rose then and went silently to his room, full of weariness.

In the morning he breakfasted without seeing her, but as he had business in the world that gave him just an hour longer at the inn before he left it for good and all, he went into the smoke-room and found her. She greeted him with curious gaze, but merrily enough, for there were other men there now—farmers, a butcher, a registrar, an old, old man. The hour passed, but not these men, and at length he donned his coat, took up his stick, and said good-bye. Her shining glances followed him to the door, and from the window as far as they could view him.

Roald Dahl

THE LANDLADY

Billy Weaver had travelled down from London on the slow after-noon train, with a change at Reading on the way, and by the time he got to Bath it was about nine o'clock in the evening and the moon was coming up out of a clear starry sky over the houses opposite the station entrance. But the air was deadly cold and the wind was like a flat blade of ice on his cheeks.

"Excuse me," he said, "but is there a fairly cheap hotel not too far away from here?"

"Try The Bell and Dragon," the porter answered, pointing down the road. "They might take you in. It's about a quarter of a mile along on the other side."

Billy thanked him and picked up his suitcase and set out to walk the quarter-mile to The Bell and Dragon. He had never been to Bath before. He didn't know anyone who lived there. But Mr. Greenslade at the Head Office in London had told him it was a splendid town. "Find your own lodgings," he had said, "and then go along and report to the Branch Manager as soon as you've got yourself settled."

Billy was seventeen years old. He was wearing a new navy-blue overcoat, a new brown trilby hat, and a new brown suit, and he was feeling fine. He walked briskly down the street. He was trying to do everything briskly these days. Briskness, he had decided, was *the* one common characteristic of all successful businessmen. The big shots up at Head Office were absolutely fantastically brisk all the time. They were amazing.

There were no shops on this wide street that he was walking along, only a line of tall houses on each side, all of them identical. They had porches and pillars and four or five steps going up to their front doors, and it was obvious that once upon a time they had been very swanky residences. But now, even in the darkness, he could see that the paint was peeling from the woodwork on their doors and windows, and that the handsome white façades were cracked and blotchy from neglect.

Suddenly, in a downstairs window that was brilliantly illuminated by a street-lamp not six yards away, Billy caught sight of a printed notice propped up against the glass in one of the upper panes. It said BED AND BREAKFAST. There was a vase of yellow chrysanthemums, tall and beautiful, standing just underneath the notice.

He stopped walking. He moved a bit closer. Green curtains (some sort of velvety material) were hanging down on either side of the window. The chrysanthemums looked wonderful beside them. He went right up and peered through the glass into the room, and the first thing he saw was a bright fire burning in the hearth. On the carpet in front of the fire, a pretty little dachshund was curled up asleep with its nose tucked into its belly. The room itself, so far as he could see in the half-darkness, was filled with pleasant furniture. There was a baby-grand piano and a big sofa and several plump armchairs; and in one corner he spotted a large parrot in a cage. Animals were usually a good sign in a place like this, Billy told himself; and all in all, it looked to him as though it would be a pretty decent house to stay in. Certainly it would be more comfortable than The Bell and Dragon.

On the other hand, a pub would be more congenial than a boarding-house. There would be beer and darts in the evenings, and lots of people to talk to, and it would probably be a good bit cheaper, too. He had stayed a couple of nights in a pub once before and he had liked it. He had never stayed in any boarding-houses, and, to be perfectly honest, he was a tiny bit frightened of them. The name itself conjured up images of watery cabbage, rapacious landladies, and a powerful smell of kippers in the living-room.

After dithering about like this in the cold for two or three minutes, Billy decided that he would walk on and take a look at The Bell and Dragon before making up his mind. He turned to go.

And now a queer thing happened to him. He was in the act of stepping back and turning away from the window when all at once his eye was caught and held in the most peculiar manner by the small notice that was there. BED AND BREAKFAST, it said. BED AND BREAKFAST, BED AND BREAKFAST, BED AND BREAKFAST. Each word was like a large black eye staring at him through the glass, holding him, compelling him, forcing him to stay where he was and not to walk away from that house, and the next thing he knew, he was actually moving across from the window to the front door of the house, climbing the steps that led up to it, and reaching for the bell.

He pressed the bell. Far away in a back room he heard it ringing, and then *at once*—it must have been at once because he hadn't even had time to take his finger from the bell-button—the door swung open and a woman was standing there.

Normally you ring the bell and you have at least a half-minute's wait before the door opens. But this dame was like a jack-in-the-box. He pressed the bell—and out she popped! It made him jump.

She was about forty-five or fifty years old, and the moment she saw him, she gave him a warm welcoming smile.

"*Please* come in," she said pleasantly. She stepped aside, holding the door wide open, and Billy found himself automatically starting forward. The compulsion or, more accurately, the desire to follow after her into that house was extraordinarily strong.

"I saw the notice in the window," he said, holding himself back.

"Yes, I know."

"I was wondering about a room."

"It's *all* ready for you, my dear," she said. She had a round pink face and very gentle blue eyes.

"I was on my way to The Bell and Dragon," Billy told her. "But the notice in your window just happened to catch my eye."

"My dear boy," she said, "why don't you come in out of the cold?"

"How much do you charge?"

"Five and sixpence a night, including breakfast."

It was fantastically cheap. It was less than half of what he had been willing to pay.

"If that is too much," she added, "then perhaps I can reduce it just a tiny bit. Do you desire an egg for breakfast? Eggs are expensive at the moment. It would be sixpence less without the egg."

"Five and sixpence is fine," he answered. "I should like very much to stay here."

"I knew you would. Do come in."

She seemed terribly nice. She looked exactly like the mother of one's best school-friend welcoming one into the house to stay for the Christmas holidays. Billy took off his hat, and stepped over the threshold.

"Just hang it there," she said, "and let me help you with your coat."

There were no other hats or coats in the hall. There were no umbrellas, no walking-sticks—nothing.

"We have it *all* to ourselves," she said, smiling at him over her shoulder as she led the way upstairs. "You see, it isn't very often I have the pleasure of taking a visitor into my little nest."

The old girl is slightly dotty, Billy told himself. But at five and sixpence a night, who gives a damn about that? "I should've thought you'd be simply swamped with applicants," he said politely.

"Oh, I am, my dear, I am, of course I am. But the trouble is that I'm inclined to be just a teeny weeny bit choosy and particular—if you see what I mean."

"Ah, yes."

"But I'm always ready. Everything is always ready day and night in this house just on the off-chance that an acceptable young gentleman will come along. And it is such a pleasure, my dear, such a very great pleasure when now and again I open the door and I see someone standing there who is just *exactly* right." She was halfway up the stairs, and she paused with one hand on the stair-rail, turning her head and smiling down at him with pale lips. "Like you," she added, and her blue eyes travelled slowly all the way down the length of Billy's body, to his feet, and then up again.

On the second-floor landing she said to him, "This floor is mine."

They climbed up another flight. "And this one is *all* yours," she said. "Here's your room. I do hope you'll like it." She took him into a small but charming front bedroom, switching on the light as she went in.

"The morning sun comes right in the window, Mr. Perkins. It *is* Mr. Perkins, isn't it?"

"No," he said. "It's Weaver."

"Mr. Weaver. How nice. I've put a water-bottle between the sheets to air them out, Mr. Weaver. It's such a comfort to have a hot water-bottle in a strange bed with clean sheets, don't you agree? And you may light the gas fire at any time if you feel chilly."

"Thank you," Billy said. "Thank you ever so much." He noticed that the bedspread had been taken off the bed, and that the bedclothes had been neatly turned back on one side, all ready for someone to get in.

"I'm so glad you appeared," she said, looking earnestly into his face. "I was beginning to get worried."

"That's all right," Billy answered brightly. "You mustn't worry about me." He put his suitcase on the chair and started to open it.

"And what about supper, my dear? Did you manage to get anything to eat before you came here?"

"I'm not a bit hungry, thank you," he said. "I think I'll just go to bed as soon as possible because tomorrow I've got to get up rather early and report to the office."

"Very well, then. I'll leave you now so that you can unpack. But before you go to bed, would you be kind enough to pop into the sitting-room on the ground floor and sign the book? Everyone has to do that because it's the law of the land, and we don't want to go breaking any laws at *this* stage in the proceedings, do we?" She gave him a little wave of the hand and went quickly out of the room and closed the door.

Now, the fact that his landlady appeared to be slightly off her rocker didn't worry Billy in the least. After all, she not only was harmless—there was no question about that—but she was also quite obviously a kind and generous soul. He guessed that she had probably lost a son in the war, or something like that, and had never gotten over it.

So a few minutes later, after unpacking his suitcase and washing his hands, he trotted downstairs to the ground floor and entered the living-room. His landlady wasn't there, but the fire was glowing in the hearth, and the little dachshund was still sleeping soundly in front of it. The room was wonderfully warm and cosy. I'm a lucky fellow, he thought, rubbing his hands. This is a bit of all right.

He found the guest-book lying open on the piano, so he took out his pen and wrote down his name and address. There were only two other entries above his on the page, and, as one always does with guest-books, he started to read them. One was a Christopher Mulholland from Cardiff. The other was Gregory W. Temple from Bristol.

That's funny, he thought suddenly. Christopher Mulholland. It rings a bell.

Now where on earth had he heard that rather unusual name before?

Was it a boy at school? No. Was it one of his sister's numerous young men, perhaps, or a friend of his father's? No, no, it wasn't any of those. He glanced down again at the book.

> *Christopher Mulholland*   *231 Cathedral Road, Cardiff*
> *Gregory W. Temple*   *27 Sycamore Drive, Bristol*

As a matter of fact, now he came to think of it, he wasn't at all sure that the second name didn't have almost as much of a familiar ring about it as the first.

"Gregory Temple?" he said aloud, searching his memory. "Christopher Mulholland? . . ."

"Such charming boys," a voice behind him answered, and he turned and saw his landlady sailing into the room with a large silver tea-tray in her hands. She was holding it well out in front of her, and rather high up, as though the tray were a pair of reins on a frisky horse.

"They sound somehow familiar," he said.

"They do? How interesting."

"I'm almost positive I've heard those names before somewhere. Isn't that odd? Maybe it was in the newspapers. They weren't famous in any way, were they? I mean famous cricketers or footballers or something like that?"

"Famous," she said, setting the tea-tray down on the low table in front of the sofa. "Oh no, I don't think they were famous. But they were incredibly handsome, both of them, I can promise you that. They were tall and young and handsome, my dear, just exactly like you."

Once more, Billy glanced down at the book. "Look here," he said, noticing the dates. "This last entry is over two years old."

"It is?"

"Yes, indeed. And Christopher Mulholland's is nearly a year before that—more than *three years* ago."

"Dear me," she said, shaking her head and heaving a dainty little sigh. "I would never have thought it. How time does fly away from us all, doesn't it, Mr. Wilkins?"

"It's Weaver," Billy said. "W-e-a-v-e-r."

"Oh, of course it is!" she cried, sitting down on the sofa. "How silly of me. I do apologize. In one ear and out the other, that's me, Mr. Weaver."

"You know something?" Billy said. "Something that's really quite extraordinary about all this?"

"No, dear, I don't."

"Well, you see, both of these names—Mulholland and Temple—I not only seem to remember each one of them separately, so to speak, but somehow or other, in some peculiar way, they both appear to be sort of connected together as well. As though they were both famous for the same sort of thing, if you see what I mean—like . . . well . . . like Dempsey and Tunney, for example, or Churchill and Roosevelt."

"How amusing," she said. "But come over here now, dear, and sit down beside me on the sofa and I'll give you a nice cup of tea and a ginger biscuit before you go to bed."

"You really shouldn't bother," Billy said. "I didn't mean you to do anything like that." He stood by the piano, watching her as she fussed about with the cups and saucers. He noticed that she had small, white, quickly moving hands, and red finger-nails.

"I'm almost positive it was in the newspapers I saw them," Billy said. "I'll think of it in a second. I'm sure I will."

There is nothing more tantalizing than a thing like this that lingers just outside the borders of one's memory. He hated to give up.

"Now wait a minute," he said. "Wait just a minute. Mulholland . . . Christopher Mulholland . . . wasn't *that* the name of the Eton schoolboy who was on a walking-tour through the West Country, and then all of a sudden . . ."

"Milk?" she said. "And sugar?"

"Yes, please. And then all of a sudden . . ."

"Eton schoolboy?" she said. "Oh no, my dear, that can't possibly be right because *my* Mr. Mulholland was certainly not an Eton schoolboy when he came to me. He was a Cambridge undergraduate. Come over here now and sit next to me and warm yourself in front of this lovely fire. Come on. Your tea's all ready for you." She patted the empty place beside her on the sofa, and she sat there smiling at Billy and waiting for him to come over.

He crossed the room slowly, and sat down on the edge of the sofa. She placed his teacup on the table in front of him.

"*There* we are," she said. "How nice and cosy this is, isn't it?"

Billy started sipping his tea. She did the same. For half a minute or so, neither of them spoke. But Billy knew that she was looking at him. Her body was half turned toward him, and he could feel her eyes resting on his face, watching him over the rim of her teacup. Now and again, he caught a whiff of a peculiar smell that seemed to emanate directly from her person. It was not in the least unpleasant, and it reminded him—well, he wasn't quite sure what it reminded him of. Pickled walnuts? New leather? Or was it the corridors of a hospital?

At length, she said, "Mr. Mulholland was a great one for his tea. Never in my life have I seen anyone drink as much tea as dear, sweet Mr. Mulholland."

"I suppose he left fairly recently," Billy said. He was still puzzling his head about the two names. He was positive now that he had seen them in the newspapers—in the headlines.

"Left?" she said, arching her brows. "But my dear boy, he never left. He's still here. Mr. Temple is also here. They're on the fourth floor, both of them together."

Billy set his cup down slowly on the table and stared at his landlady. She smiled back at him, and then she put out one of her white hands and patted him comfortingly on the knee. "How old are you, my dear?" she asked.

"Seventeen."

"Seventeen!" she cried. "Oh, it's the perfect age! Mr. Mulholland was also seventeen. But I think he was a trifle shorter than you are; in fact I'm sure he was, and his teeth weren't *quite* so white. You have the most beautiful teeth, Mr. Weaver, did you know that?"

"They're not as good as they look," Billy said. "They've got simply masses of fillings in them at the back."

"Mr. Temple, of course, was a little older," she said, ignoring his remark. "He was actually twenty-eight. And yet I never would have guessed it if he hadn't told me, never in my whole life. There wasn't a *blemish* on his body."

"A what?" Billy said.

"His skin was *just* like a baby's."

There was a pause. Billy picked up his teacup and took another sip of his tea, then he set it down again gently in its saucer. He waited for her to say something else, but she seemed to have lapsed into another of her silences. He sat there staring straight ahead of him into the far corner of the room, biting his lower lip.

"That parrot," he said at last. "You know something? It had me completely fooled when I first saw it through the window. I could have sworn it was alive."

"Alas, no longer."

"It's most terribly clever the way it's been done," he said. "It doesn't look in the least bit dead. Who did it?"

"I did."

"*You* did?"

"Of course," she said. "And have you met my little Basil as well?" She nodded toward the dachshund curled up so comfortably in front of the fire. Billy looked at it. And suddenly, he realized that this animal had all the time been just as silent and motionless as the parrot. He put out a hand and touched it gently on the top of its back. The back was hard and cold, and when he pushed the hair to one side with his fingers, he could see the skin underneath, greyish-black and dry and perfectly preserved.

"Good gracious me," he said. "How absolutely fascinating." He turned away from the dog and stared with deep admiration at the little woman beside him on the sofa. "It must be most awfully difficult to do a thing like that."

"Not in the least," she said. "I stuff *all* my little pets myself when they pass away. Will you have another cup of tea?"

"No, thank you," Billy said. The tea tasted faintly of bitter almonds, and he didn't much care for it.

"You did sign the book, didn't you?"

"Oh, yes."

"That's good. Because later on, if I happen to forget what you were called, then I could always come down here and look it up. I still do that almost every day with Mr. Mulholland and Mr. . . . . Mr. . . . ."

"Temple," Billy said. "Gregory Temple. Excuse my asking, but haven't there been *any* other guests here except them in the last two or three years?"

Holding her teacup high in one hand, inclining her head slightly to the left, she looked up at him out of the corners of her eyes and gave him another gentle little smile.

"No, my dear," she said. "Only you."

Walter de la Mare

SEATON'S AUNT

I HAD HEARD RUMOURS of Seaton's aunt long before I actually encountered her. Seaton, in the hush of confidence, or at any little show
of toleration on our part, would remark, "My aunt," or "My old aunt,
you know," as if his relative might be a kind of cement to an *entente
cordiale*.

He had an unusual quantity of pocket-money; or, at any rate, it was
bestowed on him in unusually large amounts; and he spent it freely,
though none of us would have described him as an "awfully generous
chap." "Hullo, Seaton," we would say, "the old Begum?" At the beginning of term, too, he used to bring back surprising and exotic dainties in a
box with a trick padlock that accompanied him from his first appearance
at Gummidge's in a billycock hat to the rather abrupt conclusion of his
schooldays.

From a boy's point of view he looked distastefully foreign, with his
yellow skin, and slow chocolate-coloured eyes, and lean weak figure.
Merely for his looks he was treated by most of us true-blue Englishmen
with condescension, hostility, or contempt. We used to call him "Pongo,"
but without any much better excuse for the nickname than his skin. He
was, that is, in one sense of the term what he assuredly was not in the
other sense, a sport.

Seaton and I, as I may say, were never in any sense intimate at
school; our orbits only intersected in class. I kept deliberately aloof from
him. I felt vaguely he was a sneak, and remained quite unmollified by
advances on his side, which, in a boy's barbarous fashion, unless it suited
me to be magnanimous, I haughtily ignored.

We were both of us quick-footed, and at Prisoner's Base used occasionally to hide together. And so I best remember Seaton—his narrow

watchful face in the dusk of a summer evening; his peculiar crouch, and his inarticulate whisperings and mumblings. Otherwise he played all games slackly and limply; used to stand and feed at his locker with a crony or two until his "tuck" gave out; or waste his money on some outlandish fancy or other. He bought, for instance, a silver bangle, which he wore above his left elbow, until some of the fellows showed their masterly contempt of the practice by dropping it nearly red-hot down his neck.

It needed, therefore, a rather peculiar taste, a rather rare kind of schoolboy courage and indifference to criticism, to be much associated with him. And I had neither the taste nor, perhaps, the courage. None the less, he did make advances, and on one memorable occasion went to the length of bestowing on me a whole pot of some outlandish mulberry-coloured jelly that had been duplicated in his term's supplies. In the exuberance of my gratitude I promised to spend the next half-term holiday with him at his aunt's house.

I had clean forgotten my promise when, two or three days before the holiday, he came up and triumphantly reminded me of it.

"Well, to tell you the honest truth, Seaton, old chap—" I began graciously: but he cut me short.

"My aunt expects you," he said; "she is very glad you are coming. She's sure to be quite decent to *you*, Withers."

I looked at him in sheer astonishment; the emphasis was so uncalled for. It seemed to suggest an aunt not hitherto hinted at, and a friendly feeling on Seaton's side that was far more disconcerting than welcome.

We reached his home partly by train, partly by a lift in an empty farm-cart, and partly by walking. It was a whole-day holiday, and we were to sleep the night; he lent me extraordinary night-gear, I remember. The village street was unusually wide, and was fed from a green by two converging roads, with an inn, and a high green sign at the corner. About a hundred yards down the street was a chemist's shop—a Mr. Tanner's. We descended the two steps into his dusky and odorous interior to buy, I remember, some rat poison. A little beyond the chemist's was the forge. You then walked along a very narrow path, under a fairly high wall, nodding here and there with weeds and tufts of grass, and so came to the iron garden-gates, and saw the high flat house behind its huge sycamore. A coach-house stood on the left of the house, and on the right a gate led into a kind of rambling orchard. The lawn lay away over to the left again, and at the bottom (for the whole garden sloped gently to a sluggish and rushy pond-like stream) was a meadow.

We arrived at noon, and entered the gates out of the hot dust beneath the glitter of the dark-curtained windows. Seaton led me at once through the little garden-gate to show me his tadpole pond, swarming with what (being myself not in the least interested in low life) I considered the most horrible creatures—of all shapes, consistencies, and sizes,

but with whom Seaton seemed to be on the most intimate of terms. I can see his absorbed face now as he sat on his heels and fished the slimy things out in his sallow palms. Wearying at last of these pets, we loitered about awhile in an aimless fashion. Seaton seemed to be listening, or at any rate waiting, for something to happen or for someone to come. But nothing did happen and no one came.

That was just like Seaton. Anyhow, the first view I got of his aunt was when, at the summons of a distant gong, we turned from the garden, very hungry and thirsty, to go in to luncheon. We were approaching the house when Seaton suddenly came to a standstill. Indeed, I have always had the impression that he plucked at my sleeve. Something, at least, seemed to catch me back, as it were, as he cried, "Look out, there she is!"

She was standing at an upper window which opened wide on a hinge, and at first sight she looked an excessively tall and overwhelming figure. This, however, was mainly because the window reached all but to the floor of her bedroom. She was in reality rather an under-sized woman, in spite of her long face and big head. She must have stood, I think, unusually still, with eyes fixed on us, though this impression may be due to Seaton's sudden warning and to my consciousness of the cautious and subdued air that had fallen on him at sight of her. I know that without the least reason in the world I felt a kind of guiltiness, as if I had been "caught." There was a silvery star pattern sprinkled on her black silk dress, and even from the ground I could see the immense coils of her hair and the rings on her left hand, which was held fingering the small jet buttons of her bodice. She watched our united advance without stirring, until, imperceptibly, her eyes raised and lost themselves in the distance, so that it was out of an assumed reverie that she appeared suddenly to awaken to our presence beneath her when we drew close to the house.

"So this is your friend, Mr. Smithers, I suppose?" she said, bobbing to me.

"Withers, aunt," said Seaton.

"It's much the same," she said, with eyes fixed on me. "Come in, Mr. Withers, and bring him along with you."

She continued to gaze at me—at least, I think she did so. I know that the fixity of her scrutiny and her ironical "Mr." made me feel peculiarly uncomfortable. None the less she was extremely kind and attentive to me, though, no doubt, her kindness and attention showed up more vividly against her complete neglect of Seaton. Only one remark that I have any recollection of she made to him: "When I look on my nephew, Mr. Smithers, I realize that dust we are, and dust shall become. You are hot, dirty, and incorrigible, Arthur."

She sat at the head of the table, Seaton at the foot, and I, before a wide waste of damask tablecloth, between them. It was an old and rather close dining-room, with windows thrown wide to the green garden and a wonderful cascade of fading roses. Miss Seaton's great chair faced this window, so that its rose-reflected light shone full on her yellowish face,

and on just such chocolate eyes as my schoolfellow's, except that hers were more than half-covered by unusually long and heavy lids.

There she sat, steadily eating, with those sluggish eyes fixed for the most part on my face; above them stood the deep-lined fork between her eyebrows; and above that the wide expanse of a remarkable brow beneath its strange steep bank of hair. The lunch was copious, and consisted, I remember, of all such dishes as are generally considered too rich and too good for the schoolboy digestion—lobster mayonnaise, cold game sausages, and immense veal and ham pie farced with eggs, truffles, and numberless delicious flavours; besides kickshaws, creams, and sweetmeats. We even had wine, a half-glass of old darkish sherry each.

Miss Seaton enjoyed and indulged an enormous appetite. Her example and a natural schoolboy voracity soon overcame my nervousness of her, even to the extent of allowing me to enjoy to the best of my bent so rare a spread. Seaton was singularly modest; the greater part of his meal consisted of almonds and raisins, which he nibbled surreptitiously and as if he found difficulty in swallowing them.

I don't mean that Miss Seaton "conversed" with me. She merely scattered trenchant remarks and now and then twinkled a baited question over my head. But her face was like a dense and involved accompaniment to her talk. She presently dropped the "Mr.," to my intense relief, and called me now Withers, or Wither, now Smithers, and even once towards the close of the meal distinctly Johnson, though how on earth my name suggested it, or whose face mine had reanimated in memory, I cannot conceive.

"And is Arthur a good boy at school, Mr. Wither?" was one of her many questions. "Does he please his masters? Is he first in his class? What does the Reverend Dr. Gummidge think of him, eh?"

I knew she was jeering at him, but her face was adamant against the least flicker of sarcasm or facetiousness. I gazed fixedly at a blushing crescent of lobster.

"I think you're eighth, aren't you, Seaton?"

Seaton moved his small pupils towards his aunt. But she continued to gaze with a kind of concentrated detachment at me.

"Arthur will never make a brilliant scholar, I fear," she said, lifting a dexterously-burdened fork to her wide mouth. . . .

After luncheon she preceded me up to my bedroom. It was a jolly little bedroom, with a brass fender and rugs and a polished floor, on which it was possible, I afterwards found, to play "snow-shoes." Over the washstand was a little black-framed water-colour drawing, depicting a large eye with an extremely fishlike intensity in the spark of light on the dark pupil; and in "illuminated" lettering beneath was printed very minutely, "Thou God Seest ME," followed by a long looped monogram, "S.S." in the corner. The other pictures were all of the sea: brigs on blue water; a schooner overtopping chalk cliffs; a rocky island of prodigious steepness, with two tiny sailors dragging a monstrous boat up a shelf of beach.

"This is the room, Withers, my brother William died in when a boy. Admire the view!"

I looked out of the window across the tree-tops. It was a day hot with sunshine over the green fields, and the cattle were standing swishing their tails in the shallow water. But the view at the moment was only exaggeratedly vivid because I was horribly dreading that she would presently inquire after my luggage, and I had not brought even a toothbrush. I need have had no fear. Hers was not that highly-civilized type of mind that is stuffed with sharp, material details. Nor could her ample presence be described as in the least motherly.

"I would never consent to question a schoolfellow behind my nephew's back," she said, standing in the middle of the room, "but tell me, Smithers, why is Arthur so unpopular? You, I understand, are his only close friend." She stood in a dazzle of sun, and out of it her eyes regarded me with such leaden penetration beneath their thick lids that I doubt if my face concealed the least thought from her. "But there, there," she added very suavely, stooping her head a little, "don't trouble to answer me. I never extort an answer. Boys are queer fish. Brains might perhaps have suggested his washing his hands before luncheon; but—not my choice, Smithers. God forbid! And now, perhaps, you would like to go into the garden again. I cannot actually see from here, but I should not be surprised if Arthur is now skulking behind that hedge."

He was. I saw his head come out and take a rapid glance at the windows.

"Join him, Mr. Smithers; we shall meet again, I hope, at the tea-table. The afternoon I spend in retirement."

Whether or not, Seaton and I had not been long engaged with the aid of two green switches in riding round and round a lumbering old grey horse we found in the meadow, before a rather bunched-up figure appeared, walking along the field-path on the other side of the water, with a magenta parasol studiously lowered in our direction throughout her slow progress, as if that were the magnetic needle and we the fixed Pole. Seaton at once lost all nerve in his riding. At the next lurch of the old mare's heels he toppled over into the grass, and I slid off the sleek broad back to join him where he stood, rubbing his shoulder and sourly watching the rather pompous figure till it was out of sight.

"Was that your aunt, Seaton?" I inquired; but not till then.

He nodded.

"Why didn't she take any notice of us, then?"

"She never does."

"Why not?"

"Oh, she knows all right, without; that's the dam' awful part of it." Seaton was about the only fellow at Gummidge's who ever had the ostentation to use bad language. He had suffered for it too. But it wasn't, I think, bravado. I believe he really felt certain things more intensely than most of the other fellows, and they were generally things that fortunate and average people do not feel at all—the peculiar quality, for instance, of the British schoolboy's imagination.

"I tell you, Withers," he went on moodily, slinking across the meadow with his hands covered up in his pockets, "she sees everything. And what she doesn't see she knows without."

"But how?" I said, not because I was much interested, but because the afternoon was so hot and tiresome and purposeless, and it seemed more of a bore to remain silent. Seaton turned gloomily and spoke in a very low voice.

"Don't appear to be talking of her, if you wouldn't mind. It's— because she's in league with the devil." He nodded his head and stooped to pick up a round flat pebble. "I tell you," he said, still stooping, "you fellows don't realize what it is. I know I'm a bit close and all that. But so would you be if you had that old hag listening to every thought you think."

I looked at him, then turned and surveyed one by one the windows of the house.

"Where's your *pater?*" I said awkwardly.

"Dead, ages and ages ago, and my mother too. She's not my aunt by rights."

"What is she, then?"

"I mean she's not my mother's sister, because my grandmother married twice; and she's one of the first lot. I don't know what you call her, but anyhow she's not my real aunt."

"She gives you plenty of pocket-money."

Seaton looked steadfastly at me out of his flat eyes. "She can't give me what's mine. When I come of age half of the whole lot will be mine; and what's more"—he turned his back on the house—"I'll make her hand over every blessed shilling of it."

I put my hands in my pockets and stared at Seaton; "Is it much?"

He nodded.

"Who told you?" He got suddenly very angry; a darkish red came into his cheeks, his eyes glistened, but he made no answer, and we loitered listlessly about the garden until it was time for tea. . . .

Seaton's aunt was wearing an extraordinary kind of lace jacket when we sidled sheepishly into the drawing-room together. She greeted me with a heavy and protracted smile, and bade me bring a chair close to the little table.

"I hope Arthur has made you feel at home," she said as she handed me my cup in her crooked hand. "He don't talk much to me; but then I'm an old woman. You must come again, Wither, and draw him out of his shell. You old snail!" She wagged her head at Seaton, who sat munching cake and watching her intently.

"And we must correspond, perhaps." She nearly shut her eyes at me. "You must write and tell me everything behind the creature's back." I confess I found her rather disquieting company. The evening drew on.

Lamps were brought in by a man with a nondescript face and very quiet footsteps. Seaton was told to bring out the chess-men. And we played a game, she and I, with her big chin thrust over the board at every move as she gloated over the pieces and occasionally croaked "Check!"—after which she would sit back inscrutably staring at me. But the game was never finished. She simply hemmed me defencelessly in with a cloud of men that held me impotent, and yet one and all refused to administer to my poor flustered old king a merciful *coup de grâce*.

"There," she said, as the clock struck ten—"a drawn game, Withers. We are very evenly matched. A very creditable defence, Withers. You know your room. There's supper on a tray in the dining-room. Don't let the creature over-eat himself. The gong will sound three-quarters of an hour *before* a punctual breakfast." She held out her cheek to Seaton, and he kissed it with obvious perfunctoriness. With me she shook hands.

"An excellent game," she said cordially, "but my memory is poor, and"—she swept the pieces helter-skelter into the box—"the result will never be known." She raised her great head far back. "Eh?"

It was a kind of challenge, and I could only murmur: "Oh, I was absolutely in a hole, you know!" when she burst out laughing and waved us both out of the room.

Seaton and I stood and ate our supper, with one candlestick to light us, in a corner of the dining-room. "Well, and how would you like it?" he said very softly, after cautiously poking his head round the doorway.

"Like what?"

"Being spied on—every blessed thing you do and think?"

"I shouldn't like it at all," I said, "if she does."

"And yet you let her smash you up at chess!"

"I didn't let her!" I said, indignantly.

"Well, you funked it, then."

"And I didn't funk it either," I said; "she's so jolly clever with her knights." Seaton stared fixedly at the candle. "You wait, that's all," he said slowly. And we went upstairs to bed.

I had not been long in bed, I think, when I was cautiously awakened by a touch on my shoulder. And there was Seaton's face in the candle-light—and his eyes looking into mine.

"What's up?" I said, rising quickly to my elbow.

"Don't scurry," he whispered, "or she'll hear. I'm sorry for waking you, but I didn't think you'd be asleep so soon."

"Why, what's the time, then?" Seaton wore, what was then rather unusual, a night-suit, and he hauled his big silver watch out of the pocket in his jacket.

"It's a quarter to twelve. I never get to sleep before twelve—not here."

"What do you do, then?"

"Oh, I read and listen."

"Listen?"

Seaton stared into his candle-flame as if he were listening even then. "You can't guess what it is. All you read in ghost stories, that's all rot. You can't see much, Withers, but you know all the same."

"Know what?"

"Why, that they're there."

"Who's there?" I asked fretfully, glancing at the door.

"Why, in the house. It swarms with 'em. Just you stand still and listen outside my bedroom door in the middle of the night. I have, dozens of times; they're all over the place."

"Look here, Seaton," I said, "you asked me to come here, and I didn't mind chucking up a leave just to oblige you and because I'd promised; but don't get talking a lot of rot, that's all, or you'll know the difference when we get back."

"Don't fret," he said coldly, turning away. "I shan't be at school long. And what's more, you're here now, and there isn't anybody else to talk to. I'll chance the other."

"Look here, Seaton," I said, "you may think you're going to scare me with a lot of stuff about voices and all that. But I'll just thank you to clear out; and you may please yourself about pottering about all night."

He made no answer; he was standing by the dressing-table looking across his candle into the looking-glass; he turned and stared slowly round the walls.

"Even this room's nothing more than a coffin. I suppose she told you—'It's all exactly the same as when my brother William died'—trust her for that! And good luck to him, say I. Look at that." He raised his candle close to the little water-colour I have mentioned. "There's hundreds of eyes like that in this house; and even if God does see you, He takes precious good care you don't see Him. And it's just the same with them. I tell you what, Withers, I'm getting sick of all this. I shan't stand it much longer."

The house was silent within and without, and even in the yellowish radiance of the candle a faint silver showed through the open window on my blind. I slipped off the bedclothes, wide awake, and sat irresolute on the bedside.

"I know you're only guying me," I said angrily, "but why is the house full of—what you say? Why do you hear—what you *do* hear? Tell me that, you silly fool!"

Seaton sat down on a chair and rested his candlestick on his knee. He blinked at me calmly. "She brings them," he said, with lifted eyebrows.

"Who? Your aunt?"

He nodded.

"How?"

"I told you," he answered pettishly. "She's in league. You don't know. She as good as killed my mother; I know that. But it's not only her by a long chalk. She just sucks you dry. I know. And that's what she'll do for me; because I'm like her—like my mother, I mean. She simply hates to see me alive. I wouldn't be like that old she-wolf for a million pounds. And so"—he broke off, with a comprehensive wave of his candlestick —"they're always here. Ah, my boy, wait till she's dead! She'll hear something then, I can tell you. It's all very well now, but wait till then! I wouldn't be in her shoes when she has to clear out—for something. Don't you go and believe I care for ghosts, or whatever you like to call them. We're all in the same box. We're all under her thumb."

He was looking almost nonchalantly at the ceiling at the moment, when I saw his face change, saw his eyes suddenly drop like shot birds and fix themselves on the cranny of the door he had just left ajar. Even from where I sat I could see his colour change; he went greenish. He crouched without stirring, simply fixed. And I, scarcely daring to breathe, sat with creeping skin, simply watching him. His hands relaxed, and he gave a kind of sigh.

"Was that one?" I whispered, with a timid show of jauntiness. He looked round, opened his mouth, and nodded. "What?" I said. He jerked his thumb with meaningful eyes, and I knew that he meant that his aunt had been there listening at our door cranny.

"Look here, Seaton," I said once more, wriggling to my feet. "You may think I'm a jolly noodle; just as you please. But your aunt has been civil to me and all that, and I don't believe a word you say about her, that's all, and never did. Every fellow's a bit off his pluck at night, and you may think it a fine sport to try your rubbish on me. I heard your aunt come upstairs before I fell asleep. And I'll bet you a level tanner she's in bed now. What's more, you can keep your blessed ghosts to yourself. It's a guilty conscience, I should think."

Seaton looked at me curiously, without answering for a moment. "I'm not a liar, Withers; but I'm not going to quarrel either. You're the only chap I care a button for; or, at any rate, you're the only chap that's ever come here; and it's something to tell a fellow what you feel. I don't care a fig for fifty thousand ghosts, although I swear on my solemn oath that I know they're here. But she"—he turned deliberately—"you laid a tanner she's in bed, Withers; well, I know different. She's never in bed much of the night, and I'll prove it, too, just to show you I'm not such a nolly as you think I am. Come on!"

"Come on where?"

"Why, to see."

I hesitated. He opened a large cupboard and took out a small dark dressing-gown and a kind of shawl-jacket. He threw the jacket on the bed and put on the gown. His dusky face was colourless, and I could see by the way he fumbled at the sleeves he was shivering. But it was no good showing the white feather now. So I threw the tasselled shawl over my shoulders and, leaving our candle brightly burning on the chair, we went out together and stood in the corridor.

"Now then, listen!" Seaton whispered.

We stood leaning over the staircase. It was like leaning over a well, so still and chill the air was all around us. But presently, as I suppose happens in most old houses, began to echo and answer in my ears a medley of infinite small stirrings and whisperings. Now out of the distance an old timber would relax its fibres, or a scurry die away behind the perishing wainscot. But amid and behind such sounds as these I seemed to begin to be conscious, as it were, of the lightest of footfalls, sounds as faint as the vanishing remembrance of voices in a dream. Seaton was all in obscurity except his face; out of that his eyes gleamed darkly, watching me.

"You'd hear, too, in time, my fine soldier," he muttered. "Come on!"

He descended the stairs, slipping his lean fingers lightly along the balusters. He turned to the right at the loop, and I followed him barefooted along a thickly-carpeted corridor. At the end stood a door ajar. And from here we very stealthily and in complete blackness ascended five narrow stairs. Seaton, with immense caution, slowly pushed open a door, and we stood together looking into a great pool of duskiness, out of which, lit by the feeble clearness of a night-light, rose a vast bed. A heap of clothes lay on the floor; beside them two slippers dozed, with noses each to each, two yards apart. Somewhere a little clock ticked huskily. There was a rather close smell of lavender and Eau de Cologne, mingled with the fragrance of ancient sachets, soap, and drugs. Yet it was a scent even more peculiarly commingled than that.

And the bed! I stared warily in; it was mounded gigantically, and it was empty.

Seaton turned a vague pale face, all shadows: "What did I say?" he muttered. "Who's—who's the fool now, I say? How are we going to get back without meeting her, I say? Answer me that! Oh, I wish to goodness you hadn't come here, Withers."

He stood visibly shivering in his skimpy gown, and could hardly speak for his teeth chattering. And very distinctly, in the hush that followed his whisper, I heard approaching a faint unhurried voluminous rustle. Seaton clutched my arm, dragged me to the right across the room to a large cupboard, and drew the door close to on us. And, presently, as with bursting lungs I peeped out into the long, low, curtained bedroom, waddled in that wonderful great head and body. I can see her now, all patched and lined with shadow, her tied-up hair (she must have had enormous quantities of it for so old a woman), her heavy lids above those flat, slow, vigilant eyes. She just passed across my ken in the vague dusk; but the bed was out of sight.

We waited on and on, listening to the clock's muffled ticking. Not the ghost of a sound rose up from the great bed. Either she lay archly listening or slept a sleep serener than an infant's. And when, it seemed, we had been hours in hiding and were cramped, chilled, and half-suffocated, we crept out on all fours, with terror knocking at our ribs, and so down the five narrow stairs and back to the little candlelit blue-and-gold bedroom.

Once there, Seaton gave in. He sat livid on a chair with closed eyes.

"Here," I said, shaking his arm, "I'm going to bed; I've had enough of this foolery; I'm going to bed." His lips quivered, but he made no answer. I poured out some water into my basin and, with that cold pictured azure eye fixed on us, bespattered Seaton's sallow face and forehead and dabbled his hair. He presently sighed and opened fishlike eyes.

"Come on!" I said. "Don't get shamming, there's a good chap. Get on my back, if you like, and I'll carry you into your bedroom."

He waved me away and stood up. So, with my candle in one hand, I took him under the arm and walked him along according to his direction down the corridor. His was a much dingier room than mine, and littered with boxes, paper, cages, and clothes. I huddled him into bed and turned to go. And suddenly, I can hardly explain it now, a kind of cold and deadly terror swept over me. I almost ran out of the room, with eyes fixed rigidly in front of me, blew out my candle, and buried my head under the bedclothes.

When I awoke, roused not by a gong, but by a long-continued tapping at my door, sunlight was raying in on cornice and bedpost, and birds were singing in the garden. I got up, ashamed of the night's folly, dressed quickly, and went downstairs. The breakfast-room was sweet with flowers and fruit and honey. Seaton's aunt was standing in the garden beside the open French window, feeding a great flutter of birds. I watched her for a moment, unseen. Her face was set in a deep reverie beneath the shadow of a big loose sun-hat. It was deeply lined, crooked, and, in a way I can't describe, fixedly vacant and strange. I coughed, and she turned at once with a prodigious smile to inquire how I had slept. And in that mysterious way by which we learn each other's secret thoughts without a sentence spoken I knew that she had followed every word and movement of the night before, and was triumphing over my affected innocence and ridiculing my friendly and too easy advances.

We returned to school, Seaton and I, lavishly laden, and by rail all the way. I made no reference to the obscure talk we had had, and resolutely refused to meet his eyes or to take up the hints he let fall. I was relieved—and yet I was sorry—to be going back, and strode on as fast as I could from the station, with Seaton almost trotting at my heels. But he insisted on buying more fruit and sweets—my share of which I accepted with a very bad grace. It was uncomfortably like a bribe; and, after all, I had no quarrel with his rum old aunt, and hadn't really believed half the stuff he had told me.

I saw as little of him as I could after that. He never referred to our visit or resumed his confidences, though in class I would sometimes catch his eye fixed on mine, full of a mute understanding, which I easily affected not to understand. He left Gummidge's, as I have said, rather abruptly, though I never heard of anything to his discredit. And I did not see him or have any news of him again till by chance we met one summer afternoon in the Strand.

He was dressed rather oddly in a coat too large for him and a bright silky tie. But we instantly recognized one another under the awning of a cheap jeweller's shop. He immediately attached himself to me and dragged me off, not too cheerfully, to lunch with him at an Italian restaurant near by. He chattered about our old school, which he remembered only with dislike and disgust; told me cold-bloodedly of the disastrous fate of one or two of the old fellows who had been among his chief tormentors; insisted on an expensive wine and the whole gamut of the foreign menu; and finally informed me, with a good deal of niggling, that he had come up to town to buy an engagement-ring.

And of course: "How is your aunt?" I inquired at last.

He seemed to have been awaiting the question. It fell like a stone into a deep pool, so many expressions flitted across his long un-English face.

"She's aged a good deal," he said softly, and broke off.

"She's been very decent," he continued presently after, and paused again. "In a way." He eyed me fleetingly. "I dare say you heard that—she —that is, that we—had lost a good deal of money."

"No," I said.

"Oh, yes!" said Seaton, and paused again.

And somehow, poor fellow, I knew in the clink and clatter of glass and voices that he had lied to me; that he did not possess, and never had possessed, a penny beyond what his aunt had squandered on his too ample allowance of pocket-money.

"And the ghosts?" I inquired quizzically.

He grew instantly solemn, and, though it may have been my fancy, slightly yellowed. But "You are making game of me, Withers," was all he said.

He asked for my address, and I rather reluctantly gave him my card.

"Look here, Withers," he said, as we stood together in the sunlight on the kerb, saying good-bye, "here I am, and—and it's all very well. I'm not perhaps as fanciful as I was. But you are practically the only friend I have on earth—except Alice. . . . And there—to make a clean breast of it, I'm not sure that my aunt cares much about my getting married. She doesn't say so, of course. You know her well enough for that." He looked sidelong at the rattling gaudy traffic.

"What I was going to say is this: Would you mind coming down? You needn't stay the night unless you please, though, of course, you know you would be awfully welcome. But I should like you to meet my— to meet Alice; and then, perhaps, you might tell me your honest opinion of—of the other too."

I vaguely demurred. He pressed me. And we parted with a half promise that I would come. He waved his ball-topped cane at me and ran off in his long jacket after a 'bus.

A letter arrived soon after, in his small weak handwriting, giving me full particulars regarding route and trains. And without the least curiosity, even perhaps with some little annoyance that chance should have thrown us together again, I accepted his invitation and arrived one hazy midday at his out-of-the-way station to find him sitting on a low seat under a clump of double hollyhocks, awaiting me.

His face looked absent and singularly listless; but he seemed, none the less, pleased to see me.

We walked up the village street, past the little dingy apothecary's and the empty forge, and, as on my first visit, skirted the house together, and, instead of entering by the front door, made our way down the green path into the garden at the back. A pale haze of cloud muffled the sun; the garden lay in a grey shimmer—its old trees, its snapdragoned, faintly glittering walls. But now there was an air of slovenliness where before all had been neat and methodical. In a patch of shallowly-dug soil stood a worn-down spade leaning against a tree. There was an old broken wheelbarrow. The roses had run to leaf and brier; the fruit trees were unpruned. The goddess of neglect brooded in secret.

"You ain't much of a gardener, Seaton," I said, with a sigh of ease.

"I think, do you know, I like it best like this," said Seaton. "We haven't any man now, of course. Can't afford it." He stood staring at his little dark square of freshly-turned earth. "And it always seems to me," he went on ruminatingly, "that, after all, we are nothing better than interlopers on the earth, disfiguring and staining wherever we go. I know it's shocking blasphemy to say so, but then it's different here, you see. We are further away."

"To tell you the truth, Seaton, I *don't* quite see," I said; "but it isn't a new philosophy, is it? Anyhow, it's a precious beastly one."

"It's only what I think," he replied, with all his odd old stubborn meekness.

We wandered on together, talking little, and still with that expression of uneasy vigilance on Seaton's face. He pulled out his watch as we stood gazing idly over the green meadows and the dark motionless bulrushes.

"I think, perhaps, it's nearly time for lunch," he said "Would you like to come in?"

We turned and walked slowly towards the house, across whose windows I confess my own eyes, too, went restlessly wandering in search of its rather disconcerting inmate. There was a pathetic look of draggledness, of want of means and care, rust and overgrowth and faded paint. Seaton's aunt, a little to my relief, did not share our meal. Seaton carved the cold meat, and dispatched a heaped-up plate by an elderly servant for his aunt's private consumption. We talked little and in half-suppressed tones, and sipped a bottle of Madeira which Seaton had rather heedfully fetched out of the great mahogany sideboard.

I played him a dull and effortless game of chess, yawning between the moves he himself made almost at haphazard, and with attention elsewhere engaged. About five o'clock came the sound of a distant ring, and

Seaton jumped up, overturning the board, and so ending a game that else might have fatuously continued to this day. He effusively excused himself, and after some little while returned with a slim, dark, rather sallow girl of about nineteen, in a white gown and hat, to whom I was presented with some little nervousness as his "dear old friend and schoolfellow."

We talked on in the pale afternoon light, still, as it seemed to me, and even in spite of a real effort to be clear and gay, in a half-suppressed, lacklustre fashion. We all seemed, if it were not my fancy, to be expectant, to be rather anxiously awaiting an arrival, the appearance of someone who all but filled our collective consciousness. Seaton talked least of all, and in a restless interjectory way, as he continually fidgeted from chair to chair. At last he proposed a stroll in the garden before the sun should have quite gone down.

Alice walked between us. Her hair and eyes were conspicuously dark against the whiteness of her gown. She carried herself not ungracefully, and yet without the least movement of her arms and body, and answered us both without turning her head. There was a curious provocative reserve in that impassive and rather long face, a half-unconscious strength of character.

And yet somehow I knew—I believe we all knew—that this walk, this discussion of their future plans, was a futility. I had nothing to base such a cynicism on, except only a vague sense of oppression, the foreboding remembrance of the inert invincible power in the background, to whom optimistic plans and love-making and youth are as chaff and thistledown. We came back, silent, in the last light. Seaton's aunt was there—under an old brass lamp. Her hair was as barbarously massed and curled as ever. Her eyelids, I think, hung even a little heavier in age over their slow-moving inscrutable pupils. We filed in softly out of the evening, and I made my bow.

"In this short interval, Mr. Withers," she remarked amiably, "you have put off youth, put on the man. Dear me, how sad it is to see the young days vanishing! Sit down. My nephew tells me you met by chance —or act of Providence, shall we call it?—and in my beloved Strand! You, I understand, are to be best man—yes, best man, or am I divulging secrets?" She surveyed Arthur and Alice with overwhelming graciousness. They sat apart on two low chairs and smiled in return.

"And Arthur—how do you think Arthur is looking?"

"I think he looks very much in need of a change," I said deliberately.

"A change! Indeed?" She all but shut her eyes at me and with an exaggerated sentimentality shook her head. "My dear Mr. Withers! Are we not *all* in need of a change in this fleeting, fleeting world?" She mused over the remark like a connoisseur. "And you," she continued, turning abruptly to Alice, "I hope you pointed out to Mr. Withers all my pretty bits?"

"We walked round the garden," said Alice, looking out of the window. "It's a very beautiful evening."

"*Is* it?" said the old lady, starting up violently. "Then on this very beautiful evening we will go in to supper. Mr. Withers, your arm; Arthur, bring your bride."

I can scarcely describe with what curious ruminations I led the way into the faded, heavy-aired dining-room, with this indefinable old creature leaning weightily on my arm—the large flat bracelet on the yellow-laced wrist. She fumed a little, breathed rather heavily, as if with an effort of mind rather than of body; for she had grown much stouter and yet little more proportionate. And to talk into that great white face, so close to mine, was a queer experience in the dim light of the corridor, and even in the twinkling crystal of the candles. She was naïve—appallingly naïve; she was sudden and superficial; she was even arch; and all these in the brief, rather puffy passage from one room to the other, with these two tongue-tied children bringing up the rear. The meal was tremendous. I have never seen such a monstrous salad. But the dishes were greasy and over-spiced, and were indifferently cooked. One thing only was quite unchanged—my hostess's appetite was as Gargantuan as ever. The old solid candelabra that lighted us stood before her high-backed chair. Seaton sat a little removed, with his plate almost in darkness.

And throughout this prodigious meal his aunt talked, mainly to me, mainly at Seaton, with an occasional satirical courtesy to Alice and muttered explosions of directions to the servant. She had aged, and yet, if it be not nonsense to say so, seemed no older. I suppose to the Pyramids a decade is but as the rustling down of a handful of dust. And she reminded me of some such unshakable prehistoricism. She certainly was an amazing talker—racy, extravagant, with a delivery that was perfectly overwhelming. As for Seaton—her flashes of silence were for him. On her enormous volubility would suddenly fall a hush: acid sarcasm would be left implied; and she would sit softly moving her great head, with eyes fixed full in a dreamy smile; but with her whole attention, one could see, slowly, joyously absorbing his mute discomfiture.

She confided in us her views on a theme vaguely occupying at the moment, I suppose, all our minds. "We have barbarous institutions, and so must put up, I suppose, with a never-ending procession of fools—of fools *ad infinitum*. Marriage, Mr. Withers, was instituted in the privacy of a garden; *sub rosa*, as it were. Civilization flaunts it in the glare of day. The dull marry the poor; the rich the effete; and so our New Jerusalem is peopled with naturals, plain and coloured, at either end. I detest folly; I detest still more (if I must be frank, dear Arthur) mere cleverness. Mankind has simply become a tailless host of uninstinctive animals. We should never have taken to Evolution, Mr. Withers. 'Natural Selection!'—little gods and fishes!—the deaf for the dumb. We should have used our brains —intellectual pride, the ecclesiastics call it. And by brains I mean—what do I mean, Alice?—I mean, my dear child," and she laid two gross fingers on Alice's narrow sleeve, "I mean courage. Consider it, Arthur. I read that the scientific world is once more beginning to be afraid of spiritual agencies. Spiritual agencies that tap, and actually float, bless their hearts! I think just one more of those mulberries—thank you.

"They talk about 'blind Love,'" she ran inconsequently on as she helped herself, with eyes roving on the dish, "but why blind? I think, do you know, from weeping over its rickets. After all, it is we plain women that triumph, Mr. Withers, beyond the mockery of time. Alice, now! Fleeting, fleeting is youth, my child. What's that you were confiding to your plate, Arthur? Satirical boy. He laughs at his old aunt: nay, but thou didst laugh. He detests all sentiment. He whispers the most acid asides. Come, my love, we will leave these cynics; we will go and commiserate with each other on our sex. The choice of two evils, Mr. Smithers!" I opened the door, and she swept out as if borne on a torrent of unintelligible indignation; and Arthur and I were left in the clear four-flamed light alone.

For a while we sat in silence. He shook his head at my cigarette-case, and I lit a cigarette. Presently he fidgeted in his chair and poked his head forward into the light. He paused to rise and shut again the shut door.

"How long will you be?" he said, standing by the table.

I laughed.

"Oh, it's not that!" he said, in some confusion. "Of course, I like to be with her. But it's not that. The truth is, Withers, I don't care about leaving her too long with my aunt."

I hesitated. He looked at me questioningly.

"Look here, Seaton," I said, "you know well enough that I don't want to interfere in your affairs, or to offer advice where it is not wanted. But don't you think perhaps you may not treat your aunt quite in the right way? As one gets old, you know, a little give and take. I have an old godmother, or something. She talks, too. . . . A little allowance: it does no harm. But hang it all, I'm no talker."

He sat down with his hands in his pockets and still with his eyes fixed almost incredulously on mine. "How?" he said.

"Well, my dear fellow, if I'm any judge—mind, I don't say that I am—but I can't help thinking she thinks you don't care for her; and perhaps takes your silence for—for bad temper. She has been very decent to you, hasn't she?"

" 'Decent'? My God!" said Seaton.

I smoked on in silence; but he continued to look at me with that peculiar concentration I remembered of old.

"I don't think, perhaps, Withers," he began presently, "I don't think you quite understand. Perhaps you are not quite our kind. You always did, just like the other fellows, guy me at school. You laughed at me that night you came to stay here—about the voices and all that. But I don't mind being laughed at—because I know."

"Know what?" It was the same old system of dull question and evasive answer.

"I mean I know that what we see and hear is only the smallest fraction of what is. I know she lives quite out of this. She *talks* to you; but it's all make-believe. It's all a 'parlour game.' She's not really with you; only pitting her outside wits against yours and enjoying the fooling. She's living on inside, on what you're rotten without. That's what it is—a cannibal feast. She's a spider. It doesn't much matter what you call it. It means the same kind of thing. I tell you, Withers, she hates me; and you can scarcely dream what that hatred means. I used to think I had an inkling of the reason. It's oceans deeper than that. It just lies behind: herself against myself. Why, after all, how much do we really understand of anything? We don't even know our own histories, and not a tenth, not a tenth of the reasons. What has life been to me?—nothing but a trap. And when one is set free, it only begins again. I thought you might understand; but you are on a different level: that's all."

"What on earth are you talking about?" I said contemptuously, in spite of myself.

"I mean what I say," he said gutturally. "All this outside's only make-believe—but there! what's the good of talking? So far as this is concerned I'm as good as done. You wait."

Seaton blew out three of the candles and, leaving the vacant room in semi-darkness, we groped our way along the corridor to the drawing-room. There a full moon stood shining in at the long garden windows. Alice sat stooping at the door, with her hands clasped, looking out, alone.

"Where is she?" Seaton asked in a low tone.

Alice looked up; their eyes met in a kind of instantaneous under-standing, and the door immediately afterwards opened behind us.

"*Such* a moon!" said a voice that, once heard, remained unforgetta-bly on the ear. "A night for lovers, Mr. Withers, if ever there was one. Get a shawl, my dear Arthur, and take Alice for a little promenade. I dare say we old cronies will manage to keep awake. Hasten, hasten, Romeo! My poor, poor Alice, how laggard a lover!"

Seaton returned with a shawl. They drifted out into the moonlight. My companion gazed after them till they were out of hearing, turned to me gravely, and suddenly twisted her white face into such a convulsion of contemptuous amusement that I could only stare blankly in reply.

"Dear innocent children!" she said, with inimitable unctuousness. "Well, well, Mr. Withers, we poor seasoned old creatures must move with the times. Do you sing?"

I scouted the idea.

"Then you must listen to my playing. Chess"—she clasped her fore-head with both cramped hands—"chess is now completely beyond my poor wits."

She sat down at the piano and ran her fingers in a flourish over the keys. "What shall it be? How shall we capture them, those passionate hearts? That first fine careless rapture? Poetry itself." She gazed softly into the garden a moment, and presently, with a shake of her body, began to play the opening bars of Beethoven's "Moonlight" Sonata. The piano was old and woolly. She played without music. The lamplight was rather dim. The moonbeams from the window lay across the keys. Her head was in shadow. And whether it was simply due to her personality or to some really occult skill in her playing I cannot say: I only know that she gravely and deliberately set herself to satirize the beautiful music. It brooded on the air, disillusioned, charged with mockery and bitterness. I stood at the window; far down the path I could see the white figure glimmering in that pool of colourless light. A few faint stars shone, and still that amazing woman behind me dragged out of the unwilling keys her wonderful grotesquerie of youth and love and beauty. It came to an end. I knew the player was watching me. "Please, please, go on!" I murmured, without turning. "Please go on playing, Miss Seaton."

No answer was returned to my rather fluttering sarcasm, but I knew in some indefinite way that I was being acutely scrutinized, when suddenly there followed a procession of quiet, plaintive chords which broke at last softly into the hymn, *A Few More Years Shall Roll*.

I confess it held me spellbound. There is a wistful, strained, plangent pathos in the tune; but beneath those masterly old hands it cried softly and bitterly the solitude and desperate estrangement of the world. Arthur and his lady-love vanished from my thoughts. No one could put into a rather hackneyed old hymn-tune such an appeal who had never known the meaning of the words. Their meaning, anyhow, isn't commonplace.

I turned very cautiously and glanced at the musician. She was leaning forward a little over the keys, so that at the approach of my cautious glance she had but to turn her face into the thin flood of moonlight for every feature to become distinctly visible. And so, with the tune abruptly terminated, we steadfastly regarded one another, and she broke into a chuckle of laughter.

"Not quite so seasoned as I supposed, Mr. Withers. I see you are a real lover of music. To me it is too painful. It evokes too much thought. . . ."

I could scarcely see her little glittering eyes under their penthouse lids.

"And now," she broke off crisply, "tell me, as a man of the world, what do you think of my new niece?"

I was not a man of the world, nor was I much flattered in my stiff and dullish way of looking at things by being called one; and I could answer her without the least hesitation.

"I don't think, Miss Seaton, I'm much of a judge of character. She's very charming."

"A brunette?"

"I think I prefer dark women."

"And why? Consider, Mr. Withers; dark hair, dark eyes, dark cloud, dark night, dark vision, dark death, dark grave, dark DARK!"

Perhaps the climax would have rather thrilled Seaton, but I was too thick-skinned. "I don't know much about all that," I answered rather pompously. "Broad daylight's difficult enough for most of us."

"Ah," she said, with a sly inward burst of satirical laughter.

"And I suppose," I went on, perhaps a little nettled, "it isn't the actual darkness one admires, it's the contrast of the skin, and the colour of the eyes, and—and their shining. Just as," I went blundering on, too late to turn back, "just as you only see the stars in the dark. It would be a long day without any evening. As for death and the grave, I don't suppose we shall much notice that." Arthur and his sweetheart were slowly returning along the dewy path. "I believe in making the best of things."

"How very interesting!" came the smooth answer. "I see you are a philosopher, Mr. Withers. H'm! 'As for death and the grave, I don't suppose we shall much notice that.' Very interesting. . . . And I'm sure," she added in a particularly suave voice, "I profoundly hope so." She rose slowly from her stool. "You will take pity on me again, I hope. You and I would get on famously—kindred spirits—elective affinities. And, of course, now that my nephew's going to leave me, now that his affections are centred on another, I shall be a very lonely old woman. . . . Shall I not, Arthur?"

Seaton blinked stupidly. "I didn't hear what you said, aunt."

"I was telling our old friend, Arthur, that when you are gone I shall be a very lonely old woman."

"Oh, I don't think so," he said in a strange voice.

"He means, Mr. Withers, he means, my dear child," she said, sweeping her eyes over Alice, "he means that I shall have memory for company —heavenly memory—the ghosts of other days. Sentimental boy! And did you enjoy our music, Alice? Did I really stir that youthful heart? . . . Oh, oh, oh," continued the horrible old creature, "you billers and cooers, I have been listening to such flatteries, such confessions! Beware, beware, Arthur, there's many a slip." She rolled her little eyes at me, she shrugged her shoulders at Alice, and gazed an instant stonily into her nephew's face.

I held out my hand. "Good-night, good-night!" she cried. "He that fights and runs away. Ah, good-night, Mr. Withers; come again soon!" She thrust out her cheek at Alice, and we all three filed slowly out of the room.

Black shadow darkened the porch and half the spreading sycamore. We walked without speaking up the dusty village street. Here and there a crimson window glowed. At the fork of the high-road I said good-bye. But I had taken hardly more than a dozen paces when a sudden impulse seized me.

"Seaton!" I called.

He turned in the moonlight.

"You have my address; if by any chance, you know, you should care to spend a week or two in town between this and the—the Day, we should be delighted to see you."

"Thank you, Withers, thank you," he said in a low voice.

"I dare say"—I waved my stick gallantly to Alice—"I dare say you will be doing some shopping: we could all meet," I added, laughing.

"Thank you, thank you, Withers—immensely," he repeated.
And so we parted.

But they were out of the jog-trot of my prosaic life. And being of a
stolid and incurious nature, I left Seaton and his marriage, and even his
aunt, to themselves in my memory, and scarcely gave a thought to them
until one day I was walking up the Strand again, and passed the flashing
gloaming of the covered-in jeweller's shop where I had accidentally encountered my old schoolfellow in the summer. It was one of those still
close autumnal days after a rainy night. I cannot say why, but a vivid
recollection returned to my mind of our meeting and of how suppressed
Seaton had seemed, and of how vainly he had endeavoured to appear
assured and eager. He must be married by now, and had doubtless returned from his honeymoon. And I had clean forgotten my manners, had
sent not a word of congratulation, nor—as I might very well have done,
and as I knew he would have been immensely pleased at my doing—the
ghost of a wedding present.

On the other hand, I pleaded with myself, I had had no invitation. I
paused at the corner of Trafalgar Square, and at the bidding of one of
those caprices that seize occasionally on even an unimaginative mind, I
suddenly ran after a green 'bus that was passing, and found myself bound
on a visit I had not in the least foreseen.

The colours of autumn were over the village when I arrived. A
beautiful late afternoon sunlight bathed thatch and meadow. But it was
close and hot. A child, two dogs, a very old woman with a heavy basket I
encountered. One or two incurious tradesmen looked idly up as I passed
by. It was all so rural and so still, my whimsical impulse had so much
flagged, that for a while I hesitated to venture under the shadow of the
sycamore tree to inquire after the happy pair. I deliberately passed by the
faint-blue gates and continued my walk under the high green and tufted
wall. Hollyhocks had attained their topmost bud and seeded in the little
cottage gardens beyond; the Michaelmas daisies were in flower; a sweet
warm aromatic smell of fading leaves was in the air. Beyond the cottages
lay a field where cattle were grazing, and beyond that I came to a little
churchyard. Then the road wound on, pathless and houseless, among
gorse and bracken. I turned impatiently and walked quickly back to the
house and rang the bell.

The rather colourless elderly woman who answered my inquiry informed me that Miss Seaton was at home, as if only taciturnity forbade
her adding, "But she doesn't want to see *you*."

"Might I, do you think, have Mr. Arthur's address?" I said.

She looked at me with quiet astonishment, as if waiting for an explanation. Not the faintest of smiles came into her thin face.

"I will tell Miss Seaton," she said after a pause. "Please walk in."

She showed me into the dingy undusted drawing-room, filled with
evening sunshine and with the green-dyed light that penetrated the leaves

overhanging the long French windows. I sat down and waited on and on, occasionally aware of a creaking footfall overhead. At last the door opened a little, and the great face I had once known peered round at me. For it was enormously changed; mainly, I think, because the old eyes had rather suddenly failed, and so a kind of stillness and darkness lay over its calm and wrinkled pallor.

"Who is it?" she asked.

I explained myself and told her the occasion of my visit.

She came in and shut the door carefully after her and, though the fumbling was scarcely perceptible, groped her way to a chair. She had on an old dressing-gown, like a cassock, of a patterned cinnamon colour.

"What is it you want?" she said, seating herself and lifting her blank face to mine.

"Might I just have Arthur's address?" I said deferentially. "I am so sorry to have disturbed you."

"H'm. You have come to see my nephew?"

"Not necessarily to see him, only to hear how he is, and, of course, Mrs. Seaton, too. I am afraid my silence must have appeared . . ."

"He hasn't noticed your silence," croaked the old voice out of the great mask; "besides, there isn't any Mrs. Seaton."

"Ah, then," I answered, after a momentary pause, "I have not seemed so black as I painted myself! And how is Miss Outram?"

"She's gone into Yorkshire," answered Seaton's aunt.

"And Arthur too?"

She did not reply, but simply sat blinking at me with lifted chin, as if listening, but certainly not for what I might have to say. I began to feel rather at a loss.

"You were no close friend of my nephew's, Mr. Smithers?" she said presently.

"No," I answered, welcoming the cue, "and yet, do you know, Miss Seaton, he is one of the very few of my old schoolfellows I have come across in the last few years, and I suppose as one gets older one begins to value old associations . . ." My voice seemed to trail off into a vacuum. "I thought Miss Outram," I hastily began again, "a particularly charming girl. I hope they are both quite well."

Still the old face solemnly blinked at me in silence.

"You must find it very lonely, Miss Seaton, with Arthur away?"

"I was never lonely in my life," she said sourly. "I don't look to flesh and blood for my company. When you've got to be my age, Mr. Smithers (which God forbid), you'll find life a very different affair from what you seem to think it is now. You won't seek company then, I'll be bound. It's thrust on you." Her face edged round into the clear green light, and her eyes groped, as it were, over my vacant, disconcerted face. "I dare say, now," she said, composing her mouth, "I dare say my nephew told you a good many tarradiddles in his time. Oh, yes, a good many, eh? He was always a liar. What, now, did he say of me? Tell me, now." She leant forward as far as she could, trembling, with an ingratiating smile.

"I think he is rather superstitious," I said coldly, "but, honestly, I have a very poor memory, Miss Seaton."

"Why?" she said. "*I* haven't."

"The engagement hasn't been broken off, I hope."

"Well, between you and me," she said, shrinking up and with an immensely confidential grimace, "it has."

"I'm sure I'm very sorry to hear it. And where is Arthur?"

"Eh?"

"Where is Arthur?"

We faced each other mutely among the dead old bygone furniture. Past all my scrutiny was that large, flat, grey, cryptic countenance. And then, suddenly, our eyes for the first time really met. In some indescribable way out of that thick-lidded obscurity a far small something stooped and looked out at me for a mere instant of time that seemed of almost intolerable protraction. Involuntarily I blinked and shook my head. She muttered something with great rapidity, but quite inarticulately; rose and hobbled to the door. I thought I heard, mingled in broken mutterings, something about tea.

"Please, please, don't trouble," I began, but could say no more, for the door was already shut between us. I stood and looked out on the long-neglected garden. I could just see the bright greenness of Seaton's old tadpole pond. I wandered about the room. Dusk began to gather, the last birds in that dense shadowiness of trees had ceased to sing. And not a sound was to be heard in the house. I waited on and on, vainly speculating. I even attempted to ring the bell; but the wire was broken, and only jangled loosely at my efforts.

I hesitated, unwilling to call or to venture out, and yet more unwilling to linger on, waiting for a tea that promised to be an exceedingly comfortless supper. And as darkness drew down, a feeling of the utmost unease and disquietude came over me. All my talks with Seaton returned on me with a suddenly enriched meaning. I recalled again his face as we had stood hanging over the staircase, listening in the small hours to the inexplicable stirrings of the night. There were no candles in the room; every minute the autumnal darkness deepened. I cautiously opened the door and listened, and with some little dismay withdrew, for I was uncertain of my way out. I even tried the garden, but was confronted under a veritable thicket of foliage by a padlocked gate. It would be a little too ignominious to be caught scaling a friend's garden fence!

Cautiously returning into the still and musty drawing-room, I took out my watch, and gave the incredible old woman ten minutes in which to reappear. And when that tedious ten minutes had ticked by I could scarcely distinguish its hands. I determined to wait no longer, drew open the door, and, trusting to my sense of direction, groped my way through the corridor that I vaguely remembered led to the front of the house.

I mounted three or four stairs and, lifting a heavy curtain, found myself facing the starry fanlight of the porch. From here I glanced into the gloom of the dining-room. My fingers were on the latch of the outer door when I heard a faint stirring in the darkness above the hall. I looked up and became conscious of, rather than saw, the huddled old figure looking down on me.

There was an immense hushed pause. Then, "Arthur, Arthur," whispered an inexpressibly peevish, rasping voice, "is that you? Is that you, Arthur?"

I can scarcely say why, but the question horribly startled me. No conceivable answer occurred to me. With head craned back, hand clenched on my umbrella, I continued to stare up into the gloom, in this fatuous confrontation.

"Oh, oh," the voice croaked. "It is you, is it? *That* disgusting man! . . . Go away out. Go away out."

Hesitating no longer, I caught open the door and, slamming it behind me, ran out into the garden, under the gigantic old sycamore, and so out at the open gate.

I found myself half up the village street before I stopped running. The local butcher was sitting in his shop reading a piece of newspaper by the light of a small oil-lamp. I crossed the road and inquired the way to the station. And after he had with minute and needless care directed me, I asked casually if Mr. Arthur Seaton still lived with his aunt at the big house just beyond the village. He poked his head in at the little parlour door.

"Here's a gentleman inquiring after young Mr. Seaton, Millie," he said. "He's dead, ain't he?"

"Why, yes, bless you," replied a cheerful voice from within. "Dead and buried these three months or more—young Mr. Seaton. And just before he was to be married, don't you remember, Bob?"

I saw a fair young woman's face peer over the muslin of the little door at me.

"Thank you," I replied, "then I go straight on?"

"That's it, sir; past the pond, bear up the hill a bit to the left, and then there's the station lights before your eyes."

We looked intelligently into each other's faces in the beam of the smoky lamp. But not one of the many questions in my mind could I put into words.

And again I paused irresolutely a few paces further on. It was not, I fancy, merely a foolish apprehension of what the rawboned butcher might "think" that prevented my going back to see if I could find Seaton's grave in the benighted churchyard. There was precious little use in pottering about in the muddy dark merely to discover where he was buried. And yet I felt a little uneasy. My rather horrible thought was that, so far as I was concerned—one of his extremely few friends—he had never been much better than "buried" in my mind.

E. M. Forster

THE CELESTIAL OMNIBUS

I

THE BOY WHO RESIDED at Agathox Lodge, 28, Buckingham Park Road, Surbiton, had often been puzzled by the old sign-post that stood almost opposite. He asked his mother about it, and she replied that it was a joke, and not a very nice one, which had been made many years back by some naughty young men, and that the police ought to remove it. For there were two strange things about this sign-post: firstly, it pointed up a blank alley, and, secondly, it had painted on it, in faded characters, the words, "To Heaven."

"What kind of young men were they?" he asked.

"I think your father told me that one of them wrote verses, and was expelled from the University and came to grief in other ways. Still, it was a long time ago. You must ask your father about it. He will say the same as I do, that it was put up as a joke."

"So it doesn't mean anything at all?"

She sent him up-stairs to put on his best things, for the Bonses were coming to tea, and he was to hand the cake-stand.

It struck him, as he wrenched on his tightening trousers, that he might do worse than ask Mr. Bons about the sign-post. His father, though very kind, always laughed at him—shrieked with laughter whenever he or any other child asked a question or spoke. But Mr. Bons was serious as well as kind. He had a beautiful house and lent one books, he was a churchwarden, and a candidate for the County Council; he had donated to the Free Library enormously, he presided over the Literary Society,

From *The Celestial Omnibus*, 1923.

and had Members of Parliament to stop with him—in short, he was probably the wisest person alive.

Yet even Mr. Bons could only say that the sign-post was a joke—the joke of a person named Shelley.

"Of course!" cried the mother; "I told you so, dear. That was the name."

"Had you never heard of Shelley?" asked Mr. Bons.

"No," said the boy, and hung his head.

"But is there no Shelley in the house?"

"Why, yes!" exclaimed the lady, in much agitation. "Dear Mr. Bons, we aren't such Philistines as that. Two at the least. One a wedding present, and the other, smaller print, in one of the spare rooms."

"I believe we have seven Shelleys," said Mr. Bons, with a slow smile. Then he brushed the cake crumbs off his stomach, and, together with his daughter, rose to go.

The boy, obeying a wink from his mother, saw them all the way to the garden gate, and when they had gone he did not at once return to the house, but gazed for a little up and down Buckingham Park Road.

His parents lived at the right end of it. After No. 39 the quality of the houses dropped very suddenly, and 64 had not even a separate servants' entrance. But at the present moment the whole road looked rather pretty, for the sun had just set in splendour, and the inequalities of rent were drowned in a saffron afterglow. Small birds twittered, and the breadwinners' train shrieked musically down through the cutting—that wonderful cutting which has drawn to itself the whole beauty out of Surbiton, and clad itself, like any Alpine valley, with the glory of the fir and the silver birch and the primrose. It was this cutting that had first stirred desires within the boy—desires for something just a little different, he knew not what, desires that would return whenever things were sunlit, as they were this evening, running up and down inside him, up and down, up and down, till he would feel quite unusual all over, and as likely as not would want to cry. This evening he was even sillier, for he slipped across the road towards the sign-post and began to run up the blank alley.

The alley runs between high walls—the walls of the gardens of "Ivanhoe" and "Belle Vista" respectively. It smells a little all the way, and is scarcely twenty yards long, including the turn at the end. So not unnaturally the boy soon came to a standstill. "I'd like to kick that Shelley," he exclaimed, and glanced idly at a piece of paper which was pasted on the wall. Rather an odd piece of paper, and he read it carefully before he turned back. This is what he read:

S. AND C. R. C. C.

Alteration in Service.

Owing to lack of patronage the Company are regretfully compelled to suspend the hourly service, and to retain only the

Sunrise and Sunset Omnibuses,

which will run as usual. It is to be hoped that the public will pa-
tronize an arrangement which is intended for their convenience.
As an extra inducement, the Company will, for the first time, now
issue

Return Tickets !

(available one day only), which may be obtained of the driver.
Passengers are again reminded that *no tickets are issued at the other
end*, and that no complaints in this connection will receive consideration from the Company. Nor will the Company be responsible
for any negligence or stupidity on the part of Passengers, nor for
Hailstorms, Lightning, Loss of Tickets, nor for any Act of God.

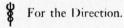 For the Direction.

Now he had never seen this notice before, nor could he imagine
where the omnibus went to. S. of course was for Surbiton, and R.C.C.
meant Road Car Company. But what was the meaning of the other C.?
Coombe and Malden, perhaps, or possibly "City." Yet it could not hope
to compete with the South-Western. The whole thing, the boy reflected,
was run on hopelessly unbusiness-like lines. Why no tickets from the
other end? And what an hour to start! Then he realized that unless the
notice was a hoax, an omnibus must have been starting just as he was
wishing the Bonses good-bye. He peered at the ground through the
gathering dusk, and there he saw what might or might not be the marks
of wheels. Yet nothing had come out of the alley. And he had never seen
an omnibus at any time in the Buckingham Park Road. No: it must be a
hoax, like the sign-post, like the fairy tales, like the dreams upon which
he would wake suddenly in the night. And with a sigh he stepped from
the alley—right into the arms of his father.

Oh, how his father laughed! "Poor, poor Popsey!" he cried. "Diddums! Diddums! Diddums think he'd walky-palky up to Evvink!" And
his mother, also convulsed with laughter, appeared on the steps of Agathox Lodge. "Don't, Bob!" she gasped. "Don't be so naughty! Oh, you'll
kill me! Oh, leave the boy alone!"

But all the evening the joke was kept up. The father implored to be
taken too. Was it a very tiring walk? Need one wipe one's shoes on the
door-mat? And the boy went to bed feeling faint and sore, and thankful
for only one thing—that he had not said a word about the omnibus. It
was a hoax, yet through his dreams it grew more and more real, and the
streets of Surbiton, through which he saw it driving, seemed instead to
become hoaxes and shadows. And very early in the morning he woke
with a cry, for he had had a glimpse of its destination.

He struck a match, and its light fell not only on his watch but also on
his calendar, so that he knew it to be half-an-hour to sunrise. It was pitch
dark, for the fog had come down from London in the night, and all
Surbiton was wrapped in its embraces. Yet he sprang out and dressed

himself, for he was determined to settle once for all which was real: the omnibus or the streets. "I shall be a fool one way or the other," he thought, "until I know." Soon he was shivering in the road under the gas lamp that guarded the entrance to the alley.

To enter the alley itself required some courage. Not only was it horribly dark, but he now realized that it was an impossible terminus for an omnibus. If it had not been for a policeman, whom he heard approaching through the fog, he would never have made the attempt. The next moment he had made the attempt and failed. Nothing. Nothing but a blank alley and a very silly boy gaping at its dirty floor. It *was* a hoax. "I'll tell papa and mamma," he decided. "I deserve it. I deserve that they should know. I am too silly to be alive." And he went back to the gate of Agathox Lodge.

There he remembered that his watch was fast. The sun was not risen; it would not rise for two minutes. "Give the bus every chance," he thought cynically, and returned into the alley.

But the omnibus was there.

II

IT HAD TWO HORSES, whose sides were still smoking from their journey, and its two great lamps shone through the fog against the alley's walls, changing their cobwebs and moss into tissues of fairyland. The driver was huddled up in a cape. He faced the blank wall, and how he had managed to drive in so neatly and so silently was one of the many things that the boy never discovered. Nor could he imagine how ever he would drive out.

"Please," his voice quavered through the foul brown air, "Please, is that an omnibus?"

"Omnibus est," said the driver, without turning round. There was a moment's silence. The policeman passed, coughing, by the entrance of the alley. The boy crouched in the shadow, for he did not want to be found out. He was pretty sure, too, that it was a Pirate; nothing else, he reasoned, would go from such odd places and at such odd hours.

"About when do you start?" He tried to sound nonchalant.

"At sunrise."

"How far do you go?"

"The whole way."

"And can I have a return ticket which will bring me all the way back?"

"You can."

"Do you know, I half think I'll come." The driver made no answer. The sun must have risen, for he unhitched the brake. And scarcely had the boy jumped in before the omnibus was off.

How? Did it turn? There was no room. Did it go forward? There was a blank wall. Yet it was moving—moving at a stately pace through the fog, which had turned from brown to yellow. The thought of warm bed and warmer breakfast made the boy feel faint. He wished he had not come. His parents would not have approved. He would have gone back to them if the weather had not made it impossible. The solitude was terrible; he was the only passenger. And the omnibus, though well-built, was cold and somewhat musty. He drew his coat round him, and in so doing chanced to feel his pocket. It was empty. He had forgotten his purse.

"Stop!" he shouted. "Stop!" And then, being of a polite disposition, he glanced up at the painted notice-board so that he might call the driver by name. "Mr. Browne! stop; oh, do please stop!"

Mr. Browne did not stop, but he opened a little window and looked in at the boy. His face was a surprise, so kind it was and modest.

"Mr. Browne, I've left my purse behind. I've not got a penny. I can't pay for the ticket. Will you take my watch, please? I am in the most awful hole."

"Tickets on this line," said the driver, "whether single or return, can be purchased by coinage from no terrene mint. And a chronometer, though it had solaced the vigils of Charlemagne, or measured the slumbers of Laura, can acquire by no mutation the double-cake that charms the fangless Cerberus of Heaven!" So saying, he handed in the necessary ticket, and, while the boy said "Thank you," continued: "Titular pretensions, I know it well, are vanity. Yet they merit no censure when uttered on a laughing lip, and in an homonymous world are in some sort useful, since they do serve to distinguish one Jack from his fellow. Remember me, therefore, as Sir Thomas Browne."

"Are you a Sir? Oh, sorry!" He had heard of these gentlemen drivers. "It *is* good of you about the ticket. But if you go on at this rate, however does your bus pay?"

"It does not pay. It was not intended to pay. Many are the faults of my equipage; it is compounded too curiously of foreign woods; its cushions tickle erudition rather than promote repose; and my horses are nourished not on the evergreen pastures of the moment, but on the dried bents and clovers of Latinity. But that it pays!—that error at all events was never intended and never attained."

"Sorry again," said the boy rather hopelessly. Sir Thomas looked sad, fearing that, even for a moment, he had been the cause of sadness. He invited the boy to come up and sit beside him on the box, and together they journeyed on through the fog, which was now changing from yellow to white. There were no houses by the road; so it must be either Putney Heath or Wimbledon Common.

"Have you been a driver always?"

"I was a physician once."

"But why did you stop? Weren't you good?"

"As a healer of bodies I had scant success, and several score of my patients preceded me. But as a healer of the spirit I have succeeded beyond my hopes and my deserts. For though my draughts were not better nor subtler than those of other men, yet, by reason of the cunning goblets wherein I offered them, the queasy soul was ofttimes tempted to sip and be refreshed."

"The queasy soul," he murmured; "if the sun sets with trees in front of it, and you suddenly come strange all over, is that a queasy soul?"

"Have you felt that?"

"Why yes."

After a pause he told the boy a little, a very little, about the journey's end. But they did not chatter much, for the boy, when he liked a person, would as soon sit silent in his company as speak, and this, he discovered, was also the mind of Sir Thomas Browne and of many others with whom he was to be acquainted. He heard, however, about the young man Shelley, who was now quite a famous person, with a carriage of his own, and about some of the other drivers who are in the service of the Company. Meanwhile the light grew stronger, though the fog did not disperse. It was now more like mist than fog, and at times would travel quickly across them, as if it was part of a cloud. They had been ascending, too, in a most puzzling way; for over two hours the horses had been pulling against the collar, and even if it were Richmond Hill they ought to have been at the top long ago. Perhaps it was Epsom, or even the North Downs; yet the air seemed keener than that which blows on either. And as to the name of their destination, Sir Thomas Browne was silent.

Crash!

"Thunder, by Jove!" said the boy, "and not so far off either. Listen to the echoes! It's more like mountains."

He thought, not very vividly, of his father and mother. He saw them sitting down to sausages and listening to the storm. He saw his own empty place. Then there would be questions, alarms, theories, jokes, consolations. They would expect him back at lunch. To lunch he would not come, nor to tea, but he would be in for dinner, and so his day's truancy would be over. If he had had his purse he would have bought them presents—not that he should have known what to get them.

Crash!

The peal and the lightning came together. The cloud quivered as if it were alive, and torn streamers of mist rushed past. "Are you afraid?" asked Sir Thomas Browne.

"What is there to be afraid of? Is it much farther?"

The horses of the omnibus stopped just as a ball of fire burst up and exploded with a ringing noise that was deafening but clear, like the noise of a blacksmith's forge. All the cloud was shattered.

"Oh, listen, Sir Thomas Browne! No, I mean look; we shall get a view at last. No, I mean listen; that sounds like a rainbow!"

The noise had died into the faintest murmur, beneath which another murmur grew, spreading stealthily, steadily, in a curve that widened but did not vary. And in widening curves a rainbow was spreading from the horses' feet into the dissolving mists.

"But how beautiful! What colours! Where will it stop? It is more like the rainbows you can tread on. More like dreams."

The colour and the sound grew together. The rainbow spanned an enormous gulf. Clouds rushed under it and were pierced by it, and still it grew, reaching forward, conquering the darkness, until it touched something that seemed more solid than a cloud.

The boy stood up. "What is that out there?" he called. "What does it rest on, out at that other end?"

In the morning sunshine a precipice shone forth beyond the gulf. A precipice—or was it a castle? The horses moved. They set their feet upon the rainbow.

"Oh, look!" the boy shouted. "Oh, listen! Those caves—or are they gateways? Oh, look between those cliffs at those ledges. I see people! I see trees!"

"Look also below," whispered Sir Thomas. "Neglect not the diviner Acheron."

The boy looked below, past the flames of the rainbow that licked against their wheels. The gulf also had cleared, and in its depths there flowed an everlasting river. One sunbeam entered and struck a green pool, and as they passed over he saw three maidens rise to the surface of the pool, singing, and playing with something that glistened like a ring.

"You down in the water—" he called.

They answered, "You up on the bridge—" There was a burst of music. "You up on the bridge, good luck to you. Truth in the depth, truth on the height."

"You down in the water, what are you doing?"

Sir Thomas Browne replied: "They sport in the mancipiary possession of their gold"; and the omnibus arrived.

III

THE BOY WAS IN DISGRACE. He sat locked up in the nursery of Agathox Lodge, learning poetry for a punishment. His father had said, "My boy! I can pardon anything but untruthfulness," and had caned him, saying at each stroke, "There is *no* omnibus, *no* driver, *no* bridge, *no* mountain; you are a *truant*, a *gutter snipe*, a *liar*." His father could be very stern at times. His mother had begged him to say he was sorry. But he could not say that. It was the greatest day of his life, in spite of the caning and the poetry at the end of it.

He had returned punctually at sunset—driven not by Sir Thomas Browne, but by a maiden lady who was full of quiet fun. They had talked of omnibuses and also of barouche landaus. How far away her gentle voice seemed now! Yet it was scarcely three hours since he had left her up the alley.

His mother called through the door. "Dear, you are to come down and to bring your poetry with you."

He came down, and found that Mr. Bons was in the smoking-room with his father. It had been a dinner party.

"Here is the great traveller!" said his father grimly. "Here is the young gentleman who drives in an omnibus over rainbows, while young ladies sing to him." Pleased with his wit, he laughed.

"After all," said Mr. Bons, smiling, "there is something a little like it in Wagner. It is odd how, in quite illiterate minds, you will find glimmers of Artistic Truth. The case interests me. Let me plead for the culprit. We have all romanced in our time, haven't we?"

"Hear how kind Mr. Bons is," said his mother, while his father said, "Very well. Let him say his Poem, and that will do. He is going away to my sister on Tuesday, and *she* will cure him of this alley-slopering." (Laughter.) "Say your Poem."

The boy began. " 'Standing aloof in giant ignorance.' "

His father laughed again—roared. "One for you, my son! 'Standing aloof in giant ignorance!' I never knew these poets talked sense. Just describes you. Here, Bons, you go in for poetry. Put him through it, will you, while I fetch up the whisky?"

"Yes, give me the Keats," said Mr. Bons. "Let him say his Keats to me."

So for a few moments the wise man and the ignorant boy were left alone in the smoking-room.

" 'Standing aloof in giant ignorance, of thee I dream and of the Cyclades, as one who sits ashore and longs perchance to visit—' "

"Quite right. To visit what?"

" 'To visit dolphin coral in deep seas,' " said the boy, and burst into tears.

"Come, come! why do you cry?"

"Because—because all these words that only rhymed before, now that I've come back they're me."

Mr. Bons laid the Keats down. The case was more interesting than he had expected. "*You?*" he exclaimed. "This sonnet, *you?*"

"Yes—and look further on: 'Aye, on the shores of darkness there is light, and precipices show untrodden green.' It *is* so, sir. All these things are true."

"I never doubted it," said Mr. Bons, with closed eyes.

"You—then you believe me? You believe in the omnibus and the driver and the storm and that return ticket I got for nothing and—"

"Tut, tut! No more of your yarns, my boy. I meant that I never doubted the essential truth of Poetry. Some day, when you have read more, you will understand what I mean."

"But, Mr. Bons, it *is* so. There *is* light upon the shores of darkness. I have seen it coming. Light and a wind."

"Nonsense," said Mr. Bons.

"If I had stopped! They tempted me. They told me to give up my ticket—for you cannot come back if you lose your ticket. They called from the river for it, and indeed I was tempted, for I have never been so happy as among those precipices. But I thought of my mother and father, and that I must fetch them. Yet they will not come, though the road starts opposite our house. It has all happened as the people up there warned me and Mr. Bons has disbelieved me like every one else. I have been caned. I shall never see that mountain again."

"What's that about me?" said Mr. Bons, sitting up in his chair very suddenly.

"I told them about you, and how clever you were, and how many books you had, and they said, 'Mr. Bons will certainly disbelieve you.'"

"Stuff and nonsense, my young friend. You grow impertinent. I—well—I will settle the matter. Not a word to your father. I will cure you. To-morrow evening I will myself call here to take you for a walk, and at sunset we will go up this alley opposite and hunt for your omnibus, you silly little boy."

His face grew serious, for the boy was not disconcerted, but leapt about the room singing, "Joy! joy! I told them you would believe me. We will drive together over the rainbow. I told them that you would come." After all, could there be anything in the story? Wagner? Keats? Shelley? Sir Thomas Browne? Certainly the case was interesting.

And on the morrow evening, though it was pouring with rain, Mr. Bons did not omit to call at Agathox Lodge.

The boy was ready, bubbling with excitement, and skipping about in a way that rather vexed the President of the Literary Society. They took a turn down Buckingham Park Road, and then—having seen that no one was watching them—slipped up the alley. Naturally enough (for the sun was setting) they ran straight against the omnibus.

"Good heavens!" exclaimed Mr. Bons. "Good gracious heavens!"

It was not the omnibus in which the boy had driven first, nor yet that in which he had returned. There were three horses—black, gray, and white, the gray being the finest. The driver, who turned round at the mention of goodness and of heaven, was a sallow man with terrifying jaws and sunken eyes. Mr. Bons, on seeing him, gave a cry as if of recognition, and began to tremble violently.

The boy jumped in.

"Is it possible?" cried Mr. Bons. "Is the impossible possible?"

"Sir; come in, sir. It is such a fine omnibus. Oh, here is his name—Dan some one."

Mr. Bons sprang in too. A blast of wind immediately slammed the omnibus door, and the shock jerked down all the omnibus blinds, which were very weak on their springs.

"Dan . . . Show me. Good gracious heavens! we're moving."

"Hooray!" said the boy.

Mr. Bons became flustered. He had not intended to be kidnapped. He could not find the doorhandle, nor push up the blinds. The omnibus was quite dark, and by the time he had struck a match, night had come on outside also. They were moving rapidly.

"A strange, a memorable adventure," he said, surveying the interior of the omnibus, which was large, roomy, and constructed with extreme regularity, every part exactly answering to every other part. Over the door (the handle of which was outside) was written, "Lasciate ogni baldanza voi che entrate"—at least, that was what was written, but Mr. Bons said that it was Lashy arty something, and that baldanza was a mistake for speranza. His voice sounded as if he was in church. Meanwhile, the boy called to the cadaverous driver for two return tickets. They were handed in without a word. Mr. Bons covered his face with his hands and again trembled. "Do you know who that is!" he whispered, when the little window had shut upon them. "It is the impossible."

"Well, I don't like him as much as Sir Thomas Browne, though I shouldn't be surprised if he had even more in him."

"More in him?" He stamped irritably. "By accident you have made the greatest discovery of the century, and all you can say is that there is more in this man. Do you remember those vellum books in my library, stamped with red lilies? This—sit still, I bring you stupendous news!— *this is the man who wrote them.*"

The boy sat quite still. "I wonder if we shall see Mrs. Gamp?" he asked, after a civil pause.

"Mrs.—?"

"Mrs. Gamp and Mrs. Harris. I like Mrs. Harris. I came upon them quite suddenly. Mrs. Gamp's bandboxes have moved over the rainbow so badly. All the bottoms have fallen out, and two of the pippins off her bedstead tumbled into the stream."

"Out there sits the man who wrote my vellum books!" thundered Mr. Bons, "and you talk to me of Dickens and of Mrs. Gamp?"

"I know Mrs. Gamp so well," he apologized. "I could not help being glad to see her. I recognized her voice. She was telling Mrs. Harris about Mrs. Prig."

"Did you spend the whole day in her elevating company?"

"Oh, no. I raced. I met a man who took me out beyond to a race-course. You run, and there are dolphins out at sea."

"Indeed. Do you remember the man's name?"

"Achilles. No; he was later. Tom Jones."

Mr. Bons sighed heavily. "Well, my lad, you have made a miserable mess of it. Think of a cultured person with your opportunities! A cultured person would have known all these characters and known what to have said to each. He would not have wasted his time with a Mrs. Gamp or a Tom Jones. The creations of Homer, of Shakespeare, and of Him who drives us now, would alone have contented him. He would not have raced. He would have asked intelligent questions."

"But, Mr. Bons," said the boy humbly, "you will be a cultured person. I told them so."

"True, true, and I beg you not to disgrace me when we arrive. No gossiping. No running. Keep close to my side, and never speak to these Immortals unless they speak to you. Yes, and give me the return tickets. You will be losing them."

The boy surrendered the tickets, but felt a little sore. After all, he had found the way to this place. It was hard first to be disbelieved and then to be lectured. Meanwhile, the rain had stopped, and moonlight crept into the omnibus through the cracks in the blinds.

"But how is there to be a rainbow?" cried the boy.

"You distract me," snapped Mr. Bons. "I wish to meditate on beauty. I wish to goodness I was with a reverent and sympathetic person."

The lad bit his lip. He made a hundred good resolutions. He would imitate Mr. Bons all the visit. He would not laugh, or run, or sing, or do any of the vulgar things that must have disgusted his new friends last time. He would be very careful to pronounce their names properly, and to remember who knew whom. Achilles did not know Tom Jones—at least, so Mr. Bons said. The Duchess of Malfi was older than Mrs. Gamp —at least, so Mr. Bons said. He would be self-conscious, reticent, and prim. He would never say he liked any one. Yet, when the blind flew up at a chance touch of his head, all these good resolutions went to the winds, for the omnibus had reached the summit of a moonlit hill, and there was the chasm, and there, across it, stood the old precipices, dreaming, with their feet in the everlasting river. He exclaimed, "The mountain! Listen to the new tune in the water! Look at the camp fires in the ravines," and Mr. Bons, after a hasty glance, retorted, "Water? Camp fires? Ridiculous rubbish. Hold your tongue. There is nothing at all."

Yet, under his eyes, a rainbow formed, compounded not of sunlight and storm, but of moonlight and the spray of the river. The three horses put their feet upon it. He thought it the finest rainbow he had seen, but did not dare to say so, since Mr. Bons said that nothing was there. He leant out—the window had opened—and sang the tune that rose from the sleeping waters.

"The prelude to Rhinegold?" said Mr. Bons suddenly. "Who taught you these *leitmotifs?*" He, too, looked out of the window. Then he behaved very oddly. He gave a choking cry, and fell back on to the omnibus floor. He writhed and kicked. His face was green.

"Does the bridge make you dizzy?" the boy asked.

"Dizzy!" gasped Mr. Bons. "I want to go back. Tell the driver."

But the driver shook his head.

"We are nearly there," said the boy. "They are asleep. Shall I call? They will be so pleased to see you, for I have prepared them."

Mr. Bons moaned. They moved over the lunar rainbow, which ever and ever broke away behind their wheels. How still the night was! Who would be sentry at the Gate?

"I am coming," he shouted, again forgetting the hundred resolutions. "I am returning—I, the boy."

"The boy is returning," cried a voice to other voices, who repeated, "The boy is returning."

"I am bringing Mr. Bons with me."

Silence.

"I should have said Mr. Bons is bringing me with him."

Profound silence.

"Who stands sentry?"

"Achilles."

And on the rocky causeway, close to the springing of the rainbow bridge, he saw a young man who carried a wonderful shield.

"Mr. Bons, it is Achilles, armed."

"I want to go back," said Mr. Bons.

The last fragment of the rainbow melted, the wheels sang upon the living rock, the door of the omnibus burst open. Out leapt the boy—he could not resist—and sprang to meet the warrior, who, stooping suddenly, caught him on his shield.

"Achilles!" he cried, "let me get down, for I am ignorant and vulgar, and I must wait for that Mr. Bons of whom I told you yesterday."

But Achilles raised him aloft. He crouched on the wonderful shield, on heroes and burning cities, on vineyards graven in gold, on every dear passion, every joy, on the entire image of the Mountain that he had discovered, encircled, like it, with an everlasting stream. "No, no," he protested, "I am not worthy. It is Mr. Bons who must be up here."

But Mr. Bons was whimpering, and Achilles trumpeted and cried, "Stand upright upon my shield!"

"Sir, I did not mean to stand! something made me stand. Sir, why do you delay? Here is only the great Achilles, whom you knew."

Mr. Bons screamed, "I see no one. I see nothing. I want to go back." Then he cried to the driver, "Save me! Let me stop in your chariot. I have honoured you. I have quoted you. I have bound you in vellum. Take me back to my world."

The driver replied, "I am the means and not the end. I am the food and not the life. Stand by yourself, as that boy has stood. I cannot save you. For poetry is a spirit; and they that would worship it must worship in spirit and in truth."

Mr. Bons—he could not resist—crawled out of the beautiful omnibus. His face appeared, gaping horribly. His hands followed, one gripping the step, the other beating the air. Now his shoulders emerged, his chest, his stomach. With a shriek of "I see London," he fell—fell against the hard moonlit rock, fell into it as if it were water, fell through it, vanished, and was seen by the boy no more.

"Where have you fallen to, Mr. Bons? Here is a procession arriving to honour you with music and torches. Here come the men and women whose names you know. The mountain is awake, the river is awake, over the race-course the sea is awaking those dolphins, and it is all for you. They want you—"

There was the touch of fresh leaves on his forehead. Some one had crowned him.

ΤΕΛΟΣ

.   .   .   .

From the *Kingston Gazette, Surbiton Times,*
and *Raynes Park Observer*

The body of Mr. Septimus Bons has been found in a shockingly mutilated condition in the vicinity of the Bermondsey gas-works. The deceased's pockets contained a sovereign-purse, a silver cigar-case, a bijou pronouncing dictionary, and a couple of omnibus tickets. The unfortunate gentleman had apparently been hurled from a considerable height. Foul play is suspected, and a thorough investigation is pending by the authorities.

W. H. Hudson

EL OMBÚ

THIS HISTORY of a house that had been was told in the shade, one summer's day, by Nicandro, that old man to whom we all loved to listen, since he could remember and properly narrate the life of every person he had known in his native place, near to the lake of Chascomus, on the southern pampas of Buenos Ayres.

I

IN ALL THIS DISTRICT, though you should go twenty leagues to this way and that, you will not find a tree as big as this ombú, standing solitary, where there is no house; therefore it is known to all as "*the ombú*," as if but one existed; and the name of all this estate, which is now ownerless and ruined, is El Ombú. From one of the higher branches, if you can climb, you will see the lake of Chascomus, two thirds of a league away, from shore to shore, and the village on its banks. Even smaller things will you see on a clear day; perhaps a red line moving across the water—a flock of flamingos flying in their usual way. A great tree standing alone, with no house near it; only the old brick foundations of a house, so overgrown with grass and weeds that you have to look closely to find them. When I am out with my flock in the summer time, I often come here to sit in the shade. It is near the main road; travellers, droves of cattle, the diligence and bullock-carts pass in sight. Sometimes, at noon, I find a traveller resting in the shade, and if he is not sleeping we talk and he tells me the news of that great world my eyes have never seen.

From *Tales of the Pampas*, 1916.

They say that sorrow and at last ruin comes upon the house on whose roof the shadow of the ombú tree falls; and on that house which now is not, the shadow of this tree came every summer day when the sun was low. They say, too, that those who sit much in the ombú shade become crazed. Perhaps, sir, the bone of my skull is thicker than in most men, since I have been accustomed to sit here all my life, and though now an old man I have not yet lost my reason. It is true that evil fortune came to the old house in the end; but into every door sorrow must enter—sorrow and death that comes to all men; and every house must fall at last.

Do you hear the mangangá, the carpenter bee, in the foliage over our heads? Look at him, like a ball of shining gold among the green leaves, suspended in one place, humming loudly! Ah, señor, the years that are gone, the people that have lived and died, speak to me thus audibly when I am sitting here by myself. These are memories; but there are other things that come back to us from the past; I mean ghosts. Sometimes, at midnight, the whole tree, from its great roots to its topmost leaves, is seen from a distance shining like white fire. What is that fire, seen of so many, which does not scorch the leaves? And, sometimes, when a traveller lies down here to sleep the siesta, he hears sounds of footsteps coming and going, and noises of dogs and fowls, and of children shouting and laughing, and voices of people talking; but when he starts up and listens, the sounds grow faint, and seem at last to pass away into the tree with a low murmur as of wind among the leaves.

As a small boy, from the time when I was able, at the age of about six years, to climb on to a pony and ride, I knew this tree. It was then what it is now; five men with their arms stretched to their utmost length could hardly encircle it. And the house stood there, where you see a bed of nettles—a long, low house, built of bricks, when there were few brick houses in this district, with a thatched roof.

The last owner was just touching on old age. Not that he looked aged; on the contrary, he looked what he was, a man among men, a head taller than most, with the strength of an ox; but the wind had blown a little sprinkling of white ashes into his great beard and his hair, which grew to his shoulders like the mane of a black horse. That was Don Santos Ugarte, known to all men in this district as the White Horse, on account of the whiteness of his skin where most men look dark; also because of that proud temper and air of authority which he had. And for still another reason—the number of children in this neighborhood of which he was said to be the father. In all houses, for many leagues around, the children were taught to reverence him, calling him "uncle," and when he appeared they would run and, dropping on their knees before him, cry out *"Bendición, mi tío."* He would give them his blessing; then, after tweaking a nose and pinching an ear or two, he would flourish his whip over their heads to signify that he had done with them, and that they must quickly get out of his way.

These were children of the wind, as the saying is, and the desire of his heart was for a legitimate son, an Ugarte by name, who would come after him at El Ombú, as he had come after his father. But though he had married thrice, there was no son born, and no child. Some thought it a mystery that one with so many sons should yet be without a son. The mystery, friend, was only for those who fail to remember that such things are not determined by ourselves. We often say, that He who is above us is too great to concern Himself with our small affairs. There are so many of us; and how shall He, seated on his throne at so great a distance, know all that passes in his dominions! But Santos was no ordinary person, and He who was greater than Santos had doubtless had his attention drawn to this man; and had considered the matter, and had said, "You shall not have your desire; for though you are a devout man, one who gives freely of his goods to the church and my poor, I am not wholly satisfied with you." And so it came to pass that he had no son and heir.

His first two wives had died, so it was said, because of his bitterness against them. I only knew the third—Doña Mericie, a silent, sad woman, who was of less account than any servant, or any slave in the house. And I, a simple boy, what could I know of the secrets of her heart? Nothing! I only saw her pale and silent and miserable, and because her eyes followed me, I feared her, and tried always to keep out of her way. But one morning, when I came to El Ombú and went into the kitchen, I found her there alone, and before I could escape she caught me in her arms, and lifting me off my feet strained me against her breast, crying, *hijo de mi alma*, and I knew not what beside; and calling God's blessing on me, she covered my face with kisses. Then all at once, hearing Santos' voice without, she dropped me and remained like a woman of stone, staring at the door with scared eyes.

She, too, died in a little while, and her disappearance made no difference in the house, and if Santos wore a black band on his arm, it was because custom demanded it and not because he mourned for her in his heart.

II

THAT SILENT GHOST of a woman being gone, no one could say of him that he was hard; nor could anything be said against him except that he was not a saint, in spite of his name. But, sir, we do not look for saints among strong men, who live in the saddle, and are at the head of big establishments. If there was one who was a father to the poor it was Santos; therefore he was loved by many, and only those who had done him an injury or had crossed him in any way had reason to fear and hate him. But let me now relate what I, a boy of ten, witnessed one day in the year 1808. This will show you what the man's temper was; and his courage, and the strength of his wrists.

It was his custom to pay a visit every two or three months to a monastery at a distance of half-a-day's journey from El Ombú.

He was greatly esteemed by the friars, and whenever he went to see them he had a led horse to carry his presents to the Brothers;—a side of fat beef, a sucking-pig or two, a couple of lambs, when they were in season, a few fat turkeys and ducks, a bunch of big partridges, a brace or two of armadillos, the breast and wings of a fat ostrich; and in summer, a dozen ostriches' eggs, and I know not what besides.

One evening I was at El Ombú, and was just starting for home, when Santos saw me, and cried out, "Get off and let your horse go, Nicandro. I am going to the monastery to-morrow, and you shall ride the laden horse, and save me the trouble of leading it. You will be like a little bird perched on his back and he will not feel your few ounces' weight. You can sleep on a sheepskin in the kitchen, and get up an hour before daybreak."

The stars were still shining when we set out on our journey the next morning, in the month of June, and when we crossed the river San-borombón at sunrise the earth was all white with hoar frost. At noon, we arrived at our destination, and were received by the friars, who embraced and kissed Santos on both cheeks, and took charge of our horses. After breakfast in the kitchen, the day being now warm and pleasant, we went and sat out of doors to sip maté and smoke, and for an hour or longer, the conversation between Santos and the Brothers had been going on when, all at once, a youth appeared coming at a fast gallop towards the gate, shouting as he came, "Los Ingleses! Los Ingleses!" We all jumped up and ran to the gate, and climbing up by the posts and bars, saw at a distance of less than half-a-league to the east, a great army of men marching in the direction of Buenos Ayres. We could see that the foremost part of the army had come to a halt on the banks of a stream which flows past the monastery and empties itself into the Plata, two leagues further east. The army was all composed of infantry, but a great many persons on horse-back could be seen following it, and these, the young man said, were neighbours who had come out to look at the English invaders; and he also said that the soldiers, on arriving at the stream, had begun to throw away their blankets, and that the people were picking them up. Santos, hearing this, said he would go and join the crowd, and mounting his horse and followed by me, and by two of the Brothers, who said they wished to get a few blankets for the monastery, we set out at a gallop for the stream.

Arrived at the spot, we found that the English, not satisfied with the ford, which had a very muddy bottom, had made a new crossing-place for themselves by cutting down the bank on both sides, and that numbers of blankets had been folded and laid in the bed of the stream where it was about twenty-five yards wide. Hundreds of blankets were also being thrown away, and the people were picking them up and loading their horses with them. Santos at once threw himself into the crowd and gath-ered about a dozen blankets, the best he could find, for the friars; then he gathered a few for himself and ordered me to fasten them on the back of my horse.

The soldiers, seeing us scrambling for the blankets, were much amused; but when one man among us cried out, "These people must be mad to throw their blankets away in cold weather—perhaps their red jackets will keep them warm when they lie down to-night"—there was one soldier who understood, and could speak Spanish, and he replied, "No, sirs, we have no further need of blankets. When we next sleep it will be in the best beds in the capital." Then Santos shouted back, "That, sirs, will perhaps be a sleep from which some of you will never awake." That speech attracted their attention to Santos, and the soldier who had spoken before returned, "There are not many men like you in these parts, therefore what you say does not alarm us." Then they looked at the friars fastening the blankets Santos had given them on to their horses, and seeing that they wore heavy iron spurs strapped on their bare feet, they shouted with laughter, and the one who talked with us cried out, "We are sorry, good Brothers, that we have not boots as well as blankets to give you."

But our business was now done, and bidding good-bye to the friars, we set out on our return journey, Santos saying that we should be at home before midnight.

It was past the middle of the afternoon, we having ridden about six leagues, when we spied at a distance ahead a great number of mounted men scattered about over the plain, some standing still, others galloping this way or that.

"El pato! el pato!" cried Santos with excitement, "Come, boys, let us go and watch the battle while it is near, and when it is passed on we will go our way." Urging his horse to a gallop, I following, we came to where the men were struggling for the ball, and stood for a while looking on. But it was not in him to remain a mere spectator for long; never did he see a cattle-marking, or parting, or races, or a dance, or any game, and above all games, el pato, but he must have a part in it. Very soon he dismounted to throw off some of the heaviest parts of his horse-gear, and ordering me to take them up on my horse and follow him, he rode in among the players.

About forty or fifty men had gathered at that spot, and were sitting quietly on their horses in a wide circle, waiting to see the result of a struggle for the Pato between three men who had hold of the ball. They were strong men, well mounted, each resolved to carry off the prize from the others. Sir, when I think of that sight, and remember that the game is no longer played because of the Tyrant who forbade it, I am ready to cry out that there are no longer men on these plains where I first saw the light! How they tugged and strained and sweated, almost dragging each other out of the saddle, their trained horses leaning away, digging their hoofs into the turf, as when they resist the shock of a lassoed animal, when the lasso stiffens and the pull comes! One of the men was a big, powerful mulatto, and the by-standers thinking the victory would be his, were only waiting to see him wrest the ball from the others to rush upon and try to deprive him of it before he could escape from the crowd.

Santos refused to stand inactive, for was there not a fourth handle to the ball to be grasped by another fighter? Spurring his horse into the group, he very soon succeeded in getting hold of the disengaged handle. A cry of resentment at this action on the part of a stranger went up from some of those who were looking on, mixed with applause at his daring from others, while the three men who had been fighting against each other, each one for himself, now perceived that they had a common enemy. Excited as they were by the struggle, they could not but be startled at the stranger's appearance—that huge man on a big horse, so white-skinned and long-haired, with a black beard, that came down over his breast, and who showed them, when he threw back his poncho, the knife that was like a sword and the big brass-barrelled pistol worn at his waist. Very soon after he joined in the fray all four men came to the earth. But they did not fall together, and the last to go down was Santos, who would not be dragged off his horse, and in the end horse and man came down on the top of the others. In coming down, two of the men had lost their hold of the ball; last of all, the big mulatto, to save himself from being crushed under the falling horse, was forced to let go, and in his rage at being beaten, he whipped out his long knife against the stranger. Santos, too quick for him, dealt him a blow on the forehead with the heavy silver handle of his whip, dropping him stunned to the ground. Of the four, Santos alone had so far escaped injury, and rising and remounting, the ball still in his hand, he rode out from among them, the crowd opening on each side to make room for him.

Now in the crowd there was one tall, imposing-looking man, wearing a white poncho, many silver ornaments, and a long knife in an embossed silver sheath; his horse, too, which was white as milk, was covered with silver trappings. This man alone raised his voice; "Friends and comrades," he cried, "is this to be the finish? If this stranger is permitted to carry the Pato away, it will not be because of his stronger wrist and better horse, but because he carries firearms. Comrades, what do you say?"

But there was no answer. They had seen the power and resolution of the man, and though they were many they preferred to let him go in peace. Then the man on a white horse, with a scowl of anger and contempt, turned from them and began following us at a distance of about fifty yards. Whenever Santos turned back to come to close quarters with him, he retired, only to turn and follow us again as soon as Santos resumed his course. In this way we rode till sunset. Santos was grave, but calm; I, being so young, was in constant terror. "Oh, uncle," I whispered, "for the love of God fire your pistol at this man and kill him, so that he may not kill us!"

Santos laughed. "Fool of a boy," he replied, "do you not know that he wants me to fire at him! He knows that I could not hit him at this distance, and that after discharging my pistol we should be equal, man to man, and knife to knife; and who knows then which would kill the other? God knows best, since He knows everything, and He has put it into my heart not to fire."

When it grew dark we rode slower, and the man then lessened the distance between us. We could hear the chink-chink of his silver trappings, and when I looked back I could see a white misty form following us like a ghost. Then, all at once, there came a noise of hoofs and a whistling sound of something thrown, and Santos' horse plunged and reared and kicked, then stood still trembling with terror. His hind legs were entangled in the bolas which had been thrown. With a curse Santos threw himself off, and, drawing his knife, cut the thong which bound the animal's legs, and remounting we went on as before, the white figure still following us.

At length, about midnight, the Sanborombón was reached, at the ford where we had crossed in the morning, where it was about forty yards wide, and the water only high as the surcingle in the deepest parts.

"Let your heart be glad, Nicandro!" said Santos, as we went down into the water; "for our time is come now, and be careful to do as I bid you."

We crossed slowly, and coming out on the south side, Santos quietly dropped off his horse, and, speaking in a low voice, ordered me to ride slowly on with the two horses and wait for him in the road. He said that the man who followed would not see him crouching under the bank, and thinking it safe would cross over, only to receive the charge fired at a few yards' distance.

That was an anxious interval that followed, I waiting alone, scarcely daring to breathe, staring into the darkness in fear of that white figure that was like a ghost, listening for the pistol shot. My prayer to heaven was to direct the bullet in its course, so that it might go to that terrible man's heart, and we be delivered from him. But there was no shot, and no sound except a faint chink of silver and sound of hoof-beats that came to my ears after a time, and soon ceased to be heard. The man, perhaps, had some suspicion of the other's plan and had given up the chase and gone away.

Nothing more do I remember of that journey which ended at El Ombú at cock-crow, except that at one spot Santos fastened a thong round my waist and bound me before and behind to the saddle to prevent my falling from my horse every time I went to sleep.

III

REMEMBER, SEÑOR, that I have spoken of things that passed when I was small. The memories of that time are few and scattered, like the fragments of tiles and bricks and rusty iron which one may find half-buried among the weeds, where the house once stood. Fragments that once formed part of the building. Certain events, some faces, and some voices, I remember, but I cannot say the year. Nor can I say how many years had gone by after Doña Mericie's death, and after my journey to the monastery. Perhaps they were few, perhaps many. Invasions had come, wars with a foreigner and with the savage, and Independence, and many things had happened at a distance. He, Santos Ugarte, was older, I know, greyer, when that great misfortune and calamity came to one whom God had created so strong, so brave, so noble. And all on account of a slave, a youth born at El Ombú, who had been preferred above the others by his master. For, as it is said, we breed crows to pick our eyes out. But I will say nothing against that poor youth, who was the cause of the disaster, for it was not wholly his fault. Part of the fault was in Santos—his indomitable temper and his violence. And perhaps, too, the time was come when He who rules over all men had said, "You have raised your voice and have ridden over others long enough. Look, Santos! I shall set My foot upon you, and under it you shall be like a wild pumpkin at the end of summer, when it is dryer and more brittle than an empty egg-shell."

Remember that there were slaves in those days, also that there was a law fixing every man's price, old or young, so that if any slave went, money in hand, to his master and offered him the price of his liberty, from that moment he became a free man. It mattered not that his master wished not to sell him. So just was the law.

Of his slaves Santos was accustomed to say, "These are my children, and serve because they love me, not because they are slaves; and if I were to offer his freedom to any one among them, he would refuse to take it." He saw their faces, not their hearts.

His favourite was Meliton, black but well favoured, and though but a youth, he had authority over the others, and dressed well, and rode his master's best horses, and had horses of his own. But it was never said of him that he gained that eminence by means of flattery and a tongue cunning to frame lies. On the contrary, he was loved by all, even by those he was set above, because of his goodness of heart and a sweet and gay disposition. He was one of those who can do almost anything better than others; whatever his master wanted done, whether it was to ride a race, or break a horse, or throw a lasso, or make a bridle, or whip, or surcingle, or play on a guitar, or sing, or dance, it was Meliton, Meliton. There was no one like him.

Now this youth cherished a secret ambition in his heart, and saved, and saved his money; and at length one day he came with a handful of silver and gold to Santos, and said, "Master, here is the price of my freedom, take it and count it, and see that it is right, and let me remain at El Ombú to serve you henceforth without payment. But I shall no longer be a slave."

Santos took the money into his hand, and spoke, "It was for this then that you saved, even the money I gave you to spend and to run with, and the money you made by selling the animals I gave you—you saved it for this! Ingrate, with a heart blacker than your skin! Take back the money, and go from my presence, and never cross my path again if you wish for a long life." And with that he hurled the handful of silver and gold into the young man's face with such force, that he was cut and bruised with the coins and well nigh stunned. He went back staggering to his horse, and mounting, rode away, sobbing like a child, the blood running down from his face.

He soon left this neighbourhood and went to live at Las Vivoras, on the Vecino river, south of Dolores, and there made good use of his freedom, buying fat animals for the market; and for a space of two years he prospered, and every man, rich or poor, was his friend. Nevertheless, he was not happy, for his heart was loyal and he loved his old master, who had been a father to him, and desired above all things to be forgiven. And, at length, hoping that Santos had outlived his resentment and would be pleased to see him again, he one day came to El Ombú and asked to see the master.

The old man came out of the house and greeted him jovially. "Ha, Meliton," he cried with a laugh, "you have returned in spite of my warning. Come down from your horse and let me take your hand once more."

The other, glad to think he was forgiven, alighted, and advancing, put out his hand. Santos took it in his, only to crush it with so powerful a grip, that the young man cried out aloud, and blinded with tears of pain, he did not see that his master had the big brass pistol in his left hand, and did not know that his last moment had come. He fell with a bullet in his heart.

Look, señor, where I am pointing, twenty yards or so from the edge of the shadow of the ombú, do you see a dark green weed with a yellow flower on a tall stem growing on the short, dry grass? It was just there, on the very spot where the yellow flower is, that poor Meliton fell, and was left lying, covered with blood, until noon the next day. For no person dared take up the corpse until the Alcalde had been informed of the matter and had come to inquire into it.

Santos had mounted his horse and gone away without a word, taking the road to Buenos Ayres. He had done that for which he would have to pay dearly; for a life is a life, whether the skin be black or white, and no man can slay another deliberately, in cold blood, and escape the penalty. The law is no respecter of persons, and when he, who commits such a deed, is a man of substance, he must expect that Advocates and Judges, with all those who take up his cause, will bleed him well before they procure him a pardon.

Ugarte cared nothing for that, he had been as good as his word, and the devil in his heart was satisfied. Only he would not wait at his estancia to be taken, nor would he go and give himself up to the authorities, who would then have to place him in confinement, and it would be many months before his liberation. That would be like suffocation to him; to such a man a prison is like a tomb. No, he would go to Buenos Ayres and embark for Montevideo, and from that place he would put the matter in motion, and wait there until it was all settled and he was free to return to El Ombú.

Dead Meliton was taken away and buried in consecrated ground at Chascomus. Rain fell, and washed away the red stains on the ground. In the spring, the swallows returned and built their nests under the eaves; but Ugarte came not back, nor did any certain tidings of him reach us. It was said, I know not whether truly or not, that the Advocate who defended him, and the Judge of First Instance, who had the case before him, had quarrelled about the division of the reward, and both being rich, proud persons, they had allowed themselves to forget the old man waiting there month after month for his pardon, which never came to him.

Better for him if he never heard of the ruin which had fallen on El Ombú during his long exile. There was no one in authority: the slaves, left to themselves, went away, and there was no person to restrain them. As for the cattle and horses, they were blown away like thistle-down, and everyone was free to pasture his herds and flocks on the land.

The house for a time was in charge of some person placed there by the authorities, but little by little it was emptied of its contents; and at last it was abandoned, and for a long time no one could be found to live in it on account of the ghosts.

IV

THERE WAS LIVING at that time, a few leagues from El Ombú, one Valerio de la Cueva, a poor man, whose all consisted of a small flock of three or four hundred sheep and a few horses. He had been allowed to make a small rancho, a mere hut, to shelter himself and his wife Donata and their one child, a boy named Bruno; and to pay for the grass his few sheep consumed he assisted in the work at the estancia house. This poor man, hearing of El Ombú, where he could have house and ground for nothing, offered himself as occupant, and in time came with wife and child and his small flock, and all the furniture he possessed—a bed, two or three chairs, a pot and kettle, and perhaps a few other things. Such poverty El Ombú had not known, but all others had feared to inhabit such a place on account of its evil name, so that it was left for Valerio, who was a stranger in the district.

Tell me, señor, have you ever in your life met with a man, who was perhaps poor, or even clothed in rags, and who yet when you had looked at and conversed with him, has caused you to say: Here is one who is like no other man in the world? Perhaps on rising and going out, on some clear morning in summer, he looked at the sun when it rose, and perceived an angel sitting in it, and as he gazed, something from that being fell upon and passed into and remained in him. Such a man was Valerio. I have known no other like him.

"Come, friend Nicandro," he would say, "let us sit down in the shade and smoke our cigarettes, and talk of our animals. Here are no politics under this old ombú, no ambitions and intrigues and animosities—no bitterness except in these green leaves. They are our laurels—the leaves of the ombú. Happy Nicandro, who never knew the life of cities! I wish that I, too, had seen the light on these quiet plains, under a thatched roof. Once I wore fine clothes and gold ornaments, and lived in a great house where there were many servants to wait on me. But happy I have never been. Every flower I plucked changed into a nettle to sting my hand. Perhaps that maleficent one, who has pursued me all my days, seeing me now so humbled and one with the poor, has left me and gone away. Yes, I am poor, and this frayed garment that covers me will I press to my lips because it does not shine with silk and gold embroidery. And this poverty which I have found will I cherish, and bequeath it as a precious thing to my child when I die. For with it is peace."

The peace did not last long; for when misfortune has singled out a man for its prey, it will follow him to the end, and he shall not escape from it though he mount up to the clouds like the falcon, or thrust himself deep down into the earth like the armadillo.

Valerio had been two years at El Ombú when there came an Indian invasion on the southern frontier. There was no force to oppose it; the two hundred men stationed at the Guardia del Azul had been besieged by a part of the invaders in the fort, while the larger number of the savages were sweeping away the cattle and horses from the country all round. An urgent order came to the commander at Chascomus to send a contingent of forty men from the department; and I, then a young man of twenty, who had seen no service, was cited to appear at the Commandancia, in readiness to march. There I found that Valerio had also been cited, and from that moment we were together. Two days later we were at the Azul, the Indians having retired with their booty; and when all the contingents from the various departments had come in, the commander, one Colonel Barboza, set out with about six hundred men in pursuit.

It was known that in their retreat the Indians had broken up their force into several parties, and that these had taken different directions, and it was thought that these bodies would reunite after a time, and that the larger number would return to their territory by way of Trinqué Lauquén, about seventy-five leagues west of Azul. Our Colonel's plan was to go quickly to this point and wait the arrival of the Indians. It was impossible that they, burdened with the thousands of cattle they had collected, could move fast, while we were burdened with nothing, the only animals we drove before us being our horses. These numbered about five thousand, but many were unbroken mares, to be used as food. Nothing but mare's flesh did we have to eat.

It was the depth of winter, and worse weather I have never known.

In this desert I first beheld that whiteness called snow, when the rain flies like cotton-down before the wind, filling the air and whitening the whole earth. All day and every day our clothes were wet, and there was no shelter from the wind and rain at night, nor could we make fires with the soaked grass and reeds, and wood there was none, so that we were compelled to eat our mare's flesh uncooked.

Three weeks were passed in this misery, waiting for the Indians and seeking for them, with the hills of Gaumini now before us in the south, and now on our left hand; and still no sight and no sign of the enemy. It seemed as if the earth had opened and swallowed him up. Our Colonel was in despair, and we now began to hope that he would lead us back to the Azul.

In these circumstances one of the men, who was thinly clad and had been suffering from a cough, dropped from his horse, and it was then seen that he was likely to die, and that in any case he would have to be left behind. Finding that there was no hope for him, he begged that those who were with him would remember, when they were at home again, that he had perished in the desert and that his soul was suffering in purgatory, and that they would give something to the priests to procure him ease. When asked by his officer to say who his relations were and where they lived, he replied that he had no one belonging to him. He said that he had spent many years in captivity among the Indians at the Salinas Grandes, and that on his return he had failed to find any one of his relations living in the district where he had been born. In answer to further questions, he said that he had been carried away when a small boy, that the Indians on that occasion had invaded the Christian country in the depth of winter, and on their retreat, instead of returning to their own homes, they had gone east, toward the sea coast, and had encamped on a plain by a small stream called Curumamuel, at Los Tres Arroyos, where there was firewood and sweet water, and good grass for the cattle, and where they found many Indians, mostly women and children, who had gone thither to await their coming; and at that spot they had remained until the spring.

The poor man died that night, and we gathered stones and piled them on his body so that the foxes and caranchos should not devour him.

At break of day next morning we were on horseback marching at a gallop toward sunrise, for our Colonel had determined to look for the Indians at that distant spot near the sea where they had hidden themselves from their pursuers so many years before. The distance was about seventy leagues, and the journey took us about nine days. And at last, in a deep valley near the sea, the enemy was discovered by our scouts, and we marched by night until we were within less than a league of their encampment, and could see their fires. We rested there for four hours, eating raw flesh and sleeping. Then every man was ordered to mount his best horse, and we were disposed in a half-moon, so that the free horses could easily be driven before us. The Colonel, sitting on his horse, ad-

dressed us, "Boys," he said, "you have suffered much, but now the victory is in our hands, and you shall not lose the reward. All the captives you take, and all the thousands of horses and cattle we succeed in recovering, shall be sold by public auction on our return, and the proceeds divided among you."

He then gave the order, and we moved quietly on for a space of half a league, and coming to the edge of the valley saw it all black with cattle before us, and the Indians sleeping in their camp; and just when the sun rose from the sea and God's light came over the earth, with a great shout we charged upon them. In a moment the multitude of cattle, struck with panic, began rushing away, bellowing in all directions, shaking the earth beneath their hoofs. Our troop of horses, urged on by our yells, were soon in the encampment, and the savages, rushing hither and thither, trying to save themselves, were shot and speared and cut down by swords. One desire was in all our hearts, one cry on all lips—kill! kill! kill! Such a slaughter had not been known for a long time, and birds and foxes and armadillos must have grown fat on the flesh of the heathen we left for them. But we killed only the men, and few escaped; the women and children we made captive.

Two days we spent in collecting the scattered cattle and horses, numbering about ten thousand; then with our spoil we set out on our return and arrived at the Azul at the end of August. On the following day the force was broken up into the separate contingents of which it was composed, and each in its turn was sent to the Colonel's house to be paid. The Chascomus contingent was the last to go up, and on presenting ourselves, each man received two months' soldiers' pay, after which Colonel Barboza came out and thanked us for our services, and ordered us to give up our arms at the fort and go back to our district, every man to his own house.

"We have spent some cold nights in the deserts together, neighbour Nicandro," said Valerio, laughing, "but we have fared well—on raw horse flesh; and now to make it better we have received money. Why, look, with all this money I shall be able to buy a pair of new shoes for Bruno. Brave little man! I can see him toddling about among the cardoon thistles, searching for hens' eggs for his mother, and getting his poor little feet full of thorns. If there should be any change left he shall certainly have some sugarplums."

But the others on coming to the fort began to complain loudly of the treatment they had received, whereupon Valerio, rebuking them, told them to act like men and tell the Colonel that they were not satisfied, or else hold their peace.

"Will you, Valerio, be our spokesman?" they cried, and he consenting, they all took up their arms again and followed him back to the Colonel's house.

Barboza listened attentively to what was said and replied that our demands were just. The captives and cattle, he said, had been placed in

charge of an officer appointed by the authorities and would be sold publicly in a few days. Let them now return to the fort and give up their
arms, and leave Valerio with him to assist in drawing up a formal demand
for their share of the spoil.

We then retired once more, giving *vivas* to our Colonel. But no
sooner had we given up our arms at the fort than we were sharply
ordered to saddle our horses and take our departure. I rode out with the
others, but seeing that Valerio did not overtake us I went back to look for
him.

This was what had happened. Left alone in his enemy's hands,
Barboza had his arms taken from him, then ordered his men to carry him
out to the patio and flay him alive. The men hesitated to obey so cruel a
command, and this gave Valerio time to speak; "My Colonel," he said,
"you put a hard task on these poor men, and my hide when taken will be
of no value to you or to them. Bid them lance me or draw a knife across
my throat, and I will laud your clemency."

"You shall not lose your hide nor die," returned the Colonel, "for I
admire your courage. Take him, boys, and stake him out, and give him
two hundred lashes; then throw him into the road so that it may be
known that his rebellious conduct has been punished."

This order was obeyed, and out upon the road he was thrown. A
compassionate storekeeper belonging to the place saw him lying there
insensible, the carrion-hawks attracted by his naked bleeding body hovering about him; and this good man took him and was ministering to him
when I found him. He was lying, face down, on a pile of rugs, racked
with pains, and all night long his sufferings were terrible; nevertheless,
when morning came, he insisted on setting out at once on our journey to
Chascomus. When his pain was greatest and caused him to cry out, the
cry, when he saw my face, would turn to a laugh. "You are too tender
hearted for this world we live in," he would say. "Think nothing of this,
Nicandro. I have tasted man's justice and mercy before now. Let us talk
of pleasanter things. Do you know that it is the first of September today? Spring has come back, though we hardly notice it yet in this cold
southern country. It has been winter, winter with us, and no warmth of
sun or fire, and no flowers and no birds' song. But our faces are towards
the north now; in a few days we shall sit again in the shade of the old
ombú, all our toil and suffering over, to listen to the mangangá humming
among the leaves and to the call of the yellow bienteveo. And better than
all, little Bruno will come to us with his hands full of scarlet verbenas.
Perhaps in a few years' time you, too, will be a father, Nicandro, and will
know what it is to hear a child's prattle. Come, we have rested long
enough, and have many leagues to ride!"

The leagues were sixty by the road, but something was gained by
leaving it, and it was easier for Valerio when the horses trod on the turf.
To gallop or to trot was impossible, and even walking I had to keep at his

side to support him with my arm; for his back was all one ever-bleeding wound, and his hands were powerless, and all his joints swollen and inflamed as a result of his having been stretched out on the stakes. Five days we travelled, and day by day and night by night he grew feebler, but he would not rest; so long as the light lasted he would be on the road; and as we slowly pressed on, I supporting him, he would groan with pain and then laugh and begin to talk of the journey's end and of the joy of seeing wife and child again.

It was afternoon on the fifth day when we arrived. The sight of the ombú which we had had for hours before us, strongly excited him; he begged me, almost with tears, to urge the horses to a gallop, but it would have killed him, and I would not do it.

No person saw our approach, but the door stood open, and when we had walked our horses to within about twenty yards we heard Bruno's voice prattling to his mother. Then suddenly Valerio slipped from the saddle before I could jump down to assist him, and staggered on for a few paces towards the door. Running to his side I heard his cry—"Donata! Bruno! let my eyes see you! one kiss!" Only then his wife heard, and running out to us, saw him sink, and with one last gasp expire in my arms.

Strange and terrible scenes have I witnessed, but never a sadder one than this! Tell me, señor, are these things told in books,—does the world know them?

Valerio was dead. He who was so brave, so generous even in his poverty, of so noble a spirit, yet so gentle; whose words were sweeter than honey to me! Of what his loss was to others—to that poor woman who was the mother of his one child, his little Bruno—I speak not. There are things about which we must be silent, or say only, turning our eyes up, Has He forgotten us! Does He know? But to me the loss was greater than all losses: for he was my friend, the man I loved above all men, who was more to me than any other, even than Santos Ugarte, whose face I should see no more.

For he, too, was dead.

And now I have once more mentioned the name of that man, who was once so great in this district, let me, before proceeding with the history of El Ombú, tell you his end. I heard of it by chance long after he had been placed under the ground.

It was the old man's custom in that house, on the other side of the Rio de la Plata where he was obliged to live, to go down every day to the waterside. Long hours would he spend there, sitting on the rocks, always with his face towards Buenos Ayres. He was waiting, waiting for the pardon which would, perhaps, in God's good time, come to him from that forgetful place. He was thinking of El Ombú; for what was life to him away from it, in that strange country? And that unsatisfied desire, and perhaps remorse, had, they say, made his face terrible to look at, for it was like the face of a dead man who had died with wide-open eyes.

One day some boatmen on the beach noticed that he was seated on the rocks far out and that when the tide rose he made no movement to escape from the water. They saw him sitting waist-deep in the sea, and when they rescued him from his perilous position and brought him to the shore, he stared at them like a great white owl and talked in a strange way.

"It is very cold and very dark," he said, "and I cannot see your faces, but perhaps you know me. I am Santos Ugarte, of El Ombú. I have had a great misfortune, friends. To-day in my anger I killed a poor youth whom I loved like a son—my poor boy Meliton! Why did he despise my warning and put himself in my way! But I will say no more about that. After killing him I rode away with the intention of going to Buenos Ayres, but on the road I repented of my deed and turned back. I said that with my own hands I would take him up and carry him in, and call my neighbours together to watch with me by his poor body. But, Sirs, the night overtook me and the Sanborombón is swollen with rains, as you no doubt know, and in swimming it I lost my horse. I do not know if he was drowned. Let me have a fresh horse, friends, and show me the way to El Ombú, and God will reward you."

In that delusion he remained till the end, a few days later, when he died. May his soul rest in peace!

V

SEÑOR, WHEN I AM HERE and remember things, I sometimes say to myself: Why, old man, do you come to this tree to sit for an hour in the shade, since there is not on all these plains a sadder or more bitter place? My answer is, To one who has lived long, there is no house and no spot of ground, overgrown with grass and weeds, where a house once stood and where men have lived, that is not equally sad. For this sadness is in us, in a memory of other days which follows us into all places. But for the child there is no past: he is born into the world light hearted like a bird; for him gladness is everywhere.

That is how it was with little Bruno, too young to feel the loss of a father or to remember him long. It was her great love of this child which enabled Donata to live through so terrible a calamity. She never quitted El Ombú. An embargo had been placed on the estancia so that it could not be sold, and she was not disturbed in her possession of the house. She now shared it with an old married couple, who, being poor and having a few animals, were glad of a place to live in rent free. The man, whose name was Pascual, took care of Donata's flock and the few cows and horses she owned along with his own. He was a simple, good-tempered old man, whose only fault was indolence, and a love of the bottle, and of play. But that mattered little, for when he gambled he invariably lost, through not being sober, so that when he had any money it was quickly gone.

Old Pascual first put Bruno on a horse and taught him to ride after the flock, and to do a hundred things. The boy was like his father, of a beautiful countenance, with black curling hair, and eyes as lively as a bird's. It was not strange that Donata loved him as no mother ever loved a son, but as he grew up a perpetual anxiety was in her heart lest he should hear the story of his father's death and the cause of it. For she was wise in this; she knew that the most dangerous of all passions is that of revenge, since when it enters into the heart all others, good or bad, are driven out, and all ties and interests and all the words that can be uttered are powerless to restrain a man; and the end is ruin. Many times she spoke of this to me, begging me with tears never to speak of my dead friend to Bruno, lest he should discover the truth, and that fatal rage should enter into his heart.

It had been Donata's custom, every day since Valerio's death, to take a pitcher of water, fresh from the well, and pour it out on the ground, on the spot where he had sunk down and expired, without that sight of wife and child, that one kiss, for which he had cried. Who can say what caused her to do such a thing? A great grief is like a delirium, and sometimes gives us strange thoughts, and makes us act like demented persons. It may have been because of the appearance of the dead face as she first saw it, dry and white as ashes, the baked black lips, the look of thirst that would give everything for a drink of cold water; and that which she had done in the days of anguish, of delirium, she had continued to do.

The spot where the water was poured each day, being but a few yards from the door of the house, was of a dryness and hardness of fire-baked bricks, trodden hard by the feet of I know not how many generations of men, and by hoofs of horses ridden every day to the door. But after a long time of watering a little green began to appear in the one spot; and the green was of a creeping plant with small round malva-like leaves, and little white flowers like porcelain shirt buttons. It spread and thickened, and was like a soft green carpet about two yards long placed on that dry ground, and it was of an emerald greenness all the year round, even in the hot weather when the grass was dead and dry and the plains were in colour like a faded yellow rag.

When Bruno was a boy of fourteen I went one day to help him in making a sheepfold, and when our work was finished in the afternoon we went to the house to sip maté. Before going in, on coming to that green patch, Bruno cried out, "Have you ever seen so verdant a spot as this, Nicandro, so soft and cool a spot to lie down on when one is hot and tired?" He then threw himself down full length upon it, and, lying at ease on his back, he looked up at Donata, who came out to us, and spoke laughingly, "Ah, little mother of my soul! A thousand times have I asked you why you poured water every day on this spot and you would not tell me. Now I have found out. It was all to make me a soft cool spot to lie on when I come back tired and hot from work. Look! is it not like a soft bed with a green and white velvet coverlid; bring water now, mother mine, and pour it on my hot, dusty face."

She laughed, too, poor woman, but I could see the tears in her eyes—the tears which she was always so careful to hide from him.

All this I remember as if it had happened yesterday; I can see and hear it all—Donata's laugh and the tears in her eyes which Bruno could not see. I remember it so well because this was almost the last time I saw her before I was compelled to go away, for my absence was long. But before I speak of that change let me tell you of something that happened about two years before at El Ombú, which brought a new happiness into that poor widow's life.

It happened that among those that had no right to be on the land, but came and settled there because there was no one to forbid them, there was a man named Sanchez, who had built himself a small rancho about half a league from the old house, and kept a flock of sheep. He was a widower with one child, a little girl named Monica. This Sanchez, although poor, was not a good man, and had no tenderness in his heart. He was a gambler, always away from his rancho, leaving the flock to be taken care of by poor little Monica. In winter it was cruel, for then the sheep travel most, and most of all on cold, rough days; and she without a dog to help her, barefooted on the thistle-grown land, often in terror at the sight of cattle, would be compelled to spend the whole day out of doors. More than once on a winter evening in bad weather I have found her trying to drive the sheep home in the face of the rain, crying with misery. It hurt me all the more because she had a pretty face: no person could fail to see its beauty, though she was in rags and her black hair in a tangle, like the mane of a horse that has been feeding among the burrs. At such times I have taken her up on my saddle and driven her flock home for her, and have said to myself: "Poor lamb without a mother, if you were mine I would seat you on the horns of the moon; but, unhappy one! he whom you call father is without compassion."

At length, Sanchez, finding himself without money, just when strangers from all places were coming to Chascomus to witness a great race, and anxious not to lose this chance of large winnings, sold his sheep, having nothing of more value to dispose of. But instead of winning he lost, and then leaving Monica in a neighbour's house he went away, promising to return for her in a few days. But he did not return, and it was believed by everybody that he had abandoned the child.

It was then that Donata offered to take her and be a mother to the orphan, and I can say, señor, that the poor child's own mother, who was dead, could not have treated her more tenderly or loved her more. And the pretty one had now been Donata's little daughter and Bruno's play-mate two years when I was called away, and I saw them not again and heard no tidings of them for a space of five years—the five longest years of my life.

VI

I WENT AWAY because men were wanted for the army, and I was taken. I was away, I have said, five years, and the five would have been ten, and the ten twenty, supposing that life had lasted, but for a lance wound in my thigh, which made me a lame man for the rest of my life. That was the reason of my discharge and happy escape from that purgatory. Once back in these plains where I first saw heaven's light, I said in my heart: I can no longer spring light as a bird on to the back of an unbroken animal and laugh at his efforts to shake me off; nor can I throw a lasso on a running horse or bull and digging my heel in the ground, pit my strength against his; nor can I ever be what I have been in any work or game on horseback or on foot; nevertheless, this lameness, and all I have lost through it, is a small price to pay for my deliverance.

But this is not the history of my life; let me remember that I speak only of those who have lived at El Ombú in my time, in the old house which no longer exists.

There had been no changes when I returned, except that those five years had made Bruno almost a man, and more than ever like his father, except that he never had that I-know-not-what something to love in the eyes which made Valerio different from all men. Donata was the same, but older. Grey hair had come to her in her affliction; now her hair which should have been black was all white—but she was more at peace, for Bruno was good to her, and as a widow's only son, was exempt from military service. There was something else to make her happy. Those two, who were everything to her, could not grow up under one roof and not love; now she could look with confidence to a union between them, and there would be no separation. But even so, that old fear she had so often spoken of to me in former days was never absent from her heart.

Bruno was now away most of the time, working as a cattle drover, his ambition being, Donata informed me, to make money so as to buy everything needed for the house.

I had been back, living in that poor rancho, half a league from El Ombú, where I first saw the light, for the best part of a year, when Bruno, who had been away with his employer buying cattle in the south, one day appeared at my place. He had not been to El Ombú, and was silent and strange in his manner, and when we were alone together I said to him: "What has happened to you, Bruno, that you have the face of a stranger and speak in an unaccustomed tone to your friend?"

He answered: "Because you, Nicandro, have treated me like a child, concealing from me that which you ought to have told me long ago, instead of leaving me to learn it by accident from a stranger."

"It has come," I said to myself, for I knew what he meant: then I spoke of his mother.

"Ah, yes," he said with bitterness, "I know now why she pours water fresh from the well every day on that spot of ground near the door. Do you, Nicandro, think that water will ever wash away that old stain and memory? A man who is a man, must in such a thing obey, not a mother's wish, nor any woman, but that something which speaks in his heart."

"Let no such thought dwell in you to make you mad," I replied. "Look, Bruno, my friend's son and my friend, leave it to God who is above us, and who considers and remembers all evil deeds that men do, and desires not that anyone should take the sword out of his hand."

"Who is he—this God you talk of?" he answered. "Have you seen or spoken with him that you tell me what his mind is in this matter? I have only this voice to tell me how a man should act in such a case," and he smote his breast; then overcome with a passion of grief he covered his face with his hands and wept.

Vainly I begged him not to lose himself, telling him what the effect of his attempt, whether he succeeded or failed, would be on Donata and on Monica—it would break those poor women's hearts. I spoke, too, of things I had witnessed in my five years' service; the cruel sentences from which there was no appeal, the torments, the horrible deaths so often inflicted. For these evils there was no remedy on earth: and he, a poor, ignorant boy, what would he do but dash himself to pieces against that tower of brass!

He replied that within that brazen tower there was a heart full of blood; and with that he went away, only asking me as a favour not to tell his mother of this visit to me.

Some ten days later she had a message from him, brought from the capital by a traveller going to the south. Bruno sent word that he was going to Las Mulitas, a place fifty leagues west of Buenos Ayres, to work on an estancia there, and would be absent some months.

Why had he gone thither? Because he had heard that General Barboza—for that man was now a General—owned a tract of land at that place, which the Government had given him as a reward for his services on the southern frontier; and that he had recently returned from the northern provinces to Buenos Ayres and was now staying at this estancia at Las Mulitas.

Donata knew nothing of his secret motives, but his absence filled her with anxiety; and when at length she fell ill I resolved to go in search of the poor youth and try to persuade him to return to El Ombú. But at Las Mulitas I heard that he was no longer there. All strangers had been taken for the army in the frontier department, and Bruno, in spite of his passport, had been forced to go.

When I returned to El Ombú with this sad news Donata resolved at once to go to the capital and try to obtain his release. She was ill, and it was a long journey for her to perform on horseback, but she had friends to go with and take care of her. In the end she succeeded in seeing the

President, and throwing herself on her knees before him, and with tears in her eyes, implored him to let her have her son back.

He listened to her, and gave her a paper to take to the War Office. There it was found that Bruno had been sent to El Rosario, and an order was despatched for his immediate release. But when the order reached its destination the unhappy boy had deserted.

That was the last that Donata ever heard of her son. She guessed why he had gone, and knew as well as if I had told her that he had found out the secret so long hidden from him. Still, being his mother, she would not abandon hope; she struggled to live. Never did I come into her presence but I saw in her face a question which she dared not put in words. If, it said, you have heard, if you know, when and how his life ended, tell me now before I go. But it also said, If you know, do not tell me so that I and Monica may go on hoping together to the end.

"I know, Nicandro," she would say, "that if Bruno returns he will not be the same—the son I have lost. For in that one thing he is not like his father. Could another be like Valerio? No misfortune and no injustice could change that heart, or turn his sweetness sour. In that freshness and gaiety of temper he was like a child, and Bruno as a child was like him. My son! my son! where are you? God of my soul, grant that he may yet come to me, though his life be now darkened with some terrible passion—though his poor hands be stained with blood, so that my eyes may see him again before I go!"

But he came not, and she died without seeing him.

VII

IF MONICA, left alone in the house with old Pascual and his wife, had been disposed to listen to those who were attracted by her face she might have found a protector worthy of her. There were men of substance among those who came for her. But it mattered nothing to her whether they had land and cattle or not, or what their appearance was, and how they were dressed. Hers was a faithful heart. And she looked for Bruno's return, not with that poor half-despairing hope which had been Donata's, and had failed to keep her alive, but with a hope that sustained and made her able to support the months and years of waiting. She looked for his coming as the night-watcher for the dawn. On summer afternoons, when the heat of the day was over, she would take her sewing outside the gate and sit there by the hour, where her sight commanded the road to the north. From that side he would certainly come. On dark, rainy nights a lantern would be hung on the wall lest he, coming at a late hour, should miss the house in the dark. Glad, she was not, nor lively; she was pale and thin, and those dark eyes that looked too large because of her thinness were the eyes of one who had beheld grief. But with it all, there was a serenity, an air of one whose tears, held back, would all be shed at the proper time, when he returned. And he would, perhaps, come to-day, or, if not to-day, then to-morrow, or perhaps the day after, as God willed.

Nearly three years had passed by since Donata's death when, one afternoon, I rode to El Ombú, and on approaching the house spied a saddled horse, which had got loose, going away at a trot. I went after, and caught, and led it back, and then saw that its owner was a traveller, an old soldier, who with or without the permission of the people of the house, was lying down and asleep in the shade of the ombú.

There had lately been a battle in the northern part of the province, and the defeated force had broken up, and the men carrying their arms had scattered themselves all over the country. This veteran was one of them.

He did not wake when I led the horse up and shouted to him. He was a man about fifty to sixty years old, grey-haired, with many scars of sword and lance wounds on his sun-blackened face and hands. His carbine was leaning against the tree a yard or two away, but he had not unbuckled his sword and what now attracted my attention as I sat on my horse regarding him, was the way in which he clutched the hilt and shook the weapon until it rattled in its scabbard. His was an agitated sleep; the sweat stood in big drops on his face, he ground his teeth and moaned, and muttered words which I could not catch.

At length, dismounting, I called to him again, then shouted in his ear, and finally shook him by the shoulder. Then he woke with a start, and struggling up to a sitting position, and staring at me like one demented, he exclaimed, "What has happened?"

When I told him about his horse he was silent, and sitting there with eyes cast down, passed his hand repeatedly across his forehead. Never in any man's face had I seen misery compared to his. "Pardon me, friend," he spoke at last. "My ears were so full of sounds you do not hear that I paid little attention to what you were saying."

"Perhaps the great heat of the day has overcome you," I said; "or maybe you are suffering from some malady caused by an old wound received in fight."

"Yes, an incurable malady," he returned, gloomily. "Have you, friend, been in the army?"

"Five years had I served when a wound which made me lame for life delivered me from that hell."

"I have served thirty," he returned, "perhaps more. I know that I was very young when I was taken, and I remember that a woman I called mother wept to see me go. That any eyes should have shed tears for me! Shall I now in that place in the south where I was born find one who remembers my name? I look not for it! I have no one but this"— and here he touched his sword.

After an interval, he continued, "We say, friend, that in the army we can do no wrong, since all responsibility rests with those who are over us;

that our most cruel and sanguinary deeds are no more a sin or crime than is the shedding of the blood of cattle, or of Indians who are not Christians, and are therefore of no more account than cattle in God's sight. We say, too, that once we have become accustomed to kill, not men only, but even those who are powerless to defend themselves—the weak and the innocent—we think nothing of it, and have no compunction nor remorse. If this be so, why does He, the One who is above, torment me before my time? Is it just? Listen: no sooner do I close my eyes than sleep brings to me that most terrible experience a man can have—to be in the midst of a conflict and powerless. The bugles call: there is a movement everywhere of masses of men, foot and horse, and every face has on it the look of one who is doomed. There is a murmur of talking all round me, the officers are shouting and waving their swords; I strive in vain to catch the word of command; I do not know what is happening; it is all confusion, a gloom of smoke and dust, a roar of guns, a great noise and shouting of the enemy charging through us. And I am helpless. I awake, and slowly the noise and terrible scene fade from my mind, only to return when sleep again overcomes me. What repose, what refreshment can I know! Sleep, they say, is a friend to everyone, and makes all equal, the rich and the poor, the guilty and the innocent; they say, too, that this forgetfulness is like a draught of cold water to the thirsty man. But what shall I say of sleep? Often with this blade would I have delivered myself from its torture but for the fear that there may be after death something even worse than this dream."

After an interval of silence, seeing that he had recovered from his agitation, I invited him to go with me to the house. "I see smoke issuing from the kitchen," I said, "let us go in so that you may refresh yourself with maté before resuming your journey."

We went in and found the old people boiling the kettle; and in a little while Monica came in and sat with us. Never did she greet me without that light which was like sunshine in her dark eyes; words were not needed to tell me of the gratitude and friendliness she felt toward me, for she was not one to forget the past. I remember that she looked well that day in her white dress with a red flower. Had not Bruno said that he liked to see her in white, and that a flower on her bosom or in her hair was an ornament that gave her most grace? And Bruno might arrive at any moment. But the sight of that grey-haired veteran in his soiled and frayed uniform, and with his clanking sword and his dark scarred face, greatly disturbed her. I noticed that she grew paler and could scarcely keep her eyes off his face while he talked.

When sipping his maté he told us of fights he had been in, of long marches and sufferings in desert places, and of some of the former men he had served under. Among them he, by chance, named General Barboza.

Monica, I knew, had never heard of that man, and on this account I feared not to speak of him. It had, I said, been reported, I knew not whether truthfully or not, that Barboza was dead.

"On that point I can satisfy you," he returned, "since I was serving with him, when his life came to an end in the province of San Luis about two years ago. He was at the head of nineteen hundred men when it happened, and the whole force was filled with amazement at the event. Not that they regretted his loss; on the contrary, his own followers feared, and were glad to be delivered from him. He exceeded most commanders in ferocity, and was accustomed to say scoffingly to his prisoners that he would not have gunpowder wasted on them. That was not a thing to complain of, but he was capable of treating his own men as he treated a spy or a prisoner of war. Many a one have I seen put to death with a blunted knife, he, Barboza, looking on, smoking a cigarette. It was the manner of his death that startled us, for never had man been seen to perish in such a way.

"It happened on this march, about a month before the end, that a soldier named Bracamonte went one day at noon to deliver a letter from his captain to the General. Barboza was sitting in his shirt sleeves in his tent when the letter was handed to him, but just when he put out his hand to take it the man made an attempt to stab him. The General throwing himself back escaped the blow, then instantly sprang like a tiger upon his assailant, and seizing him by the wrist, wrenched the weapon out of his hand only to strike it quick as lightning into the poor fool's throat. No sooner was he down than the General bending over him, before drawing out the weapon, called to those who had run to his assistance to get him a tumbler. When, tumbler in hand, he lifted himself up and looked upon them, they say that his face was of the whiteness of iron made white in the furnace, and that his eyes were like two flames. He was mad with rage, and cried out with a loud voice, 'Thus, in the presence of the army do I serve the wretch who thought to shed my blood!' Then with a furious gesture he threw down and shattered the reddened glass, and bade them take the dead man outside the camp and leave him stripped to the vultures.

"This ended the episode, but from that day it was noticed by those about him that a change had come over the General. If, friend, you have served with, or have even seen him, you know the man he was—tall and well-formed, blue eyed and fair, like an Englishman, endowed with a strength, endurance and resolution that was a wonder to every one: he was like an eagle among birds,—that great bird that has no weakness and no mercy, whose cry fills all creatures with dismay, whose pleasure it is to tear his victim's flesh with his crooked talons. But now some secret malady had fallen on him which took away all his mighty strength; the colour of his face changed to sickly paleness, and he bent forward and swayed this way and that in the saddle as he rode like a drunken man, and this strange weakness increased day by day. It was said in the army that the blood of the man he had killed had poisoned him. The doctors who accompanied us in this march could not cure him, and their failure so angered him against them that they began to fear for their own safety.

They now said that he could not be properly treated in camp, but must withdraw to some town where a different system could be followed; but this he refused to do.

"Now it happened that we had an old soldier with us who was a curandero. He was a native of Santa Fé, and was famed for his cures in his own department; but having had the misfortune to kill a man, he was arrested and condemned to serve ten years in the army. This person now informed some of the officers that he would undertake to cure the General, and Barboza, hearing of it, sent for and questioned him. The curandero informed him that his malady was one which the doctors could not cure. It was a failure of a natural heat of the blood, and only by means of animal heat, not by drugs, could health be recovered. In such a grave case the usual remedy of putting the feet and legs in the body of some living animal opened for the purpose would not be sufficient. Some very large beast should be procured and the patient placed bodily in it.

"The General agreed to submit himself to this treatment; the doctors dared not interfere, and men were sent out in quest of a large animal. We were then encamped on a wide sandy plain in San Luis, and as we were without tents we were suffering much from the great heat and the dust-laden winds. But at this spot the General had grown worse, so that he could no longer sit on his horse, and here we had to wait for his improvement.

"In due time a very big bull was brought in and fastened to a stake in the middle of the camp. A space, fifty or sixty yards round, was marked out and roped round, and ponchos hung on the rope to form a curtain so that what was being done should not be witnessed by the army. But a great curiosity and anxiety took possession of the entire force, and when the bull was thrown down and his agonizing bellowings were heard, from all sides officers and men began to move toward that fatal spot. It had been noised about that the cure would be almost instantaneous, and many were prepared to greet the reappearance of the General with a loud cheer.

"Then very suddenly, almost before the bellowings had ceased, shrieks were heard from the enclosure, and in a moment, while we all stood staring and wondering, out rushed the General, stark naked, reddened with that bath of warm blood he had been in, a sword which he had hastily snatched up in his hand. Leaping over the barrier, he stood still for an instant, then catching sight of the great mass of men before him he flew at them, yelling and whirling his sword round so that it looked like a shining wheel in the sun. The men seeing that he was raving mad fled before him, and for a space of a hundred yards or more he pursued them; then that superhuman energy was ended; the sword flew from his hand, he staggered, and fell prostrate on the earth. For some minutes no one ventured to approach him, but he never stirred, and at length, when examined, was found to be dead."

The soldier had finished his story, and though I had many questions to ask I asked none, for I saw Monica's distress, and that she had gone white even to the lips at the terrible things the man had related. But now he had ended, and would soon depart, for the sun was getting low.

He rolled up and lighted a cigarette, and was about to rise from the bench, when he said, "One thing I forgot to mention about the soldier Bracamonte, who attempted to assassinate the General. After he had been carried out and stripped for the vultures, a paper was found sewn up in the lining of his tunic, which proved to be his passport, for it contained his right description. It said that he was a native of this department of Chascomus, so that you may have heard of him. His name was Bruno de la Cueva."

Would that he had not spoken those last words! Never, though I live to be a hundred, shall I forget that terrible scream that came from Monica's lips before she fell senseless to the floor!

As I raised her in my arms, the soldier turned and said, "She is subject to fits?"

"No," I replied, "that Bruno, of whose death we have now heard for the first time, was of this house."

"It was destiny that led me to this place," he said, "or perhaps that God who is ever against me; but you, friend, are my witness that I crossed not this threshold with a drawn weapon in my hand." And with these words he took his departure, and from that day to this I have never again beheld his face.

She opened her eyes at last, but the wings of my heart drooped when I saw them, since it was easy to see that she had lost her reason; but whether that calamity or the grief she would have known is greatest who can say? Some have died of pure grief—did it not kill Donata in the end?—but the crazed may live many years. We sometimes think it would be better if they were dead; but not in all cases—not, señor, in this.

She lived on here with the old people, for from the first time she was quiet and docile as a child. Finally an order came from a person in authority at Chascomus for those who were in the house to quit it. It was going to be pulled down for the sake of the material which was required for a building in the village. Pascual died about that time, and the widow, now old and infirm, went to live with some poor relations at Chascomus and took Monica with her. When the old woman died Monica remained with these people: she lives with them to this day. But she is free to come and go at will, and is known to all in the village as *la loca del Ombú*. They are kind to her, for her story is known to them, and God has put compassion in their hearts.

To see her you would hardly believe that she is the Monica I have told you of, whom I knew as a little one, running bare-footed after her father's flock. For she has grey hairs and wrinkles now. As you ride to Chascomus from this point you will see, on approaching the lake, a very high bank on your left hand, covered with a growth of tall fennel, hoarhound, and cardoon thistle. There on most days you will find her, sitting on the bank in the shade of the tall fennel bushes, looking across the water. She watches for the flamingoes. There are many of those great birds on the lake, and they go in flocks, and when they rise and travel across the water, flying low, their scarlet wings may be seen at a great distance. And every time she catches sight of a flock moving like a red line across the lake she cries out with delight. That is her one happiness— her life. And she is the last of all those who have lived in my time at El Ombú.

D. H. Lawrence

THE MAN WHO LOVED ISLANDS

FIRST ISLAND

THERE WAS A MAN who loved islands. He was born on one, but it didn't suit him, as there were too many other people on it, besides himself. He wanted an island all of his own: not necessarily to be alone on it, but to make it a world of his own.

An island, if it is big enough, is no better than a continent. It has to be really quite small, before it *feels like* an island; and this story will show how tiny it has to be, before you can presume to fill it with your own personality.

Now circumstances so worked out, that this lover of islands, by the time he was thirty-five, actually acquired an island of his own. He didn't own it as freehold property, but he had a ninety-nine years' lease of it, which, as far as a man and an island are concerned, is as good as everlasting. Since, if you are like Abraham, and want your offspring to be numberless as the sands of the sea-shore, you don't choose an island to start breeding on. Too soon there would be overpopulation, overcrowding, and slum conditions. Which is a horrid thought, for one who loves an island for its insulation. No, an island is a nest which holds one egg, and one only. This egg is the islander himself.

The island acquired by our potential islander was not in the remote oceans. It was quite near at home, no palm-trees nor boom of surf on the reef, nor any of that kind of thing; but a good solid dwelling-house, rather gloomy, above the landing-place, and beyond, a small farm-house with sheds, and a few outlying fields. Down on the little landing bay were three cottages in a row, like coastguards' cottages, all neat and white-washed.

What could be more cozy and home-like? It was four miles if you walked all round your island, through the gorse and the blackthorn bushes, above the steep rocks of the sea and down in the little glades where the primroses grew. If you walked straight over the two humps of hills, the length of it, through the rocky fields where the cows lay chewing, and through the rather sparse oats, on into the gorse again, and so to the low cliffs' edge, it took you only twenty minutes. And when you came to the edge, you could see another, bigger island lying beyond. But the sea was between you and it. And as you returned over the turf where the short, downland cowslips nodded you saw to the east still another island, a tiny one this time, like the calf of the cow. This tiny island also belonged to the islander.

Thus it seems that even islands like to keep each other company.

Our islander loved his island very much. In early spring, the little ways and glades were a snow of blackthorn, a vivid white among the celtic stillness of close green and grey rock, blackbirds calling out in the whiteness their first long, triumphant calls. After the blackthorn and the nestling primroses came the blue apparition of hyacinths, like elfin lakes and slipping sheets of blue, among the bushes and under the glade of trees. And many birds with nests you could peep into, on the island all your own. Wonderful what a great world it was!

Followed summer, and the cowslips gone, the wild roses faintly fragrant through the haze. There was a field of hay, the foxgloves stood looking down. In a little cove, the sun was on the pale granite where you bathed, and the shadow was in the rocks. Before the mist came stealing, and you went home through the ripening oats, the glare of the sea fading from the high air as the foghorn started to moo on the other island. And then the sea-fog went, it was autumn, and oat-sheaves lying prone; the great moon, another island, rose golden out of the sea, and, rising higher, the world of the sea was white.

So autumn ended with rain, and winter came, dark skies and dampness and rain, but rarely frost. The island, your island, cowered dark, holding away from you. You could feel, down in the wet, sombre hollows, the resentful spirit coiled upon itself, like a wet dog coiled in gloom, or a snake that is neither asleep nor awake. Then in the night, when the wind left off blowing in great gusts and volleys, as at sea, you felt that your island was a universe, infinite and old as the darkness; not an island at all, but an infinite dark world where all the souls from all the other bygone nights lived on, and the infinite distance was near.

Strangely, from your little island in space, you were gone forth into the dark, great realms of time, where all the souls that never die veer and swoop on their vast, strange errands. The little earthly island has dwindled, like a jumping-off place, into nothingness, for you have jumped off, you know not how, into the dark wide mystery of time, where the past is vastly alive, and the future is not separated off.

This is the danger of becoming an islander. When, in the city, you wear your white spats and dodge the traffic with the fear of death down your spine, then you are quite safe from the terrors of infinite time. The moment is your little islet in time, it is the spatial universe that careers round you.

But once isolate yourself on a little island in the sea of space, and the moment begins to heave and expand in great circles, the solid earth is gone, and your slippery, naked dark soul finds herself out in the timeless world, where the chariots of the so-called dead dash down the old streets of centuries, and souls crowd on the footways that we, in the moment, call bygone years. The souls of all the dead are alive again, and pulsating actively around you. You are out in the other infinity.

Something of this happened to our islander. Mysterious "feelings" came upon him, that he wasn't used to; strange awarenesses of old, far-gone men, and other influences; men of Gaul, with big moustaches, who had been on his island, and had vanished from the face of it, but not out of the air of night. They were there still, hurtling their big, violent, unseen bodies through the night. And there were priests, with golden knives and mistletoe; then other priests with a crucifix; then pirates with murder on the sea.

Our islander was uneasy. He didn't believe, in the daytime, in any of this nonsense. But at night it just was so. He had reduced himself to a single point in space, and, a point being that which has neither length nor breadth, he had to step off it into somewhere else. Just as you must step into the sea, if the waters wash your foothold away, so he had, at night, to step off into the other world of undying time.

He was uncannily aware, as he lay in the dark, that the blackthorn grove that seemed a bit uncanny even in the realm of space and day, at night was crying with old men of an invisible race, around the altar stone. What was a ruin under the hornbeam trees by day, was a moaning of bloodstained priests with crucifixes, on the ineffable night. What was a cave and a hidden beach between coarse rocks, became in the invisible dark the purple-lipped imprecation of pirates.

To escape any more of this sort of awareness, our islander daily concentrated upon his material island. Why should it not be the Happy Isle at last? Why not the last small isle of the Hesperides, the perfect place, all filled with his own gracious, blossom-like spirit? A minute world of pure perfection, made by man, himself.

He began, as we begin all our attempts to regain Paradise, by spending money. The old, semi-feudal dwelling-house he restored, let in more light, put clear lovely carpets on the floor, clear, flower-petal curtains at the sullen windows, and wines in the cellars of rock. He brought over a buxom housekeeper from the world, and a soft-spoken, much-experienced butler. These too were to be islanders.

In the farm-house he put a bailiff, with two farm-hands. There were Jersey cows, tinkling a slow bell, among the gorse. There was a call to meals at midday, and the peaceful smoking of chimneys at evening, when rest descended.

A jaunty sailing-boat with a motor accessory rode in the shelter in the bay, just below the row of three white cottages. There was also a little yawl, and two row-boats drawn up on the sand. A fishing net was drying on its supports, a boat-load of new white planks stood criss-cross, a woman was going to the well with a bucket.

In the end cottage lived the skipper of the yacht, and his wife and son. He was a man from the other, large island, at home on this sea. Every fine day he went out fishing, with his son, every fine day there was fresh fish on the island.

In the middle cottage lived an old man and wife, a very faithful couple. The old man was a carpenter, and man of many jobs. He was always working, always the sound of his plane or his saw: lost in his work, he was another kind of islander.

In the third cottage was the mason, a widower with a son and two daughters. With the help of his boy, this man dug ditches and built fences, raised buttresses and erected a new outbuilding, and hewed stone from the little quarry. His daughters worked at the big house.

It was a quiet, busy little world. When the islander brought you over as his guest, you met first the dark-bearded, thin, smiling skipper, Arnold, then his boy Charles. At the house, the smooth-lipped butler who had lived all over the world valeted you, and created that curious creamy-smooth, disarming sense of luxury around you which only a perfect and rather untrustworthy servant can create. He disarmed you and had you at his mercy. The buxom housekeeper smiled and treated you with the subtly respectful familiarity, that is only dealt out to the true gentry. And the rosy maid threw a glance at you, as if you were very wonderful, coming from the great outer world. Then you met the smiling but watchful bailiff, who came from Cornwall, and the shy farm-hand from Berkshire, with his clean wife and two little children, then the rather sulky farm-hand from Suffolk. The mason, a Kent man, would talk to you by the yard, if you let him. Only the old carpenter was gruff and elsewhere absorbed.

Well then, it was a little world to itself, and everybody feeling very safe, and being very nice to you, as if you were really something special. But it was the islander's world, not yours. He was the Master. The special smile, the special attention was to the Master. They all knew how well off they were. So the islander was no longer Mr. So-and-So. To everyone on the island, even to you yourself, he was "the Master."

Well, it was ideal. The Master was no tyrant. Ah no! He was a delicate, sensitive, handsome Master, who wanted everything perfect and everybody happy. Himself, of course, to be the fount of this happiness and perfection.

But in his way, he was a poet. He treated his guests royally, his

servants liberally. Yet he was shrewd, and very wise. He never came the
boss over his people. Yet he kept his eye on everything, like a shrewd,
blue-eyed young Hermes. And it was amazing what a lot of knowledge
he had at hand. Amazing what he knew about Jersey cows, and cheese-
making, ditching and fencing, flowers and gardening, ships and the sailing
of ships. He was a fount of knowledge about everything, and this knowledge he imparted to his people in an odd, half-ironical, half-portentous
fashion, as if he really belonged to the quaint, half-real world of the gods.

They listened to him with their hats in their hands. He loved white
clothes; or creamy white; and cloaks, and broad hats. So, in fine weather,
the bailiff would see the elegant tall figure in creamy-white serge coming
like some bird over the fallow, to look at the weeding of the turnips.
Then there would be a doffing of hats, and a few minutes of whimsical,
shrewd, wise talk, to which the bailiff answered admiringly, and the farm-
hands listened in silent wonder, leaning on their hoes. The bailiff was
almost tender, to the Master.

Or, on a windy morning, he would stand with his cloak blowing in
the sticky sea-wind, on the edge of the ditch that was being dug to drain
a little swamp, talking in the teeth of the wind to the man below, who
looked up at him with steady and inscrutable eyes.

Or at evening in the rain he would be seen hurrying across the yard,
the broad hat turned against the rain. And the farm-wife would hurriedly
exclaim: "The Master! Get up, John, and clear him a place on the sofa."
And then the door opened, and it was a cry of: "Why of all things, if it
isn't the Master! Why, have ye turned out then of a night like this, to
come across to the like of we?" And the bailiff took his cloak, and the
farm-wife his hat, the two farm-hands drew their chairs to the back, he
sat on the sofa and took a child up near him. He was wonderful with
children, talked to them simply wonderful, made you think of Our
Saviour Himself, said the woman.

Always he was greeted with smiles, and the same peculiar deference,
as if he were a higher, but also frailer being. They handled him almost
tenderly, and almost with adulation. But when he left, or when they
spoke of him, they had often a subtle, mocking smile on their faces.
There was no need to be afraid of "the Master." Just let him have his own
way. Only the old carpenter was sometimes sincerely rude to him; so he
didn't care for the old man.

It is doubtful whether any of them really liked him, man to man, or
even woman to man. But then it is doubtful if he really liked any of them,
as man to man, or man to woman. He wanted them to be happy, and the
little world to be perfect. But any one who wants the world to be perfect
must be careful not to have real likes and dislikes. A general good-will is
all you can afford.

The sad fact is, alas, that general good-will is always felt as something
of an insult, by the mere object of it; and so it breeds a quite special

brand of malice. Surely general good-will is a form of egoism, that it should have such a result!

Our islander, however, had his own resources. He spent long hours in his library, for he was compiling a book of reference to all the flowers mentioned in the Greek and Latin authors. He was not a great classical scholar: the usual public-school equipment. But there are such excellent translations nowadays. And it was so lovely, tracing flower after flower as it blossomed in the ancient world.

So the first year on the island passed by. A great deal had been done. Now the bills flooded in, and the Master, conscientious in all things, began to study them. The study left him pale and breathless. He was not a rich man. He knew he had been making a hole in his capital, to get the island into running order. When he came to look, however, there was hardly anything left but hole. Thousands and thousands of pounds had the island swallowed into nothingness.

But surely the bulk of the spending was over! Surely the island would now begin to be self-supporting, even if it made no profit! Surely he was safe. He paid a good many of the bills, and took a little heart. But he had had a shock, and the next year, the coming year, there must be economy, frugality. He told his people so, in simple and touching language. And they said: "Why surely! Surely!"

So, while the wind blew and the rain lashed outside, he would sit in his library with the bailiff over a pipe and a pot of beer, discussing farm projects. He lifted his narrow handsome face, and his blue eye became dreamy. "*What* a wind!" It blew like cannon shots. He thought of his island, lashed with foam, and inaccessible, and he exulted. . . . No, he must not lose it. He turned back to the farm projects with the zest of genius, and his hands flicked white emphasis, while the bailiff intoned: "Yes, Sir! Yes, Sir! You're right, Master!"

But the man was hardly listening. He was looking at the Master's blue lawn shirt and curious pink tie with the fiery red stone, at the enamel sleeve-links, and at the ring with the peculiar scarab. The brown searching eyes of the man of the soil glanced repeatedly over the fine, immaculate figure of the Master, with a sort of slow, calculating wonder. But if he happened to catch the Master's bright, exalted glance, his own eye lit up with a careful cordiality and deference, as he bowed his head slightly.

Thus between them they decided what crops should be sown, what fertilizers should be used in different places, which breed of pigs should be imported, and which line of turkeys. That is to say, the bailiff, by continually cautiously agreeing with the Master, kept out of it, and let the young man have his own way.

The Master knew what he was talking about. He was brilliant at grasping the gist of a book, and knowing how to apply his knowledge. On the whole, his ideas were sound. The bailiff even knew it. But in the man of the soil there was no answering enthusiasm. The brown eyes smiled their cordial deference, but the thin lips never changed. The Master pursed his own flexible mouth in a boyish versatility, as he cleverly sketched in his ideas to the other man, and the bailiff made eyes of admiration, but in his heart he was not attending, he was only watching the Master as he would have watched a queer, alien animal, quite without sympathy, not implicated.

So, it was settled, and the Master rang for Elvery, the butler, to bring a sandwich. He, the Master, was pleased. The butler saw it, and came back with anchovy and ham sandwiches, and a newly opened bottle of vermouth. There was always a newly opened bottle of something.

It was the same with the mason. The Master and he discussed the drainage of a bit of land, and more pipes were ordered, more special bricks, more this, more that.

Fine weather came at last, there was a little lull in the hard work on the island. The Master went for a short cruise in his yacht. It was not really a yacht, just a neat little bit of a yawl. They sailed along the coast of the mainland, and put in at the ports. At every port some friend turned up, the butler made elegant little meals in the cabin. Then the Master was invited to villas and hotels, his people disembarked him as if he were a prince.

And oh, how expensive it turned out! He had to telegraph to the bank for money. And he went home again, to economize.

The marsh-marigolds were blazing in the little swamp where the ditches were being dug for drainage. He almost regretted, now, the work in hand. The yellow beauties would not blaze again.

Harvest came, and a bumper crop. There must be a harvest-home supper. The long barn was now completely restored and added to. The carpenter had made long tables. Lanterns hung from the beams of the high-pitched roof. All the people of the island were assembled. The bailiff presided. It was a gay scene.

Towards the end of the supper the Master, in a velvet jacket, appeared with his guests. Then the bailiff rose and proposed: "The Master! Long life and health to the Master!" All the people drank the health with great enthusiasm and cheering. The Master replied with a little speech: They were on an island in a little world of their own. It depended on them all to make this world a world of true happiness and content. Each must do his part. He hoped he himself did what he could, for his heart was in his island, and with the people of his island.

The butler responded: As long as the island had such a Master, it could not but be a little heaven for all the people on it.—This was seconded with virile warmth by the bailiff and the mason, the skipper was beside himself. Then there was dancing, the old carpenter was fiddler.

But under all this, things were not well. The very next morning came the farm-boy to say that a cow had fallen over the cliff. The Master went to look. He peered over the not very high declivity, and saw her lying dead, on a green ledge under a bit of late-flowering broom. A beautiful, expensive creature, already looking swollen. But what a fool, to fall so unnecessarily!

It was a question of getting several men to haul her up the bank: and then of skinning and burying her. No one would eat the meat. How repulsive it all was!

This was symbolic of the island. As sure as the spirits rose in the human breast, with a movement of joy, an invisible hand struck malevolently out of the silence. There must not be any joy, nor even any quiet peace. A man broke a leg, another was crippled with rheumatic fever. The pigs had some strange disease. A storm drove the yacht on a rock. The mason hated the butler, and refused to let his daughter serve at the house.

Out of the very air came a stony, heavy malevolence. The island itself seemed malicious. It would go on being hurtful and evil for weeks at a time. Then suddenly again one morning it would be fair, lovely as a morning in Paradise, everything beautiful and flowing. And everybody would begin to feel a great relief, and a hope for happiness.

Then as soon as the Master was opened out in spirit like an open flower, some ugly blow would fall. Somebody would send him an anonymous note, accusing some other person on the island. Somebody else would come hinting things against one of his servants.

"Some folks thinks they've got an easy job out here, with all the pickings they make!" the mason's daughter screamed at the suave butler, in the Master's hearing. He pretended not to hear.

"My man says this island is surely one of the lean kine of Egypt, it would swallow a sight of money, and you'd never get anything back out of it," confided the farm-hand's wife to one of the Master's visitors.

The people were not contented. They were not islanders. "We feel we're not doing right by the children," said those who had children. "We feel we're not doing right by ourselves," said those who had no children. And the various families fairly came to hate one another.

Yet the island was so lovely. When there was a scent of honeysuckle, and the moon brightly flickering down on the sea, then even the grumblers felt a strange nostalgia for it. It set you yearning, with a wild yearning; perhaps for the past, to be far back in the mysterious past of the island, when the blood had a different throb. Strange floods of passion came over you, strange violent lusts and imaginations of cruelty. The blood and the passion and the lust which the island had known. Uncanny dreams, half-dreams, half-evoked yearnings.

The Master himself began to be a little afraid of his island. He felt here strange violent feelings he had never felt before, and lustful desires that he had been quite free from. He knew quite well now that his people didn't love him at all. He knew that their spirits were secretly against him, malicious, jeering, envious, and lurking to down him. He became just as wary and secretive with regard to them.

But it was too much. At the end of the second year, several departures took place. The housekeeper went. The Master always blamed self-important women most. The mason said he wasn't going to be monkeyed about any more, so he took his departure, with his family. The rheumatic farm-hand left.

And then the year's bills came in, the Master made up his accounts. In spite of good crops, the assets were ridiculous, against the spending. The island had again lost, not hundreds but thousands of pounds. It was incredible. But you simply couldn't believe it! Where had it all gone?

The Master spent gloomy nights and days, going through accounts in the library. He was thorough. It became evident, now the housekeeper had gone, that she had swindled him. Probably everybody was swindling him. But he hated to think it, so he put the thought away.

He emerged, however, pale and hollow-eyed from his balancing of unbalanceable accounts, looking as if something had kicked him in the stomach. It was pitiable. But the money had gone, and there was an end of it. Another great hole in his capital. How could people be so heartless?

It couldn't go on, that was evident. He would soon be bankrupt. He had to give regretful notice to his butler. He was afraid to find out how much his butler had swindled him. Because the man was such a wonderful butler, after all. And the farm-bailiff had to go. The Master had no regrets in that quarter. The losses on the farm had almost embittered him.

The third year was spent in rigid cutting down of expenses. The island was still mysterious and fascinating. But it was also treacherous and cruel, secretly, fathomlessly malevolent. In spite of all its fair show of white blossom and bluebells, and the lovely dignity of foxgloves bending their rose-red bells, it was your implacable enemy.

With reduced staff, reduced wages, reduced splendour, the third year went by. But it was fighting against hope. The farm still lost a good deal. And once more, there was a hole in that remnant of capital. Another hole, in that which was already a mere remnant round the old holes. The island was mysterious in this also: it seemed to pick the very money out of your pocket, as if it were an octopus with invisible arms stealing from you in every direction.

Yet the Master still loved it. But with a touch of rancour now.

He spent, however, the second half of the fourth year intensely working on the mainland, to be rid of it. And it was amazing how difficult he found it to dispose of an island. He had thought that everybody was pining for such an island as his; but not at all. Nobody would pay any price for it. And he wanted now to get rid of it, as a man who wants a divorce at any cost.

It was not till the middle of the fifth year that he transferred it, at a considerable loss to himself, to an hotel company who were willing to speculate in it. They were to turn it into a handy honeymoon-and-golf island!

There, take that, island which didn't know when it was well off!
Now be a honeymoon-and-golf island!

SECOND ISLAND

THE ISLANDER HAD TO MOVE. But he was not going to the mainland.
Oh, no! He moved to the smaller island, which still belonged to him. And
he took with him the faithful old carpenter and wife, the couple he never
really cared for; also a widow and daughter, who had kept house for him
the last year; also an orphan lad, to help the old man.

The small island was very small; but, being a hump of rock in the sea,
it was bigger than it looked. There was a little track among rocks and
bushes, winding and scrambling up and down around the islet, so that it
took you twenty minutes to do the circuit. It was more than you would
have expected.

Still, it was an island. The islander moved himself, with all his books,
into the commonplace six-roomed house up to which you had to scramble
from the rocky landing-place. There were also two joined-together cottages. The old carpenter lived in one, with his wife and the lad, the
widow and daughter lived in the other.

At last all was in order. The Master's books filled two rooms. It was
already autumn, Orion lifting out of the sea. And in the dark nights, the
Master could see the lights on his late island, where the hotel company
were entertaining guests who would advertise the new resort for
honeymoon-golfers.

On his hump of rock, however, the Master was still master. He
explored the crannies, the odd handbreadths of grassy level, the steep
little cliffs where the last harebells hung, and the seeds of summer were
brown above the sea, lonely and untouched. He peered down the old
well. He examined the stone pen where the pig had been kept. Himself,
he had a goat.

Yes, it was an island. Always, always, underneath among the rocks the
celtic sea sucked and washed and smote its feathery greyness. How many
different noises of the sea! deep explosions, rumblings, strange long sighs
and whistling noises; then voices, real voices of people clamouring as if
they were in a market, under the waters; and again, the far-off ringing of
a bell, surely an actual bell! then a tremulous trilling noise, very long and
alarming, and an undertone of hoarse gasping.

On this island there were no human ghosts, no ghosts of any ancient
race. The sea, and the spume and the wind and the weather, had washed
them all out, washed them out, so there was only the sound of the sea
itself, its own ghost, myriad-voiced, communing and plotting and shouting all winter long. And only the smell of the sea, with a few bristly
bushes of gorse and coarse tufts of heather, among the grey, pellucid

rocks, in the grey, more pellucid air. The coldness, the greyness, even the soft, creeping fog of the sea! and the islet of rock humped up in it all, like the last point in space.

Green star Sirius stood over the sea's rim. The island was a shadow. Out at sea a ship showed small lights. Below, in the rocky cove, the row-boat and the motor-boat were safe. A light shone in the carpenter's kitchen. That was all.

Save, of course, that the lamp was lit in the house, where the widow was preparing supper, her daughter helping. The islander went in to his meal. Here he was no longer the Master, he was an islander again and he had peace. The old carpenter, the widow and daughter were all faithfulness itself. The old man worked while ever there was light to see, because he had a passion for work. The widow and her quiet, rather delicate daughter of thirty-three worked for the Master, because they loved looking after him, and they were infinitely grateful for the haven he provided them. But they didn't call him "the Master." They gave him his name: "Mr. Cathcart, Sir!" softly, and reverently. And he spoke back to them also softly, gently, like people far from the world, afraid to make a noise.

The island was no longer a "world." It was a sort of refuge. The islander no longer struggled for anything. He had no need. It was as if he and his few dependents were a small flock of sea-birds alighted on this rock, as they travelled through space, and keeping together without a word. The silent mystery of travelling birds.

He spent most of his day in his study. His book was coming along. The widow's daughter could type out his manuscript for him, she was not uneducated. It was the one strange sound on the island, the type-writer. But soon even its spattering fitted in with the sea's noises, and the wind's.

The months went by. The islander worked away in his study, the people of the island went quietly about their concerns. The goat had a little black kid with yellow eyes. There were mackerel in the sea. The old man went fishing in the row-boat, with the lad. When the weather was calm enough, they went off in the motor-boat to the biggest island, for the post. And they brought supplies, never a penny wasted. And the days went by, and the nights, without desire, without *ennui*.

The strange stillness from all desire was a kind of wonder to the islander. He didn't want anything. His soul at last was still in him, his spirit was like a dim-lit cave under water, where strange sea-foliage expands upon the watery atmosphere, and scarcely sways, and a mute fish shadowily slips in and slips away again. All still and soft and uncrying, yet alive as rooted sea-weed is alive.

The islander said to himself: "Is this happiness?" He said to himself: "I am turned into a dream. I feel nothing, or I don't know what I feel. Yet it seems to me I am happy."

Only he had to have something upon which his mental activity could work. So he spent long, silent hours in his study, working not very fast, nor very importantly, letting the writing spin softly from him as if it were drowsy gossamer. He no longer fretted whether it were good or not, what he produced. He slowly, softly spun it like gossamer, and, if it were to melt away as gossamer in autumn melts, he would not mind. It was only the soft evanescence of gossamy things which now seemed to him permanent. The very mist of eternity was in them. Whereas stone buildings, cathedrals for example, seemed to him to howl with temporary resistance, knowing they must fall at last; the tension of their long endurance seemed to howl forth from them all the time.

Sometimes he went to the mainland and to the city. Then he went elegantly, dressed in the latest style, to his club. He sat in a stall at the theatre, he shopped in Bond Street. He discussed terms for publishing his book. But over his face was that gossamy look of having dropped out of the race of progress, which made the vulgar city people feel they had won it over him, and made him glad to go back to his island.

He didn't mind if he never published his book. The years were blending into a soft mist, from which nothing obtruded. Spring came. There was never a primrose on his island, but he found a winter-aconite. There were two little sprayed bushes of blackthorn, and some wind-flowers. He began to make a list of the flowers on his islet, and that was absorbing. He noted a wild currant bush, and watched for the elder flowers on a stunted little tree, then for the first yellow rags of the broom, and wild roses. Bladder campion, orchids, stitchwort, celandine, he was prouder of them than if they had been people on his island. When he came across the golden saxifrage, so inconspicuous in a damp corner, he crouched over it in a trance, he knew not for how long, looking at it. Yet it was nothing to look at. As the widow's daughter found, when he showed it her.

He had said to her, in real triumph:

"I found the golden saxifrage this morning."

The name sounded splendid. She looked at him with fascinated brown eyes, in which was a hollow ache that frightened him a little.

"Did you, Sir? Is it a nice flower?"

He pursed his lips and tilted his brows.

"Well—not showy exactly. I'll show it you if you like."

"I should like to see it."

She was so quiet, so wistful. But he sensed in her a persistency which made him uneasy. She said she was so happy: really happy. She followed him quietly, like a shadow, on the rocky track where there was never room for two people to walk side by side. He went first, and could feel her there, immediately behind him, following so submissively, gloating on him from behind.

It was a kind of pity for her which made him become her lover: though he never realized the extent of the power she had gained over him, and how *she* willed it. But the moment he had fallen, a jangling feeling came upon him, that it was all wrong. He felt a nervous dislike of her. He had not wanted it. And it seemed to him, as far as her physical self went, she had not wanted it either. It was just her will. He went away, and climbed at the risk of his neck down to a ledge near the sea. There he sat for hours, gazing all jangled at the sea, and saying miserably to himself: "We didn't want it. We didn't really want it."

It was the automatism of sex that had caught him again. Not that he hated sex. He deemed it, as the Chinese do, one of the great life-mysteries. But it had become mechanical, automatic, and he wanted to escape that. Automatic sex shattered him, and filled him with a sort of death. He thought he had come through, to a new stillness of desirelessness. Perhaps beyond that, there was a new fresh delicacy of desire, an unentered frail communion of two people meeting on untrodden ground.

But be that as it might, this was not it. This was nothing new or fresh. It was automatic, and driven from the will. Even she, in her true self, hadn't wanted it. It was automatic in her.

When he came home, very late, and saw her face white with fear and apprehension of his feeling against her, he pitied her, and spoke to her delicately, reassuringly. But he kept himself remote from her.

She gave no sign. She served him with the same silence, the same hidden hunger to serve him, to be near where he was. He felt her love following him with strange, awful persistency. She claimed nothing. Yet now, when he met her bright, brown, curiously vacant eyes, he saw in them the mute question. The question came direct at him, with a force and a power of will he never realized.

So he succumbed, and asked her again.

"Not," she said, "if it will make you hate me."

"Why should it?" he replied, nettled. "Of course not."

"You know I would do anything on earth for you."

It was only afterwards, in his exasperation, he remembered what she had said, and was more exasperated. Why should she pretend to do this *for him*? Why not for herself? But in his exasperation, he drove himself deeper in. In order to achieve some sort of satisfaction, which he never did achieve, he abandoned himself to her. Everybody on the island knew. But he did not care.

Then even what desire he had left him, and he felt only shattered. He felt that only with her will had she wanted him. Now he was shattered and full of self-contempt. His island was smirched and spoiled. He had lost his place in the rare, desireless levels of Time to which he had at last arrived, and he had fallen right back. If only it had been true, delicate desire between them, and a delicate meeting on the third rare place where a man might meet a woman, when they were both true to the frail, sensitive, crocus flame of desire in them. But it had been no such thing: automatic, an act of will, not of true desire, it left him feeling humiliated.

He went away from the islet, in spite of her mute reproach. And he wandered about the continent, vainly seeking a place where he could stay. He was out of key; he did not fit in the world any more.

Then came a letter from Flora—her name was Flora—to say she was afraid she was going to have a child. He sat down as if he were shot, and he remained sitting. But he replied to her: "Why be afraid? If it is so, it is so, and we should rather be pleased than afraid."

At this very moment, it happened there was an auction of islands. He got the maps, and studied them. And at the auction he bought, for very little money, another island. It was just a few acres of rock away in the north, on the outer fringe of the isles. It was low, it rose out of the great ocean. There was not a building, not even a tree on it. Only northern sea-turf, a pool of rain-water, a bit of sedge, rock, and sea-birds. Nothing else. Under the weeping wet western sky.

He made a trip to visit his new possession. For several days, owing to the seas, he could not approach it. Then, in a light sea-mist, he landed, and saw it hazy, low, stretching apparently a long way. But it was illusion. He walked over the wet, springy turf, and dark-grey sheep tossed away from him, spectral, bleating hoarsely. And he came to the dark pool, with the sedge. Then on in the dampness, to the grey sea sucking angrily among the rocks.

This was indeed an island.

So he went home to Flora. She looked at him with guilty fear, but also with a triumphant brightness in her uncanny eyes. And again he was gentle, he reassured her, even he wanted her again, with that curious desire that was almost like toothache. So he took her to the mainland, and they were married, since she was going to have his child.

They returned to the island. She still brought in his meals, her own along with them. She sat and ate with him. He would have it so. The widowed mother preferred to stay in the kitchen. And Flora slept in the guest-room of his house, mistress of his house.

His desire, whatever it was, died in him with nauseous finality. The child would still be months coming. His island was hateful to him, vulgar, a suburb. He himself had lost all his finer distinction. The weeks passed in a sort of prison, in humiliation. Yet he stuck it out, till the child was born. But he was meditating escape. Flora did not even know.

A nurse appeared, and ate at table with them. The doctor came sometimes, and, if the sea were rough, he too had to stay. He was cheery over his whisky.

They might have been a young couple in Golders Green.

The daughter was born at last. The father looked at the baby, and felt depressed, almost more than he could bear. The millstone was tied round his neck. But he tried not to show what he felt. And Flora did not know. She still smiled with a kind of half-witted triumph in her joy, as she got well again. Then she began again to look at him with those aching, suggestive, somehow impudent eyes. She adored him so.

This he could not stand. He told her that he had to go away for a time. She wept, but she thought she had got him. He told her he had settled the best part of his property to her, and wrote down for her what income it would produce. She hardly listened, only looked at him with those heavy, adoring, impudent eyes. He gave her a cheque-book, with the amount of her credit duly entered. This did arouse her interest. And he told her, if she got tired of the island, she could choose her home wherever she wished.

She followed him with those aching, persistent brown eyes, when he left, and he never even saw her weep.

He went straight north, to prepare his third island.

THIRD ISLAND

THE THIRD ISLAND was soon made habitable. With cement and the big pebbles from the shingle beach, two men built him a hut, and roofed it with corrugated iron. A boat brought over a bed and table, and three chairs, with a good cupboard, and a few books. He laid in a supply of coal and paraffin and food—he wanted so little.

The house stood near the flat shingle bay where he landed, and where he pulled up his light boat. On a sunny day in August the men sailed away and left him. The sea was still and pale blue. On the horizon he saw the small mail-steamer slowly passing northwards, as if she were walking. She served the outer isles twice a week. He could row out to her if need be, in calm weather, and he could signal her from a flagstaff behind his cottage.

Half a dozen sheep still remained on the island, as company; and he had a cat to rub against his legs. While the sweet, sunny days of the northern autumn lasted, he would walk among the rocks, and over the springy turf of his small domain, always coming to the ceaseless, restless sea. He looked at every leaf, that might be different from another, and he watched the endless expansion and contraction of the water-tossed sea-weed. He had never a tree, not even a bit of heather to guard. Only the turf, and tiny turf-plants, and the sedge by the pool, the sea-weed in the ocean. He was glad. He didn't want trees or bushes. They stood up like people, too assertive. His bare, low-pitched island in the pale blue sea was all he wanted.

He no longer worked at his book. The interest had gone. He liked to sit on the low elevation of his island, and see the sea; nothing but the pale, quiet sea. And to feel his mind turn soft and hazy, like the hazy ocean. Sometimes, like a mirage, he would see the shadow of land rise hovering to northwards. It was a big island beyond. But quite without substance.

He was soon almost startled when he perceived the steamer on the near horizon, and his heart contracted with fear, lest it were going to pause and molest him. Anxiously he watched it go, and not till it was out of sight did he feel truly relieved, himself again. The tension of waiting for human approach was cruel. He did not want to be approached. He did not want to hear voices. He was shocked by the sound of his own voice, if he inadvertently spoke to his cat. He rebuked himself for having broken the great silence. And he was irritated when his cat would look up at him and mew faintly, plaintively. He frowned at her. And she knew. She was becoming wild, lurking in the rocks, perhaps fishing.

But what he disliked most was when one of the lumps of sheep opened its mouth and baa-ed its hoarse, raucous baa. He watched it, and it looked to him hideous and gross. He came to dislike the sheep very much.

He wanted only to hear the whispering sound of the sea, and the sharp cries of the gulls, cries that came out of another world to him. And best of all, the great silence.

He decided to get rid of the sheep, when the boat came. They were accustomed to him now, and stood and stared at him with yellow or colourless eyes, in an insolence that was almost cold ridicule. There was a suggestion of cold indecency about them. He disliked them very much. And when they jumped with staccato jumps off the rocks, and their hoofs made the dry, sharp hit, and the fleece flopped on their square backs—he found them repulsive, degrading.

The fine weather passed, and it rained all day. He lay a great deal on his bed, listening to the water trickling from his roof into the zinc water-butt, looking through the open door at the rain, the dark rocks, the hidden sea. Many gulls were on the island now: many sea-birds of all sorts. It was another world of life. Many of the birds he had never seen before. His old impulse came over him, to send for a book, to know their names. In a flicker of the old passion, to know the name of every-thing he saw, he even decided to row out to the steamer. The names of these birds! he must know their names, otherwise he had not got them, they were not quite alive to him.

But the desire left him, and he merely watched the birds as they wheeled or walked around him, watched them vaguely, without discrimi-nation. All interest had left him. Only there was one gull, a big handsome fellow, who would walk back and forth, back and forth in front of the open door of the cabin, as if he had some mission there. He was big, and pearl-grey, and his roundnesses were as smooth and lovely as a pearl. Only the folded wings had shut black pinions, and on the closed black feathers were three very distinct white dots, making a pattern. The is-lander wondered very much, why this bit of trimming on the bird out of the far, cold seas. And as the gull walked back and forth, back and forth in front of the cabin, strutting on pale-dusky gold feet, holding up his pale yellow beak, that was curved at the tip, with curious alien impor-tance, the man wondered over him. He was portentous, he had a meaning.

Then the bird came no more. The island, which had been full of sea-birds, the flash of wings, the sound and cut of wings and sharp eerie cries in the air, began to be deserted again. No longer they sat like living eggs on the rocks and turf, moving their heads, but scarcely rising into flight round his feet. No longer they ran across the turf among the sheep, and lifted themselves upon low wings. The host had gone. But some remained, always.

The days shortened, and the world grew eerie. One day the boat came: as if suddenly, swooping down. The islander found it a violation. It was torture to talk to those two men, in their homely clumsy clothes. The air of familiarity around them was very repugnant to him. Himself, he was neatly dressed, his cabin was neat and tidy. He resented any intrusion, the clumsy homeliness, the heavy-footedness of the two fishermen was really repulsive to him.

The letters they had brought, he left lying unopened in a little box. In one of them was his money. But he could not bear to open even that one. Any kind of contact was repulsive to him. Even to read his name on an envelope. He hid the letters away.

And the hustle and horror of getting the sheep caught and tied and put in the ship made him loathe with profound repulsion the whole of the animal creation. What repulsive god invented animals, and evil-smelling men? To his nostrils, the fishermen and the sheep alike smelled foul; an uncleanness on the fresh earth.

He was still nerve-racked and tortured when the ship at last lifted sail and was drawing away, over the still sea. And sometimes days after, he would start with repulsion, thinking he heard the munching of sheep.

The dark days of winter drew on. Sometimes there was no real day at all. He felt ill, as if he were dissolving, as if dissolution had already set in inside him. Everything was twilight, outside, and in his mind and soul. Once, when he went to the door, he saw black heads of men swimming in his bay. For some moments he swooned unconscious. It was the shock, the horror of unexpected human approach. The horror in the twilight! And not till the shock had undermined him and left him disembodied, did he realize that the black heads were the heads of seals swimming in. A sick relief came over him. But he was barely conscious, after the shock. Later on, he sat and wept with gratitude, because they were not men. But he never realized that he wept. He was too dim. Like some strange, ethereal animal, he no longer realized what he was doing.

Only he still derived his single satisfaction from being alone, absolutely alone, with the space soaking into him. The grey sea alone, and the footing of his sea-washed island. No other contact. Nothing human to bring its horror into contact with him. Only space, damp, twilit, sea-washed space! This was the bread of his soul.

For this reason, he was most glad when there was a storm, or when the sea was high. Then nothing could get at him. Nothing could come through to him from the outer world. True, the terrific violence of the wind made him suffer badly. At the same time, it swept the world utterly out of existence for him. He always liked the sea to be heavily rolling and tearing. Then no boat could get at him. It was like eternal ramparts round his island.

He kept no track of time, and no longer thought of opening a book. The print, the printed letters, so like the depravity of speech, looked obscene. He tore the brass label from the paraffin stove. He obliterated any bit of lettering in his cabin.

His cat had disappeared. He was rather glad. He shivered at her thin, obtrusive call. She had lived in the coal shed. And each morning he had put her a dish of porridge, the same as he ate. He washed her saucer with repulsion. He did not like her writhing about. But he fed her scrupulously. Then one day she did not come for her porridge: she always mewed for it. She did not come again.

He prowled about his island in the rain, in a big oil-skin coat, not knowing what he was looking at, nor what he went out to see. Time had ceased to pass. He stood for long spaces, gazing from a white, sharp face, with those keen, far-off blue eyes of his, gazing fiercely and almost cruelly at the dark sea under the dark sky. And if he saw the labouring sail of a fishing boat away on the cold waters, a strange malevolent anger passed over his features.

Sometimes he was ill. He knew he was ill, because he staggered as he walked, and easily fell down. Then he paused to think what it was. And he went to his stores and took out dried milk and malt, and ate that. Then he forgot again. He ceased to register his own feelings.

The days were beginning to lengthen. All winter the weather had been comparatively mild, but with much rain, much rain. He had forgotten the sun. Suddenly, however, the air was very cold, and he began to shiver. A fear came over him. The sky was level and grey, and never a star appeared at night. It was very cold. More birds began to arrive. The island was freezing. With trembling hands he made a fire in his grate. The cold frightened him.

And now it continued, day after day, a dull, deathly cold. Occasional crumblings of snow were in the air. The days were greyly longer, but no change in the cold. Frozen grey daylight. The birds passed away, flying away. Some he saw lying frozen. It was as if all life were drawing away, contracting away from the north, contracting southwards. "Soon," he said to himself, "it will all be gone, and in all these regions nothing will be alive." He felt a cruel satisfaction in the thought.

Then one night there seemed to be a relief: he slept better, did not tremble half awake, and writhe so much, half-conscious. He had become so used to the quaking and writhing of his body, he hardly noticed it. But when for once it slept deep, he noticed that.

He awoke in the morning to a curious whiteness. His window was muffled. It had snowed. He got up and opened his door, and shuddered. Ugh! how cold! All white, with a dark leaden sea, and black rocks curiously speckled with white. The foam was no longer pure. It seemed dirty. And the sea ate at the whiteness of the corpse-like land. Crumbles of snow were silting down the dead air.

On the ground the snow was a foot deep, white and smooth and soft, windless. He took a shovel to clear round his house and shed. The pallor of morning darkened. There was a strange rumbling of far-off thunder, in the frozen air, and through the newly-falling snow, a dim flash of lightning. Snow now fell steadily down, in the motionless obscurity.

He went out for a few minutes. But it was difficult. He stumbled and fell in the snow, which burned his face. Weak, faint, he toiled home. And when he recovered, he took the trouble to make hot milk.

It snowed all the time. In the afternoon again there was a muffled rumbling of thunder, and flashes of lightning blinking reddish through the falling snow. Uneasy, he went to bed and lay staring fixedly at nothing.

Morning seemed never to come. An eternity long he lay and waited for one alleviating pallor on the night. And at last it seemed the air was paler. His house was a cell faintly illuminated with white light. He realized the snow was walled outside his window. He got up, in the dead cold. When he opened his door, the motionless snow stopped him in a wall as high as his breast. Looking over the top of it, he felt the dead wind slowly driving, saw the snow-powder lift and travel like a funeral train. The blackish sea churned and champed, seeming to bite at the snow, impotent. The sky was grey, but luminous.

He began to work in a frenzy, to get at his boat. If he was to be shut in, it must be by his own choice, not by the mechanical power of the elements. He must get to the sea. He must be able to get at his boat.

But he was weak, and at times the snow overcame him. It fell on him, and he lay buried and lifeless. Yet every time, he struggled alive before it was too late, and fell upon the snow with the energy of fever. Exhausted, he would not give in. He crept indoors and made coffee and bacon. Long since he had cooked so much. Then he went at the snow once more. He must conquer the snow, this new, white brute force which had accumulated against him.

He worked in the awful, dead wind, pushing the snow aside, pressing it with his shovel. It was cold, freezing hard in the wind, even when the sun came out for a while, and showed him his white, lifeless surroundings, the black sea rolling sullen, flecked with dull spume, away to the horizons. Yet the sun had power on his face. It was March.

He reached the boat. He pushed the snow away, then sat down under the lee of the boat, looking at the sea, which nearly swirled to his feet, in the high tide. Curiously natural the pebbles looked, in a world gone all uncanny. The sun shone no more. Snow was falling in hard crumbs, that vanished as if by miracle as they touched the hard blackness of the sea. Hoarse waves rang in the shingle, rushing up at the snow. The wet rocks were brutally black. And all the time the myriad swooping crumbs of snow, demonish, touched the dark sea and disappeared.

During the night there was a great storm. It seemed to him he could hear the vast mass of the snow striking all the world with a ceaseless thud; and over it all, the wind roared in strange hollow volleys, in between which came a jump of blindfold lightning, then the low roll of thunder

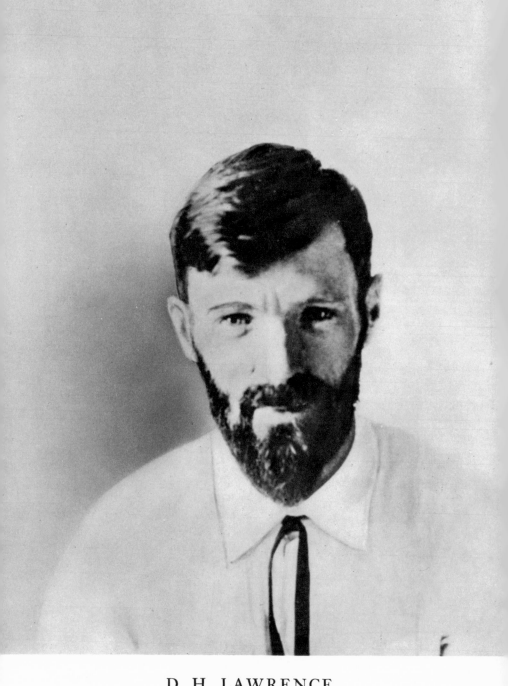

D. H. LAWRENCE

photograph by Brown Brothers

ELIZABETH BOWEN

photograph by Angus McBean

heavier than the wind. When at last the dawn faintly discoloured the dark, the storm had more or less subsided, but a steady wind drove on. The snow was up to the top of his door.

Sullenly, he worked to dig himself out. And he managed, through sheer persistency, to get out. He was in the tail of a great drift, many feet high. When he got through, the frozen snow was not more than two feet deep. But his island was gone. Its shape was all changed, great heaping white hills rose where no hills had been, inaccessible, and they fumed like volcanoes, but with snow powder. He was sickened and overcome.

His boat was in another, smaller drift. But he had not the strength to clear it. He looked at it helplessly. The shovel slipped from his hands, and he sank in the snow, to forget. In the snow itself, the sea resounded.

Something brought him to. He crept to his house. He was almost without feeling. Yet he managed to warm himself, just that part of him which leaned in snow-sleep over the coal fire. Then again, he made hot milk. After which, carefully, he built up the fire.

The wind dropped. Was it night again? In the silence, it seemed he could hear the panther-like dropping of infinite snow. Thunder rumbled nearer, crackled quick after the bleared reddened lightning. He lay in bed in a kind of stupor. The elements! The elements! His mind repeated the word dumbly. You can't win against the elements.

How long it went on, he never knew. Once, like a wraith, he got out, and climbed to the top of a white hill on his unrecognizable island. The sun was hot. "It is summer," he said to himself, "and the time of leaves." He looked stupidly over the whiteness of his foreign island, over the waste of the lifeless sea. He pretended to imagine he saw the wink of a sail. Because he knew too well there would never again be a sail on that stark sea.

As he looked, the sky mysteriously darkened and chilled. From far off came the mutter of the unsatisfied thunder, and he knew it was the signal of the snow rolling over the sea. He turned, and felt its breath on him.

Katherine Mansfield

THE FLY

Y'ARE VERY SNUG IN HERE," piped old Mr. Woodifield, and he peered out of the great, green leather armchair by his friend the boss's desk as a baby peers out of its pram. His talk was over; it was time for him to be off. But he did not want to go. Since he had retired, since his . . . stroke, the wife and the girls kept him boxed up in the house every day of the week except Tuesday. On Tuesday he was dressed up and brushed and allowed to cut back to the City for the day. Though what he did there the wife and girls couldn't imagine. Made a nuisance of himself to his friends, they supposed. . . . Well, perhaps so. All the same, we cling to our last pleasures as the tree clings to its last leaves. So there sat old Woodifield, smoking a cigar and staring almost greedily at the boss, who rolled in his office chair, stout, rosy, five years older than he, and still going strong, still at the helm. It did one good to see him.

Wistfully, admiringly, the old voice added, "It's snug in here, upon my word!"

"Yes, it's comfortable enough," agreed the boss, and he flipped the *Financial Times* with a paper-knife. As a matter of fact he was proud of his room; he liked to have it admired, especially by old Woodifield. It gave him a feeling of deep, solid satisfaction to be planted there in the midst of it in full view of that frail old figure in the muffler.

"I've had it done up lately," he explained, as he had explained for the past—how many?—weeks. "New carpet," and he pointed to the bright red carpet with a pattern of large white rings. "New furniture," and he nodded towards the massive bookcase and the table with legs like twisted treacle. "Electric heating!" He waved almost exultantly towards the five transparent, pearly sausages glowing so softly in the tilted copper pan.

But he did not draw old Woodifield's attention to the photograph over the table of a grave-looking boy in uniform standing in one of those spectral photographers' parks with photographers' storm-clouds behind him. It was not new. It had been there for over six years.

"There was something I wanted to tell you," said old Woodifield, and his eyes grew dim remembering. "Now what was it? I had it in my mind when I started out this morning." His hands began to tremble, and patches of red showed above his beard.

Poor old chap, he's on his last pins, thought the boss. And, feeling kindly, he winked at the old man, and said jokingly, "I tell you what. I've got a little drop of something here that'll do you good before you go out into the cold again. It's beautiful stuff. It wouldn't hurt a child." He took a key off his watch-chain, unlocked a cupboard below his desk, and drew forth a dark, squat bottle. "That's the medicine," said he. "And the man from whom I got it told me on the strict Q.T. it came from the cellars at Windsor Cassel."

Old Woodifield's mouth fell open at the sight. He couldn't have looked more surprised if the boss had produced a rabbit.

"It's whisky, ain't it?" he piped, feebly.

The boss turned the bottle and lovingly showed him the label. Whisky it was.

"D'you know," said he, peering up at the boss wonderingly, "they won't let me touch it at home." And he looked as though he was going to cry.

"Ah, that's where we know a bit more than the ladies," cried the boss, swooping across for two tumblers that stood on the table with the water-bottle, and pouring a generous finger into each. "Drink it down. It'll do you good. And don't put any water with it. It's sacrilege to tamper with stuff like this. Ah!" He tossed off his, pulled out his handkerchief, hastily wiped his moustaches, and cocked an eye at old Woodifield, who was rolling his in his chaps.

The old man swallowed, was silent a moment, and then said faintly, "It's nutty!"

But it warmed him; it crept into his chill old brain—he remembered.

"That was it," he said, heaving himself out of his chair. "I thought you'd like to know. The girls were in Belgium last week having a look at poor Reggie's grave, and they happened to come across your boy's. They're quite near each other, it seems."

Old Woodifield paused, but the boss made no reply. Only a quiver in his eyelids showed that he heard.

"The girls were delighted with the way the place is kept," piped the old voice. "Beautifully looked after. Couldn't be better if they were at home. You've not been across, have yer?"

"No, no!" For various reasons the boss had not been across.

"There's miles of it," quavered old Woodifield, "and it's all as neat as a garden. Flowers growing on all the graves. Nice broad paths." It was plain from his voice how much he liked a nice broad path.

The pause came again. Then the old man brightened wonderfully.

"D'you know what the hotel made the girls pay for a pot of jam?" he piped. "Ten francs! Robbery, I call it. It was a little pot, so Gertrude says, no bigger than a half-crown. And she hadn't taken more than a spoonful when they charged her ten francs. Gertrude brought the pot away with her to teach 'em a lesson. Quite right, too; it's trading on our feelings. They think because we're over there having a look around we're ready to pay anything. That's what it is." And he turned towards the door.

"Quite right, quite right!" cried the boss, though what was quite right he hadn't the least idea. He came round by his desk, followed the shuffling footsteps to the door, and saw the old fellow out. Woodifield was gone.

For a long moment the boss stayed, staring at nothing, while the grey-haired office messenger, watching him, dodged in and out of his cubby-hole like a dog that expects to be taken for a run. Then: "I'll see nobody for half an hour, Macey," said the boss. "Understand? Nobody at all."

"Very good, sir."

The door shut, the firm heavy steps recrossed the bright carpet, the fat body plumped down in the spring chair, and leaning forward, the boss covered his face with his hands. He wanted, he intended, he had arranged to weep. . . .

It had been a terrible shock to him when old Woodifield sprang that remark upon him about the boy's grave. It was exactly as though the earth had opened and he had seen the boy lying there with Woodifield's girls staring down at him. For it was strange. Although over six years had passed away, the boss never thought of the boy except as lying un-changed, unblemished in his uniform, asleep for ever. "My son!" groaned the boss. But no tears came yet. In the past, in the first months and even years after the boy's death, he had only to say those words to be over-come by such grief that nothing short of a violent fit of weeping could relieve him. Time, he had declared then, he had told everybody, could make no difference. Other men perhaps might recover, might live their loss down, but not he. How was it possible? His boy was an only son. Ever since his birth the boss had worked at building up this business for him; it had no other meaning if it was not for the boy. Life itself had come to have no other meaning. How on earth could he have slaved, denied himself, kept going all those years without the promise for ever before him of the boy's stepping into his shoes and carrying on where he left off?

And that promise had been so near being fulfilled. The boy had been in the office learning the ropes for a year before the war. Every morning they had started off together; they had come back by the same train. And what congratulations he had received as the boy's father! No wonder; he had taken to it marvellously. As to his popularity with the staff, every man jack of them down to old Macey couldn't make enough of the boy. And he wasn't in the least spoilt. No, he was just his bright, natural self, with the right word for everybody, with that boyish look and his habit of saying, "Simply splendid!"

But all that was over and done with as though it never had been. The day had come when Macey had handed him the telegram that brought the whole place crashing about his head. "Deeply regret to inform you . . ." And he had left the office a broken man, with his life in ruins.

Six years ago, six years . . . How quickly time passed! It might have happened yesterday. The boss took his hands from his face; he was puzzled. Something seemed to be wrong with him. He wasn't feeling as he wanted to feel. He decided to get up and have a look at the boy's photograph. But it wasn't a favorite photograph of his; the expression was unnatural. It was cold, even stern-looking. The boy had never looked like that.

At that moment the boss noticed that a fly had fallen into his broad inkpot, and was trying feebly but desperately to clamber out again. Help! help! said those struggling legs. But the sides of the inkpot were wet and slippery; it fell back again and began to swim. The boss took up a pen, picked the fly out of the ink, and shook it on to a piece of blotting-paper. For a fraction of a second it lay still on the dark patch that oozed round it. Then the front legs waved, took hold, and, pulling its small sodden body up, it began the immense task of cleaning the ink from its wings. Over and under, over and under, went a leg along a wing, as the stone goes over and under the scythe. Then there was a pause, while the fly, seeming to stand on the tips of its toes, tried to expand first one wing and then the other. It succeeded at last, and, sitting down, it began, like a minute cat, to clean its face. Now one could imagine that the little front legs rubbed against each other lightly, joyfully. The horrible danger was over; it had escaped; it was ready for life again.

But just then the boss had an idea. He plunged his pen back into the ink, leaned his thick wrist on the blotting paper, and as the fly tried its wings down came a great heavy blot. What would it make of that? What indeed! The little beggar seemed absolutely cowed, stunned, and afraid to move because of what would happen next. But then, as if painfully, it dragged itself forward. The front legs waved, caught hold, and, more slowly this time, the task began from the beginning.

He's a plucky little devil, thought the boss, and he felt a real admiration for the fly's courage. That was the way to tackle things; that was the right spirit. Never say die; it was only a question of . . . But the fly had again finished its laborious task, and the boss had just time to refill his pen, to shake fair and square on the new-cleaned body yet another dark drop. What about it this time? A painful moment of suspense followed. But behold, the front legs were again waving; the boss felt a rush of relief. He leaned over the fly and said to it tenderly, "You artful little b . . ." And he actually had the brilliant notion of breathing on it to help the drying process. All the same, there was something timid and weak about its efforts now, and the boss decided that this time should be the last, as he dipped the pen into the inkpot.

It was. The last blot on the soaked blotting-paper, and the draggled fly lay in it and did not stir. The back legs were stuck to the body; the front legs were not to be seen.

"Come on," said the boss. "Look sharp!" And he stirred it with his pen—in vain. Nothing happened or was likely to happen. The fly was dead.

The boss lifted the corpse on the end of the paper-knife and flung it into the waste-paper basket. But such a grinding feeling of wretchedness seized him that he felt positively frightened. He started forward and pressed the bell for Macey.

"Bring me some fresh blotting-paper," he said, sternly, "and look sharp about it." And while the old dog padded away he fell to wondering what it was he had been thinking about before. What was it? It was . . . He took out his handkerchief and passed it inside his collar. For the life of him he could not remember.

Alan Sillitoe

THE LONELINESS OF THE LONG-DISTANCE RUNNER

I

A s soon as I got to Borstal they made me a long-distance cross-country runner. I suppose they thought I was just the build for it because I was long and skinny for my age (and still am) and in any case I didn't mind it much, to tell you the truth, because running had always been made much of in our family, especially running away from the police. I've always been a good runner, quick and with a big stride as well, the only trouble being that no matter how fast I run, and I did a very fair lick even though I do say so myself, it didn't stop me getting caught by the cops after that bakery job.

You might think it a bit rare, having long-distance cross-country runners in Borstal, thinking that the first thing a long-distance cross-country runner would do when they set him loose at them fields and woods would be to run as far away from the place as he could get on a bellyful of Borstal slumgullion—but you're wrong, and I'll tell you why. The first thing is that them bastards over us aren't as daft as they most of the time look, and for another thing I'm not so daft as I would look if I tried to make a break for it on my long-distance running, because to abscond and then get caught is nothing but a mug's game, and I'm not falling for it. Cunning is what counts in this life, and even that you've got to use in the slyest way you can; I'm telling you straight: they're cunning, and I'm cunning. If only "them" and "us" had the same ideas we'd

Published 1959. Copyright © 1959 by Alan Sillitoe.

get on like a house on fire, but they don't see eye to eye with us and we don't see eye to eye with them, so that's how it stands and how it will always stand. The one fact is that all of us are cunning, and because of this there's no love lost between us. So the thing is that they know I won't try to get away from them: they sit there like spiders in that crumbly manor house, perched like jumped-up jackdaws on the roof, watching out over the drives and fields like German generals from the tops of tanks. And even when I jog-trot on behind a wood and they can't see me anymore they know my sweeping-brush head will bob along that hedge-top in an hour's time and that I'll report to the bloke on the gate. Because when on a raw and frosty morning I get up at five o'clock and stand shivering my belly off on the stone floor and all the rest still have another hour to snooze before the bells go, I slink downstairs through all the corridors to the big outside door with a permit running-card in my fist, I feel like the first and last man on the world, both at once, if you can believe what I'm trying to say. I feel like the first man because I've hardly got a stitch on and am sent against the frozen fields in a shimmy and shorts—even the first poor bastard dropped on to the earth in mid-winter knew how to make a suit of leaves, or how to skin a pterodactyl for a topcoat. But there I am, frozen stiff, with nothing to get me warm except a couple of hours' long-distance running before breakfast, not even a slice of bread-and-sheepdip. They're training me up fine for the big sports day when all the pig-faced snotty-nosed dukes and ladies—who can't add two and two together and would mess themselves like loonies if they didn't have slavies to beck-and-call—come and make speeches to us about sports being just the thing to get us leading an honest life and keep our itching finger-ends off them shop locks and safe handles and hairgrips to open gas meters. They give us a bit of blue ribbon and a cup for a prize after we've shagged ourselves out running or jumping, like race horses, only we don't get so well looked-after as race horses, that's the only thing.

So there I am, standing in the doorway in shimmy and shorts, not even a dry crust in my guts, looking out at frosty flowers on the ground. I suppose you think this is enough to make me cry? Not likely. Just because I feel like the first bloke in the world wouldn't make me bawl. It makes me feel fifty times better than when I'm cooped up in that dormitory with three hundred others. No, it's sometimes when I stand there feeling like the *last* man in the world that I don't feel so good. I feel like the last man in the world because I think that all those three hundred sleepers behind me are dead. They sleep so well I think that every scruffy head's kicked the bucket in the night and I'm the only one left, and when I look out into the bushes and frozen ponds I have the feeling that it's going to get colder and colder until everything I can see, meaning my red arms as well, is going to be covered with a thousand miles of ice, all the earth, right up to the sky and over every bit of land and sea. So I try to kick this feeling out and act like I'm the first man on earth. And that makes me feel good, so as soon as I'm steamed up enough to get this feeling in me, I take a flying leap out of the doorway, and off I trot.

I'm in Essex. It's supposed to be a good Borstal, at least that's what the governor said to me when I got here from Nottingham. "We want to trust you while you are in this establishment," he said, smoothing out his newspaper with lily-white workless hands, while I read the big words upside down: *Daily Telegraph*. "If you play ball with us, we'll play ball with you." (Honest to God, you'd have thought it was going to be one long tennis match.) "We want hard honest work and we want good athletics," he said as well. "And if you give us both these things you can be sure we'll do right by you and send you back into the world an honest man." Well, I could have died laughing, especially when straight after this I hear the barking sergeant-major's voice calling me and two others to attention and marching us off like we was Grenadier Guards. And when the governor kept saying how "we" wanted you to do this, and "we" wanted you to do that, I kept looking round for the other blokes, wondering how many of them there was. Of course, I knew there were thousands of them, but as far as I knew only one was in the room. And there *are* thousands of them, all over the poxeaten country, in shops, offices, railway stations, cars, houses, pubs—In-law blokes like you and them, all on the watch for Out-law blokes like me and us—and waiting to 'phone for the coppers as soon as we make a false move. And it'll always be there, I'll tell you that now, because I haven't finished making all my false moves yet, and I dare say I won't until I kick the bucket. If the In-laws are hoping to stop me making false moves they're wasting their time. They might as well stand me up against a wall and let fly with a dozen rifles. That's the only way they'll stop me, and a few million others. Because I've been doing a lot of thinking since coming here. They can spy on us all day to see if we're pulling our puddings and if we're working good or doing our "athletics" but they can't make an X-ray of our guts to find out what we're telling ourselves. I've been asking myself all sorts of questions, and thinking about my life up to now. And I like doing all this. It's a treat. It passes the time away and don't make Borstal seem half so bad as the boys in our street used to say it was. And this long-distance running lark is the best of all, because it makes me think so good that I learn things even better than when I'm on my bed at night. And apart from that, what with thinking so much while I'm running I'm getting to be one of the best runners in the Borstal. I can go my five miles round better than anybody else I know.

So as soon as I tell myself I'm the first man ever to be dropped into the world, and as soon as I take that first flying leap out into the frosty grass of an early morning when even birds haven't the heart to whistle, I get to thinking, and that's what I like. I go my rounds in a dream, turning at lane or footpath corners without knowing I'm turning, leaping brooks without knowing they're there, and shouting good morning to the early cow-milker without seeing him. It's a treat, being a long-distance runner, out in the world by yourself with not a soul to make you bad-tempered or tell you what to do or that there's a shop to break and enter a bit back from the next street. Sometimes I think that I've never been so free as during that couple of hours when I'm trotting up the path out of the gates and turning by that bare-faced, big-bellied oak tree at the lane end. Everything's dead, but good, because it's dead before coming alive, not dead after being alive. That's how I look at it. Mind you, I often feel frozen stiff at first. I can't feel my hands or feet or flesh at all, like I'm a ghost who wouldn't know the earth was under him if he didn't see it now and again through the mist. But even though some people would call this frost-pain suffering if they wrote about it to their mams in a letter, I don't, because I know that in half an hour I'm going to be warm, that by the time I get to the main road and am turning on to the wheatfield footpath by the bus stop I'm going to feel as hot as a potbellied stove and as happy as a dog with a tin tail.

It's a good life, I'm saying to myself, if you don't give in to coppers and Borstal-bosses and the rest of them bastard-faced In-laws. Trot-trot-trot. Puff-puff-puff. Slap-slap-slap go my feet on the hard soil. Swish-swish-swish as my arms and side catch the bare branches of a bush. For I'm seventeen now, and when they let me out of this—if I don't make a break and see that things turn out otherwise—they'll try to get me in the army, and what's the difference between the army and this place I'm in now? They can't kid me, the bastards. I've seen the barracks near where I live, and if there weren't swaddies on guard outside with rifles you wouldn't know the difference between their high walls and the place I'm in now. Even though the swaddies come out at odd times a week for a pint of ale, so what? Don't I come out three mornings a week on my long-distance running, which is fifty times better than boozing. When they first said that I was to do my long-distance running without a guard pedalling beside me on a bike I couldn't believe it; but they called it a progressive and modern place, though they can't kid me because I know it's just like any other Borstal, going by the stories I've heard, except that they let me trot about like this. Borstal's Borstal no matter what they do; but anyway I moaned about it being a bit thick sending me out so early to run five miles on an empty stomach, until they talked me round to thinking it wasn't so bad—which I knew all the time—until they called me a good sport and patted me on the back when I said I'd do it and that I'd try to win them the Borstal Blue Ribbon Prize Cup For Long Distance Cross Country Running (All England). And now the governor talks to me when he comes on his rounds, almost as he'd talk to his prize race horse, if he had one.

"All right, Smith?" he asks.

"Yes, sir," I answer.

He flicks his grey moustache: "How's the running coming along?"

"I've set myself to trot round the grounds after dinner just to keep my hand in, sir," I tell him.

The pot-bellied pop-eyed bastard gets pleased at this: "Good show. I know you'll get us that cup," he says.

And I swear under my breath: "Like boggery, I will." No, I won't get them that cup, even though the stupid tash-twitching bastard has all his hopes in me. Because what does his barmy hope mean? I ask myself. Trot-trot-trot, slap-slap-slap, over the stream and into the wood where it's almost dark and frosty-dew twigs sting my legs. It don't mean a bloody thing to me, only to him, and it means as much to him as it would mean to me if I picked up the racing paper and put my bet on a hoss I didn't know, had never seen, and didn't care a sod if I ever did see. That's what it means to him. And I'll lose that race, because I'm not a race horse at all, and I'll let him know it when I'm about to get out—if I don't sling my hook even before the race. By Christ I will. I'm a human being and I've got thoughts and secrets and bloody life inside me that he doesn't know is there, and he'll never know what's there because he's stupid. I suppose you'll laugh at this, me saying the governor's a stupid bastard when I know hardly how to write and he can read and write and add-up like a professor. But what I say is true right enough. He's stupid, and I'm not, because I can see further into the likes of him than he can see into the likes of me. Admitted, we're both cunning, but I'm more cunning and I'll win in the end even if I die in gaol at eighty-two, because I'll have more fun and fire out of my life than he'll ever get out of his. He's read a thousand books I suppose, and for all I know he might even have written a few, but I know for a dead cert, as sure as I'm sitting here, that what I'm scribbling down is worth a million to what he could ever scribble down. I don't care what anybody says, but that's the truth and can't be denied. I know when he talks to me and I look into his army mug that I'm alive and he's dead. He's as dead as a doornail. If he ran ten yards he'd drop dead. If he got ten yards into what goes on in my guts he'd drop dead as well—with surprise. At the moment it's dead blokes like him as have the whip-hand over blokes like me, and I'm almost dead sure it'll always be like that, but even so, by Christ, I'd rather be like I am—always on the run and breaking into shops for a packet of fags and a jar of jam—than have the whip-hand over somebody else and be dead from the toe nails up. Maybe as soon as you get the whip-hand over somebody you do go dead. By God, to say that last sentence has needed a few hundred miles of long-distance running. I could no more have said that at first than I could have took a million-pound note from my back pocket. But it's true, you know, now I think of it again, and has always been true, and always will be true, and I'm surer of it every time I see the governor open that door and say Goodmorning lads.

As I run and see my smoky breath going out into the air as if I had ten cigars stuck in different parts of my body I think more on the little speech the governor made when I first came. Honesty. Be honest. I laughed so much one morning I went ten minutes down in my timing because I had to stop and get rid of the stitch in my side. The governor was so worried when I got back late that he sent me to the doctor's for an X-ray and heart check. Be honest. It's like saying: Be dead, like me, and then you'll have no more pain of leaving your nice slummy house for Borstal or prison. Be honest and settle down in a cosy six pounds a week job. Well, even with all this long-distance running I haven't yet been able to decide what he means by this, although I'm just about beginning to—and I don't like what it means. Because after all my thinking I found that it adds up to something that can't be true about me, being born and brought up as I was. Because another thing people like the governor will never understand is that I *am* honest, that I've never been anything else but honest, and that I'll always be honest. Sounds funny. But it's true because I know what honest means according to me and he only knows what it means according to him. I think my honesty is the only sort in the world, and he thinks his is the only sort in the world as well. That's why this dirty great walled-up and fenced-up manor house in the middle of nowhere has been used to coop-up blokes like me. And if I had the whip-hand I wouldn't even bother to build a place like this to put all the cops, governors, posh whores, penpushers, army officers, Members of Parliament in; no, I'd stick them up against a wall and let them have it, like they'd have done with blokes like us years ago, that is, if they'd ever known what it means to be honest, which they don't and never will so help me God Almighty.

I was nearly eighteen months in Borstal before I thought about getting out. I can't tell you much about what it was like there because I haven't got the hang of describing buildings or saying how many crumby chairs and slatted windows make a room. Neither can I do much complaining, because to tell you the truth I didn't suffer in Borstal at all. I gave the same answer a pal of mine gave when someone asked him how much he hated it in the army. "I didn't hate it," he said. "They fed me, gave me a suit, and pocket-money, which was a bloody sight more than I ever got before, unless I worked myself to death for it, and most of the time they wouldn't let me work but sent me to the dole office twice a week." Well, that's more or less what I say. Borstal didn't hurt me in that respect, so since I've got no complaints I don't have to describe what they gave us to eat, what the dorms were like, or how they treated us. But in another way Borstal does something to me. No, it doesn't get my back up, because it's always been up, right from when I was born. What it does do is show me what they've been trying to frighten me with. They've got other things as well, like prison and, in the end, the rope. It's like me rushing up to thump a man and snatch the coat off his back when, suddenly, I pull up because he whips out a knife and lifts it to stick me like a pig if I come too close. That knife is Borstal, clink, the rope. But once you've seen the knife you learn a bit of unarmed combat. You have to, because you'll never get that sort of knife in your own hands, and this unarmed combat doesn't amount to much. Still, there it is, and you keep on rushing up to this man, knife or not, hoping to get one of your hands

on his wrist and the other on his elbow both at the same time, and press back until he drops the knife.

You see, by sending me to Borstal they've shown me the knife, and from now on I know something I didn't know before: that it's war between me and them. I always knew this, naturally, because I was in Remand Homes as well and the boys there told me a lot about their brothers in Borstal, but it was only touch and go then, like kittens, like boxing-gloves, like dobbie. But now that they've shown me the knife, whether I ever pinch another thing in my life again or not, I know who my enemies are and what war is. They can drop all the atom bombs they like for all I care: I'll never call it war and wear a soldier's uniform, because I'm in a different sort of war, that they think is child's play. The war they think is war is suicide, and those that go and get killed in war should be put in clink for attempted suicide because that's the feeling in blokes' minds when they rush to join up or let themselves be called up. I know, because I've thought how good it would be sometimes to do myself in and the easiest way to do it, it occurred to me, was to hope for a big war so's I could join up and get killed. But I got past that when I knew I already was in a war of my own, that I was born into one, that I grew up hearing the sound of "old soldiers" who'd been over the top at Dartmoor, half-killed at Lincoln, trapped in no-man's-land at Borstal, that sounded louder than any Jerry bombs. Government wars aren't my wars; they've got nowt to do with me, because my own war's all that I'll ever be bothered about. I remember when I was fourteen and I went out into the country with three of my cousins, all about the same age, who later went to different Borstals, and then to different regiments, from which they soon deserted, and then to different gaols where they still are as far as I know. But anyway, we were all kids then, and wanted to go out to the woods for a change, to get away from the roads of stinking hot tar one summer. We climbed over fences and went through fields, scrumping a few sour apples on our way, until we saw the wood about a mile off. Up Colliers' Pad we heard another lot of kids talking in high-school voices behind a hedge. We crept up on them and peeped through the brambles, and saw they were eating a picnic, a real posh spread out of baskets and flasks and towels. There must have been about seven of them, lads and girls sent out by their mams and dads for the afternoon. So we went on our bellies through the hedge like crocodiles and surrounded them, and then dashed into the middle, scattering the fire and batting their tabs and snatching up all there was to eat, then running off over Cherry Orchard fields into the wood, with a man chasing us who'd come up while we were ransacking their picnic. We got away all right, and had a good feed into the bargain, because we'd been clambed to death and couldn't wait long enough to get our chops ripping into them thin lettuce and ham sandwiches and creamy cakes.

Well, I'll always feel during every bit of my life like those daft kids should have felt before we broke them up. But they never dreamed that

what happened was going to happen, just like the governor of this Borstal who spouts to us about honesty and all that wappy stuff don't know a bloody thing, while I know every minute of my life that a big boot is always likely to smash any nice picnic I might be barmy and dishonest enough to make for myself. I admit that there've been times when I've thought of telling the governor all this so as to put him on his guard, but when I've got as close as seeing him I've changed my mind, thinking to let him either find out for himself or go through the same mill as I've gone through. I'm not hard-hearted (in fact I've helped a few blokes in my time with the odd quid, lie, fag, or shelter from the rain when they've been on the run) but I'm boggered if I'm going to risk being put in the cells just for trying to give the governor a bit of advice he don't deserve. If my heart's soft I know the sort of people I'm going to save it for. And any advice I'd give the governor wouldn't do him the least bit of good; it'd only trip him up sooner than if he wasn't told at all, which I suppose is what I want to happen. But for the time being I'll let things go on as they are, which is something else I've learned in the last year or two. (It's a good job I can only think of these things as fast as I can write with this stub of pencil that's clutched in my paw, otherwise I'd have dropped the whole thing weeks ago.)

By the time I'm half-way through my morning course, when after a frost-bitten dawn I can see a phlegmy bit of sunlight hanging from the bare twigs of beech and sycamore, and when I've measured my half-way mark by the short-cut scrimmage down the steep bush-covered bank and into the sunken lane, when still there's not a soul in sight and not a sound except the neighing of a piebald foal in a cottage stable that I can't see, I get to thinking the deepest and daftest of all. The governor would have a fit if he could see me sliding down the bank because I could break my neck or ankle, but I can't not do it because it's the only risk I take and the only excitement I ever get, flying flat-out like one of them pterodactyls from the "Lost World" I once heard on the wireless, crazy like a cut-balled cockerel, scratching myself to bits and almost letting myself go but not quite. It's the most wonderful minute because there's not one thought or word or picture of anything in my head while I'm going down. I'm empty, as empty as I was before I was born, and I don't let myself go, I suppose, because whatever it is that's farthest down inside me don't want me to die or hurt myself bad. And it's daft to think deep, you know, because it gets you nowhere, though deep is what I am when I've passed this half-way mark because the long-distance run of an early morning makes me think that every run like this is a life—a little life, I know—but a life as full of misery and happiness and things happening as you can ever get really around yourself—and I remember that after a lot of these runs I thought that it didn't need much know-how to tell how a life was going to end once it had got well started. But as usual I was wrong, caught first by the cops and then by my own bad brain, I could never trust myself to fly scot-free over these traps, was always tripped up sooner or later no

matter how many I got over to the good without even knowing it. Looking back I suppose them big trees put their branches to their snouts and gave each other the wink, and there I was whizzing down the bank and not seeing a bloody thing.

II

I DON'T SAY TO MYSELF: "You shouldn't have done the job and then you'd have stayed away from Borstal"; no, what I ram into my runner-brain is that my luck had no right to scram just when I was on my way to making the coppers think I hadn't done the job after all. The time was autumn and the night foggy enough to set me and my mate Mike roaming the streets when we should have been rooted in front of the telly or stuck into a plush posh seat at the pictures, but I was restless after six weeks away from any sort of work, and well you might ask me why I'd been bone-idle for so long because normally I sweated my thin guts out on a milling-machine with the rest of them, but you see, my dad died from cancer of the throat, and mam collected a cool five hundred in insurance and benefits from the factory where he'd worked, "for your bereavement," they said, or words like that.

Now I believe, and my mam must have thought the same, that a wad of crisp blue-back fivers ain't a sight of good to a living soul unless they're flying out of your hand into some shopkeeper's till, and the shopkeeper is passing you tip-top things in exchange over the counter, so as soon as she got the money, mam took me and my five brothers and sisters out to town and got us dolled-up in new clothes. Then she ordered a twenty-one-inch telly, a new carpet because the old one was covered with blood from dad's dying and wouldn't wash out, and took a taxi home with bags of grub and a new fur coat. And do you know—you wain't believe me when I tell you—she'd still near three hundred left in her bulging handbag the next day, so how could any of us go to work after that? Poor old dad, he didn't get a look in, and he was the one who'd done the suffering and dying for such a lot of lolly.

Night after night we sat in front of the telly with a ham sandwich in one hand, a bar of chocolate in the other, and a bottle of lemonade between our boots, while mam was with some fancy-man upstairs on the new bed she'd ordered, and I'd never known a family as happy as ours was in that couple of months when we'd got all the money we needed. And when the dough ran out I didn't think about anything much, but just roamed the streets—looking for another job, I told mam—hoping I suppose to get my hands on another five hundred nicker so's the nice life we'd got used to could go on and on for ever. Because it's surprising how quick you can get used to a different life. To begin with, the adverts on the telly had shown us how much more there was in the world to buy than we'd ever dreamed of when we'd looked into shop windows but hadn't seen all there was to see because we didn't have the money to buy it with anyway. And the telly made all these things seem twenty times better than we'd ever thought they were. Even adverts at the cinema were cool and tame, because now we were seeing them in private at home. We used to cock our noses up at things in shops that didn't move, but suddenly we saw their real value because they jumped and glittered around the screen and had some pasty-faced tart going head over heels to get her nail-polished grabbers on to them or her lipstick lips over them, not like the crumby adverts you saw on posters or in newspapers as dead as doornails; these were flickering around loose, half-open packets and tins, making you think that all you had to do was finish opening them before they were yours, like seeing an unlocked safe through a shop window with the man gone away for a cup of tea without thinking to guard his lolly. The films they showed were good as well, in that way, because we couldn't get our eyes unglued from the cops chasing the robbers who had satchel-bags crammed with cash and looked like getting away to spend it—until the last moment. I always hoped they would end up free to blow the lot, and could never stop wanting to put my hand out, smash into the screen (it only looked a bit of rag-screen like at the pictures) and get the copper in a half-nelson so's he'd stop following the bloke with the money-bags. Even when he'd knocked off a couple of bank clerks I hoped he wouldn't get nabbed. In fact then I wished more than ever he wouldn't because it meant the hot-chair if he did, and I wouldn't wish that on anybody no matter what they'd done, because I'd read in a book where the hot-chair worn't a quick death at all, but that you just sat there scorching to death until you were dead. And it was when these cops were chasing the crooks that we played some good tricks with the telly, because when one of them opened his big gob to spout about getting their man I'd turn the sound down and see his mouth move like a goldfish or mackerel or a minnow mimicking what they were supposed to be acting—it was so funny the whole family nearly went into fits on the brand-new carpet that hadn't yet found its way to the bed-room. It was the best of all though when we did it to some Tory telling us about how good his government was going to be if we kept on voting for them—their slack chops rolling, opening and bumbling, hands lifting to twitch moustaches and touching their buttonholes to make sure the flower hadn't wilted, so that you could see they didn't mean a word they said, especially with not a murmur coming out because we'd cut off the sound. When the governor of the Borstal first talked to me I was re-minded of those times so much that I nearly killed myself trying not to laugh. Yes, we played so many good stunts on the box of tricks that mam used to call us the Telly Boys, we got so clever at it.

My pal Mike got let off with probation because it was his first job—anyway the first they ever knew about—and because they said he would never have done it if it hadn't been for me talking him into it. They said I was a menace to honest lads like Mike—hands in his pockets so that they looked stone-empty, head bent forward as if looking for half-crowns to fill 'em with, a ripped jersey on and his hair falling into his eyes so that he could go up to women and ask them for a shilling because he was hungry—and that I was the brains behind the job, the guiding light when it came to making up anybody's mind, but I swear to God I worn't owt like that because really I ain't got no more brains than a gnat after hiding the money in the place I did. And I—being cranky like I am—got sent to Borstal because to tell you the honest truth I'd been to Remand Homes before—though that's another story and I suppose if ever I tell it it'll be just as boring as this one is. I was glad though that Mike got away with it, and I only hope he always will, not like silly bastard me.

So on this foggy night we tore ourselves away from the telly and slammed the front door behind us, setting off up our wide street like slow tugs on a river that'd broken their hooters, for we didn't know where the housefronts began what with the perishing cold mist all around. I was snatched to death without an overcoat: mam had forgotten to buy me one in the scrummage of shopping, and by the time I thought to remind her of it the dough was all gone. So we whistled "The Teddy Boys' Picnic" to keep us warm, and I told myself that I'd get a coat soon if it was the last thing I did. Mike said he thought the same about himself, adding that he'd also get some brand-new glasses with gold rims, to wear instead of the wire frames they'd given him at the school clinic years ago. He didn't twig it was foggy at first and cleaned his glasses every time I pulled him back from a lamp-post or car, but when he saw the lights on Alfreton Road looking like octopus eyes he put them in his pocket and didn't wear them again until we did the job. We hadn't got two ha-pennies between us, and though we weren't hungry we wished we'd got a bob or two when we passed the fish and chip shops because the delicious sniffs of salt and vinegar and frying fat made our mouths water. I don't mind telling you we walked the town from one end to the other and if our eyes worn't glued to the ground looking for lost wallets and watches they was swivelling around house windows and shop doors in case we saw something easy and worth nipping into.

Neither of us said as much as this to each other, but I know for a fact that that was what we was thinking. What I don't know—and as sure as I sit here I know I'll never know—is which of us was the first bastard to latch his peepers on to that baker's backyard. Oh yes, it's all right me telling myself it was me, but the truth is that I've never known whether it was Mike or not, because I do know that I didn't see the open window until he stabbed me in the ribs and pointed it out. "See it?" he said.

"Yes," I told him, "so let's get cracking."

"But what about the wall though?" he whispered, looking a bit closer.

"On your shoulders," I chipped in.

His eyes were already up there: "Will you be able to reach?" It was the only time he ever showed any life.

"Leave it to me," I said, ever-ready. "I can reach anywhere from your ham-hock shoulders."

Mike was a nipper compared to me, but underneath the scruffy draught-board jersey he wore were muscles as hard as iron, and you wouldn't think to see him walking down the street with glasses on and hands in pockets that he'd harm a fly, but I never liked to get on the wrong side of him in a fight because he's the sort that don't say a word for weeks on end—sits plugged in front of the telly, or reads a cowboy book, or just sleeps—when suddenly BIFF—half kills somebody for almost nothing at all, such as beating him in a race for the last Football Post on a Saturday night, pushing in before him at a bus stop, or bumping into him when he was day-dreaming about Dolly-on-the-Tub next door. I saw him set on a bloke once for no more than fixing him in a funny way with his eyes, and it turned out that the bloke was cock-eyed but nobody knew it because he'd just that day come to live in our street. At other times none of these things would matter a bit, and I suppose the only reason why I was pals with him was because I didn't say much from one month's end to another either.

He puts his hands up in the air like he was being covered with a Gatling-Gun, and moved to the wall like he was going to be mowed down, and I climbed up him like he was a stile or step-ladder, and there he stood, the palms of his upshot maulers flat and turned out so's I could step on 'em like they was the adjustable jack-spanner under a car, not a sound of a breath nor the shiver of a flinch coming from him. I lost no time in any case, took my coat from between my teeth, chucked it up to the glass-topped wall (where the glass worn't too sharp because the jags had been worn down by years of accidental stones) and was sitting astraddle before I knew where I was. Then down the other side, with my legs rammed up into my throat when I hit the ground, the crack coming about as hard as when you fall after a high parachute drop, that one of my mates told me was like jumping off a twelve-foot wall, which this must have been. Then I picked up my bits and pieces and opened the gate for Mike, who was still grinning and full of life because the hardest part of the job was already done. "I came, I broke, I entered," like that clever-dick Borstal song.

I didn't think about anything at all, as usual, because I never do when I'm busy, when I'm draining pipes, looting sacks, yaling locks, lifting latches, forcing my bony hands and lanky legs into making something move, hardly feeling my lungs going in-whiff and out-whaff, not realizing whether my mouth is clamped tight or gaping, whether I'm hungry, itching from scabies, or whether my flies are open and flashing dirty words like muck and spit into the late-night final fog. And when I don't know anything about all this then how can I honest-to-God say I think of anything at such times? When I'm wondering what's the best way to get a window open or how to force a door, how can I be thinking or have anything on my mind? That's what the four-eyed white-smocked bloke with the note-book couldn't understand when he asked me questions for days and days after I got to Borstal; and I couldn't explain it to him then like I'm writing it down now; and even if I'd been able to maybe he still wouldn't have caught on because I don't know whether I can understand it myself even at this moment, though I'm doing my best you can bet.

So before I knew where I was I was inside the baker's office watching Mike picking up that cash box after he'd struck a match to see where it was, wearing a tailor-made fifty-shilling grin on his square crew-cut nut as his paws closed over the box like he'd squash it to nothing. "Out," he suddenly said, shaking it so's it rattled. "Let's scram."

"Maybe there's some more," I said, pulling half a dozen drawers out of a rollertop desk.

"No," he said, like he'd already been twenty years in the game, "this is the lot," patting his tin box, "this is it."

I pulled out another few drawers, full of bills, books and letters. "How do you know, you loony sod?"

He barged past me like a bull at a gate. "Because I do."

Right or wrong, we'd both got to stick together and do the same thing. I looked at an ever-loving babe of a brand-new typewriter, but knew it was too traceable, so blew it a kiss, and went out after him. "Hang on," I said, pulling the door to, "we're in no hurry."

"Not much we aren't," he says over his shoulder.

"We've got months to splash the lolly," I whispered as we crossed the yard, "only don't let that gate creak too much or you'll have the narks tuning-in."

"You think I'm barmy?" he said, creaking the gate so that the whole street heard.

I don't know about Mike, but now I started to think, of how we'd get back safe through the streets with that money-box up my jumper. Because he'd clapped it into my hand as soon as we'd got to the main road, which might have meant that he'd started thinking as well, which only goes to show how you don't know what's in anybody else's mind unless you think about things yourself. But as far as my thinking went at that moment it wasn't up to much, only a bit of fright that wouldn't budge not even with a hot blow-lamp, about what we'd say if a copper asked us where we were off to with that hump in my guts.

"What is it?" he'd ask, and I'd say: "A growth." "What do you mean, a growth, my lad?" he'd say back, narky like. I'd cough and clutch myself like I was in the most tripe-twisting pain in the world, and screw my eyes up like I was on my way to the hospital, and Mike would take my arm like he was the best pal I'd got. "Cancer," I'd manage to say to Narker, which would make his slow punch-drunk brain suspect a thing or two. "A lad of your age?" So I'd groan again, and hope to make him feel a real bully of a bastard, which would be impossible, but anyway: "It's in the family. Dad died of it last month, and I'll die of it next month by the feel of it." "What, did he have it in the guts?" "No, in the throat. But it's got me in the stomach." Groan and cough. "Well, you shouldn't be out like this if you've got cancer, you should be in the hospital." I'd get ratty now: "That's where I'm trying to go if only you'd let me and stop asking so many questions. Aren't I, Mike?" Grunt from Mike as he un-slung his cosh. Then just in time the copper would tell us to get on our way, kind and considerate all of a sudden, saying that the outpatient department of the hospital closes at twelve, so hadn't he better call us a taxi? He would if we liked, he says, and he'd pay for it as well. But we tell him not to bother, that he's a good bloke even if he is a copper, that we know a short cut anyway. Then just as we're turning a corner he gets it into his big batchy head that we're going the opposite way to the hospital, and calls us back. So we'd start to run . . . if you can call all that thinking.

Up in my room Mike rips open that money-box with a hammer and chisel, and before we know where we are we've got seventy-eight pounds fifteen and fourpence ha'penny *each* lying all over my bed like tea spread out on Christmas Day: cake and trifle, salad and sandwiches, jam tarts and bars of chocolate: all shared and shared alike between Mike and me because we believed in equal work and equal pay, just like the comrades my dad was in until he couldn't do a stroke anymore and had no breath left to argue with. I thought how good it was that blokes like that poor baker didn't stash all his cash in one of the big marble-fronted banks that take up every corner of the town, how lucky for us that he didn't trust them no matter how many millions of tons of concrete or how many iron bars and boxes they were made of, or how many coppers kept their blue pop-eyed peepers glued on to them, how smashing it was that he believed in money-boxes when so many shopkeepers thought it old-fashioned and tried to be modern by using a bank, which wouldn't give a couple of sin-cere, honest, hardworking, conscientious blokes like Mike and me a chance.

Now you'd think, and I'd think, and anybody with a bit of imagina-tion would think, that we'd done as clean a job as could ever be done, that, with the baker's shop being at least a mile from where we lived, and with not a soul having seen us, and what with the fog and the fact that we weren't more than five minutes in the place, that the coppers should never have been able to trace us. But then, you'd be wrong, I'd be wrong, and everybody else would be wrong, no matter how much imagination was diced out between us.

Even so, Mike and I didn't splash the money about, because that would have made people think straightaway that we'd latched on to something that didn't belong to us. Which wouldn't do at all, because even in a street like ours there are people who love to do a good turn for the coppers, though I never know why they do. Some people are so mean-gutted that even if they've only got tuppence more than you and they think you're the sort that would take it if you have half the chance, they'd get you put inside if they saw you ripping lead out of a lavatory, even if it weren't their lavatory—just to keep their tuppence out of your reach. And so we didn't do anything to let on about how rich we were, nothing like going down town and coming back dressed in brand-new Teddy boy suits and carrying a set of skiffle-drums like another pal of ours who'd done a factory office about six months before. No, we took the odd bobs and pennies out and folded the notes into bundles and stuffed them up the drainpipe outside the door in the backyard. "Nobody'll ever think of looking for it there," I said to Mike. "We'll keep it doggo for a week or two, then take a few quid a week out till it's all gone. We might be thieving bastards, but we're not green."

Some days later a plain-clothes dick knocked at the door. And asked for me. I was still in bed, at eleven o'clock, and had to unroll myself from the comfortable black sheets when I heard mam calling me. "A man to see you," she said. "Hurry up, or he'll be gone."

I could hear her keeping him at the back door, nattering about how fine it had been but how it looked like rain since early this morning—and he didn't answer her except to snap out a snotty yes or no. I scrambled into my trousers and wondered why he'd come—knowing it was a copper because "a man to see you" always meant just that in our house—and if I'd had any idea that one had gone to Mike's house as well at the same time I'd have twigged it to be because of that hundred and fifty quid's worth of paper stuffed up the drainpipe outside the back door, about ten inches away from that plain-clothed copper's boot, where mam still talked to him thinking she was doing me a favour, and I wishing to God she'd ask him in, though on second thoughts realizing that that would seem more suspicious than keeping him outside, because they know we hate their guts and smell a rat if they think we're trying to be nice to them. Mam wasn't born yesterday, I thought, thumping my way down the creaking stairs.

I'd seen him before: Borstal Bernard in nicky-hat, Remand Home Ronald in rowing-boat boots, Probation Pete in a pit-prop mackintosh, three-months clink in collar and tie (all this out of a Borstal skiffle-ballad that my new mate made up, and I'd tell you it in full but it doesn't belong in this story), a 'tec who'd never had as much in his pockets as that drainpipe had up its jackses. He was like Hitler in the face, right down to the paint-brush tash, except that being six-foot tall made him seem worse. But I straightened my shoulders to look into his illiterate blue eyes—like I always do with any copper.

Then he started asking me questions, and my mother from behind said: "He's never left that television set for the last three months, so you've got nowt on him, mate. You might as well look for somebody else, because you're wasting the rates you get out of my rent and the income-tax that comes out of my pay-packet standing there like that"—which was a laugh because she'd never paid either to my knowledge, and never would, I hoped.

"Well, you know where Papplewick Street is, don't you?" the copper asked me, taking no notice of mam.

"Ain't it off Alfreton Road?" I asked him back, helpful and bright.

"You know there's a baker's half-way down on the left-hand side, don't you?"

"Ain't it next door to a pub, then?" I wanted to know.

He answered me sharp: "No, it bloody well ain't." Coppers always lose their tempers as quick as this, and more often than not they gain nothing by it. "Then I don't know it," I told him, saved by the bell.

He slid his big boot round and round on the doorstep. "Where were you last Friday night?" Back in the ring, but this was worse than a boxing match.

I didn't like him trying to accuse me of something he wasn't sure I'd done. "Was I at that baker's you mentioned? Or in the pub next door?"

"You'll get five years in Borstal if you don't give me a straight answer," he said, unbuttoning his mac even though it was cold where he was standing.

"I was glued to the telly, like mam says," I swore blind. But he went on and on with his loony questions: "Have you got a television?"

The things he asked wouldn't have taken in a kid of two, and what else could I say to the last one except: "Has the aerial fell down? Or would you like to come in and see it?"

He was liking me even less for saying that. "We know you weren't listening to the television set last Friday, and so do you, don't you?"

"P'raps not, but I was *looking* at it, because sometimes we turn the sound down for a bit of fun." I could hear mam laughing from the kitchen, and I hoped Mike's mam was doing the same if the cops had gone to him as well.

"We know you weren't in the house," he said, starting up again, cranking himself with the handle. They always say "We" "We," never "I" "I"—as if they feel braver and righter knowing there's a lot of them against only one.

"I've got witnesses," I said to him. "Mam for one. Her fancy-man, for two. Ain't that enough? I can get you a dozen more, or thirteen altogether, if it was a baker's that got robbed."

"I don't want no lies," he said, not catching on about the baker's dozen. Where do they scrape cops up from anyway? "All I want is to get from you where you put that money."

Don't get mad, I kept saying to myself, don't get mad—hearing mam setting out cups and saucers and putting the pan on the stove for bacon. I stood back and waved him inside like I was a butler. "Come and search the house. If you've got a warrant."

"Listen, my lad," he said, like the dirty bullying jumped-up bastard he was, "I don't want too much of your lip, because if we get you down to the Guildhall you'll get a few bruises and black-eyes for your trouble." And I knew he wasn't kidding either, because I'd heard about all them sort of tricks. I hoped one day though that him and all his pals would be the ones to get the black-eyes and kicks; you never knew. It might come sooner than anybody thinks, like in Hungary. "Tell me where the money is, and I'll get you off with probation."

"What money?" I asked him, because I'd heard that one before as well.

"You know what money."

"Do I look as though I'd know owt about money?" I said, pushing my fist through a hole in my shirt.

"The money that was pinched, that you know all about," he said. "You can't trick me, so it's no use trying."

"Was it three-and-eightpence ha'penny?" I asked.

"You thieving young bastard. We'll teach you to steal money that doesn't belong to you."

I turned my head around: "Mam," I called out, "get my lawyer on the blower, will you?"

"Clever, aren't you?" he said in a very unfriendly way, "but we won't rest until we clear all this up."

"Look," I pleaded, as if about to sob my socks off because he'd got me wrong, "it's all very well us talking like this, it's like a game almost, but I wish you'd tell me what it's all about, because honest-to-God I've just got out of bed and here you are at the door talking about me having pinched a lot of money, money that I don't know anything about."

He swung around now as if he'd trapped me, though I couldn't see why he might think so. "Who said anything about money? I didn't. What made you bring money into this little talk we're having?"

"It's you," I answered, thinking he was going barmy, and about to start foaming at the chops, "you've got money on the brain, like all policemen. Baker's shops as well."

He screwed his face up. "I want an answer from you: where's that money?"

But I was getting fed-up with all this. "I'll do a deal."

Judging by his flash-bulb face he thought he was suddenly on to a good thing. "What sort of a deal?"

So I told him: "I'll give you all the money I've got, one and four-pence ha'penny, if you stop this third-degree and let me go in and get my breakfast. Honest, I'm clambed to death. I ain't had a bite since yesterday. Can't you hear my guts rollin'?"

His jaw dropped, but on he went, pumping me for another half hour. A routine check-up, as they say on the pictures. But I knew I was winning on points.

Then he left, but came back in the afternoon to search the house. He didn't find a thing, not a French farthing. He asked me questions again and I didn't tell him anything except lies, lies, lies, because I can go on doing that forever without batting an eyelid. He'd got nothing on me and we both of us knew it, otherwise I'd have been down at the Guildhall in no time, but he kept on keeping on because I'd been in a Remand Home for a high-wall job before; and Mike was put through the same mill because all the local cops knew he was my best pal.

When it got dark me and Mike were in our parlour with a low light on and the telly off, Mike taking it easy in the rocking chair and me slouched out on the settee, both of us puffing a packet of Woods. With the door bolted and curtains drawn we talked about the dough we'd crammed up the drainpipe. Mike thought we should take it out and both of us do a bunk to Skegness or Cleethorpes for a good time in the arcades, living like lords in a boarding house near the pier, then at least we'd both have had a big beano before getting sent down.

"Listen, you daft bleeder," I said, "we aren't going to get caught at all, *and* we'll have a good time, later." We were so clever we didn't even go out to the pictures, though we wanted to.

In the morning old Hitler-face questioned me again, with one of his pals this time, and the next day they came, trying as hard as they could to get something out of me, but I didn't budge an inch. I know I'm showing off when I say this, but in me he'd met his match, and I'd never give in to questions no matter how long it was kept up. They searched the house a couple of times as well, which made me think they thought they really had something to go by, but I know now that they hadn't, and that it was all buckshee speculation. They turned the house upside down and inside out like an old sock, went from top to bottom and front to back but naturally didn't find a thing. The copper even poked his face up the front-room chimney (that hadn't been used or swept for years) and came down looking like Al Jolson so that he had to swill himself clean at the scullery sink. They kept tapping and pottering around the big aspidistra plant that grandma had left to mam, lifting it up from the table to look under the cloth, putting it aside so's they could move the table and get at the boards under the rug—but the big headed stupid ignorant bastards never once thought of emptying the soil out of the plant pot, where they'd have found the crumpled-up money-box that we'd buried the night we did the job. I suppose it's still there, now I think about it, and I suppose mam wonders now and again why the plant don't prosper like it used to—as if it could with a fistful of thick black tin lapped around its guts.

The last time he knocked at our door was one wet morning at five minutes to nine and I was sleep-logged in my crumby bed as usual. Mam had gone to work that day so I shouted for him to hold on a bit, and then went down to see who it was. There he stood, six-feet tall and sopping wet, and for the first time in my life I did a spiteful thing I'll never forgive myself for: I didn't ask him to come in out of the rain, because I wanted him to get double pneumonia and die. I suppose he could have pushed by me and come in if he'd wanted, but maybe he'd got used to asking questions on the doorstep and didn't want to be put off by chang-ing his ground even though it was raining. Not that I don't like being spiteful because of any barmy principle I've got, but this bit of spite, as it turned out, did me no good at all. I should have treated him as a brother I hadn't seen for twenty years and dragged him in for a cup of tea and a fag, told him about the picture I hadn't seen the night before, asked him how his wife was after her operation and whether they'd shaved her moustache off to make it, and then sent him happy and satisfied out by the front door. But no, I thought, let's see what he's got to say for himself now.

He stood a little to the side of the door, either because it was less wet there, or because he wanted to see me from a different angle, perhaps having found it monotonous to watch a bloke's face always telling lies from the same side. "You've been identified," he said, twitching raindrops from his tash. "A woman saw you and your mate yesterday and she swears blind you are the same chaps she saw going into that bakery."

I was dead sure he was still bluffing, because Mike and I hadn't even seen each other the day before, but I looked worried. "She's a menace then to innocent people, whoever she is, because the only bakery I've been in lately is the one up our street to get some cut-bread on tick for mam."

He didn't bite on this. "So now I want to know where the money is"—as if I hadn't answered him at all.

"I think mam took it to work this morning to get herself some tea in the canteen." Rain was splashing down so hard I thought he'd get washed away if he didn't come inside. But I wasn't much bothered, and went on: "I remember I put it in the telly-vase last night—it was my only one-and-three and I was saving it for a packet of tips this morning—and I nearly had a jibbering black fit just now when I saw it had gone. I was reckoning on it for getting me through today because I don't think life's worth living without a fag, do you?"

I was getting into my stride and began to feel good, twigging that this would be my last pack of lies, and that if I kept it up for long enough this time I'd have the bastards beat: Mike and me would be off to the coast in a few weeks time having the fun of our lives, playing at penny football and latching on to a couple of tarts that would give us all they were good for. "And this weather's no good for picking-up fag-ends in the street," I said, "because they'd be sopping wet. Course, I know you could dry 'em out near the fire, but it don't taste the same you know, all said and done. Rainwater does summat to 'em that don't bear thinkin' about: it turns 'em back into hoss-tods without the taste though."

I began to wonder, at the back of my brainless eyes, why old copper-lugs didn't pull me up sharp and say he hadn't got time to listen to all this, but he wasn't looking at me anymore, and all my thoughts about Skegness went bursting to smithereens in my sludgy loaf. I could have dropped into the earth when I saw what he'd fixed his eyes on.

He was looking at it, an ever-loving fiver, and I could only jabber: "The one thing is to have some real fags because new hoss-tods is always better than stuff that's been rained on and dried, and I know how you feel about not being able to find money because one-and-three's one-and-three in anybody's pocket, and naturally if I see it knocking around I'll get you on the blower tomorrow straightaway and tell you where you can find it."

I thought I'd go down in a fit: three green-backs as well had been washed down by the water, and more were following, lying flat at first after their fall, then getting tilted at the corners by wind and rainspots as if they were alive and wanted to get back into the dry snug drainpipe out of the terrible weather, and you can't imagine how I wished they'd be able to. Old Hitler-face didn't know what to make of it but just kept staring down and down, and I thought I'd better keep on talking, though I knew it wasn't much good now.

"It's a fact, I know, that money's hard to come by and half-crowns don't get found on bus seats or in dustbins, and I didn't see any in bed last night because I'd 'ave known about it, wouldn't I? You can't sleep with things like that in the bed because they're too hard, and anyway at first they're. . . ." It took Hitler-boy a long time to catch on; they were beginning to spread over the yard a bit, reinforced by the third colour of a ten-bob note, before his hand clamped itself on to my shoulder.

III

THE POP-EYED POTBELLIED GOVERNOR said to a pop-eyed potbellied Member of Parliament who sat next to his pop-eyed potbellied whore of a wife that I was his only hope for getting the Borstal Blue Ribbon Prize Cup For Long Distance Cross Country Running (All England), which I was, and it set me laughing to myself inside, and I didn't say a word to any potbellied pop-eyed bastard that might give them real hope, though I knew the governor anyway took my quietness to mean he'd got that cup already stuck on the bookshelf in his office among the few other mildewed trophies.

"He might take up running in a sort of professional way when he gets out," and it wasn't until he'd said this and I'd heard it with my own flap-tabs that I realized it might be possible to do such a thing, run for money, trot for wages on piece work at a bob a puff rising bit by bit to a guinea a gasp and retiring through old age at thirty-two because of lace-curtain lungs, a football heart, and legs like varicose beanstalks. But I'd have a wife and car and get my grinning long-distance clock in the papers and have a smashing secretary to answer piles of letters sent by tarts who'd mob me when they saw who I was as I pushed my way into Woolworth's for a packet of razor blades and a cup of tea. It was something to think about all right, and sure enough the governor knew he'd got me when he said, turning to me as if I would at any rate have to be consulted about it all: "How does this matter strike you, then, Smith, my lad?"

A line of potbellied pop-eyes gleamed at me and a row of goldfish mouths opened and wiggled gold teeth at me, so I gave them the answer they wanted because I'd hold my trump card until later. "It'd suit me fine, sir," I said.

"Good lad. Good show. Right spirit. Splendid."

"Well," the governor said, "get that cup for us today and I'll do all I can for you. I'll get you trained so that you whack every man in the Free World." And I had a picture in my brain of me running and beating everybody in the world, leaving them all behind until only I was trot-trotting across a big wide moor alone, doing a marvellous speed as I ripped between boulders and reed-clumps, when suddenly: CRACK! CRACK!—bullets that can go faster than any man running, coming from a copper's rifle planted in a tree, winged me and split my gizzard in spite of my perfect running, and down I fell.

The potbellies expected me to say something else. "Thank you, sir," I said.

Told to go, I trotted down the pavilion steps, out on to the field because the big cross-country was about to begin and the two entries from Gunthorpe had fixed themselves early at the starting line and were ready to move off like white kangaroos. The sports ground looked a treat: with big tea-tents all round and flags flying and seats for families—empty because no mam or dad had known what opening day meant—and boys still running heats for the hundred yards, and lords and ladies walk-ing from stall to stall, and the Borstal Boys Brass Band in blue uniforms; and up on the stands the brown jackets of Hucknall as well as our own grey blazers, and then the Gunthorpe lot with shirt sleeves rolled. The blue sky was full of sunshine and it couldn't have been a better day, and all of the big show was like something out of Ivanhoe that we'd seen on the pictures a few days before.

"Come on, Smith," Roach the sports master called to me, "we don't want you to be late for the big race, eh? Although I dare say you'd catch them up if you were." The others cat-called and grunted at this, but I took no notice and placed myself between Gunthorpe and one of the Aylesham trusties, dropped on my knees and plucked a few grass blades to suck on the way round. So the big race it was, for them, watching from the grandstand under a fluttering Union Jack, a race for the gover-nor, that he had been waiting for, and I hoped he and all the rest of his pop-eyed gang were busy placing big bets on me, hundred to one to win, all the money they had in their pockets, all the wages they were going to get for the next five years, and the more they placed the happier I'd be. Because here was a dead cert going to die on the big name they'd built for him, going to go down dying with laughter whether it choked him or not. My knees felt the cool soil pressing into them, and out of my eye's corner I saw Roach lift his hand. The Gunthorpe boy twitched before the signal was given; somebody cheered too soon; Medway bent forward; then the gun went, and I was away.

We went once around the field and then along a half-mile drive of elms, being cheered all the way, and I seemed to feel I was in the lead as we went out by the gate and into the lane, though I wasn't interested enough to find out. The five-mile course was marked by splashes of whitewash gleaming on gateposts and trunks and stiles and stones, and a boy with a waterbottle and bandage-box stood every half-mile waiting for those that dropped out or fainted. Over the first stile, without trying, I was still nearly in the lead but one; and if any of you want tips about running, never be in a hurry, and never let any of the other runners know you are in a hurry even if you are. You can always overtake on long-distance running without letting the others smell the hurry in you; and when you've used your craft like this to reach the two or three up front then you can do a big dash later that puts everybody else's hurry in the shade because you've not had to make haste up till then. I ran to a steady jog-trot rhythm, and soon it was so smooth that I forgot I was running, and I was hardly able to know that my legs were lifting and falling and my arms going in and out, and my lungs didn't seem to be working at all, and my heart stopped that wicked thumping I always get at the beginning of a run. Because you see I never race at all; I just run, and somehow I know that if I forget I'm racing and only jog-trot along until I don't know I'm running I always win the race. For when my eyes recognize that I'm getting near the end of the course—by seeing a stile or cottage corner—I put on a spurt, and such a fast big spurt it is because I feel that up till then I haven't been running and that I've used up no energy at all. And I've been able to do this because I've been thinking; and I wonder if I'm the only one in the running business with this system of forgetting that I'm running because I'm too busy thinking; and I wonder if any of the other lads are on to the same lark, though I know for a fact that they aren't. Off like the wind along the cobbled footpath and rutted lane, smoother than the flat grass track on the field and better for thinking because it's not too smooth, and I was in my element that afternoon knowing that nobody could beat me at running but intending to beat myself before the day was over. For when the governor talked to me of being honest when I first came in he didn't know what the word meant or he wouldn't have had me here in this race, trotting along in shimmy and shorts and sunshine. He'd have had me where I'd have had him if I'd been in his place: in a quarry breaking rocks until he broke his back. At least old Hitler-face the plain-clothes dick was honester than the governor, because he at any rate had had it in for me and I for him, and when my case was coming up in court a copper knocked at our front door at four o'clock in the morning and got my mother out of bed when she was paralytic tired, reminding her she had to be in court at dead on half past nine. It was the finest bit of spite I've ever heard of, but I would call it honest, the same as my mam's words were honest when she really told that copper what she thought of him and called him all the dirty names she'd ever heard of, which took her half an hour and woke the terrace up.

I trotted on along the edge of a field bordered by the sunken lane, smelling green grass and honeysuckle, and I felt as though I came from a long line of whippets trained to run on two legs, only I couldn't see a toy rabbit in front and there wasn't a collier's cosh behind to make me keep up the pace. I passed the Gunthorpe runner whose shimmy was already black with sweat and I could just see the corner of the fenced-up copse in front where the only man I had to pass to win the race was going all out to gain the half-way mark. Then he turned into a tongue of trees and bushes where I couldn't see him anymore, and I couldn't see anybody, and I knew what the loneliness of the long-distance runner running across country felt like, realizing that as far as I was concerned this feeling was the only honesty and realness there was in the world and I knowing it would be no different ever, no matter what I felt at odd times, and no matter what anybody else tried to tell me. The runner behind me must have been a long way off because it was so quiet, and there was even less noise and movement than there had been at five o'clock of a frosty winter morning. It was hard to understand, and all I knew was that you had to run, run, run, without knowing why you were running, but on you went through fields you didn't understand and into woods that made you afraid, over hills without knowing you'd been up and down, and shooting across streams that would have cut the heart out of you had you fallen into them. And the winning post was no end to it, even though crowds might be cheering you in, because on you had to go before you got your breath back, and the only time you stopped really was when you tripped over a tree trunk and broke your neck or fell into a disused well and stayed dead in the darkness forever. So I thought: they aren't going to get me on this racing lark, this running and trying to win, this jog-trotting for a bit of blue ribbon, because it's not the way to go on at all, though they swear blind that it is. You should think about nobody and go your own way, not on a course marked out for you by people holding mugs of water and bottles of iodine in case you fall and cut yourself so that they can pick you up—even if you want to stay where you are—and get you moving again.

On I went, out of the wood, passing the man leading without knowing I was going to do so. Flip-flap, flip-flap, jog-trot, jog-trot, crunchslap-crunchslap, across the middle of a broad field again, rhythmically running in my greyhound effortless fashion, knowing I had won the race though it wasn't half over, won it if I wanted it, could go on for ten or fifteen or twenty miles if I had to and drop dead at the finish of it, which would be the same, in the end, as living an honest life like the governor wanted me to. It amounted to: win the race and be honest, and on trot-trotting I went, having the time of my life, loving my progress because it did me good and set me thinking which by now I liked to do, but not caring at all when I remembered that I had to win this race as well as run it. One of the two, I had to win the race or run it, and I knew I could do both because my legs had carried me well in front—now coming to the short cut down the bramble bank and over the sunken road—and would carry me further because they seemed made of electric cable and easily alive to keep on slapping at those ruts and roots, but I'm not going to win because the only way I'd see I came in first would be if winning meant that I was going to escape the coppers after doing the biggest bank job of my life, but winning means the exact opposite, no matter how they try to kill or kid me, means running right into their white-gloved wall-barred hands and grinning mugs and staying there for the rest of my natural long life of stone-breaking anyway, but stone-breaking in the way I want to do it and not in the way they tell me.

Another honest thought that comes is that I could swing left at the next hedge of the field, and under its cover beat my slow retreat away from the sports ground winning post. I could do three or six or a dozen miles across the turf like this and cut a few main roads behind me so's they'd never know which one I'd taken; and maybe on the last one when it got dark I could thumb a lorry-lift and get a free ride north with somebody who might not give me away. But no, I said I wasn't daft didn't I? I won't pull out with only six months left, and besides there's nothing I want to dodge and run away from; I only want a bit of my own back on the In-laws and Potbellies by letting them sit up there on their big posh seats and watch me lose this race, though as sure as God made me I know that when I do lose I'll get the dirtiest crap and kitchen jobs in the months to go before my time is up. I won't be worth a threpp'ny-bit to anybody here, which will be all the thanks I get for being honest in the only way I know. For when the governor told me to be honest it was meant to be in his way not mine, and if I kept on being honest in the way he wanted and won my race for him he'd see I got the cushiest six months still left to run; but in my own way, well, it's not allowed, and if I find a way of doing it such as I've got now then I'll get what-for in every mean trick he can set his mind to. And if you look at it in my way, who can blame him? For this is war—and ain't I said so?—and when I hit him in the only place he knows he'll be sure to get his own back on me for not collaring that cup when his heart's been set for ages on seeing himself standing up at the end of the afternoon to clap me on the back as I take the cup from Lord Earwig or some such chinless wonder with a name like that. And so I'll hit him where it hurts a lot, and he'll do all he can to get his own back, tit for tat, though I'll enjoy it most because I'm hitting first, and because I planned it longer. I don't know why I think these thoughts are better than any I've ever had, but I do, and I don't care why. I suppose it took me a long time to get going on all this because I've had no time and peace in all my bandit life, and now my thoughts are coming pat and the only trouble is I often can't stop, even when my brain feels as if it's got cramp, frostbite and creeping paralysis all rolled into one and I have to give it a rest by slap-dashing down through the brambles of the sunken lane. And all this is another uppercut I'm getting in first at people like the governor, to show how—if I can—his races are never won even though some bloke always comes unknowingly in first, how in the end the governor is going to be doomed while blokes like me will take the pickings of his roasted bones and dance like maniacs around his Borstal's ruins. And so this story's like the race and once again I won't bring off a winner to suit the governor; no, I'm being honest like he told me to, without him knowing what he means, though I don't suppose he'll ever come in with a story of his own, even if he reads this one of mine and knows who I'm talking about.

I've just come up out of the sunken lane, kneed and elbowed, thumped and bramble-scratched, and the race is two-thirds over, and a voice is going like a wireless in my mind saying that when you've had enough of feeling good like the first man on earth of a frosty morning, and you've known how it is to be taken bad like the last man on earth on a summer's afternoon, then you get at last to being like the only man on earth and don't give a bogger about either good or bad, but just trot on with your slippers slapping the good dry soil that at least would never do you a bad turn. Now the words are like coming from a crystal-set that's broken down, and something's happening inside the shell-case of my guts that bothers me and I don't know why or what to blame it on, a grinding near my ticker as though a bag of rusty screws is loose inside me and I shake them up every time I trot forward. Now and again I break my rhythm to feel my left shoulder-blade by swinging a right hand across my chest as if to rub the knife away that has somehow got stuck there. But I know it's nothing to bother about, that more likely it's caused by too much thinking that now and again I take for worry. For sometimes I'm the greatest worrier in the world I think (as you twigged I'll bet from me having got this story out) which is funny anyway because my mam don't know the meaning of the word so I don't take after her; though dad had a hard time of worry all his life up to when he filled his bedroom with hot blood and kicked the bucket that morning when nobody was in the house. I'll never forget it, straight I won't, because I was the one that found him and I often wished I hadn't. Back from a session on the fruit-machines at the fish-and-chip shop, jingling my three-lemon loot to a nail-dead house, as soon as I got in I knew something was wrong, stood leaning my head against the cold mirror above the mantel-piece trying not to open my eyes and see my stone-cold clock—because I knew I'd gone as white as a piece of chalk since coming in as if I'd been got at by a Dracula-vampire and even my penny-pocket winnings kept quiet on purpose.

Gunthorpe nearly caught me up. Birds were singing from the briar hedge, and a couple of thrushies flew like lightning into some thorny bushes. Corn had grown high in the next field and would be cut down soon with scythes and mowers; but I never wanted to notice much while running in case it put me off my stroke, so by the haystack I decided to leave it all behind and put on such a spurt, in spite of nails in my guts, that before long I'd left both Gunthorpe and the birds a good way off; I wasn't far now from going into that last mile and a half like a knife

through margarine, but the quietness I suddenly trotted into between
two pickets was like opening my eyes underwater and looking at the
pebbles on a stream bottom, reminding me again of going back that
morning to the house in which my old man had croaked, which is funny
because I hadn't thought about it at all since it happened and even then I
didn't brood much on it. I wonder why? I suppose that since I started to
think on these long-distance runs I'm liable to have anything crop up and
pester at my tripes and innards, and now that I see my bloody dad
behind each grass-blade in my barmy runner-brain I'm not so sure I like
to think and that it's such a good thing after all. I choke my phlegm
and keep on running anyway and curse the Borstal-builders and
their athletics—flappity-flap, slop-slop, crunchslap-crunchslap-crunchslap—
who've maybe got their own back on me from the bright beginning by
sliding magic-lantern slides into my head that never stood a chance before. Only if I take whatever comes like this in my runner's stride can I
keep on keeping on like my old self and beat them back; and now I've
thought on this far I know I'll win, in the crunchslap end. So anyway
after a bit I went upstairs one step at a time not thinking anything about
how I should find dad and what I'd do when I did. But now I'm making
up for it by going over the rotten life mam led him ever since I can
remember, knocking-on with different men even when he was alive and
fit and she not caring whether he knew it or not, and most of the time he
wasn't so blind as she thought and cursed and roared and threatened to
punch her tab, and I had to stand up to stop him even though I knew she
deserved it. What a life for all of us. Well, I'm not grumbling, because if
I did I might just as well win this bleeding race, which I'm not going to
do, though if I don't lose speed I'll win it before I know where I am, and
then where would I be?

Now I can hear the sportsground noise and music as I head back for
the flags and the lead-in drive, the fresh new feel of underfoot gravel
going against the iron muscles of my legs. I'm nowhere near puffed
despite that bag of nails that rattles as much as ever, and I can still give a
big last leap like gale-force wind if I want to, but everything is under
control and I know now that there ain't another long-distance cross-
country running runner in England to touch my speed and style. Our
doddering bastard of a governor, our half-dead gangrened gaffer is hollow like an empty petrol drum, and he wants me and my running life to
give him glory, to put in him blood and throbbing veins he never had,
wants his potbellied pals to be his witnesses as I gasp and stagger up to
his winning post so's he can say: "My Borstal gets that cup, you see. I win
my bet, because it pays to be honest and try to gain the prizes I offer
to my lads, and they know it, have known it all along. They'll always be
honest now, because I made them so." And his pals will think: "He
trains his lads to live right, after all; he deserves a medal but we'll get him
made a Sir"—and at this very moment as the birds come back to whistling I can tell myself I'll never care a sod what any of the chinless

KATHERINE MANSFIELD

JOHN UPDIKE

photograph by Alfred A. Knopf

spineless In-laws think or say. They've seen me and they're cheering now and loudspeakers set around the field like elephant's ears are spreading out the big news that I'm well in the lead, and can't do anything else but stay there. But I'm still thinking of the Out-law death my dad died, telling the doctors to scat from the house when they wanted him to finish up in hospital (like a bleeding guinea-pig, he raved at them). He got up in bed to throw them out and even followed them down the stairs in his shirt though he was no more than skin and stick. They tried to tell him he'd want some drugs but he didn't fall for it, and only took the pain-killer that mam and I got from a herb-seller in the next street. It's not till now that I know what guts he had, and when I went into the room that morning he was lying on his stomach with the clothes thrown back, looking like a skinned rabbit, his grey head resting just on the edge of the bed, and on the floor must have been all the blood he'd had in his body, right from his toe-nails up, for nearly all of the lino and carpet was covered in it, thin and pink.

And down the drive I went, carrying a heart blocked up like Boulder Dam across my arteries, the nail-bag clamped down tighter and tighter as though in a woodwork vice, yet with my feet like birdwings and arms like talons ready to fly across the field except that I didn't want to give anybody that much of a show, or win the race by accident. I smell the hot dry day now as I run towards the end, passing a mountain-heap of grass emptied from cans hooked on to the fronts of lawn-mowers pushed by my pals; I rip a piece of tree-bark with my fingers and stuff it in my mouth, chewing wood and dust and maybe maggots as I run until I'm nearly sick, yet swallowing what I can of it just the same because a little birdie whistled to me that I've got to go on living for at least a bloody sight longer yet but that for six months I'm not going to smell that grass or taste that dusty bark or trot this lovely path. I hate to have to say this but something bloody-well made me cry, and crying is a thing I haven't bloody-well done since I was a kid of two or three. Because I'm slowing down now for Gunthorpe to catch me up, and I'm doing it in a place just where the drive turns in to the sportsfield—where they can see what I'm doing, especially the governor and his gang from the grandstand, and I'm going so slow I'm almost marking time. Those on the nearest seats haven't caught on yet to what's happening and are still cheering like mad ready for when I make that mark, and I keep on wondering when the bleeding hell Gunthorpe behind me is going to nip by on to the field because I can't hold this up all day, and I think Oh Christ it's just my rotten luck that Gunthorpe's dropped out and that I'll be here for half an hour before the next bloke comes up, but even so, I say, I won't budge, I won't go for that last hundred yards if I have to sit down cross-legged on the grass and have the governor and his chinless wonders pick me up and carry me there, which is against their rules so you can bet they'd never do it because they're not clever enough to break the rules—like I would be in their place—even though they are their own. No, I'll show him what honesty means if it's the last thing I do, though I'm sure he'll never understand because if he and all them like him did it'd mean they'd be on my side which is impossible. By God I'll stick this out like my dad stuck out his pain and kicked them doctors down the stairs: if he had guts for that then I've got guts for this and here I stay waiting for Gunthorpe or Aylesham to bash that turf and go right slap-up against that bit of clothes-line stretched across the winning post. As for me, the only time I'll hit that clothes-line will be when I'm dead and a comfortable coffin's been got ready on the other side. Until then I'm a long-distance runner, crossing country all on my own no matter how bad it feels.

The Essex boys were shouting themselves blue in the face telling me to get a move on, waving their arms, standing up and making as if to run at that rope themselves because they were only a few yards to the side of it. You cranky lot, I thought, stuck at that winning post, and yet I knew they didn't mean what they were shouting, were really on my side and always would be, not able to keep their maulers to themselves, in and out of cop-shops and clink. And there they were now having the time of their lives letting themselves go in cheering me which made the governor think they were heart and soul on his side when he wouldn't have thought any such thing if he'd had a grain of sense. And I could hear the lords and ladies now from the grandstand, and could see them standing up to wave me in: "Run!" they were shouting in their posh voices. "Run!" But I was deaf, daft and blind, and stood where I was, still tasting the bark in my mouth and still blubbing like a baby, blubbing now out of gladness that I'd got them beat at last.

Because I heard a roar and saw the Gunthorpe gang throwing their coats up in the air and I felt the pat-pat of feet on the drive behind me getting closer and closer and suddenly a smell of sweat and a pair of lungs on their last gasp passed me by and went swinging on towards that rope, all shagged out and rocking from side to side, grunting like a Zulu that didn't know any better, like the ghost of me at ninety when I'm heading for that fat upholstered coffin. I could have cheered him myself: "Go on, go on, get cracking. Knot yourself up on that piece of tape." But he was already there, and so I went on, trot-trotting after him until I got to the rope, and collapsed, with a murderous sounding roar going up through my ears while I was still on the wrong side of it.

It's about time to stop; though don't think I'm not still running, because I am, one way or another. The governor at Borstal proved me right; he didn't respect my honesty at all; not that I expected him to, or tried to explain it to him, but if he's supposed to be educated then he should have more or less twigged it. He got his own back right enough, or thought he did, because he had me carting dustbins about every morning from the big full-working kitchen to the garden-bottoms where I had to empty them; and in the afternoon I spread out slops over spuds and carrots growing in the allotments. In the evenings I scrubbed floors, miles and miles of them. But it wasn't a bad life for six months, which was another thing he could never understand and would have made it grimmer if he could, and it was worth it when I look back on it, considering all the thinking I did, and the fact that the boys caught on to me losing the race on purpose and never had enough good words to say about me, or curses to throw out (to themselves) at the governor.

The work didn't break me; if anything it made me stronger in many ways, and the governor knew, when I left, that his spite had got him nowhere. For since leaving Borstal they tried to get me in the army, but I didn't pass the medical and I'll tell you why. No sooner was I out, after that final run and six-months hard, that I went down with pleurisy, which means as far as I'm concerned that I lost the governor's race all right, and won my own twice over, because I know for certain that if I hadn't raced my race I wouldn't have got this pleurisy, which keeps me out of khaki but doesn't stop me doing the sort of work my itchy fingers want to do.

I'm out now and the heat's switched on again, but the rats haven't got me for the last big thing I pulled. I counted six hundred and twenty-eight pounds and am still living off it because I did the job all on my own, and after it I had the peace to write all this, and it'll be money enough to keep me going until I finish my plans for doing an even bigger snatch, something up my sleeve I wouldn't tell to a living soul. I worked out my systems and hiding-places while pushing scrubbing-brushes around them Borstal floors, planned my outward life of innocence and honest work, yet at the same time grew perfect in the razor-edges of my craft for what I knew I had to do once free; and what I'll do again if netted by the poaching coppers.

In the meantime (as they say in one or two books I've read since, useless though because all of them ended on a winning post and didn't teach me a thing) I'm going to give this story to a pal of mine and tell him that if I do get captured again by the coppers he can try and get it put into a book or something, because I'd like to see the governor's face when he reads it, if he does, which I don't suppose he will; even if he did read it though I don't think he'd know what it was all about. And if I don't get caught the bloke I give this story to will never give me away; he's lived in our terrace for as long as I can remember, and he's my pal. That I do know.

John Updike

SNOWING IN GREENWICH VILLAGE

THE MAPLES HAD MOVED just the day before to West Thirteenth Street, and that evening they had Rebecca Cune over, because now they were so close. A tall, always slightly smiling girl with an absent manner, she allowed Richard Maple to slip off her coat and scarf even as she stood gently greeting Joan. Richard, moving with an extra precision and grace because of the smoothness with which the business had been managed—though he and Joan had been married nearly two years, he was still so young-looking that people did not instinctively lay upon him hostly duties; their reluctance worked in him a corresponding hesitancy, so that often it was his wife who poured the drinks, while he sprawled on the sofa in the attitude of a favored and wholly delightful guest—entered the dark bedroom, entrusted the bed with Rebecca's clothes, and returned to the living room. Her coat had seemed weightless.

Rebecca, seated beneath the lamp, on the floor, one leg tucked under her, one arm up on the Hide-a-Bed that the previous tenants had not as yet removed, was saying, "I had known her, you know, just for the day she taught me the job, but I said okay. I was living in an awful place called a hotel for ladies. In the halls they had typewriters you put a quarter in."

Joan, straight-backed on a Hitchcock chair from her parents' home in Vermont, a damp handkerchief balled in her hand, turned to Richard and explained, "Before her apartment now, Becky lived with this girl and her boy friend."

"Yes, his name was Jacques," Rebecca said.

Richard asked, "You lived with them?" The arch composure of his tone was left over from the mood aroused in him by his successful and, in the dim bedroom, somewhat poignant—as if he were with great tact delivering a disappointing message—disposal of their guest's coat.

"Yes, and he insisted on having his name on the mailbox. He was terribly afraid of missing a letter. When my brother was in the Navy and came to see me and saw on the mailbox"—with three parallel movements of her fingers she set the names beneath one another—

> "Georgene Clyde,
> Rebecca Cune,
> Jacques Zimmerman,

he told me I had always been such a nice girl. Jacques wouldn't even move out so my brother would have a place to sleep. He had to sleep on the floor." She lowered her lids and looked in her purse for a cigarette.

"Isn't that wonderful?" Joan said, her smile broadening helplessly as she realized what an inane thing it had been to say. Her cold worried Richard. It had lasted seven days without improving. Her face was pale, mottled pink and yellow; this accentuated the Modiglianiesque quality established by her long neck and oval blue eyes and her habit of sitting to her full height, her head quizzically tilted and her hands palm downward in her lap.

Rebecca, too, was pale, but in the consistent way of a drawing, perhaps—the weight of her lids and a certain virtuosity about the mouth suggested it—by da Vinci.

"Who would like some sherry?" Richard asked in a deep voice, from a standing position.

"We have some hard stuff if you'd rather," Joan said to Rebecca; from Richard's viewpoint the remark, like those advertisements which from varying angles read differently, contained the quite legible declaration that this time *he* would have to mix the Old Fashioneds.

"The sherry sounds fine," Rebecca said. She enunciated her words distinctly, but in a faint, thin voice that disclaimed for them any consequence.

"I think, too," Joan said.

"Good." Richard took from the mantel the eight-dollar bottle of Tio Pepe that the second man on the Spanish sherry account had stolen for him. So all could share in the drama of it, he uncorked the bottle in the living room. He posingly poured out three glasses, half-full, passed them around, and leaned against the mantel (the Maples had never had a mantel before), swirling the liquid, as the agency's wine expert had told him to do, thus liberating the esters and ethers, until his wife said, as she always did, it being the standard toast in her parents' home, "Cheers, dears!"

Rebecca continued the story of her first apartment. Jacques had never worked. Georgene never held a job more than three weeks. The three of them contributed to a kitty, to which all enjoyed equal access. Rebecca had a separate bedroom. Jacques and Georgene sometimes worked on television scripts; they pinned the bulk of their hopes onto a serial titled *The IBI*—"I" for Intergalactic, or Interplanetary, or something—*in Space and Time*. One of their friends was a young Communist who never washed and always had money because his father owned half of the West Side. During the day, when the two girls were off working, Jacques flirted with a young Swede upstairs who kept dropping her mop onto the tiny balcony outside their window. "A real bombardier," Rebecca said. When Rebecca moved into a single apartment for herself and was all settled and happy, Georgene and Jacques offered to bring a mattress and sleep on her floor. Rebecca felt that the time had come for her to put her foot down. She said no. Later, Jacques married a girl other than Georgene.

"Cashews, anybody?" Richard said. He had bought a can at the corner delicatessen, expressly for this visit, though if Rebecca had not been coming, he would have bought something else there on some other excuse, just for the pleasure of buying his first thing at the store where in the coming years he would purchase so much.

"No thank you," Rebecca said. Richard was so far from expecting refusal that out of momentum he pressed them on her again, exclaiming, "Please! They're so good for you." She took two and bit one in half.

He offered the dish, a silver porringer given to the Maples as a wedding present and which they had never before had the space to unpack, to his wife, who took a greedy handful and looked so pale that he asked, "How do you feel?" not so much forgetting the presence of their guest as parading his concern, quite genuine at that, before her.

"Fine," Joan said edgily, and perhaps she did.

Though the Maples told some stories—how they had lived in a log cabin in a Y.M.C.A. camp for the first three months of their married life, how Bitsy Flaner, a mutual friend, was the only girl enrolled in Bentham Divinity School, how Richard's advertising work brought him into contact with Yogi Berra—they did not regard themselves (that is, each other) as raconteurs, and Rebecca's slight voice dominated the talk. She had a gift for odd things.

Her rich uncle lived in a metal house, furnished with auditorium chairs. He was terribly afraid of fire. Right before the depression he had built an enormous boat to take himself and some friends to Polynesia. All his friends lost their money in the crash. He did not. He made money. He made money out of everything. But he couldn't go on the trip alone, so the boat was still waiting in Oyster Bay, a huge thing, rising thirty feet out of water. The uncle was a vegetarian. Rebecca had not eaten turkey for Thanksgiving until she was thirteen years old because it was the family custom to go to the uncle's house on that holiday. The custom was dropped during the war, when the children's synthetic heels made black marks all over his asbestos floor. Rebecca's family had not spoken to the uncle since. "Yes, what got me," Rebecca said, "was the way each new wave of vegetables would come in as if it were a different course."

Richard poured the sherry around again and, because this made him the center of attention anyway, said, "Don't some vegetarians have turkeys molded out of crushed nuts for Thanksgiving?"

After a stretch of silence, Joan said, "I don't know." Her voice, unused for ten minutes, cracked on the last syllable. She cleared her throat, scraping Richard's heart.

"What would they stuff them with?" Rebecca asked, dropping an ash into the saucer beside her.

Beyond and beneath the window there arose a clatter. Joan reached the windows first, Richard next, and lastly Rebecca, standing on tiptoe, elongating her neck. Six mounted police, standing in their stirrups, were galloping two abreast down Thirteenth Street. When the Maples' exclamations had subsided, Rebecca remarked, "They do it every night at this time. They seem awfully jolly, for policemen."

"Oh, and it's snowing!" Joan cried. She was pathetic about snow; she loved it so much, and in these last years had seen so little. "On our first night here! Our first *real* night." Forgetting herself, she put her arms around Richard, and Rebecca, where another guest might have turned away, or smiled too broadly, too encouragingly, retained without modification her sweet, absent look and studied, through the embracing couple, the scene outdoors. The snow was not taking on the wet street; only the hoods and tops of parked automobiles showed an accumulation.

"I think I'd best go," Rebecca said.

"Please don't," Joan said with an urgency Richard had not expected; clearly she was very tired. Probably the new home, the change in the weather, the good sherry, the currents of affection between herself and her husband that her sudden hug had renewed, and Rebecca's presence had become in her mind the inextricable elements of one enchanting moment.

"Yes, I think I'll go because you're so snuffly and peakèd."

"Can't you just stay for one more cigarette? Dick, pass the sherry around."

"A teeny bit," Rebecca said, holding out her glass. "I guess I told you, Joan, about the boy I went out with who pretended to be a headwaiter."

Joan giggled expectantly. "No, honestly, you never did." She hooked her arm over the back of the chair and wound her hand through the slats, like a child assuring herself that her bedtime has been postponed. "What did he do? He imitated headwaiters?"

"Yes, he was the kind of guy who, when we get out of a taxi and there's a grate giving out steam, crouches down"—Rebecca lowered her head and lifted her arms—"and pretends he's the Devil."

The Maples laughed, less at the words themselves than at the way Rebecca had evoked the situation by conveying, in her understated imitation, both her escort's flamboyant attitude and her own undemonstrative nature. They could see her standing by the taxi door, gazing with no expression as her escort bent lower and lower, seized by his own joke, his fingers writhing demonically as he felt horns sprout through his scalp, flames lick his ankles, and his feet shrivel into hoofs. Rebecca's gift, Richard realized, was not that of having odd things happen to her but that of representing, through the implicit contrast with her own sane calm, all things touching her as odd. This evening too might appear grotesque in her retelling: "Six policemen on horses galloped by and she cried 'It's snowing!' and hugged him. He kept telling her how sick she was and filling us full of sherry."

"What else did he do?" Joan asked.

"At the first place we went to—it was a big night club on the roof of somewhere—on the way out he sat down and played the piano until a woman at a harp asked him to stop."

Richard asked, "Was the woman *playing* the harp?"

"Yes, she was strumming away." Rebecca made circular motions with her hands.

"Well, did he play the tune she was playing? Did he *accompany* her?" Petulance, Richard realized without understanding why, had entered his tone.

"No, he just sat down and played something else. I couldn't tell what it was."

"Is this *really* true?" Joan asked, egging her on.

"And then at the next place we went to, we had to wait at the bar for a table and I looked around and he was walking among the tables asking people if everything was all right."

"Wasn't it *aw*ful?" said Joan.

"Yes. Later he played the piano there, too. We were sort of the main attraction. Around midnight he thought we ought to go out to Brooklyn to his sister's house. I was exhausted. We got off the subway two stops too early, under the Manhattan Bridge. It was deserted, with nothing going by except black limousines. Miles above our head"—she stared up, as though at a cloud, or the sun—"was the Manhattan Bridge and he kept saying it was the el. We finally found some steps and two policemen who told us to go back to the subway."

"What does this amazing man do for a living?" Richard asked.

"He teaches school. He's quite bright." She stood up, extending in stretch a long, silvery white arm. Richard got her coat and said he'd walk her home.

"It's only three-quarters of a block," Rebecca protested in a voice free of any insistent inflection.

"You must walk her home, Dick," Joan said. "Pick up a pack of cigarettes." The idea of his walking in the snow seemed to please her, as if she were anticipating how he would bring back with him, in the snow on his shoulders and the coldness of his face, all the sensations of the walk she was not well enough to risk.

"You should stop smoking for a day or two," he told her.

Joan waved them goodbye from the head of the stairs.

· · ·

The snow, invisible except around street lights, exerted a fluttering romantic pressure on their faces. "Coming down hard now," he said.

"Yes."

At the corner, where the snow gave the green light a watery blueness, her hesitancy in following him as he turned to walk with the light across Thirteenth Street led him to ask, "It is this side of the street you live on, isn't it?"

"Yes."

"I thought I remembered from the time we drove you down from Boston." The Maples had been living in the West Eighties then. "I remember I had an impression of big buildings."

"The church and the butcher's school," Rebecca said. "Every day about ten when I'm going to work the boys learning to be butchers come out for an intermission all bloody and laughing."

Richard looked up at the church; the steeple was fragmentarily silhouetted against the scattered lit windows of a tall improvement on Seventh Avenue. "Poor church," he said. "It's hard in this city for a steeple to be the tallest thing."

Rebecca said nothing, not even her habitual "Yes." He felt rebuked for being preachy. In his embarrassment he directed her attention to the first next thing he saw, a poorly lettered sign above a great door. "Food Trades Vocational High School," he read aloud. "The people upstairs told us that the man before the man before *us* in our apartment was a wholesale meat salesman who called himself a Purveyor of Elegant Foods. He kept a woman in the apartment."

"Those big windows up there," Rebecca said, pointing up at the third story of a brownstone, "face mine across the street. I can look in and feel we are neighbors. Someone's always there; I don't know what they do for a living."

After a few more steps they halted, and Rebecca, in a voice that Richard imagined to be slightly louder than her ordinary one, said, "Do you want to come up and see where I live?"

"Sure." It seemed implausible to refuse.

They descended four concrete steps, opened a shabby orange door, entered an overheated half-basement lobby, and began to climb four flights of wooden stairs. Richard's suspicion on the street that he was trespassing beyond the public gardens of courtesy turned to certain guilt. Few experiences so savor of the illicit as mounting stairs behind a woman's fanny. Three years ago, Joan had lived in a fourth-floor walkup, in Cambridge. Richard never took her home, even when the whole business, down to the last intimacy, had become formula, without the fear that the landlord, justifiably furious, would leap from his door and devour him as they passed.

Opening her door, Rebecca said, "It's hot as hell in here," swearing for the first time in his hearing. She turned on a weak light. The room was small; slanting planes, the underside of the building's roof, intersecting the ceiling and walls, cut large prismatic volumes from Rebecca's living space. As he moved further forward, toward Rebecca, who had not yet removed her coat, Richard perceived, on his right, an unexpected area created where the steeply slanting roof extended itself to the floor. Here a double bed was placed. Tightly bounded on three sides, the bed had the appearance not so much of a piece of furniture as of a permanently installed, blanketed platform. He quickly took his eyes from it and, unable to face Rebecca at once, stared at two kitchen chairs, a metal bridge lamp around the rim of whose shade plump fish and helm wheels alternated, and a four-shelf bookcase—all of which, being slender and proximate to a tilting wall, had an air of threatened verticality.

"Yes, here's the stove on top of the refrigerator I told you about," Rebecca said. "Or did I?"

The top unit overhung the lower by several inches on all sides. He touched his fingers to the stove's white side. "This room is quite sort of nice," he said.

"Here's the view," she said. He moved to stand beside her at the windows, lifting aside the curtains and peering through tiny flawed panes into the apartment across the street.

"That guy *does* have a huge window," Richard said.

She made a brief agreeing noise of n's.

Though all the lamps were on, the apartment across the street was empty. "Looks like a furniture store," he said. Rebecca had still not taken off her coat. "The snow's keeping up."

"Yes. It is."

"Well"—this word was too loud; he finished the sentence too softly —"thanks for letting me see it. I—have you read this?" He had noticed a copy of *Auntie Mame* lying on a hassock.

"I haven't had the time," she said.

"I haven't read it either. Just reviews. That's all I ever read."

This got him to the door. There, ridiculously, he turned. It was only at the door, he decided in retrospect, that her conduct was quite inexcusable: not only did she stand unnecessarily close, but, by shifting the weight of her body to one leg and leaning her head sidewise, she lowered her height several inches, placing him in a dominating position exactly fitted to the broad, passive shadows she must have known were on her face.

"Well—" he said.

"Well." Her echo was immediate and possibly meaningless.

"Don't, don't let the b-butchers get you." The stammer of course ruined the joke, and her laugh, which had begun as soon as she had seen by his face that he would attempt something funny, was completed ahead of his utterance.

As he went down the stairs she rested both hands on the banister and looked down toward the next landing. "Good night," she said.

"Night." He looked up; she had gone into her room. Oh but they were close.

BORZOI
BOOKS
1915
1965

Drama

O NE OF THE MOST DIFFICULT, brilliant, versatile, and (for all his Communist quasi-sympathies) independent of European writers, Jean-
Paul Sartre (1905–   ) today occupies a position in the world of letters
to find a parallel for which one would have to go back almost to the
time of Goethe. His influence is partly a matter of fashion—the Existentialist position, though beginning to show signs of wear, still retains a
café glamor—but much more a consequence of genuine intellectual
power and moral dominance.

Sartre's childhood years are recounted (or rather talked about) in
his recent *The Words*, probably the first part of what is bound to be a
radically original series of memories or commentaries on memories. He
began his career as a lycée teacher in the provinces, then in Paris; studied in Germany under Husserl and Heidegger (who unfortunately affected his style as well as his thought); began to write on psychology
and, more popularly, on modern American literature; published novels
and stories that sounded the note of negativism and alienation which
was for a time his hallmark; joined the French Army in 1939; escaped
from imprisonment the following year and became a valiant intellectual
leader of the underground Resistance; produced plays, novels, and
treatises in abundance, now stressing—with a leftward slant—the necessity of commitment to whatever cause most promises to improve the
human condition.

Sartre's production, for a man still only sixty, is so prodigious that
it is difficult to single out key works. Of his novels my own preference
is still for the early *Nausea* (1938). I am incompetent to judge his monumental Existentialist exposition *Being and Nothingness* (1943). But of

his plays, all extremely interesting, I think *No Exit* the most effective. Directed by John Huston, it received a lively reception on Broadway and, with *The Flies*, has become part of the dramatic repertory of most of the civilized world. Eric Bentley believes that Sartre's plays, along with those of Camus and Brecht, "are the chief dramatic events of the present."

First produced in 1944, it is one of the latest and most contemporary variations on the endless theme of the meaning of utter spiritual perdition. Three ruined souls in a cheap hotel room, which is Hell, find the ultimate agony to be their inability to dispense with each other—or to escape from each other. "Hell is—other people." Is this a judgment on our century? Or on the human race?

Jean-Paul Sartre

NO EXIT
[HUIS CLOS]

Characters in the Play

VALET   GARCIN   ESTELLE   INEZ

Huis Clos (No Exit) was presented for the first time at the Théâtre du Vieux-Colombier, Paris, in May 1944.

SCENE

A drawing-room in Second Empire style. A massive bronze ornament stands on the mantelpiece.

GARCIN [*enters, accompanied by the* ROOM-VALET, *and glances around him*]: Hm! So here we are?

VALET: Yes, Mr. Garcin.

GARCIN: And this is what it looks like?

VALET: Yes.

GARCIN: Second Empire furniture, I observe. . . . Well, well, I dare say one gets used to it in time.

VALET: Some do. Some don't.

GARCIN: Are all the other rooms like this one?

VALET: How could they be? We cater for all sorts: Chinamen and Indians, for instance. What use would they have for a Second Empire chair?

GARCIN: And what use do you suppose *I* have for one? Do you know who I was? . . . Oh, well, it's no great matter. And, to tell the truth, I had quite a habit of living among furniture that I didn't relish, and in false positions. I'd even come to like it. A false position in a Louis-Philippe

---

dining-room—you know the style?—well, that had its points, you know. Bogus in bogus, so to speak.

VALET: And you'll find that living in a Second Empire drawing-room has its points.

GARCIN: Really? . . . Yes, yes, I dare say. . . . [*He takes another look around.*] Still, I certainly didn't expect—this! You know what they tell us down there?

VALET: What about?

GARCIN: About [*makes a sweeping gesture*] this—er—residence.

VALET: Really, sir, how could you believe such cock-and-bull stories? Told by people who'd never set foot here. For, of course, if they had—

GARCIN: Quite so. [*Both laugh. Abruptly the laugh dies from* GARCIN'S *face.*] But, I say, where are the instruments of torture?

VALET: The what?

GARCIN: The racks and red-hot pincers and all the other paraphernalia.

VALET: Ah, you must have your little joke, sir!

GARCIN: My little joke? Oh, I see. No, I wasn't joking. [*A short silence. He strolls round the room.*] No mirrors, I notice. No windows. Only to be expected. And nothing breakable. [*Bursts out angrily.*] But, damn it all, they might have left me my toothbrush!

VALET: That's good! So you haven't yet got over your—what-do-you-call-it?—sense of human dignity? Excuse me smiling.

GARCIN [*thumping ragefully the arm of an armchair*]: I'll ask you to be more polite. I quite realize the position I'm in, but I won't tolerate . . .

VALET: Sorry, sir. No offense meant. But all our guests ask me the same questions. Silly questions, if you'll pardon me saying so. Where's the torture-chamber? That's the first thing they ask, all of them. They don't bother their heads about the bathroom requisites, that I can assure you. But after a bit, when they've got their nerve back, they start in about their toothbrushes and what-not. Good heavens, Mr. Garcin, can't you use your brains? What, I ask you, would be the point of brushing your teeth?

GARCIN [*more calmly*]: Yes, of course you're right. [*He looks around again.*] And why should one want to see oneself in a looking-glass? But that bronze contraption on the mantelpiece, that's another story. I suppose there will be times when I stare my eyes out at it. Stare my eyes out—see what I mean? . . . All right, let's put our cards on the table. I assure you I'm quite conscious of my position. Shall I tell you what it feels like? A man's drowning, choking, sinking by inches, till only his eyes are just above water. And what does he see? A bronze atrocity by—what's the fellow's name?—Barbedienne. A collector's piece. As in a nightmare. That's their idea, isn't it? . . . No, I suppose you're under orders not to answer questions; and I won't insist. But don't forget, my man, I've a good notion of what's coming to me, so don't you boast you've caught me off my guard. I'm facing the situation, facing it. [*He starts pacing the room again.*] So that's that; no toothbrush. And no bed, either. One never sleeps, I take it?

VALET: That's so.

GARCIN: Just as I expected. *Why* should one sleep? A sort of drowsiness steals on you, tickles you behind the ears, and you feel your eyes closing—but why sleep? You lie down on the sofa and—in a flash, sleep flies away. Miles and miles away. So you rub your eyes, get up, and it starts all over again.

VALET: Romantic, that's what you are.

GARCIN: Will you keep quiet, please! . . . I won't make a scene, I shan't be sorry for myself, I'll face the situation, as I said just now. Face it fairly and squarely. I won't have it springing at me from behind, before I've time to size it up. And you call that being "romantic"! . . . So it comes to this; one doesn't need rest. Why bother about sleep if one isn't sleepy? That stands to reason, doesn't it? Wait a minute, there's a snag somewhere; something disagreeable. Why, now, should it be disagreeable? . . . Ah, I see; it's life without a break.

VALET: What do you mean by that?

GARCIN: What do I mean? [*Eyes the* VALET *suspiciously.*] I thought as much. That's why there's something so beastly, so damn bad-mannered, in the way you stare at me. They're paralyzed.

VALET: What are you talking about?

GARCIN: Your eyelids. We move ours up and down. Blinking, we call it. It's like a small black shutter that clicks down and makes a break. Everything goes black; one's eyes are moistened. You can't imagine how restful, refreshing, it is. Four thousand little rests per hour. Four thousand little respites—just think! . . . So that's the idea. I'm to live without eyelids. Don't act the fool, you know what I mean. No eyelids, no sleep; it follows, doesn't it? I shall never sleep again. But then —how shall I endure my own company? Try to understand. You see, I'm fond of teasing, it's a second nature with me—and I'm used to teasing myself. Plaguing myself, if you prefer; I don't tease nicely. But I can't go on doing that without a break. Down there I had my nights. I slept. I always had good nights. By way of compensation, I suppose. And happy little dreams. There was a green field. Just an ordinary field. I used to stroll in it. . . . Is it daytime now?

VALET: Can't you see? The lights are on.

GARCIN: Ah yes, I've got it. It's *your* daytime. And outside?

VALET: Outside?

GARCIN: Damn it, you know what I mean. Beyond that wall.

VALET: There's a passage.

GARCIN: And at the end of the passage?

VALET: There's more rooms, more passages, and stairs.

GARCIN: And what lies beyond them?

VALET: That's all.

GARCIN: But surely you have a day off sometimes. Where do you go?

VALET: To my uncle's place. He's the head valet here. He has a room on the third floor.

GARCIN: I should have guessed as much. Where's the light-switch?

VALET: There isn't any.

GARCIN: What? Can't one turn off the light?

VALET: Oh, the management can cut off the current if they want to. But I can't remember their having done so on this floor. We have all the electricity we want.

GARCIN: So one has to live with one's eyes open all the time?

VALET: To *live*, did you say?

GARCIN: Don't let's quibble over words. With one's eyes open. Forever. Always broad daylight in my eyes—and in my head. [*Short silence.*] And suppose I took that contraption on the mantelpiece and dropped it on the lamp—wouldn't it go out?

VALET: You can't move it. It's too heavy.

GARCIN [*seizing the bronze ornament and trying to lift it*]: You're right. It's too heavy.

[*A short silence follows.*]

VALET: Very well, sir, if you don't need me any more, I'll be off.

GARCIN: What? You're going? [*The* VALET *goes up to the door.*] Wait. [VALET *looks round.*] That's a bell, isn't it? [VALET *nods.*] And if I ring, you're bound to come?

VALET: Well, yes, that's so—in a way. But you can never be sure about that bell. There's something wrong with the wiring, and it doesn't always work. [GARCIN *goes to the bell-push and presses the button. A bell purrs outside.*]

GARCIN: It's working all right.

VALET [*looking surprised*]: So it is. [*He, too, presses the button.*] But I shouldn't count on it too much if I were you. It's—capricious. Well, I really must go now. [GARCIN *makes a gesture to detain him.*] Yes, sir?

GARCIN: No, never mind. [*He goes to the mantelpiece and picks up a paper-knife.*] What's this?

VALET: Can't you see? An ordinary paper-knife.

GARCIN: Are there books here?

VALET: No.

GARCIN: Then what's the use of this? [VALET *shrugs his shoulders.*] Very well. You can go. [VALET *goes out.*] [GARCIN *is by himself. He goes to the bronze ornament and strokes it reflectively. He sits down; then gets up, goes to the bell-push, and presses the button. The bell remains silent. He tries two or three times, without success. Then he tries to open the door, also without success. He calls the* VALET *several times, but gets no result. He beats the door with his fists, still calling. Suddenly he grows calm and sits down again. At the same moment the door opens and* INEZ *enters, followed by the* VALET.]

VALET: Did you call, sir?

GARCIN [*on the point of answering "Yes"—but then his eyes fall on* INEZ]: No.

VALET [*turning to* INEZ]: This is your room, madam. [INEZ *says nothing.*] If there's any information you require—? [INEZ *still keeps silent, and the* VALET *looks slightly huffed.*] Most of our guests have quite a lot to ask me. But I won't insist. Anyhow, as regards the toothbrush, and the electric bell, and that thing on the mantelshelf, this gentleman can tell you anything you want to know as well as I could. We've had a little chat, him and me. [VALET *goes out.*] [GARCIN *refrains from looking at* INEZ, *who is inspecting the room. Abruptly she turns to* GARCIN.]

INEZ: Where's Florence? [GARCIN *does not reply.*] Didn't you hear? I asked you about Florence. Where is she?

GARCIN: I haven't an idea.

INEZ: Ah, that's the way it works, is it? Torture by separation. Well, as far as I'm concerned, you won't get anywhere. Florence was a tiresome little fool, and I shan't miss her in the least.

GARCIN: I beg your pardon. Who do you suppose I am?

INEZ: You? Why, the torturer, of course.

GARCIN [*looks startled, then bursts out laughing*]: Well, that's a good one! Too comic for words. I the torturer! So you came in, had a look at me, and thought I was—er—one of the staff. Of course, it's that silly fellow's fault; he should have introduced us. A torturer indeed! I'm Joseph Garcin, journalist and man of letters by profession. And as we're both in the same boat, so to speak, might I ask you, Mrs.—?

INEZ [*testily*]: Not "Mrs." I'm unmarried.

GARCIN: Right. That's a start, anyway. Well, now that we've broken the ice, do you *really* think I look like a torturer? And, by the way, how does one recognize torturers when one sees them? Evidently you've ideas on the subject.

INEZ: They look frightened.

GARCIN: Frightened! But how ridiculous! Of whom should they be frightened? Of their victims?

INEZ: Laugh away, but I know what I'm talking about. I've often watched my face in the glass.

GARCIN: In the glass? [*He looks around him.*] How beastly of them! They've removed everything in the least resembling a glass. [*Short silence.*] Anyhow, I can assure you I'm not frightened. Not that I take my position lightly; I realize its gravity only too well. But I'm not afraid.

INEZ [*shrugging her shoulders*]: That's your affair. [*Silence.*] Must you be here all the time, or do you take a stroll outside, now and then?

GARCIN: The door's locked.

INEZ: Oh! . . . That's too bad.

GARCIN: I can quite understand that it bores you having me here. And I, too—well, quite frankly, I'd rather be alone. I want to think things out, you know; to set my life in order, and one does that better by oneself. But I'm sure we'll manage to pull along together somehow. I'm no talker, I don't move much; in fact I'm a peaceful sort of fellow. Only, if I may venture on a suggestion, we should make a point of being extremely courteous to each other. That will ease the situation for us both.

INEZ: I'm not polite.

GARCIN: Then I must be polite for two.

[*A longish silence.* GARCIN *is sitting on a sofa, while* INEZ *paces up and down the room.*]

INEZ [*fixing her eyes on him*]: Your mouth!

GARCIN [*as if waking from a dream*]: I beg your pardon.

INEZ: Can't you keep your mouth still? You keep twisting it about all the time. It's grotesque.

GARCIN: So sorry. I wasn't aware of it.

INEZ: That's just what I reproach you with. [GARCIN's *mouth twitches.*] There you are! You talk about politeness, and you don't even try to control your face. Remember you're not alone; you've no right to inflict the sight of your fear on me.

GARCIN [*getting up and going towards her*]: How about you? Aren't you afraid?

INEZ: What would be the use? There was some point in being afraid *before;* while one still had hope.

GARCIN [*in a low voice*]: There's no more hope—but it's still "before." We haven't yet begun to suffer.

INEZ: That's so. [*A short silence.*] Well? What's going to happen?

GARCIN: I don't know. I'm waiting.

[*Silence again.* GARCIN *sits down and* INEZ *resumes her pacing up and down the room.* GARCIN's *mouth twitches; after a glance at* INEZ *he buries his face in his hands. Enter* ESTELLE *with the* VALET. ESTELLE *looks at* GARCIN, *whose face is still hidden by his hands.*]

ESTELLE [*to* GARCIN]: No! Don't look up. I know what you're hiding with your hands. I know you've no face left. [GARCIN *removes his hands.*] What! [*A short pause. Then, in a tone of surprise*] But I don't know you!

GARCIN: I'm not the torturer, madam.

ESTELLE: I never thought you were. I—I thought someone was trying to play a rather nasty trick on me. [*To the* VALET] Is anyone else coming?

VALET: No, madam. No one else is coming.

ESTELLE: Oh! Then we're to stay by ourselves, the three of us, this gentleman, this lady, and myself. [*She starts laughing.*]

GARCIN [*angrily*]: There's nothing to laugh about.

ESTELLE [*still laughing*]: It's those sofas. They're so hideous. And just look how they've been arranged. It makes me think of New Year's Day—when I used to visit that boring old aunt of mine, Aunt Mary.

Her house is full of horrors like that. . . . I suppose each of us has a sofa of his own. Is that one mine? [*To the* VALET] But you can't expect me to sit on that one. It would be too horrible for words. I'm in pale blue and it's vivid green.

INEZ: Would you prefer mine?

ESTELLE: That claret-colored one, you mean? That's very sweet of you, but really—no, I don't think it'd be so much better. What's the good of worrying, anyhow? We've got to take what comes to us, and I'll stick to the green one. [*Pauses.*] The only one which might do, at a pinch, is that gentleman's. [*Another pause.*]

INEZ: Did you hear, Mr. Garcin?

GARCIN [*with a slight start*]: Oh—the sofa, you mean. So sorry. [*He rises.*] Please take it, madam.

ESTELLE: Thanks. [*She takes off her coat and drops it on the sofa. A short silence.*] Well, as we're to live together, I suppose we'd better introduce ourselves. My name's Rigault. Estelle Rigault. [GARCIN *bows and is going to announce his name, but* INEZ *steps in front of him.*]

INEZ: And I'm Inez Serrano. Very pleased to meet you.

GARCIN [*bowing again*]: Joseph Garcin.

VALET: Do you require me any longer?

ESTELLE: No, you can go. I'll ring when I want you. [*Exit* VALET, *with polite bows to everyone.*]

INEZ: You're very pretty. I wish we'd had some flowers to welcome you with.

ESTELLE: Flowers? Yes, I loved flowers. Only they'd fade so quickly here, wouldn't they? It's so stuffy. Oh, well, the great thing is to keep as cheerful as we can, don't you agree? Of course, you, too, are—

INEZ: Yes. Last week. What about you?

ESTELLE: I'm—quite recent. Yesterday. As a matter of fact, the ceremony's not quite over. [*Her tone is natural enough, but she seems to be seeing what she describes.*] The wind's blowing my sister's veil all over the place. She's trying her best to cry. Come, dear! Make another effort. That's better. Two tears, two little tears are twinkling under the black veil. Oh dear! What a sight Olga looks this morning! She's holding my sister's arm, helping her along. She's not crying, and I don't blame her; tears always mess one's face up, don't they? Olga was my bosom friend, you know.

INEZ: Did you suffer much?

ESTELLE: No. I was only half conscious, mostly.

INEZ: What was it?

ESTELLE: Pneumonia. [*In the same tone as before*] It's over now, they're leaving the cemetery. Good-by. Good-by. Quite a crowd they are. My husband's stayed at home. Prostrated with grief, poor man. [*To* INEZ] How about you?

INEZ: The gas stove.

ESTELLE: And you, Mr. Garcin?

GARCIN: Twelve bullets through my chest. [ESTELLE *makes a horrified gesture.*] Sorry! I fear I'm not good company among the dead.

ESTELLE: Please, please don't use that word. It's so—so crude. In terribly bad taste, really. It doesn't mean much, anyhow. Somehow I feel we've never been so much alive as now. If we've absolutely got to mention this—this state of things, I suggest we call ourselves—wait!—absentees. Have you been—been absent for long?

GARCIN: About a month.

ESTELLE: Where do you come from?

GARCIN: From Rio.

ESTELLE: I'm from Paris. Have you anyone left down there?

GARCIN: Yes, my wife. [*In the same tone as* ESTELLE *has been using*] She's waiting at the entrance of the barracks. She comes there every day. But they won't let her in. Now she's trying to peep between the bars. She doesn't yet know I'm—absent, but she suspects it. Now she's going away. She's wearing her black dress. So much the better, she won't need to change. She isn't crying, but she never did cry, anyhow. It's a bright sunny day and she's like a black shadow creeping down the empty street. Those big tragic eyes of hers—with that martyred look they always had. Oh, how she got on my nerves!

[*A short silence.* GARCIN *sits on the central sofa and buries his head in his hands.*]

INEZ: Estelle!

ESTELLE: Please, Mr. Garcin!

GARCIN: What is it?

ESTELLE: You're sitting on my sofa.

GARCIN: I beg your pardon. [*He gets up.*]

ESTELLE: You looked so—so far away. Sorry I disturbed you.

GARCIN: I was setting my life in order. [INEZ *starts laughing.*] You may laugh, but you'd do better to follow my example.

INEZ: No need. My life's in perfect order. It tidied itself up nicely of its own accord. So I needn't bother about it now.

GARCIN: Really? You imagine it's so simple as that. [*He runs his hand over his forehead.*] Whew! How hot it is here! Do you mind if—? [*He begins taking off his coat.*]

ESTELLE: How dare you! [*More gently*] No, please don't. I loathe men in their shirt-sleeves.

GARCIN [*putting on his coat again*]: All right. [*A short pause.*] Of course, I used to spend my nights in the newspaper office, and it was a regular Black Hole, so we never kept our coats on. Stiflingly hot it could be. [*Short pause. In the same tone as previously*] Stifling, that it *is*. It's night now.

ESTELLE: That's so. Olga's undressing; it must be after midnight. How quickly the time passes, on earth!

INEZ: Yes, after midnight. They've sealed up my room. It's dark, pitch-dark, and empty.

GARCIN: They've slung their coats on the backs of the chairs and rolled up their shirt-sleeves above the elbow. The air stinks of men and cigar-smoke. [*A short silence.*] I used to like living among men in their shirt-sleeves.

ESTELLE [*aggressively*]: Well, in that case our tastes differ. That's all it proves. [*Turning to* INEZ] What about you? Do you like men in their shirt-sleeves?

INEZ: Oh, I don't care much for men any way.

ESTELLE [*looking at the other two with a puzzled air*]: Really I can't imagine why they put us three together. It doesn't make sense.

INEZ [*stifling a laugh*]: What's that you said?

ESTELLE: I'm looking at you two and thinking that we're going to live to-gether. . . . It's so absurd. I expected to meet old friends, or relatives.

INEZ: Yes, a charming old friend—with a hole in the middle of his face.

ESTELLE: Yes, him too. He danced the tango so divinely. Like a profes-sional. . . . But why, why should we of all people be put together?

GARCIN: A pure fluke, I should say. They lodge folks as they can, in the order of their coming. [*To* INEZ] Why are you laughing?

INEZ: Because you amuse me, with your "flukes." As if they left anything to chance! But I suppose you've got to reassure yourself somehow.

ESTELLE [*hesitantly*]: I wonder, now. Don't you think we may have met each other at some time in our lives?

INEZ: Never. I shouldn't have forgotten you.

ESTELLE: Or perhaps we have friends in common. I wonder if you know the Dubois-Seymours?

INEZ: Not likely.

ESTELLE: But *everyone* went to their parties.

INEZ: What's their job?

ESTELLE: Oh, they don't do anything. But they have a lovely house in the country, and hosts of people visit them.

INEZ: I didn't. I was a post-office clerk.

ESTELLE [*recoiling a little*]: Ah, yes. . . . Of course, in that case— [*A pause.*] And you, Mr. Garcin?

GARCIN: We've never met. I always lived in Rio.

ESTELLE: Then you must be right. It's mere chance that has brought us together.

INEZ: Mere chance? Then it's by chance this room is furnished as we see it. It's an accident that the sofa on the right is a livid green, and that one on the left's wine-red. Mere chance? Well, just try to shift the sofas and you'll see the difference quick enough. And that statue on the mantelpiece, do you think it's there by accident? And what about the heat here? How about that? [*A short silence.*] I tell you they've thought it all out. Down to the last detail. Nothing was left to chance. This room was all set for us.

ESTELLE: But really! Everything here's so hideous; all in angles, so un-comfortable. I always loathed angles.

INEZ [*shrugging her shoulders*]: And do you think *I* lived in a Second
Empire drawing-room?

ESTELLE: So it was all fixed up beforehand?

INEZ: Yes. And they've put us together deliberately.

ESTELLE: Then it's not mere chance that *you* precisely are sitting opposite *me?* But what can be the idea behind it?

INEZ: Ask me another! I only know they're waiting.

ESTELLE: I never could bear the idea of anyone's expecting something
from me. It always made me want to do just the opposite.

INEZ: Well, do it. Do it if you can. You don't even know what they
expect.

ESTELLE [*stamping her foot*]: It's outrageous! So something's coming to
me from you two? [*She eyes each in turn.*] Something nasty, I suppose. There are some faces that tell me everything at once. Yours
don't convey anything.

GARCIN [*turning abruptly towards* INEZ]: Look here! Why are we together? You've given us quite enough hints, you may as well come
out with it.

INEZ [*in a surprised tone*]: But I know nothing, absolutely nothing about
it. I'm as much in the dark as you are.

GARCIN: We've *got* to know. [*Ponders for a while.*]

INEZ: If only each of us had the guts to tell—

GARCIN: Tell what?

INEZ: Estelle!

ESTELLE: Yes?

INEZ: What have you done? I mean, why have they sent you here?

ESTELLE [*quickly*]: That's just it. I haven't a notion, not the foggiest. In
fact, I'm wondering if there hasn't been some ghastly mistake.
[*To* INEZ] Don't smile. Just think of the number of people who—
who become absentees every day. There must be thousands and
thousands, and probably they're sorted out by—by understrappers,
you know what I mean. Stupid employees who don't know their
job. So they're bound to make mistakes sometimes. . . . Do stop
smiling. [*To* GARCIN] Why don't you speak? If they made a mistake in my case, they may have done the same about you. [*To* INEZ]
And you, too. Anyhow, isn't it better to think we've got here by
mistake?

INEZ: Is that all you have to tell us?

ESTELLE: What else should I tell? I've nothing to hide. I lost my parents
when I was a kid, and I had my young brother to bring up. We were
terribly poor and when an old friend of my people asked me to
marry him I said yes. He was very well off, and quite nice. My
brother was a very delicate child and needed all sorts of attention, so
really that was the right thing for me to do, don't you agree? My
husband was old enough to be my father, but for six years we had a
happy married life. Then two years ago I met the man I was fated

to love. We knew it the moment we set eyes on each other. He asked me to run away with him, and I refused. Then I got pneumonia and it finished me. That's the whole story. No doubt, by certain standards, I did wrong to sacrifice my youth to a man nearly three times my age. [*To* GARCIN] Do *you* think that could be called a sin?

GARCIN: Certainly not. [*A short silence.*] And now, tell me, do you think it's a crime to stand by one's principles?

ESTELLE: Of course not. Surely no one could blame a man for that!

GARCIN: Wait a bit! I ran a pacifist newspaper. Then war broke out. What was I to do? Everyone was watching me, wondering: "Will he dare?" Well, I dared. I folded my arms and they shot me. Had I done anything wrong?

ESTELLE [*laying her hand on his arm*]: Wrong? On the contrary. You were—

INEZ [*breaks in ironically*]: —a hero! And how about your wife, Mr. Garcin?

GARCIN: That's simple. I'd rescued her from—from the gutter.

ESTELLE [*to* INEZ]: You see! You see!

INEZ: Yes, I see. [*A pause.*] Look here! What's the point of play-acting, trying to throw dust in each other's eyes? We're all tarred with the same brush.

ESTELLE [*indignantly*]: How dare you!

INEZ: Yes, we are criminals—murderers—all three of us. We're in hell, my pets; they never make mistakes, and people aren't damned for nothing.

ESTELLE: Stop! For heaven's sake—

INEZ: In hell! Damned souls—that's us, all three!

ESTELLE: Keep quiet! I forbid you to use such disgusting words.

INEZ: A damned soul—that's you, my little plaster saint. And ditto our friend there, the noble pacifist. We've had our hour of pleasure, haven't we? There have been people who burned their lives out for our sakes—and we chuckled over it. So now we have to pay the reckoning.

GARCIN [*raising his fist*]: Will you keep your mouth shut, damn it!

INEZ [*confronting him fearlessly, but with a look of vast surprise*]: Well, well! [*A pause.*] Ah, I understand now. I know why they've put us three together.

GARCIN: I advise you to—to think twice before you say any more.

INEZ: Wait! You'll see how simple it is. Childishly simple. Obviously there aren't any physical torments—you agree, don't you? And yet we're in hell. And no one else will come here. We'll stay in this room together, the three of us, for ever and ever. . . . In short, there's someone absent here, the official torturer.

GARCIN [*sotto voce*]: I'd noticed that.

INEZ: It's obvious what they're after—an economy of man-power—or devil-power, if you prefer. The same idea as in the cafeteria, where customers serve themselves.

ESTELLE: What ever do you mean?

INEZ: I mean that each of us will act as torturer of the two others.

[*There is a short silence while they digest this information.*]

GARCIN [*gently*]: No, I shall never be your torturer. I wish neither of you any harm, and I've no concern with you. None at all. So the solution's easy enough; each of us stays put in his or her corner and takes no notice of the others. You here, you here, and I there. Like soldiers at our posts. Also, we mustn't speak. Not one word. That won't be difficult; each of us has plenty of material for self-communings. I think I could stay ten thousand years with only my thoughts for company.

ESTELLE: Have *I* got to keep silent, too?

GARCIN: Yes. And that way we—we'll work out our salvation. Looking into ourselves, never raising our heads. Agreed?

INEZ: Agreed.

ESTELLE [*after some hesitation*]: I agree.

GARCIN: Then—good-by.

[*He goes to his sofa and buries his head in his hands. There is a long silence; then* INEZ *begins singing to herself.*]

INEZ [*singing*]:

What a crowd in Whitefriars Lane!
They've set trestles in a row,
With a scaffold and the knife,
And a pail of bran below.
Come, good folks, to Whitefriars Lane,
Come to see the merry show!

The headsman rose at crack of dawn,
He'd a long day's work in hand,
Chopping heads off generals,
Priests and peers and admirals,
All the highest in the land.
What a crowd in Whitefriars Lane!

See them standing in a line,
Ladies all dressed up so fine.
But their heads have got to go,
Heads and hats roll down below.
Come, good folks, to Whitefriars Lane,
Come to see the merry show!

[*Meanwhile* ESTELLE *has been plying her powder-puff and lipstick. She looks round for a mirror, fumbles in her bag, then turns towards* GARCIN.]

ESTELLE: Excuse me, have you a glass? [GARCIN *does not answer.*] Any sort of glass, a pocket-mirror will do. [GARCIN *remains silent.*] Even if you won't speak to me, you might lend me a glass.

[*His head still buried in his hands,* GARCIN *ignores her.*]

INEZ [*eagerly*]: Don't worry. I've a glass in my bag. [*She opens her bag. Angrily*] It's gone! They must have taken it from me at the entrance.

ESTELLE: How tiresome!

[*A short silence.* ESTELLE *shuts her eyes and sways, as if about to faint.* INEZ *runs forward and holds her up.*]

INEZ: What's the matter?

ESTELLE [*opens her eyes and smiles*]: I feel so queer. [*She pats herself.*] Don't you ever get taken that way? When I can't see myself I begin to wonder if I really and truly exist. I pat myself just to make sure, but it doesn't help much.

INEZ: You're lucky. I'm always conscious of myself—in my mind. Painfully conscious.

ESTELLE: Ah yes, in your mind. But everything that goes on in one's head is so vague, isn't it? It makes one want to sleep. [*She is silent for a while.*] I've six big mirrors in my bedroom. There they are. I can see them. But they don't see me. They're reflecting the carpet, the settee, the window—but how empty it is, a glass in which I'm absent! When I talked to people I always made sure there was one near by in which I could see myself. I watched myself talking. And somehow it kept me alert, seeing myself as the others saw me. . . . Oh dear! My lipstick! I'm sure I've put it on all crooked. No, I can't do without a looking-glass for ever and ever, I simply can't.

INEZ: Suppose I try to be your glass? Come and pay me a visit, dear. Here's a place for you on my sofa.

ESTELLE: But— [*Points to* GARCIN.]

INEZ: Oh, he doesn't count.

ESTELLE: But we're going to—to hurt each other. You said it yourself.

INEZ: Do I look as if I wanted to hurt you?

ESTELLE: One never can tell.

INEZ: Much more likely *you'll* hurt me. Still, what does it matter? If I've got to suffer, it may as well be at your hands, your pretty hands. Sit down. Come closer. Closer. Look into my eyes. What do you see?

ESTELLE: Oh, I'm there! But so tiny I can't see myself properly.

INEZ: But *I* can. Every inch of you. Now ask me questions. I'll be as candid as any looking-glass.

[ESTELLE *seems rather embarrassed and turns to* GARCIN, *as if appealing to him for help.*]

ESTELLE: Please, Mr. Garcin. Sure our chatter isn't boring you?

[GARCIN *makes no reply.*]

INEZ: Don't worry about him. As I said, he doesn't count. We're by ourselves. . . . Ask away.

ESTELLE: Are my lips all right?

INEZ: Show! No, they're a bit smudgy.

ESTELLE: I thought as much. Luckily [*throws a quick glance at* GARCIN] no one's seen me. I'll try again.

INEZ: That's better. No. Follow the line of your lips. Wait! I'll guide your hand. There. That's quite good.

ESTELLE: As good as when I came in?

INEZ: Far better. Crueler. Your mouth looks quite diabolical that way.

ESTELLE: Good gracious! And you say you like it! How maddening, not being able to see for myself! You're quite sure, Miss Serrano, that it's all right now?

INEZ: Won't you call me Inez?

ESTELLE: Are you sure it looks all right?

INEZ: You're lovely, Estelle.

ESTELLE: But how can I rely upon your taste? Is it the same as *my* taste? Oh, how sickening it all is, enough to drive one crazy!

INEZ: I *have* your taste, my dear, because I like you so much. Look at me. No, straight. Now smile. I'm not so ugly, either. Am I not nicer than your glass?

ESTELLE: Oh, I don't know. You scare me rather. My reflection in the glass never did that; of course, I knew it so well. Like something I had tamed. . . . I'm going to smile, and my smile will sink down into your pupils, and heaven knows what it will become.

INEZ: And why shouldn't you "tame" *me?* [*The women gaze at each other,* ESTELLE *with a sort of fearful fascination.*] Listen! I want you to call me Inez. We must be great friends.

ESTELLE: I don't make friends with women very easily.

INEZ: Not with postal clerks, you mean? Hullo, what's that—that nasty red spot at the bottom of your cheek? A pimple?

ESTELLE: A pimple? Oh, how simply foul! Where?

INEZ: There. . . . You know the way they catch larks—with a mirror? I'm your lark-mirror, my dear, and you can't escape me. . . . There isn't any pimple, not a trace of one. So what about it? Suppose the mirror started telling lies? Or suppose I covered my eyes—as he is doing—and refused to look at you, all that loveliness of yours would be wasted on the desert air. No, don't be afraid, I can't help looking at you, I shan't turn my eyes away. And I'll be nice to you, ever so nice. Only you must be nice to me, too.

[*A short silence.*]

ESTELLE: Are you really—attracted by me?

INEZ: Very much indeed.

[*Another short silence.*]

ESTELLE [*indicating* GARCIN *by a slight movement of her head*]: But I wish he'd notice me, too.

INEZ: Of course! Because he's a Man! [*To* GARCIN] You've won. [GARCIN *says nothing.*] But look at her, damn it! [*Still no reply from* GARCIN.] Don't pretend. You haven't missed a word of what we've said.

GARCIN: Quite so; not a word. I stuck my fingers in my ears, but your voices thudded in my brain. Silly chatter. Now will you leave me in peace, you two? I'm not interested in you.

INEZ: Not in me, perhaps—but how about this child? Aren't you interested in her? Oh, I saw through your game; you got on your high horse just to impress her.

GARCIN: I asked you to leave me in peace. There's someone talking about me in the newspaper office and I want to listen. And, if it'll make you any happier, let me tell you that I've no use for the "child," as you call her.

ESTELLE: Thanks.

GARCIN: Oh, I didn't mean it rudely.

ESTELLE: You cad!

[*They confront each other in silence for some moments.*]

GARCIN: So's that's that. [*Pause.*] You know I begged you not to speak.

ESTELLE: It's *her* fault; she started. I didn't ask anything of her and she came and offered me her—her glass.

INEZ: So you say. But all the time you were making up to him, trying every trick to catch his attention.

ESTELLE: Well, why shouldn't I?

GARCIN: You're crazy, both of you. Don't you see where this is leading us? For pity's sake, keep your mouths shut. [*Pause.*] Now let's all sit down again quite quietly; we'll look at the floor and each must try to forget the others are there.

[*A longish silence.* GARCIN *sits down. The women return hesitantly to their places. Suddenly* INEZ *swings round on him.*]

INEZ: To forget about the others? How utterly absurd! I *feel* you there, in every pore. Your silence clamors in my ears. You can nail up your mouth, cut your tongue out—but you can't prevent your *being there.* Can you stop your thoughts? I hear them ticking away like a clock, tick-tock, tick-tock, and I'm certain you hear mine. It's all very well skulking on your sofa, but you're everywhere, and every sound comes to me soiled, because you've intercepted it on its way. Why, you've even stolen my face; you know it and I don't! And what about her, about Estelle? You've stolen her from me, too; if she and I were alone do you suppose she'd treat me as she does? No, take your hands from your face, I won't leave you in peace—that would suit your book too well. You'd go on sitting there, in a sort of trance, like a yogi, and even if I didn't see her I'd feel it in my bones—that she was making every sound, even the rustle of her dress, for your benefit, throwing you smiles you didn't see. . . . Well, I won't stand for that, I prefer to choose my hell; I prefer to look you in the eyes and fight it out face to face.

GARCIN: Have it your own way. I suppose we were bound to come to this; they knew what they were about, and we're easy game. If they'd put me in a room with men—men can keep their mouths shut. But it's no use wanting the impossible. [*He goes to* ESTELLE *and lightly fondles her neck.*] So I attract you, little girl? It seems you were making eyes at me?

ESTELLE: Don't touch me.

GARCIN: Why not? We might, anyhow, be natural. . . . Do you know, I used to be mad about women? And some were fond of me. So we may as well stop posing, we've nothing to lose. Why trouble about politeness, and decorum, and the rest of it? We're between ourselves. And presently we shall be naked as—as new-born babes.

ESTELLE: Oh, let me be!

GARCIN: As new-born babes. Well, I'd warned you, anyhow. I asked so little of you, nothing but peace and a little silence. I'd put my fingers in my ears. Gomez was spouting away as usual, standing in the center of the room, with all the pressmen listening. In their shirt-sleeves. I tried to hear, but it wasn't too easy. Things on earth move so quickly, you know. Couldn't you have held your tongues? Now it's over, he's stopped talking, and what he thinks of me has gone back into his head. Well, we've got to see it through some-how. . . . Naked as we were born. So much the better; I want to know whom I have to deal with.

INEZ: You know already. There's nothing more to learn.

GARCIN: You're wrong. So long as each of us hasn't made a clean breast of it—why they've damned him or her—we know nothing. Nothing that counts. You, young lady, you shall begin. Why? Tell us why. If you are frank, if we bring our specters into the open, it may save us from disaster. So—out with it! Why?

ESTELLE: I tell you I haven't a notion. They wouldn't tell me why.

GARCIN: That's so. They wouldn't tell me, either. But I've a pretty good idea. . . . Perhaps you're shy of speaking first? Right. I'll lead off. [*A short silence.*] I'm not a very estimable person.

INEZ: No need to tell us that. We know you were a deserter.

GARCIN: Let that be. It's only a side-issue. I'm here because I treated my wife abominably. That's all. For five years. Naturally, she's suffering still. There she is: the moment I mention her, I see her. It's Gomez who interests me, and it's she I see. Where's Gomez got to? For five years. There! They've given her back my things; she's sitting by the window, with my coat on her knees. The coat with the twelve bullet-holes. The blood's like rust; a brown ring round each hole. It's quite a museum-piece, that coat; scarred with history. And I used to wear it, fancy! . . . Now, can't you shed a tear, my love? Surely you'll squeeze one out—at last? No? You can't manage it? . . . Night after night I came home blind drunk, stinking of wine and women. She'd sat up for me, of course. But she never cried, never uttered a word of reproach. Only her eyes spoke. Big, tragic eyes. I don't regret anything. I must pay the price, but I shan't whine. . . . It's snowing in the street. Won't you cry, confound you? That woman was a born martyr, you know; a victim by vocation.

INEZ [*almost tenderly*]: Why did you hurt her like that?

GARCIN: It was so easy. A word was enough to make her flinch. Like a sensitive-plant. But never, never a reproach. I'm fond of teasing. I watched and waited. But no, not a tear, not a protest. I'd picked her up out of the gutter, you understand. . . . Now she's stroking the coat. Her eyes are shut and she's feeling with her fingers for the bullet-holes. What are you after? What do you expect? I tell you I regret nothing. The truth is, she admired me too much. Does that mean anything to you?

INEZ: No. Nobody admired *me*.

GARCIN: So much the better. So much the better for you. I suppose all this strikes you as very vague. Well, here's something you can get your teeth into. I brought a half-caste girl to stay in our house. My wife slept upstairs; she must have heard—everything. She was an early riser and, as I and the girl stayed in bed late, she served us our morning coffee.

INEZ: You brute!

GARCIN: Yes, a brute, if you like. But a well-beloved brute. [*A far-away look comes to his eyes.*] No, it's nothing. Only Gomez, and he's not talking about *me*. . . . What were you saying? Yes, a brute. Certainly. Else why should I be here? [*To* INEZ] Your turn.

INEZ: Well, I was what some people down there called "a damned bitch." Damned already. So it's no surprise, being here.

GARCIN: Is that all you have to say?

INEZ: No. There was that affair with Florence. A dead men's tale. With three corpses to it. He to start with; then she and I. So there's no one left, I've nothing to worry about; it was a clean sweep. Only that room. I see it now and then. Empty, with the doors locked. . . . No, they've just unlocked them. "To Let." It's to let; there's a notice on the door. That's—too ridiculous.

GARCIN: Three. Three deaths, you said?

INEZ: Three.

GARCIN: One man and two women?

INEZ: Yes.

GARCIN: Well, well. [*A pause.*] Did he kill himself?

INEZ: He? No, he hadn't the guts for that. Still, he'd every reason; we led him a dog's life. As a matter of fact, he was run over by a tram. A silly sort of end. . . . I was living with them; he was my cousin.

GARCIN: Was Florence fair?

INEZ: Fair? [*Glances at* ESTELLE.] You know, I don't regret a thing; still, I'm not so very keen on telling you the story.

GARCIN: That's all right. . . . So you got sick of him?

INEZ: Quite gradually. All sorts of little things got on my nerves. For instance, he made a noise when he was drinking—a sort of gurgle. Trifles like that. He was rather pathetic really. Vulnerable. Why are you smiling?

GARCIN: Because I, anyhow, am *not* vulnerable.

INEZ: Don't be too sure. . . . I crept inside her skin, she saw the world through my eyes. When she left him, I had her on my hands. We shared a bed-sitting-room at the other end of the town.

GARCIN: And then?

INEZ: Then that tram did its job. I used to remind her every day: "Yes, my pet, we killed him between us." [*A pause.*] I'm rather cruel, really.

GARCIN: So am I.

INEZ: No, you're not cruel. It's something else.

GARCIN: What?

INEZ: I'll tell you later. When I say I'm cruel, I mean I can't get on without making people suffer. Like a live coal. A live coal in others' hearts. When I'm alone I flicker out. For six months I flamed away in her heart, till there was nothing but a cinder. One night she got up and turned on the gas while I was asleep. Then she crept back into bed. So now you know.

GARCIN: Well! Well!

INEZ: Yes? What's in your mind?

GARCIN: Nothing. Only that it's not a pretty story.

INEZ: Obviously. But what matter?

GARCIN: As you say, what matter? [*To* ESTELLE] Your turn. What have you done?

ESTELLE: As I told you, I haven't a notion. I rack my brain, but it's no use.

GARCIN: Right. Then we'll give you a hand. That fellow with the smashed face, who was he?

ESTELLE: Who—who do you mean?

INEZ: You know quite well. The man you were so scared of seeing when you came in.

ESTELLE: Oh, him! A friend of mine.

GARCIN: Why were you afraid of him?

ESTELLE: That's my business, Mr. Garcin.

INEZ: Did he shoot himself on your account?

ESTELLE: Of course not. How absurd you are!

GARCIN: Then why should you have been so scared? He blew his brains out, didn't he? That's how his face got smashed.

ESTELLE: Don't! Please don't go on.

GARCIN: Because of you. Because of you.

INEZ: He shot himself because of you.

ESTELLE: Leave me alone! It's—it's not fair, bullying me like that. I want to go! I want to go!

[*She runs to the door and shakes it.*]

GARCIN: Go if you can. Personally, I ask for nothing better. Unfortunately, the door's locked.

[ESTELLE *presses the bell-push, but the bell does not ring.* INEZ *and* GARCIN *laugh.* ESTELLE *swings round on them, her back to the door.*]

ESTELLE [*in a muffled voice*]: You're hateful, both of you.

INEZ: Hateful? Yes, that's the word. Now get on with it. That fellow who killed himself on your account—you were his mistress, eh?

GARCIN: Of course she was. And he wanted to have her to himself alone. That's so, isn't it?

INEZ: He danced the tango like a professional, but he was poor as a church mouse—that's right, isn't it?

[*A short silence.*]

GARCIN: Was he poor or not? Give a straight answer.

ESTELLE: Yes, he was poor.

GARCIN: And then you had your reputation to keep up. One day he came and implored you to run away with him, and you laughed in his face.

INEZ: That's it. You laughed at him. And so he killed himself.

ESTELLE: Did you use to look at Florence in that way?

INEZ: Yes.

[*A short pause, then* ESTELLE *bursts out laughing.*]

ESTELLE: You've got it all wrong, you two. [*She stiffens her shoulders, still leaning against the door, and faces them. Her voice grows shrill, truculent.*] He wanted me to have a baby. So there!

GARCIN: And you didn't want one?

ESTELLE: I certainly didn't. But the baby came, worse luck. I went to Switzerland for five months. No one knew anything. It was a girl. Roger was with me when she was born. It pleased him no end, having a daughter. It didn't please *me!*

GARCIN: And then?

ESTELLE: There was a balcony overlooking the lake. I brought a big stone. He could see what I was up to and he kept on shouting: "Estelle, for God's sake, don't!" I hated him then. He saw it all. He was leaning over the balcony and he saw the rings spreading on the water—

GARCIN: Yes? And then?

ESTELLE: That's all. I came back to Paris—and he did as he wished.

GARCIN: You mean he blew his brains out?

ESTELLE: It was absurd of him, really, my husband never suspected anything. [*A pause.*] Oh, how I loathe you! [*She sobs tearlessly.*]

GARCIN: Nothing doing. Tears don't flow in this place.

ESTELLE: I'm a coward. A coward! [*Pause.*] If you knew how I hate you!

INEZ [*taking her in her arms*]: Poor child! [*To* GARCIN] So the hearing's over. But there's no need to look like a hanging judge.

GARCIN: A hanging judge? [*He glances around him.*] I'd give a lot to be able to see myself in a glass. [*Pause.*] How hot it is! [*Unthinkingly he takes off his coat.*] Oh, sorry! [*He starts putting it on again.*]

ESTELLE: Don't bother. You can stay in your shirt-sleeves. As things are—

GARCIN: Just so. [*He drops his coat on the sofa.*] You mustn't be angry with me, Estelle.

ESTELLE: I'm not angry with you.

INEZ: And what about me? Are you angry with me?

ESTELLE: Yes.

[*A short silence.*]

INEZ: Well, Mr. Garcin, now you have us in the nude all right. Do you understand things any better for that?

GARCIN: I wonder. Yes, perhaps a trifle better. [*Timidly*] And now suppose we start trying to help each other.

INEZ: I don't need help.

GARCIN: Inez, they've laid their snare damned cunningly—like a cobweb. If you make any movement, if you raise your hand to fan yourself, Estelle and I feel a little tug. Alone, none of us can save himself or herself; we're linked together inextricably. So you can take your choice. [*A pause.*] Hullo? What's happening?

INEZ: They've let it. The windows are wide open, a man is sitting on my bed. *My* bed, if you please! They've let it, let it! Step in, step in, make yourself at home, you brute! Ah, there's a woman, too. She's going up to him, putting her hands on his shoulders. . . . Damn it, why don't they turn the lights on! It's getting dark. Now he's going to kiss her. But that's my room, *my* room! Pitch-dark now. I can't see anything, but I hear them whispering, whispering. Is he going to make love to her on *my* bed? What's that she said? That it's noon and the sun is shining? I must be going blind. [*A pause.*] Blacked out. I can't see or hear a thing. So I'm done with the earth, it seems. No more alibis for me! [*She shudders.*] I feel so empty, desiccated— really dead at last. All of me's here, in this room. [*A pause.*] What were you saying? Something about helping me, wasn't it?

GARCIN: Yes.

INEZ: Helping me to do what?

GARCIN: To defeat their devilish tricks.

INEZ: And what do you expect me to do, in return?

GARCIN: To help *me*. It only needs a little effort, Inez; just a spark of human feeling.

INEZ: Human feeling. That's beyond my range. I'm rotten to the core.

GARCIN: And how about me? [*A pause.*] All the same, suppose we try?

INEZ: It's no use. I'm all dried up. I can't give and I can't receive. How could *I* help you? A dead twig, ready for the burning. [*She falls silent, gazing at* ESTELLE, *who has buried her head in her hands.*] Florence was fair, a natural blonde.

GARCIN: Do you realize that this young woman's fated to be your torturer?

INEZ: Perhaps I've guessed it.

GARCIN: It's through her they'll get you. I, of course, I'm different—aloof. I take no notice of her. Suppose you had a try—

INEZ: Yes?

GARCIN: It's a trap. They're watching you, to see if you'll fall into it.

INEZ: I know. And you're another trap. Do you think they haven't fore-known every word you say? And of course there's a whole nest of pitfalls that we can't see. Everything here's a booby-trap. But what do I care? I'm a pitfall, too. For her, obviously. And perhaps I'll catch her.

GARCIN: You won't catch anything. We're chasing after each other, round and round in a vicious circle, like the horses on a roundabout. That's part of their plan, of course. . . . Drop it, Inez. Open your hands and let go of everything. Or else you'll bring disaster on all three of us.

INEZ: Do I look the sort of person who lets go? I know what's coming to me. I'm going to burn, and it's to last forever. Yes, I *know* everything. But do you think I'll let go? I'll catch her, she'll see you through my eyes, as Florence saw that other man. What's the good of trying to enlist my sympathy? I assure you I know everything, and I can't feel sorry even for myself. A trap! Don't I know it, and that I'm in a trap myself, up to the neck, and there's nothing to be done about it? And if it suits their book, so much the better!

GARCIN [*gripping her shoulders*]: Well, *I*, anyhow, can feel sorry for you, too. Look at me, we're naked, naked right through, and I can see into your heart. That's one link between us. Do you think I'd want to hurt you? I don't regret anything, I'm dried up, too. But for you I can still feel pity.

INEZ [*who has let him keep his hands on her shoulders until now, shakes herself loose*]: Don't. I hate being pawed about. And keep your pity for yourself. Don't forget, Garcin, that there are traps for you, too, in this room. All nicely set for you. You'd do better to watch your own interests. [*A pause.*] But, if you will leave us in peace, this child and me, I'll see I don't do you any harm.

GARCIN [*gazes at her for a moment, then shrugs his shoulders*]: Very well.

ESTELLE [*raising her head*]: Please, Garcin.

GARCIN: What do you want of me?

ESTELLE [*rises and goes up to him*]: You can help *me*, anyhow.

GARCIN: If you want help, apply to her.

[INEZ *has come up and is standing behind* ESTELLE, *but without touching her. During the dialogue that follows she speaks almost in her eyes. But* ESTELLE *keeps her eyes on* GARCIN, *who observes her without speaking, and she addresses her answers to him, as if it were he who is questioning her.*]

ESTELLE: I implore you, Garcin—you gave me your promise, didn't you?

Help me quick. I don't want to be left alone. Olga's taken him to a cabaret.

INEZ: Taken whom?

ESTELLE: Peter. . . . Oh, now they're dancing together.

INEZ: Who's Peter?

ESTELLE: Such a silly boy. He called me his glancing stream—just fancy! He was terribly in love with me. . . . She's persuaded him to come out with her tonight.

INEZ: Do you love him?

ESTELLE: They're sitting down now. She's puffing like a grampus. What a fool the girl is to insist on dancing! But I dare say she does it to reduce. . . . No, of course I don't love him; he's only eighteen, and I'm not a baby-snatcher.

INEZ: Then why bother about them? What difference can it make?

ESTELLE: He belonged to me.

INEZ: Nothing on earth belongs to you any more.

ESTELLE: I tell you he was mine. All mine.

INEZ: Yes, he *was* yours—once. But now— Try to make him hear, try to touch him. Olga can touch him, talk to him as much as she likes. That's so, isn't it? She can squeeze his hand, rub herself against him—

ESTELLE: Yes, look! She's pressing her great fat chest against him, puffing and blowing in his face. But, my poor little lamb, can't you see how ridiculous she is? Why don't you laugh at her? Oh, once I'd have only had to glance at them and she'd have slunk away. Is there really nothing, nothing left of me?

INEZ: Nothing whatever. Nothing of you's left on earth—not even a shadow. All you own is here. Would you like that paper-knife? Or that ornament on the mantelpiece? That blue sofa's yours. And I, my dear, am yours forever.

ESTELLE: You mine! That's good! Well, which of you two would dare to call me his glancing stream, his crystal girl? You know too much about me, you know I'm rotten through and through. . . . Peter dear, think of me, fix your thoughts on me, and save me. All the time you're thinking "my glancing stream, my crystal girl," I'm only half here, I'm only half wicked, and half of me is down there with you, clean and bright and crystal-clear as running water. . . . Oh, just look at her face, all scarlet, like a tomato. No, it's absurd, we've laughed at her together, you and I, often and often. . . . What's that tune?— I always loved it. Yes, the *St. Louis Blues*. . . . All right, dance away, dance away. Garcin, I wish you could see her, you'd die of laughing. Only—she'll never know I *see* her. Yes, I see you, Olga, with your hair all anyhow, and you do look a dope, my dear. Oh, now you're treading on his toes. It's a scream! Hurry up! Quicker! Quicker! He's dragging her along, bundling her round and round—it's too ghastly! He always said I was so light, he loved to dance with me. [*She is dancing as she speaks.*] I tell you, Olga, I can see you. No, she doesn't care, she's dancing through my gaze. What's that? What's that you said? "Our poor dear Estelle"? Oh, don't be such a humbug! You didn't even shed a tear at the funeral. . . . And she has the nerve to talk to him about her poor dear friend Estelle! How dare she discuss me with Peter? Now then, keep time. She never could dance and talk at once. Oh, what's that? No, no. Don't tell him. Please, please don't tell him. You can keep him, do what you like with him, but please don't tell him about—that! [*She has stopped dancing.*] All right. You can have him now. Isn't it *foul*, Garcin? She's told him every-thing, about Roger, my trip to Switzerland, the baby. "Poor Estelle wasn't exactly—" No, I wasn't exactly— True enough. He's looking grave, shaking his head, but he doesn't seem so very much surprised, not what one would expect. Keep him, then—I won't haggle with you over his long eyelashes, his pretty girlish face. They're yours for the asking. His glancing stream, his crystal. Well, the crystal's shattered into bits. "Poor Estelle!" Dance, dance, dance. On with it. But do keep time. One, two. One, two. How I'd love to go down to earth for just a moment, and dance with him again. [*She dances again for some moments.*] The music's growing fainter. They've turned down the lights, as they do for a tango. Why are they playing so softly? Louder, please. I can't hear. It's so far away, so far away. I—I can't hear a sound. [*She stops dancing.*] All over. It's the end. The earth has left me. [*To* GARCIN] Don't turn from me—please. Take me in your arms. [*Behind* ESTELLE'S *back,* INEZ *signs to* GARCIN *to move away.*]

INEZ [*commandingly*]: Now then, Garcin!

[GARCIN *moves back a step, and, glancing at* ESTELLE, *points to* INEZ.]

GARCIN: It's to her you should say that.

ESTELLE [*clinging to him*]: Don't turn away. You're a man, aren't you, and surely I'm not such a fright as all that! Everyone says I've lovely hair and, after all, a man killed himself on my account. You have to look at something, and there's nothing here to see except the sofas and that awful ornament and the table. Surely I'm better to look at than a lot of stupid furniture. Listen! I've dropped out of their hearts like a little sparrow fallen from its nest. So gather me up, dear, fold me to your heart—and you'll see how nice I can be.

GARCIN [*freeing himself from her, after a short struggle*]: I tell you it's to that lady you should speak.

ESTELLE: To her? But she doesn't count, she's a woman.

INEZ: Oh, I don't count? Is that what you think? But, my poor little fallen nestling, you've been sheltering in my heart for ages, though you didn't realize it. Don't be afraid; I'll keep looking at you for ever and ever, without a flutter of my eyelids, and you'll live in my gaze like a mote in a sunbeam.

ESTELLE: A sunbeam indeed! Don't talk such rubbish! You've tried that trick already, and you should know it doesn't work.

INEZ: Estelle! My glancing stream! My crystal!

ESTELLE: *Your* crystal? It's grotesque. Do you think you can fool me with that sort of talk? Everyone knows by now what I did to my baby. The crystal's shattered, but I don't care. I'm just a hollow dummy, all that's left of me is the outside—but it's not for you.

INEZ: Come to me, Estelle. You shall be whatever you like: a glancing stream, a muddy stream. And deep down in my eyes you'll see yourself just as you want to be.

ESTELLE: Oh, leave me in peace. You haven't any eyes. Oh, damn it, isn't there anything I can do to get rid of you? I've an idea. [*She spits in* INEZ's *face*.] There!

INEZ: Garcin, you shall pay for this.

[*A pause.* GARCIN *shrugs his shoulders and goes to* ESTELLE.]

GARCIN: So it's a man you need?

ESTELLE: Not *any* man. You.

GARCIN: No humbug now. Any man would do your business. As I happen to be here, you want me. Right! [*He grips her shoulders*.] Mind, I'm not your sort at all, really; I'm not a young nincompoop and I don't dance the tango.

ESTELLE: I'll take you as you are. And perhaps I shall change you.

GARCIN: I doubt it. I shan't pay much attention; I've other things to think about.

ESTELLE: What things?

GARCIN: They wouldn't interest you.

ESTELLE: I'll sit on your sofa and wait for you to take some notice of me. I promise not to bother you at all.

INEZ [*with a shrill laugh*]: That's right, fawn on him, like the silly bitch you are. Grovel and cringe! And he hasn't even good looks to commend him!

ESTELLE [*to* GARCIN]: Don't listen to her. She has no eyes, no ears. She's nothing.

GARCIN: I'll give you what I can. It doesn't amount to much. I shan't love you; I know you too well.

ESTELLE: Do you want me, anyhow?

GARCIN: Yes.

ESTELLE: I ask no more.

GARCIN: In that case— [*He bends over her*.]

INEZ: Estelle! Garcin! You must be going crazy. You're not alone. I'm here too.

GARCIN: Of course—but what does it matter?

INEZ: Under my eyes? You couldn't—couldn't do it.

ESTELLE: Why not? I often undressed with my maid looking on.

INEZ [*gripping* GARCIN's *arm*]: Let her alone. Don't paw her with your dirty man's hands.

GARCIN [*thrusting her away roughly*]: Take care. I'm no gentleman, and I'd have no compunction about striking a woman.

INEZ: But you promised me; you promised. I'm only asking you to keep your word.

GARCIN: Why should I, considering you were the first to break our agreement?

[INEZ *turns her back on him and retreats to the far end of the room.*]

INEZ: Very well, have it your own way. I'm the weaker party, one against two. But don't forget I'm here, and watching. I shan't take my eyes off you, Garcin; when you're kissing her, you'll feel them boring into you. Yes, have it your own way, make love and get it over. We're in hell; my turn will come.

[*During the following scene she watches them without speaking.*]

GARCIN [*coming back to* ESTELLE *and grasping her shoulders*]: Now then. Your lips. Give me your lips. [*A pause. He bends to kiss her, then abruptly straightens up.*]

ESTELLE [*indignantly*]: Really! [*A pause.*] Didn't I tell you not to pay any attention to her?

GARCIN: You've got it wrong. [*Short silence.*] It's Gomez; he's back in the press-room. They've shut the windows; it must be winter down there. Six months since I— Well, I warned you I'd be absent-minded sometimes, didn't I? They're shivering, they've kept their coats on. Funny they should feel the cold like that, when I'm feeling so hot. Ah, this time he's talking about me.

ESTELLE: Is it going to last long? [*Short silence.*] You might at least tell me what he's saying.

GARCIN: Nothing. Nothing worth repeating. He's a swine, that's all. [*He listens attentively.*] A god-damned bloody swine. [*He turns to* ESTELLE.] Let's come back to—to ourselves. Are you going to love me?

ESTELLE [*smiling*]: I wonder now!

GARCIN: Will you trust me?

ESTELLE: What a quaint thing to ask! Considering you'll be under my eyes all the time, and I don't think I've much to fear from Inez, so far as you're concerned.

GARCIN: Obviously. [*A pause. He takes his hands off* ESTELLE's *shoulders.*] I was thinking of another kind of trust. [*Listens.*] Talk away, talk away, you swine. I'm not there to defend myself. [*To* ESTELLE] Estelle, you *must* give me your trust.

ESTELLE: Oh, what a nuisance you are! I'm giving you my mouth, my arms, my whole body—and everything could be so simple. . . . My trust! I haven't any to give, I'm afraid, and you're making me terribly embarrassed. You must have something pretty ghastly on your conscience to make such a fuss about my trusting you.

GARCIN: They shot me.

ESTELLE: I know. Because you refused to fight. Well, why shouldn't you?

GARCIN: I—I didn't exactly refuse. [*In a far-away voice*] I must say he talks well, he makes out a good case against me, but he never says what I should have done instead. Should I have gone to the general and said: "General, I decline to fight"? A mug's game; they'd have promptly locked me up. But I wanted to show my colors, my true colors, do you understand? I wasn't going to be silenced. [*To* ESTELLE] So I—I took the train. . . . They caught me at the frontier.

ESTELLE: Where were you trying to go?

GARCIN: To Mexico. I meant to launch a pacifist newspaper down there. [*A short silence.*] Well, why don't you speak?

ESTELLE: What could I say? You acted quite rightly, as you didn't want to fight. [GARCIN *makes a fretful gesture.*] But, darling, how on earth can I guess what you want me to answer?

INEZ: Can't you guess? Well, *I* can. He wants you to tell him that he bolted like a lion. For "bolt" he did, and that's what's biting him.

GARCIN: "Bolted," "went away"—we won't quarrel over words.

ESTELLE: But you *had* to run away. If you'd stayed they'd have sent you to jail, wouldn't they?

GARCIN: Of course. [*A pause.*] Well, Estelle, am I a coward?

ESTELLE: How can I say? Don't be so unreasonable, darling. I can't put myself in your skin. You must decide that for yourself.

GARCIN [*wearily*]: I can't decide.

ESTELLE: Anyhow, you must remember. You must have had reasons for acting as you did.

GARCIN: I had.

ESTELLE: Well?

GARCIN: But were they the real reasons?

ESTELLE: You've a twisted mind, that's your trouble. Plaguing yourself over such trifles!

GARCIN: I'd thought it all out, and I wanted to make a stand. But was that my real motive?

INEZ: Exactly. That's the question. Was that your real motive? No doubt you argued it out with yourself, you weighed the pros and cons, you found good reasons for what you did. But fear and hatred and all the dirty little instincts one keeps dark—they're motives too. So carry on, Mr. Garcin, and try to be honest with yourself—for once.

GARCIN: Do I need you to tell me that? Day and night I paced my cell, from the window to the door, from the door to the window. I pried into my heart, I sleuthed myself like a detective. By the end of it I felt as if I'd given my whole life to introspection. But always I harked back to the one thing certain—that I had acted as I did, I'd taken that train to the frontier. But why? Why? Finally I thought: My death will settle it. If I face death courageously, I'll prove I am no coward.

INEZ: And how did you face death?

GARCIN: Miserably. Rottenly. [INEZ *laughs.*] Oh, it was only a physical lapse—that might happen to anyone; I'm not ashamed of it. Only everything's been left in suspense, forever. [*To* ESTELLE] Come here,

Estelle. Look at me. I want to feel someone looking at me while they're talking about me on earth. . . . I like green eyes.

INEZ: Green eyes! Just hark to him! And you, Estelle, do you like cowards?

ESTELLE: If you knew how little I care! Coward or hero, it's all one—provided he kisses well.

GARCIN: There they are, slumped in their chairs, sucking at their cigars. Bored they look. Half-asleep. They're thinking: "Garcin's a coward." But only vaguely, dreamily. One's got to think of something. "That chap Garcin was a coward." That's what they've decided, those dear friends of mine. In six months' time they'll be saying: "Cowardly as that skunk Garcin." You're lucky, you two; no one on earth is giving you another thought. But I—I'm long in dying.

INEZ: What about your wife, Garcin?

GARCIN: Oh, didn't I tell you? She's dead.

INEZ: Dead?

GARCIN: Yes, she died just now. About two months ago.

INEZ: Of grief?

GARCIN: What else should she die of? So all is for the best, you see; the war's over, my wife's dead, and I've carved out my place in history. [*He gives a choking sob and passes his hand over his face.* ESTELLE *catches his arm.*]

ESTELLE: My poor darling! Look at me. Please look. Touch me. Touch me. [*She takes his hand and puts it on her neck.*] There! Keep your hand there. [GARCIN *makes a fretful movement.*] No, don't move. Why trouble what those men are thinking? They'll die off one by one. Forget them. There's only me, now.

GARCIN: But *they* won't forget *me*, not they! They'll die, but others will come after them to carry on the legend. I've left my fate in their hands.

ESTELLE: You think too much, that's your trouble.

GARCIN: What else is there to do now? I was a man of action once. . . . Oh, if only I could be with them again, for just one day—I'd fling their lie in their teeth. But I'm locked out; they're passing judgment on my life without troubling about me, and they're right, because I'm dead. Dead and done with. [*Laughs.*] A back number.

[*A short pause.*]

ESTELLE [*gently*]: Garcin.

GARCIN: Still there? Now listen! I want you to do me a service. No, don't shrink away. I know it must seem strange to you, having someone asking you for help; you're not used to that. But if you'll make the effort, if you'll only *will* it hard enough, I dare say we can really love each other. Look at it this way. A thousand of them are proclaiming I'm a coward; but what do numbers matter? If there's someone, just one person, to say quite positively I did not run away, that

I'm not the sort who runs away, that I'm brave and decent and the rest of it—well, that one person's faith would save me. Will you have that faith in me? Then I shall love you and cherish you for ever. Estelle—will you?

ESTELLE [*laughing*]: Oh, you dear silly man, do you think I could love a coward?

GARCIN: But just now you said—

ESTELLE: I was only teasing you. I like men, my dear, who're real men, with tough skin and strong hands. You haven't a coward's chin, or a coward's mouth, or a coward's voice, or a coward's hair. And it's for your mouth, your hair, your voice, I love you.

GARCIN: Do you mean this? *Really* mean it?

ESTELLE: Shall I swear it?

GARCIN: Then I snap my fingers at them all, those below and those in here. Estelle, we shall climb out of hell. [INEZ *gives a shrill laugh. He breaks off and stares at her.*] What's that?

INEZ [*still laughing*]: But she doesn't mean a word of what she says. How can you be such a simpleton? "Estelle, am I a coward?" As if she cared a damn either way.

ESTELLE: Inez, how dare you? [*To* GARCIN] Don't listen to her. If you want me to have faith in you, you must begin by trusting me.

INEZ: That's right! That's right! Trust away! She wants a man—that far you can trust her—she wants a man's arm round her waist, a man's smell, a man's eyes glowing with desire. And that's all she wants. She'd assure you you were God Almighty if she thought it would give you pleasure.

GARCIN: Estelle, is this true? Answer me. Is it true?

ESTELLE: What do you expect me to say? Don't you realize how maddening it is to have to answer questions one can't make head or tail of? [*She stamps her foot.*] You do make things difficult. . . . Anyhow, I'd love you just the same, even if you were a coward. Isn't that enough? [*A short pause.*]

GARCIN [*to the two women*]: You disgust me, both of you. [*He goes towards the door.*]

ESTELLE: What are you up to?

GARCIN: I'm going.

INEZ [*quickly*]: You won't get far. The door is locked.

GARCIN: I'll *make* them open it. [*He presses the bell-push. The bell does not ring.*]

ESTELLE: Please! Please!

INEZ [*to* ESTELLE]: Don't worry, my pet. The bell doesn't work.

GARCIN: I tell you they shall open. [*Drums on the door.*] I can't endure it any longer, I'm through with you both. [ESTELLE *runs to him; he pushes her away.*] Go away. You're even fouler than she. I won't let myself get bogged in your eyes. You're soft and slimy. Ugh! [*Bangs on the door again.*] Like an octopus. Like a quagmire.

ESTELLE: I beg you, oh, I beg you not to leave me. I'll promise not to speak again, I won't trouble you in any way—but don't go. I daren't be left alone with Inez, now she's shown her claws.

GARCIN: Look after yourself. I never asked you to come here.

ESTELLE: Oh, how mean you are! Yes, it's quite true you're a coward.

INEZ [*going up to* ESTELLE]: Well, my little sparrow fallen from the nest, I hope you're satisfied now. You spat in my face—playing up to him, of course—and we had a tiff on his account. But he's going, and a good riddance it will be. We two women will have the place to ourselves.

ESTELLE: You won't gain anything. If that door opens, I'm going, too.

INEZ: Where?

ESTELLE: I don't care where. As far from you as I can. [GARCIN *has been drumming on the door while they talk.*]

GARCIN: Open the door! Open, blast you! I'll endure anything, your red-hot tongs and molten lead, your racks and prongs and garrotes—all your fiendish gadgets, everything that burns and flays and tears—I'll put up with any torture you impose. Anything, anything would be better than this agony of mind, this creeping pain that gnaws and fumbles and caresses one and never hurts quite enough. [*He grips the door-knob and rattles it.*] Now will you open? [*The door flies open with a jerk, and he just avoids falling.*] Ah! [*A long silence.*]

INEZ: Well, Garcin? You're free to go.

GARCIN [*meditatively*]: Now I wonder why that door opened.

INEZ: What are you waiting for? Hurry up and go.

GARCIN: I shall not go.

INEZ: And you Estelle? [ESTELLE *does not move.* INEZ *bursts out laughing.*] So what? Which shall it be? Which of the three of us will leave? The barrier's down, why are we waiting? . . . But what a situation! It's a scream! We're—inseparables!

[ESTELLE *springs at her from behind.*]

ESTELLE: Inseparables? Garcin, come and lend a hand. Quickly. We'll push her out and slam the door on her. That'll teach her a lesson.

INEZ [*struggling with* ESTELLE]: Estelle! I beg you, let me stay. I won't go, I won't go! Not into the passage.

GARCIN: Let go of her.

ESTELLE: You're crazy. She hates you.

GARCIN: It's because of her I'm staying here.

[ESTELLE *releases* INEZ *and stares dumbfoundedly at* GARCIN.]

INEZ: Because of me? [*Pause.*] All right, shut the door. It's ten times hotter here since it opened. [GARCIN *goes to the door and shuts it.*] Because of me, you said?

GARCIN: Yes. *You*, anyhow, know what it means to be a coward.

INEZ: Yes, I know.

GARCIN: And you know what wickedness is, and shame, and fear. There were days when you peered into yourself, into the secret places of your heart, and what you saw there made you faint with horror. And then, next day, you didn't know what to make of it, you couldn't interpret the horror you had glimpsed the day before. Yes, you know what evil *costs*. And when you say I'm a coward, you know from experience what that means. Is that so?

INEZ: Yes.

GARCIN: So it's you whom I have to convince; you are of my kind. Did you suppose I meant to go? No, I couldn't leave you here, gloating over my defeat, with all those thoughts about me running in your head.

INEZ: Do you really wish to convince me?

GARCIN: That's the one and only thing I wish for now. I can't hear them any longer, you know. Probably that means they're through with me. For good and all. The curtain's down, nothing of me is left on earth—not even the name of coward. So, Inez, we're alone. Only you two remain to give a thought to me. She—she doesn't count. It's you who matter; you who hate me. If you'll have faith in me I'm saved.

INEZ: It won't be easy. Have a look at me. I'm a hard-headed woman.

GARCIN: I'll give you all the time that's needed.

INEZ: Yes, we've lots of time in hand. *All* time.

GARCIN [*putting his hands on her shoulders*]: Listen! Each man has an aim in life, a leading motive; that's so, isn't it? Well, I didn't give a damn for wealth, or for love. I aimed at being a real man. A tough, as they say. I staked everything on the same horse. . . . Can one possibly be a coward when one's deliberately courted danger at every turn? And can one judge a life by a single action?

INEZ: Why not? For thirty years you dreamt you were a hero, and condoned a thousand petty lapses—because a hero, of course, can do no wrong. An easy method, obviously. Then a day came when you were up against it, the red light of real danger—and you took the train to Mexico.

GARCIN: I "dreamt," you say. It was no dream. When I chose the hardest path, I made my choice deliberately. A man is what he wills himself to be.

INEZ: Prove it. Prove it was no dream. It's what one does, and nothing else, that shows the stuff one's made of.

GARCIN: I died too soon. I wasn't allowed time to—to do my deeds.

INEZ: One always dies too soon—or too late. And yet one's whole life is complete at that moment, with a line drawn neatly under it, ready for summing up. You are—your life, and nothing else.

GARCIN: What a poisonous woman you are! With an answer for every-thing.

INEZ: Now then! Don't lose heart. It shouldn't be so hard, convincing me. Pull yourself together, man, rake up some arguments. [GARCIN *shrugs his shoulders*.] Ah, wasn't I right when I said you were vulnerable?

now you're going to pay the price, and what a price! You're a coward, Garcin, because I wish it. I wish it—do you hear?—I wish it. And yet, just look at me, see how weak I am, a mere breath on the air, a gaze observing you, a formless thought that thinks you. [*He walks towards her, opening his hands.*] Ah, they're open now, those big hands, those coarse, man's hands! But what do you hope to do? You can't throttle thoughts with hands. So you've no choice, you must convince me, and you're at my mercy.

ESTELLE: Garcin!

GARCIN: What?

ESTELLE: Revenge yourself.

GARCIN: How?

ESTELLE: Kiss me, darling—then you'll hear her squeal.

GARCIN: That's true, Inez. I'm at your mercy, but you're at mine as well.

[*He bends over* ESTELLE. INEZ *gives a little cry.*]

INEZ: Oh, you coward, you weakling, running to women to console you!

ESTELLE: That's right, Inez. Squeal away.

INEZ: What a lovely pair you make! If you could see his big paw splayed out on your back, rucking up your skin and creasing the silk. Be careful, though! He's perspiring, his hand will leave a blue stain on your dress.

ESTELLE: Squeal away, Inez, squeal away! . . . Hug me tight, darling; tighter still—that'll finish her off, and a good thing too!

INEZ: Yes, Garcin, she's right. Carry on with it, press her to you till you feel your bodies melting into each other; a lump of warm, throbbing flesh. . . . Love's a grand solace, isn't it, my friend? Deep and dark as sleep. But I'll see you don't sleep.

[GARCIN *makes a slight movement.*]

ESTELLE: Don't listen to her. Press your lips to my mouth. Oh, I'm yours, yours, yours.

INEZ: Well, what are you waiting for? Do as you're told. What a lovely scene: coward Garcin holding baby-killer Estelle in his manly arms! Make your stakes, everyone. Will coward Garcin kiss the lady, or won't he dare? What's the betting? I'm watching you, everybody's watching, I'm a crowd all by myself. Do you hear the crowd? Do you hear them muttering, Garcin? Mumbling and muttering. "Coward! Coward! Coward! Coward!"—that's what they're saying. . . . It's no use trying to escape, I'll never let you go. What do you hope to get from her silly lips? Forgetfulness? But I shan't forget you, not I! "It's I you must convince." So come to me. I'm waiting. Come along, now. . . . Look how obedient he is, like a well-trained dog who comes when his mistress calls. You can't hold him, and you never will.

GARCIN: Will night never come?

INEZ: Never.

GARCIN: You will always see me?

INEZ: Always.

[GARCIN *moves away from* ESTELLE *and takes some steps across the room. He goes to the bronze ornament.*]

GARCIN: This bronze. [*Strokes it thoughtfully.*] Yes, now's the moment; I'm looking at this thing on the mantelpiece, and I understand that I'm in hell. I tell you, everything's been thought out beforehand. They knew I'd stand at the fireplace stroking this thing of bronze, with all those eyes intent on me. Devouring me. [*He swings round abruptly.*] What? Only two of you? I thought there were more; many more. [*Laughs.*] So this is hell. I'd never have believed it. You remember all we were told about the torture-chambers, the fire and brimstone, the "burning marl." Old wives' tales! There's no need for red-hot pokers. Hell is—other people!

ESTELLE: My darling! Please—

GARCIN [*thrusting her away*]: No, let me be. She is between us. I cannot love you when she's watching.

ESTELLE: Right! In that case, I'll stop her watching. [*She picks up the paper-knife from the table, rushes at* INEZ, *and stabs her several times.*]

INEZ [*struggling and laughing*]: But, you crazy creature, what do you think you're doing? You know quite well I'm dead.

ESTELLE: Dead?

[*She drops the knife. A pause.* INEZ *picks up the knife and jabs herself with it regretfully.*]

INEZ: Dead! Dead! Dead! Knives, poison, ropes—all useless. It has happened *already*, do you understand? Once and for all. So here we are, forever. [*Laughs.*]

ESTELLE [*with a peal of laughter*]: Forever. My God, how funny! Forever.

GARCIN [*looks at the two women, and joins in the laughter*]: For ever, and ever, and ever.

[*They slump onto their respective sofas. A long silence. Their laughter dies away and they gaze at each other.*]

GARCIN: Well, well, let's get on with it. . . .

CURTAIN

Reportage and Essays

T HESE TWENTY-THREE ESSAYS or miscellanea, in a few cases excerpted from larger works, have little in common beyond the fact that they make interesting reading. In only a few cases do they rise to the level of literature. These few are worth pointing out: pre-eminently Conrad's memories of Stephen Crane; T. S. Eliot's well-known seminal discussion of the relations between the writer and his tradition; Romains's still-moving set piece, drawn from *Verdun*, one of the volumes of his great *roman-fleuve;* and perhaps that is all, though to many Unamuno's great cry may seem to belong to the same high category.

Rereading the acceptance speeches of the Nobel Prize winners for Literature over the past few decades is a dismal experience. For one thing, literary men rarely have a flair for oratory; rhetoric and the imagination make a poor team. Furthermore the writer does not know how to address the whole world; he misses the interposing screen of white paper, desk, solitude. Finally, writers exude only with much unease the bland moral truths that are expected at Stockholm, for their job is to disturb rather than soothe human beings. Camus's acceptance speech therefore is exceptional. It combines nobility and sincerity, a real voice vibrates through it, a man is meditating rather than addressing posterity or the wire services.

Joseph Conrad's low-toned, perfectly controlled memoir of the author of *The Red Badge of Courage* appeared as the introduction to Thomas Beer's life (1923) of Stephen Crane (1871–1900). I believe it the best, surely the most sympathetic, portrait in existence of that "hurried visitor on this earth on which he had so little reason to be joyous." It also as a by-product supplies the reader with a glimpse of the way real artists talk to each other. The life of Joseph Conrad (1857–1924) is too familiar to call for any recapitulation. As with Raymond Chandler and D. H. Lawrence, one of the more interesting events in his biography occurred posthumously. I suppose his literary reputation stands higher today than it ever did during his lifetime. Justly so: he will rank with James, Balzac, Stendhal at the final reckoning, if there is any final reckoning.

Partly as a consequence of the delightful long-run dramatizations by Howard Lindsay and Russel Crouse, the reputation of Clarence Day (1874–1935) rests a little too heavily on *Life with Father* (1935) and *Life with Mother* (1936). They are unique, of course, though they have spawned a numerous progeny—most of the Great Eccentric American Family memoirs that have flooded the market during the last quarter-century owe much to them. (Not, however, Thurber's *My Life and Hard Times*, a masterpiece whose humor far surpasses Day's.) I have included a far too brief excerpt from Clarence Day's first and for me still his best book, *This Simian World* (1920).

Day, who spent most of his life immobilized in bed, is one of the most adultly cheerful and unsentimentally courageous of American writers. To his moral qualities was added the mysterious gift of style: his sentences are his own and color-fast.

On October 19, 1963, at the annual convention of the Western History Association in Salt Lake City, Mr. Knopf announced the establishment of a five-thousand-dollar award, in addition to royalties, for the best-written manuscript in the field of Western American history. The terms of his announcement are noteworthy: "Such a manuscript would have to be really well written: to award the prize to a work, however sound in scholarship or interesting in other ways, which was badly written, would disgrace us all and defeat my whole purpose."

Mr. Knopf is here calling attention to an unhappy fact. Our historians, whose level of conscientious scholarship is higher than it has ever been, have failed, because they have little interest in the English language, to endow their work with the magnetic power that created large publics for such men as Michelet and Macaulay. There are exceptions to this stricture (Bruce Catton, for example, and at his best Samuel Eliot Morison) but they are few.

If the reader of these pages will turn to Professor Morison's "History as a Literary Art" he will find an authority making the same complaint and backing Mr. Knopf to the hilt. The difficulty perhaps roots in the fact that many English historians (such as Trevelyan) almost instinctively see the past in narrative and dramatic terms, whereas many of our most respected American scholars see it as a dividable field of stern investigation. This was not the view of Parkman or Prescott; and so, though they are full of errors, omissions, and narrow perspectives, they are still a pleasure to read.

Representative work by four historians is here included. As noted, Professor Morison (1887–) is represented by a fine "hortatory essay" rather than by his more professional labors. What he has to say should be weighed by the reader in connection with two sample historical studies by two of our better scholars: David Donald (1920–) on Herndon and Mrs. Lincoln, drawn from *Lincoln Reconsidered;* and Richard Hofstadter (1916–) on Calhoun, contained in his *The American Political Tradition.* One can say for these excerpted chapters that they are clear, interesting, and doubtless well-founded. That they lack charm, wit, and dynamism the authors would probably cheerfully admit, adding perhaps that the display of such qualities is irrelevant to their purposes as scholars.

I have also included a brief section from *The Decline of the West,* by Oswald Spengler (1880–1936), a figure presently occupying a considerable amount of space in the historical doghouse. Spengler of course was not, unless you accept his terms, a historian. He was not even, some would say, a philosopher of history. But he was a poet of history. His relation to history has some kinship with that of Dante to theology. He is a visionary. The question sensible historians put is: How far does his vision correspond with the checkable facts? The question the layman puts is: What insights can Spengler, by force of his visionary power, give me into the grand processes of change? I submit that both questions have point—and that the second one has enough point to warrant my including in this book a part of Spengler's grandiose historical dream of the immediate future. However you may judge its truth, here is *writing.*

This year marked the death of T. S. Eliot (1888–1965), American-born, a dweller in England from his twenty-sixth year, a British subject from his thirty-ninth year, and one of the half dozen greatest poets of our century. His life and his work have both been so well absorbed into the modern temper that no recapitulation of either is called for.

As the house of Knopf was closely associated with his first publication in our country, it seemed proper, almost as a memorial gesture, to reprint in this semi-centennial volume some examples of his early work in both prose and poetry. The obvious thing to say is also the true one: that neither "Tradition and the Individual Talent" nor "The Love Song of J. Alfred Prufrock" shows any sign of dating. The first is clearly one of those seminal critical utterances that are subject to debate but never to neglect. The second announced with absolute self-confidence a new poetical mode of looking at the contemporary world.

Good prose stemming from patriotism is rare. The emotion, however admirable in itself, seems to generate platitudes and the most inadmissible kind of rhetoric. As Oscar Wilde said about the death of Little Nell, he is a hard-hearted man who could read the peroration of Webster's speech of January 26–27, 1830, without laughing—though the rest of it still makes solid sense.

The brief address of Judge Learned Hand (1872–1961) to his fellow citizens is good patriotism and good prose. It cannot be too often anthologized. It is drawn from a book of Judge Hand's papers and addresses, *The Spirit of Liberty*, edited by Irving Dilliard. The collection is typical of one of the many Borzoi intellectual preoccupations, in this case the field of jurisprudence.

The Knopfs were and, I should think, are great admirers of the books of Joseph Hergesheimer (1880–1954). I am not; and, after poring once again over his many novels and short stories, I fear I shall never change my view. But the reconsideration of Hergesheimer introduced me to a brief and to me hitherto unfamiliar essay from his hand. Mr. Knopf once published a complete set of Stephen Crane, each volume preceded by an introduction by a well-known literary name. Of them all Hergesheimer's seemed to me the best, as well as excellent in itself. I had never thought of him as a critic (all his novels appeared deficient in mere brain-power) and I do not so think of him now. But here, for some reason, his mind met a book that drew out what was justest and finest in his powers of appreciation.

Perhaps there are a few of my readers who have not been exposed to John Hersey's *Hiroshima*. Perhaps there are others who regret having lent the little book to a friend and would like to have it on their shelves. Neither of these is a particularly good reason for its inclusion. It is here preserved because it is a prime historical document, written by a master journalist who can feel and think as well as see, but who knows perfectly how, by concealing them, to give added force to his feelings and thoughts.

John Hersey, born in 1914, is one of the leading writers of his generation, a Pulitzer Prize winner in 1945 (*A Bell for Adano*), an undiscourageable experimenter with the novel, and, as *Hiroshima* makes quite clear, one of the few journalists of our time able to give status and permanence to a record of transient occurrences. It is possible that, though less dramatically, *Hiroshima* has had as much effect on Americans as *Uncle Tom's Cabin* did in its day.

The surest way to become a good writer is to arrange to be born a Huxley. Julian Huxley (1887–   ) is the brother of the late Aldous, the grandson of Thomas Huxley, the great-nephew of Matthew Arnold, and in one way or another related to half a dozen other distinguished English families. He possesses his grandfather's talent for lucid

scientific exposition, adding to it (as is evidenced in the fantastic speculation here included) wit, humor, and even a kind of drollery. Respected
by his scholarly colleagues as a leading biologist, he is known to the general public as a persuasive exponent of a humanist creed devoid of soft
edges. I do not think he ever did anything better in its particular line
than "Philosophic Ants." It starts with an emendation of Lewis Carroll,
ends with a parody of a scientific paper's bibliography, and in between
offers entertainment and perfect sense in harmonious mixture.

Though he occupies a privileged position in the firm, Alfred A.
Knopf is not one of his own authors and does not think of himself as a
writer. His essay "The National Park Idea" is here reprinted not as part
of a semi-centennial gesture, but because it is a sound piece of prose
about an institution important to us as Americans and the progenitors
of future Americans. I wanted somehow to represent Mr. Knopf's serious interest in the conservation and preservation of our magnificent
natural world. Though he has sponsored many fine books in this field,
I do not think any one of his authors has put the central idea more
sanely and tellingly than he himself in this short paper. It is drawn from
a collection of essays, *This Is Dinosaur*, a beautiful book of wise conser-
vationist argument edited by Wallace Stegner and dealing with the
Echo Park country and its "magic rivers." The back pages list notes on
the contributors. The reference to Mr. Knopf includes this statement:
"He annually practices what he preaches, and takes his refreshment
and restoration in the parks which he has done much to protect and
support."

The exchange of letters in December 1936 between Thomas Mann
and the dean of the philosophical faculty of the Friedrich-Wilhelm University of Bonn is here included in order to reveal to the reader a side
of Mann not displayed in his fiction; because it is a magnificent statement of the eternal opposition between the Word and the spirit of to-
talitarianism; and because it is good for us to remember.

In the twenties and thirties the association of Mencken and Knopf
was as close as that of ham and eggs and no less nutritious. H. L. Mencken
(1880–1956)—let us say it baldly—was not only one of the greatest journalists who ever lived but also one of the best writers of American prose of his time and just conceivably in our whole history. The
judgment can stand only if our canons are non-academic. Mencken was
impolite, noisy, and unschoolmarmish. He used exaggeration, vitupera-
tion, catch-as-catch-can epithets, slang, facetious Teutonisms, facetious
Latinisms, sesquipedalian jocularity. Fowler would have execrated him.
Any professor would.

Nonetheless, look sharply at the form of any of the hundreds of thousands of sentences he wrote during his tirelessly productive life. Observe their shape, their economy of structure. Note how he builds his paragraphs, how he develops an idea, how every allusion is made to count, how concrete (like those of Thoreau, otherwise so unlike him) are the images that flow off his typewriter platen. Then ask yourself *why* he employed his unique (though much-imitated) style. I think you will conclude that *it works*. He knew what effects he wanted to produce and what would most efficiently produce them. And at the same time there is nothing ostensibly calculated here. The voice is his own, the voice of a whole, vigorous man.

I hope this shows to advantage in the two essays (and even in the little epitaph) here reprinted, one on a man he hated but somehow respected, one on a man he respected and perhaps even loved. Are his judgments accurate? Time will tell. Do the judgments live a powerful life of their own decades after they were made? I think so.

The Knopfs' lifelong interest in music is reflected in these pages through two writers, Ernest Newman and J. W. N. Sullivan.

Nowadays I suppose the musicologists think little of Ernest Newman (1868–1959). It is not easy for a music critic who wrote as well as he did, with such *brio* and charm, to retain his reputation among the learned. No matter. His four-volume life of Richard Wagner (1933–46) will stand; his championship of Gluck and Hugo Wolf will be remembered by some; and name me another music critic who wrote as much as he did, under the conditions imposed by periodical journalism, and who did as much (well, perhaps Shaw) to lift the English public out of its tonal philistinism.

Like Coppard (and George Meredith), Newman was the son of a tailor. He worked as a bank clerk for fourteen years; taught himself music, as well as German, Russian, Latin, Greek, French, Italian, Spanish, Swedish, and Hebrew; wrote not only on music but on banking, boxing, literature, biology, and religion (he was a stubborn free-thinker). He was indomitable and almost unkillable, for he died at ninety-one. For the non-specialist reader the best approach to this phenomenon is the volume of selected writings called *Testament of Music*, assembled by Herbert Van Thal. From it I have taken the long autobiographical memoir "Confessions of a Musical Critic" in which Newman presents himself with as much vigor as he presented a less agreeable fellow, Richard Wagner.

To balance Newman's informality I have chosen a careful and, I believe, searching piece of music criticism by J. W. N. Sullivan (1886–1937). "The Last Quartets and the Final Stage" comprises the terminal chapters of his beautiful book *Beethoven: His Spiritual Development* (1927). Sullivan was an unhappy man who never quite managed to understand the competitive world. His basic talent lay in the field of scientific exposition, particularly of mathematics. But his splendid popularizations cannot in the nature of things endure. His *Beethoven*, making claims for music not acceptable to musical purists, I hope will.

One of the most courageous programs ever undertaken by the Knopfs was the publication year after year of the twenty-seven French volumes of *Men of Good Will* by Jules Romains (1885–). This vast effort to present in fiction almost every aspect of French life from 1908 to 1933 could not possibly have succeeded, surely not with our impatient and short-memoried American audience. However, it deserves far more attention than is now paid it. Perhaps the reprinting of "How Verdun Managed to Hold Out" may help to win Romains a few new readers. Though torn bodily from *Verdun* (one of the finest volumes in the series) it stands by itself, and should be comprehensible without any setting of the scene.

"The Man of Flesh and Bone" is drawn from a book of essays by the intensely Spanish philosopher, poet, and novelist Miguel de Unamuno (1864–1936). The essence of Unamuno is to be found in his book *The Tragic Sense of Life*. But the essence of the essence may be found in these half-dozen pages.

Unamuno, of Basque ancestry, held the chair of Greek at Salamanca but never really became a professor. He lived a passionate inner life, as one can discern from the essay here reprinted. His external career was one of difficulty and unhappiness. From 1924 to 1930 he was banished because of his political convictions. But he was unable to make any easier accommodation to the Republican regime. Today he is considered one of the immediate forerunners of Existentialism. Hardly a great thinker, he had perhaps only one central conviction: *I do not want to die.* Out of this passionate feeling he constructed one remarkable book and several lesser ones.

Our section of Reportage and Essays terminates pleasurably with a charming picture of a man who in his day was probably the greatest restaurateur in the world, Fernand Point. Joseph Wechsberg (1907–) writes well on politics, music, and food—but perhaps best on food. As books on food and wine constitute an appreciable fraction of the Knopf list, it would have been remiss not to represent the art of gastronomy in these Borzoian pages.

Albert Camus

SPEECH OF ACCEPTANCE UPON THE AWARD OF THE NOBEL PRIZE FOR LITERATURE, DELIVERED IN STOCKHOLM ON THE TENTH OF DECEMBER, NINETEEN HUNDRED AND FIFTY-SEVEN

CITATION

TO ALBERT CAMUS ON HIS RECEIVING THE
NOBEL PRIZE FOR LITERATURE · 1957

*For his important literary production,
which with clear-sighted earnestness
illuminates the problems of
the human conscience in our time.*

(read by Dr. Anders Osterling
of the Swedish Academy)

Published 1958. Translated from the French by Justin O'Brien. Copyright © 1958 by Alfred A. Knopf, Inc.

U PON RECEIVING THE DISTINCTION with which your free Academy
has seen fit to honor me, I measured the extent to which that
reward exceeded my personal deserts, and this only increased my gratitude. Every man and, even more understandably, every artist, wants
recognition. I want it too. But it was not possible for me to learn of your
decision without comparing its repercussions with whatever merits I
really have. How could a man still almost young, possessed only of his
doubts and of a work still in progress, accustomed to live in the isolation
of work or the seclusion of friendship—how could he have failed to feel
a sort of panic upon learning of a choice that suddenly focused a harsh
spotlight on him, alone and reduced to himself? And in what spirit
could he receive that honor at a moment when other European writers,
often the greatest among them, are reduced to silence, and at a time
when his native land is experiencing prolonged suffering?

I felt that shock and that perplexity. I could recover my peace of
mind, in short, only by adapting myself to an over-generous fate. And
inasmuch as I could not measure up to it through my own merits, I could
think of no other help than what has always comforted me throughout
life, even in the most adverse circumstances: the idea I entertain of my
art and of the writer's role. Please allow me to express my gratitude and
friendship by telling you, as simply as I can, just what that idea is.

I cannot live as a person without my art. And yet I have never set
that art above everything else. It is essential to me, on the contrary,
because it excludes no one and allows me to live, just as I am, on a
footing with all. To me art is not a solitary delight. It is a means of
stirring the greatest number of men by providing them with a privileged
image of our common joys and woes. Hence it forces the artist not to
isolate himself; it subjects him to the humblest and most universal truth.
And the man who, as often happens, chose the path of art because he was
aware of his difference soon learns that he can nourish his art, and his
difference, solely by admitting his resemblance to all. The artist fashions
himself in that ceaseless oscillation from himself to others, midway between the beauty he cannot do without and the community from which
he cannot tear himself. This is why true artists scorn nothing. They
force themselves to understand instead of judging. And if they are to
take sides in this world, they can do so only with a society in which,
according to Nietzsche's profound words, the judge will yield to the
creator, whether he be a worker or an intellectual.

By the same token, the writer's function is not without arduous
duties. By definition, he cannot serve today those who make history; he
must serve those who are subject to it. Otherwise he is alone and deprived of his art. All the armies of tyranny with their millions of men
cannot people his solitude—even, and especially, if he is willing to fall
into step with them. But the silence of an unknown prisoner subjected to

humiliations at the other end of the world is enough to tear the writer from exile, every time at least that he manages, amid the privileges of freedom, not to forget that silence but to relieve it, making it re-echo by means of art.

No one of us is great enough for such a vocation. Yet in all the circumstances of his life, unknown or momentarily famous, bound by tyranny or temporarily free to express himself, the writer can recapture the feeling of a living community that will justify him. But only if he accepts as completely as possible the two trusts that constitute the nobility of his calling: the service of truth and the service of freedom. Because his vocation is to unite the greatest possible number of men, it cannot countenance falsehood and slavery, which breed solitudes wherever they prevail. Whatever our personal frailties may be, the nobility of our calling will always be rooted in two commitments difficult to observe: refusal to lie about what we know and resistance to oppression.

For more than twenty years of absolutely insane history, lost hopelessly like all those of my age in the convulsions of the epoch, I derived comfort from the vague impression that writing was an honor today because the act itself obligated a man, obligated him to more than just writing. It obligated me in particular, such as I was, with whatever strength I possessed, to bear—along with all the others living the same history—the tribulation and hope we shared. Those men born at the beginning of the First World War who had reached the age of twenty just as Hitler was seizing power and the first revolutionary trials were taking place, who then had to complete their education by facing up to war in Spain, the Second World War, the regime of concentration camps, a Europe of torture and prisons, must today bring their children and their works to maturity in a world threatened with nuclear destruction. No one, I suppose, can expect them to be optimistic. I even go so far as to feel that, without ceasing to struggle against those who, through an excess of despair, insisted upon their right to dishonor and hurled themselves into the current nihilisms, we must understand their error. Nonetheless, most of us in my country and in Europe rejected that nihilism and strove to find some form of legitimacy. They had to fashion for themselves an art of living in times of catastrophe in order to be reborn before fighting openly against the death-instinct at work in our history.

Probably every generation sees itself as charged with remaking the world. Mine, however, knows that it will not remake the world. But its task is perhaps even greater, for it consists in keeping the world from destroying itself. As the heir of a corrupt history that blends blighted revolutions, misguided techniques, dead gods, and worn-out ideologies, in which second-rate powers can destroy everything today, but are unable to win anyone over, in which intelligence has stooped to becoming the servant of hatred and oppression, that generation, starting from nothing but its own negations, has had to re-establish both within and without itself a little of what constitutes the dignity of life and death. Faced with a world threatened with disintegration, in which our grand inquisitors may set up once and for all the kingdoms of death, that generation knows that, in a sort of mad race against time, it ought to re-establish among nations a peace not based on slavery, to reconcile labor and culture again, and to reconstruct with all men an Ark of the Covenant. Perhaps it can never accomplish that vast undertaking, but most certainly throughout the world it has already accepted the double challenge of truth and liberty and, on occasion, has shown that it can lay down its life without hatred. That generation deserves to be acclaimed and encouraged wherever it happens to be, and especially wherever it is sacrificing itself. And to it, at all events, with your basic agreement, of which I feel sure, I should like to transfer the honor you have just done me.

At the same time, after having extolled the nobility of the writer's calling, I should have taken the writer down a peg, showing him as he is with no other rights than those he shares with his fellow-fighters, vulnerable but stubborn, unjust and eager for justice, constructing his work without shame or pride within sight of all, constantly torn between pain and beauty, and devoted to extracting from his dual nature the creations he obstinately strives to raise up in the destructive fluctuation of history. Who, after that, could expect of him ready-made solutions and fine moral codes? Truth is mysterious, elusive, ever to be won anew. Liberty is dangerous, as hard to get along with as it is exciting. We must progress toward those two objectives, painfully but resolutely, sure in advance that we shall weaken and flinch on such a long road. Consequently, what writer would dare, with a clear conscience, to become a preacher of virtue? As for me, I must say once more that I am far from all that. I have never been able to forget the sunlight, the delight in life, the freedom in which I grew up. But although that nostalgia explains many of my mistakes and shortcomings, it doubtless helped me to understand my calling, and it still helps me to stand implicitly beside all those silent men who, throughout the world, endure the life that has been made for them only because they remember or fleetingly re-experience free moments of happiness.

Reduced in this way to what I am in reality, to my limits, to my liabilities, as to my difficult faith, I feel freer to show you in conclusion the extent and generosity of the distinction you have just granted me, freer likewise to tell you that I should like to receive it as a tribute paid to all those who, sharing the same fight, have received no reward, but on the contrary have known only woe and persecution. It remains for me then to thank you from the bottom of my heart and to make you publicly, as a personal token of gratitude, the same age-old promise of allegiance that every true artist, every day, makes to himself, in silence.

Joseph Conrad

INTRODUCTION TO
STEPHEN CRANE BY THOMAS BEER

O N A RAINY DAY OF MARCH of the year 1923, listening to the author of this biography telling me of his earnest labours for the memory of a man who was certainly unique in his generation I exclaimed to myself with wonder: "And so it has come to pass after all—this thing which I did not expect to see!" In truth I had never expected the biography of Stephen Crane to appear in my lifetime. My immense pleasure was affected by the devastating touch of time which like a muddy flood covers under a mass of daily trivialities things of value: moments of affectionate communion with kindred spirits, words spoken with the careless freedom of perfect confidence, the deepest emotions of joy and sorrow—together with such things of merely historical importance as the recollection of dates, for instance. After hearing from Mr. Beer of his difficulties in fixing certain dates in the history of Stephen Crane's life I discovered that I was unable to remember with any kind of precision the initial date of our friendship. Indeed life is but a dream—especially for those of us who have never kept a diary or possessed a note-book in their lives.

In this extremity I had recourse to another friend of Stephen Crane, who had appreciated him intuitively almost as soon as I did myself and who is a woman of excellent memory. My wife's recollection is that Crane and I met in London in October, 1897, and that he came to see us for the first time in our Essex home in the following November.

I have mentioned in a short paper written two years ago that it was Mr. S. S. Pawling, partner in the publishing firm of Mr. Heinemann, who brought us together. It was done at Stephen Crane's own desire. I was told by Mr. Pawling that when asked whom he wanted to

meet Crane mentioned two names, of which one was of a notable journalist (who had written some novels) whom he knew in America, I
believe, and the other was mine. At that time the only facts we knew
about each other were that we both had the same publisher in England.
The only other fact I knew about Stephen Crane was that he was quite a
young man. I had of course read his *Red Badge of Courage* of which
people were writing and talking at that time. I certainly did not know
that he had the slightest notion of my existence, or that he had seen a
single line (there were not many of them then) of my writing. I can
safely say that I earned this precious friendship by something like ten
months of strenuous work with my pen. It took me just that time to
write *The Nigger of the Narcissus* working at what I always considered
a very high pressure. It was on the ground of the authorship of that
book that Crane wanted to meet me. Nothing could have been more
flattering, than to discover that the author of *The Red Badge of Courage*
appreciated my effort to present a group of men held together by a
common loyalty and a common perplexity in a struggle not with human
enemies but with the hostile conditions testing their faithfulness to the
conditions of their own calling.

Apart from the imaginative analysis of his own temperament tried
by the emotions of a battlefield Stephen Crane dealt in his book with the
psychology of the mass—the army; while I—in mine—had been dealing
with the same subject on a much smaller scale and in more specialized
conditions—the crew of a merchant ship, brought to the test of what I
may venture to call the moral problem of conduct. This may be thought
a very remote connection between these two works and the idea may
seem too far-fetched to be mentioned here; but that was my undoubted
feeling at the time. It is a fact that I considered Crane, by virtue of his
creative experience with *The Red Badge of Courage*, as eminently fit to
pronounce a judgment on my first consciously planned attempt to
render the truth of a phase of life in the terms of my own temperament
with all the sincerity of which I was capable.

I had, of course, my own opinion as to what I had done; but I
doubted whether anything of my ambitiously comprehensive aim would
be understood. I was wrong there; but my doubt was excusable since I
myself would have been hard put to it if requested to give my complex
intentions the form of a concise and definite statement. In that period of
misgivings which so often follows an accomplished task I would often
ask myself who in the world could be interested in such a thing? It was
after reading *The Red Badge* which came into my hands directly after
its publication in England that I said to myself: "Here's a man who may
understand—if he ever sees the book; though of course that would not
mean that he would like it." I do not mean to say that I looked towards
the author of *The Red Badge* as the only man in the world. It would
have been stupid and ungrateful. I had the moral support of one or two
intimate friends and the solid fact of Mr. W. H. Henley's acceptance of

my tale for serial publication in *The New Review* to give me confidence, while I awaited the larger verdict.

It seems to me that in trying to recall my memories of Stephen Crane I have been talking so far only about myself; but that is unavoidable, since this introduction, which I am privileged to write, can only trace what is left on earth of our personal intercourse which was even more short and fleeting than it may appear from the record of dates. October, 1897–May, 1900. And out of that beggarly tale of months must be deducted the time of his absence from England during the Spanish-American war, and of his visit to the United States shortly before the beginning of his last illness. Even when he was in England our intercourse was not so close and frequent as the warmth of our friendship would have wished it to be. We both lived in the country and, though not very far from each other, in different counties. I had my work to do, always in conditions which made it a matter of urgency. He had his own tasks and his own visions to attend to. I do not think that he had more friendships to claim him than I, but he certainly had more acquaintances and more calls on his time.

This was only natural. It must be remembered that as an author he was my senior, as I used to remind him now and then with affected humility which always provoked his smiles. He had a quiet smile that charmed and frightened one. It made you pause by something revelatory it cast over his whole physiognomy, not like a ray but like a shadow. I often asked myself what it could be, that quality that checked one's carefree mood and now I think I have had my answer. It was the smile of a man who knows that his time will not be long on this earth.

I would not for a moment wish to convey the impression of melancholy in connection with my memories of Stephen Crane. I saw his smile first over the table-cloth in a restaurant. We shook hands with intense gravity and a direct stare at each other, after the manner of two children told to make friends. It was under the encouraging gaze of Sidney Pawling who, a much bigger man than either of us and possessed of a deep voice, looked like a grown-up person entertaining two strange small boys—protecting and slightly anxious as to the experiment. He knew very little of either of us. I was a new author and Crane was a new arrival. It was the meeting of *The Red Badge* and *The Nigger* in the presence of their publisher; but as far as our personalities went we were three strangers breaking bread together for the first time. Yet it was as pleasantly easy a meal as any I can remember. Crane talked in his characteristic deliberate manner about Greece, at war. I had already sensed the man's intense earnestness underlying his quiet surface. Every time he raised his eyes that secret quality (for his voice was careless) of his soul was betrayed in a clear flash. Most of the true Stephen Crane was in his eyes, most of his strength at any rate, though it was apparent also in his other features, as for instance in the structure of his forehead, the deep solid arches under the fair eyebrows.

Some people saw traces of weakness in the lower part of his face. What I could see there was a hint of the delicacy of sentiment, of the inborn fineness of nature which this man, whose life had been anything but a stroll through a rose-garden, had managed to preserve like a sacred heritage. I say heritage, not acquisition, for it was not and could not have been acquired. One could depend on it on all occasions; whereas the cultivated kind is apt to show ugly gaps under very slight provocation. The coarseness of the professedly delicate must be very amusing to the misanthrope. But Crane was no enemy of his kind. That sort of thing did not amuse him. As to his own temper it was proof against anger and scorn, as I can testify, having seen him both angry and scornful, always quietly, on fitting occasions. Contempt and indignation never broke the surface of his moderation simply because he had no surface. He was all through of the same material, incapable of affectation of any kind, of any pitiful failure of generosity for the sake of personal advantage, or even from sheer exasperation which must find its relief.

Many people imagined him a fiery individuality. Certainly he was not cold-blooded. But his was an equable glow, morally and temperamentally. I would have said the same of his creative power (I have seen him sit down before a blank sheet of paper, dip his pen, write the first line at once and go on without haste and without pause for a couple of hours), had he not confided to me that his mentality did flag at times. I do not think it was anything more than every writer is familiar with at times. Another man would have talked of his "failing inspiration." It is very characteristic of Crane that I have never heard him use that word when talking about his work.

His phraseology was generally of a very modest cast. That unique and exquisite faculty, which Edward Garnett, another of his friends, found in his writing—"of disclosing an individual scene by an odd simile" was not apparent in his conversation. It was interesting of course, but its charm consisted mainly in the freshness of his impressions set off by an acute simplicity of view and expressed with an amusing deliberation. Super-abundance of words was not his failing when communing with those whom he liked and felt he could trust. With the other kind of "friends" he followed the method of a sort of suspended silence. On a certain occasion (it was at Brede Place) after two amazingly conceited idiots had gone away I said to him, "Stevie, you brood like a distant thunder-cloud." He had retired early to the other end of the room, and from there had sent out, now and then, a few words, more like the heavy drops of rain that precede the storm than growls of thunder. Poor Crane, if he could look black enough at times, never thundered; though I have no doubt he could have been dangerous if he had liked. There always seemed to be something (not timidity) which restrained him, not from within but, I could not help fancying, from outside, with an effect as of a whispered *memento mori* in the ear of a reveller not lost to the sense of grace.

That of course was a later impression. It must be stated clearly that I know very little of Stephen Crane's life. We did not feel the need to tell each other formally the story of our lives. That did not prevent us from being very intimate and also very open with each other from the first. Our affection would have been "everlasting" as he himself qualified it, had not the jealous death intervened with her cruel capriciousness by striking down the younger man. Our intimacy was really too close to admit of indiscretions; not that he did not speak amusingly of his experiences and of his hardships, and warmly of the men that helped him in his early days, like Mr. Hamlin Garland for instance, or men kindly encouraging to him, like Mr. Howells. Many other names he used to utter lovingly have been forgotten by me after so many years.

It is a fact that I heard more of his adventures than of his trials, privations and difficulties. I know he had many. He was the least recriminatory of men (though one of the most sensitive, I should say), but, in any case, nothing I could have learned would have shaken the independent judgment I had formed for myself of his trustworthiness as a man and a friend. Though the word is discredited now and may sound pretentious, I will say that there was in Crane a strain of chivalry which made him safe to trust with one's life. To be recognizably a man of honour carries no immunity against human weaknesses, but comports more rigid limitations in personal relations than the status of an "honourable man," however recognizable that too may be. Some men are "honourable" by courtesy, others by the office they hold, or simply by belonging to some popular assembly, the election to which is not generally secured by a dignified accuracy of statement and a scrupulous regard for the feelings of others. Many remain honourable (because of their great circumspection in the conduct of their affairs) without holding within themselves any of these restraints which are inherent in the character of a man of honour, however weak or luckless he may be.

I do not know everything about the strength of Crane's circumspection, but I am not afraid of what the biography which follows may disclose to us; though I am convinced that it will be free from hypocritical reservations. I think I have understood Stephen Crane, and from my too short acquaintance with his biographer I am confident he will receive the most humane and sympathetic treatment. What I discovered very early in our acquaintance was that Crane had not the face of a lucky man. That certitude came to me at our first meeting while I sat opposite him listening to his simple tales of Greece, while Mr. Pawling presided at the initiatory feast—friendly and debonair, looking solidly anchored in the stream of life, and very reassuring, like a big, prosperous ship to the sides of which we two in our tossing little barks could hook on for safety. He was interested in the tales too; and the best proof of it is that when he looked at his watch and jumped up, saying, "I must leave you two now," it was very near four o'clock. Nearly a whole afternoon wasted, for an English business man.

No such consideration of waste or duty agitated Crane and myself. The sympathy that, even in regard of the very few years allotted to our friendship, may be said to have sprung up instantaneously between us, was the most undemonstrative case of that sort in the last century. We not only did not tell each other of it (which would have been missish) but even without entering formally into a previous agreement to remain together we went out and began to walk side by side in the manner of two tramps without home, occupation, or care for the next night's shelter. We certainly paid no heed to direction. The first thing I noticed were the Green Park railings, when to my remark that he had seen no war before he went to Greece Crane made answer: "No. But *The Red Badge* is all right." I assured him that I never had doubted it; and, since the title of the work had been pronounced for the first time, feeling I must do something to show I had read it, I said shyly: "I like your General." He knew at once what I was alluding to but said not a word. Nothing could have been more tramp-like than our silent pacing, elbow to elbow, till, after we had left Hyde Park Corner behind us, Crane uttered with his quiet earnestness, the words: "I like your young man—I can just see him." Nothing could have been more characteristic of the depth of our three-hour-old intimacy than that each of us should have selected for praise the merest by-the-way vignette of a minor character.

This was positively the only allusion we made that afternoon to our immortal works. Indeed we talked very little of them at any time, and then always selecting some minor point for particular mention; which, after all, is not a bad way of showing an affectionate appreciation of a piece of work done by a friend. A stranger would have expected more, but, in a manner of speaking, Crane and I have never been strangers. We took each other's work for granted from the very first, I mean from the moment we had exchanged those laudatory remarks alongside the Green Park railings. Henceforth mutual recognition kept to that standard. It consisted often of an approving grunt, sometimes of the mention of some picked out paragraph, or of a line or only of a few words that had caught our fancy and would, for a time, be applied more or less aptly to the turns of our careless, or even serious, talks.

Thus, for instance, there was a time when I persecuted poor Crane with the words "barbarously abrupt." They occur in that marvellous story "The Open Boat" and are applied by him to the waves of the sea (as seen by men tossing in a small dinghy) with an inspired audacity of epithet which was one of Crane's gifts that gave me most delight. How amazingly apt these words are where they stand, anybody can see by looking at that story, which is altogether a big thing, and has remained an object of my confirmed admiration. I was always telling Crane that this or that was "barbarously abrupt," or begging him not to be so "barbarously abrupt" himself, with a keen enjoyment of the incongruity; for no human being could be less abrupt than Crane. As to his humanity (in contra-distinction to barbarity) it was a shining thing

without a flaw. It is possible that he may have grown at length weary of my little joke but he invariably received it with a smile, thus proving his consistent humanity toward his kind. But, after all, he too liked that story of his, of four men in a very small boat, which by the deep and simple humanity of presentation seems somehow to illustrate the essentials of life itself, like a symbolic tale. It opens with a phrase that anybody could have uttered but which, in relation to what is to follow, acquires the poignancy of a meaning almost universal. Once, much later in our acquaintance, I made use of it to him. He came on a flying visit to Pent Farm where we were living then. I noticed that he looked harassed. I, too, was feeling for the moment as if things were getting too much for me. He lay on the couch and I sat on a chair opposite. After a longish silence in which we both could have felt how uncertain was the issue of life envisaged as a deadly adventure in which we were both engaged like two men trying to keep afloat in a small boat, I said suddenly across the width of the mantel-piece.

"None of them knew the colour of the sky."

He raised himself sharply. The words had struck him as familiar, though I believe he failed to place them at first. "Don't you know that quotation?" I asked. (These words form the opening sentence of his tale.) The startled expression passed off his face. "Oh, yes," he said quietly, and lay down again. Truth to say it was a time when neither he nor I had the leisure to look up idly at the sky. The waves just then were too "barbarously abrupt."

I do not mean to say that it was always so. Now and then we were permitted to snatch a glance at the colour of the sky. But it is a fact that in the history of our essentially undemonstrative friendship (which is nearly as difficult to recapture as a dream) that first long afternoon is the most care-free instant, and the only one that had a character of enchantment about it. It was spread out over a large portion of central London. After the Green Park the next thing I remember are the Kensington Gardens where under the lofty and historical trees I was vouchsafed a glimpse of the low mesquit bush overspreading the plum-coloured infinities of the great Texas plains. Then after a long tramp amongst an orderly multitude of grimy brick houses—from which the only things I carried off were the impressions of the coloured rocks of Mexico (or was it Arizona?), and my first knowledge of a locality called the Painted Desert—there came suddenly Oxford Street. I don't know whether the inhabitants of London were keeping indoors or had gone into the country that afternoon, but I don't remember seeing any people in the streets except for a figure, now and then, unreal, flitting by, obviously negligible. The wheeled traffic, too, was stopped; yet, it seems, not entirely, because I remember Crane seizing my arm and jerking me back on the pavement with the calm remark: "You will get run over." I love to think that the dear fellow had saved my life and that it seemed to amuse him. As to London's enormous volume of business all I know is

that one A.B.C. shop had remained open. We went through the depressing ceremony of having tea there; but our interest in each other mitigated its inherent horrors and gave me a good idea of Crane's stoicism. At least I suppose we had tea, otherwise they would not have let us sit there so long. To be left alone was all we wanted. Neither of us had then a club to entertain the other in. It will give a good notion of our indomitable optimism (on that afternoon) when I say that it was there, in those dismal surroundings, we reached the conclusion that though the world had grown old and weary, yet the scheme of creation remained as obscure as ever, and (from our own particular point of view) there was still much that was interesting to expect from Gods and men.

As if intoxicated by this draught of hope we rolled out of that A.B.C. shop, but I kept my head sufficiently to guess what was coming and to send a warning telegram to my wife in our Essex home. Crane then was, I believe, staying temporarily in London. But he seemed to have no care in the world; and so we resumed our tramping—east and north and south again, steering through uncharted mazes the streets, forgetting to think of dinner but taking a rest here and there, till we found ourselves, standing in the middle of Piccadilly Circus, blinking at the lights like two authentic night-birds. By that time we had been (in Tottenham Court Road) joined by Balzac. How he came in I have no idea. Crane was not given to literary curiosities of that kind. Somebody he knew, or something he had read, must have attracted lately his attention to Balzac. And now suddenly at ten o'clock in the evening he demanded insistently to be told in particular detail all about the Comédie Humaine, its contents, its scope, its plan, and its general significance, together with a critical description of Balzac's style. I told him hastily that it was just black on white; and for the rest, I said, he would have to wait till we got across to Monico and had eaten some supper. I hoped he would forget Balzac and his Comédie. But not a bit of it; and I had no option but to hold forth over the remnants of a meal, in the rush of hundreds of waiters and the clatter of tons of crockery, caring not what I said (for what could Stephen want with Balzac), in the comfortable assurance that the Monstrous Shade, even if led by some strange caprice to haunt the long room of Monico's, did not know enough English to understand a single word I said. I wonder what Crane made of it all. He did not look bored, and it was eleven o'clock before we parted at the foot of that monumentally heavy abode of frivolity, the Pavilion, with just a hand-shake and a good-night—no more—without making any arrangements for meeting again, as though we had lived in the same town from childhood and were sure to run across each other next day.

It struck me directly I left him that we had not even exchanged addresses; but I was not uneasy. Sure enough, before the month was out there arrived a post card (from Ravensbrook) asking whether he might come to see us. He came, was received as an old friend, and before the end of the day conquered my wife's sympathy, as undemonstrative and

sincere as his own quiet friendliness. The friendship that sprang up between them was confirmed by the interest Crane displayed in our first child, a boy who came on the scene not quite two months afterwards. How strong was that interest on the part of Stephen Crane and his wife in the boy is evidenced by the fact that at the age of six weeks he was invited to come for a long visit to Ravensbrook. He was in fact impatiently expected there. He arrived in state bringing with him not only his parents but also a young aunt, and was welcomed like a prince. This visit, during which I suffered from a sense of temporary extinction, is commemorated by a group photograph taken by an artist summoned with his engine (regardless of expense) to Ravensbrook. Though the likenesses are not bad it is a very awful thing. Nobody looks like him or herself in it. The best yet are the Crane dogs, a very important part of the establishment and quite conscious of it, belonging apparently to some order of outlandish poodles, amazingly sedate and yet the most restless animals I have ever met. They pervaded, populated and filled the whole house. Whichever way one looked at any time, down the passage, up the stairs, into the drawing-room, there was always a dog in sight. Had I been asked on the first day how many there were I would have guessed about thirty. As a matter of fact there were only three, but I think they never sat down, except in Crane's study, where they had their entrée at all hours.

A scratching would be heard at the door, Crane would drop his pen with alacrity to throw it open—and the dogs would enter sedately in single file, taking a lot of time about it, too. Then the room would resound for a while with grunts, sniffs, yawns, heavy flops, followed by as much perhaps as three whole minutes of silence. Then the dogs would get up, one after another, never all together, and direct their footsteps to the door in an impressive and ominous manner. The first arrival waited considerately for the others before trying to attract attention by means of scratching on the bottom panel. Then, never before, Crane would raise his head, go meekly to the door—and the procession would file out at the slowest possible pace. The recurrent sedateness of the proceedings, the utter unconsciousness of the dogs, dear Stephen's absurd gravity while playing his part in those ceremonies, without ever a muscle of his face moving, were irresistibly, exasperatingly funny. I tried to preserve my gravity (or at least to keep calm), with fair success. Only one afternoon on the fifth or sixth repetition I could not help bursting into a loud interminable laugh and then the dear fellow asked me in all innocence what was the matter. I managed to conceal my nervous irritation from him and he never learned the secret of that laugh in which there was a beginning of hysteria.

If the definition that man is a laughing animal be true then Crane was neither one nor the other; indeed he was but a hurried visitor on this earth on which he had so little reason to be joyous. I might say that I never heard him laugh, except in connection with the baby. He loved children; but his friendship with our child was of the kind that put our

mutual sentiment, by comparison, somewhere within the arctic region. The two could not be compared; at least I have never detected Crane stretched full length and sustained on his elbows on a grass plot, in order to gaze at me; on the other hand this was his usual attitude of communion with the small child—with him who was called *the Boy*, and whose destiny it was to see more war before he came of age than the author of *The Red Badge* had time to see in all the allotted days of his life. In the gravity of its disposition the baby came quite up to Crane; yet those two would sometimes find something to laugh at in each other. Then there would be silence, and glancing out of the low window of my room I would see them, very still, staring at each other with a solemn understanding that needed no words or perhaps was beyond words altogether. I could not object on any ground to their profound intimacy but I do not see why Crane should have developed such an unreasonable suspicion as to my paternal efficiency. He seemed to be everlastingly taking the boy's part. I could not see that the baby was being oppressed, hectored over, or in any way deprived of its rights, or ever wounded in its feelings by me; but Crane seemed always to nurse some vague unexpressed grievance as to my conduct. I was inconsiderate. For instance—why could I not get a dog for the boy? One day he made me quite a scene about it. He seemed to imply I should drop everything and go look for a dog. I sat under the storm and said nothing. At last he cried "Hang it all, a boy ought to have a dog." It was an appeal to first principles but for an answer I pointed at the window and said: "Behold the boy." . . . He was sitting on a rug spread on the grass, with his little red stocking-cap very much over one eye (a fact of which he seemed unaware), and propped round with many pillows on account of his propensity to roll over on his side helplessly. My answer was irresistible. This is one of the few occasions on which I heard Stephen Crane laugh outright. He dropped his preaching on the dog theme and went out to the boy while I went on with my work. But he was strangely incorrigible. When he came back after an hour or so, his first words were, "Joseph, I will teach your boy to ride." I closed with the offer at once—but it was not to be. He was not given the time.

The happiest mental picture my wife and I preserve of Crane is on the occasion of our first visit to Brede Place when he rode to meet us at the Park gate. He looked at his best on horseback. On that day he must have been feeling well. As usual, he was happy in the saddle. As he went on trotting by the side of the open trap I said to him: "If you give the boy your seat I will be perfectly satisfied." I knew this would please him; and indeed his face remained wreathed in smiles all the way to the front door. He looked about him at that bit of the world, down the green slopes and up the brown fields, with an appreciative serenity and the confident bearing of a man who is feeling very sure of the present and of the future. All because he was looking at life from the saddle, with a good morning's work behind him. Nothing more is needed to give a man a blessed moment of illusion. The more I think of that morning the more I

believe it was just that; that it had really been given me to see Crane perfectly happy for a couple of hours; and that it was under this spell that directly we arrived he led me impatiently to the room in which he worked when at Brede. After we got there he said to me, "Joseph, I will give you something." I had no idea what it would be, till I saw him sit down to write an inscription in a very slim volume. He presented it to me with averted head. It was *The Black Riders*. He had never spoken to me of his verse before. It was while holding the book in my hand that I learned that they were written years before in America. I expressed my appreciation of them that afternoon in the usual half a dozen, or dozen, words which we allowed ourselves when completely pleased with each other's work. When the pleasure was not so complete the words would be many. And that was a great waste of breath and time. I must confess that we were no critics, I mean temperamentally. Crane was even less of a critic than myself. Criticism is very much a matter of a vocabulary, very consciously used; with us it was the intonation that mattered. The tone of a grunt could convey an infinity of meaning between us.

The articulate literary conscience at our elbow was Edward Garnett. He, of course, was worth listening to. His analytical appreciation (or appreciative analysis) of Crane's art, in the London Academy of 17th Dec., 1898, goes to the root of the matter with Edward's almost uncanny insight, and a well balanced sympathy with the blind, pathetic striving of the artist towards a complete realization of his individual gift. How highly Edward Garnett rated Crane's gift is recorded in the conclusions of that admirable and, within the limits of its space, masterly article of some two columns, where at the end are set down such affirmative phrases as: "The chief impressionist of the age" . . . "Mr. Crane's talent is unique" . . . and where he hails him as "the creator of fresh rhythms and phrases," while the very last words state confidently that: "Undoubtedly, of the young school it is Mr. Crane who is the genius—the others have their talents."

My part here being not that of critic but of private friend all I will say is that I agreed warmly at the time with that article which from the quoted phrases might be supposed a merely enthusiastic pronouncement, but on reading will be found to be based on that calm sagacity which Edward Garnett, for all his fiery zeal in the cause of letters, could always summon for the judgment of matters emotional—as all response to the various forms of art must be in the main. I had occasion to re-read it last year in its expanded form in a collection of literary essays of great, now almost historical, interest in the record of American and English imaginative literature. I found there a passage or two, not bearing precisely on Crane's work but giving a view of his temperament, on which of course his art was based; and of the conditions moral and material under which he had to put forth his creative faculties and his power of steady composition. On those matters, as a man who had the opportunity to look at

Crane's life in England I wish to offer a few remarks before closing my contribution to the memory of my friend.

I do not know that he was ever dunned for money and had to work under a threat of legal proceedings. I don't think he was ever dunned in the sense in which such a phrase is used about a spendthrift unscrupulous in incurring debts. No doubt he was sometimes pressed for money. He lived by his pen and the prices he obtained were not great. Personally he was not extravagant; and I will not quarrel with him for not choosing to live in a garret. The tenancy of Brede Place was held by him at a nominal rent. That glorious old place was not restored then, and the greatest part of it was uninhabitable. The Cranes had furnished in a modest way six or seven of the least dilapidated rooms, which even then looked bare and half empty. Certainly there was a horse, and at one time even two, but that luxury was not so very expensive at that time. One man looked after them. Riding was the only exercise open to Crane; and if he did work so hard surely he was entitled to some relaxation, if only for the preservation of his unique talent.

His greatest extravagance was hospitality of which I, too, had my share; often in the company, I am sorry to say, of men who after sitting at his board chose to speak of him and of his wife slightingly. Having some rudimentary sense of decency their behaviour while actually under the Cranes' roof often produced on me a disagreeable impression. Once I ventured to say to him, "You are too good-natured, Stephen." He gave me one of his quiet smiles, that seemed to hint so poignantly at the vanity of all things, and after a period of silence remarked: "I am glad those Indians are gone." He was surrounded by men who, secretly envious, hostile to the real quality of his genius (and a little afraid of it), were also in antagonism with the essential fineness of his nature. But enough of them. *Pulvis et umbra sunt.* I mean even those that may be alive yet. They were ever hardly anything else; one would have forgotten them if it were not for the legend (if one may dignify perfidious and contemptible gossip by that name), they created in order to satisfy that same obscure instinct of base humanity, which in the past would often bring against any exceptional man the charge of consorting with the devil. It was just as vague, just as senseless and in its implications just as lying as the mediaeval kind. I have heard one of these "friends" hint before several other Philistines that Crane could not write his tales without getting drunk!

Putting aside the gross palpable stupidity of such a statement—which the creature gave out as an instance of the artistic temperament—I am in a position to disclose what may have been the foundation of this piece of gossip. I have seen repeatedly Crane at work. A small jug of still smaller ale would be brought into the study at about ten o'clock; Crane would pour out some of it into a glass and settle himself at the long table at which he used to write in Brede Place. I would take a book and settle myself at the other end of the same table, with my back to him; and for two hours or so not a sound would be heard in that room. At the end of that time Crane would say suddenly: "I won't do any more now, Joseph." He would have covered three of his large sheets with his regular, legible, perfectly controlled, handwriting, with no more than half a dozen erasures—mostly single words—in the whole lot. It seemed to me always a perfect miracle in the way of mastery over material and expression. Most of the ale would be still in the glass, and how flat by that time I don't like to think! The most amusing part was to see Crane, as if moved by some obscure sense of duty, drain the last drop of that untempting remnant before we left the room to stroll to and fro in front of the house while waiting for lunch. Such is the origin of some of these gleeful whispers making up the Crane legend of "unrestrained temperament." I have known various sorts of temperaments—some perfidious and some lying—but "unrestrained temperament" is mere parrot talk. It has no meaning. But it was suggestive. It was founded on Crane's visits to town during which I more than once met him there. We used to spend afternoons and evenings together and I did not see any of his supposed revels in progress; nor yet have I ever detected any after effects of them on any occasion. Neither have I ever seen anybody who would own to having been a partner in those excesses—if only to the extent of standing by charitably—which would have been a noble part to play. I daresay all those "excesses" amounted to very little more than the one in which he asked me to join him in the following letter. It is the only note I have kept from the very few which we exchanged. The reader will see why it is one of my most carefully preserved possessions.

RAVENSBROOK.
OXTED.
17 March. (1899)

MY DEAR CONRAD: I am enclosing you a bit of MS. under the supposition that you might like to keep it in remembrance of my warm and endless friendship for you. I am still hoping that you will consent to Stokes' invitation to come to the Savage on Saturday night. Cannot you endure it? Give my affectionate remembrances to Mrs. Conrad and my love to the boy.

Yours always,
STEPHEN CRANE.

P.S. You must accept says Cora—and I—our invitation to come home with me on Sat. night.

I joined him. We had a very amusing time with the Savages. Afterwards Crane refused to go home till the last train. Evidence of what somebody has called his "unrestrained temperament," no doubt. So we went and sat at Gatti's, I believe; unless it was in a Bodega which existed then in that neighbourhood, and talked. I have a vivid memory of this awful debauch because it was on that evening that Crane told me of a subject for a story—a very exceptional thing for him to do. He called it "The Predecessor." I could not recall now by what capricious turns and odd associations of thought he reached the enthusiastic conclusion that it would make a good play, and that we must do it together. He wanted me to share in a certain success—"a dead sure thing," he said. His was an unrestrainedly generous temperament. But let that pass. I must have been specially predisposed, because I caught the infection at once. There and then we began to build up the masterpiece, interrupting each other eagerly, for, I don't know how it was, the air around us had suddenly grown thick with felicitous suggestions. We carried on this collaboration as far as the railway time-table would let us, and then made a break for the last train. Afterwards we did talk of our collaboration now and then, but no attempt at it was ever made. Crane had other stories to write; I was immersed deeply in *Lord Jim*, of which I had to keep up the instalments in *Blackwood's*; difficulties in presenting the subject on the stage rose one after another before our experience. The general subject consisted in a man personating his "predecessor" (who had died) in the hope of winning a girl's heart. The scenes were to include a ranch at the foot of the Rocky Mountains, I remember, and the action I fear would have been frankly melodramatic. Crane insisted that one of the situations should present the man and the girl on a boundless plain standing by their dead ponies after a furious ride (a truly Crane touch). I made some objections. A boundless plain in the light of a sunset could be got into a back-cloth, I admitted; but I doubted whether we could induce the management of any London theatre to deposit two stuffed horses on its stage.

Recalling now those earnestly fantastic discussions it occurs to me that Crane and I must have been unconsciously penetrated by a prophetic sense of the technique and of the very spirit of film-plays of which even the name was unknown then to the world. But if gifted with prophetic sense we must have been strangely ignorant of ourselves, since it must be obvious to any one who has read a page of our writings that a collaboration between us two could never come to anything in the end—could never even have been begun. The project was merely the expression of our affection for each other. We were fascinated for a moment by the will-of-the-wisp of close artistic communion. It would in no case have led us into a bog. I flatter myself we both had too much regard for each other's gifts not to be clear-eyed about them. We would not have followed the lure very far. At the same time it can not be denied that there were profound, if not extensive, similitudes in our temperaments which could create for a moment that fascinating illusion. It is not to be regretted, for it had, at any rate, given us some of the most light-hearted moments in the clear but sober atmosphere of our intimacy. From the force of circumstances there could not be much sunshine in it. "None of them saw the colour of the sky!" And alas! it stood already written that it was the younger man who would fail to make a landing through the surf. So I am glad to have that episode to remember, a brotherly serio-comic interlude, played under the shadow of coming events. But I would not have alluded to it at all if it had not come out in the course of my most interesting talk with the author of this biography, that Crane had thought it worth while to mention it in his correspondence, whether seriously or humorously, I know not. So here it is without the charm which it had for me but which can not be reproduced in the mere relation of its outward characteristics: a clear gleam on us two, succeeded by the Spanish-American war into which Crane disappeared like a wilful man walking away into the depths of an ominous twilight.

The cloudy afternoon when we two went rushing all over London together, was for him the beginning of the end. The problem was to find £60 that day, before the sun set, before dinner, before the "six forty" train to Oxted, at once, that instant—lest peace should be declared and the opportunity of seeing a war be missed. I had not £60 to lend him. Sixty shillings was nearer my mark. We tried various offices but had no luck, or rather we had the usual luck of money hunting enterprises. The man was either gone out to see about a dog, or would take no interest in the Spanish-American war. In one place the man wanted to know what was the hurry? He would have liked to have forty-eight hours to think the matter over. As we came downstairs Crane's white-faced excitement frightened me. Finally it occurred to me to take him to Messrs. William Blackwood & Sons' London office. There he was received in a most friendly way. Presently I escorted him to Charing Cross where he took the train for home with the assurance that he would have the means to start "for the war" next day. That is the reason I can not to this day read his tale "The Price of the Harness" without a pang. It has done nothing more deadly than pay his debt to Messrs. Blackwood; yet now and then I feel as though that afternoon I had led him by the hand to his doom. But, indeed, I was only the blind agent of the fate that had him in her grip! Nothing could have held him back. He was ready to swim the ocean.

Thirteen years afterwards I made use, half consciously, of the shadow of the primary idea of "The Predecessor," in one of my short tales which were serialized in the *Metropolitan Magazine*. But in that tale the dead man in the background is not a Predecessor but merely an assistant on a lonely plantation; and instead of the ranch, the mountains and the plains, there is a cloud-capped island, a bird-haunted reef and the sea. All this the mere distorted shadow of what we two used to talk about in a fantastic mood; but now and then, as I wrote, I had the feeling that he had the right to come and look over my shoulder. But he never came. I received no suggestions from him, subtly conveyed without words. There will never be any collaboration for us now. But I wonder, were he alive, whether he would be pleased with the tale. I don't know. Perhaps not. Or, perhaps, after picking up the volume with that detached air I remember so well, and turning over page after page in silence, he would suddenly read aloud a line or two and then looking straight into my eyes as was his wont on such occasions, say with all the intense earnestness of affection that was in him: "I—like—that, Joseph."

Clarence Day

From THIS SIMIAN WORLD

I T HAS ALWAYS BEEN a serious matter for men when a civilization de-
cayed. But it may at some future day prove far more serious still.
Our hold on the planet is not absolute. Our descendants may lose it.

Germs may do them out of it. A chestnut fungus springs up, defies
us, and kills all our chestnuts. The boll weevil very nearly baffles us. The
fly seems unconquerable. Only a strong civilization, when such foes are
about, can preserve us. And our present efforts to cope with such beings
are fumbling and slow.

We haven't the habit of candidly facing this danger. We read our
biological history but we don't take it in. We blandly assume we were
always "intended" to rule, and that no other outcome could even be
considered by Nature. This is one of the remnants of ignorance certain
religions have left: but it's odd that men who don't believe in Easter
should still believe this. For the facts are of course this is a hard and
precarious world, where every mistake and infirmity must be paid for in
full.

If mankind ever is swept aside as a failure however, what a brilliant
and enterprising failure he at least will have been. I felt this with a kind of
warm suddenness only today, as I finished these dreamings and drove
through the gates of the park. I had been shutting my modern surroundings out of my thoughts, so completely, and living as it were in the wild
world of ages ago, that when I let myself come back suddenly to the
twentieth century, and stare at the park and the people, the change was
tremendous. All around me were the well-dressed descendants of primi-

tive animals, whizzing about in bright motors, past tall, soaring buildings. What gifted, energetic achievers they suddenly seemed!

I thought of a photograph I had once seen, of a ship being torpedoed. There it was, the huge, finely made structure, awash in the sea, with tiny black spots hanging on to its side—crew and passengers. The great ship, even while sinking, was so mighty, and those atoms so helpless. Yet, it was those tiny beings that had created that ship. They had planned it and built it and guided its bulk through the waves. They had also invented a torpedo that could rend it asunder.

It is possible that our race may be an accident, in a meaningless universe, living its brief life uncared-for, on this dark, cooling star: but even so—and all the more—what marvelous creatures we are! What fairy story, what tale from the Arabian Nights of the jinns, is a hundredth part as wonderful as this true fairy story of simians! It is so much more heartening, too, than the tales we invent. A universe capable of giving birth to many such accidents is—blind or not—a good world to live in, a promising universe.

And if there are no other such accidents, if we stand alone, if all the uncountable armies of planets are empty, or peopled by animals only, with no keys to thought, then we have done something so mighty, what may it not lead to! What powers may we not develop before the Sun dies! We once thought we lived on God's footstool: it may be a throne.

This is no world for pessimists. An amoeba on the beach, blind and helpless, a mere bit of pulp—that amoeba has grandsons today who read Kant and play symphonies. Will those grandsons in turn have descendants who will sail through the void, discover the foci of forces, the means to control them, and learn how to marshal the planets and grapple with space? Would it after all be any more startling than our rise from the slime?

No sensible amoeba would have ever believed for a minute that any of his most remote children would build and run dynamos. Few sensible men of today stop to feel, in their hearts, that we live in the very same world where that miracle happened.

This world, and our racial adventure, are magical still.

* * *

YET ALTHOUGH for high-spirited marchers the march is sufficient, there still is that other way of looking at it that we dare not forget. Our adventure may satisfy *us:* does it satisfy Nature? She is letting us camp for a while here among the wrecked graveyards of mightier dynasties, not one of which met her tests. Their bones are the message the epochs she murdered have left us: we have learned to decipher their sickening warning at last.

. . .

Yes, and even if we are permitted to have a long reign, and are not laid away with the failures, are we a success?

We need so much spiritual insight, and we have so little. Our airships may some day float over the hills of Arcturus, but how will that help us if we cannot find the soul of the world? Is that soul alive and loving? or cruel? or callous? or dead?

We have no sure vision. Hopes, guesses, beliefs—that is all.

There are sounds we are deaf to, there are strange sights invisible to us. There are whole realms of splendor, it may be, of which we are heedless; and which we are as blind to as ants to the call of the sea.

Life is enormously flexible—look at all that we've done to our dogs—but we carry our hairy past with us wherever we go. The wise St. Bernards and the selfish toy lap-dogs are brothers, and some things are possible for them and others are not. So with us. There are definite limits to simian civilizations, due in part to some primitive traits that help keep us alive, and in part to the mere fact that every being has to be something, and when one is a simian one is not also everything else. Our main-springs are fixed, and our principal traits are deep-rooted. We cannot now re-live the ages whose imprint we bear.

We have but to look back on our past to have hope in our future: but—it will be only *our* future, not some other race's. We shall win our own triumphs, yet know that they would have been different, had we cared above all for creativeness, beauty, or love.

So we run about, busy and active, marooned on this star, always violently struggling, yet with no clearly seen goal before us. Men, animals, insects—what tribe of us asks any object, except to keep trying to satisfy its own master appetite? If the ants were earth's lords they would make no more use of their lordship than to learn and enjoy every possible method of toiling. Cats would spend their span of life, say, trying new kinds of guile. And we, who crave so much to know, crave so little but knowing. Some of us wish to know Nature most; those are the scientists. Others, the saints and philosophers, wish to know God. Both are alike in their hearts, yes, in spite of their quarrels. Both seek to assuage, to no end, the old simian thirst.

If we wanted to *be* Gods—but ah, can we grasp that ambition?

Clarence Day

MY FATHER'S RELIGION

M Y FATHER'S IDEAS OF RELIGION seemed straightforward and simple. He had noticed when he was a boy that there were buildings called churches; he had accepted them as a natural part of the surroundings in which he had been born. He would never have invented such things himself. Nevertheless they were here. As he grew up he regarded them as unquestioningly as he did banks. They were substantial old structures, they were respectable, decent, and venerable. They were frequented by the right sort of people. Well, that was enough.

On the other hand he never allowed churches—or banks—to dictate to him. He gave each the respect that was due to it from his point of view; but he also expected from each of them the respect he felt due to him.

As to creeds, he knew nothing about them, and cared nothing either; yet he seemed to know which sect he belonged with. It had to be a sect with the minimum of nonsense about it; no total immersion, no exhorters, no holy confession. He would have been a Unitarian, naturally, if he'd lived in Boston. Since he was a respectable New Yorker, he belonged in the Episcopal Church.

As to living a spiritual life, he never tackled that problem. Some men who accept spiritual beliefs try to live up to them daily: other men, who reject such beliefs, try sometimes to smash them. My father would have disagreed with both kinds entirely. He took a more distant attitude. It disgusted him when atheists attacked religion: he thought they were vulgar. But he also objected to have religion make demands upon him— he felt that religion too was vulgar, when it tried to stir up men's feelings. It had its own proper field of activity, and it was all right there, of course; but there was one place religion should let alone, and that was a man's soul. He especially loathed any talk of walking hand in hand with his Saviour. And if he had ever found the Holy Ghost trying to soften his heart, he would have regarded Its behavior as distinctly uncalled for; even ungentlemanly.

The only religious leader or prophet I can think of who might have suited my father was Confucius—though even Confucius would have struck him as addled. Confucius was an advocate of peace, and of finding the path; and he enjoined the Golden Rule on his followers long before Christ. My father would not have been his follower in any of these. Finding "the path"? Not even Confucius could have made him see what that meant. He was too busy for that, too hot-tempered for peace, and the Golden Rule he regarded as claptrap; how could things work both ways? Whatever he did unto others he was sure was all right, but that didn't mean that he would have allowed them to do the same things to him. He saw other men as disorderly troops, and himself as a general; and the Golden Rule was plainly too mushy to apply in such circumstances. He disciplined himself quite as firmly as he tried to discipline others, but it wasn't necessarily by any means the same kind of discipline. There was one saying of Confucius', however, with which he would have agreed: "Respect spiritual beings—if there are any—but keep aloof from them." My father would have regarded that principle as thoroughly sound.

When Confucius was asked about the rule to return good for evil, he said: "What then will you return for good? No: return good for good; for evil, return justice." If my father had been asked to return good for evil he would have been even more pithy—his response would have consisted of a hearty and full-throated "Bah!"

If he had been let alone, he would have brought up his sons in this spirit. But my mother's feelings and teachings were different, and this complicated things for us. Like my father, she had accepted religion without any doubtings, but she had accepted more of it. She was far more devout. And she loved best the kind of faith that comforted her and sweetened her thoughts. My father didn't object to this at all—it was all right enough—for a woman: but it led to her giving us instructions that battled with his.

They both insisted strongly, for example, on our going to church, but they didn't agree in their reasons. It was the right thing to do, Father said. "But why do we have to go, Father?" "Because I wish to bring you up properly. Men who neglect going to church are a lazy, disreputable lot." A few might be good fellows, he would admit, but they were the exceptions. As a rule, non-churchgoers were not solid, respectable citizens. All respectable citizens owed it to themselves to attend.

My mother put it differently to us. She said we owed it to God. Church to her was a place where you worshiped, and learned to be good. My father never dreamed of attending for any such reason. In his moral instructions to us he never once mentioned God. What he dwelt on was integrity. My mother once wrote in my plush-covered autograph album, "Fear God and keep His commandments"; but the motto that Father had written on the preceding page, over his bolder signature, was: "Do your duty and fear no one." And nobody could tell him his duty—he knew it without that, it seemed. It wasn't written down in any book, certainly not in the Bible, but it was a perfectly definite and indisputable thing nevertheless. It was a code, a tradition. It was to be upright and fearless and honorable, and to brush your clothes properly; and in general always to do the right thing in every department of life. The right thing to do for religion was to go to some good church on Sundays.

When Father went to church and sat in his pew, he felt he was doing enough. Any further spiritual work ought to be done by the clergy.

When hymns were sung he sometimes joined in mechanically, for the mere sake of singing; but usually he stood as silent as an eagle among canaries and doves, leaving others to abase themselves in sentiments that he didn't share. The hymns inculcated meekness and submission, and dependence on God; but Father was quick to resent an injury, and he had no meekness in him.

> Jesus, lover of my soul,
>   Let me to thy bosom fly,
> While the nearer waters roll,
>   While the tempest still is nigh.

How could Father sing that? He had no desire to fly to that bosom.

> Hide me, O my Saviour, hide,
>   Till the storm of life be past;
> Safe into the haven guide,
>   Oh receive my soul at last . . .
> All my trust on thee is stayed;
>   All my help from thee I bring;
> Cover my defenseless head
>   With the shadow of thy wing.

But Father's head was far from defenseless, and he would have scorned to hide, or ask shelter. As he stood there, looking critically about him, high-spirited, resolute, I could imagine him marching with that same independence through space—a tiny speck masterfully dealing with death and infinity.

When our rector talked of imitating the saints, it seemed drivel to Father. What! imitate persons who gave their whole lives to religion, and took only a perfunctory interest in the affairs of this world? Father regarded himself as a more all-round man than the saints. They had neglected nine-tenths of their duties from this point of view—they had no business connections, no families, they hadn't even paid taxes. In a word, saints were freaks. If a freak spent an abnormal amount of time being religious, what of it?

The clergy were a kind of freaks also. A queer lot. Father liked Bishop Greer and a few others, but he hadn't much respect for the rest of them. He thought of most clergymen as any busy man of action thinks of philosophers, or of those scholars who discuss the fourth dimension, which is beyond human knowing. He regarded the self-alleged intimacy of our rector with that fourth dimension most sceptically. He himself neither was nor wished to be intimate with a thing of that sort. But this didn't mean that he doubted the existence of God. On the contrary, God and Father had somehow contrived to achieve a serene and harmonious relation that the clergy themselves might have envied.

How did Father think God felt towards my mother? Why, about the way he did. God probably knew she had faults, but He saw she was lovely and good; and—in spite of some mistaken ideas that she had about money—He doubtless looked on her most affectionately. Father didn't expect God to regard *him* affectionately—they stood up man to man—but naturally God loved my mother, as everyone must. At the gate of Heaven, if there was any misunderstanding about his own ticket, Father counted on Mother to get him in. That was her affair.

This idea runs far back, or down, into old human thoughts. "The unbelieving husband is sanctified by the wife." (First Corinthians, vii, 14.) Medical missionaries report that today, in some primitive tribes, a healthy woman will propose to swallow medicine in behalf of her sick husband. This plan seems to her husband quite reasonable. It seemed so—in religion—to Father.

As to his mental picture of God, I suppose that Father was vague, but in a general way he seemed to envisage a God in his own image. A God who had small use for emotionalism and who prized strength and dignity. A God who probably found the clergy as hard to bear as did Father himself. In short Father and God, as I said, usually saw eye to eye. They seldom met, or even sought a meeting, their spheres were so different; but they had perfect confidence in each other—at least at most moments. The only exceptions were when God seemed to be neglecting His job—Father's confidence in Him was then withdrawn, instantly. But I'll come to this later.

As to the nature of God's sphere, namely Heaven, compared to Father's, the earth, Heaven wasn't nearly so solid and substantial. Father had all the best of it. Life here on earth was trying, but it shouldn't be—it was all right intrinsically—he felt it was only people's damned carelessness that upset things so much. Heaven on the other hand had a more serious and fundamental defect: the whole place was thin and peculiar. It didn't inspire much confidence. Father saw glumly that the time would come when he'd have to go there, but he didn't at all relish the prospect. He clung to his own battered realm.

Yet its faults and stupidities weighed on his spirit at times: all the chuckle-headed talk and rascality in business and politics. He was always getting indignant about them, and demanding that they be stamped out;

and when he saw them continually spreading everywhere, it was maddening. Nature too, though in general sound and wholesome, had a treacherous streak. He hated and resented decay, and failing powers. He hated to see little children or animals suffer. His own aches and pains were an outrage; he faced them with anger. And aside from these treacheries, there was a spirit of rebellion in things. He would come in from a walk over his fields—which to me had seemed pleasant—oppressed by the balky disposition both of his fields and his farmer. He would get up from an inspection of his account books with the same irritation: there were always some bonds in his box that hadn't behaved as they should. And twice a day, regularly, he would have a collision, or bout, with the newspaper: it was hard to see why God had made so many damned fools and democrats.

I would try to persuade him sometimes—in my argumentative years —that it would be better for him to accept the world as it was and adapt himself to it, since he could scarcely expect to make the planet over, and change the whole earth single-handed. Father listened to this talk with suspicion, as to an advocatus diaboli. If he ever was tempted to give in, it was only in his weak moments; a minute later he was again on the warpath, like a materialistic Don Quixote.

There was one kind of depression that afflicted Mother which Father was free from: he never once had any moments of feeling "unworthy." This was a puzzle to Mother, and it made her look at Father with a mixture of awe and annoyance. Other people went to church to be made better, she told him. Why didn't he? He replied in astonishment that he had no need to be better—he was all right as he was. Mother couldn't get over his taking this stand, but she never could get him to see what the matter was with it. It wasn't at all easy for Father to see that he had any faults; and if he did, it didn't even occur to him to ask God to forgive them. He forgave them himself. In his moments of prayer, when he and God tried to commune with each other, it wasn't his own shortcomings that were brought on the carpet, but God's.

He expected a good deal of God, apparently. Not that he wanted God's help, of course; or far less His guidance. No, but it seemed that God—like the rest of us—spoiled Father's plans. He, Father, was always trying to bring this or that good thing to pass, only to find that there were obstacles in the way. These of course roused his wrath. He would call God's attention to such things. They should not have been there. He didn't actually accuse God of gross inefficiency, but when he prayed his tone was loud and angry, like that of a dissatisfied guest in a carelessly managed hotel.

I never saw Father kneel in supplication on such occasions. On the contrary he usually talked with God lying in bed. My room was just above Father's, and he could easily be heard through the floor. On those rare nights when he failed to sleep well, the sound of damns would float up—at first deep and tragic and low, then more loud and exasperated.

Fragments of thoughts and strong feelings came next, or meditations on current bothers. At the peak of these, God would be summoned. I would hear him call "Oh God?" over and over, with a rising inflection, as though he were demanding that God should present himself instantly, and sit in the fat green chair in the corner, and be duly admonished. Then when Father seemed to feel that God was listening, he would begin to expostulate. He would moan in a discouraged but strong voice: "Oh God, it's too much. Amen . . . I say it's too damned much . . . No, no, I can't stand it. Amen." After a pause, if he didn't feel better, he would seem to suspect that God might be trying to sneak back to Heaven without doing anything, and I would hear him shout warningly: "Oh God! I *won't* stand it! Amen. Oh damnation! A-a-men." Sometimes he would ferociously bark a few extra Amens, and then, soothed and satisfied, peacefully go back to sleep . . . And one night in the country, when the caretaker of our house in town telephoned to Father that the rain was pouring in through a hole in the roof, I heard so much noise that I got out of bed and looked over the banisters, and saw Father standing alone in the hall, shaking his fist at the ceiling, and shouting in hot indignation to Heaven, "What next?"

But Father was patient with God after all. If he didn't forgive, he forgot. His wrath didn't last—he had other things to think of—and he was genial at heart. The very next Sunday after an outburst he would be back in church. Not perhaps as a worshiper or a devotee, but at least as a patron.

A caricature of Clarence Day by himself.

David Donald

HERNDON AND MRS. LINCOLN

I

Aɴɴ Rᴜᴛʟᴇᴅɢᴇ ᴡᴀs ᴛʜᴇ ᴏɴʟʏ ᴡᴏᴍᴀɴ Lincoln ever loved. But after his removal to Springfield he was trapped by the ambitious and aggressive Mary Todd into a promise of marriage. The appointed day came, the feast was prepared, the guests were waiting, the bride was decked out in her finery—but the groom did not appear. Lincoln felt he could not marry this woman he did not love. Later, however, consideration of his plighted honor forced him to go through with the ceremony, and Mary Todd became Mrs. Abraham Lincoln. From that day in November 1842 Lincoln's home life was a domestic hell. Mary Lincoln made it so unpleasant for him that he was forced to interest himself in politics. He was driven from home into the White House.

Most people believe that this is the story of Abraham Lincoln's married life. Many can cite one story or another to "prove" their point. These ideas have become so widespread as to form an accepted part of a great national tradition, and the recent publication of two admirable defenses of Mary Lincoln has done little to upset these stereotypes. Yet they are one-hundred-per-cent incorrect.

There is a fascination in tracing this legend back to its origin and in seeing how it developed and grew. The Ann Rutledge story, the defaulting-bridegroom incident, and the anecdotes of married strife all go back to one man, to Abraham Lincoln's law partner and biographer, William Henry Herndon. This man Herndon was in many ways as interesting as Lincoln himself. A curiously divided personality, he was on the

From *Lincoln Reconsidered*, 1956. Copyright 1950, © 1956 by David Donald. Originally published in *Books at Brown* by Brown University.

one hand a fighting idealist, a champion of causes, a man of drums and trumpets; on the other, he was a man of the common people, of barnyard vulgarity, who knew men's talk about drinking and cockfights and horses and women. Born in Kentucky in 1818 (just twelve days after Mary Todd saw the light in cultured Lexington), he was early taken by his father to pioneer in Illinois, in the wild Sangamon country. In the 1820's Herndon's father moved to the hamlet of Springfield, where he opened the Indian Queen, the first tavern in the community. Here young Billy got to know the leaders of the ambitious village, learned to laugh at their jokes and to understand their talk of politics. Here, too, he acquired that taste for liquor which was so tragically to blight his later years.

But there was more to this youth than the hanger-on at the tavern. He did well in the Springfield schools and his proud father sent him at an almost unheard-of expense to attend the preparatory division of Illinois College. He had one exciting year at Jacksonville. He dimly saw vistas of sweeping fields of knowledge; from the library, where he was permitted to borrow two small volumes or one large book each week, he caught an insatiable appetite for reading. But at the end of the year he failed in mathematics and was not allowed to register for college courses.

Back in Springfield, Herndon clerked for Joshua Speed and slept with Speed, Abraham Lincoln, and another clerk in the big room above the store. Then he married and began raising a family. And, most important of all, he started studying law with the two best lawyers the Illinois capital could offer—Logan and Lincoln. Lincoln wrote that Herndon was "a laborious studious young man, . . . far better informed on almost all subjects than I have been." It was not surprising, then, that Lincoln in 1844 should choose this promising student for his new law partner. The association thus formed lasted without interruption until Lincoln went to Washington, and in 1865 the Lincoln & Herndon shingle still creaked over the office door. Herndon became a competent lawyer and did the "book work" for the firm. In politics, too, he helped—so well that Springfield newspapers called him "Lincoln's man Friday."

Herndon was an eager and earnest young man. There was something almost pathetic in the way he sought knowledge. He loved books, the deeper and more "philisophic" the better. He was fascinated by the rolling periods of grandiloquent oratory and by the lofty abstractions of metaphysicians. He read Kant and Comte, Holyoke and Hobbes. He reveled in speculations of the more abstruse sort: What is law? What is the nature of the mind? What is the ultimate source of knowledge? His speculative turn was stimulated by a long series of letters which he exchanged with Theodore Parker, the Boston Unitarian radical. Herndon poured out his soul to this man; he told him everything—of politics and philosophy and the slavery controversy and the law office, and sometimes of his partner, "Mr. Lincoln."

It is important to understand how Herndon went about his almost desperate search for Truth. Truth was not something that could be found in books, not even the Bible; nor was Truth spoken by the Sage alone. Given a Divine Providence and a soul in the individual man, it was the belief of the Transcendentalists—Parker, Emerson, Thoreau, for all of whom Herndon had an almost painful admiration—that Truth could be found by introspection. If you wished to explain a man's actions, look to your own soul, where you would find identical motives reflected. All men operate on the same laws, and these laws can explain any human behavior.

There were many problems that Herndon wanted to solve. He sought to know the laws of the "All-All" and of "zo-ophyte & man." He was puzzled by the secrets of the winds and of the hibernacle surrounding the tiny leaf bud, the mystery of the sun and the rain. But there were human problems facing him, too. One of them was his office mate. Herndon could never quite figure Lincoln out. He behaved queerly—i.e., differently from Herndon. He seemed to drip melancholy as he walked, but his fits of deep depression would alternate with gusty outbreaks of humor. There must be something wrong with this man.

In groping for an explanation, Herndon did not go far. He promptly concluded that the trouble with Lincoln was Mrs. Lincoln. Herndon had never liked Mary Todd. When she first came to Illinois he had met her at a ball given by Colonel Allen. This youth back from college had danced with the belle, and, thinking to compliment her, had informed Mary that she waltzed with the grace of a serpent. Miss Todd, never distinguished for a sense of humor, had flashed back: "Mr. Herndon, comparison to a serpent is rather severe irony, especially to a newcomer"—and she left him on the dance floor. Neither ever forgot the scene. Twenty years later, when Herndon visited the Lincolns at the White House, he wrote a friend that Mrs. Lincoln was becoming more "excentric" every day; that she had, to his personal knowledge, made Lincoln's life desolate since they were married. Of course, it was not all friction between them, for a wife cannot completely snub her husband's partner. Mary Lincoln occasionally borrowed small sums from Herndon while her husband was out on the circuit, and after Lincoln's death she spoke graciously to Herndon of "my beloved husband's, *truly*, affectionate regard for *you*." So far the amenities of life would carry her, but not further; she never invited Herndon to have a meal at her home.

It was in this atmosphere of mutual dislike that Herndon did his thinking about his partner's melancholy and his sudden moods. By a comparison with his own home life, he could easily tell what was wrong. Herndon hated to spend a night away from his family; Lincoln would go off sometimes for months on the circuit without returning to Springfield. It was obvious, thought Herndon, that his partner's home life was unhappy. Herndon would invite a casual acquaintance to dinner without giving his wife any notice; Lincoln had guests only when Mary specially asked them. It must be, said Herndon, that Mrs. Lincoln was of a shrewish and inhospitable temperament. When the Herndon children came to

the law office—which was not often—they were given lawbooks and told
to sit quietly on a bench; when the Lincoln boys were brought in by
their father, Herndon wrote, "they would take down the books from the
shelves—scatter them over the floor—mash up gold pens—spill the ink all
over the floor." Clearly, Herndon thought, the Lincolns lacked discipline.

Before Lincoln's death Herndon kept his views largely to himself,
but in 1865 he decided to write a biography of the man he had known so
well and at the same time so little. It was to be a subjective, personal
biography explaining why Lincoln acted and thought as he did. One of
the springs of Lincoln's nature Herndon found in gathering reminiscences
from New Salem acquaintances. From twisted recollections of events
more than thirty years past, from hearsay and gossip, from inferences as
to what must have been, and from speculations as to what might have
been, he wove the fabric of the Ann Rutledge story, which he spread
before the Springfield people in a long lecture in 1866. In lush periods of
purple phrases he told his fellow citizens that Ann was the only woman
Lincoln had ever loved, that as late as 1860 he had still cherished his
affection for her alone.

Mrs. Lincoln, her sons, and her friends were outraged. It was, it
should be remembered, a romantic age, this mid-Victorian period when
ladies had limbs and not legs, when marriage meant—or was supposed to
mean—invariable connubial bliss, when debunking was not dreamed of.
The true lady, etiquette books of the day pronounced, should be mentioned in the newspapers only twice—when she married and when she
died; if her name occurred in print at any other time, a male relative
ought to visit the editor with a shotgun. Mrs. Lincoln was a proud,
sensitive lady, the more so now that she was alone in the world. She
retaliated upon Herndon by declaring that her husband had always
thought of him as a drunkard and a wastrel. And Herndon came back
with a blistering excoriation: Mrs. Lincoln was a liar, subject to spas-
modic fits of insanity. From then on it was open warfare. Year after year
went by, and Herndon became more and more bitter. Age and drink cast
a cloud over his brilliant mind and made trivial details stand out with
sharp poignancy. Mrs. Lincoln, he now thought, was the "she wolf of this
section," "soured . . . gross . . . material—avaricious—insolent," "a ti-
gress," "terribly aristocratic . . . and haughty," "as cold as a chunk of
ice." He brooded over real and imagined slights and stirred up his
memory. Twenty years after Lincoln's death he concluded that Mary
Lincoln was *the female wild cat of the age.*

II

IT IS ONLY BY DISCOUNTING these belated recollections and garbled
introspections that one can hope to arrive at a true picture of Mary
Lincoln. Herndon assiduously collected backstairs gossip about Mrs.
Lincoln and spread it as truth. He did not consciously misinterpret

facts, for he was really determined to "do justice" to Mrs. Lincoln. But
he was eager to accept stories that fitted in with his preconceived ideas.
Any thinking person will realize how difficult it is to remember correctly
the back-fence gossip of twenty to forty years earlier, even assuming that
the gossip was ever correct in the first place.

By following strictly contemporary accounts one gets a different
view of Mrs. Lincoln. When Miss Mary Todd came to Springfield in
1839 to make her home with her sister, Mrs. Ninian W. Edwards, she
came as a belle, as an interesting and attractive young woman destined to
be the center of social life and gaiety. The Todds were a proud and
distinguished family in Kentucky, numbering two governors, a couple of
Cabinet members, and a score of less-distinguished officials as close relatives. It was the Todds, together with the Crittendens and the Clays, who
set the social tone for Lexington. Yet the Todd name carried with it a less
desirable heritage, too—a sort of mental taint, a tendency toward abnormally intense personalities, ill adapted to severe crises or harsh shocks.
The medical record shows that Mary Todd's own brother became a
mental case.

But all this was in the future. For Miss Todd was a brilliant addition
to Springfield society in the 1830's. She had been well educated at Mme.
Mentelle's, both in English fundamentals and in French, which she read
fluently. She could write a gracious and well-expressed letter. She could
dance and hold sprightly conversations with men. She was a born co-
quette. When life with her stepmother in Kentucky became unendurable,
it was natural that she should visit her Springfield sister, for here she
might find an attractive husband and a home. Women are always at a
premium in a frontier society, and it is not surprising that the Edwards
house in the winters of 1839 and 1840 was a center of gaiety. There were
balls and sleigh rides and excursions and parties. Half a dozen young men
danced in attendance upon the new queen—James C. Conkling, Joshua
Speed, Stephen A. Douglas, and a gawky young lawyer called Abraham
Lincoln. Mary was excited and delighted by such attentions. In a letter of
the time a friend described her as "the very creature of excitement," who
"never enjoy[ed] herself more than when in society and surrounded by a
company of merry friends."

"Mary," as her niece remembered her, "although not strictly beautiful,
was more than pretty. She had a broad, white forehead, eyebrows sharply
but delicately marked, a straight nose, short upper lip, and an expressive
mouth curling into an adorable, slow coming smile that brought dimples
into her cheeks and glinted in her long-lashed, blue eyes." Observers
noted her "Plump round figure," her "lovely complexion," her "soft
brown hair." One of the clearest pictures of Mary Todd at this time
comes from Herndon himself: "of a short build—chunky—compact and
about of the average height—and waid [*sic*] . . . about 130 pounds . . .
haughtily dignified—moved easily . . . a fine conversationa[li]st—witty
and sometimes terribly sarcastic . . . intelligent—quick—intuitive." Others

also noted Miss Todd's sharp tongue, even while admitting her charm. She could be gracious, but she could also flash out with an ungovernable temper—possibly a reflection of her lack of early home training.

She was ambitious, intelligently so. She came to find a husband, and she intended to make a good choice. Half laughingly, Mary said that she was going to marry the man who would become President of the United States. It is not hard to understand why she rejected one widower, referring to his motherless children as "two *sweet little objections.*" The extent of Stephen A. Douglas's attentions has probably been exaggerated, but he was very often in the Edwards parlor. But it was Abraham Lincoln with whom she finally fell in love. It must have been an amusing courtship—for an outsider. Awkward and rough and a little embarrassed in the presence of ladies, Lincoln would sit and listen fascinated by Mary's prattle, but he could not carry on the conversation himself. Friends advised Mary against the match, pointing out Lincoln's poor prospects and his even poorer present. Exactly what happened during those winter months of 1840–1 is not clear, but apparently there was an engagement of some sort, or at least an understanding.

The commonly accepted story, started by Herndon and spread by fiction-writers, is that the two were to be married. To quote Herndon's version: "The time fixed for the marriage was the first day in January, 1841. Careful preparations for the happy occasion were made at the Edwards mansion. The house underwent the customary renovation; . . . the supper [was] prepared, and the guests invited. The latter assembled on the evening in question, and awaited in expectant pleasure the interesting ceremony of marriage. The bride, bedecked in veil and silken gown, and nervously toying with the flowers in her hair, sat in the adjoining room. Nothing was lacking but the groom." Hours passed, and Lincoln failed to appear. The wedding plans were abandoned, and the guests quietly departed.

This is not the place to examine this wedding story in detail. It is enough to realize that the whole episode was created from self-contradictory reminiscences given years after the event; that no contemporary letter by Mary Todd, Lincoln, or their friends mentions a projected marriage for the couple; that Lincoln did not take out a marriage license in 1840; and that Springfield gossips did not spread the tale until after Lincoln's death.

But if there was no deserted bride, no waiting guests or garlanded house, there was certainly a major emotional crisis about this time. Lincoln referred to the day as "that fatal first of Jany. '41," and he considered himself "the most miserable man living." "If what I feel were equally distributed to the whole human family," he wrote disconsolately, "there would not be one cheerful face on the earth." A friend remarked that "he is reduced and emaciated in appearance and seems scarcely to possess strength enough to speak above a whisper," and laughingly called

Lincoln a "poor, hapless simple swain who loved most true but was not loved again."

Mary Todd, though she carried on the round of parties and entertainment, was none too happy either. Lincoln, she wrote to a bosom companion, "deems me unworthy of notice, as I have not met *him* in the gay world for months. . . . others were as seldom gladdened by his presence as my humble self, yet I would that . . . he would once more resume his station in Society, that 'Richard should be himself again,' much, much happiness would it afford me."

The best reconstruction that can now be made of the whole tangle is as follows: About the first of January 1841, Lincoln, realizing his poverty and doubting his ability to make a sensitive and cultured woman happy, asked to be released from his engagement. Mary consented, though letting it be known that she would consider the question still open. Thus the crisis passed.

It was not until nearly two years later that their marriage actually took place. During that time Lincoln was comforted by the knowledge that the marriage of his friend Joshua Speed was successful. He was also rising to a more secure financial position as one of the leading lawyers in Springfield. The estranged couple was brought together through the agency of Mrs. Simeon Francis, a common friend, and the engagement was renewed. There was no public announcement, for Mary said "that the world, woman and man, were uncertain and slippery and that it was best to keep the secret courtship from all eyes and ears." Some months later, on November 4, 1842, the two were married.

The Lincolns at first stayed at the Globe Tavern, where they got room and board for four dollars a week. It was here that their first son, Robert Todd, was born. In 1846 a second child, Edward Baker, came, and the same year Lincoln was elected to Congress. For a part of his term the family lived in Washington with him, rooming at Mrs. Sprigg's. But some of the time Mrs. Lincoln stayed at her father's in Kentucky. The letters between husband and wife during this period reveal the tender affection that united the couple and their deep devotion to their children. Writing from Washington in 1848, Lincoln found himself lonesome for his wife in Kentucky. To occupy his time he went shopping for plaid stockings to fit "Eddy's dear little feet." "All the house," he wrote Mary, "or rather, all with whom you were on decided good terms—send their love to you— The others say nothing." He was concerned with his "Molly's" health. "Are you entirely free from headaches?" he asked. "That is good. . . . I am afraid you will get so well, and fat, and young, as to be wanting to marry again."

She replied in kind, telling the family news, how little "Eddy" had recovered from a spell of sickness, and how the children had adopted a homeless kitten. She concluded: "Do not fear the children, have forgotten you, I was only jesting. Even E-eyes brighten at the mention of your name." Other letters at this period tell of a husband's anxiety to see his wife—provided she would "be a *good girl* in all things" when she came East—and of his worry about an accumulation of debts. Later Lincoln wrote impatiently that he had "expected to see you all sooner" and closed with "Kiss and love the dear rascals." These were the sort of letters that an understanding and adjusted couple would write.

When the term in Congress was over, Lincoln returned to Springfield, to the practice of law and the pursuit of politics. Mary was a help to her husband; she had influential family connections; she could guard against social blunders; she read books for Lincoln; she understood politics and was a good judge of character; she carried on the church responsibilities for the pair; she could entertain and charm visiting politicians. In short, she was the wife Lincoln needed.

III

How CAN ONE SUMMARIZE twenty-two years of married life—the endless round of domestic duties, the cycle of birth and growth, the silent adjustments of man and wife? Springfield was home to the Lincolns. The house on Eighth Street was where their children grew up. Every foot, every inch of it had memories, suggestions of the compromises and truces, the shared joys and griefs, the whispered hopes and silent dreams that make up a marriage. Little Eddy died in his fourth year, but his place was filled by two more sons, the ubiquitous and exuberant Tad, with his slight stammer, and bright little Willie, who was to die in Washington in 1862. Everyone agreed that the Lincolns were devoted parents. Perhaps they were overindulgent, and perhaps they loved their children too much. But any mother who could bring up three of four children in an age of terrific infant mortality, when cholera epidemics swept the country, before the days of the most rudimentary sanitation or sewerage, must have been a competent one.

A lawyer's income is irregular and somewhat uncertain, and Mary Todd Lincoln had at times to manage with meager resources. She did her own and the boys' sewing and sometimes did all the cooking for the family. When he was home, Mr. Lincoln milked the cow, curried the horse, and chopped wood for the stove. There was no time to plant and grow flowers about the place; even the garden the Lincolns tried one year was too much of a burden.

Springfield store records tell a good deal about this family of Lincolns. The books of John Williams & Co., drygoods merchants, carry such items as "2½ yds. Muslin per Lady," "1 pair Boys Boots," "4½ yds. Velvet Ribbon @ .06¼," "½ lb Gun Powder Tea @ 1.25," "2 pair Heavy Drawers @ 1.25," and "36 yds Buff Linen @ .25"—all charged to the Lincoln account. At Corneau & Diller's drugstore their purchases included "Castor Oil," "Calomel," "Bottle Vermifuge," "1 paper Horse Powder," "2 bottles Extract Vanella," "Cough Candy," "Toilet Soap," and more than one "Bottle Allen's Restorative." Tradition has it that Mary Lincoln was a shopper difficult to please and that she frequently exchanged goods she had purchased.

The Lincolns had their share in the social life of Springfield. There were teas and dinners, even though Mrs. Lincoln sometimes had to make up for them by a scanty everyday table. The children as well as the grown-ups had their parties. On one special occasion the Lincolns issued over five hundred invitations to an entertainment, and more than three hundred persons actually attended the gathering at the Eighth Street residence. Letters of the period frequently mention "Mr. Lincoln & Cousin Mary" as being present at suppers, at political receptions, at charity socials.

Mary's sister has left a picture of the Lincolns at this time: "Mr. Lincoln enjoyed his home and he and Mary idolized their children. So far as I could see there was complete harmony and loving kindness between Mary and her husband, consideration for each other's wishes and a taste for the same books. They seemed congenial in all things."

IV

IT IS A MISTAKE, however, to think of this marriage as one of un-interrupted happiness and tranquility. The Lincolns had sharply con-trasting personalities, and there was friction, as in every home. Mary had difficulties with housemaids, icemen, storekeepers, and delivery boys, and her husband must have understood that her outbursts of temper were connected directly with the violent headaches of which she had com-plained for years. When there was trouble, Mary Lincoln's temper some-times got the better of her, and she would become momentarily irrespon-sible. There were many pressures beating on this woman, and she was not adapted either by temperament or by training to make a successful ad-justment. Lincoln's law practice kept him on the circuit nearly half of the year, leaving his wife with two or three small children anxiously worry-ing at Springfield. There is something pathetic in Mary Lincoln's confi-dence to a neighbor: "She always said that if her husband had stayed at home as he ought to that she could love him better. . . ."

And when Lincoln was at home, there were disagreements that some-times became tempestuous. Mrs. Lincoln could never get used to seeing her husband stretched out on the floor of the parlor, reading; and Lincoln could never break himself of the habit of answering the doorbell in his shirt sleeves or of using his own spoon in the sugar bowl. He was a man of long silences and brooding melancholy; she wanted lively talk and gay company. There were disputes over the children and how they should be trained. And there was the constant problem of servants, who were, for the most part, idle and inefficient and utterly unable to get along with the temperamental Mrs. Lincoln. After one particularly bad wrangle with a new servant girl, Mary sighed: "Well, one thing is certain: If Mr. Lincoln should happen to die, his spirit will never find me living outside the boundaries of a slave state."

When the strain became too great, Mrs. Lincoln would, as Herndon put it, "get the devil in her" and fly up in uncontrollable anger. At such times Lincoln would first of all ignore her. Then, if she did not calm down, he would take one of the children and leave the house until her fury was spent. There are a number of stories about these rages of hers; Springfield gossips were to smack their lips over them for fifty years. One man recalled passing the Lincoln house one Sunday and seeing "a woman chasing a man with a table knife or butcher knife in her hand"; when they came to a group of Springfield worthies returning from church, Lincoln "turned suddenly around, caught his wife by the shoulder with one hand and with the other caught his wife at the heavy end, her hips, if you please, and quickly hustled her to the back door of his house and . . . pushed her in, at the same time . . . spanking her heavy end, saying . . . 'There, d—n it, now stay in the house and don't disgrace us before the eyes of the world.' "

Once, so the story goes, Mary "blazed away with her sharp and sarcastic tongue" at a man who called at the house on business. She called him "a dirty villain—a vile creature & the like." When he complained to Lincoln, that unchivalrous gentleman is supposed to have said: *"Friend* . . . , can't you endure this one wrong . . . for old friendship's sake while I have had to bear it without complaint and without a murmur for lo these last fifteen years?"

Not all the temper, rumor had it, was on one side. One day Springfield citizens were shocked to see Mrs. Lincoln ejected forcibly from the Lincoln house, her husband shouting: "You make the house intolerable, damn you, get out of it."

One cannot ignore or dismiss such incidents. At the same time, it ought to be remembered that such disturbances were not the usual thing in the Lincoln home. In every marriage there are tensions and stresses, and in many marriages the partners may lose their tempers. Furthermore, such stories are of the kind likely to be exaggerated and repeated with endless variations. Most such anecdotes come from unreliable sources and were recorded long after the event. That Mary Lincoln lost control of herself at times is admitted. Against this should be set the facts that she was a faithful and loving wife, that she was a capable, if indulgent, mother, that she managed a growing household with commendable economy, that she performed graciously her duties as wife of a leading politician and lawyer. If storms occasionally struck the Lincoln house with unusual violence, disaster was avoided by the spirit of tender love and deep understanding which united the couple around their home and children. James Gourley, who lived next door to the Lincolns for nineteen years, gave a pretty fair verdict: "Mrs & Mr Lincoln were good neighbors."

The history of Mary Lincoln in the White House is another story, too long and too painful to be related here. Subject to the pitiless searchlight of unfavorable publicity, engulfed in the tidal wave of hate engendered by the war, bruised by the terrific responsibilities of her position, and desolated by intolerable grief, first over the death of a dearly loved son and then over the assassination of a husband more than life to her, her mind gave way. In her last tragic years, in that ceaseless seeking for peace which sent her searching over two continents, finally to seal herself in a shuttered, candle-lit room in Springfield, her mind must often have wandered back—to the days of her marriage, to the birth of her children, to home and husband. She counted over her hours of past happiness like a rosary. Endlessly she fingered the gold wedding ring inscribed: "Love is Eternal." And as her wretchedly aching brain relived the past, she could clearly remember two things: she was Mrs. Abraham Lincoln, and she had made her husband a home.

T. S. Eliot

TRADITION AND THE INDIVIDUAL TALENT

I

IN ENGLISH WRITING we seldom speak of tradition, though we occasionally apply its name in deploring its absence. We cannot refer to "the tradition" or to "a tradition"; at most, we employ the adjective in saying that the poetry of So-and-so is "traditional" or even "too traditional." Seldom, perhaps, does the word appear except in a phrase of censure. If otherwise, it is vaguely approbative, with the implication, as to the work approved, of some pleasing archæological reconstruction. You can hardly make the word agreeable to English ears without this comfortable reference to the reassuring science of archæology.

Certainly the word is not likely to appear in our appreciations of living or dead writers. Every nation, every race, has not only its own creative, but its own critical turn of mind; and is even more oblivious of the shortcomings and limitations of its critical habits than of those of its creative genius. We know, or think we know, from the enormous mass of critical writing that has appeared in the French language the critical method or habit of the French; we only conclude (we are such unconscious people) that the French are "more critical" than we, and sometimes even plume ourselves a little with the fact, as if the French were the less spontaneous. Perhaps they are; but we might remind ourselves that criticism is as inevitable as breathing, and that we should be none the worse for articulating what passes in our minds when we read a book and feel an emotion about it, for criticizing our own minds in their work of criticism.

From *The Sacred Wood: Essays on Poetry and Criticism*, 1921. Subsequently published in *Selected Essays: New Edition*. Copyright 1932, 1936, 1950 by Harcourt, Brace & World, Inc. Copyright © 1960, 1964 by T. S. Eliot. Reprinted by permission of the publishers.

One of the facts that might come to light in this process is our tendency to insist, when we praise a poet, upon those aspects of his work in which he least resembles anyone else. In these aspects or parts of his work we pretend to find what is individual, what is the peculiar essence of the man. We dwell with satisfaction upon the poet's difference from his predecessors, especially his immediate predecessors; we endeavor to find something that can be isolated in order to be enjoyed. Whereas if we approach a poet without this prejudice we shall often find that not only the best, but the most individual parts of his work may be those in which the dead poets, his ancestors, assert their immortality most vigorously. And I do not mean the impressionable period of adolescence, but the period of full maturity.

Yet if the only form of tradition, of handing down, consisted in following the ways of the immediate generation before us in a blind or timid adherence to its successes, "tradition" should positively be discouraged. We have seen many such simple currents soon lost in the sand; and novelty is better than repetition. Tradition is a matter of much wider significance. It cannot be inherited, and if you want it you must obtain it by great labour. It involves, in the first place, the historical sense, which we may call nearly indispensable to anyone who would continue to be a poet beyond his twenty-fifth year; and the historical sense involves a perception, not only of the pastness of the past, but of its presence; the historical sense compels a man to write not merely with his own generation in his bones, but with a feeling that the whole of the literature of Europe from Homer and within it the whole of the literature of his own country has a simultaneous existence and composes a simultaneous order. This historical sense, which is a sense of the timeless as well as of the temporal and of the timeless and of the temporal together, is what makes a writer traditional. And it is at the same time what makes a writer most acutely conscious of his place in time, of his contemporaneity.

No poet, no artist of any art, has his complete meaning alone. His significance, his appreciation is the appreciation of his relation to the dead poets and artists. You cannot value him alone; you must set him, for contrast and comparison, among the dead. I mean this as a principle of æsthetic, not merely historical, criticism. The necessity that he shall conform, that he shall cohere, is not one-sided; what happens when a new work of art is created is something that happens simultaneously to all the works of art which preceded it. The existing monuments form an ideal order among themselves, which is modified by the introduction of the new (the really new) work of art among them. The existing order is complete before the new work arrives; for order to persist after the supervention of novelty, the *whole* existing order must be, if ever so slightly, altered; and so the relations, proportions, values of each work of art toward the whole are readjusted; and this is conformity between the old and the new. Whoever has approved this idea of order, of the form of European, of English literature, will not find it preposterous that the past should be altered by the present as much as the present is directed by the past. And the poet who is aware of this will be aware of great difficulties and responsibilities.

In a peculiar sense he will be aware also that he must inevitably be judged by the standards of the past. I say judged, not amputated, by them; not judged to be as good as, or worse or better than, the dead; and certainly not judged by the canons of dead critics. It is a judgment, a comparison, in which two things are measured by each other. To conform merely would be for the new work not really to conform at all; it would not be new, and would therefore not be a work of art. And we do not quite say that the new is more valuable because it fits in; but its fitting in is a test of its value—a test, it is true, which can only be slowly and cautiously applied, for we are none of us infallible judges of conformity. We say: it appears to conform, and is perhaps individual, or it appears individual, and may conform; but we are hardly likely to find that it is one and not the other.

To proceed to a more intelligible exposition of the relation of the poet to the past: he can neither take the past as a lump, an indiscriminate bolus, nor can he form himself wholly on one or two private admirations, nor can he form himself wholly upon one preferred period. The first course is inadmissible, the second is an important experience of youth, and the third is a pleasant and highly desirable supplement. The poet must be very conscious of the main current, which does not at all flow invariably through the most distinguished reputations. He must be quite aware of the obvious fact that art never improves, but that the material of art is never quite the same. He must be aware that the mind of Europe—the mind of his own country—a mind which he learns in time to be much more important than his own private mind—is a mind which changes, and that this change is a development which abandons nothing *en route*, which does not superannuate either Shakespeare, or Homer, or the rock drawing of the Magdalenian draughtsmen. That this development, refinement perhaps, complication certainly, is not, from the point of view of the artist, any improvement. Perhaps not even an improvement from the point of view of the psychologist or not to the extent which we imagine; perhaps only in the end based upon a complication in economics and machinery. But the difference between the present and the past is that the conscious present is an awareness of the past in a way and to an extent which the past's awareness of itself cannot show.

Some one said: "The dead writers are remote from us because we *know* so much more than they did." Precisely, and they are that which we know.

I am alive to a usual objection to what is clearly part of my programme for the *métier* of poetry. The objection is that the doctrine requires a ridiculous amount of erudition (pedantry), a claim which can be rejected by appeal to the lives of poets in any pantheon. It will even be affirmed that much learning deadens or perverts poetic sensibility. While, however, we persist in believing that a poet ought to know as much as will not encroach upon his necessary receptivity and necessary laziness, it is not desirable to confine knowledge to whatever can be put into a useful shape for examinations, drawing-rooms, or the still more pretentious modes of publicity. Some can absorb knowledge, the more tardy must sweat for it. Shakespeare acquired more essential history from Plutarch than most men could from the whole British Museum. What is to be insisted upon is that the poet must develop or procure the consciousness of the past and that he should continue to develop this consciousness throughout his career.

What happens is a continual surrender of himself as he is at the moment to something which is more valuable. The progress of an artist is a continual self-sacrifice, a continual extinction of personality.

There remains to define this process of depersonalization and its relation to the sense of tradition. It is in this depersonalization that art may be said to approach the condition of science. I shall, therefore, invite you to consider, as a suggestive analogy, the action which takes place when a bit of finely filiated platinum is introduced into a chamber containing oxygen and sulphur dioxide.

II

HONEST CRITICISM and sensitive appreciation is directed not upon the poet but upon the poetry. If we attend to the confused cries of the newspaper critics and the susurrus of popular repetition that follows, we shall hear the names of poets in great numbers; if we seek not Blue-book knowledge but the enjoyment of poetry, and ask for a poem, we shall seldom find it. In the last article I tried to point out the importance of the relation of the poem to other poems by other authors, and suggested the conception of poetry as a living whole of all the poetry that has ever been written. The other aspect of this Impersonal theory of poetry is the relation of the poem to its author. And I hinted, by an analogy, that the mind of the mature poet differs from that of the immature one not precisely in any valuation of "personality," not being necessarily more interesting, or having "more to say," but rather by being a more finely perfected medium in which special, or very varied, feelings are at liberty to enter into new combinations.

The analogy was that of the catalyst. When the two gases previously mentioned are mixed in the presence of a filament of platinum, they form sulphurous acid. This combination takes place only if the platinum is present; nevertheless the newly formed acid contains no trace of platinum, and the platinum itself is apparently unaffected; has remained inert, neutral, and unchanged. The mind of the poet is the shred of platinum. It may partly or exclusively operate upon the experience of the man himself; but, the more perfect the artist, the more completely separate in him will be the man who suffers and the mind which creates; the more per-

fectly will the mind digest and transmute the passions which are its
material.

The experience, you will notice, the elements which enter the presence of the transforming catalyst, are of two kinds: emotions and feelings. The effect of a work of art upon the person who enjoys it is an
experience different in kind from any experience not of art. It may be
formed out of one emotion, or may be a combination of several; and
various feelings, inhering for the writer in particular words or phrases or
images, may be added to compose the final result. Or great poetry may be
made without the direct use of any emotion whatever: composed out of
feelings solely. Canto XV of the *Inferno* (Brunetto Latini) is a working
up of the emotion evident in the situation; but the effect, though single as
that of any work of art, is obtained by considerable complexity of detail.
The last quatrain gives an image, a feeling attaching to an image, which
"came," which did not develop simply out of what precedes, but which
was probably in suspension in the poet's mind until the proper combination arrived for it to add itself to. The poet's mind is in fact a receptacle
for seizing and storing up numberless feelings, phrases, images, which
remain there until all the particles which can unite to form a new compound are present together.

If you compare several representative passages of the greatest poetry
you see how great is the variety of types of combination, and also how
completely any semi-ethical criterion of "sublimity" misses the mark. For
it is not the "greatness," the intensity, of the emotions, the components,
but the intensity of the artistic process, the pressure, so to speak, under
which the fusion takes place, that counts. The episode of Paolo and
Francesca employs a definite emotion, but the intensity of the poetry is
something quite different from whatever intensity in the supposed experience it may give the impression of. It is no more intense, furthermore,
than Canto XXVI, the voyage of Ulysses, which has not the direct dependence upon an emotion. Great variety is possible in the process of
transmutation of emotion: the murder of Agamemnon, or the agony of
Othello, gives an artistic effect apparently closer to a possible original
than the scenes from Dante. In the *Agamemnon*, the artistic emotion approximates to the emotion of an actual spectator; in *Othello* to the emotion
of the protagonist himself. But the difference between art and the event is
always absolute; the combination which is the murder of Agamemnon is
probably as complex as that which is the voyage of Ulysses. In either case
there has been a fusion of elements. The ode of Keats contains a number of
feelings which have nothing particular to do with the nightingale, but
which the nightingale, partly, perhaps, because of its attractive name, and
partly because of its reputation, served to bring together.

The point of view which I am struggling to attack is perhaps related
to the metaphysical theory of the substantial unity of the soul: for my
meaning is, that the poet has, not a "personality" to express, but a particular medium, which is only a medium and not a personality, in which

JEAN-PAUL SARTRE

Photo Pic

LEARNED HAND

impressions and experiences combine in peculiar and unexpected ways. Impressions and experiences which are important for the man may take no place in the poetry, and those which become important in the poetry may play quite a negligible part in the man, the personality.

I will quote a passage which is unfamiliar enough to be regarded with fresh attention in the light—or darkness—of these observations:

> And now methinks I could e'en chide myself
> For doating on her beauty, though her death
> Shall be revenged after no common action.
> Does the silkworm expend her yellow labours
> For thee? For thee does she undo herself?
> Are lordships sold to maintain ladyships
> For the poor benefit of a bewildering minute?
> Why does yon fellow falsify highways,
> And put his life between the judge's lips,
> To refine such a thing—keeps horse and men
> To beat their valours for her? . . .

In this passage (as is evident if it is taken in its context) there is a combination of positive and negative emotions: an intensely strong attraction toward beauty and an equally intense fascination by the ugliness which is contrasted with it and which destroys it. This balance of contrasted emotion is in the dramatic situation to which the speech is pertinent, but that situation alone is inadequate to it. This is, so to speak, the structural emotion, provided by the drama. But the whole effect, the dominant tone, is due to the fact that a number of floating feelings, having an affinity to this emotion by no means superficially evident, have combined with it to give us a new art emotion.

It is not in his personal emotions, the emotions provoked by particular events in his life, that the poet is in any way remarkable or interesting. His particular emotions may be simple, or crude, or flat. The emotion in his poetry will be a very complex thing, but not with the complexity of the emotions of people who have very complex or unusual emotions in life. One error, in fact, of eccentricity in poetry is to seek for new human emotions to express; and in this search for novelty in the wrong place it discovers the perverse. The business of the poet is not to find new emotions, but to use the ordinary ones and, in working them up into poetry, to express feelings which are not in actual emotions at all. And emotions which he has never experienced will serve his turn as well as those familiar to him. Consequently, we must believe that "emotion recollected in tranquillity" is an inexact formula. For it is neither emotion, nor recollection, nor, without distortion of meaning, tranquillity. It is a concentration, and a new thing resulting from the concentration, of a very great number of experiences which to the practical and active person would not seem to be experiences at all; it is a concentration which does not happen consciously or of deliberation. These experiences are not "recollected," and they finally unite in an atmosphere which is "tranquil" only in that it is a passive attending upon the event. Of course this is not quite the whole story. There is a great deal, in the writing of poetry, which must be conscious and deliberate. In fact, the bad poet is usually unconscious where he ought to be conscious, and conscious where he ought to be unconscious. Both errors tend to make him "personal." Poetry is not a turning loose of emotion, but an escape from emotion; it is not the expression of personality, but an escape from personality. But, of course, only those who have personality and emotions know what it means to want to escape from these things.

III

ὁ δὲ νοῦ, ἴσω, θειότερόν τι καὶ ἀπαθές ἐστιν

THIS ESSAY PROPOSES to halt at the frontier of metaphysics or mysticism, and confine itself to such practical conclusions as can be applied by the responsible person interested in poetry. To divert interest from the poet to the poetry is a laudable aim: for it would conduce to a juster estimation of actual poetry, good and bad. There are many people who appreciate the expression of sincere emotion in verse, and there is a smaller number of people who can appreciate technical excellence. But very few know when there is expression of *significant* emotion, emotion which has its life in the poem and not in the history of the poet. The emotion of art is impersonal. And the poet cannot reach this impersonality without surrendering himself wholly to the work to be done. And he is not likely to know what is to be done unless he lives in what is not merely the present, but the present moment of the past, unless he is conscious, not of what is dead, but of what is already living.

Learned Hand

THE SPIRIT OF LIBERTY

IN THE critical World War II year of 1944 a vast "I Am an American Day" ceremony was held in Central Park, New York City, on May 21. Many thousands of people were present, including a large number of new citizens. Learned Hand's brief address was so eloquent and so moving that the text immediately became the object of wide demand. It was quickly printed and reprinted and also put into anthologies. The impact was so great that the speaker was invited to address a similar gathering the next year. [Ed.]

WE HAVE GATHERED HERE to affirm a faith, a faith in a common purpose, a common conviction, a common devotion. Some of us have chosen America as the land of our adoption; the rest have come from those who did the same. For this reason we have some right to consider ourselves a picked group, a group of those who had the courage to break from the past and brave the dangers and the loneliness of a strange land. What was the object that nerved us, or those who went before us, to this choice? We sought liberty; freedom from oppression, freedom from want, freedom to be ourselves. This we then sought; this we now believe that we are by way of winning. What do we mean when we say that first of all we seek liberty? I often wonder whether we do not rest our hopes too much upon constitutions, upon laws and upon courts. These are false hopes; believe me, these are false hopes. Liberty lies in the hearts of men and women; when it dies there, no constitution, no law, no court can save it; no constitution, no law, no court can even do much to help it. While it lies there it needs no constitution, no law, no court to save it. And what is this liberty which must lie in the hearts of men and women? It is not the ruthless, the unbridled will; it is not freedom to do as one likes. That is the denial of liberty, and leads straight to its overthrow. A society in which men recognize no check upon their freedom soon becomes a society where freedom is the possession of only a savage few; as we have learned to our sorrow.

What then is the spirit of liberty? I cannot define it; I can only tell you my own faith. The spirit of liberty is the spirit which is not too sure that it is right; the spirit of liberty is the spirit which seeks to understand the minds of other men and women; the spirit of liberty is the spirit which weighs their interest alongside its own without bias; the spirit of liberty remembers that not even a sparrow falls to earth unheeded; the spirit of liberty is the spirit of Him who, near two thousand years ago, taught mankind that lesson it has never learned, but has never quite forgotten;[1] that there may be a kingdom where the least shall be heard and considered side by side with the greatest. And now in that spirit, that spirit of an America which has never been, and which may never be; nay, which never will be except as the conscience and courage of Americans create it; yet in the spirit of that America which lies hidden in some form in the aspirations of us all; in the spirit of that America for which our young men are at this moment fighting and dying; in that spirit of liberty and of America I ask you to rise and with me pledge our faith in the glorious destiny of our beloved country.

[1] This clause was taken in substance from the following clause in H. G. Wells's *The Outline of History* (Vol. II, p. 632, George Newnes, Ltd., London): ". . . whose pitiless and difficult doctrine of self-abandonment and self-forgetfulness we can neither disregard nor yet bring ourselves to obey." L.H.

Joseph Hergesheimer

INTRODUCTION TO
THE RED BADGE OF COURAGE
BY STEPHEN CRANE

IT IS ONE OF THE MINOR TREACHERIES of time that twenty-nine years have vanished almost—as more than a quarter of a century—unnoticed since I first read *The Red Badge of Courage*. I was, then, fifteen years old, and beyond all doubt a better reader than I am now. I had an enormous enthusiasm for the books I liked, a private and unquestioned and passionate allegiance to them long ago diluted by my own experience and difficulties, and by the inevitable development of considerations not always admirable. I do not mean that I wouldn't, to-day, if I were reading it for the first time, completely surrender myself to Stephen Crane's young private of the Civil War; I would, of course; for his is a created story of inescapable fineness. But in the present I would regard it, in part at least, as a deliberate accomplishment in composed periods; while at fifteen it was a great and personal experience.

I read it at once upon its publication—books have a habit of reaching their specially right readers—and I was deeply engaged even before I had opened the straw-coloured buckram, printed in black and red and gold, of its binding. It had come to me widely heralded, borne on the excitement, the derision and praise and curiosity, its appearance had instantly upraised. I have no way of knowing what, at that day, made a large sale; it may be that the interest in *The Red Badge of Courage* was limited to a changelessly small superior public. It may be, but it isn't in my memory that it was; trying to recall those circumstances it seems to me that Crane's novel of battle brought out a very general, and heated, warfare in itself.

You see, it was everywhere regarded as fantastically modern, and one sentence in it, a paragraph, really, became particularly celebrated:

The red sun was pasted in the sky like a wafer.

That phrase, actually, was made into the standard, the flag—like the flag the youth himself twisted from a dying standard-bearer and carried forward—about which the climax of the action revolved. It was regarded in one camp as a superb piece of imagery, a line which invested one of the oldest of observations with a new and living freshness and vigour; and by the other as a strained and artificial figure. When I reached it I hadn't, for that single instance, an entirely virgin attention; already the struggle had given it an exaggerated importance; and I was appropriately amazed. I thought of an actual red wafer, such as druggists fixed to their bottles; it had a definite, a limited, size for me, an established clear vermilion colour.

I thought of it, for the moment, constantly, repeating it for the benefit of any who could be persuaded to listen; I was, in a minute way, part of the noise that made it notable. But there was no doubt about my opinion of such a remarkable, and modern, paragraph—I was convinced that it was marvellous. The sun itself was diminished, in the sky like a wafer, a wafer of glazed vermilion paper with a regularly serrated edge. For the rest, I felt, together with my enthusiasm, an impatience at what, then, appeared to be a large lack of story; I had no recognition of an underlying structure and ordered whole.

It was, however, a slight compensation for the passage of so many swift years that I could, now, grasp that: the order and progression, the singleness of purpose, were exact . . . and not entirely modern, even in 1895. It was the story of the birth, in a boy, of a knowledge of himself and of self-command; the beginning, in short, of the fixed pattern of maturity. And, as was usual in such forms, it was a birth out of a tragic agony and doubt, a success scarcely won from the edge of eternal defeat.

What, I realized, had worried me at fifteen was that *The Red Badge of Courage* was not at all the story of the practically nameless youth of whom, apparently, it was written; Crane's interest in him, as an individual, was small—he was present for what, as universally as possible, he represented. This coldness to the boy himself, this aloofness from a specific sympathy—from, in reality, sentimentality—left me, too, the implicated reader, more than a little cold. It was the true, the singular, mark of an authentic classical accomplishment; but at fifteen I wasn't aware of so much.

I was perfectly merged with the subject of the book, he was a vessel carrying me over a threatening sea; his undignified cowardice, the temporary spiritual meanness of flight, were mine; when he ran I ran, when he skulked I skulked; when, in the wavering line of the retreating wounded, he was asked where he had been hit, my acute shame was his. Even the eventual firmness and triumph did not, completely, restore me to a necessary warm glow of reassurance. I had, it seemed, been studied by an essentially wise but, where I was intimately concerned, a detached intellect. Stephen Crane might have been a doctor exploring me, to my ultimate good, with frigid and unerring fingers.

I didn't then, and then I was abjectly synonymous with what is called the reading public, want to be so justly regarded, so unsparingly valued; what I did want was to be filled with praise, to hum with a beautiful valour rewarded by all material good; I wanted to be decorated before all the files of men alive, and before the loveliest lady imaginable. This Stephen Crane would not allow; and so my enthusiasm was a little subdued; privately I was even slightly bored; yet, in spite of that, *The Red Badge of Courage* had my devoted, if youngly uncritical, support.

I was not then, naturally, separately conscious of its words, they had to be indicated to me; I discovered no pleasure in them as accomplishments and ends; but I was highly responsive to their effects. Two novels, in that past, made clearer than all others what might, perhaps, be called scenes in nature—*The Red Badge of Courage* and *Jane Eyre*. The battlefields and wooded hills, the ruined peace of little valleys, of the first, shrouded in the smoke of guns, were as vivid as the headlong action. The men dead and dying, their sounds and pallors and last rigidity, held a fearful reality which came from the perfection of Stephen Crane's visualization, a quality not alone optical:

He saw them emotionally, in the mystery of creative perception, and put them down in a simplicity of words that cast back, like the reflection in a clear mirror, every leaf and hurt that passed through his imagination. The transition from his conception to its formal expression was as instantaneous, as untroubled, as the flight of a bar of music to a receptive brain and heart.

The whole form of *The Red Badge of Courage* is amazing for, as much as anything, its directness and candour. That was not, merely, the result of an æsthetic sophistication—simplicity usually is—but the effect on the entire book of the character of the pictured youth. He is singularly candid; and all the sentences, all the pages, have an air of coming from him. Even the lyrical beauty of the objective descriptions, impossible for him to formulate, take the shape and fervour of his inherited reactions to them. When, with his fellows, he moves across a field, the field and the youth are seen together; he walks or desperately charges and the grass is beaten down by his passage; he marches over the roads in loose formation or is momentarily soothed by the peace of casual meadows . . . the shuffling tramp of feet accompanies him or he is set in a calm with idly floating butterflies.

And, through it all, the army, the soldiers, talk; they talk in a dialect which seems hopelessly arbitrary, a mere scrambling of disjointed syllables; but actually it is as easy to read, its intent is as plain, as the wording on a sign-board. It's the actual living American language, or, rather, the language that was American—the talk of multitudes of small towns and farming districts. It isn't so much a dialect as it is the flexible and successful record of what promised to be the new language of a new land. This, in the sequel, it did not become; a new land, for reasons inherent in the fatality of humanity, failed to appear; but its pastoral speech, as valid and charming as the rustic measures in Theocritus, has been saved in *The Red Badge of Courage*.

There is, too—a part of Stephen Crane's accomplishment here—a strong sense of humour behind everything said; there isn't a breath, a suspicion, of satire; the spirit of the ludicrous, ungainly like the soldiers themselves, permeates their heated or philosophical or rebellious phrases. The men are eternally complaining or arguing or predicting; they are always beginning bitter quarrels that fade into diminishing curses in turn obliterated by the roll of the cannon. It is possible that no book had ever been written with so much and such a literal transcription of general and particularized talk.

That, the humour investing the things said, was a result of the detached attitude of which, at fifteen, I was critical. Crane was not his youth, the voice of one was not the voice of the other; no, the writer was a completely understanding listener. An unfailing sense of proportion—the heart of humour—gave each uttered sound its true place in the harmony of the whole, no one was covered with decorative ribbons in the face of a silent and respectful masculine world, under the tender gaze of an appealing loveliness. The tumult of the world was not stopped in order to let one voice dominate fate and the law of physics . . . in the character of the youth I was slovenly in speech and often hysterical in expression. I had a small habit of mumbling to myself; and it was evident that a great deal I said was humiliating nonsense. Yes, it was funny! The difference between what I was and what I thought and said of myself was made too easily discoverable for my pleasure.

The controversy over what was referred to as the extremely modern form of *The Red Badge of Courage* has, naturally and long ago, died; and what, on that plane, remains is the realization that it is neither modern nor conservative. There is literally nothing in its treatment which suggests the period that saw it produced; its underlying spirit belongs to no current fashion. Its situations and development were seen not in relation to what else was then being written—it wasn't, in that sense, a piece of the time—but as independent and unliterary facts. Being, in a very fine sense indeed, literature it wasn't concerned with literary values at all. It must have fallen into its period with the effect of a shell from a heavy mortar. The result was as final—thereafter all novels about war must be different; the old pretentious attack was for ever obliterated.

Novels such as, at fifteen, I demanded would continue to satisfy the private vanity of the public; and quite admirable they were; but they had no part in the engagement that held Stephen Crane. They came and went; but here, after twenty-nine years, I was writing a preface to a book that had survived death—the story of a boy who went to war, who fell a victim to fear, and who recovered. That pattern would not have been sufficient for the writers of current successes; in it they could not have discovered a pattern at all. No romance! Nothing prepared at the beginning and no more solved at the end. Yes, and profane . . . at the expense of God, pronounced Gawd, and the dignity of men. Where, in all *The Red Badge of Courage*, was the nobility of a cause even hinted at? Where was Lincoln bearing his benevolence like a tendered pardon to fault? Where was Grant with his half-consumed cigar? Where, above everything, was General Lee?

The truth is that they were absent for the reason that they weren't needed; they could have added nothing to Crane's narrative of the Civil War. In writing, so late, the word narrative, which is supposed to carry a different meaning from the word novel, I realize that I am inviting the patronage of the learned. A narrative is not a novel. But in such a confusion of definitions I was, at least, deliberate. *The Red Badge of Courage* is both a novel and a narrative; since the difference between realism and romance has never been defined it may, as well, be both romantic and realistic. At once, I mean. I have an idea, too, that it is poetry, lyrical as well as epic; no one, certainly, can deny that it is completely classic in its movement, its pace and return.

It is all these things, and, in addition, it is life; and it can no more be neatly fitted into a definition than can the mystery of birth. As a child it disturbed and excited and challenged me; and as a man—it would be more precise to say as a writer—it satisfies me. A tranquil countryside is torn for a little by human strife, the stillness is broken by a hideous clamour of explosions and cries, and then the quiet comes back with evening. The dead are removed, the trees are healed, the brooks are again softly audible. Wars are unimportant; individuals are unimportant—actually there are no individuals, but only connected and momentary activities, one fading into the other in a march from dark to dark. That is the burden of *The Red Badge of Courage*, it is the meaning of its title, since courage is not a means but an end. Its incentives are chimeras.

John Hersey

HIROSHIMA

I · A Noiseless Flash

A T EXACTLY fifteen minutes past eight in the morning, on August 6, 1945, Japanese time, at the moment when the atomic bomb flashed above Hiroshima, Miss Toshiko Sasaki, a clerk in the personnel department of the East Asia Tin Works, had just sat down at her place in the plant office and was turning her head to speak to the girl at the next desk. At that same moment, Dr. Masakazu Fujii was settling down cross-legged to read the Osaka *Asahi* on the porch of his private hospital, overhanging one of the seven deltaic rivers which divide Hiroshima; Mrs. Hatsuyo Nakamura, a tailor's widow, stood by the window of her kitchen, watching a neighbor tearing down his house because it lay in the path of an air-raid-defense fire lane; Father Wilhelm Kleinsorge, a German priest of the Society of Jesus, reclined in his underwear on a cot on the top floor of his order's three-story mission house, reading a Jesuit magazine, *Stimmen der Zeit;* Dr. Terufumi Sasaki, a young member of the surgical staff of the city's large, modern Red Cross Hospital, walked along one of the hospital corridors with a blood specimen for a Wassermann test in his hand; and the Reverend Mr. Kiyoshi Tanimoto, pastor of the Hiroshima Methodist Church, paused at the door of a rich man's house in Koi, the city's western suburb, and prepared to unload a handcart full of things he had evacuated from town in fear of the massive B-29 raid which everyone expected Hiroshima to suffer. A hundred thousand people were killed by the atomic bomb, and these six were among the survivors. They still wonder why they lived when so many others died. Each of them counts

---

Published 1946. Copyright 1946 by John Hersey. Originally published in *The New Yorker.*

many small items of chance or volition—a step taken in time, a decision to go indoors, catching one streetcar instead of the next—that spared him. And now each knows that in the act of survival he lived a dozen lives and saw more death than he ever thought he would see. At the time, none of them knew anything.

The Reverend Mr. Tanimoto got up at five o'clock that morning. He was alone in the parsonage, because for some time his wife had been commuting with their year-old baby to spend nights with a friend in Ushida, a suburb to the north. Of all the important cities of Japan, only two, Kyoto and Hiroshima, had not been visited in strength by B-san, or Mr. B, as the Japanese, with a mixture of respect and unhappy familiarity, called the B-29; and Mr. Tanimoto, like all his neighbors and friends, was almost sick with anxiety. He had heard uncomfortably detailed accounts of mass raids on Kure, Iwakuni, Tokuyama, and other nearby towns; he was sure Hiroshima's turn would come soon. He had slept badly the night before, because there had been several air-raid warnings. Hiroshima had been getting such warnings almost every night for weeks, for at that time the B-29s were using Lake Biwa, northeast of Hiroshima, as a rendezvous point, and no matter what city the Americans planned to hit, the Super-fortresses streamed in over the coast near Hiroshima. The frequency of the warnings and the continued abstinence of Mr. B with respect to Hiroshima had made its citizens jittery; a rumor was going around that the Americans were saving something special for the city.

Mr. Tanimoto is a small man, quick to talk, laugh, and cry. He wears his black hair parted in the middle and rather long; the prominence of the frontal bones just above his eyebrows and the smallness of his mustache, mouth, and chin give him a strange, old-young look, boyish and yet wise, weak and yet fiery. He moves nervously and fast, but with a restraint which suggests that he is a cautious, thoughtful man. He showed, indeed, just those qualities in the uneasy days before the bomb fell. Besides having his wife spend the nights in Ushida, Mr. Tanimoto had been carrying all the portable things from his church, in the close-packed residential district called Nagaragawa, to a house that belonged to a rayon manufacturer in Koi, two miles from the center of town. The rayon man, a Mr. Matsui, had opened his then unoccupied estate to a large number of his friends and acquaintances, so that they might evacuate whatever they wished to a safe distance from the probable target area. Mr. Tanimoto had had no difficulty in moving chairs, hymnals, Bibles, altar gear, and church records by pushcart himself, but the organ console and an upright piano required some aid. A friend of his named Matsuo had, the day before, helped him get the piano out to Koi; in return, he had promised this day to assist Mr. Matsuo in hauling out a daughter's belongings. That is why he had risen so early.

Mr. Tanimoto cooked his own breakfast. He felt awfully tired. The effort of moving the piano the day before, a sleepless night, weeks of worry and unbalanced diet, the cares of his parish—all combined to make him feel hardly adequate to the new day's work. There was another thing, too: Mr. Tanimoto had studied theology at Emory University, in Atlanta, Georgia; he had graduated in 1940; he spoke excellent English; he dressed in American clothes; he had corresponded with many American friends right up to the time the war began; and among a people obsessed with a fear of being spied upon—perhaps almost obsessed himself—he found himself growing increasingly uneasy. The police had questioned him several times, and just a few days before, he had heard that an influential acquaintance, a Mr. Tanaka, a retired officer of the Toyo Kisen Kaisha steamship line, anti-Christian, a man famous in Hiroshima for his showy philanthropies and notorious for his personal tyrannies, had been telling people that Tanimoto should not be trusted. In compensation, to show himself publicly a good Japanese, Mr. Tanimoto had taken on the chairmanship of his local *tonarigumi*, or Neighborhood Association, and to his other duties and concerns this position had added the business of organizing air-raid defense for about twenty families.

Before six o'clock that morning, Mr. Tanimoto started for Mr. Matsuo's house. There he found that their burden was to be a *tansu*, a large Japanese cabinet, full of clothing and household goods. The two men set out. The morning was perfectly clear and so warm that the day promised to be uncomfortable. A few minutes after they started, the air-raid siren went off—a minute-long blast that warned of approaching planes but indicated to the people of Hiroshima only a slight degree of danger, since it sounded every morning at this time, when an American weather plane came over. The two men pulled and pushed the handcart through the city streets. Hiroshima was a fan-shaped city, lying mostly on the six islands formed by the seven estuarial rivers that branch out from the Ota River; its main commercial and residential districts, covering about four square miles in the center of the city, contained three-quarters of its population, which had been reduced by several evacuation programs from a wartime peak of 380,000 to about 245,000. Factories and other residential districts, or suburbs, lay compactly around the edges of the city. To the south were the docks, an airport, and the island-studded Inland Sea. A rim of mountains runs around the other three sides of the delta. Mr. Tanimoto and Mr. Matsuo took their way through the shopping center, already full of people, and across two of the rivers to the sloping streets of Koi, and up them to the outskirts and foothills. As they started up a valley away from the tight-ranked houses, the all-clear sounded. (The Japanese radar operators, detecting only three planes, supposed that they comprised a reconnaissance.) Pushing the handcart up to the rayon man's house was tiring, and the men, after they had maneuvered their load into the driveway and to the front steps, paused to rest awhile. They stood with a wing of the house between them and the city. Like most homes in this part of Japan, the house consisted of a wooden frame and wooden walls supporting a heavy tile roof. Its front hall, packed with rolls of bedding and clothing, looked like a cool cave full of fat cushions. Opposite the house, to the right of the front door, there was a large, finicky rock garden. There was no sound of planes. The morning was still; the place was cool and pleasant.

Then a tremendous flash of light cut across the sky. Mr. Tanimoto has a distinct recollection that it travelled from east to west, from the city toward the hills. It seemed a sheet of sun. Both he and Mr. Matsuo reacted in terror—and both had time to react (for they were 3,500 yards, or two miles, from the center of the explosion). Mr. Matsuo dashed up the front steps into the house and dived among the bedrolls and buried himself there. Mr. Tanimoto took four or five steps and threw himself between two big rocks in the garden. He bellied up very hard against one of them. As his face was against the stone, he did not see what happened. He felt a sudden pressure, and then splinters and pieces of board and fragments of tile fell on him. He heard no roar. (Almost no one in Hiroshima recalls hearing any noise of the bomb. But a fisherman in his sampan on the Inland Sea near Tsuzu, the man with whom Mr. Tanimoto's mother-in-law and sister-in-law were living, saw the flash and heard a tremendous explosion; he was nearly twenty miles from Hiroshima, but the thunder was greater than when the B-29s hit Iwakuni, only five miles away.)

When he dared, Mr. Tanimoto raised his head and saw that the rayon man's house had collapsed. He thought a bomb had fallen directly on it. Such clouds of dust had risen that there was a sort of twilight around. In panic, not thinking for the moment of Mr. Matsuo under the ruins, he dashed out into the street. He noticed as he ran that the concrete wall of the estate had fallen over—toward the house rather than away from it. In the street, the first thing he saw was a squad of soldiers who had been burrowing into the hillside opposite, making one of the thousands of dugouts in which the Japanese apparently intended to resist invasion, hill by hill, life for life; the soldiers were coming out of the hole, where they should have been safe, and blood was running from their heads, chests, and backs. They were silent and dazed.

Under what seemed to be a local dust cloud, the day grew darker and darker.

AT NEARLY MIDNIGHT, the night before the bomb was dropped, an announcer on the city's radio station said that about two hundred B-29s were approaching southern Honshu and advised the population of Hiroshima to evacuate to their designated "safe areas." Mrs. Hatsuyo Nakamura, the tailor's widow, who lived in the section called Nobori-cho and who had long had a habit of doing as she was told, got her three children —a ten-year-old boy, Toshio, an eight-year-old girl, Yaeko, and a five-year-old girl, Myeko—out of bed and dressed them and walked with them to the military area known as the East Parade Ground, on the

northeast edge of the city. There she unrolled some mats and the children
lay down on them. They slept until about two, when they were
awakened by the roar of the planes going over Hiroshima.

As soon as the planes had passed, Mrs. Nakamura started back with
her children. They reached home a little after two-thirty and she immediately turned on the radio, which, to her distress, was just then broad-
casting a fresh warning. When she looked at the children and saw how
tired they were, and when she thought of the number of trips they had
made in past weeks, all to no purpose, to the East Parade Ground, she
decided that in spite of the instructions on the radio, she simply could not
face starting out all over again. She put the children in their bedrolls on
the floor, lay down herself at three o'clock, and fell asleep at once, so
soundly that when planes passed over later, she did not waken to their
sound.

The siren jarred her awake at about seven. She arose, dressed
quickly, and hurried to the house of Mr. Nakamoto, the head of her
Neighborhood Association, and asked him what she should do. He said
that she should remain at home unless an urgent warning—a series of
intermittent blasts of the siren—was sounded. She returned home, lit the
stove in the kitchen, set some rice to cook, and sat down to read that
morning's Hiroshima *Chugoku*. To her relief, the all-clear sounded at
eight o'clock. She heard the children stirring, so she went and gave each
of them a handful of peanuts and told them to stay on their bedrolls,
because they were tired from the night's walk. She had hoped that they
would go back to sleep, but the man in the house directly to the south
began to make a terrible hullabaloo of hammering, wedging, ripping, and
splitting. The prefectural government, convinced, as everyone in Hiroshima was, that the city would be attacked soon, had begun to press with
threats and warnings for the completion of wide fire lanes, which, it was
hoped, might act in conjunction with the rivers to localize any fires
started by an incendiary raid; and the neighbor was reluctantly sacrificing
his home to the city's safety. Just the day before, the prefecture had
ordered all able-bodied girls from the secondary schools to spend a few
days helping to clear these lanes, and they started work soon after the all-
clear sounded.

Mrs. Nakamura went back to the kitchen, looked at the rice, and
began watching the man next door. At first, she was annoyed with him
for making so much noise, but then she was moved almost to tears by
pity. Her emotion was specifically directed toward her neighbor, tearing
down his home, board by board, at a time when there was so much
unavoidable destruction, but undoubtedly she also felt a generalized,
community pity, to say nothing of self-pity. She had not had an easy
time. Her husband, Isawa, had gone into the Army just after Myeko was
born, and she had heard nothing from or of him for a long time, until, on
March 5, 1942, she received a seven-word telegram: "Isawa died an honorable death at Singapore." She learned later that he had died on February

15th, the day Singapore fell, and that he had been a corporal. Isawa had been a not particularly prosperous tailor, and his only capital was a San-koku sewing machine. After his death, when his allotments stopped coming, Mrs. Nakamura got out the machine and began to take in piecework herself, and since then had supported the children, but poorly, by sewing.

As Mrs. Nakamura stood watching her neighbor, everything flashed whiter than any white she had ever seen. She did not notice what happened to the man next door; the reflex of a mother set her in motion toward her children. She had taken a single step (the house was 1,350 yards, or three-quarters of a mile, from the center of the explosion) when something picked her up and she seemed to fly into the next room over the raised sleeping platform, pursued by parts of her house.

Timbers fell around her as she landed, and a shower of tiles pommelled her; everything became dark, for she was buried. The debris did not cover her deeply. She rose up and freed herself. She heard a child cry, "Mother, help me!," and saw her youngest—Myeko, the five-year-old—buried up to her breast and unable to move. As Mrs. Nakamura started frantically to claw her way toward the baby, she could see or hear nothing of her other children.

In the days right before the bombing, Dr. Masakazu Fujii, being prosperous, hedonistic, and at the time not too busy, had been allowing himself the luxury of sleeping until nine or nine-thirty, but fortunately he had to get up early the morning the bomb was dropped to see a house guest off on a train. He rose at six, and half an hour later walked with his friend to the station, not far away, across two of the rivers. He was back home by seven, just as the siren sounded its sustained warning. He ate breakfast and then, because the morning was already hot, undressed down to his underwear and went out on the porch to read the paper. This porch—in fact, the whole building—was curiously constructed. Dr. Fujii was the proprietor of a peculiarly Japanese institution: a private, single-doctor hospital. This building, perched beside and over the water of the Kyo River, and next to the bridge of the same name, contained thirty rooms for thirty patients and their kinfolk—for, according to Japanese custom, when a person falls sick and goes to a hospital, one or more members of his family go and live there with him, to cook for him, bathe, massage, and read to him, and to offer incessant familial sympathy, without which a Japanese patient would be miserable indeed. Dr. Fujii had no beds—only straw mats—for his patients. He did, however, have all sorts of modern equipment: an X-ray machine, diathermy apparatus, and a fine tiled laboratory. The structure rested two-thirds on the land, one-third on piles over the tidal waters of the Kyo. This overhang, the part of the building where Dr. Fujii lived, was queer-looking, but it was cool in summer and from the porch, which faced away from the center of the city, the prospect of the river, with pleasure boats drifting up and down it, was always refreshing. Dr. Fujii had occasionally had anxious moments when the Ota and its mouth branches rose to flood, but the piling was apparently firm enough and the house had always held.

Dr. Fujii had been relatively idle for about a month because in July, as the number of untouched cities in Japan dwindled and as Hiroshima seemed more and more inevitably a target, he began turning patients away, on the ground that in case of a fire raid he would not be able to evacuate them. Now he had only two patients left—a woman from Yano, injured in the shoulder, and a young man of twenty-five recovering from burns he had suffered when the steel factory near Hiroshima in which he worked had been hit. Dr. Fujii had six nurses to tend his patients. His wife and children were safe; his wife and one son were living outside Osaka, and another son and two daughters were in the country on Kyushu. A niece was living with him, and a maid and a manservant. He had little to do and did not mind, for he had saved some money. At fifty, he was healthy, convivial, and calm, and he was pleased to pass the evenings drinking whiskey with friends, always sensibly and for the sake of conversation. Before the war, he had affected brands imported from Scotland and America; now he was perfectly satisfied with the best Japanese brand, Suntory.

Dr. Fujii sat down cross-legged in his underwear on the spotless matting of the porch, put on his glasses, and started reading the Osaka *Asahi*. He liked to read the Osaka news because his wife was there. He saw the flash. To him—faced away from the center and looking at his paper—it seemed a brilliant yellow. Startled, he began to rise to his feet. In that moment (he was 1,550 yards from the center), the hospital leaned behind his rising and, with a terrible ripping noise, toppled into the river. The Doctor, still in the act of getting to his feet, was thrown forward and around and over; he was buffeted and gripped; he lost track of everything, because things were so speeded up; he felt the water.

Dr. Fujii hardly had time to think that he was dying before he realized that he was alive, squeezed tightly by two long timbers in a V across his chest, like a morsel suspended between two huge chopsticks—held upright, so that he could not move, with his head miraculously above water and his torso and legs in it. The remains of his hospital were all around him in a mad assortment of splintered lumber and materials for the relief of pain. His left shoulder hurt terribly. His glasses were gone.

FATHER WILHELM KLEINSORGE, of the Society of Jesus, was, on the morning of the explosion, in rather frail condition. The Japanese wartime diet had not sustained him, and he felt the strain of being a foreigner in an increasingly xenophobic Japan; even a German, since the defeat of the Fatherland, was unpopular. Father Kleinsorge had, at thirty-eight, the look of a boy growing too fast—thin in the face, with a prominent Adam's apple, a hollow chest, dangling hands, big feet. He walked clumsily, leaning forward a little. He was tired all the time. To make matters worse, he had suffered for two days, along with Father Cieslik, a fellow-priest, from a rather painful and urgent diarrhea, which they blamed on the beans and black ration bread they were obliged to eat. Two other priests then living in the mission compound, which was in the Nobori-cho section—Father Superior LaSalle and Father Schiffer—had happily escaped this affliction.

Father Kleinsorge woke up about six the morning the bomb was dropped, and half an hour later—he was a bit tardy because of his sickness—he began to read Mass in the mission chapel, a small Japanese-style wooden building which was without pews, since its worshippers knelt on the usual Japanese matted floor, facing an altar graced with splendid silks, brass, silver, and heavy embroideries. This morning, a Monday, the only worshippers were Mr. Takemoto, a theological student living in the mission house; Mr. Fukai, the secretary of the diocese; Mrs. Murata, the mission's devoutly Christian housekeeper; and his fellow-priests. After Mass, while Father Kleinsorge was reading the Prayers of Thanksgiving, the siren sounded. He stopped the service and the missionaries retired across the compound to the bigger building. There, in his room on the ground floor, to the right of the front door, Father Kleinsorge changed into a military uniform which he had acquired when he was teaching at the Rokko Middle School in Kobe and which he wore during air-raid alerts.

After an alarm, Father Kleinsorge always went out and scanned the sky, and in this instance, when he stepped outside, he was glad to see only the single weather plane that flew over Hiroshima each day about this time. Satisfied that nothing would happen, he went in and breakfasted with the other Fathers on substitute coffee and ration bread, which, under the circumstances, was especially repugnant to him. The Fathers sat and talked awhile, until, at eight, they heard the all-clear. They went then to various parts of the building. Father Schiffer retired to his room to do some writing. Father Cieslik sat in his room in a straight chair with a pillow over his stomach to ease his pain, and read. Father Superior LaSalle stood at the window of his room, thinking. Father Kleinsorge went up to a room on the third floor, took off all his clothes except his underwear, and stretched out on his right side on a cot and began reading his *Stimmen der Zeit*.

After the terrible flash—which, Father Kleinsorge later realized, reminded him of something he had read as a boy about a large meteor colliding with the earth—he had time (since he was 1,400 yards from the center) for one thought: A bomb has fallen directly on us. Then, for a few seconds or minutes, he went out of his mind.

Father Kleinsorge never knew how he got out of the house. The next things he was conscious of were that he was wandering around in the mission's vegetable garden in his underwear, bleeding slightly from small cuts along his left flank; that all the buildings round about had fallen down except the Jesuits' mission house, which had long before been braced and double-braced by a priest named Gropper, who was terrified of earthquakes; that the day had turned dark; and that Murata-*san*, the housekeeper, was nearby, crying over and over, "*Shu Jesusu, awaremi tamai!* Our Lord Jesus, have pity on us!"

ON THE TRAIN on the way into Hiroshima from the country, where he lived with his mother, Dr. Terufumi Sasaki, the Red Cross Hospital surgeon, thought over an unpleasant nightmare he had had the night before. His mother's home was in Mukaihara, thirty miles from the city, and it took him two hours by train and tram to reach the hospital. He had slept uneasily all night and had wakened an hour earlier than usual, and, feeling sluggish and slightly feverish, had debated whether to go to the hospital at all; his sense of duty finally forced him to go, and he had started out on an earlier train than he took most mornings. The dream had particularly frightened him because it was so closely associated, on the surface at least, with a disturbing actuality. He was only twenty-five years old and had just completed his training at the Eastern Medical University, in Tsingtao, China. He was something of an idealist and was much distressed by the inadequacy of medical facilities in the country town where his mother lived. Quite on his own, and without a permit, he had begun visiting a few sick people out there in the evenings, after his eight hours at the hospital and four hours' commuting. He had recently learned that the penalty for practicing without a permit was severe; a fellow-doctor whom he had asked about it had given him a serious scolding. Nevertheless, he had continued to practice. In his dream, he had been at the bedside of a country patient when the police and the doctor he had consulted burst into the room, seized him, dragged him outside, and beat him up cruelly. On the train, he just about decided to give up the work in Mukaihara, since he felt it would be impossible to get a permit, because the authorities would hold that it would conflict with his duties at the Red Cross Hospital.

At the terminus, he caught a streetcar at once. (He later calculated that if he had taken his customary train that morning, and if he had had to wait a few minutes for the streetcar, as often happened, he would have been close to the center at the time of the explosion and would surely have perished.) He arrived at the hospital at seven-forty and reported to the chief surgeon. A few minutes later, he went to a room on the first floor and drew blood from the arm of a man in order to perform a Wassermann test. The laboratory containing the incubators for the test was on the third floor. With the blood specimen in his left hand, walking in a kind of distraction he had felt all morning, probably because of the dream and his restless night, he started along the main corridor on his way toward the stairs. He was one step beyond an open window when the light of the bomb was reflected, like a gigantic photographic flash, in the corridor. He ducked down on one knee and said to himself, as only a Japanese would, "Sasaki, *gambare!* Be brave!" Just then (the building was 1,650 yards from the center), the blast ripped through the hospital. The glasses he was wearing flew off his face; the bottle of blood crashed against one wall; his Japanese slippers zipped out from under his feet—but otherwise, thanks to where he stood, he was untouched.

Dr. Sasaki shouted the name of the chief surgeon and rushed around to the man's office and found him terribly cut by glass. The hospital was in horrible confusion: heavy partitions and ceilings had fallen on patients, beds had overturned, windows had blown in and cut people, blood was spattered on the walls and floors, instruments were everywhere, many of the patients were running about screaming, many more lay dead. (A colleague working in the laboratory to which Dr. Sasaki had been walking was dead; Dr. Sasaki's patient, whom he had just left and who a few moments before had been dreadfully afraid of syphilis, was also dead.) Dr. Sasaki found himself the only doctor in the hospital who was unhurt.

Dr. Sasaki, who believed that the enemy had hit only the building he was in, got bandages and began to bind the wounds of those inside the hospital; while outside, all over Hiroshima, maimed and dying citizens turned their unsteady steps toward the Red Cross Hospital to begin an invasion that was to make Dr. Sasaki forget his private nightmare for a long, long time.

Miss Toshiko Sasaki, the East Asia Tin Works clerk, who is not related to Dr. Sasaki, got up at three o'clock in the morning on the day the bomb fell. There was extra housework to do. Her eleven-month-old brother, Akio, had come down the day before with a serious stomach upset; her mother had taken him to the Tamura Pediatric Hospital and was staying there with him. Miss Sasaki, who was about twenty, had to cook breakfast for her father, a brother, a sister, and herself, and—since the hospital, because of the war, was unable to provide food—to prepare a whole day's meals for her mother and the baby, in time for her father, who worked in a factory making rubber earplugs for artillery crews, to take the food by on his way to the plant. When she had finished and had cleaned and put away the cooking things, it was nearly seven. The family lived in Koi, and she had a forty-five-minute trip to the tin works, in the section of town called Kannonmachi. She was in charge of the personnel records in the factory. She left Koi at seven, and as soon as she reached the plant, she went with some of the other girls from the personnel department to the factory auditorium. A prominent local Navy man, a former employee, had committed suicide the day before by throwing himself under a train—a death considered honorable enough to warrant a memorial service, which was to be held at the tin works at ten o'clock that morning. In the large hall, Miss Sasaki and the others made suitable preparations for the meeting. This work took about twenty minutes.

Miss Sasaki went back to her office and sat down at her desk. She was quite far from the windows, which were off to her left, and behind her were a couple of tall bookcases containing all the books of the factory library, which the personnel department had organized. She settled herself at her desk, put some things in a drawer, and shifted papers. She thought that before she began to make entries in her lists of new employees, discharges, and departures for the Army, she would chat for a moment with the girl at her right. Just as she turned her head away from the windows, the room was filled with a blinding light. She was paralyzed by fear, fixed still in her chair for a long moment (the plant was 1,600 yards from the center).

Everything fell, and Miss Sasaki lost consciousness. The ceiling dropped suddenly and the wooden floor above collapsed in splinters and the people up there came down and the roof above them gave way; but principally and first of all, the bookcases right behind her swooped forward and the contents threw her down, with her left leg horribly twisted and breaking underneath her. There, in the tin factory, in the first moment of the atomic age, a human being was crushed by books.

II · The Fire

IMMEDIATELY AFTER the explosion, the Reverend Mr. Kiyoshi Tanimoto, having run wildly out of the Matsui estate and having looked in wonderment at the bloody soldiers at the mouth of the dugout they had been digging, attached himself sympathetically to an old lady who was walking along in a daze, holding her head with her left hand, supporting a small boy of three or four on her back with her right, and crying, "I'm hurt! I'm hurt! I'm hurt!" Mr. Tanimoto transferred the child to his own back and led the woman by the hand down the street, which was darkened by what seemed to be a local column of dust. He took the woman to a grammar school not far away that had previously been designated for use as a temporary hospital in case of emergency. By this solicitous behavior, Mr. Tanimoto at once got rid of his terror. At the school, he was much surprised to see glass all over the floor and fifty or sixty injured people already waiting to be treated. He reflected that, although the all-clear had sounded and he had heard no planes, several bombs must have been dropped. He thought of a hillock in the rayon man's garden from which he could get a view of the whole of Koi—of the whole of Hiroshima, for that matter—and he ran back up to the estate.

From the mound, Mr. Tanimoto saw an astonishing panorama. Not just a patch of Koi, as he had expected, but as much of Hiroshima as he could see through the clouded air was giving off a thick, dreadful miasma. Clumps of smoke, near and far, had begun to push up through the general dust. He wondered how such extensive damage could have been dealt out of a silent sky; even a few planes, far up, would have been audible. Houses nearby were burning, and when huge drops of water the size of marbles began to fall, he half thought that they must be coming from the hoses of firemen fighting the blazes. (They were actually drops of condensed moisture falling from the turbulent tower of dust, heat, and fission fragments that had already risen miles into the sky above Hiroshima.)

Mr. Tanimoto turned away from the sight when he heard Mr. Matsuo call out to ask whether he was all right. Mr. Matsuo had been safely cushioned within the falling house by the bedding stored in the front hall and had worked his way out. Mr. Tanimoto scarcely answered. He had thought of his wife and baby, his church, his home, his parishioners, all of them down in that awful murk. Once more he began to run in fear— toward the city.

Mrs. Hatsuyo Nakamura, the tailor's widow, having struggled up from under the ruins of her house after the explosion, and seeing Myeko, the youngest of her three children, buried breast-deep and unable to move, crawled across the debris, hauled at timbers, and flung tiles aside, in a hurried effort to free the child. Then, from what seemed to be caverns far below, she heard two small voices crying, "*Tasukete! Tasukete!* Help! Help!"

She called the names of her ten-year-old son and eight-year-old daughter: "Toshio! Yaeko!"

The voices from below answered.

Mrs. Nakamura abandoned Myeko, who at least could breathe, and in a frenzy made the wreckage fly above the crying voices. The children had been sleeping nearly ten feet apart, but now their voices seemed to come from the same place. Toshio, the boy, apparently had some freedom to move, because she could feel him undermining the pile of wood and tiles as she worked from above. At last she saw his head, and she hastily pulled him out by it. A mosquito net was wound intricately, as if it had been carefully wrapped, around his feet. He said he had been blown right across the room and had been on top of his sister Yaeko under the wreckage. She now said, from underneath, that she could not move, because there was something on her legs. With a bit more digging, Mrs. Nakamura cleared a hole above the child and began to pull her arm. "*Itai!* It hurts!" Yaeko cried. Mrs. Nakamura shouted, "There's no time now to say whether it hurts or not," and yanked her whimpering daughter up. Then she freed Myeko. The children were filthy and bruised, but none of them had a single cut or scratch.

Mrs. Nakamura took the children out into the street. They had nothing on but underpants, and although the day was very hot, she worried rather confusedly about their being cold, so she went back into the wreckage and burrowed underneath and found a bundle of clothes she had packed for an emergency, and she dressed them in pants, blouses, shoes, padded-cotton air-raid helmets called *bokuzuki*, and even, irrationally, overcoats. The children were silent, except for the five-year-old, Myeko, who kept asking questions: "Why is it night already? Why did our house fall down? What happened?" Mrs. Nakamura, who did not know what had happened (had not the all-clear sounded?), looked around and saw through the darkness that all the houses in her neighborhood had collapsed. The house next door, which its owner had been tearing down to make way for a fire lane, was now very thoroughly, if crudely, torn down; its owner, who had been sacrificing his home for the community's safety, lay dead. Mrs. Nakamoto, wife of the head of the local air-raid-defense Neighborhood Association, came across the street with her head all bloody, and said that her baby was badly cut; did Mrs. Nakamura have any bandage? Mrs. Nakamura did not, but she crawled into the remains of her house again and pulled out some white cloth that she had been using in her work as a seamstress, ripped it into strips, and gave it to Mrs. Nakamoto. While fetching the cloth, she noticed her sewing machine; she went back in for it and dragged it out. Obviously, she could not carry it with her, so she unthinkingly plunged her symbol of livelihood into the receptacle which for weeks had been her symbol of safety—the cement tank of water in front of her house, of the type every household had been ordered to construct against a possible fire raid.

A nervous neighbor, Mrs. Hataya, called to Mrs. Nakamura to run away with her to the woods in Asano Park—an estate, by the Kyo River not far off, belonging to the wealthy Asano family, who once owned the Toyo Kisen Kaisha steamship line. The park had been designated as an evacuation area for their neighborhood. Seeing fire breaking out in a nearby ruin (except at the very center, where the bomb itself ignited some fires, most of Hiroshima's citywide conflagration was caused by inflammable wreckage falling on cookstoves and live wires), Mrs. Nakamura suggested going over to fight it. Mrs. Hataya said, "Don't be foolish. What if planes come and drop more bombs?" So Mrs. Nakamura started out for Asano Park with her children and Mrs. Hataya, and she carried her rucksack of emergency clothing, a blanket, an umbrella, and a suitcase of things she had cached in her air-raid shelter. Under many ruins, as they hurried along, they heard muffled screams for help. The only building they saw standing on their way to Asano Park was the Jesuit mission house, alongside the Catholic kindergarten to which Mrs. Nakamura had sent Myeko for a time. As they passed it, she saw Father Kleinsorge, in bloody underwear, running out of the house with a small suitcase in his hand.

RIGHT AFTER the explosion, while Father Wilhelm Kleinsorge, S. J., was wandering around in his underwear in the vegetable garden, Father Superior LaSalle came around the corner of the building in the darkness. His body, especially his back, was bloody; the flash had made him twist away from his window, and tiny pieces of glass had flown at him. Father Kleinsorge, still bewildered, managed to ask, "Where are the rest?" Just then, the two other priests living in the mission house appeared—Father Cieslik, unhurt, supporting Father Schiffer, who was covered with blood that spurted from a cut above his left ear and who was very pale. Father

Cieslik was rather pleased with himself, for after the flash he had dived into a doorway, which he had previously reckoned to be the safest place inside the building, and when the blast came, he was not injured. Father LaSalle told Father Cieslik to take Father Schiffer to a doctor before he bled to death, and suggested either Dr. Kanda, who lived on the next corner, or Dr. Fujii, about six blocks away. The two men went out of the compound and up the street.

The daughter of Mr. Hoshijima, the mission catechist, ran up to Father Kleinsorge and said that her mother and sister were buried under the ruins of their house, which was at the back of the Jesuit compound, and at the same time the priests noticed that the house of the Catholic-kindergarten teacher at the front of the compound had collapsed on her. While Father LaSalle and Mrs. Murata, the mission housekeeper, dug the teacher out, Father Kleinsorge went to the catechist's fallen house and began lifting things off the top of the pile. There was not a sound underneath; he was sure the Hoshijima women had been killed. At last, under what had been a corner of the kitchen, he saw Mrs. Hoshijima's head. Believing her dead, he began to haul her out by the hair, but suddenly she screamed, "*Itai! Itai!* It hurts! It hurts!" He dug some more and lifted her out. He managed, too, to find her daughter in the rubble and free her. Neither was badly hurt.

A public bath next door to the mission house had caught fire, but since there the wind was southerly, the priests thought their house would be spared. Nevertheless, as a precaution, Father Kleinsorge went inside to fetch some things he wanted to save. He found his room in a state of weird and illogical confusion. A first-aid kit was hanging undisturbed on a hook on the wall, but his clothes, which had been on other hooks nearby, were nowhere to be seen. His desk was in splinters all over the room, but a mere papier-mâché suitcase, which he had hidden under the desk, stood handle-side up, without a scratch on it, in the doorway of the room, where he could not miss it. Father Kleinsorge later came to regard this as a bit of Providential interference, inasmuch as the suitcase contained his breviary, the account books for the whole diocese, and a considerable amount of paper money belonging to the mission, for which he was responsible. He ran out of the house and deposited the suitcase in the mission air-raid shelter.

At about this time, Father Cieslik and Father Schiffer, who was still spurting blood, came back and said that Dr. Kanda's house was ruined and that fire blocked them from getting out of what they supposed to be the local circle of destruction to Dr. Fujii's private hospital, on the bank of the Kyo River.

DR. MASAKAZU FUJII's hospital was no longer on the bank of the Kyo River; it was in the river. After the overturn, Dr. Fujii was so stupefied and so tightly squeezed by the beams gripping his chest that he was unable to move at first, and he hung there about twenty minutes in the darkened morning. Then a thought which came to him—that soon the tide would be running in through the estuaries and his head would be submerged—inspired him to fearful activity; he wriggled and turned and exerted what strength he could (though his left arm, because of the pain in his shoulder, was useless), and before long he had freed himself from the vise. After a few moments' rest, he climbed onto the pile of timbers and, finding a long one that slanted up to the river-bank, he painfully shinnied up it.

Dr. Fujii, who was in his underwear, was now soaking and dirty. His undershirt was torn, and blood ran down it from bad cuts on his chin and back. In this disarray, he walked out onto Kyo Bridge, beside which his hospital had stood. The bridge had not collapsed. He could see only fuzzily without his glasses, but he could see enough to be amazed at the number of houses that were down all around. On the bridge, he encountered a friend, a doctor named Machii, and asked in bewilderment, "What do you think it was?"

Dr. Machii said, "It must have been a *Molotoffano hanakago*"—a Molotov flower basket, the delicate Japanese name for the "bread basket," or self-scattering cluster of bombs.

At first, Dr. Fujii could see only two fires, one across the river from his hospital site and one quite far to the south. But at the same time, he and his friend observed something that puzzled them, and which, as doctors, they discussed: although there were as yet very few fires, wounded people were hurrying across the bridge in an endless parade of misery, and many of them exhibited terrible burns on their faces and arms. "Why do you suppose it is?" Dr. Fujii asked. Even a theory was comforting that day, and Dr. Machii stuck to his. "Perhaps because it was a Molotov flower basket," he said.

There had been no breeze earlier in the morning when Dr. Fujii had walked to the railway station to see his friend off, but now brisk winds were blowing every which way; here on the bridge the wind was easterly. New fires were leaping up, and they spread quickly, and in a very short time terrible blasts of hot air and showers of cinders made it impossible to stand on the bridge any more. Dr. Machii ran to the far side of the river and along a still unkindled street. Dr. Fujii went down into the water under the bridge, where a score of people had already taken refuge, among them his servants, who had extricated themselves from the wreckage. From there, Dr. Fujii saw a nurse hanging in the timbers of his hospital by her legs, and then another painfully pinned across the breast. He enlisted the help of some of the others under the bridge and freed both of them. He thought he heard the voice of his niece for a moment, but he could not find her; he never saw her again. Four of his nurses and the two patients in the hospital died, too. Dr. Fujii went back into the water of the river and waited for the fire to subside.

· · ·

THE LOT OF Drs. Fujii, Kanda, and Machii right after the explosion—and, as these three were typical, that of the majority of the physicians and surgeons of Hiroshima—with their offices and hospitals destroyed, their equipment scattered, their own bodies incapacitated in varying degrees, explained why so many citizens who were hurt went untended and why so many who might have lived died. Of a hundred and fifty doctors in the city, sixty-five were already dead and most of the rest were wounded. Of 1,780 nurses, 1,654 were dead or too badly hurt to work. In the biggest hospital, that of the Red Cross, only six doctors out of thirty were able to function, and only ten nurses out of more than two hundred. The sole uninjured doctor on the Red Cross Hospital staff was Dr. Sasaki. After the explosion, he hurried to a storeroom to fetch bandages. This room, like everything he had seen as he ran through the hospital, was chaotic—bottles of medicines thrown off shelves and broken, salves spattered on the walls, instruments strewn everywhere. He grabbed up some bandages and an unbroken bottle of mercurochrome, hurried back to the chief surgeon, and bandaged his cuts. Then he went out into the corridor and began patching up the wounded patients and the doctors and nurses there. He blundered so without his glasses that he took a pair off the face of a wounded nurse, and although they only approximately compensated for the errors of his vision, they were better than nothing. (He was to depend on them for more than a month.)

Dr. Sasaki worked without method, taking those who were nearest him first, and he noticed soon that the corridor seemed to be getting more and more crowded. Mixed in with the abrasions and lacerations which most people in the hospital had suffered, he began to find dreadful burns. He realized then that casualties were pouring in from outdoors. There were so many that he began to pass up the lightly wounded; he decided that all he could hope to do was to stop people from bleeding to death. Before long, patients lay and crouched on the floors of the wards and the laboratories and all the other rooms, and in the corridors, and on the stairs, and in the front hall, and under the porte-cochère, and on the stone front steps, and in the driveway and courtyard, and for blocks each way in the streets outside. Wounded people supported maimed people; disfigured families leaned together. Many people were vomiting. A tremendous number of schoolgirls—some of those who had been taken from their classrooms to work outdoors, clearing fire lanes—crept into the hospital. In a city of two hundred and forty-five thousand, nearly a hundred thousand people had been killed or doomed at one blow; a hundred thousand more were hurt. At least ten thousand of the wounded made their way to the best hospital in town, which was altogether unequal to such a trampling, since it had only six hundred beds, and they had all been occupied. The people in the suffocating crowd inside the hospital wept and cried, for Dr. Sasaki to hear, "*Sensei!* Doctor!," and the less seriously wounded came and pulled at his sleeve and begged him to go to the aid of the worse wounded. Tugged here and there in his stockinged feet, bewildered by the numbers, staggered by so much raw flesh, Dr. Sasaki lost all sense of profession and stopped working as a skillful surgeon and a sympathetic man; he became an automaton, mechanically wiping, daubing, winding, wiping, daubing, winding.

SOME OF THE WOUNDED in Hiroshima were unable to enjoy the questionable luxury of hospitalization. In what had been the personnel office of the East Asia Tin Works, Miss Sasaki lay doubled over, unconscious, under the tremendous pile of books and plaster and wood and corrugated iron. She was wholly unconscious (she later estimated) for about three hours. Her first sensation was of dreadful pain in her left leg. It was so black under the books and debris that the borderline between awareness and unconsciousness was fine; she apparently crossed it several times, for the pain seemed to come and go. At the moments when it was sharpest, she felt that her leg had been cut off somewhere below the knee. Later, she heard someone walking on top of the wreckage above her, and anguished voices spoke up, evidently from within the mess around her: "Please help! Get us out!"

FATHER KLEINSORGE stemmed Father Schiffer's spurting cut as well as he could with some bandage that Dr. Fujii had given the priests a few days before. When he finished, he ran into the mission house again and found the jacket of his military uniform and an old pair of gray trousers. He put them on and went outside. A woman from next door ran up to him and shouted that her husband was buried under her house and the house was on fire; Father Kleinsorge must come and save him.

Father Kleinsorge, already growing apathetic and dazed in the presence of the cumulative distress, said, "We haven't much time." Houses all around were burning, and the wind was now blowing hard. "Do you know exactly which part of the house he is under?" he asked.

"Yes, yes," she said. "Come quickly."

They went around to the house, the remains of which blazed violently, but when they got there, it turned out that the woman had no idea where her husband was. Father Kleinsorge shouted several times, "Is anyone there?" There was no answer. Father Kleinsorge said to the woman, "We must get away or we will all die." He went back to the Catholic compound and told the Father Superior that the fire was coming closer on the wind, which had swung around and was now from the north; it was time for everybody to go.

Just then, the kindergarten teacher pointed out to the priests Mr. Fukai, the secretary of the diocese, who was standing in his window on the second floor of the mission house, facing in the direction of the explosion, weeping. Father Cieslik, because he thought the stairs unusable, ran around to the back of the mission house to look for a ladder. There he heard people crying for help under a nearby fallen roof. He called to passers-by running away in the street to help him lift it, but nobody paid any attention, and he had to leave the buried ones to die. Father Kleinsorge ran inside the mission house and scrambled up the stairs, which were awry and piled with plaster and lathing, and called to Mr. Fukai from the doorway of his room.

Mr. Fukai, a very short man of about fifty, turned around slowly, with a queer look, and said, "Leave me here."

Father Kleinsorge went into the room and took Mr. Fukai by the collar of his coat and said, "Come with me or you'll die."

Mr. Fukai said, "Leave me here to die."

Father Kleinsorge began to shove and haul Mr. Fukai out of the room. Then the theological student came up and grabbed Mr. Fukai's feet, and Father Kleinsorge took his shoulders, and together they carried him downstairs and outdoors. "I can't walk!" Mr. Fukai cried. "Leave me here!" Father Kleinsorge got his paper suitcase with the money in it and took Mr. Fukai up pickaback, and the party started for the East Parade Ground, their district's "safe area." As they went out of the gate, Mr. Fukai, quite childlike now, beat on Father Kleinsorge's shoulders and said, "I won't leave. I won't leave." Irrelevantly, Father Kleinsorge turned to Father LaSalle and said, "We have lost all our possessions but not our sense of humor."

The street was cluttered with parts of houses that had slid into it, and with fallen telephone poles and wires. From every second or third house came the voices of people buried and abandoned, who invariably screamed, with formal politeness, "*Tasukete kure!* Help, if you please!" The priests recognized several ruins from which these cries came as the homes of friends, but because of the fire it was too late to help. All the way, Mr. Fukai whimpered, "Let me stay." The party turned right when they came to a block of fallen houses that was one flame. At Sakai Bridge, which would take them across to the East Parade Ground, they saw that the whole community on the opposite side of the river was a sheet of fire; they dared not cross and decided to take refuge in Asano Park, off to their left. Father Kleinsorge, who had been weakened for a couple of days by his bad case of diarrhea, began to stagger under his protesting burden, and as he tried to climb up over the wreckage of several houses that blocked their way to the park, he stumbled, dropped Mr. Fukai, and plunged down, head over heels, to the edge of the river. When he picked himself up, he saw Mr. Fukai running away. Father Kleinsorge shouted to a dozen soldiers, who were standing by the bridge, to stop him. As Father Kleinsorge started back to get Mr. Fukai, Father LaSalle called out, "Hurry! Don't waste time!" So Father Kleinsorge just requested the soldiers to take care of Mr. Fukai. They said they would, but the little, broken man got away from them, and the last the priests could see of him, he was running back toward the fire.

. . .

MR. TANIMOTO, fearful for his family and church, at first ran toward them by the shortest route, along Koi Highway. He was the only person making his way into the city; he met hundreds and hundreds who were fleeing, and every one of them seemed to be hurt in some way. The eyebrows of some were burned off and skin hung from their faces and hands. Others, because of pain, held their arms up as if carrying something in both hands. Some were vomiting as they walked. Many were naked or in shreds of clothing. On some undressed bodies, the burns had made patterns—of undershirt straps and suspenders and, on the skin of some women (since white repelled the heat from the bomb and dark clothes absorbed it and conducted it to the skin), the shapes of flowers they had had on their kimonos. Many, although injured themselves, supported relatives who were worse off. Almost all had their heads bowed, looked straight ahead, were silent, and showed no expression whatever.

After crossing Koi Bridge and Kannon Bridge, having run the whole way, Mr. Tanimoto saw, as he approached the center, that all the houses had been crushed and many were afire. Here the trees were bare and their trunks were charred. He tried at several points to penetrate the ruins, but the flames always stopped him. Under many houses, people screamed for help, but no one helped; in general, survivors that day assisted only their relatives or immediate neighbors, for they could not comprehend or tolerate a wider circle of misery. The wounded limped past the screams, and Mr. Tanimoto ran past them. As a Christian he was filled with compassion for those who were trapped, and as a Japanese he was overwhelmed by the shame of being unhurt, and he prayed as he ran, "God help them and take them out of the fire."

He thought he would skirt the fire, to the left. He ran back to Kannon Bridge and followed for a distance one of the rivers. He tried several cross streets, but all were blocked, so he turned far left and ran out to Yokogawa, a station on a railroad line that detoured the city in a wide semicircle, and he followed the rails until he came to a burning train. So impressed was he by this time by the extent of the damage that he ran north two miles to Gion, a suburb in the foothills. All the way, he overtook dreadfully burned and lacerated people, and in his guilt he turned to right and left as he hurried and said to some of them, "Excuse me for having no burden like yours." Near Gion, he began to meet country people going toward the city to help, and when they saw him, several exclaimed, "Look! There is one who is not wounded." At Gion, he bore toward the right bank of the main river, the Ota, and ran down it until he reached fire again. There was no fire on the other side of the river, so he threw off his shirt and shoes and plunged into it. In midstream, where the current was fairly strong, exhaustion and fear finally caught up with him—he had run nearly seven miles—and he became limp and drifted in the water. He prayed, "Please, God, help me to cross. It would be nonsense for me to be drowned when I am the only uninjured one." He managed a few more strokes and fetched up on a spit down-stream.

Mr. Tanimoto climbed up the bank and ran along it until, near a large Shinto shrine, he came to more fire, and as he turned left to get around it, he met, by incredible luck, his wife. She was carrying their infant son. Mr. Tanimoto was now so emotionally worn out that nothing could surprise him. He did not embrace his wife; he simply said, "Oh, you are safe." She told him that she had got home from her night in Ushida just in time for the explosion; she had been buried under the parsonage with the baby in her arms. She told how the wreckage had pressed down on her, how the baby had cried. She saw a chink of light, and by reaching up with a hand, she worked the hole bigger, bit by bit. After about half an hour, she heard the crackling noise of wood burning. At last the opening was big enough for her to push the baby out, and afterward she crawled out herself. She said she was now going out to Ushida again. Mr. Tanimoto said he wanted to see his church and take care of the people of his Neighborhood Association. They parted as casually—as bewildered—as they had met.

Mr. Tanimoto's way around the fire took him across the East Parade Ground, which, being an evacuation area, was now the scene of a grue-some review: rank on rank of the burned and bleeding. Those who were burned moaned, "*Mizu, mizu!* Water, water!" Mr. Tanimoto found a basin in a nearby street and located a water tap that still worked in the crushed shell of a house, and he began carrying water to the suffering strangers. When he had given drink to about thirty of them, he realized he was taking too much time. "Excuse me," he said loudly to those nearby who were reaching out their hands to him and crying their thirst. "I have many people to take care of." Then he ran away. He went to the river again, the basin in his hand, and jumped down onto a sandspit. There he saw hundreds of people so badly wounded that they could not get up to go farther from the burning city. When they saw a man erect and unhurt, the chant began again: "*Mizu, mizu, mizu.*" Mr. Tanimoto could not resist them; he carried them water from the river—a mistake, since it was tidal and brackish. Two or three small boats were ferrying hurt people across the river from Asano Park, and when one touched the spit, Mr. Tanimoto again made his loud, apologetic speech and jumped into the boat. It took him across to the park. There, in the underbrush, he found some of his charges of the Neighborhood Association, who had come there by his previous instructions, and saw many acquaint-ances, among them Father Kleinsorge and the other Catholics. But he missed Fukai, who had been a close friend. "Where is Fukai-*san?*" he asked.

"He didn't want to come with us," Father Kleinsorge said. "He ran back."

. . .

WHEN MISS SASAKI heard the voices of the people caught along with her in the dilapidation at the tin factory, she began speaking to them. Her nearest neighbor, she discovered, was a high-school girl who had been drafted for factory work, and who said her back was broken. Miss Sasaki replied, "I am lying here and I can't move. My left leg is cut off."

Some time later, she again heard somebody walk overhead and then move off to one side, and whoever it was began burrowing. The digger released several people, and when he had uncovered the high-school girl, she found that her back was not broken, after all, and she crawled out. Miss Sasaki spoke to the rescuer, and he worked toward her. He pulled away a great number of books, until he had made a tunnel to her. She could see his perspiring face as he said, "Come out, Miss." She tried. "I can't move," she said. The man excavated some more and told her to try with all her strength to get out. But books were heavy on her hips, and the man finally saw that a bookcase was leaning on the books and that a heavy beam pressed down on the bookcase. "Wait," he said. "I'll get a crowbar."

The man was gone a long time, and when he came back, he was ill-tempered, as if her plight were all her fault. "We have no men to help you!" he shouted in through the tunnel. "You'll have to get out by yourself."

"That's impossible," she said. "My left leg . . ." The man went away.

Much later, several men came and dragged Miss Sasaki out. Her left leg was not severed, but it was badly broken and cut and it hung askew below the knee. They took her out into a courtyard. It was raining. She sat on the ground in the rain. When the downpour increased, someone directed all the wounded people to take cover in the factory's air-raid shelters. "Come along," a torn-up woman said to her. "You can hop." But Miss Sasaki could not move, and she just waited in the rain. Then a man propped up a large sheet of corrugated iron as a kind of lean-to, and took her in his arms and carried her to it. She was grateful until he brought two horribly wounded people—a woman with a whole breast sheared off and a man whose face was all raw from a burn—to share the simple shed with her. No one came back. The rain cleared and the cloudy afternoon was hot; before nightfall the three grotesques under the slanting piece of twisted iron began to smell quite bad.

THE FORMER HEAD of the Nobori-cho Neighborhood Association to which the Catholic priests belonged was an energetic man named Yoshida. He had boasted, when he was in charge of the district air-raid defenses, that fire might eat away all of Hiroshima but it would never come to Nobori-cho. The bomb blew down his house, and a joist pinned him by the legs, in full view of the Jesuit mission house across the way and of the people hurrying along the street. In their confusion as they hurried past, Mrs. Nakamura, with her children, and Father Kleinsorge, with Mr. Fukai on his back, hardly saw him; he was just part of the general blur of misery through which they moved. His cries for help brought no response from them; there were so many people shouting for help that they could not hear him separately. They and all the others went along. Nobori-cho became absolutely deserted, and the fire swept through it. Mr. Yoshida saw the wooden mission house—the only erect building in the area—go up in a lick of flame, and the heat was terrific on his face. Then flames came along his side of the street and entered his house. In a paroxysm of terrified strength, he freed himself and ran down the alleys of Nobori-cho, hemmed in by the fire he had said would never come. He began at once to behave like an old man; two months later his hair was white.

As Dr. Fujii stood in the river up to his neck to avoid the heat of the fire, the wind blew stronger and stronger, and soon, even though the expanse of water was small, the waves grew so high that the people under the bridge could no longer keep their footing. Dr. Fujii went close to the shore, crouched down, and embraced a large stone with his usable arm. Later it became possible to wade along the very edge of the river, and Dr. Fujii and his two surviving nurses moved about two hundred yards upstream, to a sandspit near Asano Park. Many wounded were lying on the sand. Dr. Machii was there with his family; his daughter, who had been outdoors when the bomb burst, was badly burned on her hands and legs but fortunately not on her face. Although Dr. Fujii's shoulder was by now terribly painful, he examined the girl's burns curiously. Then he lay down. In spite of the misery all around, he was ashamed of his appearance, and he remarked to Dr. Machii that he looked like a beggar, dressed as he was in nothing but torn and bloody underwear. Later in the afternoon, when the fire began to subside, he decided to go to his parental house, in the suburb of Nagatsuka. He asked Dr. Machii to join him, but the Doctor answered that he and his family were going to spend the night on the spit, because of his daughter's injuries. Dr. Fujii, together with his nurses, walked first to Ushida, where, in the partially damaged house of some relatives, he found first-aid materials he had stored there. The two nurses bandaged him and he them. They went on. Now not many people walked in the streets, but a great number sat and lay on the pavement, vomited, waited for death, and died. The number of corpses on the way to Nagatsuka was more and more puzzling. The Doctor wondered: Could a Molotov flower basket have done all this?

Dr. Fujii reached his family's house in the evening. It was five miles from the center of town, but its roof had fallen in and the windows were all broken.

All day, people poured into Asano Park. This private estate was far enough away from the explosion so that its bamboos, pines, laurel, and

maples were still alive, and the green place invited refugees—partly because they believed that if the Americans came back, they would bomb
only buildings; partly because the foliage seemed a center of coolness
and life, and the estate's exquisitely precise rock gardens, with their quiet
pools and arching bridges, were very Japanese, normal, secure; and also
partly (according to some who were there) because of an irresistible
atavistic urge to hide under leaves. Mrs. Nakamura and her children
were among the first to arrive, and they settled in the bamboo grove
near the river. They all felt terribly thirsty, and they drank from the
river. At once they were nauseated and began vomiting, and they
retched the whole day. Others were also nauseated; they all thought
(probably because of the strong odor of ionization, an "electric smell"
given off by the bomb's fission) that they were sick from a gas the
Americans had dropped. When Father Kleinsorge and the other priests
came into the park, nodding to their friends as they passed, the
Nakamuras were all sick and prostrate. A woman named Iwasaki, who
lived in the neighborhood of the mission and who was sitting near the
Nakamuras, got up and asked the priests if she should stay where she was
or go with them. Father Kleinsorge said, "I hardly know where the
safest place is." She stayed there, and later in the day, though she had
no visible wounds or burns, she died. The priests went farther along the
river and settled down in some underbrush. Father LaSalle lay down and
went right to sleep. The theological student, who was wearing slippers,
had carried with him a bundle of clothes, in which he had packed two
pairs of leather shoes. When he sat down with the others, he found that
the bundle had broken open and a couple of shoes had fallen out and
now he had only two lefts. He retraced his steps and found one right.
When he rejoined the priests, he said, "It's funny, but things don't
matter any more. Yesterday, my shoes were my most important possessions. Today, I don't care. One pair is enough."

Father Cieslik said, "I know. I started to bring my books along, and
then I thought, 'This is no time for books.'"

When Mr. Tanimoto, with his basin still in his hand, reached the
park, it was very crowded, and to distinguish the living from the dead
was not easy, for most of the people lay still, with their eyes open. To
Father Kleinsorge, an Occidental, the silence in the grove by the river,
where hundreds of gruesomely wounded suffered together, was one of
the most dreadful and awesome phenomena of his whole experience. The
hurt ones were quiet; no one wept, much less screamed in pain; no one
complained; none of the many who died did so noisily; not even the
children cried; very few people even spoke. And when Father Kleinsorge gave water to some whose faces had been almost blotted out by
flash burns, they took their share and then raised themselves a little and
bowed to him, in thanks.

Mr. Tanimoto greeted the priests and then looked around for other

JOHN HERSEY

photograph by Russell O. Kuhner

JOSEPH HERGESHEIMER

photograph by Hal Phyfe

friends. He saw Mrs. Matsumoto, wife of the director of the Methodist School, and asked her if she was thirsty. She was, so he went to one of the pools in the Asanos' rock gardens and got water for her in his basin. Then he decided to try to get back to his church. He went into Nobori-cho by the way the priests had taken as they escaped, but he did not get far; the fire along the streets was so fierce that he had to turn back. He walked to the riverbank and began to look for a boat in which he might carry some of the most severely injured across the river from Asano Park and away from the spreading fire. Soon he found a good-sized pleasure punt drawn up on the bank, but in and around it was an awful tableau—five dead men, nearly naked, badly burned, who must have expired more or less all at once, for they were in attitudes which suggested that they had been working together to push the boat down into the river. Mr. Tanimoto lifted them away from the boat, and as he did so, he experienced such horror at disturbing the dead—preventing them, he momentarily felt, from launching their craft and going on their ghostly way—that he said out loud, "Please forgive me for taking this boat. I must use it for others, who are alive." The punt was heavy, but he managed to slide it into the water. There were no oars, and all he could find for propulsion was a thick bamboo pole. He worked the boat upstream to the most crowded part of the park and began to ferry the wounded. He could pack ten or twelve into the boat for each crossing, but as the river was too deep in the center to pole his way across, he had to paddle with the bamboo, and consequently each trip took a very long time. He worked several hours that way.

Early in the afternoon, the fire swept into the woods of Asano Park. The first Mr. Tanimoto knew of it was when, returning in his boat, he saw that a great number of people had moved toward the riverside. On touching the bank, he went up to investigate, and when he saw the fire, he shouted, "All the young men who are not badly hurt come with me!" Father Kleinsorge moved Father Schiffer and Father LaSalle close to the edge of the river and asked people there to get them across if the fire came too near, and then joined Tanimoto's volunteers. Mr. Tanimoto sent some to look for buckets and basins and told others to beat the burning underbrush with their clothes; when utensils were at hand, he formed a bucket chain from one of the pools in the rock gardens. The team fought the fire for more than two hours, and gradually defeated the flames. As Mr. Tanimoto's men worked, the frightened people in the park pressed closer and closer to the river, and finally the mob began to force some of the unfortunates who were on the very bank into the water. Among those driven into the river and drowned were Mrs. Matsumoto, of the Methodist School, and her daughter.

When Father Kleinsorge got back after fighting the fire, he found Father Schiffer still bleeding and terribly pale. Some Japanese stood around and stared at him, and Father Schiffer whispered, with a weak smile, "It is as if I were already dead." "Not yet," Father Kleinsorge said. He had brought Dr. Fujii's first-aid kit with him, and he had noticed Dr. Kanda in the crowd, so he sought him out and asked him if he would dress Father Schiffer's bad cuts. Dr. Kanda had seen his wife and daughter dead in the ruins of his hospital; he sat now with his head in his hands. "I can't do anything," he said. Father Kleinsorge bound more bandage around Father Schiffer's head, moved him to a steep place, and settled him so that his head was high, and soon the bleeding diminished.

The roar of approaching planes was heard about this time. Someone in the crowd near the Nakamura family shouted, "It's some Grummans coming to strafe us!" A baker named Nakashima stood up and commanded, "Everyone who is wearing anything white, take it off." Mrs. Nakamura took the blouses off her children, and opened her umbrella and made them get under it. A great number of people, even badly burned ones, crawled into bushes and stayed there until the hum, evidently of a reconnaissance or weather run, died away.

It began to rain. Mrs. Nakamura kept her children under the umbrella. The drops grew abnormally large, and someone shouted, "The Americans are dropping gasoline. They're going to set fire to us!" (This alarm stemmed from one of the theories being passed through the park as to why so much of Hiroshima had burned: it was that a single plane had sprayed gasoline on the city and then somehow set fire to it in one flashing moment.) But the drops were palpably water, and as they fell, the wind grew stronger and stronger, and suddenly—probably because of the tremendous convection set up by the blazing city—a whirlwind ripped through the park. Huge trees crashed down; small ones were uprooted and flew into the air. Higher, a wild array of flat things revolved in the twisting funnel—pieces of iron roofing, papers, doors, strips of matting. Father Kleinsorge put a piece of cloth over Father Schiffer's eyes, so that the feeble man would not think he was going crazy. The gale blew Mrs. Murata, the mission housekeeper, who was sitting close by the river, down the embankment at a shallow, rocky place, and she came out with her bare feet bloody. The vortex moved out onto the river, where it sucked up a waterspout and eventually spent itself.

After the storm, Mr. Tanimoto began ferrying people again, and Father Kleinsorge asked the theological student to go across and make his way out to the Jesuit Novitiate at Nagatsuka, about three miles from the center of town, and to request the priests there to come with help for Fathers Schiffer and LaSalle. The student got into Mr. Tanimoto's boat and went off with him. Father Kleinsorge asked Mrs. Nakamura if she would like to go out to Nagatsuka with the priests when they came. She said she had some luggage and her children were sick—they were still vomiting from time to time, and so, for that matter, was she—and therefore she feared she could not. He said he thought the fathers from the Novitiate could come back the next day with a pushcart to get her.

Late in the afternoon, when he went ashore for a while, Mr. Tanimoto, upon whose energy and initiative many had come to depend, heard people begging for food. He consulted Father Kleinsorge, and they decided to go back into town to get some rice from Mr. Tanimoto's Neighborhood Association shelter and from the mission shelter. Father Cieslik and two or three others went with them. At first, when they got among the rows of prostrate houses, they did not know where they were; the change was too sudden, from a busy city of two hundred and forty-five thousand that morning to a mere pattern of residue in the afternoon. The asphalt of the streets was still so soft and hot from the fires that walking was uncomfortable. They encountered only one person, a woman, who said to them as they passed, "My husband is in those ashes." At the mission, where Mr. Tanimoto left the party, Father Kleinsorge was dismayed to see the building razed. In the garden, on the way to the shelter, he noticed a pumpkin roasted on the vine. He and Father Cieslik tasted it and it was good. They were surprised at their hunger, and they ate quite a bit. They got out several bags of rice and gathered up several other cooked pumpkins and dug up some potatoes that were nicely baked under the ground, and started back. Mr. Tanimoto rejoined them on the way. One of the people with him had some cooking utensils. In the park, Mr. Tanimoto organized the lightly wounded women of his neighborhood to cook. Father Kleinsorge offered the Nakamura family some pumpkin, and they tried it, but they could not keep it on their stomachs. Altogether, the rice was enough to feed nearly a hundred people.

Just before dark, Mr. Tanimoto came across a twenty-year-old girl, Mrs. Kamai, the Tanimotos' next-door neighbor. She was crouching on the ground with the body of her infant daughter in her arms. The baby had evidently been dead all day. Mrs. Kamai jumped up when she saw Mr. Tanimoto and said, "Would you please try to locate my husband?"

Mr. Tanimoto knew that her husband had been inducted into the Army just the day before; he and Mrs. Tanimoto had entertained Mrs. Kamai in the afternoon, to make her forget. Kamai had reported to the Chugoku Regional Army Headquarters—near the ancient castle in the middle of town—where some four thousand troops were stationed. Judging by the many maimed soldiers Mr. Tanimoto had seen during the day, he surmised that the barracks had been badly damaged by whatever it was that had hit Hiroshima. He knew he hadn't a chance of finding Mrs. Kamai's husband, even if he searched, but he wanted to humor her. "I'll try," he said.

"You've got to find him," she said. "He loved our baby so much. I want him to see her once more."

III · Details Are Being Investigated

EARLY IN THE EVENING of the day the bomb exploded, a Japanese naval launch moved slowly up and down the seven rivers of Hiroshima. It stopped here and there to make an announcement—alongside the crowded sandspits, on which hundreds of wounded lay; at the bridges, on which others were crowded; and eventually, as twilight fell, opposite Asano Park. A young officer stood up in the launch and shouted through a megaphone, "Be patient! A naval hospital ship is coming to take care of you!" The sight of the shipshape launch against the background of the havoc across the river; the unruffled young man in his neat uniform; above all, the promise of medical help—the first word of possible succor anyone had heard in nearly twelve awful hours —cheered the people in the park tremendously. Mrs. Nakamura settled her family for the night with the assurance that a doctor would come and stop their retching. Mr. Tanimoto resumed ferrying the wounded across the river. Father Kleinsorge lay down and said the Lord's Prayer and a Hail Mary to himself, and fell right asleep; but no sooner had he dropped off than Mrs. Murata, the conscientious mission housekeeper, shook him and said, "Father Kleinsorge! Did you remember to repeat your evening prayers?" He answered rather grumpily, "Of course," and he tried to go back to sleep but could not. This, apparently, was just what Mrs. Murata wanted. She began to chat with the exhausted priest. One of the questions she raised was when he thought the priests from the Novitiate, for whom he had sent a messenger in midafternoon, would arrive to evacuate Father Superior LaSalle and Father Schiffer.

THE MESSENGER Father Kleinsorge had sent—the theological student who had been living at the mission house—had arrived at the Novitiate, in the hills about three miles out, at half past four. The sixteen priests there had been doing rescue work in the outskirts; they had worried about their colleagues in the city but had not known how or where to look for them. Now they hastily made two litters out of poles and boards, and the student led half a dozen of them back into the devastated area. They worked their way along the Ota above the city; twice the heat of the fire forced them into the river. At Misasa Bridge, they encountered a long line of soldiers making a bizarre forced march away from the Chugoku Regional Army Headquarters in the center of the town. All were grotesquely burned, and they supported themselves with staves or leaned on one another. Sick, burned horses, hanging their heads, stood on the bridge. When the rescue party reached the park, it was after dark, and progress was made extremely difficult by the tangle of fallen trees of all sizes that had been knocked down by the whirlwind that afternoon. At last—not long after Mrs. Murata asked her question—they reached their friends, and gave them wine and strong tea.

The priests discussed how to get Father Schiffer and Father LaSalle out to the Novitiate. They were afraid that blundering through the park with them would jar them too much on the wooden litters, and that the wounded men would lose too much blood. Father Kleinsorge thought of Mr. Tanimoto and his boat, and called out to him on the river. When Mr. Tanimoto reached the bank, he said he would be glad to take the injured priests and their bearers upstream to where they could find a clear roadway. The rescuers put Father Schiffer onto one of the stretchers and lowered it into the boat, and two of them went aboard with it. Mr. Tanimoto, who still had no oars, poled the punt upstream.

About half an hour later, Mr. Tanimoto came back and excitedly asked the remaining priests to help him rescue two children he had seen standing up to their shoulders in the river. A group went out and picked them up—two young girls who had lost their family and were both badly burned. The priests stretched them on the ground next to Father Kleinsorge and then embarked Father LaSalle. Father Cieslik thought he could make it out to the Novitiate on foot, so he went aboard with the others. Father Kleinsorge was too feeble; he decided to wait in the park until the next day. He asked the men to come back with a handcart, so that they could take Mrs. Nakamura and her sick children to the Novitiate.

Mr. Tanimoto shoved off again. As the boatload of priests moved slowly upstream, they heard weak cries for help. A woman's voice stood out especially: "There are people here about to be drowned! Help us! The water is rising!" The sounds came from one of the sandspits, and those in the punt could see, in the reflected light of the still-burning fires, a number of wounded people lying at the edge of the river, already partly covered by the flooding tide. Mr. Tanimoto wanted to help them, but the priests were afraid that Father Schiffer would die if they didn't hurry, and they urged their ferryman along. He dropped them where he had put Father Schiffer down and then started back alone toward the sandspit.

THE NIGHT WAS HOT, and it seemed even hotter because of the fires against the sky, but the younger of the two girls Mr. Tanimoto and the priests had rescued complained to Father Kleinsorge that she was cold. He covered her with his jacket. She and her older sister had been in the salt water of the river for a couple of hours before being rescued. The younger one had huge, raw flash burns on her body; the salt water must have been excruciatingly painful to her. She began to shiver heavily, and again said it was cold. Father Kleinsorge borrowed a blanket from someone nearby and wrapped her up, but she shook more and

more, and said again, "I am so cold," and then she suddenly stopped
shivering and was dead.

MR. TANIMOTO FOUND about twenty men and women on the
sandspit. He drove the boat onto the bank and urged them to get aboard.
They did not move and he realized that they were too weak to lift
themselves. He reached down and took a woman by the hands, but her
skin slipped off in huge, glove-like pieces. He was so sickened by this
that he had to sit down for a moment. Then he got out into the water
and, though a small man, lifted several of the men and women, who were
naked, into his boat. Their backs and breasts were clammy, and he
remembered uneasily what the great burns he had seen during the day
had been like: yellow at first, then red and swollen, with the skin
sloughed off, and finally, in the evening, suppurated and smelly. With
the tide risen, his bamboo pole was now too short and he had to paddle
most of the way across with it. On the other side, at a higher spit, he
lifted the slimy living bodies out and carried them up the slope away
from the tide. He had to keep consciously repeating to himself, "These
are human beings." It took him three trips to get them all across the
river. When he had finished, he decided he had to have a rest, and he
went back to the park.

As Mr. Tanimoto stepped up the dark bank, he tripped over someone, and someone else said angrily, "Look out! That's my hand." Mr.
Tanimoto, ashamed of hurting wounded people, embarrassed at being
able to walk upright, suddenly thought of the naval hospital ship, which
had not come (it never did), and he had for a moment a feeling of blind,
murderous rage at the crew of the ship, and then at all doctors. Why
didn't they come to help these people?

DR. FUJII LAY in dreadful pain throughout the night on the floor of
his family's roofless house on the edge of the city. By the light of a
lantern, he had examined himself and found: left clavicle fractured;
multiple abrasions and lacerations of face and body, including deep cuts
on the chin, back, and legs; extensive contusions on chest and trunk; a
couple of ribs possibly fractured. Had he not been so badly hurt, he
might have been at Asano Park, assisting the wounded.

BY NIGHTFALL, ten thousand victims of the explosion had invaded
the Red Cross Hospital, and Dr. Sasaki, worn out, was moving aimlessly
and dully up and down the stinking corridors with wads of bandage and
bottles of mercurochrome, still wearing the glasses he had taken from
the wounded nurse, binding up the worst cuts as he came to them. Other
doctors were putting compresses of saline solution on the worst burns.
That was all they could do. After dark, they worked by the light of the
city's fires and by candles the ten remaining nurses held for them. Dr.
Sasaki had not looked outside the hospital all day; the scene inside was so

terrible and so compelling that it had not occurred to him to ask any questions about what had happened beyond the windows and doors. Ceilings and partitions had fallen; plaster, dust, blood, and vomit were everywhere. Patients were dying by the hundreds, but there was nobody to carry away the corpses. Some of the hospital staff distributed biscuits and rice balls, but the charnel-house smell was so strong that few were hungry. By three o'clock the next morning, after nineteen straight hours of his gruesome work, Dr. Sasaki was incapable of dressing another wound. He and some other survivors of the hospital staff got straw mats and went outdoors—thousands of patients and hundreds of dead were in the yard and on the driveway—and hurried around behind the hospital and lay down in hiding to snatch some sleep. But within an hour wounded people had found them; a complaining circle formed around them: "Doctors! Help us! How can you sleep?" Dr. Sasaki got up again and went back to work. Early in the day, he thought for the first time of his mother, at their country home in Mukaihara, thirty miles from town. He usually went home every night. He was afraid she would think he was dead.

NEAR THE SPOT upriver to which Mr. Tanimoto had transported the priests, there sat a large case of rice cakes which a rescue party had evidently brought for the wounded lying thereabouts but hadn't distributed. Before evacuating the wounded priests, the others passed the cakes around and helped themselves. A few minutes later, a band of soldiers came up, and an officer, hearing the priests speaking a foreign language, drew his sword and hysterically asked who they were. One of the priests calmed him down and explained that they were Germans—allies. The officer apologized and said that there were reports going around that American parachutists had landed.

The priests decided that they should take Father Schiffer first. As they prepared to leave, Father Superior LaSalle said he felt awfully cold. One of the Jesuits gave up his coat, another his shirt; they were glad to wear less in the muggy night. The stretcher bearers started out. The theological student led the way and tried to warn the others of obstacles, but one of the priests got a foot tangled in some telephone wire and tripped and dropped his corner of the litter. Father Schiffer rolled off, lost consciousness, came to, and then vomited. The bearers picked him up and went on with him to the edge of the city, where they had arranged to meet a relay of other priests, left him with them, and turned back and got the Father Superior.

The wooden litter must have been terribly painful for Father La-Salle, in whose back scores of tiny particles of window glass were embedded. Near the edge of town, the group had to walk around an automobile burned and squatting on the narrow road, and the bearers on one side, unable to see their way in the darkness, fell into a deep ditch. Father LaSalle was thrown onto the ground and the litter broke in two.

One priest went ahead to get a handcart from the Novitiate, but he soon found one beside an empty house and wheeled it back. The priests lifted Father LaSalle into the cart and pushed him over the bumpy road the rest of the way. The rector of the Novitiate, who had been a doctor before he entered the religious order, cleaned the wounds of the two priests and put them to bed between clean sheets, and they thanked God for the care they had received.

THOUSANDS OF PEOPLE had nobody to help them. Miss Sasaki was one of them. Abandoned and helpless, under the crude lean-to in the courtyard of the tin factory, beside the woman who had lost a breast and the man whose burned face was scarcely a face any more, she suffered awfully that night from the pain in her broken leg. She did not sleep at all; neither did she converse with her sleepless companions.

IN THE PARK, Mrs. Murata kept Father Kleinsorge awake all night by talking to him. None of the Nakamura family were able to sleep, either; the children, in spite of being very sick, were interested in everything that happened. They were delighted when one of the city's gas-storage tanks went up in a tremendous burst of flame. Toshio, the boy, shouted to the others to look at the reflection in the river. Mr. Tanimoto, after his long run and his many hours of rescue work, dozed uneasily. When he awoke, in the first light of dawn, he looked across the river and saw that he had not carried the festered, limp bodies high enough on the sandspit the night before. The tide had risen above where he had put them; they had not had the strength to move; they must have drowned. He saw a number of bodies floating in the river.

EARLY THAT DAY, August 7th, the Japanese radio broadcast for the first time a succinct announcement that very few, if any, of the people most concerned with its content, the survivors in Hiroshima, happened to hear: "Hiroshima suffered considerable damage as the result of an attack by a few B-29s. It is believed that a new type of bomb was used. The details are being investigated." Nor is it probable that any of the survivors happened to be tuned in on a short-wave rebroadcast of an extraordinary announcement by the President of the United States, which identified the new bomb as atomic: "That bomb had more power than twenty thousand tons of TNT. It had more than two thousand times the blast power of the British Grand Slam, which is the largest bomb ever yet used in the history of warfare." Those victims who were able to worry at all about what had happened thought of it and discussed it in more primitive, childish terms—gasoline sprinkled from an airplane, maybe, or some combustible gas, or a big cluster of incendiaries, or the work of parachutists; but, even if they had known the truth, most of them were too busy or too weary or too badly hurt to care that they were the objects of the first great experiment in the use of atomic power, which (as the voices on the short wave shouted) no country except the United States, with its industrial know-how, its willingness to throw two billion gold dollars into an important wartime gamble, could possibly have developed.

Mr. Tanimoto was still angry at doctors. He decided that he would personally bring one to Asano Park—by the scruff of the neck, if necessary. He crossed the river, went past the Shinto shrine where he had met his wife for a brief moment the day before, and walked to the East Parade Ground. Since this had long before been designated as an evacuation area, he thought he would find an aid station there. He did find one, operated by an Army medical unit, but he also saw that its doctors were hopelessly overburdened, with thousands of patients sprawled among corpses across the field in front of it. Nevertheless, he went up to one of the Army doctors and said, as reproachfully as he could, "Why have you not come to Asano Park? You are badly needed there."

Without even looking up from his work, the doctor said in a tired voice, "This is my station."

"But there are many dying on the river bank over there."

"The first duty," the doctor said, "is to take care of the slightly wounded."

"Why—when there are many who are heavily wounded on the riverbank?"

The doctor moved to another patient. "In an emergency like this," he said, as if he were reciting from a manual, "the first task is to help as many as possible—to save as many lives as possible. There is no hope for the heavily wounded. They will die. We can't bother with them."

"That may be right from a medical standpoint—" Mr. Tanimoto began, but then he looked out across the field, where the many dead lay close and intimate with those who were still living, and he turned away without finishing his sentence, angry now with himself. He didn't know what to do; he had promised some of the dying people in the park that he would bring them medical aid. They might die feeling cheated. He saw a ration stand at one side of the field, and he went to it and begged some rice cakes and biscuits, and he took them back, in lieu of doctors, to the people in the park.

The morning, again, was hot. Father Kleinsorge went to fetch water for the wounded in a bottle and a teapot he had borrowed. He had heard that it was possible to get fresh tap water outside Asano Park. Going through the rock gardens, he had to climb over and crawl under the trunks of fallen pine trees; he found he was weak. There were many dead in the gardens. At a beautiful moon bridge, he passed a naked, living woman who seemed to have been burned from head to toe and was red all over. Near the entrance to the park, an Army doctor was working, but the only medicine he had was iodine, which he painted

over cuts, bruises, slimy burns, everything—and by now everything that
he painted had pus on it. Outside the gate of the park, Father Kleinsorge
found a faucet that still worked—part of the plumbing of a vanished
house—and he filled his vessels and returned. When he had given the
wounded the water, he made a second trip. This time, the woman by the
bridge was dead. On his way back with the water, he got lost on a
detour around a fallen tree, and as he looked for his way through the
woods, he heard a voice ask from the underbrush, "Have you anything
to drink?" He saw a uniform. Thinking there was just one soldier, he
approached with the water. When he had penetrated the bushes, he saw
there were about twenty men, and they were all in exactly the same
nightmarish state: their faces were wholly burned, their eyesockets were
hollow, the fluid from their melted eyes had run down their cheeks.
(They must have had their faces upturned when the bomb went off;
perhaps they were anti-aircraft personnel.) Their mouths were mere
swollen, pus-covered wounds, which they could not bear to stretch
enough to admit the spout of the teapot. So Father Kleinsorge got a large
piece of grass and drew out the stem so as to make a straw, and gave
them all water to drink that way. One of them said, "I can't see anything." Father Kleinsorge answered, as cheerfully as he could, "There's a
doctor at the entrance to the park. He's busy now, but he'll come soon
and fix your eyes, I hope."

Since that day, Father Kleinsorge has thought back to how queasy
he had once been at the sight of pain, how someone else's cut finger
used to make him turn faint. Yet there in the park he was so benumbed
that immediately after leaving this horrible sight he stopped on a path by
one of the pools and discussed with a lightly wounded man whether it
would be safe to eat the fat, two-foot carp that floated dead on the
surface of the water. They decided, after some consideration, that it
would be unwise.

Father Kleinsorge filled the containers a third time and went back to
the riverbank. There, amid the dead and dying, he saw a young woman
with a needle and thread mending her kimono, which had been slightly
torn. Father Kleinsorge joshed her. "My, but you're a dandy!" he said.
She laughed.

He felt tired and lay down. He began to talk with two engaging
children whose acquaintance he had made the afternoon before. He
learned that their name was Kataoka; the girl was thirteen, the boy five.
The girl had been just about to set out for a barbershop when the bomb
fell. As the family started for Asano Park, their mother decided to turn
back for some food and extra clothing; they became separated from her
in the crowd of fleeing people, and they had not seen her since. Occasionally they stopped suddenly in their perfectly cheerful playing and
began to cry for their mother.

It was difficult for all the children in the park to sustain the sense of
tragedy. Toshio Nakamura got quite excited when he saw his friend

Seichi Sato riding up the river in a boat with his family, and he ran to the bank and waved and shouted, "Sato! Sato!"

The boy turned his head and shouted, "Who's that?"

"Nakamura."

"Hello, Toshio!"

"Are you all safe?"

"Yes. What about you?"

"Yes, we're all right. My sisters are vomiting, but I'm fine."

Father Kleinsorge began to be thirsty in the dreadful heat, and he did not feel strong enough to go for water again. A little before noon, he saw a Japanese woman handing something out. Soon she came to him and said in a kindly voice, "These are tea leaves. Chew them, young man, and you won't feel thirsty." The woman's gentleness made Father Kleinsorge suddenly want to cry. For weeks, he had been feeling oppressed by the hatred of foreigners that the Japanese seemed increasingly to show, and he had been uneasy even with his Japanese friends. This stranger's gesture made him a little hysterical.

Around noon, the priests arrived from the Novitiate with the handcart. They had been to the site of the mission house in the city and had retrieved some suitcases that had been stored in the air-raid shelter and had also picked up the remains of melted holy vessels in the ashes of the chapel. They now packed Father Kleinsorge's papier-mâché suitcase and the things belonging to Mrs. Murata and the Nakamuras into the cart, put the two Nakamura girls aboard, and prepared to start out. Then one of the Jesuits who had a practical turn of mind remembered that they had been notified some time before that if they suffered property damage at the hands of the enemy, they could enter a claim for compensation with the prefectural police. The holy men discussed this matter there in the park, with the wounded as silent as the dead around them, and decided that Father Kleinsorge, as a former resident of the destroyed mission, was the one to enter the claim. So, as the others went off with the handcart, Father Kleinsorge said goodbye to the Kataoka children and trudged to a police station. Fresh, clean-uniformed policemen from another town were in charge, and a crowd of dirty and disarrayed citizens crowded around them, mostly asking after lost relatives. Father Kleinsorge filled out a claim form and started walking through the center of the town on his way to Nagatsuka. It was then that he first realized the extent of the damage; he passed block after block of ruins, and even after all he had seen in the park, his breath was taken away. By the time he reached the Novitiate, he was sick with exhaustion. The last thing he did as he fell into bed was request that someone go back for the motherless Kataoka children.

ALTOGETHER, Miss Sasaki was left two days and two nights under the piece of propped-up roofing with her crushed leg and her two unpleasant comrades. Her only diversion was when men came to the factory air-raid shelters, which she could see from under one corner of her shelter, and hauled corpses up out of them with ropes. Her leg became discolored, swollen, and putrid. All that time, she went without food and water. On the third day, August 8th, some friends who supposed she was dead came to look for her body and found her. They told her that her mother, father, and baby brother, who at the time of the explosion were in the Tamura Pediatric Hospital, where the baby was a patient, had all been given up as certainly dead, since the hospital was totally destroyed. Her friends then left her to think that piece of news over. Later, some men picked her up by the arms and legs and carried her quite a distance to a truck. For about an hour, the truck moved over a bumpy road, and Miss Sasaki, who had become convinced that she was dulled to pain, discovered that she was not. The men lifted her out at a relief station in the section of Inokuchi, where two Army doctors looked at her. The moment one of them touched her wound, she fainted. She came to in time to hear them discuss whether or not to cut off her leg; one said there was gas gangrene in the lips of the wound and predicted she would die unless they amputated, and the other said that was too bad, because they had no equipment with which to do the job. She fainted again. When she recovered consciousness, she was being carried somewhere on a stretcher. She was put aboard a launch, which went to the nearby island of Ninoshima, and she was taken to a military hospital there. Another doctor examined her and said that she did not have gas gangrene, though she did have a fairly ugly compound fracture. He said quite coldly that he was sorry, but this was a hospital for operative surgical cases only, and because she had no gangrene, she would have to return to Hiroshima that night. But then the doctor took her temperature, and what he saw on the thermometer made him decide to let her stay.

THAT DAY, August 8th, Father Cieslik went into the city to look for Mr. Fukai, the Japanese secretary of the diocese, who had ridden unwillingly out of the flaming city on Father Kleinsorge's back and then had run back crazily into it. Father Cieslik started hunting in the neighborhood of Sakai Bridge, where the Jesuits had last seen Mr. Fukai; he went to the East Parade Ground, the evacuation area to which the secretary might have gone, and looked for him among the wounded and dead there; he went to the prefectural police and made inquiries. He could not find any trace of the man. Back at the Novitiate that evening, the theological student, who had been rooming with Mr. Fukai at the mission house, told the priests that the secretary had remarked to him, during an air-raid alarm one day not long before the bombing, "Japan is dying. If there is a real air raid here in Hiroshima, I want to die with our country." The priests concluded that Mr. Fukai had run back to immolate himself in the flames. They never saw him again.

·   ·   ·

AT THE RED CROSS HOSPITAL, Dr. Sasaki worked for three straight days with only one hour's sleep. On the second day, he began to sew up the worst cuts, and right through the following night and all the next day he stitched. Many of the wounds were festered. Fortunately, some-one had found intact a supply of *narucopon*, a Japanese sedative, and he gave it to many who were in pain. Word went around among the staff that there must have been something peculiar about the great bomb, because on the second day the vice-chief of the hospital went down in the basement to the vault where the X-ray plates were stored and found the whole stock exposed as they lay. That day, a fresh doctor and ten nurses came in from the city of Yamaguchi with extra bandages and antiseptics, and the third day another physician and a dozen more nurses arrived from Matsue—yet there were still only eight doctors for ten thousand patients. In the afternoon of the third day, exhausted from his foul tailoring, Dr. Sasaki became obsessed with the idea that his mother thought he was dead. He got permission to go to Mukaihara. He walked out to the first suburbs, beyond which the electric train service was still functioning, and reached home late in the evening. His mother said she had known he was all right all along; a wounded nurse had stopped by to tell her. He went to bed and slept for seventeen hours.

BEFORE DAWN ON August 8th, someone entered the room at the Novi-tiate where Father Kleinsorge was in bed, reached up to the hanging light bulb, and switched it on. The sudden flood of light, pouring in on Father Kleinsorge's half sleep, brought him leaping out of bed, braced for a new concussion. When he realized what had happened, he laughed confusedly and went back to bed. He stayed there all day.

On August 9th, Father Kleinsorge was still tired. The rector looked at his cuts and said they were not even worth dressing, and if Father Kleinsorge kept them clean, they would heal in three or four days. Father Kleinsorge felt uneasy; he could not yet comprehend what he had been through; as if he were guilty of something awful, he felt he had to go back to the scene of the violence he had experienced. He got up out of bed and walked into the city. He scratched for a while in the ruins of the mission house, but he found nothing. He went to the sites of a couple of schools and asked after people he knew. He looked for some of the city's Japanese Catholics, but he found only fallen houses. He walked back to the Novitiate, stupefied and without any new understanding.

AT TWO MINUTES after eleven o'clock on the morning of August 9th, the second atomic bomb was dropped, on Nagasaki. It was several days before the survivors of Hiroshima knew they had company, be-cause the Japanese radio and newspapers were being extremely cautious on the subject of the strange weapon.

· · ·

On August 9th, Mr. Tanimoto was still working in the park. He went to the suburb of Ushida, where his wife was staying with friends, and got a tent which he had stored there before the bombing. He now took it to the park and set it up as a shelter for some of the wounded who could not move or be moved. Whatever he did in the park, he felt he was being watched by the twenty-year-old girl, Mrs. Kamai, his former neighbor, whom he had seen on the day the bomb exploded, with her dead baby daughter in her arms. She kept the small corpse in her arms for four days, even though it began smelling bad on the second day. Once, Mr. Tanimoto sat with her for a while, and she told him that the bomb had buried her under their house with the baby strapped to her back, and that when she had dug herself free, she had discovered that the baby was choking, its mouth full of dirt. With her little finger, she had carefully cleaned out the infant's mouth, and for a time the child had breathed normally and seemed all right; then suddenly it had died. Mrs. Kamai also talked about what a fine man her husband was, and again urged Mr. Tanimoto to search for him. Since Mr. Tanimoto had been all through the city the first day and had seen terribly burned soldiers from Kamai's post, the Chugoku Regional Army Headquarters, everywhere, he knew it would be impossible to find Kamai, even if he were living, but of course he didn't tell her that. Every time she saw Mr. Tanimoto, she asked whether he had found her husband. Once, he tried to suggest that perhaps it was time to cremate the baby, but Mrs. Kamai only held it tighter. He began to keep away from her, but whenever he looked at her, she was staring at him and her eyes asked the same question. He tried to escape her glance by keeping his back turned to her as much as possible.

The Jesuits took about fifty refugees into the exquisite chapel of the Novitiate. The rector gave them what medical care he could—mostly just the cleaning away of pus. Each of the Nakamuras was provided with a blanket and a mosquito net. Mrs. Nakamura and her younger daughter had no appetite and ate nothing; her son and other daughter ate, and lost, each meal they were offered. On August 10th, a friend, Mrs. Osaki, came to see them and told them that her son Hideo had been burned alive in the factory where he worked. This Hideo had been a kind of hero to Toshio, who had often gone to the plant to watch him run his machine. That night, Toshio woke up screaming. He had dreamed that he had seen Mrs. Osaki coming out of an opening in the ground with her family, and then he saw Hideo at his machine, a big one with a revolving belt, and he himself was standing beside Hideo, and for some reason this was terrifying.

On August 10th, Father Kleinsorge, having heard from someone that Dr. Fujii had been injured and that he had eventually gone to the summer house of a friend of his named Okuma, in the village of Fukawa, asked Father Cieslik if he would go and see how Dr. Fujii was. Father Cieslik went to Misasa station, outside Hiroshima, rode for twenty minutes on an electric train, and then walked for an hour and a half in a terribly hot sun to Mr. Okuma's house, which was beside the Ota River at the foot of a mountain. He found Dr. Fujii sitting in a chair in a kimono, applying compresses to his broken collarbone. The Doctor told Father Cieslik about having lost his glasses and said that his eyes bothered him. He showed the priest huge blue and green stripes where beams had bruised him. He offered the Jesuit first a cigarette and then whiskey, though it was only eleven in the morning. Father Cieslik thought it would please Dr. Fujii if he took a little, so he said yes. A servant brought some Suntory whiskey, and the Jesuit, the Doctor, and the host had a very pleasant chat. Mr. Okuma had lived in Hawaii, and he told some things about Americans. Dr. Fujii talked a bit about the disaster. He said that Mr. Okuma and a nurse had gone into the ruins of his hospital and brought back a small safe which he had moved into his air-raid shelter. This contained some surgical instruments, and Dr. Fujii gave Father Cieslik a few pairs of scissors and tweezers for the rector at the Novitiate. Father Cieslik was bursting with some inside dope he had, but he waited until the conversation turned naturally to the mystery of the bomb. Then he said he knew what kind of bomb it was; he had the secret on the best authority—that of a Japanese newspaperman who had dropped in at the Novitiate. The bomb was not a bomb at all; it was a kind of fine magnesium powder sprayed over the whole city by a single plane, and it exploded when it came into contact with the live wires of the city power system. "That means," said Dr. Fujii, perfectly satisfied, since after all the information came from a newspaperman, "that it can only be dropped on big cities and only in the daytime, when the tram lines and so forth are in operation."

AFTER FIVE DAYS of ministering to the wounded in the park, Mr. Tanimoto returned, on August 11th, to his parsonage and dug around in the ruins. He retrieved some diaries and church records that had been kept in books and were only charred around the edges, as well as some cooking utensils and pottery. While he was at work, a Miss Tanaka came and said that her father had been asking for him. Mr. Tanimoto had reason to hate her father, the retired shipping-company official who, though he made a great show of his charity, was notoriously selfish and cruel, and who, just a few days before the bombing, had said openly to several people that Mr. Tanimoto was a spy for the Americans. Several times he had derided Christianity and called it un-Japanese. At the moment of the bombing, Mr. Tanaka had been walking in the street in front of the city's radio station. He received serious flash burns, but he was able to walk home. He took refuge in his Neighborhood Association shelter and from there tried hard to get medical aid. He expected all the doctors of Hiroshima to come to him, because he was so rich and so famous for giving his money away. When none of them came, he angrily set out to look for them; leaning on his daughter's arm, he walked from private hospital to private hospital, but all were in ruins, and he went back and lay down in the shelter again. Now he was very weak and knew he was going to die. He was willing to be comforted by any religion.

Mr. Tanimoto went to help him. He descended into the tomblike shelter and, when his eyes were adjusted to the darkness, saw Mr. Tanaka, his face and arms puffed up and covered with pus and blood, and his eyes swollen shut. The old man smelled very bad, and he moaned constantly. He seemed to recognize Mr. Tanimoto's voice. Standing at the shelter stairway to get light, Mr. Tanimoto read loudly from a Japanese-language pocket Bible: "For a thousand years in Thy sight are but as yesterday when it is past, and as a watch in the night. Thou carriest the children of men away as with a flood; they are as a sleep; in the morning they are like grass which groweth up. In the morning it flourisheth and groweth up; in the evening it is cut down, and withereth. For we are consumed by Thine anger and by Thy wrath are we troubled. Thou hast set our iniquities before Thee, our secret sins in the light of Thy countenance. For all our days are passed away in Thy wrath: we spend our years as a tale that is told. . . ."

Mr. Tanaka died as Mr. Tanimoto read the psalm.

On August 11th, word came to the Ninoshima Military Hospital that a large number of military casualties from the Chugoku Regional Army Headquarters were to arrive on the island that day, and it was deemed necessary to evacuate all civilian patients. Miss Sasaki, still running an alarmingly high fever, was put on a large ship. She lay out on deck, with a pillow under her leg. There were awnings over the deck, but the vessel's course put her in the sunlight. She felt as if she were under a magnifying glass in the sun. Pus oozed out of her wound, and soon the whole pillow was covered with it. She was taken ashore at Hatsukaichi, a town several miles to the southwest of Hiroshima, and put in the Goddess of Mercy Primary School, which had been turned into a hospital. She lay there for several days before a specialist on fractures came from Kobe. By then her leg was red and swollen up to her hip. The doctor decided he could not set the breaks. He made an incision and put in a rubber pipe to drain off the putrescence.

At the Novitiate, the motherless Kataoka children were inconsolable. Father Cieslik worked hard to keep them distracted. He put riddles to them. He asked, "What is the cleverest animal in the world?," and after the thirteen-year-old girl had guessed the ape, the elephant, the horse, he said, "No, it must be the hippopotamus," because in Japanese that animal is *kaba*, the reverse of *baka*, stupid. He told Bible stories, beginning, in the order of things, with the Creation. He showed them a scrapbook of snapshots taken in Europe. Nevertheless, they cried most of the time for their mother.

Several days later, Father Cieslik started hunting for the children's family. First, he learned through the police that an uncle had been to the authorities in Kure, a city not far away, to inquire for the children. After that, he heard that an older brother had been trying to trace them through the post office in Ujina, a suburb of Hiroshima. Still later, he heard that the mother was alive and was on Goto Island, off Nagasaki. And at last, by keeping a check on the Ujina post office, he got in touch with the brother and returned the children to their mother.

ABOUT A WEEK after the bomb dropped, a vague, incomprehensible rumor reached Hiroshima—that the city had been destroyed by the energy released when atoms were somehow split in two. The weapon was referred to in this word-of-mouth report as *genshi bakudan*—the root characters of which can be translated as "original child bomb." No one understood the idea or put any more credence in it than in the powdered magnesium and such things. Newspapers were being brought in from other cities, but they were still confining themselves to extremely general statements, such as Domei's assertion on August 12th: "There is nothing to do but admit the tremendous power of this inhuman bomb." Already, Japanese physicists had entered the city with Lauritsen electroscopes and Neher electrometers; they understood the idea all too well.

ON AUGUST 12TH, the Nakamuras, all of them still rather sick, went to the nearby town of Kabe and moved in with Mrs. Nakamura's sister-in-law. The next day, Mrs. Nakamura, although she was too ill to walk much, returned to Hiroshima alone, by electric car to the outskirts, by foot from there. All week, at the Novitiate, she had worried about her mother, brother, and older sister, who had lived in the part of town called Fukuro, and besides, she felt drawn by some fascination, just as Father Kleinsorge had been. She discovered that her family were all dead. She went back to Kabe so amazed and depressed by what she had seen and learned in the city that she could not speak that evening.

A COMPARATIVE ORDERLINESS, at least, began to be established at the Red Cross Hospital. Dr. Sasaki, back from his rest, undertook to classify his patients (who were still scattered everywhere, even on the stairways). The staff gradually swept up the debris. Best of all, the nurses and attendants started to remove the corpses. Disposal of the dead, by decent cremation and enshrinement, is a greater moral responsibility to the Japanese than adequate care of the living. Relatives identified most of the first day's dead in and around the hospital. Beginning on the second day, whenever a patient appeared to be moribund, a piece of paper with his name on it was fastened to his clothing. The corpse detail carried the bodies to a clearing outside, placed them on pyres of wood from ruined houses, burned them, put some of the ashes in envelopes intended for exposed X-ray plates, marked the envelopes with the names of the deceased, and piled them, neatly and respectfully, in stacks in the main office. In a few days, the envelopes filled one whole side of the impromptu shrine.

IN KABE, on the morning of August 15th, ten-year-old Toshio Nakamura heard an airplane overhead. He ran outdoors and identified it with a professional eye as a B-29. "There goes Mr. B!" he shouted.

One of his relatives called out to him, "Haven't you had enough of Mr. B?"

The question had a kind of symbolism. At almost that very moment, the dull, dispirited voice of Hirohito, the Emperor Tenno, was speaking for the first time in history over the radio: "After pondering deeply the general trends of the world and the actual conditions obtaining in Our Empire today, We have decided to effect a settlement of the present situation by resorting to an extraordinary measure. . . ."

Mrs. Nakamura had gone to the city again, to dig up some rice she had buried in her Neighborhood Association air-raid shelter. She got it and started back for Kabe. On the electric car, quite by chance, she ran into her younger sister, who had not been in Hiroshima the day of the bombing. "Have you heard the news?" her sister asked.

"What news?"

"The war is over."

"Don't say such a foolish thing, sister."

"But I heard it over the radio myself." And then, in a whisper, "It was the Emperor's voice."

"Oh," Mrs. Nakamura said (she needed nothing more to make her give up thinking, in spite of the atomic bomb, that Japan still had a chance to win the war), "in that case . . ."

SOME TIME LATER, in a letter to an American, Mr. Tanimoto described the events of that morning. "At the time of the Post-War, the marvelous thing in our history happened. Our Emperor broadcasted his own voice through radio directly to us, common people of Japan. Aug. 15th we were told that some news of great importance could be heard & all of us should hear it. So I went to Hiroshima railway station. There set a loud-speaker in the ruins of the station. Many civilians, all of them were in boundage, some being helped by shoulder of their daughters, some sustaining their injured feet by sticks, they listened to the broadcast and when they came to realize the fact that it was the Emperor, they cried with full tears in their eyes, 'What a wonderful blessing it is that Tenno himself call on us and we can hear his own voice in person. We are thoroughly satisfied in such a great sacrifice.' When they came to know the war was ended—that is, Japan was defeated, they, of course, were deeply disappointed, but followed after their Emperor's commandment in calm spirit, making whole-hearted sacrifice for the everlasting peace of the world—and Japan started her new way."

IV · Panic Grass and Feverfew

ON AUGUST 18TH, twelve days after the bomb burst, Father Klein-sorge set out on foot for Hiroshima from the Novitiate with his papier-mâché suitcase in his hand. He had begun to think that this bag, in which he kept his valuables, had a talismanic quality, because of the way he had found it after the explosion, standing handle-side up in the doorway of his room, while the desk under which he had previously hidden it was in splinters all over the floor. Now he was using it to carry the yen belonging to the Society of Jesus to the Hiroshima branch of the Yokohama Specie Bank, already reopened in its half-ruined building. On the whole, he felt quite well that morning. It is true that the minor cuts he had received had not healed in three or four days, as the rector of the Novitiate, who had examined them, had positively promised they would, but Father Kleinsorge had rested well for a week and considered that he was again ready for hard work. By now he was accustomed to the terrible scene through which he walked on his way into the city: the large rice field near the Novitiate, streaked with brown; the houses on the outskirts of the city, standing but decrepit, with broken windows and dishevelled tiles; and then, quite suddenly, the beginning of the four square miles of reddish-brown scar, where nearly everything had been buffeted down and burned; range on range of collapsed city blocks, with here and there a crude sign erected on a pile of ashes and tiles ("Sister, where are you?" or "All safe and we live at Toyosaka"); naked trees and canted telephone poles; the few standing, gutted buildings only accentuating the horizontality of everything else (the Museum of Science and Industry, with its dome stripped to its steel frame, as if for an autopsy; the modern Chamber of Commerce Building, its tower as cold, rigid, and unassailable after the blow as before; the huge, low-lying, camouflaged city hall; the row of dowdy banks, caricaturing a shaken economic system); and in the streets a macabre traffic—hundreds of crumpled bicycles, shells of streetcars and automobiles, all halted in mid-motion. The whole way, Father Kleinsorge was oppressed by the thought that all the damage he saw had been done in one instant by one bomb. By the time he reached the center of town, the day had become very hot. He walked to the Yokohama Bank, which was doing business in a temporary wooden stall on the ground floor of its building, deposited the money, went by the mission compound just to have another look at the wreckage, and then started back to the Novitiate. About halfway there, he began to have peculiar sensations. The more or less magical suitcase, now empty, suddenly seemed terribly heavy. His knees grew weak. He felt excruciatingly tired. With a considerable expenditure of spirit, he managed to reach the Novitiate. He did not think his weakness was worth mentioning to the other Jesuits. But a couple of days later, while attempting to say Mass, he had an onset of faintness and even after three attempts was unable to go through with the service, and the next morning the rector, who had examined Father Kleinsorge's apparently negligible but unhealed cuts daily, asked in surprise, "What have you done to your wounds?" They had suddenly opened wider and were swollen and inflamed.

As she dressed on the morning of August 20th, in the home of her sister-in-law in Kabe, not far from Nagatsuka, Mrs. Nakamura, who had suffered no cuts or burns at all, though she had been rather nauseated all through the week she and her children had spent as guests of Father Kleinsorge and the other Catholics at the Novitiate, began fixing her hair and noticed, after one stroke, that her comb carried with it a whole handful of hair; the second time, the same thing happened, so she stopped combing at once. But in the next three or four days, her hair kept falling out of its own accord, until she was quite bald. She began living indoors, practically in hiding. On August 26th, both she and her younger daughter, Myeko, woke up feeling extremely weak and tired, and they stayed on their bedrolls. Her son and other daughter, who had shared every experience with her during and after the bombing, felt fine.

At about the same time—he lost track of the days, so hard was he working to set up a temporary place of worship in a private house he had rented in the outskirts—Mr. Tanimoto fell suddenly ill with a general malaise, weariness, and feverishness, and he, too, took to his bedroll on the floor of the half-wrecked house of a friend in the suburb of Ushida.

These four did not realize it, but they were coming down with the strange, capricious disease which came later to be known as radiation sickness.

MISS SASAKI lay in steady pain in the Goddess of Mercy Primary School, at Hatsukaichi, the fourth station to the southwest of Hiroshima on the electric train. An internal infection still prevented the proper setting of the compound fracture of her lower left leg. A young man who was in the same hospital and who seemed to have grown fond of her in spite of her unremitting preoccupation with her suffering, or else just pitied her because of it, lent her a Japanese translation of de Maupassant, and she tried to read the stories, but she could concentrate for only four or five minutes at a time.

The hospitals and aid stations around Hiroshima were so crowded in the first weeks after the bombing, and their staffs were so variable, depending on their health and on the unpredictable arrival of outside help, that patients had to be constantly shifted from place to place. Miss Sasaki, who had already been moved three times, twice by ship, was taken at the end of August to an engineering school, also at Hatsukaichi. Because her leg did not improve but swelled more and more, the doctors at the school bound it with crude splints and took her by car, on September 9th, to the Red Cross Hospital in Hiroshima. This was the first chance she had had to look at the ruins of Hiroshima; the last time she had been carried through the city's streets, she had been hovering on the edge of unconsciousness. Even though the wreckage had been described to her, and though she was still in pain, the sight horrified and amazed her, and there was something she noticed about it that particularly gave her the creeps. Over everything—up through the wreckage of the city, in gutters, along the riverbanks, tangled among tiles and tin roofing, climbing on charred tree trunks—was a blanket of fresh, vivid, lush, optimistic green; the verdancy rose even from the foundations of ruined houses. Weeds already hid the ashes, and wild flowers were in bloom among the city's bones. The bomb had not only left the underground organs of plants intact; it had stimulated them. Everywhere were bluets and Spanish bayonets, goosefoot, morning glories and day lilies, the hairy-fruited bean, purslane and clotbur and sesame and panic grass and fever-few. Especially in a circle at the center, sickle senna grew in extraordinary regeneration, not only standing among the charred remnants of the same plant but pushing up in new places, among bricks and through cracks in the asphalt. It actually seemed as if a load of sickle-senna seed had been dropped along with the bomb.

At the Red Cross Hospital, Miss Sasaki was put under the care of Dr. Sasaki. Now, a month after the explosion, something like order had been reëstablished in the hospital; which is to say that the patients who still lay in the corridors at least had mats to sleep on and that the supply of medicines, which had given out in the first few days, had been replaced, though inadequately, by contributions from other cities. Dr. Sasaki, who had had one seventeen-hour sleep at his home on the third night, had ever since then rested only about six hours a night, on a mat at the hospital; he had lost twenty pounds from his very small body; he still wore the borrowed glasses.

Since Miss Sasaki was a woman and was so sick (and perhaps, he afterward admitted, just a little bit because she was named Sasaki), Dr. Sasaki put her on a mat in a semi-private room, which at that time had only eight people in it. He questioned her and put down on her record card, in the correct, scrunched-up German in which he wrote all his records: "*Mittelgrosse Patientin in gutem Ernährungszustand. Fraktur am linken Unterschenkelknochen mit Wunde; Anschwellung in der linken Unterschenkelgegend. Haut und sichtbare Schleimhäute mässig durchblutet und kein Oedema,*" noting that she was a medium-sized female patient in good general health; that she had a compound fracture of the left tibia, with swelling of the left lower leg; that her skin and visible mucous membranes were heavily spotted with *petechiae*, which are hemorrhages about the size of grains of rice, or even as big as soybeans; and, in addition, that her head, eyes, throat, lungs, and heart were apparently normal; and that she had a fever. He wanted to set her fracture and put her leg in a cast, but he had run out of plaster of Paris long since, so he just stretched her out on a mat and prescribed aspirin for her fever, and glucose intravenously and diastase orally for her undernourishment (which he had not entered on her record because everyone suffered from it). She exhibited only one of the queer symptoms so many of his patients were just then beginning to show—the spot hemorrhages.

Dr. Fujii was still pursued by bad luck, which still was connected with rivers. Now he was living in the summer house of Mr. Okuma, in Fukawa. This house clung to the steep banks of the Ota River. Here his injuries seemed to make good progress, and he even began to treat refugees who came to him from the neighborhood, using medical supplies he had retrieved from a cache in the suburbs. He noticed in some of his patients a curious syndrome of symptoms that cropped out in the third and fourth weeks, but he was not able to do much more than swathe cuts and burns. Early in September, it began to rain, steadily and heavily. The river rose. On September 17th, there came a cloudburst and then a typhoon, and the water crept higher and higher up the bank. Mr. Okuma and Dr. Fujii became alarmed and scrambled up the mountain to a peasant's house. (Down in Hiroshima, the flood took up where the bomb had left off—swept away bridges that had survived the blast, washed out streets, undermined foundations of buildings that still stood—and ten miles to the west, the Ono Army Hospital, where a team of experts from Kyoto Imperial University was studying the delayed affliction of the patients, suddenly slid down a beautiful, pine-dark mountainside into the Inland Sea and drowned most of the investigators and their mysteriously diseased patients alike.) After the storm, Dr. Fujii and Mr. Okuma went down to the river and found that the Okuma house had been washed altogether away.

Because so many people were suddenly feeling sick nearly a month after the atomic bomb was dropped, an unpleasant rumor began to move around, and eventually it made its way to the house in Kabe where Mrs. Nakamura lay bald and ill. It was that the atomic bomb had deposited some sort of poison on Hiroshima which would give off deadly emanations for seven years; nobody could go there all that time. This especially upset Mrs. Nakamura, who remembered that in a moment of confusion on the morning of the explosion she had literally sunk her entire means of livelihood, her Sankoku sewing machine, in the small cement water tank in front of what was left of her house; now no one would be able to go and fish it out. Up to this time, Mrs. Nakamura and her relatives had been quite resigned and passive about the moral issue of the atomic bomb, but this rumor suddenly aroused them to more hatred and resentment of America than they had felt all through the war.

Japanese physicists, who knew a great deal about atomic fission (one of them owned a cyclotron), worried about lingering radiation at Hiroshima, and in mid-August, not many days after President Truman's disclosure of the type of bomb that had been dropped, they entered the city to make investigations. The first thing they did was roughly to determine a center by observing the side on which telephone poles all around the heart of the town were scorched; they settled on the torii gateway of the Gokoku Shrine, right next to the parade ground of the Chugoku Regional Army Headquarters. From there, they worked north and south with Lauritsen electroscopes, which are sensitive to both beta particles and gamma rays. These indicated that the highest intensity of radioactivity, near the torii, was 4.2 times the average natural "leak" of ultra-short waves for the earth of that area. The scientists noticed that the flash of the bomb had discolored concrete to a light reddish tint, had scaled off the surface of granite, and had scorched certain other types of building material, and that consequently the bomb had, in some places, left prints of the shadows that had been cast by its light. The experts found, for instance, a permanent shadow thrown on the roof of the Chamber of Commerce Building (220 yards from the rough center) by the structure's rectangular tower; several others in the lookout post on top of the Hypothec Bank (2,050 yards); another in the tower of the Chugoku Electric Supply Building (800 yards); another projected by the handle of a gas pump (2,630 yards); and several on granite tombstones in the Gokoku Shrine (385 yards). By triangulating these and other such shadows with the objects that formed them, the scientists determined that the exact center was a spot a hundred and fifty yards south of the torii and a few yards southeast of the pile of ruins that had once been the Shima Hospital. (A few vague human silhouettes were found, and these gave rise to stories that eventually included fancy and precise details. One story told how a painter on a ladder was monumentalized in a kind of bas-relief on the stone façade of a bank building on which he was at work, in the act of dipping his brush into his paint can; another, how a man and his cart on the bridge near the Museum of Science and Industry, almost under the center of the explosion, were cast down in an embossed shadow which made it clear that the man was about to whip his horse.) Starting east and west from the actual center, the scientists, in early September, made new measurements, and the highest radiation they found this time was 3.9 times the natural "leak." Since radiation of at least a thousand times the natural "leak" would be required to cause serious effects on the human body, the scientists announced that people could enter Hiroshima without any peril at all.

As soon as this reassurance reached the household in which Mrs. Nakamura was concealing herself—or, at any rate, within a short time, after her hair had started growing back again—her whole family relaxed their extreme hatred of America, and Mrs. Nakamura sent her brother-in-law to look for the sewing machine. It was still submerged in the water tank, and when he brought it home, she saw, to her dismay, that it was all rusted and useless.

BY THE END of the first week in September, Father Kleinsorge was in bed at the Novitiate with a fever of 102.2, and since he seemed to be getting worse, his colleagues decided to send him to the Catholic International Hospital in Tokyo. Father Cieslik and the rector took him as far as Kobe and a Jesuit from that city took him the rest of the way, with a message from a Kobe doctor to the Mother Superior of the International Hospital: "Think twice before you give this man blood transfusions, because with atomic-bomb patients we aren't at all sure that if you stick needles in them, they'll stop bleeding."

When Father Kleinsorge arrived at the hospital, he was terribly pale and very shaky. He complained that the bomb had upset his digestion and given him abdominal pains. His white blood count was three thousand (five to seven thousand is normal), he was seriously anemic, and his temperature was 104. A doctor who did not know much about these strange manifestations—Father Kleinsorge was one of a handful of atomic patients who had reached Tokyo—came to see him, and to the patient's face he was most encouraging. "You'll be out of here in two weeks," he said. But when the doctor got out into the corridor, he said to the Mother Superior, "He'll die. All these bomb people die—you'll see. They go along for a couple of weeks and then they die."

The doctor prescribed suralimentation for Father Kleinsorge. Every three hours, they forced some eggs or beef juice into him, and they fed him all the sugar he could stand. They gave him vitamins, and iron pills and arsenic (in Fowler's solution) for his anemia. He confounded both the doctor's predictions; he neither died nor got up in a fortnight. Despite the fact that the message from the Kobe doctor deprived him of transfusions, which would have been the most useful therapy of all, his fever and his digestive troubles cleared up fairly quickly. His white count went up for a while, but early in October it dropped again, to 3,600; then, in ten days, it suddenly climbed above normal, to 8,800; and it finally settled at 5,800. His ridiculous scratches puzzled everyone. For a few days, they would mend, and then, when he moved around, they would open up again. As soon as he began to feel well, he enjoyed himself tremendously. In Hiroshima he had been one of thousands of sufferers; in Tokyo he was a curiosity. American Army doctors came by the dozen to observe him. Japanese experts questioned him. A newspaper interviewed him. And once, the confused doctor came and shook his head and said, "Baffling cases, these atomic-bomb people."

MRS. NAKAMURA LAY indoors with Myeko. They both continued sick, and though Mrs. Nakamura vaguely sensed that their trouble was caused by the bomb, she was too poor to see a doctor and so never knew exactly what the matter was. Without any treatment at all, but merely resting, they began gradually to feel better. Some of Myeko's hair fell out, and she had a tiny burn on her arm which took months to heal. The boy, Toshio, and the older girl, Yaeko, seemed well enough, though they, too, lost some hair and occasionally had bad headaches. Toshio was still having nightmares, always about the nineteen-year-old mechanic, Hideo Osaki, his hero, who had been killed by the bomb.

On his back with a fever of 104, Mr. Tanimoto worried about all the funerals he ought to be conducting for the deceased of his church. He thought he was just overtired from the hard work he had done since the bombing, but after the fever had persisted for a few days, he sent for a doctor. The doctor was too busy to visit him in Ushida, but he dispatched a nurse, who recognized his symptoms as those of mild radiation disease and came back from time to time to give him injections of vitamin B_1. A Buddhist priest with whom Mr. Tanimoto was acquainted called on him and suggested that moxibustion might give him relief; the priest showed the pastor how to give himself the ancient Japanese treatment, by setting fire to a twist of the stimulant herb moxa placed on the wrist pulse. Mr. Tanimoto found that each moxa treatment temporarily reduced his fever one degree. The nurse had told him to eat as much as possible, and every few days his mother-in-law brought him vegetables and fish from Tsuzu, twenty miles away, where she lived. He spent a month in bed, and then went ten hours by train to his father's home in Shikoku. There he rested another month.

Dr. Sasaki and his colleagues at the Red Cross Hospital watched the unprecedented disease unfold and at last evolved a theory about its nature. It had, they decided, three stages. The first stage had been all over before the doctors even knew they were dealing with a new sickness; it was the direct reaction to the bombardment of the body, at the moment when the bomb went off, by neutrons, beta particles, and gamma rays. The apparently uninjured people who had died so mysteriously in the first few hours or days had succumbed in this first stage. It killed ninety-five per cent of the people within a half mile of the center, and many thousands who were farther away. The doctors realized in retrospect that even though most of these dead had also suffered from burns and blast effects, they had absorbed enough radiation to kill them. The rays simply destroyed body cells—caused their nuclei to degenerate and broke their walls. Many people who did not die right away came down with nausea, headache, diarrhea, malaise, and fever, which lasted several days. Doctors could not be certain whether some of these symptoms were the result of radiation or nervous shock. The second stage set in ten or fifteen days after the bombing. Its first symptom was falling hair. Diarrhea and fever, which in some cases went as high as 106, came next. Twenty-five to thirty days after the explosion, blood disorders appeared: gums bled, the white-blood-cell count dropped sharply, and *petechiae* appeared on the skin and mucous membranes. The drop in the number of white blood corpuscles reduced the patient's capacity to resist infection, so open wounds were unusually slow in healing and many of the sick developed sore throats and mouths. The two key symptoms, on which the doctors came to base their prognosis, were fever and the lowered white-corpuscle count. If fever remained steady and high, the patient's chances for survival were poor. The white count almost always dropped below four thousand; a patient whose count fell below one thousand had little hope of living. Toward the end of the second stage, if the patient survived, anemia, or a drop in the red blood count, also set in. The third stage was the reaction that came when the body struggled to compensate for its ills—when, for instance, the white count not only returned to normal but increased to much higher than normal levels. In this stage, many patients died of complications, such as infections in the chest cavity. Most burns healed with deep layers of pink, rubbery scar tissue, known as keloid tumors. The duration of the disease varied, depending on the patient's constitution and the amount of radiation he had received. Some victims recovered in a week; with others the disease dragged on for months.

As the symptoms revealed themselves, it became clear that many of them resembled the effects of overdoses of X-ray, and the doctors based their therapy on that likeness. They gave victims liver extract, blood transfusions, and vitamins, especially B_1. The shortage of supplies and instruments hampered them. Allied doctors who came in after the surrender found plasma and penicillin very effective. Since the blood disorders were, in the long run, the predominant factor in the disease, some of the Japanese doctors evolved a theory as to the seat of the delayed sickness. They thought that perhaps gamma rays, entering the body at the time of the explosion, made the phosphorus in the victims' bones radioactive, and that they in turn emitted beta particles, which, though they could not penetrate far through flesh, could enter the bone marrow, where blood is manufactured, and gradually tear it down. Whatever its source, the disease had some baffling quirks. Not all the patients exhibited all the main symptoms. People who suffered flash burns were protected, to a considerable extent, from radiation sickness. Those who had lain quietly for days or even hours after the bombing were much less liable to get sick than those who had been active. Gray hair seldom fell out. And, as if nature were protecting man against his own ingenuity, the reproductive processes were affected for a time; men became sterile, women had miscarriages, menstruation stopped.

FOR TEN DAYS after the flood, Dr. Fujii lived in the peasant's house on the mountain above the Ota. Then he heard about a vacant private clinic in Kaitaichi, a suburb to the east of Hiroshima. He bought it at once, moved there, and hung out a sign inscribed in English, in honor of the conquerors:

M. FUJII, M.D.

MEDICAL & VENEREAL

Quite recovered from his wounds, he soon built up a strong practice, and he was delighted, in the evenings, to receive members of the occupying forces, on whom he lavished whiskey and practiced English.

GIVING MISS SASAKI a local anaesthetic of procaine, Dr. Sasaki made an incision in her leg on October 23rd, to drain the infection, which still lingered on eleven weeks after the injury. In the following days, so much pus formed that he had to dress the opening each morning and evening. A week later, she complained of great pain, so he made another incision; he cut still a third, on November 9th, and enlarged it on the twenty-sixth. All this time, Miss Sasaki grew weaker and weaker, and her spirits fell low. One day, the young man who had lent her his translation of de Maupassant at Hatsukaichi came to visit her; he told her that he was going to Kyushu but that when he came back, he would like to see her again. She didn't care. Her leg had been so swollen and painful all along that the doctor had not even tried to set the fractures, and though an X-ray taken in November showed that the bones were mending, she could see under the sheet that her left leg was nearly three inches shorter than her right and that her left foot was turning inward. She thought often of the man to whom she had been engaged. Someone told her he was back from overseas. She wondered what he had heard about her injuries that made him stay away.

FATHER KLEINSORGE was discharged from the hospital in Tokyo on December 19th and took a train home. On the way, two days later, at Yokogawa, a stop just before Hiroshima, Dr. Fujii boarded the train. It was the first time the two men had met since before the bombing. They sat together. Dr. Fujii said he was going to the annual gathering of his family, on the anniversary of his father's death. When they started talking about their experiences, the Doctor was quite entertaining as he told how his places of residence kept falling into rivers. Then he asked Father Kleinsorge how he was, and the Jesuit talked about his stay in the hospital. "The doctors told me to be cautious," he said. "They ordered me to have a two-hour nap every afternoon."

Dr. Fujii said, "It's hard to be cautious in Hiroshima these days. Everyone seems to be so busy."

A NEW MUNICIPAL GOVERNMENT, set up under Allied Military Government direction, had gone to work at last in the city hall. Citizens who had recovered from various degrees of radiation sickness were coming back by the thousand—by November 1st, the population, mostly crowded into the outskirts, was already 137,000, more than a third of the wartime peak—and the government set in motion all kinds of projects to put them to work rebuilding the city. It hired men to clear the streets, and others to gather scrap iron, which they sorted and piled in mountains opposite the city hall. Some returning residents were putting up their own shanties and huts, and planting small squares of winter wheat beside them, but the city also authorized and built four hundred one-family "barracks." Utilities were repaired—electric lights shone again, trams started running, and employees of the waterworks fixed seventy thousand leaks in mains and plumbing. A Planning Conference, with an enthusiastic young Military Government officer, Lieutenant John D. Montgomery, of Kalamazoo, as its adviser, began to consider what sort of city the new Hiroshima should be. The ruined city had flourished—and had been an inviting target— mainly because it had been one of the most important military-command and communication centers in Japan, and would have become the Imperial headquarters had the islands been invaded and Tokyo been captured. Now there would be no huge military establishments to help revive the city. The Planning Conference, at a loss as to just what importance Hiroshima could have, fell back on rather vague cultural and paving projects. It drew maps with avenues a hundred yards wide and thought seriously of erecting a group of buildings as a monument to the disaster, and naming them the Institute of International Amity. Statistical workers gathered what figures they could on the effects of the bomb. They reported that 78,150 people had been killed, 13,983 were missing, and 37,425 had been injured. No one in the city government pretended that these figures were accurate—though the Americans accepted them as official— and as the months went by and more and more hundreds of corpses were dug up from the ruins, and as the number of unclaimed urns of ashes at the Zempoji Temple in Koi rose into the thousands, the statisticians began to say that at least a hundred thousand people had lost their lives in the bombing. Since many people died of a combination of causes, it was impossible to figure exactly how many were killed by each cause, but the statisticians calculated that about twenty-five per cent had died of direct burns from the bomb, about fifty per cent from other injuries, and about twenty per cent as a result of radiation effects. The statisticians' figures on property damage were more reliable: sixty-two thousand out of ninety thousand buildings destroyed, and six thousand more damaged beyond repair. In the heart of the city, they found only five modern buildings that could be used again without major repairs. This small number was by no means the fault of flimsy Japanese construction. In fact, since the 1923 earthquake, Japanese building regulations had required that the roof of each large building be able to bear a minimum load of seventy pounds per square foot, whereas American regulations do not normally specify more than forty pounds per square foot.

Scientists swarmed into the city. Some of them measured the force that had been necessary to shift marble gravestones in the cemeteries, to knock over twenty-two of the forty-seven railroad cars in the yards at Hiroshima station, to lift and move the concrete roadway on one of the bridges, and to perform other noteworthy acts of strength, and concluded that the pressure exerted by the explosion varied from 5.3 to 8.0 tons per square yard. Others found that mica, of which the melting point is 900° C., had fused on granite gravestones three hundred and eighty yards from the center; that telephone poles of *Cryptomeria japonica*, whose carbonization temperature is 240° C., had been charred at forty-four hundred yards from the center; and that the surface of gray clay tiles of the type used in Hiroshima, whose melting point is 1,300° C., had dissolved at six hundred yards; and, after examining other significant ashes and melted bits, they concluded that the bomb's heat on the ground at the center must have been 6,000° C. And from further measurements of radiation, which involved, among other things, the scraping up of fission fragments from roof troughs and drainpipes as far away as the suburb of Takasu, thirty-three hundred yards from the center, they learned some far more important facts about the nature of the bomb. General Mac-Arthur's headquarters systematically censored all mention of the bomb in Japanese scientific publications, but soon the fruit of the scientists' calculations became common knowledge among Japanese physicists, doctors, chemists, journalists, professors, and, no doubt, those statesmen and military men who were still in circulation. Long before the American public had been told, most of the scientists and lots of non-scientists in Japan knew—from the calculations of Japanese nuclear physicists—that a uranium bomb had exploded at Hiroshima and a more powerful one, of plutonium, at Nagasaki. They also knew that theoretically one ten times as powerful—or twenty—could be developed. The Japanese scientists thought they knew the exact height at which the bomb at Hiroshima was exploded and the approximate weight of the uranium used. They estimated that, even with the primitive bomb used at Hiroshima, it would require a shelter of concrete fifty inches thick to protect a human being entirely from radiation sickness. The scientists had these and other details which remained subject to security in the United States printed and mimeographed and bound into little books. The Americans knew of the existence of these, but tracing them and seeing that they did not fall into the wrong hands would have obliged the occupying authorities to set up, for this one purpose alone, an enormous police system in Japan. Altogether, the Japanese scientists were somewhat amused at the efforts of their conquerors to keep security on atomic fission.

LATE IN FEBRUARY, 1946, a friend of Miss Sasaki's called on Father Kleinsorge and asked him to visit her in the hospital. She had been growing more and more depressed and morbid; she seemed little interested in living. Father Kleinsorge went to see her several times. On his first visit, he kept the conversation general, formal, and yet vaguely sympathetic, and did not mention religion. Miss Sasaki herself brought it up the second time he dropped in on her. Evidently she had had some talks with a Catholic. She asked bluntly, "If your God is so good and kind, how can he let people suffer like this?" She made a gesture which took in her shrunken leg, the other patients in her room, and Hiroshima as a whole.

"My child," Father Kleinsorge said, "man is not now in the condition God intended. He has fallen from grace through sin." And he went on to explain all the reasons for everything.

It came to Mrs. Nakamura's attention that a carpenter from Kabe was building a number of wooden shanties in Hiroshima which he rented for fifty yen a month—\$3.33, at the fixed rate of exchange. Mrs. Nakamura had lost the certificates for her bonds and other wartime savings, but fortunately she had copied off all the numbers just a few days before the bombing and had taken the list to Kabe, and so, when her hair had grown in enough for her to be presentable, she went to her bank in Hiroshima, and a clerk there told her that after checking her numbers against the records the bank would give her her money. As soon as she got it, she rented one of the carpenter's shacks. It was in Nobori-cho, near the site of her former house, and though its floor was dirt and it was dark inside, it was at least a home in Hiroshima, and she was no longer dependent on the charity of her in-laws. During the spring, she cleared away some nearby wreckage and planted a vegetable garden. She cooked with utensils and ate off plates she scavenged from the debris. She sent Myeko to the kindergarten which the Jesuits reopened, and the two older children attended Nobori-cho Primary School, which, for want of buildings, held classes out of doors. Toshio wanted to study to be a mechanic, like his hero, Hideo Osaki. Prices were high; by midsummer Mrs. Nakamura's savings were gone. She sold some of her clothes to get food. She had once had several expensive kimonos, but during the war one had been stolen, she had given one to a sister who had been bombed out in Tokuyama, she had lost a couple in the Hiroshima bombing, and now she sold her last one. It brought only a hundred yen, which did not last long. In June, she went to Father Kleinsorge for advice about how to get along, and in early August, she was still considering the two alternatives he suggested—taking work as a domestic for some of the Allied occupation forces, or borrowing from her relatives enough money, about five hundred yen, or a bit more than thirty dollars, to repair her rusty sewing machine and resume the work of a seamstress.

When Mr. Tanimoto returned from Shikoku, he draped a tent he owned over the roof of the badly damaged house he had rented in Ushida. The roof still leaked, but he conducted services in the damp living room. He began thinking about raising money to restore his church in the city. He became quite friendly with Father Kleinsorge and saw the Jesuits often. He envied them their Church's wealth; they seemed to be able to do anything they wanted. He had nothing to work with except his own energy, and that was not what it had been.

THE SOCIETY OF JESUS had been the first institution to build a relatively permanent shanty in the ruins of Hiroshima. That had been while Father Kleinsorge was in the hospital. As soon as he got back, he began living in the shack, and he and another priest, Father Laderman, who had joined him in the mission, arranged for the purchase of three of the standardized "barracks," which the city was selling at seven thousand yen apiece. They put two together, end to end, and made a pretty chapel of them; they ate in the third. When materials were available, they commissioned a contractor to build a three-story mission house exactly like the one that had been destroyed in the fire. In the compound, carpenters cut timbers, gouged mortises, shaped tenons, whittled scores of wooden pegs and bored holes for them, until all the parts for the house were in a neat pile; then, in three days, they put the whole thing together, like an Oriental puzzle, without any nails at all. Father Kleinsorge was finding it hard, as Dr. Fujii had suggested he would, to be cautious and to take his naps. He went out every day on foot to call on Japanese Catholics and prospective converts. As the months went by, he grew more and more tired. In June, he read an article in the Hiroshima *Chugoku* warning survivors against working too hard—but what could he do? By July, he was worn out, and early in August, almost exactly on the anniversary of the bombing, he went back to the Catholic International Hospital, in Tokyo, for a month's rest.

WHETHER OR NOT Father Kleinsorge's answers to Miss Sasaki's questions about life were final and absolute truths, she seemed quickly to draw physical strength from them. Dr. Sasaki noticed it and congratulated Father Kleinsorge. By April 15th, her temperature and white count were normal and the infection in the wound was beginning to clear up. On the twentieth, there was almost no pus, and for the first time she jerked along a corridor on crutches. Five days later, the wound had begun to heal, and on the last day of the month she was discharged.

During the early summer, she prepared herself for conversion to Catholicism. In that period she had ups and downs. Her depressions were deep. She knew she would always be a cripple. Her fiancé never came to see her. There was nothing for her to do except read and look out, from her house on a hillside in Koi, across the ruins of the city where her parents and brother died. She was nervous, and any sudden noise made her put her hands quickly to her throat. Her leg still hurt; she rubbed it often and patted it, as if to console it.

IT TOOK SIX MONTHS for the Red Cross Hospital, and even longer for Dr. Sasaki, to get back to normal. Until the city restored electric power, the hospital had to limp along with the aid of a Japanese Army generator in its back yard. Operating tables, X-ray machines, dentist chairs, everything complicated and essential came in a trickle of charity from other cities. In Japan, face is important even to institutions, and long before the Red Cross Hospital was back to par on basic medical equipment, its directors put up a new yellow brick veneer façade, so the hospital became the handsomest building in Hiroshima—from the street. For the first four months, Dr. Sasaki was the only surgeon on the staff and he almost never left the building; then, gradually, he began to take an interest in his own life again. He got married in March. He gained back some of the weight he lost, but his appetite remained only fair; before the bombing, he used to eat four rice balls at every meal, but a year after it he could manage only two. He felt tired all the time. "But I have to realize," he said, "that the whole community is tired."

A YEAR AFTER the bomb was dropped, Miss Sasaki was a cripple; Mrs. Nakamura was destitute; Father Kleinsorge was back in the hospital; Dr. Sasaki was not capable of the work he once could do; Dr. Fujii had lost the thirty-room hospital it took him many years to acquire, and had no prospects of rebuilding it; Mr. Tanimoto's church had been ruined and he no longer had his exceptional vitality. The lives of these six people, who were among the luckiest in Hiroshima, would never be the same. What they thought of their experiences and of the use of the atomic bomb was, of course, not unanimous. One feeling they did seem to share, however, was a curious kind of elated community spirit, something like that of the Londoners after their blitz—a pride in the way they and their fellow-survivors had stood up to a dreadful ordeal. Just before the anniversary, Mr. Tanimoto wrote in a letter to an American some words which expressed this feeling: "What a heartbreaking scene this was the first night! About midnight I landed on the riverbank. So many injured people lied on the ground that I made my way by striding over them. Repeating 'Excuse me,' I forwarded and carried a tub of water with me and gave a cup of water to each one of them. They raised their upper bodies slowly and accepted a cup of water with a bow and drunk quietly and, spilling any remnant, gave back a cup with hearty expression of their thankfulness, and said, 'I couldn't help my sister, who was buried under the house, because I had to take care of my mother who got a deep wound on her eye and our house soon set fire and we hardly escaped. Look, I lost my home, my family, and at last my-self bitterly injured. But now I have gotted my mind to dedicate what I have and to complete the war for our country's sake.' Thus they pledged to me, even women and children did the same. Being entirely tired I lied down on the ground among them, but couldn't sleep at all. Next morning I found many men and women dead, whom I gave water last night. But, to my great surprise, I never heard any one cried in disorder, even though they suffered in great agony. They died in silence, with no grudge, setting their teeth to bear it. All for the country!

"Dr. Y. Hiraiwa, professor of Hiroshima University of Literature and Science, and one of my church members, was buried by the bomb under the two storied house with his son, a student of Tokyo University. Both of them could not move an inch under tremendously heavy pressure. And the house already caught fire. His son said, 'Father, we can do nothing except make our mind up to consecrate our lives for the country. Let us give *Banzai* to our Emperor.' Then the father followed after his son, '*Tenno-heika, Banzai, Banzai, Banzai!*' In the result, Dr. Hiraiwa said, 'Strange to say, I felt calm and bright and peaceful spirit in my heart, when I chanted *Banzai* to Tenno.' Afterward his son got out and digged down and pulled out his father and thus they were saved. In thinking of their experience of that time Dr. Hiraiwa repeated, 'What a fortunate that we are Japanese! It was my first time I ever tasted such a beautiful spirit when I decided to die for our Emperor.'

"Miss Kayoko Nobutoki, a student of girl's high school, Hiroshima Jazabuin, and a daughter of my church member, was taking rest with her friends beside the heavy fence of the Buddhist Temple. At the moment the atomic bomb was dropped, the fence fell upon them. They could not move a bit under such a heavy fence and then smoke entered into even a crack and choked their breath. One of the girls begun to sing *Kimi ga yo*, national anthem, and others followed in chorus and died. Meanwhile one of them found a crack and struggled hard to get out. When she was taken in the Red Cross Hospital she told how her friends died, tracing back in her memory to singing in chorus our national anthem. They were just 13 years old.

"Yes, people of Hiroshima died manly in the atomic bombing, believing that it was for Emperor's sake."

A surprising number of the people of Hiroshima remained more or less indifferent about the ethics of using the bomb. Possibly they were too terrified by it to want to think about it at all. Not many of them even bothered to find out much about what it was like. Mrs. Nakamura's conception of it—and awe of it—was typical. "The atom bomb," she would say when asked about it, "is the size of a matchbox. The heat of it is six thousand times that of the sun. It exploded in the air. There is some radium in it. I don't know just how it works, but when the radium is put together, it explodes." As for the use of the bomb, she would say, "It was war and we had to expect it." And then she would add, "*Shikata ga nai*," a Japanese expression as common as, and corresponding to, the Russian word "*nichevo*": "It can't be helped. Oh, well. Too bad." Dr. Fujii said approximately the same thing about the use of the bomb to Father Kleinsorge one evening, in German: "*Da ist nichts zu machen.* There's nothing to be done about it."

Many citizens of Hiroshima, however, continued to feel a hatred for Americans which nothing could possibly erase. "I see," Dr. Sasaki once said, "that they are holding a trial for war criminals in Tokyo just now. I think they ought to try the men who decided to use the bomb and they should hang them all."

Father Kleinsorge and the other German Jesuit priests, who, as foreigners, could be expected to take a relatively detached view, often discussed the ethics of using the bomb. One of them, Father Siemes, who was out at Nagatsuka at the time of the attack, wrote in a report to the Holy See in Rome: "Some of us consider the bomb in the same category as poison gas and were against its use on a civilian population. Others were of the opinion that in total war, as carried on in Japan, there was no difference between civilians and soldiers, and that the bomb itself was an effective force tending to end the bloodshed, warning Japan to surrender and thus to avoid total destruction. It seems logical that he who supports total war in principle cannot complain of a war against civilians. The crux of the matter is whether total war in its present form is justifiable, even when it serves a just purpose. Does it not have material and spiritual evil as its consequences which far exceed whatever good might result? When will our moralists give us a clear answer to this question?"

It would be impossible to say what horrors were embedded in the minds of the children who lived through the day of the bombing in Hiroshima. On the surface, their recollections, months after the disaster, were of an exhilarating adventure. Toshio Nakamura, who was ten at the time of the bombing, was soon able to talk freely, even gaily, about the experience, and a few weeks before the anniversary he wrote the following matter-of-fact essay for his teacher at Nobori-cho Primary School: "The day before the bomb, I went for a swim. In the morning, I was eating peanuts. I saw a light. I was knocked to little sister's sleeping place. When we were saved, I could only see as far as the tram. My mother and I started to pack our things. The neighbors were walking around burned and bleeding. Hataya-*san* told me to run away with her. I said I wanted to wait for my mother. We went to the park. A whirlwind came. At night a gas tank burned and I saw the reflection in the river. We stayed in the park one night. Next day I went to Taiko Bridge and met my girl friends Kikuki and Murakami. They were looking for their mothers. But Kikuki's mother was wounded and Murakami's mother, alas, was dead."

Richard Hofstadter

JOHN C. CALHOUN:
THE MARX OF THE MASTER CLASS

It would be well for those interested to reflect whether there now exists, or ever has existed, a wealthy and civilized community in which one portion did not live on the labor of another; and whether the form in which slavery exists in the South is not but one modification of this universal condition. . . . Let those who are interested remember that labor is the only source of wealth, and how small a portion of it, in all old and civilized countries, even the best governed, is left to those by whose labor wealth is created.

JOHN C. CALHOUN

I

JACKSON LED THROUGH force of personality, not intellect; his successors in the White House were remarkable for neither, and yielded preeminence to Congressional politicians. Of the three greatest, Clay, Webster, and Calhoun, the last showed the most striking mind. His problem, that of defending a minority interest in a democracy, offered the toughest challenge to fresh thinking.

As nationalists closely allied with capitalistic interests, Clay and Webster could both use the ideas of the Founding Fathers as they were transmitted through the Federalist tradition. Clay, content to leave theoretical elaboration of his "American system" to economists like Mathew Carey and Hezekiah Niles, never presumed to be a thinker, and his great-

From *The American Political Tradition: And the Men Who Made It*, 1948. Copyright 1948 by Alfred A. Knopf, Inc.

est contribution to the political art was to demonstrate how a Hamiltonian program could gain strength by an admixture of the Jeffersonian spirit. Webster, who was satisfied, on the whole, to follow the conservative republicanism of the Fathers, is rightly remembered best as the quasi-official rhapsodist of American nationalism. He felt no need to attempt a new synthesis for his own time.

Calhoun, representing a conscious minority with special problems, brought new variations into American political thinking. Although his concepts of nullification and the concurrent voice have little more than antiquarian interest for the twentieth-century mind, he also set forth a system of social analysis that is worthy of considerable respect. Calhoun was one of a few Americans of his age—Richard Hildreth and Orestes Brownson were others—who had a keen sense for social structure and class forces. Before Karl Marx published the *Communist Manifesto,* Calhoun laid down an analysis of American politics and the sectional struggle which foreshadowed some of the seminal ideas of Marx's system. A brilliant if narrow dialectician, probably the last American statesman to do any primary political thinking, he placed the central ideas of "scientific" socialism in an inverted framework of moral values and produced an arresting defense of reaction, a sort of intellectual Black Mass.

Calhoun was born in 1782 into a Scotch-Irish family that had entered the colonies in Pennsylvania and migrated to the Southern back country in the middle of the century. His paternal grandmother had been killed by Indians on the frontier in 1760 and his mother's brother, John Caldwell, after whom he was named, had been murdered by Tories during the Revolution. Patrick Calhoun, his father, acquired over thirty slaves in an area where slaves were rare, became a prominent citizen of the South Carolina hinterland and a member of the state legislature, and opposed the federal Constitution. When John was fourteen, Patrick died. The boy was tutored for a time by his brother-in-law, Moses Waddel, soon to become one of the South's outstanding educators; he graduated from Yale in 1804, studied law at Tapping Reeve's famous school in Litchfield, and joined the Carolina bar.

Calhoun's warmest attachment during these years, and perhaps all his life, was to an older woman, Floride Bonneau Calhoun, his father's cousin by marriage. After years of close friendship and constant correspondence, he married her eighteen-year-old daughter, whose name was also Floride. It was customary for a bride to keep control of her own fortune, but the young planter indelicately insisted that she place her property in his hands. It was so arranged. Besides these extensive landholdings, the connection brought Calhoun an assured position among gentlefolk of the seaboard.

In 1808, three years before his marriage and shortly after his admission to the bar, Calhoun was elected to the South Carolina legislature. In 1810 he was elected to Congress, where he promptly became a leader among the young "war hawks." When the war with Britain began, he became the foremost advocate of war appropriations, and for fifteen years he remained the most ardent worker for national unity and national power. He was for more troops, more funds, for manufactures, federal roads, a higher tariff, and a new national bank. Impatient with "refined arguments on the Constitution," he waved all constitutional objections aside. In 1817 he became Secretary of War in James Monroe's Cabinet and put through an ambitious program of fortifications and administrative improvement. John Quincy Adams, his colleague in the Cabinet, wrote in his diary that Calhoun was

> a man of fair and candid mind, of honorable principles, of clear and quick understanding, of cool self-possession, of enlarged philosophic views, and of ardent patriotism. He is above all sectional and factional prejudices more than any other statesman of this Union with whom I have ever acted.

Calhoun took a conciliatory view of sectional issues. When the question of slavery first appeared in the controversy over Missouri, he stood for moderation. "We to the South ought not to assent easily to the belief that there is a conspiracy either against our property or just weight in the Union," he wrote to a friend, adding that he favored supporting such measures and men "without a regard to sections, as are best calculated to advance the general interest." One must agree with William E. Dodd: Calhoun's whole early life as a public man had been built upon nationalism, and at heart he remained a Unionist as well as a Southerner. What he wanted was not for the South to leave the Union, but to dominate it. Even as late as 1838 he cautioned his daughter against the disunionist school of thought. "Those who make it up, do not think of the difficulty involved in the word; how many bleeding [pores] must be taken up on passing the knife of separation through a body politic. . . . *We must remember, it is the most difficult process in the world to make two people of one.*"

Changes at home converted the reluctant Calhoun from a nationalist to a sectionalist. As the cotton economy spread, South Carolina became entirely a staple-growing state. Her planters, working exhausted land, and hard pressed to compete with the fresh soil of the interior, found it impossible to submit quietly any longer to the exactions of the protective tariff. Before long a fiery local group of statesmen made it impossible for any politician to stay in business who did not take a strong stand for sectional interests.

Calhoun, who aspired to be much more than a regional leader, managed for some years to soft-pedal his swing to a sectional position. His initial strategy was to make an alliance with the Jackson supporters in the hope that Jackson, himself a Southern planter and an old Republican, would pursue policies favorable to the South and eventually pass the presidency on to Calhoun. Then Calhoun would cement an alliance between the agrarian South and West against the capitalistic East. Both in

1824, when Jackson was defeated by the Clay-Adams bargain, and in 1828, when he was elected, Calhoun was his vice-presidential running mate.[1]

During the campaign of 1828 the exorbitant Tariff of Abominations became law, and Calhoun wrote his first great document on the sectional question, the *Exposition and Protest*, the authorship of which remained secret for some time for political reasons.[2] Denouncing the tariff bitterly, Calhoun declared: "We are the serfs of the system." After giving an impressive analysis of the costs of the tariff to the plantation economy, he came to political remedies. "No government based on the naked principle that the majority ought to govern, however true the maxim in its proper sense, and under proper restrictions, can preserve its liberty even for a single generation." Only those governments which provide checks on power, "which limit and restrain within proper bounds the power of the majority," have had a prolonged and happy existence. Seeking for some constitutional means, short of secession, of resisting the majority, Calhoun seized upon the idea of state nullification. The powers of sovereignty, he contended, belonged of right entirely to the several states and were only delegated, in part, to the federal government. Therefore the right of judging whether measures of policy were infractions of their rights under the Constitution belonged to the states. When a state convention, called for the purpose, decided that constitutional rights were violated by any statute, the state had a right to declare the law null and void within its boundaries and refuse to permit its enforcement there. Nullification would be binding on both the citizens of the state and the federal government. The *Exposition* closed with the hope that Jackson would be elected and would make a practical test of nullification unnecessary.

Calhoun and the South were soon disappointed with Old Hickory. Personal grievances—among them Jackson's discovery that Calhoun as Secretary of War had wanted to repudiate his free and easy conduct in the Seminole campaign—caused the general to break with the Carolinian. The final breach came during the nullification crisis of 1832, when Jackson turned all his wrath upon South Carolina and incontinently threatened to hang Calhoun. At its close Calhoun, having resigned from the vice-presidency, sat in the Senate for his state, planning to join the anti-Jackson coalition, and militant Southerners were thinking about new ways of stemming Northern capital. Calhoun's trajectory toward the presidency had been forcibly deflected. Henceforth his life became a long polemical exercise, his career a series of maneuvers to defend the South and propel himself into the White House. Nourished on ambition and antagonism, he grew harder, more resolute, and more ingenious.

---

[1] Because of the unusual circumstances of the election of 1824, Calhoun became Vice President although Jackson was defeated.

[2] Calhoun's report was not officially adopted, but because the lower house of the Carolina legislature ordered a printing of five thousand copies, it was generally taken as an official statement.

II

CHARLESTON WAS the great cultural center of the Old South, a city with a flavor of its own and an air of cosmopolitan taste and breeding, and Charleston was the one part of South Carolina for which Calhoun had no use. He hated the life of ease and relaxation enjoyed by the absentee planters who were the mainstay of its social and cultural distinction. In 1807, when malaria was ravaging the city, he wrote to Floride Bonneau Calhoun with ill-disguised relish that every newspaper brought a long list of deaths. This, he thought, was due far less to the climate of the place than to "the misconduct of the inhabitants; and may be considered as a curse for their intemperance and debaucheries."

Debaucheries of any kind Calhoun was never accused of. There is no record that he ever read or tried to write poetry, although there is a traditional gibe to the effect that he once began a poem with "Whereas," and stopped. Once in his life he read a novel—this at the request of a lady who asked for his judgment on it. A friend, Mary Bates, observed that she "never heard him utter a jest," and Daniel Webster in his eulogy said he had never known a man "who wasted less of life in what is called recreation, or employed less of it in any pursuits not immediately connected with the discharge of his duty." Duty is the word, for duty was the demonic force in Calhoun. "I hold the duties of life to be greater than life itself," he once wrote. ". . . I regard this life very much as a struggle against evil, and that to him who acts on proper principle, the reward is in the struggle more than in victory itself, although that greatly enhances it." In adult life to relax and play are in a certain sense to return to the unrestrained spirits of childhood. There is reason to believe that Calhoun was one of those people who have had no childhood to return to. This, perhaps, was what Harriet Martineau sensed when she said that he seemed never to have been born. His political lieutenant, James H. Hammond, remarked after his death: "Mr. Calhoun had no youth, to our knowledge. He sprang into the arena like Minerva from the head of Jove, fully grown and clothed in armor: a man every inch himself, and able to contend with any other man."

For men whom he took seriously, this white-hot intensity was difficult to bear. Senator Dixon Lewis of Alabama, who weighed four hundred and thirty pounds and found relaxation a natural necessity, once wrote to Calhoun's friend Richard K. Crallé during an election year:

> Calhoun is now my principal associate, and he is too intelligent, too industrious, too intent on the struggle of politics to suit me except as an occasional companion. There is no *relaxation* with him. On the contrary, when I seek relaxation with him, he screws me only the higher in some sort of excitement.

Judge Prioleau, when he first met Calhoun, told an inquirer he hoped never to see him again. For three hours he had been trying to follow

Calhoun's dialectic "through heaven and earth," and he was exhausted
with the effort. "I hate a man who makes me think so much . . . and I hate
a man who makes me feel my own inferiority." Calhoun seldom made
himself congenial. He once admitted that he was almost a stranger five
miles from his home, and we can be sure that his political popularity was
not personal, but abstract. Nor is there any reason to believe that he often
felt lonesome, except for his family. He loved an audience, but he did not
especially care for company. He enjoyed spending long hours in solitary
thought.

Colleagues in the Senate who were used to the harangues of this tall,
gaunt, sickly man with his traplike mouth and harsh voice, suited, as
someone said, to a professor of mathematics, respected him deeply for his
extraordinary mind and his unquestionable integrity, but found him on
occasion just a bit ludicrous. Clay has left a memorable caricature of
him—"tall, careworn, with furrowed brow, haggard and intensely gazing,
looking as if he were dissecting the last abstraction which sprung from
metaphysician's brain, and muttering to himself, in half-uttered tones,
'This is indeed a real crisis.' "

There is testimony to Calhoun's gentleness and charm, to the winning quality of his very seriousness at times. "He talked," reports one
admirer, "on the most abstruse subjects with the guileless simplicity of a
prattling child." Benjamin F. Perry, a bitter political opponent, testified
to his kindness, but observed: "He liked very much to talk of himself."
He saved his charm and indulgence particularly for women and children,
whose world, one imagines, he considered to be a world entirely apart
from the serious things of life. There is a brief and touching picture of
him at his daughter's wedding removing the ornaments of a cake to save
them for a little child. It is easy enough to believe that he never spoke
impatiently to any member of his family, for he could always discharge
his aggressions upon a senator. And two of the most effective character-
izations have been left by women: it was Harriet Martineau who called
him "the cast iron man who looks as if he had never been born, and could
never be extinguished," and Varina Howell Davis who described him as
"a mental and moral abstraction."

It would be interesting to know what Mrs. John C. Calhoun thought
of him. That he was devoted to her one can readily imagine, but devotion
in a man like Calhoun is not an ordinary man's devotion. When he was
thinking of marrying her, he wrote to her mother: "After a careful
examination, I find none but those qualities in her character which are
suited to me." In the course of their exemplary married life she bore him
nine children, whom he treated with paternal tenderness. But there survives a curious letter written to his cherished mother-in-law on the death
of his first-born daughter in her second year of life, which reads in part:

> So fixed in sorrow is her distressed mother that every topick of
> consolation which I attempt to offer but seems to grieve her the
> more. It is in vain I tell her it is the lot of humanity; that almost all

parents have suffered equal calamity; that Providence may have intended it in kindness to her and ourselves, as no one can say what, had she lived, would have been her condition, whether it would have been happy or miserable; and above all we have the consolation to know that she is far more happy than she could be here with us. She thinks only of her dear child; and recalls to her mind every thing that made her interesting, thus furnishing additional food for her grief.

Here surely is a man who lived by abstractions; it is amazing, and a little pathetic, that he sought to make his business the management of human affairs.

Calhoun had a touching faith in his ability to catch life in logic. His political reasoning, like so many phases of his personal life, was a series of syllogisms. Given a premise, he could do wonders, but at times he showed a fantastic lack of judgment in choosing his premises, and he was often guilty of terrible logic-chopping.[3] His trust in logic led to an almost insane self-confidence. "Whether it be too great confidence in my own opinion I cannot say," he once wrote, "but what I think I see, I see with so much apparent clearness as not to leave me a choice to pursue any other course, which has always given me the impression that I acted with the force of destiny." "In looking back," he wrote to Duff Green six years before his death, "I see nothing to regret and little to correct."

That all Calhoun's ability and intensity were focused on making himself president was the accepted view of his contemporaries, friend and foe, and has not been denied by his friendliest biographers. But he himself never acknowledged or understood it. "I am no aspirant—never have been," he declared fervently to the Senate in 1847. "I would not turn on my heel for the Presidency." On this score he thought himself "the most misunderstood man in the world." A certain relative purity of motive, however, must be credited to him. He was not primarily an opportunist. He generally sought to advance himself on the basis of some coherent and well-stated body of principles in which he actually believed. It was quite in keeping that he could on occasion be devious with individual men—as he was with Jackson for years—but not with ideas. His scruples about money were matched only by those of Adams, and might have been held up as an example to Webster. He supported a large family—seven of the nine children survived to adulthood—on his declining plantation enterprises, and sincerely professed his indifference to money-making. In 1845 he applied to Webster's rich Boston patron, Abbott Lawrence, for a loan of thirty thousand dollars, and when Lawrence replied in language sug-

[3] Typical of Calhoun at his worst was his assault on the philosophy of the Declaration of Independence, which he read as "all men are born free and equal": "Taking the proposition literally . . . there is not a word of truth in it. It begins with 'all men are born,' which is utterly untrue. Men are not born. Infants are born. They grow to be men. . . . They are not born free. While infants they are incapable of freedom. . . ." Anyone whose introduction to Calhoun came through such portions of his work would find it hard to believe that he had sound and trenchant criticisms of the natural-rights philosophy, and yet he did.

gesting that for a man of Calhoun's personal eminence he might be generous beyond the call of commercial duty, Calhoun withdrew his request in a letter of supreme dignity.

Calhoun's failure to understand that politics works through people and requires sustained personal loyalty as well as fidelity to ideas was resented by his followers and partisans. James H. Hammond once complained that the leader was "always buying over enemies and never looks after friends." Again: "He marches and countermarches all who follow him until after having broken from the bulk of his followers he breaks from his friends one by one and expends them in breaking down his late associates—so all ends in ruin." Rhett and Hammond both agreed that he was too unyielding and impersonal to be a great party leader. As Rhett put it, "he understood principles . . . but he did not understand how best to control and use . . . man."

Calhoun, of course, was a slavemaster, and his view of himself in this capacity was what might be expected: "My character as a master is, I trust, unimpeachable, as I hope it is in all the other relations of life." He looked upon his relation to his slaves, he asserted, "in the double capacity of master and guardian." His neighbors testified that he was kind to them, and by the lights of his section and class there is little reason to doubt it. But the only record of his relation to a slave suggests that kindness to slaves was a mixed quality in the South. In 1831 a house servant, Aleck, committed some offense to Mrs. Calhoun for which she promised a severe whipping, and he ran away. When he was caught in Abbeville a few days later, Calhoun left instructions with a friend:

> I wish you would have him lodged in jail for one week, to be fed on bread and water, and to employ some one for me to give him 30 lashes well laid on at the end of the time. . . . I deem it necessary to our proper security to prevent the formation of the habit of running away, and I think it better to punish him before his return home than afterwards.

The case of Aleck and the "thirty lashes well laid on" does more for our understanding of the problem of majorities and minorities than all Calhoun's dialectics on nullification and the concurrent majority.

III

In 1788 Patrick Henry, arguing against the federal Constitution, asked: "How can the Southern members prevent the adoption of the most oppressive mode of taxation in the Southern States, as there is a majority of the Northern States?" This anxiety about the North's majority ripened like the flora of the Southern swamplands. As the years went by, the South grew, but the North grew faster. In 1790, when Calhoun was eight years old, populations North and South were practically equal. By 1850, the year of his death, the North's was 13,527,000, the South's only 9,612,000. This preponderance was reflected in Congress. Although Southern politicians held a disproportionate number of executive offices, federal policy continued to favor Northern capital, and Southern wealth funneled into the pockets of Northern shippers, bankers, and manufacturers. Of course, the greater part of the drain of Southern resources was the inevitable result of a relationship between a capitalistic community and an agrarian one that did little of its own shipping, banking, or manufacturing. But a considerable portion too came from what Southerners considered an "artificial" governmental intrusion—the protective tariff. It was tariffs, not slavery, that first made the South militant. Planters were understandably resentful as the wealth of the Southern fields, created by the hard labor of the men, women, and children they owned, seemed to be slipping away from them. "All we want to be rich is to let us have what we make," said Calhoun.

Southern leaders began to wonder where all this was going to stop. Given its initial advantage, what was to prevent the North from using the federal government to increase the span between the political power of the sections still further, and then, presuming upon the South's growing weakness, from pushing exploitation to outrageous and unbearable extremes? Humiliated by their comparative economic backwardness, frightened at its political implications, made uneasy by the world's condemnation of their "peculiar institution," Southern leaders reacted with the most intense and exaggerated anxiety to every fluctuation in the balance of sectional power. How to maintain this balance was Calhoun's central problem, and for twenty-two years his terrible and unrelenting intensity hung upon it. "The South," he lamented as early as 1831, ". . . is a fixed and hopeless minority," and five years later he declared in significant hyperbole on the floor of the Senate: "We are here but a handful in the midst of an overwhelming majority." In 1833, speaking on the Force Bill, he saw the South confronted with "a system of hostile legislation . . . an oppressive and unequal imposition of taxes . . . unequal and profuse appropriations . . . rendering the entire labor and capital of the weaker interest subordinate to the stronger."

After 1830, when abolitionism began to be heard, the South's revolt was directed increasingly against this alleged menace. There is little point in debating whether fear of abolition or fear of further economic exploitation was more important in stimulating Southern militancy and turning the Southern mind toward secession. The North, if the balance of power turned completely in its favor, could both reduce the planter class to economic bondage and emancipate its slaves. Southern leaders therefore concentrated on fighting for the sectional equilibrium without making any artificial distinctions about their reasons. As Calhoun put it in 1844, "plunder and agitation" were "kindred and hostile measures." "While the tariff takes from us the proceeds of our labor, abolition strikes at the labor itself."

Of course, voluntary emancipation was out of the question. To understand the mind of the Old South it is necessary to realize that emancipation meant not merely the replacement of slave labor by hired labor, but the loss of white supremacy, the overthrow of the caste system—in brief, the end of a civilization. Although Calhoun once condemned the slave trade as an "odious traffic," there is no evidence that he ever shared the Jeffersonian view of slavery, widespread in the South during his youth, that slavery was a necessary but temporary evil. During a conversation with John Quincy Adams in 1820 he revealed how implicitly he accepted the caste premises of slavery. Adams spoke of equality, of the dignity and worth of human life. Calhoun granted that Adams's beliefs were "just and noble," but added in a matter-of-fact way that in the South they were applied only to white men. Slavery, he said, was "the best guarantee to equality among the whites. It produced an unvarying level among them . . . did not even admit of inequalities, by which one white man could domineer over another."

Calhoun was the first Southern statesman of primary eminence to say openly in Congress what almost all the white South had come to feel. Slavery, he affirmed in the Senate in 1837, "is, instead of an evil, a good— a positive good." By this he did not mean to imply that slavery was always better than free labor relations, but simply that it was the best relation between blacks and whites. Slavery had done much for the Negro, he argued. "In few countries so much is left to the share of the laborer, and so little exacted from him, or . . . more kind attention paid to him in sickness or infirmities of age." His condition is greatly superior to that of poorhouse inmates in the more civilized portions of Europe. As for the political aspect of slavery, "I fearlessly assert that the existing relation between the two races in the South . . . forms the most solid and durable foundation on which to rear free and stable political institutions."

The South thought of emancipation as an apocalyptic catastrophe. In a manifesto prepared in 1849 Calhoun portrayed a series of devices by which he thought abolitionists would gradually undermine slavery until at last the North could "monopolize all the territories," add a sufficient number of states to give her three fourths of the whole, and then pass an emancipation amendment. The disaster would not stop with this. Since the two races "cannot live together in peace, or harmony, or to their mutual advantage, except in their present relation," one or the other must dominate. After emancipation the ex-slaves would be raised "to a political and social equality with their former owners, by giving them the right of voting and holding public offices under the Federal Government." They would become political associates of their Northern friends, acting with them uniformly, "holding the white race at the South in complete subjection." The blacks and the profligate whites that might unite with them would become the principal recipients of federal offices and patronage and would "be raised above the whites of the South in the political and social scale." The only resort of the former master race would be to abandon the homes of its ancestors and leave the country to the Negroes.[4]

Faced with such peril, the South should be content with nothing less than the most extreme militancy, stand firm, meet the enemy on the frontier, rather than wait till she grew weaker. Anything less than decisive victory was unthinkable. "What! acknowledged inferiority! The surrender of life is nothing to sinking down into acknowledged inferiority!"

It was one of Calhoun's merits that in spite of his saturation in the lore of constitutional argument he was not satisfied with a purely formal or constitutional interpretation of the sectional controversy, but went beyond it to translate the balance of sections into a balance of classes. Although he did not have a complete theory of history, he saw class struggle and exploitation in every epoch of human development. He was sure that "there never has yet existed a wealthy and civilized society in which one portion of the community did not, in point of fact, live on the labor of the other." It would not be too difficult "to trace out the various devices by which the wealth of all civilized communities has been so unequally divided, and to show by what means so small a share has been allotted to those by whose labor it was produced, and so large a share to the non-producing classes." Concerning one such device he had no doubts; the tariff was a certain means of making "the poor poorer and the rich richer." As early as 1828 he wrote of the tariff system in his *Exposition and Protest*:

> After we [the planters] are exhausted, the contest will be between the capitalists and operatives [workers]; for into these two classes it must, ultimately, divide society. The issue of the struggle here must be the same as it has been in Europe. Under the operation of the system, wages must sink more rapidly than the prices of the necessaries of life, till the operatives will be reduced to the lowest point,—when the portion of the products of their labor left to them, will be barely sufficient to preserve existence.

In his *Disquisition on Government* Calhoun predicted that as the community develops in wealth and population, "the difference between the rich and poor will become more strongly marked," and the proportion of "ignorant and dependent" people will increase. Then "the tendency to conflict between them will become stronger; and, as the poor and dependent become more numerous in proportion there will be, in governments of the numerical majority, no want of leaders among the wealthy and ambitious, to excite and direct them in their efforts to obtain the control."

Such arguments were not merely for public consumption. In 1831 a friend recorded a conversation in which Calhoun "spoke of the tendency

---

[4] Setting aside its valuations and demagogic language, Calhoun's forecast bears a strong resemblance to the plans actually adopted by the Radical Republicans during Reconstruction.

of Capital to destroy and absorb the property of society and produce a
collision between itself and operatives." "The capitalist owns the instruments of labor," Calhoun once told Albert Brisbane, "and he seeks to
draw out of labor all the profits, leaving the laborer to shift for himself in
age and disease." In 1837 he wrote to Hammond that he had had "no
conception that the lower class had made such great progress to equality
and independence" as Hammond had reported. "Modern society seems to
me to be rushing to some new and untried condition." "What I dread,"
he confessed to his daughter Anna in 1846, "is that progress in political
science falls far short of progress in that which relates to matter, and
which may lead to convulsions and revolutions, that may retard, or even
arrest the former." During the peak of the Jacksonian bank war he wrote
to his son James that the views of many people in the North were inclining toward Southern conceptions. They feared not only Jackson's power,
but "the needy and corrupt in their own section. They begin to feel what
I have long foreseen, that they have more to fear from their own people
than we from our slaves."

In such characteristic utterances there is discernible a rough parallel
to several ideas that were later elaborated and refined by Marx: the idea
of pervasive exploitation and class struggle in history; a labor theory of
value and of a surplus appropriated by the capitalists; the concentration of
capital under capitalistic production; the fall of working-class conditions
to the level of subsistence; the growing revolt of the laboring class against
the capitalists; the prediction of social revolution. The difference was that
Calhoun proposed that no revolution should be allowed to take place. To
forestall it he suggested consistently—over a period of years—what
Richard Current has called "planter-capitalist collaboration against the
class enemy." In such a collaboration the South, with its superior social
stability, had much to offer as a conservative force. In return, the conservative elements in the North should be willing to hold down aboli-
tionist agitation; and they would do well to realize that an overthrow of
slavery in the South would prepare the ground for social revolution in the
North.

> There is and always has been [he said in the Senate] in an ad-
> vanced stage of wealth and civilization, a conflict between labor
> and capital. The condition of society in the South exempts us from
> the disorders and dangers resulting from this conflict; and which
> explains why it is that the political condition of the slave-holding
> states has been so much more stable and quiet than that of the
> North. . . . The experience of the next generation will fully test
> how vastly more favorable our condition of society is to that of
> other sections for free and stable institutions, provided we are not
> disturbed by the interference of others, or shall . . . resist promptly
> and successfully such interference.

On January 9, 1838, Calhoun explained further why it was impossible
in the South for the conflict "between labor and capital" to take place,
"which makes it so difficult to establish and maintain free institutions in

all wealthy and highly civilized nations where such institutions as ours do not exist." It was because the Southern states were an aggregate of communities, not of individuals. "Every plantation is a little community, with the master at its head, who concentrates in himself the united interests of capital and labor, of which he is the common representative." In the Southern states labor and capital are "equally represented and perfectly harmonized." In the Union as a whole, the South, accordingly, becomes

> the balance of the system; the great conservative power, which prevents other portions, less fortunately constituted, from rushing into conflict. In this tendency to conflict in the North, between labor and capital, which is constantly on the increase, the weight of the South has been and ever will be found on the conservative side; against the aggression of one or the other side, whichever may tend to disturb the equilibrium of our political system.

In 1836 Calhoun had pointed out to "the sober and considerate" Northerners

> who have a deep stake in the existing institutions of the country that the assaults which are now directed against the institutions of the Southern States may be very easily directed against those which uphold their own property and security. A very slight modification of the arguments used against the institutions [of the South] would make them equally effectual against the institutions of the North, including banking, in which so vast an amount of its property and capital is invested.

In 1847 he again reminded Northern conservatives how much interest they had "in upholding and preserving the equilibrium of the slaveholding states." "Let gentlemen then be warned that while warring on us, they are warring on themselves." Two years later he added that the North, without the South, "would have no central point of union, to bind its various and conflicting interests together; and would . . . be subject to all the agitations and conflicts growing out of the divisions of wealth and poverty." All these warnings were merely the consequence of a longstanding conviction which Calhoun had expressed to Josiah Quincy that "the interests of the *gentlemen* of the North and of the South are identical." The Carolinian had no serious expectation that his appeals and predictions would change Northern public opinion, but he hoped that events might. Growing discontent among the masses might drive Northern conservatives into the arms of the planters, but as he confessed to Duff Green in 1835, whether the intelligence of the North would see the situation "in time to save themselves and the institutions of the Country God only knows."

Calhoun had an ingenious solution for the sectional problem: in return for the South's services as a balance wheel against labor agitation, the solid elements in the North should join her in a common front against all agitation of the slavery issue. His program for the tariff problem was best expressed in a letter to Abbott Lawrence in 1845: Northern manufacturers should join the planters in producing for the export market. At best it would be impossible for manufacturers to attain prosperity in the home market alone; "the great point is to get possession of the foreign market," and for that the high-duty tariff is nothing but an obstruction. The North should emulate English manufacturers by lowering duties, importing cheap raw materials, and competing aggressively for foreign trade. "When that is accomplished all conflict between the planter and the manufacturer would cease."

IV

DURING THE LAST SEVEN YEARS of Calhoun's life the sectional conflict centered more and more on the acquisition of new territory and its division between slave and free society. Nullification had failed for lack of unity within the South. The alliance with the West was unstable and uncertain. The proposed alliance with Northern capital Calhoun could not bring about. Hence the problem of defense turned increasingly upon the attempt to acquire new slave territory in Texas, Mexico, and the vast area wrested from Mexico by war, and keeping the North from taking the West for free labor.

Calhoun's interest in Texas was defensive in intent, but exorbitantly aggressive in form. Great Britain, eager for a new market and an independent source of cotton, was encouraging Texas to remain independent by offering financial aid and protection. During 1843, when Lord Brougham and Lord Aberdeen both openly confessed Britain's intent to foster abolition along with national independence in Texas, Calhoun, then Secretary of State, stepped forward in alarm to link the annexation issue with a thoroughgoing defense of slavery. Southerners feared that another refuge for fugitive slaves and the example of an independent, free-labor cotton-producing country on their border would be a grave menace to their social structure. Britain, Calhoun frankly told the British Minister, was trying to destroy in Texas an institution "essential to the peace, safety, and prosperity of the United States"! In 1844 he published an interpretation of Britain's motives. Having freed the slaves in her own colonial empire, he charged, she had lost ground in world production of tropical products, including cotton, had endangered the investment in her empire, and had reduced it to far poorer condition than such areas as the Southern United States and Brazil, where slavery survived. Britain, in her effort "to regain and keep a superiority in tropical cultivation, commerce, and influence," was desperately trying to "cripple or destroy the productions of her successful rivals" by undermining their superior labor system.

Ardent as he had been for annexation of Texas, Calhoun was frightened during the war with Mexico by sentiment in the South for conquest and annexation of all Mexico. If Mexico were taken, he feared that the necessity of controlling her would give the executive tremendous powers and vast patronage, bring about precisely the centralization of federal power that he so feared, and finally destroy the constitutional system. He predicted that conflict between North and South over disposition of the acquired territory might easily disrupt the Union. "Mexico is for us the forbidden fruit; the penalty of eating it would be to subject our institutions to political death."

In 1846 the introduction of the Wilmot Proviso, which banned slavery from all territory to be taken from Mexico, excited the South as nothing had before. Calhoun felt that it involved a matter of abstract right upon which no compromise should be considered, even though it was unlikely that slavery would go into the territories in question. In December he told President Polk that he "did not desire to extend slavery," that it would "probably never exist" in California and New Mexico. Still he would vote against any treaty that included the Wilmot Proviso, because "it would involve a principle."[5]

Calhoun became obsessed with the North's tendency to "monopolize" the territories for free labor. In 1847, when Iowa had entered the Union and Wisconsin was ready for statehood, he expressed his fear that the territories would yield twelve or fifteen more free states. The South was fast losing that parity in the Senate which was its final stronghold of equality in the federal government. In March of that year he called for a united Southern party to force a showdown on Southern rights. In his last great speech, which was read to the Senate for him because he was dying, he declared with finality that the balance of power had already been lost. The South no longer had "any adequate means of protecting itself against . . . encroachment and oppression." Reviewing the growth of Northern preponderance, the exploitation of the South, and the progressive disintegration of the moral bonds of Union, Calhoun warned that the nation could be saved only by conceding to the South an equal right in the newly acquired Western territory[6] and amending the Constitution to restore to her the power of self-protection that she had had before the sectional balance was destroyed.

An amendment to the Constitution would be a guarantee of equality to the South. Calhoun demanded that this guarantee should take the form of the concurrent majority, which was the king pin in his political system. All through his sectional phase Calhoun had been preaching for the concurrent majority. He expressed it as early as 1833 in his speech on the Force Bill and last formulated it in the *Disquisition on Government*, published after his death. Government by numerical majorities, he always insisted, was inherently unstable; he proposed to replace it with what he called government by the whole community—that is, a government that would organically represent both majority and minority. Society should

---

[5] This was not his view alone. "It cannot be a slave country," wrote Robert Toombs to J. J. Crittenden, January 22, 1849. "We have only the point of honor to save . . . and [to] rescue the country from all danger of agitation."

[6] It is not certain whether Calhoun had changed his mind about not expecting slavery to go into the territory, as he had admitted to Polk, or whether he still considered that the mere victory on principle was of that much importance.

not be governed by counting heads but by considering the great economic interests, the geographical and functional units, of the nation. In
order to prevent the plunder of a minority interest by a majority interest,
each must be given an appropriate organ in the constitutional structure
which would provide it with "either a concurrent voice in making and
executing the laws or a veto on their execution." Only by such a device
can the "different interests, orders, classes, or portions" of the community be protected, "and all conflict and struggle between them prevented."[7]

Time had persuaded Calhoun that a dual executive would be the best
means of employing the concurrent majority in the United States. The
nation should have two presidents, each representing one of the two great
sections, each having a veto power over acts of Congress. No measure
could pass that did not win the approval of the political agents of both
sections. The equality between sections that had existed at the beginning
of the government would thus be restored.

Calhoun's analysis of American political tensions certainly ranks
among the most impressive intellectual achievements of American statesmen. Far in advance of the event, he forecast an alliance between Northern conservatives and Southern reactionaries, which has become one of
the most formidable aspects of American politics. The South, its caste
system essentially intact, has proved to be for an entire century more
resistant to change than the North, its influence steadily exerted to retard
serious reform and to curb the power of Northern labor. Caste prejudice
and political conservatism have made the South a major stronghold of
American capitalism.

But prescient and ingenious as Calhoun was, he made critical mis-
calculations for the sectional struggle of his own time. He had a remarkable sense for the direction of social evolution, but failed to measure its
velocity. His fatal mistake was to conclude that the conflict between
labor and capital would come to a head before the conflict between
capital and the Southern planter. Marx out of optimism and Calhoun out
of pessimism both overestimated the revolutionary capacities of the working class. It was far easier to reconcile the Northern masses to the profit
system than Calhoun would ever admit. He failed to see that the expand-

---

[7] The concurrent majority was actually operative in South Carolina from the
time of Calhoun's entrance into politics, when apportionment of the state legislature
was so arranged as to give one house to the seaboard plantation area and the other
to the upcountry farmers. William A. Schaper has pointed out, however, that the
concurrent-majority principle could work there because the minority, the planters,
kept possession of power "until it had won over the majority to its interests and its
institutions."
   Some Southerners hoped that since the South had a faction in both major parties,
she could exercise an informal equivalent of the concurrent majority within the
bisectional party system rather than the Constitution itself. This plan worked for
some time, but Calhoun had no faith in it for the long run. He argued that parties
must ultimately partake "more or less of a sectional character," a tendency that would
grow stronger with the passage of time. And if parties became sectional, the concurrent voice could be found only in a formal constitutional amendment.

ing Northern free society, by offering broad opportunities to the lower and middle classes, provided itself with a precious safety valve for popular discontents. He also failed to see that the very restlessness which he considered the North's weakness was also a secret of its strength. "The main spring to progress," he realized, "is the desire of individuals to better their condition," but he could not admit how much more intensely free society stimulated that essential desire in its working population than his cherished slave system with its "thirty lashes well laid on."

Calhoun, in brief, failed to appreciate the staying power of capitalism. At the very time when it was swinging into its period of most hectic growth he spoke as though it had already gone into decline. The stirrings of the Jackson era particularly misled him; mass discontent, which gained further opportunities for the common man in business and politics, and thus did so much in the long run to strengthen capitalism, he misread as the beginning of a revolutionary upsurge. Calhoun was, after all, an intense reactionary, and to the reactionary ear every whispered criticism of the elite classes has always sounded like the opening shot of an uprising.

Calhoun's social analysis lacked the rough pragmatic resemblance to immediate reality that any analysis must have if it is to be translated into successful political strategy. He never did find a large capitalist group in the North that would see the situation as he did. Although he joined the Whig Party for a few years after his disappointment with Jackson, a long-term alliance with such firm spokesmen of capitalist tariff economics as Clay and Webster was unthinkable. Under the Van Buren administration he returned to the Democratic fold on the subtreasury issue, and there he remained. During the late thirties, while he was still appealing to Northern conservatives to join hands with the planters, he admitted that the Whig Party, the party most attractive to Northern capital, was more difficult than the Democrats on both the tariff and abolition.

Ironically, for a long time Northern labor was ideologically closer than Northern capital to the planters. The workers had little sympathy for abolitionism, but responded with interest when Southern politicians unleashed periodic assaults on Northern wage slavery. When Francis W. Pickens, one of Calhoun's own lieutenants, rose in the House in the fall of 1837 to point out that the planters stood in relation to Northern capital "precisely in the same situation as the laborer of the North" and that they were "the only class of capitalists . . . which, as a class, are identified with the laborers of the country," Ely Moore, a labor spokesman, endorsed his position. And eight years after Calhoun's death, when James H. Hammond lashed out in a famous speech against "wage slavery," he received many letters of thanks from Northern workers for exposing their condition. Calhoun himself, organizing his presidential drive between 1842 and 1844, found strong support among many members of the former left wing of Northern democracy. Fitzwilliam Byrdsall, ardent democrat and historian of the Locofocos, wrote to him from New York City that "the radical portion of the Democratic party here, to whom free suffrage is dear and sacred, is the very portion most favorable to you." Calhoun had not long before expected this sort of man to frighten the capitalists into the arms of the planters!

The essence of Calhoun's mistake as a practical statesman was that he tried to achieve a static solution for a dynamic situation. The North, stimulated by invention and industry and strengthened by a tide of immigration, was growing in population and wealth, filling the West, and building railroads that bound East and West together. No concurrent majority, nor any other principle embodied in a parchment, could stem the tide that was measured every ten years in the census returns. William H. Seward touched upon the South's central weakness in his speech of March 11, 1850, when he observed that what the Southerners wanted was "a *political* equilibrium. Every political equilibrium requires a physical equilibrium to rest upon, and is valueless without it." In the face of all realities, the Southerners kept demanding that equality of territory and approximate equality of populations be maintained. "And this," taunted Seward, "must be perpetual!"

Moreover, the Calhoun dialectic was so starkly reactionary in its implications that it became self-defeating. There was disaster even for the South in the premise that every civilized society must be built upon a submerged and exploited labor force—what Hammond called a "mudsill" class. If there must always be a submerged and exploited class at the base of society, and *if* the Southern slaves, as such a class, were better off than Northern free workers, and *if* slavery was the safest and most durable base on which to found political institutions, then there seemed to be no reason why *all* workers, white or black, industrial or agrarian, should not be slave rather than free. Calhoun shrank from this conclusion, but some Southerners did not. George Fitzhugh won himself quite a reputation in the fifties arguing along these lines. The fact that some Southerners, however few, followed Fitzhugh was an excellent one for Northern politicians to use to rouse freemen, especially those who were indifferent to the moral aspects of slavery, to take a stand against the spread of the institution.

Calhoun could see and expound very plausibly every weakness of Northern society, but his position forced him to close his eyes to the vulnerability of the South. Strong as he was on logical coherence, he had not the most elementary moral consistency. Here it is hard to follow those who, like Professor Wiltse, find in him "the supreme champion of minority rights and interests everywhere." It is true that Calhoun superbly formulated the problem of the relation between majorities and minorities, and his work at this point may have the permanent significance for political theory that is often ascribed to it. But how can the same value be assigned to his practical solutions? Not in the slightest was he concerned with minority rights as they are chiefly of interest to the modern liberal mind—the rights of dissenters to express unorthodox opinions, of the individual conscience against the State, least of all of ethnic minorities. At bottom he was not interested in any minority that was not a propertied minority. The concurrent majority itself was a device without relevance to the protection of dissent, but designed specifically to protect a vested interest of considerable power. Even within the South Calhoun had not the slightest desire to protect intellectual minorities, critics, and dissenters. Professor Clement Eaton, in his *Freedom of Thought in the Old South*, places him first among those politicians who "created stereotypes in the minds of the Southern people that produced intolerance." Finally, it was minority privileges rather than rights that he really proposed to protect. He wanted to give to the minority not merely a proportionate but an *equal* voice with the majority in determining public policy. He would have found incomprehensible the statement of William H. Roane, of Virginia, that he had "never thought that [minorities] had any other *Right* than that of freely, peaceably, & *legally* converting themselves into a *majority* whenever they can." This elementary right Calhoun was prompt to deny to any minority, North or South, that disagreed with him on any vital question. In fact, his first great speeches on the slavery question were prompted by his attempt to deny the right of petition to a minority.

Calhoun was a minority spokesman in a democracy, a particularist in an age of nationalism, a slaveholder in an age of advancing liberties, and an agrarian in a furiously capitalistic country. Quite understandably he developed a certain perversity of mind. It became his peculiar faculty, the faculty of a brilliant but highly abstract and isolated intellect, to see things that other men never dreamt of and to deny what was under his nose, to forecast with uncanny insight several major trends of the future and remain all but oblivious of the actualities of the present. His weakness was to be inhumanly schematic and logical, which is only to say that he thought as he lived. His mind, in a sense, was *too* masterful—it imposed itself upon realities. The great human, emotional, moral complexities of the world escaped him because he had no private training for them, had not even the talent for friendship, in which he might have been schooled. It was easier for him to imagine, for example, that the South had produced upon its slave base a better culture than the North because he had no culture himself, only a quick and muscular mode of thought. It may stand as a token of Calhoun's place in the South's history that when he did find culture there, at Charleston, he wished a plague on it.

Julian Huxley

PHILOSOPHIC ANTS:
A BIOLOGIC FANTASY[1]

PHILOSOPHIC—ANTS?

Amoeba has her picture in the book,
  Proud Protozoon!—Yet beware of pride.
  All she can do is fatten and divide;
She cannot even read, or sew, or cook . . .

The Worm can crawl—but has no eyes to look:
  The Jelly-fish can swim—but lacks a bride:
  The Fly's a very Ass personified:
And speech is absent even from the Rook.

The Ant herself cannot philosophize—
  While Man does that, and sees, and keeps a wife,
And flies, and talks, and is extremely wise . . .
  Will our Philosophy to later Life
Seem but a crudeness of the planet's youth,
Our Wisdom but a parasite of Truth?

Incomprehensibility; that's what I say.
LEWIS CARROLL (*amended*)

ACCORDING TO A RECENT STUDY by Mr. Shapley (Proc. Nat. Acad. Sci., Philadelphia, vol. vi, p. 204), the normal rate of progression of ants—or at least of the species of ant which he studied—is a function of temperature. For each rise of ten degrees centigrade, the ants go about double as fast. So complete is the dependence that the ants may be

---

[1] Read before the Heretics Club, Cambridge, May 1922.

---

employed as a thermometer, measurement of their rate of locomotion giving the temperature to within one degree centigrade.

The simple consequence—easy of apprehension by us, but infinite puzzlement to ants—is that on a warm day an ant will get through a task four or five times as heavy as she will on a cold one. She does more, thinks more, lives more: more Bergsonian duration is hers.

There was a time, we learn in the myrmecine annals, when ants were simple unsophisticated folk, barely emerged from entomological barbarism. Some stayed at home to look after the young brood and tend the houses, others went afield to forage. It was not long before they discovered that the days differed in length. At one season of the year they found the days insufferably long; they must rest five or six times if they were, by continuing work while light lasted, to satisfy their fabulous instinct for toil. At the opposite season, they needed no rest at all, for they only carried through a fifth of the work. This irregularity vexed them: and what is more, time varied from day to day, and this hindered them in the accurate execution of any plans.

But as the foragers talked with the household servants, and with those of their own number who through illness or accident were forced to stay indoors, they discovered that the home-stayers noticed a much slighter difference in time between the seasons.

It is easy for us to see this as due to the simple fact that the temperature of the nest varies less, summer and winter, than does that of the outer air: but it was a hard nut for them, and there was much head-scratching. It was of course made extremely difficult by the fact that they were not sensitive to gradual changes in temperature as such, the change being as it were taken up in the altered rate of living. But as their processes of thought kept pace in alteration with their movements, they found it simplest and most natural to believe in the fixity and uniformity of their own life and its processes, and to refer all changes to the already obvious mutability of external nature.

The Wise Ants were summoned: they were ordered by the Queen to investigate the matter; and so, after consultation, decided to apply the test of experiment. Several of their numbers, at stated intervals throughout the year, stayed in and went out on alternate days, performing identical tasks on the two occasions. The task was the repeated recitation of the most efficacious of the myrmecine sacred formulæ.

The rough-and-ready calculations of the workers were speedily corroborated. "Great is God, and we are the people of God" could be recited out-of-doors some twenty thousand times a day in summer, less than four thousand times in winter; while the corresponding indoor figures were about fifteen thousand and six thousand.

There was the fact; now for the explanation. After many conclaves, a most ingenious hypothesis was put forward, which found universal credence. Let me give it in an elegant and logical form.

(1)   It was well-known—indeed self-evident—that the Ant race was the offspring and special care of the Power who made and ruled the universe.

(1.1)   Therefore a great deal of the virtue and essence of that Power inhered in the race of Ants. Ants, indeed, were made in the image of God.

(1.2)   It was, alas, common knowledge that this Power, although Omnipotent and Omniscient, was confronted by another power, the power of disorder, of irregularity, who prevented tasks, put temptations in the way of workers, and was in fact the genius of Evil.

(2)   Further, it was a received tradition among them that there had been a fall from the grace of a Golden Age, when there were no neuters, but all enjoyed married bliss; and the ant-cows gave milk and honey from their teats.

(2.1)   And that this was forfeited by a crime (unmentionable, I regret to say, in modern society) on the part of a certain Queen of Ants in the distant past. The Golden Age was gone; the poor neuters—obligate spinsters—were brought into being; work became the order of the day. Ant-lions with flaming jaws were set round that kingdom of Golden Age, from which all ants were thenceforth expelled.

(2.2.1) This being so, it was natural to conclude that the fall from grace involved a certain loss of divine qualities.

(2.2.2) The general conclusion to be drawn was that in the race of ants there still resided a certain quantity of these virtues that give regularity to things and events; although not sufficient wholly to counterbalance the machinations of the power of evil and disorder.

(2.2.3) That where a number of ants had their home and were congregated together, there the virtue resided in larger bulk and with greater effect, but that abroad, where ants were scattered and away from hearth, home, and altar, the demon of irregularity exerted greater sway.

This doctrine held the field for centuries.

But at last a philosopher arose. He was not satisfied with the current explanation, although this had been held for so long that it had acquired the odour and force of a religious dogma. He decided to put the matter to the test. He took a pupa (*anglice* "ant's egg") and on a windless day suspended it from a twig outside the nest. There he had it swung back and forth, counting its swings. He then (having previously obtained permission from the Royal Sacerdotal College) suspended the pupa by the same length of thread from the roof of the largest chamber of the nest—a dome devoted to spiritual exercise—and repeated the swinging and the counting. The living pendulum-bob achieved the same daily number of oscillations inside the nest as outside, although it was full summer, and the foragers found the day quite twice as long as did the home-stayers. The trial was repeated with another pupa and other lengths of thread; the result was always the same.

It was then that he laid the foundations of ant science by his bold pronouncement that neither the combat of spiritual powers nor the expansion or contraction of the store of divine grace had anything to do with the strange alteration of diurnal length; but that the cause of it lay in the Ants themselves, who varied with the varying of something for which he invented the word *Temperature*, not in a contraction or expansion of Time.

This he announced in public, thinking that a tested truth must be well-received, and would of necessity some day prove useful to society. But the consequence was a storm of protest, horror, and execration.

Did this impious creature think to overthrow the holy traditions with impunity? Did he not realize that to impugn one sentence, one word, one letter of the Sacred Books was to subvert the whole? Did he think that a coarse, simple, verifiable experiment was to weigh against the eternal verity of subtle and mysterious Revelation? No! and again a thousand times No!!

He was brought before the Wise Ants, and cross-questioned by them. It was finally decided that he was to abjure his heretical opinion and to recant in public, reciting aloud to the four winds of heaven: "the Ant is the norm of all"—

Μύρμηξ παντὸς νόμος

He said it. But Truth stirred within him, and under his breath he muttered "Eppur si muove . . ." This was overheard, and he was condemned (loneliness being much hated and dreaded by ants) to a solitary banishment.

Later philosophers, however, by using this same pendulum method, were enabled to find that the movements of sap in plants differed in rate according to the length of day, and later discovered that the expansion of water in hollow stems also followed these changes. By devising machines for registering these movements, they were enabled to prophesy with considerable success the amount of work to be got through on a given day, and so to render great aid to the smooth working of the body politic. Thus, gradually, the old ideas fell into desuetude among the educated classes—which, however, did not prevent the common people from remaining less than half-convinced and from regarding the men of science with suspicion and disapproval.

We happen to be warm-blooded—to have had the particular problem faced by our philosophic ants solved for us during the passage of evolutionary time, not by any taking of thought on our part or on the part of our ancestors, but by the casual processes of variation and natural selection. But a succession of similar problems presses upon us. Relativity is in the air; it is so much in the air that it becomes almost stifling at times; but even so, its sphere so far has been the inorganic sciences, and biological relativity, though equally important, has been little mentioned.

We have all heard the definition of life as "one damn thing after another"; it would perhaps be more accurate to substitute some term such as *relatedness* for *thing*.

When I was a small boy, my mother wrote down in a little book a number of my infant doings and childish sayings, the perusal of which I find an admirable corrective to any excessive moral or intellectual conceit. What, for instance, is to be thought of a scientist of whom the following incident is recorded, even if the record refers to the age of four years?

I (for convenience one must assign the same identity to oneself at different ages, although again it is but a relative sameness that persists) —I had made some particularly outrageous statement which was easily proved false: to which proof, apparently without compunction, I answered, "Oh, well, I always ex*agg*-erate when it's a fine day. . . ."

The converse of this I came across recently in a solemn treatise of psychology: a small girl of five or six, in the course of an "essay" in school, affirmed that the sun was shining and the day was fine; while as a matter of fact it had been continuously overcast and gloomy: on being pressed for a reason, she explained that she felt so happy that particular morning that she had been sure it was a fine day.

If the weather can affect one's statements of fact, and one's emotions can affect the apparent course of meteorological events, where is the line to be drawn? What is real? The only things of which we have immediate cognizance are, of course, happenings in our minds: and the precise nature and quality of each of these happenings depends on two things—on the constitution and state of our mind and its train on the one hand; on the other hand upon events or relations between events outside that system. That sounds very grand; but all it means after all is that you need a cause to produce an effect, a machine to register as well as a something to be registered.

As further consequence, since this particular machine (if I may be permitted to use the odious word in a purely metaphorical sense), this mind of ours, is never the same for two succeeding instants, but continually varies both in the quantity of its activity and the quality of its state, it follows that variations in mental happenings depend very largely on variations in the machine that registers, not by any means solely upon variations in what is to be registered.

Few (at least among Englishmen) would dispute the thesis that food, properly cooked and served, and of course adapted to the hour, is attractive four times in the day. But to a large proportion among us, even sausages and marmalade at nine, or roast beef and potatoes on a Sabbath noon, would prove not only not attractive but positively repellent if offered us on a small steamer on a rough day. I will not labour the point.

We all know how the size of sums of money appears to vary in a remarkable way according as they are being paid in or paid out. We all know to our cost the extraordinary superiority of the epochs when our more elderly relatives were youthful. The fact remains that we are always prone to regard the registering machine as a constant, and to believe that all the variation comes from outside. It is easy to discount the inner variation in ourselves when we are seasick, or in others when they are old and reminiscent, but not only is this discounting sometimes far more difficult, it is sometimes not even attempted.

What, for instance, are we to say to those who profess to find a harmony in the universe, those to whom poverty and discomfort and hard work appear the merest accidents, to whom even disease, pain, loss, death, and disaster are "somehow good"? You and I would probably retort that we have a rooted dislike to discomfort, that we should most strongly deny that the loss of a friend or even of a leg was anything but bad, that a toothache was not damnably unpleasant. But I think that if they were philosophically inclined (which they probably would not be), they might justifiably retort that the difference between their universe and ours was due to a difference in their mental machinery, which they had succeeded in adjusting so that it registered in a different and a better way.

It is at least clear that something of the sort can happen in the intellectual sphere. To the uneducated, the totality of things, if ever reflected upon, is a compound of fog and chaos: advance is painfully slow, and interlarded with unpleasant falls into pits and holes of illogicality and inconsequence; to those who have taken the trouble to push on, however, an orderly system at last reveals itself.

The problem of the origin and relationship of species gave such mental distress to those zoologists of the first half of the nineteenth century who were conscientious enough to struggle with it, that many of them ended by a mental suppression of the problem and a refusal to discuss it further. The publication of Darwin's *Origin of Species* was to them what psycho-analysis is (or may be) to a patient with a repressed complex. Or again, no one can read accounts of the physicists' recent work on the structure of the atom without experiencing an extraordinary feeling of satisfaction. Instead of wallowing in unrelated facts, we fly on wings of principle; not only can we better cut our way through the jungle of things, but we are allowed a privilege that has universally been considered one of the attributes of Gods—the calm and untroubled understanding of things and processes.

The Gods are happy.
They turn on all sides

Their shining eyes,
And see below them
The earth and men.

This being so, what is to prevent us from believing that, once certain adjustments are made in the mental sausage-machine, we shall discover that what we once found impossibly tough meat will pass smoothly through and become done up into the most satisfactory of sausages? In other words, that the values are there if we choose to make them—an Euckenish doctrine which, for all that it arouses instinctive suspicion, may none the less be true.

But even when we have made all possible discounts of this kind, evolved the smoothest-running machinery, converted the raw and meaty material of being into every conceivable kind of tidy sausage, the fact remains that there are feats beyond the power of our machine—beyond its power because of the very quality of its being.

We live at a certain rhythm in time, at a certain level of size and space; beyond certain limits, events in the outer world are not directly appreciable by the ordinary channels of sense, although a symbolic picture of them may be presented to us by the intellect.

When we are listening to the organ, sometimes there come notes which are on the border-line between sound and feeling: their separate vibrations are distinguishable and pulse through us, and the more the vibrations are separable, the more they are felt as mechanical shocks, the less as sound. However, we know perfectly well that all sounds as a matter of fact depend on vibratory disturbance, and that it is only some peculiarity of the registering machinery, in ear or brain, which enables us to hear a note as continuous.

Still more remarkable are the facts of vision. As I write I see the tulips in my garden, red against the green grass: the red is a continuous sensation; but the physicists appear to be justified in telling us that the eye is being bombarded every second with a series of waves, not the few hundred or thousand that give us sound, but the half-billion or so which conspire to illuminate our vision.

With sound, we alter the frequency of the waves and we get a difference of tone which seems to be merely a difference of more or less: but alter the frequency of light-waves, and the whole quality of the sensation changes, as when I look from the tulips to the sky. The change of registering mechanism is here more profound than the change in outer event.

Or again, to choose an example that depends more on size than rhythm, how very difficult it is to remember that the pressure of air on our bodies is not the uniform gentle embrace of some homogeneous substance, but the bombardment of an infinity of particles. The particles are not even all alike: some are of oxygen, others of nitrogen, of carbonic acid gas, of water vapour. They are not all travelling at uniform speeds; collisions are all the time occurring, and the molecules are continuously changing their rate of travel as they clash and bump.

We have only to look down a microscope to convince ourselves of the alteration in our experience that it would mean if we were to become sufficiently diminished. The tiniest solid particles in fluids can be seen to be in a continuous state of agitation—inexplicable until it was pointed out that this mysterious "Brownian" movement was the inevitable result of impacts by the faster-moving molecules of the fluid. Many living things that we can still see are small enough to live permanently in such agitation; the longest diameter of many bacteria is but half a micron (a two-thousandth of a millimetre), and there are many ultra-microscopic organisms which, owing to their closer approximation to molecular dimensions, must pass their lives in erratic excursions many times more violent than any visible Brownian motion.

If we could shrink, like Alice, at the persuasion of some magic mushroom, the rain of particles on our skin, now as unfelt as midges by a rhinoceros, would at last begin to be perceptible. We should find ourselves surrounded by an infinity of motes; titillated by a dance of sand-grains; bruised by a rain of marbles; pounded by flights of fives-balls. What is more, the smaller we became, the more individuality and apparent free-will should we detect in the surrounding particles. As we got still smaller, we should, now and again, find the nearly uniform bombardment replaced by a concerted attack on one side or the other, and we should be hurled for perhaps double our own length in one direction. If we could conceivably enter into a single inorganic molecule, we should find ourselves one of a moving host of similar objects: and we should further perceive that these objects were themselves complex, some like double stars, others star-clusters, others single suns, and all again built of lesser units held in a definite plan, in an architecture reminding us (if we still had memory) of a solar system in petto. If we were lucky enough to be in a complicated fluid like sea-water, we should be intrigued by the relations of the different kinds of particles. They would be continually coming up to other particles of different kinds, and would then sometimes enter into intimate union with them. If we could manage to follow their history, we should find that after a time they would separate, and seek new partners, of the same or of different species. Some kinds of the units, or people as we should be inclined to call them, would spend most of their existence in the married state, others would apparently prefer to remain single, or, if they married, would within no long time obtain divorce.

We should be forcibly reminded of life in some cosmopolitan city like London or New York. If there existed a registrar to note down the events of these little beings' existence, and we were privileged to inspect the register, we should find that each had its own history, different from that of every other in its course and its matrimonial adventures.

If we were near the surface we should find that the outer beings always arranged themselves in a special and coherent layer, apparently to protect themselves against the machinations of the different beings inhabiting the region beyond; for every now and again one would seem to be pulled from the water and be lost among the more scattered inhabitants of the air.

If we could now revert to our old size, we might remember, as we listened to the scientist enunciating the simple formulæ of the gas-laws, or giving numerical expression to vapour-pressures and solubilities, that this simplicity and order which he enabled us to find in inorganic nature was only simplicity when viewed on a large enough scale, and that it was needful to deal in millions and billions before chance aberrations faded into insignificance, needful to experience molecules from the standpoint of a unit almost infinitely bigger before individual behaviour could be neglected and merged in the orderly average. And we might be tempted to wonder how the personal idiosyncrasies of our human units might appear to a being as much larger than we as we are larger than a molecule—whether kings and beggars would not fare alike, and all the separate, striving, feeling, conflicting personalities, with their individual histories, their ancestors, successes, marriages, friendships, pains, and pleasures, be merged in some homogeneous and simple effect, altering in response to circumstances, with changes capable of expression in some formula as simple as Boyle's or Avogadro's Law.

Almost more startling might be the effect of altering the rhythm at which we live, or rather at which we experience events.

If only I were Mr. H. G. Wells, I could make a mint of money by a story based on this idea of rhythm of living.[2] Let us see . . . First there would be Mercaptan the distinguished inventor, who would lead me (lay, uninstructed, Watsonish me, after the fashion of narrators) into his laboratory. There on the table would be the machine—all but complete: handles, coils of wire, quartz terminals, gauges of rock-crystal in which oscillated coloured fluids, platinum cogwheels . . . dot . . . dot . . . dot . . . dot. . . . He hardly dared to make the final connections, all clear and calculable though they were. He had put so much of himself into it: so many hopes . . . fears . . . dots. . . .

Then there would be the farewell dinner-party—first the inventor's voice on the wireless telephone, summoning Wagrom the explorer, Glosh of the *Evening Post,* Stewartson Ampill the novelist, and the rest of our old friends: then the warm friendly light of the candles, the excellent port, the absence of women, the reminiscences, the asterisks, the. . . .

[2] The reading of this paper brought a string of informants eager to let me know that Mr. Wells had already written a story on this theme. I was grateful to them for having caused me to read the *New Accelerator,* which by some strange chance I had managed to miss: but Mr. Wells's treatment is so wholly different from that which I have sketched that I feel no scruples in letting it stand: and, if amends are needed, at least I make him a present of the germ of a new tale, and so feel that honour should be satisfied.

Mercaptan refuses to allow the rest to come into the laboratory, in case something should go wrong. He straps the machine on his shoulders, makes a final connection; his life processes begin to work faster, faster, ever faster. The first effect of course was a change of colour. The blue oblong of the window became green—yellow—orange—red. Meanwhile each wave-length of the ultra-violet became blue, and itself ran down the gamut of colour. Then came the turn of the X-rays—by their dim light he groped about, till they too became relatively too slow for his retina. That ought to make him blind, of course—but no! Mr. Wells had thought that all out; and he came into a state of nearly maximum speed where he perceived a brilliant, phosphorescent light given out by all objects, generated by disturbances of a wave-length unimaginably, undiscoverably small. Meanwhile he had passed through an amazing experience—he had heard the veritable music of the spheres! That had happened when in his acceleration he had, so to speak, caught up with the light-waves, until they were tuned to his ear's organ of Corti: and all that had been visible in his ordinary life was now to be appreciated by hearing. Unfortunately, as his ears possessed no lens, this universal music was to him of course merely a hideous babel of sound.

At last, as the workings of his body approached the rapidity of light's own oscillations, he entered on a new phase—surrounded on every side by an ocean of waves which lapped softly against his body—waves, waves, and still more waves. . . .

He was in that region not unlike that from which life has escaped when it ceased to be infinitely little, a region in which none of the events that make up our ordinary life, none of the bodies that are our normal environment, have existence any more—all reduced to a chaos of billows ceaselessly and meaninglessly buffeting his being.

"Mi ritrovai in una selva oscura."

Life is a wood, dark and trackless enough to be sure; but Mercaptan could not even see that it was a wood—for the trees.

Yet it was soothing: the very meaninglessness of the wave-rocking released one of responsibility, and it was delicious to float upon this strange etheric sea.

Then his scientific mind reasserted itself. He realized that he had magnified his rate of life and was consuming his precious days at an appalling speed. The lever was thrown into reverse, and he passed gradually back to what he had been accustomed to think of as reality.

Back to it; and then beyond it, slowing his vital rhythm. This time he was able by an ingenious arrangement to eliminate much of the disturbing effect of his rhythm-change on his vision. It was an idea of which he was very proud: every alternate light-wave was cut out when he doubled the capacity of each process of life, and so on in automatic correspondence. As a result he was enabled to get a picture of the outer world very similar to that obtained in the ordinary accelerations of slow processes that are made possible by running slow-taken cinema records at high speed. He saw the snowdrops lift their matutinal heads and drop them again at evening—an instant later; the spring was an alarming burst of living energy, the trees' budding and growth of leaves became a portent, like the bristling of hairs on the backs of vegetable cats. As his rate changed and he comprehended more and more in each pulse, the flowers faded and fell before he could think of plucking them, autumnal apples rotted in his grasp, day was a flash and night a wink of the eye, the two blending at last in a continuous half-light.

After a time ordinary objects ceased to be distinguishable; then the seasons shared the fate of day and night. The lever was now nearly hard over, and the machine was reaching its limits. He was covering nearly a thousand of men's years with each of his own seconds.

The cinema effect was almost useless to him now; and he discarded this apparatus. Now followed what he had so eagerly awaited, something deducible in general but unpredictable in all particulars. As the repeated separate impacts of the ether waves had condensed, at his old ordinary rate, to form the continuous sensation of light, so now the events of nature coalesced to give new objects, new kinds of sensation. Especially was this so with life: the repeated generations seemed to act like separate repeated waves of light, blending to give a picture of the species changing and evolving before his eyes.

Other experiences he could explain less well. He was conscious of strange sensations that he thought were probably associated with changes in energy-distribution, in entropy; others which he seemed to perceive directly, by some form of telepathy, concerning the type of mental process occurring around him. It was all strange: but of one thing he was sure—that if only he could find a way of nourishing and maintaining himself in this new state, he would be able, as a child does in the first few years of life, to correlate his puzzling new sensations, and that when he had done this he would obtain a different and more direct view of reality than any he had ever obtained or thought of obtaining before.

As the individual light-waves were summed to give light, as the microcosm of gas-molecules cancelled out to give a uniformity of pressure, so now the repetition of the years coalesced into what could be described as visible time, a sensation of cosmic rate; the repeated pullulations of living things fused into something perceived as organic achievement: and the infinite variety of organisms, their conflicts and interactions, resolved itself, through the mediation of his sense-organs and brain at their new rhythm, into a direct perception of life as a whole, an entity with a pressure on its environment, a single slowly-evolving form, a motion and direction.

He put the lever to its limit: the rhythm of the cosmos altered again in relation to his own. He had an extraordinary sense of being on the verge of a revelation. The universe—that was the same; but what he experienced of it was totally different. He had immediate experience of the waxing and waning of suns, of the condensation of nebulæ, the slowing down and speeding up of evolutionary processes.

The curious, apparently telepathic sense which he had had of the mental side of existence was intensified. Through it, the world began to be perceived as a single Being, with all its parts in interaction. The shadowy lineaments of this being were half seen by his mental vision—vast, colossal, slowly changing; but they appeared only to disappear again, like a picture in the fire.

Strive as he might, he could not see its real likeness. Now it appeared benign; at its next dim reappearance there would be a feeling of capricious irresponsibility about it: at another instant it was cold, remote; once or twice terrible, impending over and filling everything with a black demoniacal power which brought only horror with it.

If he could but accelerate the machine! He wanted to *know*—to know whether this phantom were a reality, to know above all if it were a thing of evil or of good: and he could not know unless he could advance that last final step necessary to fuse the rhythm of separate events into the sensation of the single whole.

He sat straining all his faculties: the machine whirred and rocked: but in vain. And at last, feeling desperately hungry, for he had forgotten to take food with him, he gradually brought back the lever to its neutral-point.

Of course, Mr. Wells would have done it much better than this.

And then there would have to be an ending. I think the newspaper man would take his opportunity to slink off into the laboratory and get on the machine with the idea of making a scoop for his paper; . . . and then he would put the lever in too violently, and be thrown backwards. His head hit the corner of a bench, and he remained stunned; but by evil chance, the handles of the machine still made connection with his body after the fall. The machine was making him adjust his rhythm to that of light; so that he was living at an appalling rate. He had gone into the laboratory late at night. Next morning they found him—dead: and dead of senile decay—grey-haired, shrivelled, atrophic.

Then of course the machine is smashed up; and Mr. Wells begins to write another book.

I have spent so much time in frivolous discussion of rhythm and size and commonplaces that I have not pointed out another fundamental fact of biological relativity—to wit, that we are but parochial creatures endowed only with sense-organs giving information about the agencies normally found in our own little environment. Mind without the objects of mind is the very Chimaera bombinating *in vacuo*.

Out of all the ether waves we are sensitive to an octave as light, and some few others as heat. X-rays and ultra-violet destroy us, but we know nothing about them until they begin to give us pain; while the low swell of Hertzian waves passes by and through us harmless and unheeded. Electrical sense again we have none.

Imagine what it would be for inhabitants of another planet where changes in Hertzian waves were the central, pivotal changes in environment, where accordingly life had become sensitive to "wireless" and to nought else save perhaps touch—imagine such beings broadcast upon the face of the Earth. With a little practice and ingenuity they would no doubt be able to decipher the messages floating through our atmosphere, would feel the rhythms of the Black Hamitic Band transmitting Jazz to a million homes, and be able to follow, night by night, the soporific but benevolent fairy-stories of Uncle Archibald. I wonder what they would make of it all. They would at intervals, of course, be bumping into things and people. But would touch and radio-sense alone make our world intelligible? I wonder. . . .

When we begin trying to quit our anthropocentry and discover what the world might be like if only we had other organs of body and mind for its assaying, we must flounder and bump in a not dissimilar fashion.

Even the few senses that we do possess are determined by our environment. Sweet things are pleasant to us: sugar is sweet: so is "sugar of lead"—lead acetate; sugar is nutritious, lead acetate a poison. The biologist will conclude, and with perfect reason, that if sugar was as rare as lead acetate in nature, lead acetate as common as sugar, we should then abominate and reject sweet things as emphatically as we now do filth or acids or over-hot liquids.

But I must pause, and find a moral for my tale; for all will agree that a moral has been so long out of fashion that it is now fast becoming fashionable again.

Every schoolboy, as Macaulay would say, knows William of Occam's Razor—that philosophical tool of admirable properties:—"Entia non multiplicanda praeter necessitatem."

We want another razor—a Relativist Razor; and with that we will carry out barbering operations worthy of another Shaving of Shagpat: we will shave the Absolute.

The hoary Absolute, enormous and venerable, grey-bearded and grey-locked—he sits enthroned, wielding tremendous power, filling young minds with fear and awe.

Up, barbers, and at him! Heat the water of your enthusiasm: lather those disguising appurtenances. See the tufts collapse into the white foam —feel the hairy jungles melt away before your steel! And at the end, when the last hair falls, you will wipe away the lather, and look upon that face and see—ah, what indeed?

I will not be so banal as to attempt to describe that sight in detail. You will have seen it already in your mind's eye: "or else" (to quote Mr. Belloc)—"or else you will not; I cannot be positive which." If not, you never will; if yes, what need to waste more of the compositor's time? But of him who forges that razor, who arms those barbers, who gives them courage for their colossal task, of him shall a new Lucretius sing.

BIBLIOGRAPHY

BELLOC, H. "The Bad Child's Book of Beasts."
BERGSON, H. "Time and Free-Will."
CARROLL, L. "Alice in Wonderland."
——— "Alice Through the Looking-Glass."
CLERK MAXWELL. "Collected Papers."
EINSTEIN. See KANT.
HEGEL. See EINSTEIN.
KANT. See HEGEL.
LEAR, E. "Nonsense Songs and Stories."
LUCRETIUS. "De Rerum Natura."
MACAULAY, LORD. "Essays."
MEE, A. "Children's Encyclopaedia."
MEREDITH, G. "The Shaving of Shagpat."
OCCAM, W. DE. "Opera Omnia."
SHAPLEY. Proc. Nat. Ac. Sci., vi, 204.
SWIFT, J. "Gulliver's Travels."
WELLS, H. G. "The New Accelerator."
WHEELER, W. M. "Ants" (Columbia University Series).

Alfred A. Knopf

THE NATIONAL PARK IDEA

DINOSAUR NATIONAL MONUMENT, established in 1915 and enlarged in 1938, is a part of the National Park System, and to be a part of that system is to be dedicated to certain clearly defined principles and uses. A National Park or Monument is a scenic or archæological or in some way unique preserve, and it is also playground, campground, natural schoolroom, wildlife sanctuary. It is not a resort, though there will always be those who try to make it so. And the very special purposes of recreation, education, refreshment, and inspiration for which Parks and Monuments have been set aside prohibit many economic uses which are thoroughly legitimate elsewhere.

Dinosaur is actually a year older than the service which administers it, but it and all other Parks and Monuments are operated according to the organic law which created the National Park Service in 1916. That Act of Congress ordered the conservation of "the scenery and the national and historic objects and the wild life" of the designated regions, and provided for "the enjoyment of the same in such manner and by such means *as will leave them unimpaired for the enjoyment of future generations.*"

The key word is "unimpaired," and the dictionary defines it as "not to diminish in quantity, value, or strength; not to injure or weaken or make worse; not to harm, hurt, mar, or spoil." It is an important point to remember.

There persists an old confusion between the National Parks and the National Forests—two very different things. The Forests provide the people, all the people, with magnificent facilities for recreation, and with vital watershed protection, and so do the Parks. But there the similarity

From *This Is Dinosaur*, 1955. Edited by Wallace Stegner. Copyright © 1955 by Alfred A. Knopf, Inc.

ends. For the Forests are consistently put to economic use under policies prescribed by Congress and administered by the National Forest Service, a bureau of the Department of Agriculture. The Forests sell lumber and grazing, and can be developed for mining, irrigation, and power. The Parks sell nothing, although, like the Forests, they contract with concessioners to supply food and lodging and services to visitors. The Forests are open to grazing, under permit, and as a result have their troubles with some cattlemen. The same cattlemen yearn for grazing permits in the Parks, but there, in principle at least, they do not get them. Where cattle are seen in what appear to be Park lands, these are lands still held in private ownership within the Park's borders, and the Service is making every effort to eliminate them. Or the stock-owners are holders of pre-park permits which will not be renewed after their lifetime.

The Parks are set aside for other than dollar uses, to be kept without impairment for the enjoyment of the people. They cannot tolerate exploitation of any resource, for exploitation uses up, makes over, mars, and changes the things that according to wise law must be kept natural. If a tree falls in a Park, unless it blocks a road or endangers a building or human life it must lie where it has fallen, slowly to return to the earth out of which it grew. Grass can renew itself if properly used and cared for; so can a forest. But a mountain or a canyon or archæological remains cannot. If you cut a great swath up a hillside to put in a ski lift, the gash will remain for a very long time, perhaps long after you have abandoned the lift. If you flood a canyon, as it is proposed to flood the Dinosaur canyons with dams in Echo Park and Split Mountain, that canyon is gone forever, buried first under water and eventually under silt. And the lake you create will not be there for many generations to see or use. It has been stated on good authority that 38 per cent of our dams have a useful life of under fifty years. Four hundred thousand tons of sediment are dumped into Lake Mead, on the Colorado, every twenty-four hours. You do not ever dig canyons out from under that kind of load. And the Green and Yampa are silt-laden where they flow through the Dinosaur canyons.

Moreover, no permanent growth can take hold on the shores of a reservoir if the water fluctuates as much as ten feet. The margin of any draw-down reservoir is a broad ugly mudbank except at extreme high water—and the average reservoir is full no oftener than once in four years. When I saw it in October 1954, the lake behind Fontana Dam in the Great Smokies was something dismal to behold. After three dry summers the water had receded many, many yards, exposing bleak banks of dried mud, bare of vegetation of any sort. There is no pleasure in sailing on such a lake as that, no pleasure in swimming in it, certainly none in looking at it, and the fishing has been well described as "honeymoon fishing." Some idea of what would happen to the scenery in Dinosaur if the proposed Echo Park dam were to go in can be gained from reminding oneself that the lake impounded behind this dam would fluctuate in depth 208 feet between the thirty-to-forty-year wet and dry cycles. When full, the lake would be 107 miles long and would cover 43,000 acres. When periodically drawn down to its silt pool, it would be about 70 miles long and cover about 9,000 acres. That leaves 34,000 acres of pretty drearily impaired scenery at low water.

The National Parks embrace areas of great natural beauty, of a splendor on which man cannot hope to improve. Who that has seen Glacier, Yosemite, Yellowstone, or the Tetons can doubt this? Simply to travel through them with open eyes is an uplifting and ennobling experience. The figures on what the Service calls "visitation"—a horrible word—demonstrate that the people need and want and use the Parks. Indeed, as one writer remarked, the people are loving the Parks to death. City and suburban folk increasingly feel the need to get away into the quiet and beauty of unspoiled natural scenery, and for this sort of recreation—an ambiguous word at best—the Parks are supreme, though the Forests, especially some of the designated wilderness areas, may be a close second.

Forty-two million people visited the National Parks, Monuments, and Historical Sites in 1953. Cut that number in half to allow for those who visited more than one Park and for those who made pilgrimages to the Statue of Liberty and the Franklin D. Roosevelt home in Hyde Park. Allow further for those who go to a Park looking for what isn't there— golf, tennis, night clubs, and resort activities—and there remain probably between fifteen and twenty million separate users of the National Park areas. That number, moreover, increases by ten per cent every year in spite of the inadequate budgets and strained facilities on which the Service is forced to operate. Think what the Parks give those millions of Americans: honest, intelligent information, exhibits, demonstrations, museums and lectures and films that explain the Park's geology, history, flora and fauna. As public education there is nothing to approach it. There is no charge, once the trifling entrance fee is paid: you take as much or as little as you want. You make use of the good trails provided for hikers and riders, the good campgrounds, the hotel and cottage and cabin accommodations at rates controlled by the government. You enjoy roads that are unmarred by signboards, that ease through forests and mountains and canyons with a minimum of scarring of the natural beauty, so that driving is not a tense duel with death along a strip of man-made ugliness but a restful and enriching experience.

In a Park a citizen gets back something, and in a form he sees and appreciates, for the taxes he pays. No one can watch Park rangers or archæologists or naturalists working with visitors without being impressed by the eagerness of the visitors to be informed and the pleasure they take in what is given them. And there is something about the atmosphere of a National Park that makes people behave well—much better, for instance, than many Americans traveling abroad. Perhaps this general decency of behavior arises from some consciousness of the friendliness and good order of the Parks, the air of cheerful public service on a completely impartial and democratic basis. Perhaps it springs from an awareness that the supreme experience of solitude, the blessing of almost absolute quiet, is only a short distance away from the crowds.

With so many friends, it is difficult to understand why the Parks are so bedeviled by threats, and seem always to be fighting for their very existence. The story is an old one. There are frequent occasions when people see nothing wrong with harming, hurting, marring, or spoiling when there are valuable resources of water, power, timber, oil, or minerals to be exploited within Park boundaries.

The Service, moreover, is not always in a position to make a vigorous defense. For one thing, it is always short of money. It is small, as federal bureaus go, and the small bureau often has a hard time getting money from Congress. Thus Congress, the very branch of government which set them aside, sometimes offers a threat—of omission—to the Parks. Other threats are not so indirect.

Thirty-five years ago one George K. Davol wanted to build a cableway across the Grand Canyon of the Colorado. To Stephen T. Mather, the first Director of the National Park Service, this seemed, as it would seem to almost anyone today, simply monstrous. John Barton Payne, his Secretary of the Interior, supported Mather's denial of the request, and that was that. Another proposal called for the building of an elevator alongside the 308-foot Great Falls of the Yellowstone. And Secretary Franklin K. Lane was at one time eager to use Yellowstone Lake—the largest body of water in America at so great an altitude, 7,731 feet—for irrigation. That would have made it a draw-down reservoir, with results to its beauty that we can imagine but do not like to visualize. In his 1919 report, Mather wrote: "Is there not some place in this great nation of ours where lakes can be preserved in their natural state; where we and all generations to follow us can enjoy the beauty and charm of mountain waters in the midst of primeval forests? The country is large enough to spare a few such lakes and beauty spots. The nation has wisely set apart a few national parks where a state of nature is to be preserved. If the lakes and forests of these parks cannot be spared from the hand of commercialization, what hope can there be for the preservation of any scenic features of the mountains in the interest of posterity?"

The story of the years-long attempt by Ralph Henry Cameron, onetime Senator from Arizona, to keep the Grand Canyon region from being adequately developed as a Park is too long to tell here. Mining-claims were the chief basis of Cameron's power, and only the Supreme Court was able finally to polish him off.

There are always some people who want to mine in the Parks, cut timber, graze cattle, build ski lifts and aerial tramways, turn into four-lane super-highways the roads that now are quiet and self-effacing and built so that those who drive them can see in peace and relaxation what they came to see. There is constant pressure to develop resort and recreational facilities which could not be placed in any Park without impairing it for the present as well as for future generations. Such facilities, moreover, are not needed in the Parks; they exist in abundance outside, in hundreds of resort areas as well as on most Reclamation lakes and to a limited degree within the National Forests.

Greatest of all threats to the Parks today is the pressure to build dams. The Bureau of Reclamation is a big bureau with an annual budget many times larger than the National Parks could ever hope for, and with the additional opportunity of financing new projects with funds accruing from the sale of power. The long-range appeal is two-fold: water for irrigation and hydroelectric power for homes, farms, and industry. There is a local, short-range appeal too: a big payroll and the business that results in the nearest town during the construction period. In the case of the proposed dams in Dinosaur, the nearest town would be Vernal, Utah. As one would expect, some of the most relentless propaganda for the dams comes from there.

In his 1920 report Mather foresaw the sort of threat that is now made to Dinosaur. Once anything like a power project is authorized in any National Park, he wrote, "it will not only be illogical but impossible to keep irrigation dams and ditches, and even commercial lumbering, out of all our national parks. Then the next step will be to open these areas to hunting in season, as is the case with the national forests. Once a small dam is authorized for irrigation or other purposes, other dams will follow. Once a small lake is raised and a small amount of timber is destroyed . . . once start the national parks toward national forest status, and it will be logically impossible to stop short of all. One misstep is fatal."

Every reasonably informed person knows how important water is to the mountain states. Every reasonably informed person wants to see us get on with a wise development of the Upper Colorado River Basin. There is good reason to believe that the public opposition which the proposed Echo Park and Split Mountain dams aroused in 1954 would not have been aroused if the dam sites had lain outside the boundaries of the National Monument and the question of a damaging precedent of raids against the Parks had not been involved.

This is not the place for a detailed summary of arguments pro and con, or for a debate of the controversial problems such as evaporation loss at Echo Park as compared with evaporation loss at alternative sites. On that particular issue the anti-dam forces had definitely the better of the argument in 1954, and forced Reclamation to scale down its previously announced figures by a very large amount. It was for that reason, probably, among others, that the 83rd Congress allowed the dam recommendations to die without coming to a vote. But the Parks win battles only; the war goes on forever.

Those who would protect the Parks and Monuments must rest their case always on the organic law that created the National Park Service.

Any attempt to change that law would certainly bring on an instant and nation-wide and wholly bi-partisan explosion of protest. The danger is not that the law will be repealed or changed, but that it will be whittled away through special concessions and permits. It is necessary to bear in mind Stephen Mather's wise warnings when an advocate of whittling insists that he intends to create no precedents. With the best intentions in the world, he could not help creating a precedent. His successors in office might not agree with him about precedents, and they would have his own precedent to use against him.

The people, to whom the Parks belong, should be given the full facts on which to base a judgment, whenever the question of intrusion on Park lands arises. The people, as taxpayers who foot the bill, should also know, with fair exactness, and from a responsible reviewing body, how much a reclamation project is going to cost them, whether in a Park or not. The Upper Colorado River Basin development will involve expenditures to give anyone pause.

The attitude of Americans toward nature has been changing— slowly, perhaps, but inexorably. Fifty thousand persons camped out in one Park, the Great Smokies, in a single summer month of 1954. That same summer I spent a night at Manitou Experimental Forest, in which a near-by campground, run by the Forest Service and at that moment without a water supply, was expected to be used by fifty thousand people before winter. In 1951 Glacier National Park had a half-million visitors; in 1953 it had more than 630,000. In that same year, the last for which total figures are available, Grand Canyon had 830,000 odd, Yellowstone 1,300,000 and Yosemite just short of a million. Those figures are impressive no matter how you take them. They mean that what the Parks and Monuments provide and preserve *without impairment* is increasingly appreciated and increasingly needed by more and more millions of American families.

In 1925 Mather said: "I believe that today the National Park Service is a model bureau from the standpoint of efficiency in expenditure of public monies, adherence to the federal budget system, individual output of employees, co-operation with other government bureaus, low overhead expenses, and high morale and public spirit of personnel." He could, if he were alive today, put it even more strongly. It is hard to imagine more dedicated people than those who run the Parks. I have never met a single one whom I would not be glad to meet again, and I have invariably regretted the time to say good-by. The range of their interests, their high intelligence, their devotion, make them a separate and wonderful breed. Their love of their work often takes the form— sometimes very strange!—of believing the place they are stationed at to be the best in the entire system. Most remarkable of all, perhaps, is their cheerful willingness to work hours far beyond what the law prescribes, and their pride in the job they and their associates are doing.

There remain a few personal words to be said about Dinosaur. It *is* hard to get to. The roads into the interior of the Monument are abominable, and they stretch for miles and miles. To get the best view of Steamboat Rock, where the Green and Yampa meet, you must make a long rough drive and then walk an up-and-down trail for three miles—either that, or you must come in by river.

But remember that Yellowstone, which in 1955 will have close to a million and a half visitors, was once even more inaccessible. And inaccessible though Dinosaur yet is, nearly a thousand people made a several-day river trip through it in 1954. Dinosaur is not expendable wasteland, not a profitless desert, but a scenic resource of incalculable value that has been preserved this long precisely because of its inaccessibility. As a wilderness playground, there is nothing wrong with it that appropriations and wise use couldn't quickly cure—that and one or two improved (and most carefully planned) roads. Then people by the tens of thousands could annually drive into it and float down its marvelous rivers, and their coming and going would leave the canyons virtually unmarked. It is from the rivers that Dinosaur can best be seen, for it is from the rivers that you see the full glory of the canyon colors. You cannot judge the Dinosaur country from black-and-white photographs, beautiful as those often are. They often make it look harsh, even forbidding. It isn't. It is colorful and warm, and the spectacular Canyon of Lodore must be seen to be believed.

Three days in Dinosaur in the summer of 1954, two of them in a boat running down the Green, convinced me that America has here scenery to rank with that of the very greatest of our Parks—and that is saying a great deal. It is scenery that could not survive dams at Echo Park and Split Mountain.

Dinosaur deserves to be more visited. If it were, there is no doubt that the American people, who can recognize a superlative thing when they see it, would once again, as in the past, line up in favor of the organic law of the National Park Service and the dedicated and devoted men who run it. That is all it would take, that democratic groundswell, to insure that Dinosaur and the other superlative places will be passed on, unimpaired, to our grandchildren's grandchildren.

Thomas Mann

AN EXCHANGE OF LETTERS

Philosophical Faculty
of the Friedrich-Wilhelm University
Bonn-am-Rhein

Bonn, December 19, 1936

To HERR THOMAS MANN, WRITER: By the request of the Rector of the University of Bonn I must inform you that as a consequence of your loss of citizenship the Philosophical Faculty finds itself obliged to strike your name off its roll of honorary doctors. Your right to use this title is cancelled in accordance with Article VIII of the regulations concerning the conferring of degrees.

[signature illegible]
—DEAN

TO THE DEAN OF THE PHILOSOPHICAL FACULTY OF THE UNIVERSITY OF BONN:

I have received the melancholy communication which you addressed to me on the nineteenth of December. Permit me to reply to it as follows:

The German universities share a heavy responsibility for all the present distresses which they called down upon their heads when they tragically misunderstood their historic hour and allowed their soil to nourish the ruthless forces which have devastated Germany morally, politically, and economically. This responsibility of theirs long ago destroyed my pleasure in my academic honour and prevented me from making any use of it whatever. Moreover, I hold today an honorary degree of Doctor of Letters conferred upon me more recently by Harvard University. I cannot refrain from explaining to you the grounds upon which it was conferred. My diploma contains a sentence which, translated from the Latin, runs as follows: ". . . we the President and Fellows with the approval of the honorable Board of Overseers of the University in solemn session have designated and appointed as honorary Doctor of Letters Thomas Mann, famous author, who has interpreted life to many of our fellow-citizens and together with a very few contemporaries sustains the high dignity of German culture; and we have granted to him all the rights and privileges appertaining to this degree."

In such terms, so curiously contradictory to the current German view, do free and enlightened men across the ocean think of me—and, I may add, not only there. It would never have occurred to me to boast of the words I have quoted; but here and today I may, nay, I must repeat them. If you, Herr Dean (I am ignorant of the procedure involved), have posted a copy of your communication to me on the bulletin board of your university, it would gratify me to have this reply of mine receive the same honour. Perhaps some member of the university, some student or professor, may be visited by a sudden fear, a dismaying and swiftly suppressed presentiment, on reading a document which gives him in his disgracefully enforced isolation and ignorance a brief revealing glimpse of the free world of the intellect that still exists outside.

Here I might close. And yet at this moment certain further explanations seem to me desirable or at least permissible. I made no statement when my loss of civil rights was announced, though I was more than once asked to do so. But I regard the academic divestment as a suitable occasion for a brief personal declaration. I would beg you, Herr Dean (I have not even the honour of knowing your name), to regard yourself as merely the chance recipient of a communication not designed for you in a personal sense.

I have spent four years in an exile which it would be euphemistic to call voluntary since if I had remained in Germany or gone back there I should probably not be alive today. In these four years the odd blunder committed by fortune when she put me in this situation has never once ceased to trouble me. I could never have dreamed, it could never have been prophesied of me at my cradle, that I should spend my later years as an émigré, expropriated, outlawed, and committed to inevitable political protest. From the beginning of my intellectual life I had felt myself in happiest accord with the temper of my nation and at home in its intellectual traditions. I am better suited to represent those traditions than to become a martyr for them; far more fitted to add a little to the gaiety of the world than to foster conflict and hatred in it. Something very wrong must have happened to make my life take so false and unnatural a turn. I tried to check it, this very wrong thing, so far as my weak powers were able—and in so doing I called down on myself the fate which I must now learn to reconcile with a nature essentially foreign to it.

Certainly I challenged the wrath of these despots by remaining away and giving evidence of my irrepressible disgust. But it is not merely in the last four years that I have done so. I felt thus long before and was driven to it because I saw—earlier than my now desperate countrymen—who and what would emerge from all this. But when Germany had actually fallen into those hands I thought to keep silent. I believed that by the sacrifice I had made I had earned the right to silence; that it would enable me to preserve something dear to my heart, the contact with my public within Germany. My books, I said to myself, are written for Germans, for them above all; the outside world and its sympathy have always been for me only a happy accident. They are, these books of mine, the product of a mutually nourishing bond between nation and author and depend on conditions which I myself have helped to create in Germany. Such bonds as these are delicate and of high importance; they ought not to be rudely sundered by politics. Though there might be impatient ones at home who, muzzled themselves, would take ill the silence of a free man, I was still able to hope that a great majority of Germans would understand my reserve, perhaps even thank me for it.

These were my assumptions. They were not justified. I could not have lived or worked, I should have suffocated, had I not been able now and again to cleanse my heart, so to speak, to give from time to time free vent to my abysmal disgust at what was happening at home—the contemptible words and still more contemptible deeds. Justly or not, my name had once and for all been connected for the world with the conception of a Germany which it loved and honoured. The disquieting challenge rang in my ears: that I and no other must in clear terms contradict the ugly falsification which this conception of Germany was now suffering. That challenge disturbed all the free-flowing creative fancies to which I would so gladly have yielded. It was a challenge hard to resist for one to whom it had always been given to express himself, to release himself through language, to whom experience had always been one with the purifying and preserving Word.

The mystery of the Word is great; the responsibility for it and its purity is of a symbolic and spiritual kind; it has not only an artistic but also a general ethical significance; it is responsibility itself, human responsibility quite simply, also the responsibility for one's own people, the duty of keeping pure its image in the sight of humanity. In the Word is involved the unity of humanity, the wholeness of the human problem, which permits nobody, and today less than ever, to separate the intellectual and artistic from the political and social and to isolate himself within the ivory tower of the "cultural" alone. This true totality is equated with humanity itself, and anyone—whoever he be—is making a criminal attack upon humanity when he undertakes to "totalize" a segment of human life: I mean politics, I mean the State.

A German author accustomed to this responsibility of the Word, a German whose patriotism, perhaps naïvely, expresses itself in a belief in the infinite moral significance of whatever happens in Germany—should he be silent, wholly silent, in the face of the inexpiable evil that is done daily in my country to bodies, souls, and minds, to right and truth, to men and mankind? And should he be silent in the face of the frightful danger to the whole continent presented by this soul-destroying régime, which exists in abysmal ignorance of the hour that has struck today in the world? It was not possible for me to be silent. And so, contrary to my intentions, came the utterances, the unavoidably compromising gestures which have now resulted in the absurd and deplorable business of my national excommunication. The mere knowledge of who these men are who happen to possess the pitiful outward power to deprive me of my German birthright is enough to make the act appear in all its absurdity. I, forsooth, am supposed to have dishonoured the Reich, Germany, in acknowledging that I am against *them!* They have the incredible effrontery to confuse themselves with Germany! When, after all, perhaps the moment is not far off when it will be of supreme importance to the German people not to be confused with them.

To what a pass, in less than four years, have they brought Germany! Ruined, sucked dry body and soul by armaments with which they threaten the whole world, holding up the whole world and hindering it in its real task of peace, loved by nobody, regarded with fear and cold aversion by all, it stands on the brink of economic disaster, while its "enemies" stretch out their hands to snatch back from the abyss so important a member of the future family of nations, to help it, if only it will come to its senses and try to understand the real needs of the world at this hour, instead of dreaming dreams about mythical "sacred necessities." Yes, after all, it must be helped by those whom it hinders and menaces, in order that it may not drag down the rest of the continent with it and unleash the war upon which as the *ultima ratio* it keeps its eyes ever fixed. The mature and cultural states—by which I mean those which understand the fundamental fact that war is no longer permissible —treat this endangered and endangering country, or rather the impossible leaders into whose hands it has fallen, as doctors treat a sick man: with the utmost tact and caution, with inexhaustible if not very flattering patience. But it thinks it must play politics—the politics of power and hegemony—with the doctors. That is an unequal game. If one side plays politics when the other no longer thinks of politics but of peace, then for a time the first side reaps certain advantages. Anachronistic ignorance of the fact that war is no longer permissible results for a while of course in "successes" against those who are aware of the truth. But woe to the people which, not knowing what way to turn, at last actually seeks its way out through the abomination of war, hated of God and man! Such a people will be lost. It will be so vanquished that it can never rise again.

The meaning and purpose of the National-Socialist State is this alone and can be only this: to put the German people in readiness for the "coming war" by ruthless repression, elimination, extirpation of every stirring of opposition; to make of them an instrument of war, infinitely compliant, without a single critical thought, driven by a blind and fanatical ignorance. Any other meaning and purpose, any other excuse this system cannot have; all the sacrifices of freedom, justice, human happiness, including the secret and open crimes for which it has blithely been responsible, can be justified only by the end—absolute fitness for war. If the idea of war as an aim in itself disappeared, the system would mean nothing but the exploitation of the people; it would be utterly senseless and superfluous.

Truth to tell, it *is* both of these, senseless and superfluous, not only because war will not be permitted it, but also because its leading idea, the absolute readiness for war, will result in precisely the opposite of what it is striving for. No other people on earth is today so utterly incapable of war, so little in condition to endure one. That Germany would have no allies, not a single one in the world, is the first consideration but the smallest. Germany would be forsaken—terrible of course even in her isolation—but the really frightful thing would be the fact that she had forsaken herself. Intellectually reduced and humbled, morally gutted, inwardly torn apart by her deep mistrust of her leaders and the mischief they have done her in these years, profoundly uneasy herself, ignorant of the future, of course, but full of forebodings of evil, she would go into war not in the condition of 1914 but, even physically, of 1917 or 1918. The ten per cent of direct beneficiaries of the system—half even of them fallen away—would not be enough to win a war in which the majority of the rest would only see the opportunity of shaking off the shameful oppression that has weighed upon them so long—a war, that is, which after the first inevitable defeat would turn into a civil war.

No, this war is impossible; Germany cannot wage it; and if its dictators are in their senses, then their assurances of readiness for peace are not tactical lies repeated with a wink at their partisans; they spring from a faint-hearted perception of just this impossibility. But if war cannot and shall not be—then why these robbers and murderers? Why isolation, world hostility, lawlessness, intellectual interdict, cultural darkness, and every other evil? Why not rather Germany's voluntary return to the European system, her reconciliation with Europe, with all the inward accompaniments of freedom, justice, well-being, and human decency and a jubilant welcome from the rest of the world? Why not? Only because a régime which in word and deed denies the rights of man, which wants above all else to remain in power, would stultify itself and be abolished, if, since it cannot make war, it actually made peace!

I had forgotten, Herr Dean, that I was actually addressing you.

Certainly I may console myself with the reflection that you long since ceased to read this letter, aghast at language which in Germany has long been unspoken, terrified because somebody dares use the German tongue with the ancient freedom. I have not spoken out of arrogant presumption, but out of a concern and a distress from which your usurpers did not release me when they decreed that I was no longer a German—a mental and spiritual distress from which for four years not an hour of my life has been free, and struggling with which I have had to accomplish my creative work day by day. The pressure was great. And as a man who out of diffidence in religious matters will seldom or never either by tongue or pen let the name of the Deity escape him, yet in moments of deep emotion cannot refrain, let me—since after all one cannot say everything—close this letter with a brief and fervent prayer: *God help our darkened and desecrated country and teach it to make its peace with the world and with itself!*

H. L. Mencken

IN MEMORIAM: W.J.B.

H AS IT BEEN DULY MARKED by historians that the late William Jennings Bryan's last secular act on this globe of sin was to catch flies? A curious detail, and not without its sardonic overtones. He was the most sedulous fly-catcher in American history, and in many ways the most successful. His quarry, of course, was not *Musca domestica* but *Homo neanderthalensis*. For forty years he tracked it with coo and bellow, up and down the rustic backways of the Republic. Wherever the flambeaux of Chautauqua smoked and guttered, and the bilge of Idealism ran in the veins, and Baptist pastors dammed the brooks with the sanctified, and men gathered who were weary and heavy laden, and their wives who were full of Peruna and as fecund as the shad (*Alosa sapidissima*)—there the indefatigable Jennings set up his traps and spread his bait. He knew every country town in the South and West, and he could crowd the most remote of them to suffocation by simply winding his horn. The city proletariat, transiently flustered by him in 1896, quickly penetrated his buncombe and would have no more of him; the cockney gallery jeered him at every Democratic national convention for twenty-five years. But out where the grass grows high, and the horned cattle dream away the lazy afternoons, and men still fear the powers and principalities of the air—out there between the corn-rows he held his old puissance to the end. There was no need of beaters to drive in his game. The news that he was coming was enough. For miles the flivver dust would choke the roads. And when he rose at the end of the day to discharge his Message there would be such breathless attention, such a rapt and enchanted ecstasy, such a sweet rustle of amens as the world had not known since Johann fell to Herod's ax.

There was something peculiarly fitting in the fact that his last days were spent in a one-horse Tennessee village, and that death found him

From *Prejudices, Fifth Series*, 1926. Copyright 1926 by Alfred A. Knopf, Inc. Renewal copyright 1954 by H. L. Mencken. Originally published, in somewhat different form, in the Baltimore *Evening Sun* and subsequently, with some revisions, in *The American Mercury*.

there. The man felt at home in such simple and Christian scenes. He
liked people who sweated freely, and were not debauched by the re-
finements of the toilet. Making his progress up and down the Main street
of little Dayton, surrounded by gaping primates from the upland valleys
of the Cumberland Range, his coat laid aside, his bare arms and hairy
chest shining damply, his bald head sprinkled with dust—so accoutred
and on display he was obviously happy. He liked getting up early in the
morning, to the tune of cocks crowing on the dunghill. He liked the
heavy, greasy victuals of the farmhouse kitchen. He liked country lawyers, country pastors, all country people. He liked the country sounds
and country smells. I believe that this liking was sincere—perhaps the
only sincere thing in the man. His nose showed no uneasiness when a
hillman in faded overalls and hickory shirt accosted him on the street,
and besought him for light upon some mystery of Holy Writ. The simian
gabble of the cross-roads was not gabble to him, but wisdom of an occult
and superior sort. In the presence of city folks he was palpably uneasy.
Their clothes, I suspect, annoyed him, and he was suspicious of their too
delicate manners. He knew all the while that they were laughing at
him—if not at his baroque theology, then at least at his alpaca panta-
loons. But the yokels never laughed at him. To them he was not the
huntsman but the prophet, and toward the end, as he gradually forsook
mundane politics for more ghostly concerns, they began to elevate him
in their hierarchy. When he died he was the peer of Abraham. His old
enemy, Wilson, aspiring to the same white and shining robe, came down
with a thump. But Bryan made the grade. His place in Tennessee hagi-
ography is secure. If the village barber saved any of his hair, then it is
curing gall-stones down there today.

But what label will he bear in more urbane regions? One, I fear, of a
far less flattering kind. Bryan lived too long, and descended too deeply
into the mud, to be taken seriously hereafter by fully literate men, even
of the kind who write school-books. There was a scattering of sweet
words in his funeral notices, but it was no more than a response to
conventional sentimentality. The best verdict the most romantic edi-
torial writer could dredge up, save in the humorless South, was to the
general effect that his imbecilities were excused by his earnestness—that
under his clowning, as under that of the juggler of Notre Dame, there was
the zeal of a steadfast soul. But this was apology, not praise; precisely the
same thing might be said of Mary Baker G. Eddy, the late Czar Nicholas, or Czolgosz. The truth is that even Bryan's sincerity will probably
yield to what is called, in other fields, definitive criticism. Was he sincere
when he opposed imperialism in the Philippines, or when he fed it with
deserving Democrats in Santo Domingo? Was he sincere when he tried
to shove the Prohibitionists under the table, or when he seized their
banner and began to lead them with loud whoops? Was he sincere when
he bellowed against war, or when he dreamed of himself as a tin-soldier
in uniform, with a grave reserved among the generals? Was he sincere

when he denounced the late John W. Davis, or when he swallowed Davis? Was he sincere when he fawned over Champ Clark or when he betrayed Clark? Was he sincere when he pleaded for tolerance in New York, or when he bawled for the faggot and the stake in Tennessee?

This talk of sincerity, I confess, fatigues me. If the fellow was sincere, then so was P. T. Barnum. The word is disgraced and degraded by such uses. He was, in fact, a charlatan, a mountebank, a zany without shame or dignity. His career brought him into contact with the first men of his time; he preferred the company of rustic ignoramuses. It was hard to believe, watching him at Dayton, that he had traveled, that he had been received in civilized societies, that he had been a high officer of state. He seemed only a poor clod like those around him, deluded by a childish theology, full of an almost pathological hatred of all learning, all human dignity, all beauty, all fine and noble things. He was a peasant come home to the barnyard. Imagine a gentleman, and you have imagined everything that he was not. What animated him from end to end of his grotesque career was simply ambition—the ambition of a common man to get his hand upon the collar of his superiors, or, failing that, to get his thumb into their eyes. He was born with a roaring voice, and it had the trick of inflaming half-wits. His whole career was devoted to raising those half-wits against their betters, that he himself might shine. His last battle will be grossly misunderstood if it is thought of as a mere exercise in fanaticism—that is, if Bryan the Fundamentalist Pope is mistaken for one of the bucolic Fundamentalists. There was much more in it than that, as everyone knows who saw him on the field. What moved him, at bottom, was simply hatred of the city men who had laughed at him so long, and brought him at last to so tatterdemalion an estate. He lusted for revenge upon them. He yearned to lead the anthropoid rabble against them, to punish them for their execution upon him by attacking the very vitals of their civilization. He went far beyond the bounds of any merely religious frenzy, however inordinate. When he began denouncing the notion that man is a mammal even some of the hinds at Dayton were agape. And when, brought upon Darrow's cruel hook, he writhed and tossed in a very fury of malignancy, bawling against the baldest elements of sense and decency like a man frantic—when he came to that tragic climax of his striving there were snickers among the hinds as well as hosannas.

Upon that hook, in truth, Bryan committed suicide, as a legend as well as in the body. He staggered from the rustic court ready to die, and he staggered from it ready to be forgotten, save as a character in a third-rate farce, witless and in poor taste. It was plain to everyone who knew him, when he came to Dayton, that his great days were behind him—that, for all the fury of his hatred, he was now definitely an old man, and headed at last for silence. There was a vague, unpleasant manginess about his appearance; he somehow seemed dirty, though a close glance showed him as carefully shaven as an actor, and clad in immaculate linen. All the

hair was gone from the dome of his head, and it had begun to fall out, too,
behind his ears, in the obscene manner of the late Samuel Gompers. The
resonance had departed from his voice; what was once a bugle blast had
become reedy and quavering. Who knows that, like Demosthenes, he
had a lisp? In the old days, under the magic of his eloquence, no one
noticed it. But when he spoke at Dayton it was always audible.

When I first encountered him, on the sidewalk in front of the office
of the rustic lawyers who were his associates in the Scopes case, the trial
was yet to begin, and so he was still expansive and amiable. I had printed
in the *Nation*, a week or so before, an article arguing that the Tennessee
anti-evolution law, whatever its wisdom, was at least constitutional—that
the rustics of the State had a clear right to have their progeny taught
whatever they chose, and kept secure from whatever knowledge violated
their superstitions. The old boy professed to be delighted with the
argument, and gave the gaping bystanders to understand that I was a
publicist of parts. Not to be outdone, I admired the preposterous country shirt that he wore—sleeveless and with the neck cut very low. We
parted in the manner of two ambassadors. But that was the last touch
of amiability that I was destined to see in Bryan. The next day the battle
joined and his face became hard. By the end of the week he was simply a
walking fever. Hour by hour he grew more bitter. What the Christian
Scientists call malicious animal magnetism seemed to radiate from him
like heat from a stove. From my place in the courtroom, standing upon a
table, I looked directly down upon him, sweating horribly and pumping
his palm-leaf fan. His eyes fascinated me; I watched them all day long.
They were blazing points of hatred. They glittered like occult and sinister gems. Now and then they wandered to me, and I got my share, for
my reports of the trial had come back to Dayton, and he had read them.
It was like coming under fire.

Thus he fought his last fight, thirsting savagely for blood. All sense
departed from him. He bit right and left, like a dog with rabies. He
descended to demagogy so dreadful that his very associates at the trial
table blushed. His one yearning was to keep his yokels heated up—to
lead his forlorn mob of imbeciles against the foe. That foe, alas, refused
to be alarmed. It insisted upon seeing the whole battle as a comedy. Even
Darrow, who knew better, occasionally yielded to the prevailing spirit.
One day he lured poor Bryan into the folly I have mentioned: his
astounding argument against the notion that man is a mammal. I am glad
I heard it, for otherwise I'd never believe in it. There stood the man who
had been thrice a candidate for the Presidency of the Republic—there he
stood in the glare of the world, uttering stuff that a boy of eight would
laugh at! The artful Darrow led him on: he repeated it, ranted for it,
bellowed it in his cracked voice. So he was prepared for the final slaughter. He came into life a hero, a Galahad, in bright and shining armor. He
was passing out a poor mountebank.

The chances are that history will put the peak of democracy in

America in his time; it has been on the downward curve among us since the campaign of 1896. He will be remembered perhaps, as its supreme impostor, the *reductio ad absurdum* of its pretension. Bryan came very near being President. In 1896, it is possible, he was actually elected. He lived long enough to make patriots thank the inscrutable gods for Harding, even for Coolidge. Dullness has got into the White House, and the smell of cabbage boiling, but there is at least nothing to compare to the intolerable buffoonery that went on in Tennessee. The President of the United States may be an ass, but he at least doesn't believe that the earth is square, and that witches should be put to death, and that Jonah swallowed the whale. The Golden Text is not painted weekly on the White House wall, and there is no need to keep ambassadors waiting while Pastor Simpson, of Smithville, prays for rain in the Blue Room. We have escaped something—by a narrow margin, but still we have escaped.

That is, so far. The Fundamentalists, once apparently sweeping all before them, now face minorities prepared for battle even in the South— here and there with some assurance of success. But it is too early, it seems to me, to send the firemen home; the fire is still burning on many a far-flung hill, and it may begin to roar again at any moment. The evil that men do lives after them. Bryan, in his malice, started something that it will not be easy to stop. In ten thousand country towns his old heelers, the evangelical pastors, are propagating his gospel, and everywhere the yokels are ready for it. When he disappeared from the big cities, the big cities made the capital error of assuming that he was done for. If they heard of him at all, it was only as a crimp for real-estate speculators —the heroic foe of the unearned increment hauling it in with both hands. He seemed preposterous, and hence harmless. But all the while he was busy among his old lieges, preparing for a *jacquerie* that should floor all his enemies at one blow. He did his job competently. He had vast skill at such enterprises. Heave an egg out of a Pullman window, and you will hit a Fundamentalist almost everywhere in the United States today. They swarm in the country towns, inflamed by their *shamans*, and with a saint, now, to venerate. They are thick in the mean streets behind the gas-works. They are everywhere where learning is too heavy a burden for mortal minds to carry, even the vague, pathetic learning on tap in little red schoolhouses. They march with the Klan, with the Christian Endeavor Society, with the Junior Order of United American Mechanics, with the Epworth League, with all the rococo bands that poor and unhappy folk organize to bring some light of purpose into their lives. They have had a thrill, and they are ready for more.

Such is Bryan's legacy to his country. He couldn't be President, but he could at least help magnificently in the solemn business of shutting off the Presidency from every intelligent and self-respecting man. The storm, perhaps, won't last long, as time goes in history. It may help, indeed, to break up the democratic delusion, now already showing weakness, and so hasten its own end. But while it lasts it will blow off some roofs.

H. L. Mencken

HUNEKER: A MEMORY

THERE WAS A STIMULATING aliveness about him always, an air of living eagerly and a bit recklessly, a sort of defiant resiliency. In his very frame and form something provocative showed itself—an insolent singularity, obvious to even the most careless glance. That Caligulan profile of his was more than simply unusual in a free republic, consecrated to good works; to a respectable American, encountering it in the lobby of the Metropolitan or in the smoke-room of a *Doppelschraubenschnellpostdampfer*, it must have suggested inevitably the dark enterprises and illicit metaphysics of a Heliogabalus. More, there was always something rakish and defiant about his hat—it was too white, or it curled in the wrong way, or a feather peeped from the band—and a hint of antinomianism in his cravat. Yet more, he ran to exotic tastes in eating and drinking, preferring occult goulashes and risi-bisis to honest American steaks, and great floods of Pilsner to the harsh beverages of God-fearing men. Finally, there was his talk, that cataract of sublime trivialities: gossip lifted to the plane of the gods, the unmentionable bedizened with an astounding importance, and even profundity.

In his early days, when he performed the tonal and carnal prodigies that he liked to talk of afterward, I was at nurse, and too young to have any traffic with him. When I encountered him at last he was in the high flush of the middle years, and had already become a tradition in the little world that critics inhabit. We sat down to luncheon at one o'clock; I think it must have been at Lüchow's, his favorite refuge and rostrum to the end. At six, when I had to go, the waiter was hauling in his tenth (or was it twentieth?) *Seidel* of Pilsner, and he was bringing to a close *prestissimo* the most amazing monologue that these ears (up to that time) had ever funnelled into this consciousness. What a stew, indeed! Berlioz and the question of the clang-tint of the viola, the psychopathological causes of the suicide of Tschaikowsky, why Nietzsche had to leave Sils Maria between days in 1887, the echoes of Flaubert in Joseph Conrad (then but newly dawned), the precise topography of the warts of Liszt, George Bernard Shaw's heroic but vain struggles to throw off Presbyterianism, how Frau Cosima saved Wagner from the libidinous Swedish baroness, what to drink when playing Chopin, what Cézanne thought of his disciples, the defects in the structure of "Sister Carrie," Anton Seidl and the musical union, the complex love affairs of Gounod, the early days of David Belasco, the varying talents and idiosyncrasies of Lillian Russell's earlier husbands, whether a girl educated at Vassar could ever really learn to love, the exact composition of chicken paprika, the correct tempo of the Vienna waltz, the style of William Dean Howells, what George Moore said about German bathrooms, the true inwardness of the affair between D'Annunzio and Duse, the origin of the theory that all oboe players are crazy, why Löwenbräu survived exportation better than Hofbräu, Ibsen's loathing of Norwegians, the best remedy for Rhine wine *Katzenjammer*, how to play Brahms, the degeneration of the Bal Bullier, the sheer physical impossibility of getting Dvořák drunk, the genuine last words of Walt Whitman. . . .

I left in a sort of fever, and it was a couple of days later before I began to sort out my impressions, and formulate a coherent image. Was the man allusive in his books—so allusive that popular report credited him with the actual manufacture of authorities? Then he was ten times as allusive in his discourse—a veritable geyser of unfamiliar names, shocking epigrams in strange tongues, unearthly philosophies out of the backwaters of Scandinavia, Transylvania, Bulgaria, the Basque country, the Ukraine. And did he, in his criticism, pass facilely from the author to the man, and from the man to his wife, and to the wives of his friends? Then at the *Biertisch* he began long beyond the point where the last honest wife gives up the ghost, and so, full tilt, ran into such complexities of adultery that a plain sinner could scarcely follow him. I try to give you, ineptly and grotesquely, some notion of the talk of the man, but I must fail inevitably. It was, in brief, chaos, and chaos cannot be described. But it was chaos made to gleam and corruscate with every device of the seven arts—chaos drenched in all the colors imaginable, chaos scored for an orchestra which made the great band of Berlioz seem like a fife and drum corps. One night a few months before the war, I sat in the Paris Opera House listening to the first performance of Richard Strauss's "Josef's Legend," with Strauss himself conducting. On the stage there was a riot of hues that swung the eyes 'round and 'round in a crazy mazurka; in the orchestra there were such volleys and explosions of tone that the ears (I fall into a Hunekeran trope) began to go pale and clammy with surgical shock. Suddenly, above all the uproar, a piccolo launched into a new and saucy tune—in an unrelated key! . . . Instantly and quite naturally, I thought of the incomparable James. When he gave a show at Lüchow's he never forgot that anarchistic passage for the piccolo.

I observe a tendency since his death to estimate him in terms of the content of his books. Even Frank Harris, who certainly should know better, goes there for the facts about him. Nothing could do him worse injustice. In those books, of course, there is a great deal of perfectly sound stuff; the wonder is, in truth, that so much of it holds up so well today—for example, the essays on Strauss, on Brahms and on Nietzsche, and the whole volume on Chopin. But the real Huneker never got himself formally between covers, if one forgets "Old Fogy" and parts of "Painted Veils." The volumes of his regular canon are made up, in the main, of articles written for the more intellectual magazines and newspapers of their era, and they are full of a conscious striving to qualify for respectable company. Huneker, always curiously modest, never got over the notion that it was a singular honor for a man such as he—a mere diurnal scribbler, innocent of academic robes—to be published by so austere a publisher as Scribner. More than once, anchored at the beer-table, we discussed the matter at length, I always arguing that all the honor was enjoyed by Scribner. But Huneker, I believe in all sincerity, would not have it so, any more than he would have it that he was a better music critic than his two colleagues, the pedantic Krehbiel and the nonsensical Finck. This illogical modesty, of course, had its limits; it made him cautious about expressing himself, but it seldom led him into downright assumptions of false personality. Nowhere in all his books will you find him doing the things that every right-thinking Anglo-Saxon critic is supposed to do—the Middleton Murry, Paul Elmer More, Clutton-Brock sort of puerility—solemn essays on Coleridge and Addison, abysmal discussions of the relative merits of Schumann and Mendelssohn, horrible treatises upon the relations of Goethe to the Romantic Movement, dull scratchings in a hundred such exhausted and sterile fields. Such enterprises were not for Huneker; he kept himself out of that black coat. But I am convinced that he always had his own raiment pressed carefully before he left Lüchow's for the temple of Athene—and maybe changed cravats, and put on a boiled shirt, and took the feather out of his hat. The simon-pure Huneker, the Huneker who was the true essence and prime motor of the more courtly Huneker—remained behind. This real Huneker survives in conversations that still haunt the rafters of the beer-halls of two continents, and in a vast mass of newspaper impromptus, thrown off too hastily to be reduced to complete decorum, and in two books that stand outside the official canon, and yet contain the man himself as not even "Iconoclasts" or the Chopin book contains him, to wit, the "Old Fogy" aforesaid and the "Painted Veils" of his last year. Both were published, so to speak, out of the back door—the former by a music publisher in Philadelphia and the latter in a small and expensive edition for the admittedly damned. There is a chapter in "Painted Veils" that is Huneker to every last hitch of the shoulders and twinkle of the eye—the chapter in which the hero soliloquizes on art, life, immortality, and women—especially women. And there are half a dozen chapters in "Old Fogy"—superficially buffoonery, but how penetrating! how gorgeously flavored! how learned!—that come completely up to the same high specification. If I had to choose one Huneker book and give up all the others, I'd choose "Old Fogy" instantly. In it Huneker is utterly himself. In it the last trace of the pedagogue vanishes. Art is no longer, even by implication, a device for improving the mind. It is wholly a magnificent adventure.

That notion of it is what Huneker brought into American criticism, and it is for that bringing that he will be remembered. No other critic of his generation had a tenth of his influence. Almost single-handed he overthrew the aesthetic theory that had flourished in the United States since the death of Poe, and set up an utterly contrary aesthetic theory in its place. If the younger men of today have emancipated themselves from the Puritan aesthetic, if the schoolmaster is now palpably on the defensive, and no longer the unchallenged assassin of the fine arts that he once was, if he has already begun to compromise somewhat absurdly with new and sounder ideas, and even to lift his voice in artificial hosannahs, then Huneker certainly deserves all the credit for the change. What he brought back from Paris was precisely the thing that was most suspected in the America of those days: the capacity for gusto. Huneker had that capacity in a degree unmatched by any other critic. When his soul went adventuring among masterpieces it did not go in Sunday broadcloth; it went with vine leaves in its hair. The rest of the appraisers and criers-up—even Howells, with all his humor—could never quite rid themselves of the professorial manner. When they praised it was always with some hint of ethical, or, at all events, of cultural purpose; when they condemned that purpose was even plainer. The arts, to them, constituted a sort of school for the psyche; their aim was to discipline and mellow the spirit. But to Huneker their one aim was always to make the spirit glad—to set it, in Nietzsche's phrase, to dancing with arms and legs. He had absolutely no feeling for extra-aesthetic valuations. If a work of art that stood before him was honest, if it was original, if it was beautiful and thoroughly alive, then he was for it to his last corpuscle. What if it violated all the accepted canons? Then let the accepted canons go hang! What if it lacked all purpose to improve and lift up? Then so much the better! What if it shocked all right-feeling men, and made them blush and tremble? Then damn all men of right feeling forevermore.

With this ethical atheism, so strange in the United States and so abhorrent to most Americans, there went something that was probably also part of the loot of Paris: an insatiable curiosity about the artist as man. This curiosity was responsible for two of Huneker's salient characters: his habit of mixing even the most serious criticism with cynical and often scandalous gossip, and his pervasive foreignness. I believe that it is almost literally true to say that he could never quite make up his mind about a new symphony until he had seen the composer's mistress, or at all events a good photograph of her. He thought of Wagner, not alone in terms of melody and harmony, but also in terms of the Tribschen idyl and the Bayreuth tragi-comedy. Go through his books and you will see how often he was fascinated by mere eccentricity of personality. I doubt that even Huysmans, had he been a respectable French Huguenot, would have interested him; certainly his enthusiasm for Verlaine, Villiers de l'Isle Adam and other such fantastic fish was centered upon the men quite as much as upon the artists. His foreignness, so often urged against him by defenders of the national tradition, was grounded largely on the fact that such eccentric personalities were rare in the Republic—rare, and well watched by the *Polizei*. When one bobbed up, he was alert at once—even though the newcomer was only a Roosevelt. The rest of the American people he dismissed as a horde of slaves, goose-steppers, cads, Methodists; he could not imagine one of them becoming a first-rate artist, save by a miracle. Even the American executant was under his suspicion, for he knew very well that playing the fiddle was a great deal more than scraping four strings of copper and catgut with a switch from a horse's tail. What he asked himself was how a man could play Bach decently, and then, after playing, go from the hall to a soda-fountain, or a political meeting, or a lecture at the Harvard Club. Overseas there was a better air for artists, and overseas Huneker looked for them.

These fundamental theories of his, of course, had their defects. They were a bit too simple, and often very much too hospitable. Huneker, clinging to them, certainly did his share of whooping for the sort of revolutionist who is here today and gone tomorrow; he was fugleman, in his time, for more than one cause that was lost almost as soon as it was stated. More, his prejudices made him somewhat anæsthetic, at times, to the new men who were not brilliant in color but respectably drab, and who tried to do their work within the law. Particularly in his later years, when the old gusto began to die out and all that remained of it was habit, he was apt to go chasing after strange birds and so miss seeing the elephants go by. I could put together a very pretty list of frauds that he praised. I could concoct another list of genuine *arrivés* that he overlooked. But all that is merely saying that there were human limits to him; the professors, on their side, have sinned far worse, and in both directions. Looking back over the whole of his work, one must needs be amazed by the general soundness of his judgments. He discerned, in the main, what was good and he described it in terms that were seldom bettered afterward. His successive heroes, always under fire when he first championed them, almost invariably moved to secure ground and became solid men, challenged by no one save fools—Ibsen, Nietzsche, Brahms, Strauss, Cézanne, Stirner, Synge, the Russian composers, the Russian novelists. He did for this Western world what Georg Brandes was doing for Continental Europe—sorting out the new comers with sharp eyes, and giving mighty lifts to those who deserved it. Brandes did it in terms of the old academic bombast; he was never more the professor than when he was arguing for some hobgoblin of the professors. But Huneker did it with verve and grace; he made it, not schoolmastering, but a glorious deliverance from schoolmastering. As I say, his influence was enormous. The fine arts, at his touch, shed all their Anglo-American lugubriousness, and became provocative and joyous. The spirit of senility got out of them and the spirit of youth got into them. His criticism, for all its French basis, was thoroughly American—vastly more American, in fact, than the New England ponderosity that it displaced. Though he was an Easterner and a cockney of the cockneys, he picked up some of the Western spaciousness that showed itself in Mark Twain. And all the young men followed him.

A good many of them, I daresay, followed him so ardently that they got a good distance ahead of him, and often, perhaps, embarrassed him by taking his name in vain. For all his enterprise and iconoclasm, indeed, there was not much of the Berserker in him, and his floutings of the national aesthetic tradition seldom took the form of forthright challenges. Here the strange modesty that I have mentioned always stayed him as a like weakness stayed Mark Twain. He could never quite rid himself of the feeling that he was no more than an amateur among the gaudy doctors who roared in the reviews, and that it would be unseemly for him to forget their authority. I have a notion that this feeling was born in the days when he stood almost alone, with the whole faculty grouped in a pained circle around him. He was then too miserable a worm to be noticed at all. Later on, gaining importance, he was lectured somewhat severely for his violation of decorum; in England even Max Beerbohm made an idiotic assault upon him. It was the Germans and the French, in fact, who first praised him intelligently—and these friends were too far away to help a timorous man in a row at home. This sensation of isolation and littleness, I suppose, explains his fidelity to the newspapers, and the otherwise inexplicable joy that he always took in his forgotten work for the *Musical Courier*, in his day a very dubious journal. In such waters he felt at ease. There he could disport without thought of the dignity of publishers and the eagle eyes of campus reviewers. Some of the connections that he formed were full of an ironical inappropriateness. His discomforts in his *Puck* days showed themselves in the feebleness of his work; when he served the *Times* he was as well placed as a Cabell at a colored ball. Perhaps the *Sun*, in the years before it was munseyized, offered him the best berth that he ever had, save it were his old one on *Mlle. New York*. But whatever the flag, he served it loyally, and got a lot of fun out of the business. He liked the pressure of newspaper work; he liked the associations that it involved, the gabble in the press-room of the Opera House, the exchanges of news and gossip; above all, he liked the relative ease of the intellectual harness. In a newspaper article he could

say whatever happened to pop into his mind, and if it looked thin the next
day, then there was, after all, no harm done. But when he sat down to
write a book—or rather to compile it, for all of his volumes were re-
worked magazine (and sometimes newspaper) articles—he became self-
conscious, and so knew uneasiness. The tightness of his style, its one
salient defect, was probably the result of this weakness. The corrected
clippings that constituted most of his manuscripts are so beladen with
revisions and rerevisions that they are almost indecipherable.

Thus the growth of Huneker's celebrity in his later years filled him
with wonder, and never quite convinced him. He was certainly wholly
free from any desire to gather disciples about him and found a school.
There was, of course, some pride of authorship in him, and he liked to
know that his books were read and admired; in particular, he was pleased
by their translation into German and Czech. But it seemed to me that he
shrank from the bellicosity that so often got into praise of them—that he
disliked being set up as the opponent and superior of the professors whom
he always vaguely respected and the rival newspaper critics whose friendship he esteemed far above their professional admiration, or even respect.
I could never draw him into a discussion of these rivals, save perhaps a
discussion of their historic feats at beer-guzzling. He wrote vastly better
than any of them and knew far more about the arts than most of them,
and he was undoubtedly aware of it in his heart, but it embarrassed him
to hear this superiority put into plain terms. His intense gregariousness
probably accounted for part of this reluctance to pit himself against
them; he could not imagine a world without a great deal of easy comradeship in it, and much casual slapping of backs. But under it all was the
chronic underestimation of himself that I have discussed—his fear that
he had spread himself over too many arts, and that his equipment was
thus defective in every one of them. "Steeplejack" is full of this apologetic timidity. In its very title, as he explains it, there is a confession of
inferiority that is almost maudlin: "Life has been the Barmecide's feast to
me," and so on. In the book itself he constantly takes refuge in triviality
from the harsh challenges of critical parties, and as constantly avoids facts
that would shock the Philistines. One might reasonably assume, reading it
from end to end, that his early days in Paris were spent in the fashion of a
Y.M.C.A. secretary. A few drinking bouts, of course, and a love affair in
the manner of Dubuque, Iowa—but where are the wenches?

More than once, indeed, the book sinks to downright equivocation—
for example, in the Roosevelt episodes. Certainly no one who knew
Huneker in life will ever argue seriously that he was deceived by the
Roosevelt buncombe, or that his view of life was at all comparable to that
of the great demagogue. He stood, in fact, at the opposite pole. He saw
the world, not as a moral show, but as a sort of glorified Follies. He was
absolutely devoid of that obsession with the problem of conduct which
was Roosevelt's main virtue in the eyes of a stupid and superstitious
people. More, he was wholly against Roosevelt on many concrete issues—

the race suicide banality, the Panama swindle, the war. He was far too much the realist to believe in the American case, either before or after 1917, and the manner in which it was urged, by Roosevelt and others, violated his notions of truth, honor and decency. I assume nothing here; I simply record what he told me himself. Nevertheless, the sheer notoriety of the Rough Rider—his picturesque personality and talent as a mountebank—had its effect on Huneker, and so he was a bit flattered when he was summoned to Oyster Bay, and there accepted gravely the nonsense that was poured into his ear, and even repeated some of it without a cackle in his book. To say that he actually believed in it would be to libel him. It was precisely such hollow tosh that he stood against in his rôle of critic of art and life; it was by exposing its hollowness that he lifted himself above the general. The same weakness induced him to accept membership in the National Institute of Arts and Letters. The offer of it to a man of his age and attainments, after he had been passed over year after year in favor of all sorts of cheapjack novelists and tenth-rate compilers of college textbooks, was intrinsically insulting; it was almost as if the Musical Union had offered to admit a Brahms. But with the insult went a certain gage of respectability, a certain formal forgiveness for old frivolities, a certain abatement of old doubts and self-questionings and so Huneker accepted. Later on, reviewing the episode in his own mind, he found it the spring of doubts that were even more uncomfortable. His last letter to me was devoted to the matter. He was by then eager to maintain that he had got in by a process only partly under his control, and that, being in, he could discover no decorous way of getting out.

But perhaps I devote too much space to the elements in the man that worked against his own free development. They were, after all, grounded upon qualities that are certainly not to be deprecated—modesty, goodwill to his fellow-men, a fine sense of team-work, a distaste for acrimonious and useless strife. These qualities gave him great charm. He was not only humorous; he was also good-humored; even when the crushing discomforts of his last illness were upon him his amiability never faltered. And in addition to humor there was wit, a far rarer thing. His most casual talk was full of this wit, and it bathed everything that he discussed in a new and brilliant light. I have never encountered a man who was further removed from dullness; it seemed a literal impossibility for him to open his mouth without discharging some word or phrase that arrested the attention and stuck in the memory. And under it all, giving an extraordinary quality to the verbal fireworks, there was a solid and apparently illimitable learning. The man knew as much as forty average men, and his knowledge was well-ordered and instantly available. He had read everything and had seen everything and heard everything, and nothing that he had ever read or seen or heard quite passed out of his mind.

Here, in three words, was the main virtue of his criticism—its gigantic richness. It had the dazzling charm of an ornate and intricate design, a blazing fabric of fine silks. It was no mere pontifical statement of one man's reactions to a set of ideas; it was a sort of essence of the reactions of many men—of all the men, in fact, worth hearing. Huneker discarded their scaffolding, their ifs and whereases, and presented only what was important and arresting in their conclusions. It was never a mere *pastiche;* the selection was made delicately, discreetly, with almost unerring taste and judgment. And in the summing up there was always the clearest possible statement of the whole matter. What finally emerged was a body of doctrine that came, I believe, very close to the truth. Into an assembly of national critics who had long wallowed in dogmatic puerilities, Huneker entered with a taste infinitely surer and more civilized, a learning infinitely greater, and an address infinitely more engaging. No man was less the reformer by inclination, and yet he became a reformer beyond compare. He emancipated criticism in America from its old slavery to stupidity, and with it he emancipated all the arts themselves.

RICHARD HOFSTADTER

photograph by Alfred A. Knopf

H. L. MENCKEN

photograph by Alfred A. Knopf

and Bancroft, Parkman and Fiske, were great literary craftsmen. Their many-volumed works sold in sufficient quantities to give them handsome returns; even today they are widely read. But the first generation of seminar-trained historians, educated in Germany or by teachers trained there, imagined that history would tell itself, provided one were honest, thorough, and painstaking. Some of them went so far as to regard history as pure science and to assert that writers thereof had no more business trying to be "literary" than did writers of statistical reports or performers of scientific experiments. Professors warned their pupils (quite unnecessarily) against "fine writing," and endeavored to protect their innocence from the seductive charm of Washington Irving or the masculine glamour of Macaulay. And in this flight of history from literature the public was left behind. American history became a bore to the reader and a drug on the market; even historians with something to say and the talent for saying it (Henry Adams, for instance) could not sell their books. The most popular American histories of the period 1890-1905 were those of John Fiske, a philosopher who had no historical training, but wrote with life and movement.

Theodore Roosevelt in his presidential address before the American Historical Association in 1912 made a ringing plea to the young historian to do better:

> He must ever remember that while the worst offense of which he can be guilty is to write vividly and inaccurately, yet that unless he writes vividly he cannot write truthfully; for no amount of dull, painstaking detail will sum up the whole truth unless the genius is there to paint the truth.

And although American historians cannot hope as Theodore Roosevelt did to "watch the nearing chariots of the champions," or look forward to the day when "for us the war-horns of King Olaf shall wail across the flood, and the harps sound high at festivals in forgotten halls," we may indeed "show how the land which the pioneers won slowly and with incredible hardship was filled in two generations by the overflow from the countries of western and central Europe." We may describe the race, class, and religious conflicts that immigration has engendered, and trace the rise of the labor movement with a literary art that compels people to read about it. You do not need chariots and horsemen, harps and war-horns to make history interesting.

Theodore Roosevelt's trumpet call fell largely on deaf ears, at least in the academic historical profession. A whole generation has passed without producing any really great works on American history. Plenty of good books, valuable books, and new interpretations and explorations of the past; but none with fire in the eye, none to make a young man want to fight for his country in war or live to make it a better country in peace. There has been a sort of chain reaction of dullness. Professors who have risen to positions of eminence by writing dull, solid, valuable monographs that nobody reads outside the profession, teach graduate students to write

dull, solid, valuable monographs like theirs; the road to academic security
is that of writing dull, solid, valuable monographs. And so the young men
who have a gift for good writing either leave the historical field for
something more exciting, or write more dull, solid, valuable monographs.
The few professional historians who have had a popular following or
appeal during the last thirty years are either men like Allan Nevins who
were trained in some juicier profession like journalism, or men and
women like the Beards who had the sense to break loose young from
academic trammels.

In the meantime, the American public has become so sated by dull
history textbooks in school and college that it won't read history unless
disguised as something else under a title such as "The Flowering of Florida," "The Epic of the East," or "The Growth of the American Republic." Or, more often, they get what history they want from historical
novels.

Now I submit, this is a very bad situation. The tremendous plowing
up of the past by well-trained scholars is all to the good, so far as it goes.
Scholars know more about America's past than ever; they are opening
new furrows and finding new artifacts, from aboriginal arrowheads to
early twentieth-century corset stays. But they are heaping up the pay dirt
for others. Journalists, novelists, and free-lance writers are the ones that
extract the gold; and they deserve every ounce they get because they are
the ones who know how to write histories that people care to read. What
I want to see is a few more Ph.D.'s in history winning book-of-the-
month adoptions and reaping the harvest of dividends. They can do it,
too, if they will only use the same industry at presenting history as they
do in compiling it.

Mind you, I intend no disparagement of historians who choose to
devote their entire energies to teaching. Great teachers do far more good
to the cause of history than mediocre writers. Such men, for instance, as
the late H. Morse Stephens, who stopped writing (which he never liked)
as soon as he obtained a chair in this country, and the late Edwin F. Gay,
who never began writing, inspired thousands of young men and initiated
scores of valuable books. Thank God for these gifted teachers, I say;
universities should seek out, encourage, and promote them far more than
they do. My remarks are addressed to young people who have the urge to
write history, and wish to write it effectively.

There are no special rules for writing history; any good manual of
rhetoric or teacher of composition will supply the rules for writing English. But what terrible stuff passes for English in Ph.D. dissertations,
monographs, and articles in historical reviews! Long, involved sentences
that one has to read two or three times in order to grasp their meaning;
poverty in vocabulary, ineptness of expression, weakness in paragraph
structure, frequent misuse of words, and, of late, the introduction of
pseudo-scientific and psychological jargon. There is no fundamental cure
for this except better teaching of English in our schools and colleges, and

by every teacher, whatever his other subject may be. If historical writing is infinitely better in France than in America, and far better in the British Isles and Canada than in the United States, it is because every French and British teacher of history drills his pupils in their mother tongue, requiring a constant stream of essays and reports, and criticizing written work not only as history but as literature. The American university teacher who gives honor grades to students who have not yet learned to write English, for industrious compilations of facts or feats of memory, is wanting in professional pride or competency.

Of course, what we should all like to attain in writing history is style. "The sense for style," says Whitehead in his *Aims of Education*, "is an aesthetic sense, based on admiration for the direct attainment of a foreseen end, simply and without waste. Style in art, style in literature, style in science, style in logic, style in practical execution, have fundamentally the same aesthetic qualities, namely attainment and restraint. Style, in its finest sense, is the last acquirement of the educated mind; it is also the most useful. It pervades the whole being. . . . Style is the ultimate morality of mind."

Unfortunately, there is no royal road to style. It cannot be attained by mere industry; it can never be achieved through imitation, although it may be promoted by example. Reading the greatest literary artists among historians will help; but do not forget that what was acceptable style in 1850 might seem turgid today. We can still read Macaulay with admiration and pleasure, we can still learn paragraph structure and other things from Macaulay, but anyone who tried to imitate Macaulay today would be a pompous ass.

Just as Voltaire's ideal curé advises his flock not to worry about going to heaven, but to do right and probably by God's grace they will get there; so the young writer of history had better concentrate on day-by-day improvement in craftsmanship. Then perhaps he may find some day that his prose appeals to a large popular audience; that, in other words, he has achieved style through simple, honest, straightforward writing.

A few hints as to the craft may be useful to budding historians. First and foremost, *get writing!* Young scholars generally wish to secure the last fact before writing anything, like General McClellan refusing to advance (as people said) until the last mule was shod. It is a terrible strain, isn't it, to sit down at a desk with your notes all neatly docketed, and begin to write? You pretend to your wife that you mustn't be interrupted; but, actually, you welcome a ring of the telephone, a knock at the door, or a bellow from the baby as an excuse to break off. Finally, after smoking sundry cigarettes and pacing about the house two or three times, you commit a lame paragraph or two to paper. By the time you get to the third, one bit of information you want is lacking. What a relief! Now you must go back to the library or the archives to do some more digging. That's where you are happy! And what you turn up there leads to more questions and prolongs the delicious process of research. Half the pleas I have heard from graduate students for more time or another grant-in-aid are mere excuses to postpone the painful drudgery of writing.

There is the "indispensablest beauty in knowing how to get done," said Carlyle. In every research there comes a point, which you should recognize like a call of conscience, when you must get down to writing. And when you once are writing, go on writing as long as you can; there will be plenty of time later to shove in the footnotes or return to the library for extra information. Above all, *start* writing. Nothing is more pathetic than the "gonna" historian, who from graduate school on is always "gonna" write a magnum opus but never completes his research on the subject, and dies without anything to show for a lifetime's work.

Dictation is usually fatal to good historical writing. Write out your first draft in longhand or, if you compose easily on the typewriter, type it out yourself, revise with pencil or pen, and have it retyped clean. Don't stop to consult your notes for every clause or sentence; it is better to get what you have to say clearly in your mind and dash it off; then, after you have it down, return to your notes and compose your next few pages or paragraphs. After a little experience you may well find that you think best with your fingers on the typewriter keys or your fountain pen poised over the paper. For me, the mere writing of a few words seems to point up vague thoughts and make jumbled facts array themselves in neat order. Whichever method you choose, composing before you write or as you write, do not return to your raw material or verify facts and quotations or insert footnotes until you have written a substantial amount, an amount that will increase with practice. It is significant that two of our greatest American historians, Prescott and Parkman, were nearly blind during a good part of their active careers. They had to have the sources read to them and turn the matter over and over in their minds before they could give anything out; and when they gave, *they gave!*

Now, the purpose of this quick, warm synthesis between research, thinking, and writing is to attain the three prime qualities of historical composition—clarity, vigor, and objectivity. You must think about your facts, analyze your material, and decide exactly what you mean before you can write it so that the average reader will understand. Do not fall into the fallacy of supposing that "facts speak for themselves." Most of the facts that you excavate, like other relics of past human activity, are dumb things; it is for you to make them speak by proper selection, arrangement, and emphasis. Dump your entire collection of facts on paper, and the result will be unreadable if not incomprehensible.

So, too, with vigor. If your whole paragraph or chapter is but a hypothesis, say so at the beginning, but do not bore and confuse the reader with numerous "buts," "excepts," "perhaps," "howevers," and "possiblys." Use direct rather than indirect statements, the active rather than the passive voice, and make every sentence and paragraph an organic whole. Above all, if you are writing historical narrative, make it move.

Do not take time out in the middle of a political or military campaign to introduce special developments or literary trends, as McMaster did to the confusion of his readers. Place those admittedly important matters in a chapter or chapters by themselves so that your reader's attention will not be lost by constant interruption.

That brings us to the third essential quality—objectivity. Keep the reader constantly in mind. You are not writing history for yourself or for the professors who are supposed to know more about it than you do. Assume that you are writing for intelligent people who know nothing about your particular subject but whom you wish to interest and attract. I once asked the late Senator Beveridge why his *Life of John Marshall,* despite its great length and scholarly apparatus, was so popular. He replied: "The trouble with you professors of history is that you write for each other. I write for people almost completely ignorant of American history, as I was when I began my research."

A few more details. Even if the work you are writing does not call for footnotes, keep them in your copy until the last draft, for they will enable you to check up on your facts, statements, and quotations. And since accuracy is the prime virtue of the historian, this checking must be done, either by the author or by someone else. You will be surprised by the mistakes that creep in between a first rough draft and a final typed copy. And the better you write, the more your critics will enjoy finding misquotations and inaccuracies.

The matter of handling quotations seems to be a difficult one for young historians. There is nothing that adds so much to the charm and effectiveness of a history as good quotations from the sources, especially if the period be somewhat remote. But there is nothing so disgusting to the reader as long, tedious, broken quotations in small print, especially those in which, to make sense, the author has to interpolate words in brackets. Young writers are prone to use quotations in places where their own words would be better, and to incorporate in the text source excerpts that belong in footnotes or appendices. Avoid ending chapters with quotations, and never close your book with one.

Above all, do not be afraid to revise and rewrite. Reading aloud is a good test—historians' wives have to stand a lot of that! A candid friend who is not a historian and so represents the audience you are trying to reach, is perhaps the best "dog" to try it on. Even if he has little critical sense, it is encouraging to have him stay awake. My good friend Lucien Price years ago listened with a pained expression to a bit of my early work. "Now, just what do you mean by that?" he asked after a long, involved, pedantic, and quote-larded paragraph. I told him in words of one syllable, or perhaps two. "Fine!" said he, "I understand that. Now write down what you said; throw the other away!"

Undoubtedly the writer of history can enrich his mind and broaden his literary experience as well as better his craftsmanship by his choice of leisure reading. If he is so fortunate as to have had a classical education, no time will be better spent in making him an effective historian than in reading Latin and Greek authors. Both these ancient languages are such superb instruments of thought that a knowledge of them cures slipshod English and helps one to attain a clear, muscular style. All our greatest historical stylists—notably Prescott, Parkman, Fiske, and Frederick J. Turner—had a classical education and read the ancient historians in the original before they approached American history.

If you have little Latin and less Greek and feel unable to spare the time and effort to add them to your stock of tools, read the ancient classics in the best literary translations, such as North's Plutarch, Rawlinson's Herodotus, John J. Chapman's Aeschylus, Gilbert Murray's Euripides, and, above all, Jowett's or Livingstone's Thucydides. Through them you will gain the content and spirit of the ancient classics, which will break down your provincialism, refresh your spirit, and give you a better philosophical insight into the ways of mankind than most of such works as the new science of psychology has brought forth. Moreover, you will be acquiring the same background as many of the great Americans of past generations, thus aiding your understanding of them.

The reading of English classics will tend in the same direction, and will also be a painless and unconscious means of improving your literary style. Almost every English or American writer of distinction is indebted to Shakespeare and the English Bible. The Authorized Version is not only the great source book of spiritual experience of English-speaking peoples; it is a treasury of plain, pungent words and muscular phrases, beautiful in themselves and with long associations, which we are apt to replace by smooth words lacking in punch, or by hackneyed or involved phrases. Here are a few examples chosen in five minutes from my desk Bible: I Samuel i, 28: "I have lent him to the Lord." What an apt phrase for anyone bringing up their son for the Church! Why say "loaned" instead of "lent"? Isaiah xxii, 5: "For it is a day of trouble, and of treading down, and of perplexity." In brief, just what we are going through today. But most modern historians would not feel that they were giving the reader his money's worth unless they wrote: "It is an era of agitation, of a progressive decline in the standard of living, and of uncertainty as to the correct policy." Romans xi, 25: "Wise in your own conceits." This epigram has often been used, but a modern writer would be tempted to express the thought in some such cumbrous manner as "Expert within the limits of your own fallacious theories."

Of course much of the Biblical phraseology is obsolete, and there are other literary quarries for historians. You can find many appropriate words, phrases, similes, and epigrams in American authors such as Mark Twain, Emerson, and Thoreau. I have heard an English economist push home a point to a learned audience with a quotation from *Alice in Wonderland;* American historians might make more use of *Huckleberry Finn.*

The historian can learn much from the novelist. Most writers of fiction are superior to all but the best historians in characterization and description. If you have difficulty in making people and events seem real, see if you cannot learn the technique from American novelists such as Sherwood Anderson, Joseph Hergesheimer and Margaret Mitchell. For me, the greatest master of all is Henry James. He used a relatively simple and limited vocabulary; but what miracles he wrought with it! What precise and perfect use he makes of words to convey the essence of a human situation to the reader! If you are not yet acquainted with Henry James, try the selection of his shorter novels and stories edited by Clifton Fadiman, and then read some of the longer novels, like *Roderick Hudson* and *The American*. And, incidentally, you will learn more about the top layers of American and European society in the second half of the nineteenth century than you can ever glean from the works of social historians.

What is the place of imagination in history? A historian or biographer is under restrictions unknown to a novelist. He has no right to override facts by his own imagination. If he is writing on a remote or obscure subject about which few facts are available, his imagination may legitimately weave them into a pattern. But to be honest he must make clear what is fact and what is hypothesis. The quality of imagination, if properly restrained by the conditions of historical discipline, is of great assistance in enabling one to discover problems to be solved, to grasp the significance of facts, to form hypotheses, to discern causes in their first beginnings, and, above all, to relate the past creatively to the present. There are many opportunities in historical narrative for bold, imaginative expressions. "A complete statement in the imaginative form of an important truth arrests attention," wrote Emerson, "and is repeated and remembered." Imagination used in this way invests an otherwise pedestrian narrative with vivid and exciting qualities.

Finally, the historian should have frequent recourse to the book of life. The richer his personal experience, the wider his human contacts, the more likely he is to effect a living contact with his audience. In writing, similes drawn from the current experience of this mechanical age rather than those rifled from the literary baggage of past eras, are the ones that will go home to his reader. Service on a jury or a local committee may be a revelation as to the political thoughts and habits of mankind. A month's labor in a modern factory would help any young academician to clarify his ideas of labor and capital. A camping trip in the woods will tell him things about Western pioneering that he can never learn in books. The great historians, with few exceptions, are those who have not merely studied, but lived; and whose studies have ranged over a much wider field than the period or subject of which they write.

The veterans of World War II who, for the most part, have completed their studies in college or graduate school, should not regard the years of their war service as wasted. Rather should they realize that the war gave them a rich experience of life, which is the best equipment for a historian. They have "been around," they have seen mankind at his best and his worst, they have shared the joy and passion of a mighty effort, and they can read man's doings in the past with far greater understanding than if they had spent these years in sheltered academic groves.

To these young men especially, and to all young men I say (as the poet Chapman said to the young Elizabethan): "Be free, all worthy spirits, and stretch yourselves!" Bring all your knowledge of life to bear on everything that you write. Never let yourself bog down in pedantry and detail. Bring History, the most humane and noble form of letters, back to the proud position she once held; knowing that your words, if they be read and remembered, will enter into the stream of life, and perhaps move men to thought and action centuries hence, as do those of Thucydides after more than two thousand years.

Ernest Newman

CONFESSIONS OF A MUSICAL CRITIC

I

MUSICAL CRITICS, apparently, were not invented in Dante's day, or he would certainly have shown them having one of the worst times possible in the worst circle possible in hell. Nobody loves the musical critic; and when I come to think of it I can't see any reason why people should. He is, in the popular estimation, one of those objectionable fellows who profess to be able to tell you how to do everything without being able to do it himself. He could not write even a First symphony; but he can tell you what is wrong with the Ninth. He would not know a vocal cord if he saw it, and if you gave him one would probably show his ignorance by trying to tie a parcel up with it; but he can tell Caruso what is wrong with his "production." Pachmann, Kreisler, Cortot, Casals, Wood—he can put them all in their places.

And yet, somehow or other, these creatures are read; indeed, they have a bigger clientèle, when you think of it, than the people who call themselves "artistes" (a spelling carefully adopted in many cases, one presumes, to indicate that they are not artists). I think it may be taken as an axiom that for every man or woman who goes to this concert or that, at least five hundred will read what some critic or other has to say about it. In a really civilized society, writers so widely read would be regarded as benefactors of the race; they would have wealth and honours showered upon them. As it is, they are treated as dogs, as pariahs, as criminals; and are mostly so badly paid that their continuing to exercise the functions of their profession can be attributed only to the reluctance of philanthro-

From *Testament of Music*, 1963. Edited by Herbert Van Thal. Copyright © 1963 by Mrs. Ernest Newman. Originally published in the *New York Post*, 1923.

pists to deprive the world of pearls of price, richly as the world deserves it.

Young men sometimes come to me and ask me how they can become
musical critics. I invariably try to persuade them to give up the idea;
there are at least fifty other forms of crime, I tell them, that are more
pleasant and more profitable, that require less intelligence and less application, that have fewer working hours and longer holidays. The misguided
young men generally persist in their inquiry, however; and then I have to
tell them that I know nothing of how other men have become musical
critics. I know a good many of them, but I cannot remember any of them
ever talking about how he began.

When I come to think of it, this strikes me as being suspicious—
almost sinister. It suggests that they are ashamed to be what they are, and
are unwilling to let the world into the secret of their first fall. I think
they are wrong in this; they ought to set forth, as a warning to the
young, how they first came to tread the path of shame. It will be found, I
am sure, that, in music as in morals, the first step on that path is so small a
one that the unsuspecting person who takes it has not the slightest previ-
sion of where it will ultimately land him. Many a critic is so only by
accident—as, indeed, the cynical public may already have suspected. The
young man may have been shaping nicely for an honourable and lucrative
career in business, in politics, or in sport; then one fine day something
lured him down a side path, and he went on and on pursuing the gleam
till in the end he found himself changed, by some evil enchantment, into a
musical critic.

That, at any rate, was my experience; and I propose now to tell the
story of my ruin, not because I am so lost to shame as to be past blushing
for it, but solely as a possible warning to others.

I shall be compelled to inflict a few autobiographical details upon the
reader, and indeed to use the first person singular more than I like. I have
no desire to talk about myself, except in the interests of science. A critic is
a man who every day of his working life is confidently giving his opinions upon art and artists. His right to do so may well be challenged.
"Who set thee up as a ruler and a judge over us?" may legitimately be
asked of him. If he is a fool, or at any rate not ideally wise, he may not be
able to do much harm—not nearly as much as is popularly supposed, for
readers soon take a critic's measure—but he can certainly inflict good
deal of unnecessary pain and arouse a good deal of unnecessary anger.
At the best, most people hold, he can express only a personal point of
view; what right has he to impose that point of view upon others?

For most professions a course of careful preparation is needed—nay,
insisted on, in the interest of the public. What preparation does a critic
get for such delicate and responsible work as judging? It is not enough
that he shall be a musician. It is not merely as a practical musician that he
is addressing the public; it is as a judge of music and musicians. To do the
work efficiently he needs to be in the first place a very sensitive instru-

ment, and in the second place to be able to play coolly upon that instrument as if it were something not inside but outside himself. It is not sufficient that he shall merely react in this or that way to this or that music. Anyone can do that; but his opinions, interesting as they may be as an expression of his own personality, do not necessarily amount to criticism in the proper sense of the word. A man, for instance, may quite honestly think Bach a dullard, but that opinion does not throw much light on Bach, however much light it may throw on him.

The plain man is at liberty to say "I don't like Bach," just as he is at liberty to say "I don't like apples." The critic, however, is expected, and rightly, to express something more than a mere physiological or even psychological reaction. He is expected to be not a dogmatist, but a judge, and a just judge. But what training does he get in the art of judging— supposing there to be such an art? None whatever, except what training he can give himself in the course of the exercise of his profession. Granted that his judgments are simply an expression of himself, ought we not to know just what that self is, and how it has come to be what it is? If we knew that, we might be able to account for many of his judgments with which we disagree, and so discount them.

The critic who is trying to see a composer as he really is learns as much as possible about him—what kind of man he was, especially what were the early influences he came under. Ought not the reader, if he wishes to understand why a critic thinks this or that, to know in particular what the influences were that have helped to give his mind its special cast? The conscientious critic, indeed, sooner or later, asks questions of this kind about himself; and I think he ought to tell the reader also something of what he has learned about himself, not out of egoism, not because he thinks himself of any interest to the world *qua* critic Brown or critic Jones or critic Robinson, but because he may be of interest to a few inquiring people *qua* critic, as a case for psychological study. It is in that spirit solely that I shall talk of myself.

II

THE RECORDS OF MY FAMILY, so far as I have been able to delve into them, had never before been stained by a musical critic. So little thought had my parents of their child sinking so low that they did not even trouble to have me taught music. I have had only one music lesson in my life, and that lasted no more than half an hour. It was, I often think, my good fortune to have parents who did not take the slightest interest in my intellectual development; they left me free to get my own culture where and how I liked, or not to get any at all. Few students of art, and particularly of music, can have grown up so completely alone. Most of them, even if they do not pass through a conservatoire, have at any rate a teacher and fellow-student to talk to. I had one boyish friend, with whom I used to discuss literature, but my school education was of the usual

type, with no special reference to art, and my association with my school-mates went no further than playing with them and fighting with them.

Search my memory how I will I cannot discover how or when I learned the rudiments of music. I suppose it was from some instruction book or other. But I fancy that, once having learned the notes, reading music was as simple a process with me as reading a book. At first every-thing was done quite unsystematically. I found myself playing the piano, after a fashion, without having learned anything of piano technique.

I have often wondered if one could draw up a balance sheet showing accurately the profit and loss of an education such as mine, an education without masters and without system. No doubt such a student benefits in some ways. He comes into contact with the great artists at first hand. He goes straight for the greatest things; it is on these that his taste is nour-ished. He enjoys every work of art he takes up, because he takes up only those he hopes to enjoy; and every work he enjoys sends him hotfoot after another.

With a master, even the most intelligent master (and very few mas-ters are really intelligent), he is always being held back. His exuberance is curbed. He is told that he must learn to walk before he can run, and his early walks, under a master, condemn him to so much uninteresting coun-try! He is kept at exercises that bore him, and at "pieces" that may indeed be suited to the then stage of his technical development, but beyond which he may have travelled miles, intellectually and temperamentally. If he dislikes the drudgery with which it is associated, his first enthusiasm may be chilled.

It is surely better for him to learn to love music by approaching it from the wrong road than to hate it by approaching it from the right one. It is surely better for him to play *Tristan* abominably before he has learned to finger a scale properly, but yet to get at the heart of the opera in his own way, than to spend hours at the piano over a trifling Mozart sonata that he sees through in a couple of days, and so to conceive a prejudice against Mozart that may endure for years.

On the other hand, there is a good deal to be said for a systematic education, obvious as some of its disadvantages may be. A system sums up, however imperfectly, the combined experiences of many others who have travelled the same road before us, who have looked back after they have arrived, and have seen what, after all, was the shortest way, all things considered, from the starting point to the goal, deceptively easy as one or two alternative routes seemed at the moment. None of us is so wise or so clever that he can afford to condemn the slowly built up experience of generations. The youth dislikes system because it means discipline, and there is nothing youth chafes under so much as discipline. In ordinary life, many a man may perhaps be all the better for growing up wild; but not, perhaps, in art. Sooner or later, if he is at all conscientious and self-critical, he will realize that he, too, must go through the mill—not neces-sarily the academic mill, but certainly some sort of mill. He will see that

it has taken humanity hundreds of years of painful effort to discover a few stable truths, a few safe guiding principles, in art; he cannot, unless he is absurdly vain, hope to discover for himself all that it has taken generations to work out. Sooner or later he must go to school.

III

THIS IS WHAT HAPPENED TO ME. I do not refer to piano-playing, which I have never regarded as indispensable to a musician, though even there I soon realized how impossible it is to learn to play the piano by just sitting down and hitting the keys with a score of *Parsifal* in front of you. I found I had to settle down and do a little sensible practice in order to be able to play even moderately badly. I may say, in parenthesis, that I never became more than a bad pianist. For one thing, I always grudged even the little time I spent in practising, for I felt that in the same time I could be learning some more music. I never had any ambition to play before others, and I was content to go on for a long time with the moderate technique that enabled me to play what I could of a work, my mind supplying, when I came to difficulty, what my fingers would not do.

But it was not to piano-playing that I was referring when I spoke of my realizing, one fine day, that I would have to study music in the school way as well as in my own. I cannot remember the time when I could not read music as one reads a book. I suppose it was natural to me, for I had no lessons of any kind, and I cannot trace any stages in the process of learning. It seems to me that I was reading music, and playing it my own amateurish way, from early childhood. For some reason or other, I was most interested as a boy, in vocal music, and particularly in opera. I lived in Liverpool at that time, and I used to get from one of the public libraries some operatic scores in a series that I have never come across since. I have often wondered who published them. As well as I recollect, they belonged to the first half of the nineteenth century, and had what I then thought were very interesting prefaces. Like most young people, I was not particularly attracted to Mozart. He seemed cold to me, in my ignorance—too simple, even superficial. I liked many of his operatic arias, but as an opera composer, I thought Gluck greatly his superior in those days, and I would have been prepared to cut anyone's throat who thought otherwise.

Again, like most young people, I had unbounded faith in my own judgment, and I used to wonder how the writers who fell into ecstasies over Mozart could be so easily taken in. I suppose it was because—once more like most young people—I was more susceptible to ideas than to pure beauty.

I supposed I liked Gluck and Wagner and Schumann better than Mozart or Schubert because the former seemed to me to be dealing with a bigger order of humanity. Iphigenia, Tristan, the girl in the *Woman's Life and Love* cycle, seemed to the ardent humanitarian that I was in those unspoilt days, more truly human than Cherubino or Masetto or the Hurdy Gurdy Man. I liked Mozart and Schubert well enough in a way, but I put them with Rossini and Auber and Bellini and the other pretty tune-makers, though of course, somewhat in front of these.

IV

IT IS ONLY AS ONE GETS OLDER, I think, that one learns to appreciate pure beauty in music, the beauty that begins and ends with itself, that is all-sufficient to itself. This would account for something that happens to us all in the long run—drawing nearer to Mozart as we grow older. That, at any rate, has been my experience; I have shed a good many of my early enthusiasms, both in poetry and in music, while my delight in Mozart has gone on increasing since I first came completely under his spell some fifteen or twenty years ago.

My earliest tastes were all for the strenuous, the highly-charged poetic, in music. It was always the slow movement that transported me into what was then, and for a long time afterwards, my favourite world— the world of Goethe's *Faust* and Wordsworth's *Intimations of Immortality* ode, the world of brooding introspection and philosophic melancholy. I had no ears for the pure, simple beauty of a Mozart symphony; but I worked myself into frenzies of spiritual self-torture over the agonized adagio of Beethoven's great "Hammerclavier" sonata.

We are curiously constituted. This adagio was for me, as a boy, the expression of the quintessence of human suffering: I always had a vision, when I played or read it, of Beethoven as a chained Prometheus, the eagle gnawing him. In the course of many years, when I had outgrown my youthful romanticism, this adagio and all the German music of which it is the type lost something of its power over me.

Artists who indulge themselves too much in images of suffering are like the people we meet with in ordinary life who insist on telling us their ailments at great length. We get a little tired of them both; we feel that it is something of the same kind of weakness, the same womanish craving for sympathy, that prompts the over-long story of the spiritual as of the bodily *malaise*. Paradoxically, it is those of us who are by nature the most sensitive to suffering and the most inclined to brood over it who come to resent most, in time, any excess of this kind of expression in artists.

I suppose the explanation is that some self-protective instinct within us warns us at last that it is as bad for us to keep the spiritual sores in us open as it is to keep our bodily sores; perhaps, at bottom it is the same perilous morbidity that makes us torture, and at the same time delight, ourselves with the bittersweet of Amfortas' terrible cry as makes it difficult for the sufferer from a skin disease to keep from scratching himself, though he knows it will be worse for him in the long run. There are sores of the soul as of the body; and one day it happens to all of us who have over-indulged ourselves in our youth in the morbidities of romanticism that we feel the need of a bracing mental and spiritual hygiene.

There came a time when I felt myself reacting against the introspection and self-torture of the German romanticists; and since the most intense expression of all this was, for me, the adagio of the Hammerclavier sonata, it was against that that I most consciously and most energetically revolted—very much in the way that, when we change our political party, it is against the leader of our old party that we turn our sharpest arrows. Not, of course, that the adagio ever came to be abhorrent to me, or that it does not still move me. But I can no longer give myself up to it and what it stands for as I used to do; and I think Beethoven would have been greater had he kept more control of himself in moments like this. Bach is greater because, with the very rarest of exceptions, he universalizes his sorrow.

Too often, with Beethoven and Liszt and Schumann and Chopin, we are over-conscious of the man himself. We see him straining under a load he cannot carry without an exhausting effort. In poignant things like the aria "Have mercy, oh Lord," or the "Eli, Eli, lama sabachthani" of the Matthew Passion, Bach does not strain in the least. We feel this suffering not as something merely personal to him, as we do in many of the overwrought moments of Beethoven and Chopin and Tchaikovsky, but as the suffering of the cosmos itself—not the tears of a fretted individual, but the tears that are in mortal things.

A good deal of the present-day revolt against Beethoven and Tchaikovsky is due to the revolt of a world that has been hardened by adversity against the men who indulge themselves in their weaknesses, who scratch their sores in secret instead of giving them to the sunlight and fresh air to heal.

When, a little while ago, I printed a letter I had had from a well-known Englishman of letters, in which he tried to account for his antipathy to anything in waltz rhythm by tracing it to some childish "complex" or other—some occasion on which he may have suffered while a waltz was going on—another and more sceptical friend permitted himself a little genial humour at the expense of us both. But I see nothing improbable myself in the explanation. There must be many such complexes in all of us.

I am tempted to explain the extraordinary popularity of Scriabine among women by the curiously catlike quality of his music, in which one cannot say where eroticism ends and spirituality begins, or by his liberation of certain centuries-long suppressed complexes in them. I fancy they get something of the same kind of pleasure from Scriabine's soft curves and insinuating harmonies that they get from scents and the sheen of satins and the subtle electricity of furs. The critic who wants to understand himself must try to trace his own complexes, if only to rescue himself from them when they are likely to bar the way to his sympathetic understanding of every kind of music.

V

I SPOKE OF THE UNSYSTEMATIC NATURE of my first musical education, and of my realization, long before I was out of my teens, of the need of supplementing my haphazard study of music as an art by a study of music as a science.

I said I have had only one music lesson in my whole life, and that this lasted no more than half an hour. It must have been when I was about seventeen. At that time I was at the Liverpool College. As well as I remember, music was no part of the set educational course; indeed, it could not have been, or I should have had more than this one lesson. Yet I suppose music must have been taught in some way to someone or other, for there was a Mr. (perhaps Dr.) Richard Crowe there, who officiated at the organ in the college theatre on great occasions, and no doubt had other duties in the place.

I have no clear recollection of him except that he was a little man, that he was irreverently referred to by us boys as Dicky Crowe, and that we did not think much of him because he had nothing to do with our games. What his musical qualifications were I cannot say. To him I went one afternoon after school hours and had a short first lesson in harmony. I never repeated the experiment, for the lesson was only a repetition of a disappointment and a disillusionment that I had already experienced in private. When I had decided that it was time I learned something of the science and the technique of the art, I bought one or two text-books on harmony and counterpoint and settled down to them with something of the emotion Lord Carnarvon must have felt when he was breaking through the wall on the other side of which was the tomb of King Tutankhamen, with all its long-hidden treasures. Try to imagine what Lord Carnarvon would feel like if, after getting into the last chamber, he found it as empty as Madame Humbert's safe, and you will have a faint idea of what I felt like when first I began the study of musical text-books.

Remember that by this time I had dozens of scores in my head. I knew most of them by heart—all the pianoforte sonatas and the symphonies of Beethoven and the Forty-eight Preludes of Bach, many of Mozart's piano sonatas and piano duets, practically the whole of Wagner, Beethoven's *Fidelio*, all of Gluck's operas that are obtainable in modern editions (*Orfeo, Armide, Paris and Helen, Iphigenia in Aulis, Iphigenia in Tauris,* and *Alceste*), thirty or forty other operas of all schools, including *Der Freischütz, Fra Diavolo, William Tell, The Barber of Seville,* Paisiello's *Barber,* and Cimarosa's *Il Matrimonio Segreto,* one or two of the oratorios and a few of the clavier works of Handel, a few specimens of the older church music, such as Palestrina's "Pope Marcellus" Mass and "Stabat Mater," and the "Stabat Mater" of Pergolesi (also the latter's little opera *La Serva Padrona*), a few old English and Italian madrigals, a good deal of Schubert, Schumann, Mendelssohn and Chopin (I was very fond not only of Schumann's songs, but of his opera *Genoveva* and the big ensemble works like *Faust* and *Manfred*), and a heap of other music of all sorts, all periods, all schools.

For years I had been reading music daily, with the ardour with which schoolgirls used to read novelettes, or schoolboys adventure stories. When I was about twenty I had, in my simplicity, the idea that it would be possible, in another year or two, to have learned virtually all the music that really mattered. I rarely went to concerts at that time. I never saw a musical journal, and I do not suppose I knew that there was such a thing as musical criticism in the newspapers—in any case, newspapers hardly ever came my way in my schoolboy days.

The music I lived with was that of the classics, from Palestrina to Schumann. Of contemporary composers I knew next to nothing, with the exception of Wagner, who had seized upon my imagination from the first, and whose operas were my daily bread. I had no musical friends. I had an old history or two of music, that gave me at any rate the great names and showed the development of the chief schools. I had the catalogues of the popular editions of Peters and Litolff, and in my innocence I thought that all I had to do to know all about the real music that had ever been written was to work steadily through the chief works of the best-known men in these catalogues. I gave myself three or four years to complete this task, and thought the allowance ample. I did not then know how much interesting music lies off the beaten track. I did not know that contemporary composers were pouring out works as a fountain spouts water—what a race it was to try to catch up with them in later years! I did not then realize that of all students the student of music has the heaviest task.

A man whose job is literature may be interested in European literature as a whole, but what he really knows of it comes down in the long run to a close knowledge of the books of his own country, a pretty fair knowledge of the books of one foreign country, and a smattering of the literature of the others. But in music there is no language bar, and the musical periods of the various nations are part and parcel of each other. The student of music has to know the music of at least half a dozen countries as well as he knows the music of any one of them.

But however much I did not know of music in my early youth, at any rate I knew something of it, and what I knew had been learned at first hand. I had grown up in the art unhampered by theory. You can perhaps dimly imagine my puzzlement when, with all this music in my head—most of it first-rate—I began to work at the text-books. I found myself being solemnly taught a number of things that I had learned for myself long ago—nay, I had not learned them, for they were natural and self-evident; one might as well speak of having learned to move the eyelids or to secrete bile.

Music was to me a living language: I spoke it and understood it as one speaks and understands one's native tongue, not so much learning it as unconsciously absorbing it out of the air around. To my amazement I found myself being taught in the text-books things that it seemed simply incredible to me that anyone should need to "learn." I was like a man who has read Shakespeare through with complete understanding and enjoyment, and then is expected to listen dutifully while an elementary school teacher solemnly tells him that an English verb must agree with its noun in number. "Of course it does," he would reply. "What else *could* it do? You might as well tell me that in order to walk I must put first one foot foremost, then the other. How else *could* I walk?"

VI

I BEGAN TO DESCRIBE the perplexities in which I found myself when, after a long saturation in music itself, I began to study the theory of music as set forth in the text-books.

My difficulty was twofold—I had to listen to things being explained to me that seemed so obvious and natural as not to need explanation; and I was always being told it was wrong to do something or other that I knew the great masters made no scruple about doing.

It took me a little time to realize that much of what was taught in the text-books as essential for the right practice of music had next to nothing to do with the art of composition.

If it were necessary to know all about—or even anything about—the theory of harmony in order to understand music, then concert-going would be restricted to a handful of trained theoreticians in each town. The plain lover of music no more knows the names of the chords he is listening to than the plain lover of poetry knows that this poem is in alexandrines, this in alcaics, this in sapphics. But just as, in the latter case, ignorance of the name of the metre is no bar to the enjoyment of the rhythm of the poem, so, in the former case, ignorance of the names of the chords is no bar to the understanding of what it is that the composer is saying through the chords.

The man in the seat next to me at *Parsifal* may not know a chord of the diminished seventh from an ichthyosaurus, or a minor ninth from a pterodactyl; but when Wagner stabs him with one of these chords his soul is hurt in the same way and to the same extent as mine is. He listens to Scriabine's *Prometheus* in blissful ignorance that the composer is here working on a new harmonic system of his own, building his chord out of fourths placed one on top of the other; but the man does not need to know anything of this to understand what Scriabine is talking to him about.

Indeed, in many cases the composer himself could not tell us the proper name of some of the new chords he is using. He only knows that he "feels like that"—that he had something in him he wanted to say, and, without his volition, it said itself through these novel harmonies. He leaves it to the theoretician to name them.

Musical minds *think* in music as other minds do in prose or verse—

music, to them, is a natural language. It has always been a difficulty to me to understand how people need to be *taught* music—it has always seemed to me as natural as speech. This may be, in part, because I grew up in the *practice* of music, where I spent some years before I went on to the theory of it.

When I found the text-books telling me that this was the way to resolve certain chords, or this the way to modulate from one key to another, I was astonished—not at the information, but at the fact that there were people interested in music who needed such information. It all seemed to me self-evident. But while a great deal of what the text-books told me struck me as superfluous, a great deal more struck me as nonsense.

I found myself being "forbidden" to do things that I had seen the great composers frequently doing. I was told, indeed, that sometimes even the great composers were naughty boys, who did not keep to the rules, but that no good boy who wanted to get on would follow their bad example—unless and until he happened to become a great master himself, when, of course, he would be allowed to do what he liked, subject to the censure of the pedagogues.

It was all very puzzling. I could not help thinking that Wagner and Bach must have known more about composition than Macfarren or Rockstro or Prout. (I am not sticking strictly to chronology now. I fancy Prout's treatises did not appear till a few years after the period in my development that I am now describing. I cite him as a type; and my soul's conflicts with the text-books lasted for many years.)

It shocked me to learn that hardly one of Bach's fugues was correctly written, and that so little did composers like Palestrina know about the "rules" of counterpoint that Rockstro could hardly cite a single example from their works to illustrate the "rules" but had to write examples of his own!

I was still young enough to have some respect for authority, and to believe what I saw in print. There must be something in what all these people say, I used to murmur to myself.

Sometimes I felt sorry for Bach and Palestrina and the rest of them, who, poor fellows, had been born too soon to profit by the instruction of such masters as Macfarren and Prout. At other times I would wonder what one of these theorists would do if he had an innovating genius to teach—a Wagner, say. Would he tell him, as he tells me, to observe the rules, or would he grant him that "licence" which, it seems, only a master was allowed to take out? And at what age did a master qualify for a licence?

No doubt Beethoven and the rest of them began by observing the rules as little boys, and only ventured to flout them when they became masters. But would it not be as possible for one master to break a rule with safety at sixteen as for another to break it at sixty? Suppose, then, that Macfarren had a genius of sixteen for a pupil. Would he recognize his genius at that age?

It was all very well to wink at the peccadilloes of a composer whom the world for a hundred years had called a master; Macfarren could hardly say this or that passage should have been written otherwise without being laughed at. But might not some boy of sixteen talk as sound musical sense in defiance of the "rules" as, say, the mature Bach or Beethoven? If he did, how would Macfarren handle him?

It was easy enough to spot a winner when the crowd was applauding him after the race had been won; but could Macfarren spot a winner in his own class, before the race began? I remember how little perception Cherubini, when head of the Paris Conservatoire, had of the genius of the erratic young Berlioz; and I had my doubts.

VII

I WAS SOON MADE TO REALIZE, however, the need for a more solid grounding in musical technique when I began to compose. Mr. Squeers, in my opinion, has always been a much misunderstood and unfairly disparaged man. His own spelling may not have been above suspicion, but there is a good deal to be said for his practical way of teaching spelling; when he said, "W-i-n-d-e-r, go and clean it," he was combining, and teaching his boys to combine theory with practice.

Like all ardent young men with music in them, I had an itch for composition. It was while I was under the staggering blow of my first acquaintance with harmonic theory that I began. As I have already told the reader, nearly half of what I read in the harmony text-books seemed to me to be disputed by the practice of the great masters, and nearly half the remainder seemed so obvious that I could not understand why people should need to be told such things; and as my reading, at this time, had mostly been among harmonic rather than contrapuntal music, I had as yet no idea of the difficulties of musical composition.

It appeared to me, indeed, quite as easy as writing poetry or prose; you had something to say, and you just said it. There was, of course, a good deal of difference between the things said by one composer and those said by another; that simply meant, as in poetry, that one composer was endowed by Providence with better ideas than another.

At the age I was then, sixteen or seventeen, I naturally was quite convinced that my own ideas were excellent. All I had to do, then, was to put the thoughts on paper.

And that is where the trouble began. Then I realized that the understanding of an art was one thing, and the practice of it another. It is possible for any of us to lean back in his seat and explain why Carpentier is a good boxer, what harmony of forces goes to make that quick correlation between eye and brain and muscle. But to get a similar harmony of our own is quite another matter.

The best way to realize that such a harmony is necessary is to put on the gloves with a boxer; our conceit in ourselves will not survive the first short round. The best way to realize that swimming is an art is to fall into the water, or to go into it after something we very much want, and to scramble back to safety with difficulty, and without the thing we went in for.

When I tried to put my turbulent flood of musical ideas into notes, I soon saw the wisdom and the meaning of musical discipline. A little while ago, in the course of a removal from one house to another, I happened to come across some long-forgotten manuscripts of that period, settings of poems by Swinburne, Rossetti, Blake, Herbert and other poets. Some of the ideas were perhaps not hopelessly bad, but the technique! The clumsiness, the helplessness of it! I had the good sense to realize, even then, that this sort of thing would never do.

It was my first initiation into a truth that I have, I am afraid, often annoyed other young composers since by insisting on—that "ideas" in music, in the sense of thematic invention, and more especially the invention of a theme to illustrate a poetic or pictorial idea, are the smallest and easiest part of musical composition. This may seem an extreme statement, but every experienced musician knows that it is no exaggeration.

Thousands of second-rate composers can invent quite good themes, but they cannot make good compositions out of them. On the other hand, many of the greatest of the world's works are made out of fragments of material that in and by themselves are nothing, or even, superficially considered, worse than nothing.

Composers like Liszt have a decided faculty for inventing expressive illustrative themes, but they never succeed in building up a first-rate long work. Rimsky-Korsakov is another composer with the gift of conceiving one enchanting tune after another; but when he tries to write an overture or a symphonic movement he can do little more than go on repeating his tunes.

Beethoven and Bach, on the other hand, often perform their greatest marvels with bits of material that are in themselves quite insignificant. If we did not know the Fifth Symphony, and saw the two subjects of the first movement quoted in music type, we would feel merely a sort of pitying contempt for the composer. The first subject in particular would convey nothing to us; it is not even a tune, as the second subject is. Yet out of these two tiny fragments of wood and mud grows the gigantic tree of that wonderful first movement.

Give Bach just three notes—say those of the opening phrase of the third Brandenburg Concerto, which strictly speaking, are only two notes (G, F sharp, G)—and he will go on spinning the most delightful fabrics of tone out of them until the dinner-bell rings.

Wagner was so bad an influence upon the young composers who followed him, precisely because of his incomparable gift of inventing significant themes. His powers in this respect have perhaps not had full justice done to them; but anyone who wants to realize it for himself has only to run over in his mind the leading motives of the *"Ring"* alone. There must be well over a hundred of them. Each of them hits off to a nicety the character or the force or the object of which it is the symbol.

And many people are so absorbed in the pure expressiveness of the themes as themes that they do not realize that Wagner is not merely a great inventor, but, like Bach and Beethoven, a consummate architect and builder.

As later composers found to their cost, a musical drama or a symphonic poem is not written when expressive themes have been hit upon for the salient moments of the story. And there are composers, such as Bach and Beethoven, who do not even need striking themes in order to build up, somehow or other, great palaces of sound that have the logic of a fine building and the expressiveness of a fine poem.

VIII

I HAVE SAID THAT MY FIRST STUDIES in theoretical harmony taught me virtually nothing that I had not already learned practically at first hand from the great composers. Counterpoint, canon and fugue, however, are technical things that come to no man by the mere grace of God. As soon as I realized that the art of musical composition was not so simple a thing as the composing of poetry, and that a technique was necessary, I set myself to the acquiring of this technique. I may say at once that I very soon gave up the idea of shining as a composer. Whether the surrender was to be attributed to modesty or to vanity I cannot say— whether to the humble feeling that with so much splendid music in the world there was really no call for me or anyone else to write inferior music, or to the proud feeling that since I could not produce anything first-rate I would not appear before my fellow-men as a third- or fifth-rater. Anyhow, for a few years during which I composed I had the sense to keep my efforts to myself. Some of them were pretty ambitious; I particularly remember a big work—big I mean, in that it ran to some hundreds of pages of score—based on Shelley's "Prometheus Unbound"— a sort of mystical blend of opera and symphony, inspired, I should now imagine, by Schumann's *Manfred*.

But I am anticipating somewhat. This and sundry other masterpieces occupied some five years of my time, and during those five years I was working hard at the technique of music. On second thoughts, no doubt it was a rational humility that made me ultimately give up composing, and never succumb later to the temptation to attempt anything more in that line. I saw that, however important my music might be to myself as a kind of emotional catharsis, it was very ordinary stuff compared with the real thing of the real composers. What I then felt about myself I now feel about a great many of the young composers of today. I am often accused of being "unsympathetic" to these people and their works. I repel the charge indignantly. I am extremely sympathetic towards them. So far from discouraging them, I always encourage them to go on composing their songs and symphonies and concertos and operas. I assure them they will feel better when they get it out of their system. Writing music or poetry is to the average emotional young man merely the psychical equivalent of the Turkish bath. As this promotes a healthy action of the skin, composition promotes a healthy action of the soul. Hygiene demands the elimination of the spiritual no less than of the physical toxins; but the process, though highly beneficial to the subject, is not a matter of great interest to the rest of the world.

I am, then, anything but unsympathetic to the average composer; all I object to is his assumption that I ought to take a passionate interest in the average outpourings of his average soul. This I cannot do. Frankly, I have no use for average composers, or average artists of any kind. A musical friend once startled me by telling me I was a hero-worshipper. I jibbed at the description at first; but in a little while I saw that he understood me better than I understood myself. I reserve my enthusiasms for first-rate minds and first-rate things, and it is in the company of these, and these alone, that I would spend all my time if I were free to choose.

There is too much great music in the world that I do not know as intimately as I should like for me to be willing to give up any more time than I can help to music that has not even a flavour of greatness about it.

But though I soon, comparatively speaking, gave up the vain idea of being a composer, I worked hard at the study of musical technique for critical purposes. In this, as in everything else, I preferred to study alone. I hardly know what it is in my make-up that has always rendered it difficult for me to put myself in the hands of a "master." Perhaps it is an incurable native scepticism, the impossibility of believing that the whole truth, on any subject, is with any one man or any one school or any one party. It took very little study of musical theory for me to discover that the "authorities" were often at variance; I would find, for instance, one pundit declaring positively that the second subject of the Beethoven sonata began in a certain bar, and another pundit declaring, with equal positiveness, that it began in quite another bar. Little things of this kind aroused my suspicions, and confirmed my natural distrust of authority.

My way of study has always been to get as many books as possible on the subject in hand, and make each of them supplement the deficiencies, or show up the fallacies of the others. In counterpoint, canon, fugue and form I worked steadily for several years through text-books like those of Cherubini, Ouseley, Rockstro, Prout, Richter, Jadassohn, Higgs, Bridge, Stainer, Marx and others; one of the works from which I derived great benefit was August Reissmann's *Lehrbuch der musikalischen Komposition* in two large volumes—an excellent treatise for its time (1866).[1] Frederick Iliffe's useful analysis of Bach's "48" was not published, I think, at that time; I fancy it appeared some time in the eighteen-nineties. But I well remember the portentous seriousness with which I

[1] Grove records three volumes [*Ed.*].

went over Bach again under Iliffe's guidance; only the other day, hunting
for some lost papers, I came across a big, sprawling volume I had manufactured for myself by interleaving Iliffe's book with the preludes and
fugues from a torn-up copy of Ernst Pauer's edition of Bach. But, needless to say, my real teachers were not these theorists, but Bach, Palestrina,
Wagner, Beethoven, Mozart, and others of that great family. I soon discovered how grey, as Goethe says, is all theory. The essentials of musical
theory and musical technique are very simple, easily taught and easily
learned. The applied technique of the masters is always an individual
affair, and to the study of this there is no end.

IX

WHEN I BEGAN THESE garrulous Confessions, it was with the laudable intention of trying to account for myself, both to myself and to
others. A critic is generally so occupied with explaining other people that
it does not occur to him that he may stand in need of explanation himself,
though it may be an agreeable part of his job to explain his colleagues, to
account for this one having such bad taste, say, where Schumann is concerned, or for that one having written such egregious nonsense about
Brahms. It is true that the public, in its often justifiable irritation with us,
explains us all in a rough-and-ready way; it puts our grumblings down to
our livers. But that is really doing us an injustice.

The other day a very capable young artist described critics as
"mostly disappointed men, earning hardly enough to keep body and soul
together." I understand that great gratification was expressed in critical
circles at this handsome recognition that critics *had* souls, which I have
known some singers and fiddlers deny. As for critics being disappointed
men, I am afraid we must all plead guilty. Our life is just one disappointment after another.

But the sin is not on our shoulders, but on the shoulders of those who
disappoint us. In any case, our disappointments do not sour us. A more
cheerful, kindly body of men I never met. Where else would you find
people persistently passing off their sufferings with a joke! You do not
find the man who has just writhed under the surgeon's knife regarding
the surgeon and his knife as two of the funniest things on earth; but I
have often seen two or three critics, after enduring at the hands of a
singer's larynx, as the Irishmen might say, more excruciating pain than
any knife could inflict (and, remember, we never had chloroform for *our*
operations), turn to each other with a smile that was most expressive of
their appreciation of the joke of such a person getting up in a public hall
and calling herself a singer. Nor would the critics dream of saying anything unpleasant about her, in spite of her having paid for an advertisement.

I assure the reader that the picture generally painted of critics by
disgruntled "artists" is a false one; they have the patience of Job, the

endurance of a horse, and the sweetness of an angel. They may not get their reward in this world; but if there is any justice in the scheme of things they will get it in the next; they will be sent to some place where the singers cease from troubling and the fiddlers are at rest.

No, it is not by our livers that we critics are to be explained; as a matter of fact, I think our livers are in particularly good fettle, owing to the fresh air and exercise we get sprinting from one hall to another. But, after all, it is writing about music, not about performers, that is, or at least should be, the critic's business; and since the oddities of critical judgment that we meet with every day are to be accounted for by some idiosyncrasy of the critic, we ought to know as much as possible about the mental make-up and the bringing-up of the critic. Sometimes it is easy enough to trace a critic's opinions to something that has happened to him—when, for instance, we find a young man flagrantly unfair to German music because he had a bad time during the war. But it is in the earliest years of his life that a critic is really made, for better or for worse, and when we get to middle age we cannot help looking back and trying to see ourselves as if we were someone else we were studying, trying to account for our present attitude towards music in terms of our earliest influences and associations.

We do this as a matter of course in the case of composers; we find out where and how they lived in their early manhood, with whom they studied, and so on. But a critic does not, like a composer, go through a formal process of learning his business. There are no schools in which he can study, no masters at whose feet he can sit. He learns—if he ever learns at all—by practising at other people's expense an art he has never been taught.

He begins with an unbounded, pathetic confidence in himself; he ends with the most painful doubts about himself. I know that there is a school that regards criticism as purely a personal matter, the play of the critic's temperament upon a work of art, regardless of questions and rightness or wrongness of judgment. But rightness or wrongness of judgment assuredly enters into the question. Criticism is not merely a personal coltish kicking up of the heels in the meadows of art; it is an attempt to induce other people to see the thing as we see it—which implies a belief that one way of looking at the thing is essentially right, and the opposite way, essentially wrong, that *Gerontius*, for instance, is a greater work than *The Woman of Samaria*, not merely for Brown or Jones, but for all who know anything about names.

"The whole man thinks," said George Henry Lewes truly. Into each of our judgments upon music goes the whole man that heredity, early training and life have made us.

Looking back on my own case, I can see that the solitariness of my earliest intellectual life has had its effects on me. It has made me, for one thing, a poor party man. Having got my first musical culture by myself, without schools, without masters, without even friends, I never formed any strong ties, either personal or clannish. When I see some of my most respected colleagues behaving indulgently, to say the least of it, towards poor work because it comes from a particular coterie, they seem to me merely a sort of trade unionist marching behind the banner of their union—a sad thing, perhaps, for artists to be doing. All the same, people, in this imperfect world, can only get certain big things done by acting together and sinking some of their purely personal predilections. It is my misfortune, no doubt, that I find it difficult to do this in matters of art. I dislike joining Societies, because I feel—absurdly enough, perhaps—that it hampers my freedom of judgment on details.

X

When I look back upon my adolescence it seems to me that one of the strongest influences in my life was my love of sculpture—especially Greek sculpture—and architecture. I sometimes attribute to my early experiences among these arts my later impatience with shapelessness of design or crudity of workmanship in music, for sculpture and architecture are the two arts in which any deficiency or excess of substance, any ungainliness of line, or any failure of harmony is most quickly noticed and most intolerable.

Yet the influence may have been the other way round. Perhaps we were always inclined to confuse cause and effect in matters of the spirit.

We put certain traits of the early Wagner, as man and as artist—his hectic living, for example, or his occasional lack of artistic refinement—to his having spent so many years as a boy and as a young man in the theatre or in the company of theatrical people.

The true explanation may be that he haunted theatrical society and adopted a theatrical career in the first place because his inborn instinct for the hectic and the overblown, both in life and in art, led him unconsciously to the theatre. We say that another composer's work owes its sexless quality to the fact that he was brought up among prim women and became a choir-boy at an early age, but it is equally probable that it was the passionless nature of his mental substance that sent him in the first place to the prim ladies and the choir stalls.

It is the old problem of which came first—the egg or the chicken? Does the "influence" make the man, or does the boy instinctively and unconsciously select his own "influence"? Perhaps the latter is the truer explanation. Probably none of us would ever have been moulded by life into our present mental shape if—to put it paradoxically—we had not been that shape from our birth, and would never have come under this formative influence or that had not the unconscious desire of the soul to realize itself along its own lines made us turn in the direction where the influence was to be found.

At the same time it is no doubt true that had we not come under the particular influence we should not have become so completely ourselves.

the second into the navy.) The boy said he hadn't thought about the matter yet, but was prepared to give it his careful consideration.

A few days after, his father asked him if he had settled what he would like to do in life. He said he had; he would like to read. His father thought it an excellent idea, and was delighted that after the display of military ardour on the part of the two older boys, the youngest son should so early display a preference for one of the learned professions. But he would like a little more definite information: reading for what— the church, the bar, medicine, or what? The boy hastened to correct this misapprehension; he didn't want to read for anything in particular; he just wanted to go through life reading, poetry for preference.

That had been my own case, even at a later age than his. I should have been quite happy reading, if only grown-up people would have left me alone and not pestered me with tiresome talk about examinations.

However, Providence intervened to save India from me. My health broke down a little while before the examination. My heart was badly strained, and my doctor told me that even if I got through the examination the medical examiners would not pass me for an Eastern climate. So that settled it; I gave up India without a pang. I had never really wanted to go there, because I felt I should be cut off from my two greatest joys in life, books and music.

Somehow or other, I got into a bank in Liverpool. There I spent a good many years of my life, learning a little about banking, but more about music and literature. By one of those beautiful combinations of circumstance that make it simply impossible to doubt that there is a beneficent design in Nature, banks are always built near cafés. This en-ables bank clerks to economize time in passing from the serious business of life, which is reading or playing dominoes in a café, to the minor interests of passbooks and produce warrants and bills of lading.

From the first I had an instinct that for success in life it was neces-sary to form good habits. Guided by this sure instinct, I used to go every morning to a conveniently adjacent café to read. I was the better able to do this inasmuch as I was an exceptionally fast worker, and could always catch up the lost hour or so in the office before lunch time. So ingrained did this habit become in me that to this day I am unhappy if I do not get my coffee every morning at eleven—something like Mr. Barry Pain's gardener Edwards, who used to suspend his arduous duties every morning for what he called his elevenses. For some years my duties at the bank were "out-telling," going round with bills for acceptance or payments, etc. The reader will see what scope this delightful occupation offered to any clerk with a taste for literature.

There were various devices, known only to the initiated, by which the time actually spent in going the round could be curtailed, while the time theoretically occupied by the round was multiplied, and by which the round could be made to run in the more desirable districts. By hand-ing over to a junior colleague, for instance, some acceptance that would have taken me into the purlieus of the distant docks, and keeping for myself one that took me up Islington way, I could get half an hour in at the Walker Art Gallery or the Picton Reading Room. And, of course, one could always read as one walked; in Liverpool streets alone, in those years, I must have read hundreds of volumes.

Street-reading, though, has its perils. I remember that once, wrestling in spirit with Hegel, I banged my forehead against a lamp-post, and went about for the next fortnight looking like a unicorn. I had not thought much of the Hegelian philosophy before that, and I thought still less of it after.

XII

I AM VERY OFTEN ASKED by young men how they can become musical critics. I almost invariably recommend them to give up the mad idea, for it is not a very pleasant life, and the same amount of energy and intelligence put into commerce, speculation, betting or practising the confidence trick on guileless American visitors would bring fifty times the pecuniary reward. I used to laugh at the doctrine of metempsychosis until I became a musical critic. Now I believe firmly in it, as I often used to tell my dear old dog when his conduct had not been quite irreproachable. I used to explain to him that I had probably been a dog in some previous existence, had led a life of sin and crime, and was now working out my punishment in concert rooms, listening to singers who cannot sing, and to fiddlers who cannot fiddle; and I warned him that if he was not a better dog he might be made a musical critic in his next incarnation.

Every time a young man asks me how he can make a start as a critic I look at him sadly. Here, I say to myself, is another poor soul whose conduct as a hyena or an armadillo did not come up to the standard demanded by the too exacting gods. They are plainly being driven by the Fates, for nothing will induce them to give up the idea. I paint the profession in the blackest colours, but they insist on seeing it in the rose-pink of their imagination. To them it is a blissful succession of free seats for concerts and operas, and liberty to pour out every day those words of wisdom upon art, for which, they are convinced, an expectant world has been waiting for generations. Poor fellows, they do not foresee the time when a batch of tickets draws from the critic more groans than a demand for income tax does, the time when he feels he would like to have a short heart-to-heart talk with Tubal Cain, or Orpheus, or whoever it was invented music, and tell him just what he thought of him.

But when the young man is quite resolved to become a musical critic, and only seeks me out to learn from me how he is to begin, I am reluctantly compelled to tell him that I do not know. All I can do is tell him how I myself began. Perhaps that way is as good as any other, and better than most. It is this—to go on into business, practise writing as a sideline,

JULES ROMAINS

photograph by Meerson, Paris

ERNEST NEWMAN
photograph by Alfred A. Knopf

and stay in business till your writing has brought you reputation enough to justify your trusting wholly to it for a living.

I need not say that, in spite of the fun I often had in the bank, I was not really happy in business. I could study music and literature—apart from the hour or two I might snatch from my duties inside the bank, in the manner I have already described—only in the early morning and late at night, which meant very hard work. Often I would read from six or so in the morning until about half-past eight, and then curse the fate that tore me from my book and drove me to the office. But I can see now that there was a rough kindness in the Fates' treatment of me. Not being under the necessity of earning my living by literature, I could afford to write, when I did write, on a subject of my own choosing, and to take as long as I liked over the preparation for it. I had somehow made the acquaintance of Mr.—now the Right Honourable—John M. Robertson, man of letters, philosopher, economist and politician, to whom I owe more than to any other living individual for help and sympathy and guidance in my early days. I used to write on literature and music for one or two journals under his editorship. They had only small circulations, but they were read by a few people who took an interest in ideas.

About 1895 Mr. Robertson was finishing a book on *Buckle and his Critics* that he had had on hand for some years. It occurred to him to publish it by subscription, and to this end he gave a copious summary of its contents in the *Free Review*. He knew that I had in manuscript a book on Gluck. This had begun as an essay some years before, and had grown into a book without my quite knowing how it had happened. Mr. Robertson generously suggested my giving him an outline of the work for publication along with that of *Buckle and his Critics*. This was done. A fair number of subscribers enrolled themselves. One, I remember, lived in Japan. There were not enough, however, to justify my undertaking the expense of publication. One morning, to my great surprise, I received a letter from Mr. Bertram Dobell, the well-known Charing Cross Road book-seller, the friend and publisher of James Thomson, and later the discoverer of Traherne. He had, it seems, read several of my essays and had liked them. The summary of *Gluck and the Opera* had taken his fancy, and he declared his willingness to publish the book. He did me a very great service, for I am certain that no other publisher in England at that time would have taken a work on such a subject. I had had a light on the state of affairs when the one big publisher to whom I had written about the book replied courteously that he would not even trouble me to send him the manuscript, as there was no sale for books on music in this country.

The only thing I have to regret in connection with this affair was that I inadvertently caused the death of Sir Charles Hallé. Mr. Dobell had had the summary of the book reprinted, and copies of this I sent to a number of prominent people in the musical world who, I thought in my innocence, would be delighted to put themselves down for, at any rate,

one copy each, though I fondly hoped for more. Some of the replies I got
were very curious. The most unexpected people subscribed, and the most
expected people did not. One well-known musical critic, who was said to
be very well-to-do, replied that he could not subscribe (the price, I think,
was five shillings), but he would review the book if it were sent to
the —— for that purpose. I well remember posting a copy of the circular
to Sir Charles Hallé one afternoon. It must have reached him by the
morning post next day, and before the afternoon he was dead. It was the
first of many crimes with which my literary conscience is burdened.

XIII

I AM OFTEN ACCUSED of being unsympathetic towards "the young
composer," whereas the truth is that I am unsympathetic only towards
the young composer who has nothing of any moment to say. There is one
person, however, for whom I always feel the greatest sympathy—the
young student who, anxious to do original musical research, finds himself
checked at every turn by the difficulty of getting the necessary material.
This was my own case when I was writing *Gluck and the Opera*. (I may
add that though the book was not published till I was about twenty-
seven, it had been written some four or five years earlier.) Gluck
affected me as powerfully in those days as Wagner and Brahms, Elgar and
Wolf and others were to do in later years. Had I been free I would gladly
have devoted my whole time to research in the Continental libraries. But
not much research of that kind is possible to a young man who is cooped
up in business all day for eleven and a half months of the year: it was
impossible even for me to visit the British Museum.

I did the best I could under the circumstances. I had a fair amount of
material at my disposal in the Picton Library, Liverpool, and I bought all
the books and music I could. For biographical information I necessarily
had to rely on the exhaustive volumes of such writers upon Gluck as
Marx, Schmid,[2] Desnoiresterres[3] and Reissmann; but I made as independent a study as I could of the music and literature of the period—German,
Italian, French and English—and I tried to see the aesthetic of the opera
as it appeared to the man of the eighteenth century, and to define Gluck's
relation to this aesthetic. I have not glanced at the book for twenty years
or more, and shall probably never do so until I happen to write on Gluck
again. But I chanced a little while ago upon a critique of it, which I am
sure sums it up pretty accurately, by a German expert, Dr. Stephen
Wortsmann,[4] in a book surveying the whole field of Gluck literature,
published by the Gluckgemeinde—a Gluck Society founded a few years
before the War, but now presumably extinct.

Dr. Wortsmann points out, quite rightly, my indebtedness to Marx

---

[2] Schmid's great work on Gluck was published in Leipzig in 1854.
[3] *Gluck et Piccini* (Paris, 1875).
[4] *Die deutsche Gluck-Literatur* (Nuremberg, 1914) [*Ed.*].

and the others in the matter of biographical detail, but—this amuses me— he says that "the imagination of the author has painted some episodes, particularly in Gluck's early life, in such lively colours that the uniniti- ated reader . . . will come to the conclusion that he is dealing with an extraordinarily well-equipped Gluck expert. For none of his conjectures, however, has Newman brought forward the least new evidence; he has only, by means of his own combinations, conjured up pictures which, it cannot be denied, have a good deal of probability, against which, how- ever, the reader must be warned, since mere hypotheses are stated much too positively." Dr. Wortsmann thinks the second part of the book— dealing with Gluck as artist, and with the eighteenth-century theory of the opera—the better of the two.

I am sure if I were to re-read the book I should agree with him. I was so fired by my subject that I have not the least doubt I wrote about the incidents of Gluck's career as if I had personally been a witness of them. I was very young, very ardent, and Gluck-drunk. Gluck was more real to me than most of the people I rubbed shoulders with every day.

The book was generously received by the English reviewers, and Mr. Dobell suggested that I should do a book on Wagner, which he would publish. I gladly fell in with the suggestion. Here the material for the kind of book I then wanted to do was easily accessible even to a young student in a town so remote from civilization as Liverpool. A Study of Wagner was a biggish book of some four hundred pages. It took me, with only the evenings in which to work at it after the tiring day's labour in the bank, a good three years to write, and it was published by Mr. Dobell in 1899.

This was the second of the great services this good old man did to a young author whom he as yet did not know personally. His constant kindness and thoughtfulness I shall never forget. In his capacity as second- hand bookseller he frequently came across literature that he thought might be useful to me in my studies, and this he always sent to me. He produced both the Gluck and the Wagner in handsome style. They had a fair and steady sale, and I hope he did not lose much over them. These were the last books of mine that he published. I issued various volumes through other publishers during the next few years—books asked for by them, so I could not have offered them to Mr. Dobell. Some thirteen or fourteen years after the Study of Wagner I worked at another big book on that composer, which was published, under the title of Wagner as Man and Artist, in 1914. I received a letter from Mr. Dobell, from whom I had not heard for many years, gently reproaching me for not having given him an opportunity to publish this book also. I was touched by the generous old man's continued interest in me and his willingness to risk his money on me, and could only explain that even had I thought of asking him to make any further sacrifice on my behalf (for of course he had not the business organization of the bigger publishers) I was not free in this particular case. Thereupon he asked me to do for him a volume of literary essays (Nietzsche, Amiel, Meredith, and other subjects upon which I had already written in various magazines), and to prepare a new edition of *Gluck and the Opera*, which was now out of print. Before I could fulfill either task Mr. Dobell died. I have never forgotten his many kindnesses to me; it was he who gave me my first real footing on the ladder.

XIV

I IMAGINE THERE CAN BE few professions that are such a delight to the new hand and such a horror to the old hand as musical criticism. Someone in Dickens comments on the remarkable fact that no one ever sees a dead donkey. But there is a greater rarity even than this—a musical critic of twenty years' standing who is enthusiastic about concerts. So rare is this phenomenon, indeed, that I have never yet come upon it. I know no middle-aged critics who would not prefer a good dinner to a bad concert any day.

This weariness, this disillusion, does not, I think, take place in anything like the same proportion in the other learned professions, except, perhaps, the Church, of which I am not competent to speak from inside knowledge. I have often asked a doctor or a dentist, in whose hands I happened to be for a moment, if he did not get tired of his work. Each of them has assured me that his interest in it increased as he grew older. Even the burglar, I am sure, never conceives so profound a distaste for his profession that he has to brace himself, by a supreme effort of the will, before he can go out to "crack" another crib. But then the burglar's business offers just that perpetual touch of new adventure that is lacking from the musical critic's. Send the same burglar out night after night to "crack" the same crib, with the window-catch already slipped and everything else made ridiculously easy for him, and with nothing in the way of swag to show for his skill and toil at the end of it all but a brass farthing and a paste jewel or two, and it will not be long before he throws up pathetic hands to heaven and asks Providence why it made him a burglar.

That is the trouble with musical criticism as a profession, which means, of course, a great deal of concert reporting. It involves a fearful amount of the most appalling monotony on earth, and it involves physical as well as mental pain for the poor critics. The dentist or the surgeon may feel sorry for you when he is putting you through it, but his is a purely imaginative pain. But the average concert performer inflicts an actual positive, physical pain upon the critic. The plain man who reads this will know what it would feel like to have some unpleasantly rough fabric passed over his bare skin a thousand times an hour. He can perhaps dimly imagine, then, what a man with a sensitive musical ear suffers when a violinist or a singer plays or sings persistently out of tune during the greater part of an evening. There is, for the musical critic, only one more painful experience than to be hurt and irritated by this kind of thing, and that is not to be hurt or irritated by it. For in the latter case the horrified reflection occurs to him that he must be losing his ear, that his auditory nerve has become so brutalized by long ill-treatment that it no longer resents ugliness, much in the way that a man who has slipped away from virtue by slow stages may suddenly pull himself up one day and realize, to his horror, that he is doing something as a matter of course that a year ago he would have blushed to find himself even contemplating.

Let me not dwell further at the moment, however, on these more painful aspects of the musical critic's life. I may have occasion to recur to them later. Here I wish to speak rather of those first blissful years in which everything is so delightful and everything seems so easy. In later years doubts come to the critic. The magnanimous thought sometimes comes to him that he may be wrong; he finds in the air around him a hundred opinions upon this, that or the other, and, if he is a man of great intelligence, he will probably see that all these opinions cannot possibly be right, and that there is at least a probability that Providence has chosen someone other than himself as the receptacle for the first truth and the final wisdom of things. This is an awful feeling and, to do myself and my colleagues justice, the critic rarely gives way to it. But when he does, you may be sure that he is pretty old in the craft. The younger members of it never feel like that.

I speak from experience. I began newspaper criticism in, I think, 1905, when I was invited by the *Manchester Guardian* to succeed Arthur Johnstone—a cultured and brilliant man whose untimely death was a great loss to English musical criticism. Had it been suggested to me in those first bright days that I might have been wrong on any subject, I should probably have had serious doubts as to the sanity of the person making the suggestion. Precisely to what extent I may have made an ass of myself I cannot now say, for that would mean re-reading my articles of that time, and I have always been curiously shy of my own older work. But without enduring that painful ordeal, I fancy I can see my then self in one or two of my younger colleagues of today—brave, bright spirits who tweak the nose of an Elgar or a Hugo Wolf with as much unconcern as they would swat some too obtrusive fly on the window pane.

In those days I used to feel as, I suppose, these young friends of mine feel now—that there certainly was one right way among the hundred wrong ways of criticism, and that I, by the special grace of heaven, had been put upon it the first moment my tiny feet could toddle. As we get older, the problems of criticism become more and more perplexing; we see men for whose gifts and whose judgment we have the greatest respect thinking the direct opposite from us on a certain subject, and we are bound to ask ourselves why. In later years we spend a good deal of our time trying to understand not only a composer or a work, but also the critics who express such contradictory opinions upon him or it. But in youth we do not trouble much about these things. It is all very simple: if the other people differ from us they are wrong, and that is all there is to it. The possibility that it is we who may be wrong never occurs to us. Often now, when I see a young critic confidently laying down the law on some subject on which he can have had only a limited experience, my mind runs on the words addressed by Cromwell to the ministers of the Scotch Kirk after Dunbar: "By your hard and subtle words you have begotten prejudice in those who do too much in matters of conscience (wherein every soul has to answer for itself in God) depend upon you. Your own guilt is too much for you to bear. . . . Is it therefore infallibly agreeable to the word of God, all that you say? I beseech you in the bowels of Christ, think it possible that you may be mistaken."

XV

I SPOKE OF THE PAINS of the musical critic's life. But the life has its pleasant side also, especially at first. Only a few weeks ago I quoted elsewhere the remark of an old French musician to the effect that in his youth he had enjoyed music as a mistress, while now it was merely a wife. We all come to feel more or less like that about our art or, at all events, about that portion of it that is connected with our professional duties. Long experience has convinced me that the only way to find enduring happiness in music is to be an intelligent amateur of it—to retain it for ever, in fact, as a mistress. There was a celebrated old French nobleman of the eighteenth century who used to spend every evening of his life in the salon of a middle-aged Parisian lady whose conversation had an especial charm for him. A friend suggested that as he was so fond of the lady's society the obviously sensible thing was to marry her. The old marquis held up his hands in horror. "God forbid!" he said. "Marry her? Where would I spend my evenings?"

I always tell this story as a warning to those young men who come to me to ask me how they can begin as musical critics. My advice to them is put the awful thought away from them at once, before it gets the mastery of them. I tell them to do anything rather than make music their profession—to go into business and enjoy music in the evenings, to make commerce their wife and keep music for a mistress. Let them take a leaf from the book of our educationists. As everyone knows, the aim of the British educational system is not to teach the young Briton either art or science, but to make him proficient in sport. But the wise men who run the system know better than to let the boy see this. They know that that would be the surest way to put him off sport for the rest of his life. So they keep up the pretence that the only reason for his being at school is that he may learn the names of the rivers of England that flow into the North Sea, or how many angles of a triangle it takes to make two right angles: but they frown upon cricket as a trap laid by Satan for the immortal soul of the boy, with the natural result that the boy loves cricket and hates geography and Euclid. If he were compelled by the school regulations to play cricket for so many hours each day, to show instead of his books his gloves and pads whenever the master took it into his head to have an inspection, to learn by heart the batting and bowling averages for the last fifty years, and to work out on paper the angle at which a ball with a given trajectory would be likely to fly off a bat that meets it at a certain degree of inclination, the boy would come to hate the sight of the school cricket professional as he now hates the sight of the mathematics master, and we should find him risking a caning for playing truant to study the integral calculus in secret.

The ancient Spartans had also evidently hit upon the great truth that the best way to make a thing sought after is to frown upon it. In Sparta the young married men were kept apart from their wives and allowed to visit them only by stealth, severe penalties, I suppose, being inflicted on them if they were caught. For the young Spartan, in consequence, a marriage remained a perpetual romance. For the critic music is a romance only when it has a touch of the clandestine about it. I shall never give a young man any other than my usual advice—to keep up his liking for music as the old Frenchman kept up his liking for the lady, by spending his evenings with her as a lover, not as a husband.

At first, to be sure, the life of the musical critic has all the fascination of an engagement and none of the ennui of marriage. Concert-going is a glorious adventure. His ear is as yet unwearied, his nerves fresh and quick to react. At almost every concert he hears something or somebody for the first time, and his brain plays upon the new experience with delight and a godlike sense of intellectual power; the universe seems to be unrolling itself before him simply that he may understand it. His pen is as yet virgin—a virginity miraculously renewed with each fresh experience. His first *Tristan*, his first *Eroica*, his first Pachmann, draws the burning words from him without the least effort on his part. He not only tastes a new vintage every day, he drinks deep of it. A few years later he becomes the musical equivalent of those melancholy men the professional "tasters" of teas and wines, who, I am told, merely let the sample roll over their tongues to get the savour and estimate the quality of it, but never swallow any of it. They have long ago lost all stomach for the beverage; their one concern now is not to let their palate be corrupted any more than it is already.

But even the tea-taster is more fortunate than the critic. The former, as he ruefully spits out the mouthful he has been compelled to sample professionally, simply says "Good" or "Bad." The poor musical critic has to find fresh epithets each time for the same work or the same performer for perhaps twenty or thirty unhappy years. I have pondered long and deeply over this matter, and I have come to the conclusion that there are only two ways by which this martyrdom might be spared him. One is to abolish the present system of expressing our opinions in words, and let us express them by figures. I still hope to live to see the day, when, instead of racking his brains to find yet another way (the two hundred and fiftieth) of saying that Madame Larynxia was in fairly good voice, apart from her bad vibrato and a tendency to hit each note anywhere but in the centre, and that her Isolde would not have been half bad but for the fact that she did not look the part, could not act, and had evidently not the faintest idea what Wagner was driving at, the critic will just "mark" the lady in the style of an adjudicator at a competition festival: Tone 13, Intonation 5, Phrasing 2, Rhythm 2, Interpretation and General Effect 24, and so on. It would save him trouble, the newspaper space, and the reader time.

My alternative suggestion is that the newspaper should adopt the "circuit" system that is, I believe, in vogue in Wesleyan and other churches. No critic would be allowed to remain more than three years in any town. At the end of that time he would be drafted elsewhere. The readers in each town would thus get a welcome change, while the critic, instead of having to be always thinking out new ways of saying the old things, as he has when he addresses the same circle of readers year after year, would be able to work off on, say, Newport Pagnell, all the phrases, the jokes and epigrams he has elaborated in Ashby-De-la-Zouch, while the latter town, just beginning to weary of the too sustained brilliance of its own critic, would be toned up afresh by the coming of a new type of expert from Hayling Island.

Failing the general adoption of this system, we might have at any rate an occasional interchange of pulpits. Why should not newspapers now and then have a "guest" critic, as an opera company has a "guest" tenor?

Jules Romains

HOW VERDUN MANAGED TO
HOLD OUT

ON LEAVING THE BOULEVARDS, they wandered down to the quays beside the Siene and, as pilgrims might, moved slowly along the left bank towards Notre-Dame. Jerphanion thus found himself on his direct road home.

"Look here," he said to Jallez, "if you're free this evening, why not come and dine with us? Odette's made no preparations, but that doesn't matter. I'll buy something on the way. Odette'll be delighted to see you. She wanted to come with me to our appointment. It was I who asked her to let me meet you alone. I felt sure that we should talk frankly about all our concerns. As you know, she is very intelligent. There's nothing she can't understand, and in fact I never hide anything from her. But there are certain harshnesses of judgment, certain bitternesses, certain extremes of suffering, that I soft-pedal when I am with her, because they would rouse in her such a terror of despair that she would cry suddenly aloud: 'You mustn't go back!'"

Jallez was caught in a quick wave of emotion at the hint of tragedy which his friend's last words had disclosed.

"Of course I'll come," he said. "I have such happy memories of hours spent with you two when—there still seemed a hope of happiness for the world. We've spoken so much about the war that perhaps we can turn the conversation to other subjects before Odette, eh?"

"If you like . . . we'll see. . . . If you've anything in your mind that

---

From *Verdun*, 1939. Volume VIII of the series *Men of Good Will*. Translated from the French by Gerard Hopkins. Copyright 1939 by Alfred A. Knopf, Inc. Originally published in *Les Hommes de Bonne Volonté*. XVI: *Verdun*. Copyright 1938 by Ernest Flammarion, Paris.

might offer a little comfort for the future, anything that might bring the prospect of peace a little nearer . . . it would be very welcome."

"I'll do my best, old man."

"But until we get there, don't put any constraint on yourself. Ask me anything you still want to know."

Jallez spoke with considerable hesitation:

"No . . . I feel that I'm raking things up unnecessarily . . . things that you'd much rather forget while you're here."

"Not at all. . . . Just the reverse, in fact. I like getting it off my chest. During all this hideous experience I've become more than ever convinced that Epictetus, Marcus Aurelius . . . Pascal . . . were right. There's only one really heroic remedy for an excess of misery: to think the misery through honestly to the end. I told myself that I would keep a journal, in imitation of the philosopher Emperor; but I lacked the strength of character. A conversation such as we've just had takes its place. Besides, I've never forgotten what you once said on the subject of 'bearing witness.' do you remember? It was on the day of our first walk together, our very first, in the neighbourhood of the rue Claude-Bernard and the avenue des Gobelins. . . . The *Road to Emmaus*. . . . The light striking the top of a wall. . . . Doesn't it all come back? . . . What beauty we knew then! How lovely life could be! . . . And look at us now, creatures of shreds and patches! . . . Selfishly speaking, the greatest comfort I could have found in this war would have been to have you beside me in the trenches, as I have had good old Fabre . . . so that we might have 'borne witness' together . . . so that, at certain moments, I might have been able to say: 'Do you see this? . . . Did you see that? . . .' But fate ruled otherwise. . . . It is terribly important, though, for me to be able, in spite of everything, to make you a witness . . . to think all these things with you beside me. . . . One of the Disciples at Emmaus was absent from the room when the Figure appeared. His comrade, who witnessed all, could not rest until he had explained what he had seen, until he had made the moment 'live again' for him. That was what he was after—to make the moment live again for his friend. . . . So please go on; ask away."

His face took on the expression of a man setting himself to listen intently. At the same time, in an access of melting tenderness, his eyes took in the magnificent pageant of the river, closed at its far end by the mass of Notre-Dame.

"You've told me much that I find thrilling," said Jallez in measured tones; "but there is a good deal that still remains obscure. I don't yet understand the nature of that strength which can support millions of men in the life of an endless purgatory. You have mentioned the trivial aids, the little thoughts that buoy them up. . . . But are they really enough to account for what is happening? These men of yours are such as we all have known: men cradled, more or less, by civilization. It was not idealism that swept them along. . . . Enthusiasm? For a few days, perhaps, but not for years. How does it come about that these coddled, these matter-of-fact homunculi can endure so much, and over such long periods?"

"The first step was what counted. Once you've begun a thing, it exercises a terrible authority over you. That is one of the laws of existence about which I have fewest doubts. But if one's honest with oneself, one's got to admit that there is yet another authority which governs everything else. One's always realizing that one has somehow avoided mentioning it. Why? . . . Because it's axiomatic? . . . Because one's shy about putting it into words? . . . Even when one does take it into account one disguises it in borrowed plumage that gives it an air more flattering to self-pride: one calls it duty, patriotism, and so forth. . . . Its true name is something much cruder: nothing more or less than the pressure of society. Society today has willed that men should suffer and die on the battlefield. Well then, they just suffer and die. That's all there is to it. At other periods it has willed other things, and men have acted accordingly. The only disconcerting feature about what is happening now is this: that for a long time now men have been told that society no longer had this mystic power over them; that they had certain absolute rights as individuals; that no one could any longer demand of them anything that was not wholly reasonable from the point of view of their own personal existence. Now, from such a point of view, it does seem unreasonable that a man should be asked to give his life—in other words, his all—just to defend that part of the collective interest, often a very small part, which concerns him as an individual. Let him do it if he is moved to do it of his own free will, but no one can 'reasonably' demand it of him. Well, the only explanation to account for what we are seeing is that mankind has not yet learned to take this new theory at its face value. Certainly no one has been sufficiently assured to claim immunity as a right."

"Perhaps you're right. What seems so extraordinary to me is that this pressure should at all times be strong enough to overcome even physical fear."

"It might be truer to say that man's fear of society is still stronger than his fear of shells."

"I suppose that's it. . . . The soldier says to himself: 'If I refuse to go forward, if I run away, I shall be shot.' "

"That's not it exactly, either. . . . Some do have to think something like that; but for most of them such deliberate argument is unnecessary. Their fear of society is not a physical fear. It concerns the spirit rather than the body. Man is so made that usually fear for his body is less strong than fear that touches his spirit."

"Even to the extent of controlling his immediate reactions? . . . You start going over the top . . . shells are bursting all around . . . you find yourself in a machine-gun's field of fire. . . ."

"The point is that the mystical, the spiritual, fear of society can take forms which themselves produce immediate response. On one side of the balance is the fear of shells; on the other the fear of what your pals, what your officer, what your men, if you happen to be an officer, will think. In some ways it needs more courage to make the average man face being dubbed a coward than to get him to stand up to shell-fire."

They spoke of fear. Jerphanion maintained that at the front everyone was afraid, just as everyone is cold when it freezes, the only difference in the way fear manifested itself being due to variations in temperament. The constant presence of danger did, of course, harden men to a certain degree of insensitiveness, but not always. Often, indeed, it had just the opposite effect, screwed the nerves up to an abnormal pitch of exasperation, giving an added horror to anticipation.

"And then, you see, one never entirely gets rid of the fear one has had on previous occasions. The thought of the advance in which I was wounded last year still terrifies me. If I had to go over the top again, I should be far more frightened than I was the first time. Fear, too, has its periods; it goes in waves. There are days when one trembles all over, when one just can't control one's limbs, and other days when one is almost indifferent. Why it's impossible to say. I've found out that one of the best cures for fear is to say to oneself that it's completely useless (the same holds true of courage). One goes on saying to oneself: 'Don't be a fool. Is your stomach in your boots? Are you all strung up? Do your teeth want to chatter? Well, that won't make the slightest difference to the trajectory of the next shell or the path of the next bullets. It's merely so much fatigue the more.' On such occasions one tries to behave as though it were simply a question of going out in the rain, harmless, ordinary rain. It falls in big, heavy drops, but one just thinks of something else, like a cop huddled up in his cloak at a street-crossing. . . . See the kind of thing I mean? . . . Or else one tries to imagine that one is a pedestrian stranded in a swirl of cars in the middle of the Place de la Concorde. Each of them, dashing at full speed across the square, is more than capable of killing a man; and since they are all converging from different directions, it seems that before five minutes are out, one must crush the poor wayfarer. . . . And yet, if you're a hardened Parisian, you don't tremble, your teeth don't chatter. . . . You realize the guile of my system? One just pretends to believe that each shell will miss one as each car misses one, and that one can be killed only by the particular projectile loosed with that deliberate object by some mysterious power. . . . You remember Napoleon's famous phrase about the bullet that hadn't yet been cast? It's not much of a self-deception, but it works. Little things like that are all one has left in such situations. . . . I'm not sure, if it comes to that, that it is so little. It's just fatalism in a new dress. 'I've got a feeling that destiny has not willed that I should die today. If it has, then there's nothing I can do about it, so why worry?' When one's lived some time under the constant threat of danger, one begins to realize that fatalism is a necessary drug, just as alcohol is a necessary stimulant to a man on an arctic expedition. One of the secret virtues of fatalism is that it implies, against one's better judgment, a belief in the supernatural. 'If destiny has so far taken charge of me as to fix the moment of my death, it's not likely that it's going to leave me in the lurch afterwards. It will take me through to another stage. The adventure isn't finished yet.' Fundamentally all that man asks is that the adventure should not be ended. He doesn't want to know what happens next; he's perfectly willing to let the future remain a mystery. So long as the adventure is not finished, he can bear anything. The shells hurtling down on the trench, the advancing wave of which he forms a part, the storm of 77's and machine-gun bullets which will probably knock him over two yards farther on and leave him with his head smashed to pulp near that little tree—all these things become merely an episode. . . . You've no idea, my dear Jallez, of the depths of inherited belief that are stirred by such tornadoes of death."

"Yes, I have, and the thought moves me deeply." (Far ahead, but nearer now than it had been, rose Notre-Dame, with its gargoyles and its dreaming spires.)

"What I want to make you realize is the way that all these ideas swarm and jostle and come and go, quite arbitrarily, in a man's mind. That's why all formulas that try to generalize our reactions to life in the front line are false. There may be some men gifted with an abnormal strength of mind, whose attitude never varies . . . but they can't be many. . . . I can look back now, for instance, and see myself as I was on the second of those foodless days in the valley of Haudromont, about ten o'clock in the morning. A good many 77's were falling. Heavy shrapnel was bursting high up between our trenches and the crest to our rear, which meant that the bullets had a good chance of coming straight down into what shelter we had. As a matter of fact, I had one killed and four wounded that morning. But my own mood was one of almost complete resignation. I could hear the snapping of the branches, the burst of shells in the damp earth. It was as though I were standing aside from my own destiny. What might happen to me seemed no longer to have any significance. I didn't even have to take refuge behind my little tricks of mental comfort. My attitude was something that had been produced without any conscious exercise of my will. 'This is marvellous,' I said to myself; 'this is how a man ought to feel. Let's hope it continues.' And then, two hours later, when, if anything, the shelling was rather less intense, I found myself in a mood of hysterical and undisciplined excitement. But note this: that these ups and downs of the spirit can often have very awkward sequels. A man may be perfectly impotent in the face of shell-fire; still, the care or the speed with which he takes certain precautions may result in his being killed within the next three minutes, or finding himself still alive at the day's end. During those periods of superb indifference he may scorn to crouch or lie flat, may carelessly show his head above the parapet. When he becomes excited, on the other hand, he may get himself killed as the result of a clumsy excess of precautions, such as changing his position every few minutes, and the like. But the body is wiser than the mind. It draws the necessary inferences, adjusts the balance, looks after its own safety. The man of calm resignation and the hysterical worrier, taking the lead successively in each one of us, perform almost precisely the same automatic movements of self-preservation."

They were walking very slowly. Every few moments they stopped, the better to pick out for scrutiny some particular idea, just as woodcutters pause to choose one log rather than another.

A little later, after an effort, which clearly showed in the expression of his face, to assemble his ideas, Jerphanion said:

"I've been pondering again that question of yours. . . . Yes, the great operative influence is, I'm quite sure, the sense of social pressure. A man's got to stay where he is. He's caught like a rat in a trap, in a tangle of intersecting threads—the fear of a firing squad, a sense of shame, of dishonour, the moral impossibility of doing otherwise, a sort of mystical terror—on all sides he is hemmed in. Naturally, he is free, if he pleases, to be transported by ecstasy, free to declare that he is where he is because he wants to do his duty, because he loves his country. He is free *into the bargain* to accept his presence there as an act of will. . . . And that will may be perfectly sincere. . . . If we were intent on splitting hairs, we could prove easily enough that even this free and sincere will to sacrifice was something that he would never have come by unaided, that it is the product of that silly nonsense called education, or, in other words, of society's most cunning trick to mould a man to its design. But never mind. That's not what I meant. . . . No. . . . My point is that man is like any other animal: when there's no alternative, he gives in. Even the wild beasts give in under such conditions. . . . Men can screw themselves up to resist or to rebel when the authority that enjoins obedience shows signs of weakness. It may be all very depressing, but it's true. In the old days my 'optimism' wouldn't let me believe it. But the war has only too clearly shown me that I was wrong. Where now is man's vaunted spirit of revolt, of 'revolution'? Isn't it obvious that all such talk was never anything but a bad joke? The 'governed' make revolutions not when the governors most abuse their privileges, but when, having been guilty of abuses—not, perhaps, very grave abuses—they lack the courage to abide by their actions. . . . As my friend Griollet said, just think of the revolutionary fervour displayed by men like Pataud, Puget, Merrheim, and all the working-class leaders when they risked nothing. . . . Are they quite so keen now? Show me a single factory hand conscripted on war work, no matter how militant he was in days gone by, who refuses to turn out shells or agitates for a munition strike among his pals to stop the slaughter of the proletariat. . . . If the governments of the world don't deduce from what's happening certain philosophic and cynically Machiavellian truths for use in the post-war period, that'll only be because they are incapable of digesting any lesson of experience. In short, man is an animal who does what he is made to do very much more readily than one is inclined to believe. But once he has realized that, whatever happens, he has got to do what he is told, he likes nothing so much as to believe that the initial order came from himself. . . ."

Jerphanion paused a moment, then continued:

"To be fair, one must recognize that, in a sense, it does. No matter how strong or how cunning the collective will may be, it could not compel, and continue to compel, the individual to actions that were at complete variance with his nature. One must always reckon, for instance, with the love of destruction, which is deeply rooted in humanity. Man loves to demolish what he has himself created. Don't mothers say: 'Children are so destructive'? Think of the rows we used to make over the food at college. Most of us were only too delighted to discover once or twice a term that the stew was uneatable, because it gave us an excuse for throwing our plates on the ground and smashing them. Men are always ready to revenge themselves on the increasing complexity of material civilization. The ordered life of society forces us to give too much time to the making of too many things, and compels us to an over-nice exercise of care in using them. Bang, bang, bang, go the guns—partly to give release to the nerves of men who have heard nothing since childhood but 'Don't touch that!' 'Don't upset that!' 'Don't break that!' . . . Then there's an emotion of a totally different kind to reckon with—humanity's liking for sacrifice. I'm convinced that it exists, that it is no mere fantasy of a morbid literary taste. It's the only thing that can explain the success, the fanatical success, that cruel religions have always had. No matter how ferocious the inventions of their leaders, whether lay or priestly, there has never been any lack of willing victims. No master has ever succeeded in getting men to accept such things against their wishes. The most dearly loved leaders have always been the most bloodthirsty. There has never ceased to be a deep complicity between martyr and executioner. Certain German theorists—you know more about these things than I do—have assumed a connexion between this taste for sacrifice and sexual perversion. That is being unnecessarily ingenious. I have studied my own reactions and those of others in the course of this war. My impression is that, unless they are under the strict control of reason, men are an easy prey to the attraction, the lure, of great emotional thrills. For anyone in the prime of life there is no thrill comparable to the horror of being tortured and killed. . . . The anticipation of some such thrill does, of course, explain most perversions and the delight of the sexual act in general. And, apropos of sex, you must always remember that among the influences that conspire to keep the soldier in the trenches, exposed to constant shell-fire, sex is by no means the least. . . ."

"Hm!" interrupted Jallez. "Isn't that a bit far-fetched? . . . You can't have much time to think about sex, surely?"

"In the crude, carnal sense, no—except when we are in quiet rest-billets. But the thought of women never leaves us. I'm not talking of the girls in pink undies cut out of the *Vie Parisienne* and pinned up in every

hut and every dug-out . . . though they are not without their significance.
I'm talking of the idea that women exist, 'way back, out of the war
zone. . . ."

"Whom it's up to you to defend?"

"Well, yes, if you like to put it that way, but it's not quite that, not
so sentimental as that. . . . What I mean is that we're always conscious of
them standing, as it were, on the walls of some ancient fortified city,
watching and criticizing. . . ."

"Isn't that all a bit literary? Aren't you rather modulating on a
traditional theme?"

"No. When the common or garden poilu dreams of getting a soft
job, one argument above all others makes him pause, especially if he
happens to be young. . . . I've used it myself, more shame to me, in talking
to country lads; and that is: 'What'll the girls at home say? They'll never
look at you again.' Carry that same motive a little further, think of it as
animating the man going over the top with his rifle at the trail. 'The
women are watching,' he says to himself; 'watching to see whether I'm
making as good a showing as the rest . . . watching to see whether I turn
tail . . . whether I'm going to sneak into a shell-hole while the others go
forward.' And if that constant obsession is not enough, there are always
the war 'godmothers'—that admirable invention of the people at home
for keeping the soldier in a constant state of slightly amorous excitation
which, it is supposed, will be ultimately translated into patriotic ardour.
Think of all those 'godmothers' going to bed with their protégés when
they're on leave, and kissing them good-bye at the end of it, with a 'Be
brave, darling,' which merely means: 'Do the sensible thing and get yourself killed. . . .' How thrilling it must be for all these women, many of
them no longer young, to have such interludes of love with fresh, virile
boys, always with the thought at the back of their minds that the lover is
going from their arms straight to death. . . . The purely sensual delight of
the female insect. Sweep away all women—women in the narrow sense of
the word—from the back areas; leave no one there but mothers, old men,
and children (to make use of the categories beloved of the official mind),
and I don't mind betting that the war would soon be over."

"It's certainly worth thinking about," said Jallez. "What it all comes
to is that war touches springs that lie deep at the heart of humanity."

"Of course it does. In a way that's all it does. But even that's not the
only thing I'm after. The frightful thing about war is that, as a subject,
it's inexhaustible. One's eye is always being caught by some new aspect of
the business. My real point is this: that for the men in the trenches—for
all of them, that is, who are above the purely animal level, for whom, as
you must see for yourself, it is most necessary to find an explanation—the
idea that they must stay where they are and get on with their job because
there is no real alternative is not enough to keep them in spirits, to
prevent their moral collapse. Each one of them has got to find some effective suggestion that will touch him personally, some thought, some fixed

idea, the secret of which is known to him alone, the essence of which he can absorb drop by drop. Sometimes he has several among which he can take his choice. No sooner does one begin to lose its potency than he can change over to others. Take my own case, for instance. For quite a while I managed very comfortably on the idea that I was the kind of man who could 'rise superior to circumstances'—the circumstances in question being partly composed of mental distress, partly of bodily discomfort. 'I'd like,' said I, 'to see those circumstances to which I could not rise superior!' While shrapnel pattered round me (it was at the time when a good deal of shrapnel was being used), I would recite to myself like a sort of magic formula, those terrific lines of Horace:

> *Si fractus illabatur orbis*
> *Impavidum ferient ruinae. . . .*

It really is a magic formula. And then, one day, it no longer worked. My mental distress became too great, my fear became too great, and I just wanted to burst into tears and cry 'Mamma!' like a little boy. . . . Then take the young second lieutenant fresh from Saint-Cyr, all innocence and splendid bravery, who says to himself: 'If France is conquered, life will be impossible. I shall feel personally dishonoured. Far rather would I have my name on a headstone with the words: "Died on the field of honour," than live on disgraced.' Another example is that of the reservist with a taste for serious reading and an equipment of large-hearted ideals, the kind of man who says to himself: 'This is the war that will end war. We are bringing peace to the whole world. Thanks to our sacrifice, our children will be spared knowledge of such horrors.' Standing next to him in the same trench will be some fellow who thinks: 'This is the end of the world. We're all in for it. What does it matter if I get killed a little sooner or a little later?' Another there may be who believes in a coming reign of justice, who is still convinced that victory for the democracies will mean freedom for the oppressed everywhere in the world, the end of the domination of money and social iniquity, who would be willing even to die if only he could be sure that his death would mean greater happiness for men yet unborn. Then there's the sentimentalist, for whom nothing counts but personal relationships, whose world is made up of just a few dear friends, who argues: 'Most of my pals are dead. If they all go, what is there left to live for?' There's the man whose wife left him as soon as he was called up, and ran off with someone else; who gets no letters and no parcels; who feels himself too old to start life afresh, who would just as soon be dead, for whom the very fact of danger is a distraction, because it gives him the illusion that life is still sweet. There is the man who exists in a world of dreams and takes things as they come. 'Everything is predestined,' says he; 'I always knew it. No use fighting against fate. We must just go with the tide.' There is the man who has never had a chance, who has always felt himself to be the victim of injustice and insult, who has always envied the good fortune of others, who so relishes the taste of equality bred of a general misery that he pays but lip service to the desire for peace with all the bitterness that it will bring for him in its train. Close beside him is another in whom the war has waked a deep-seated strain of pessimism, who thinks sincerely: 'The universe is a foul absurdity. It was always pretty obvious, but the war has proved it beyond the shadow of a doubt. Why cling to a foul absurdity?' or: 'Humanity is the work of the Devil, a blot on the face of the earth, born for murder and self-slaughter. So much the worse for humanity (and for me, who am part of humanity and so of the whole putrescent mess).' There is the fanatical Catholic, who thinks: 'This is God's punishment wrought on a corrupt and faithless generation. If God has decided that I too must pay the penalty, even for the faults of others, who am I to question His will?' There is the gentle Catholic who carries tucked away in his pack a tiny edition of the *Imitation*, who, when night falls, says his prayers in his shell-hole, very quietly, so that no one shall notice him, and murmurs: 'Let me suffer, as You suffered, Jesu mine. Why should I be spared, since You suffered a thousand deaths hanging on Your cross? Give me strength that I may be not too unworthy of You.' Finally, there is the man"—and Jerphanion made a gesture towards Notre-Dame, which was now imme-diately opposite them, across the river, its pinnacles just touched by the fading day—"who says: 'All that matters to me in this world is the language of France, the cathedrals of our French countryside, the quays of the Seine, landscapes that can be found nowhere else in the world, a way of life that is unique. If all that is to be taken away, life has no longer any point. If, by dying, I can ensure that all these things will live on after me, then death is right and proper. . . .' Picture to yourself trench after trench filled with men thinking such thoughts, and you will find the answer to your question. . . . That is why Verdun still stands."

Oswald Spengler

THE FORM-WORLD OF ECONOMIC LIFE

The Machine

I

TECHNIQUE IS AS OLD as free-moving life itself. Only the plant—so far as we can see into Nature—is the mere theatre of technical processes. The animal, in that it moves, has a technique of movement so that it may nourish and protect itself.

The original relation between a waking-microcosm and its macrocosm—"Nature"—consists in a touch through the senses which rises from mere sense-*impressions* to sense-*judgment*, so that already it works critically (that is, separately) or, what comes to the same thing, *causal-analytically*. The stock of what has been determined then is enlarged into a system, as complete as may be, of the most primary experiences—identifying marks—a spontaneous method by which one is enabled to feel at home in one's world; in the case of many animals this has led to an amazing richness of experience that no human science has transcended. But the primary waking-being is always an *active* one, remote from mere theory of all sorts, and thus it is in the minor technique of everyday life,

---

From *The Decline of the West*. Volume II: *Perspectives of World-History*, 1928. Translated from the German by Charles Francis Atkinson. Copyright 1928 by Alfred A. Knopf, Inc. Renewal copyright 1956 by Alfred A. Knopf, Inc. Originally published in *Der Untergang des Abendlandes: Welthistorische Perspektiven*. Copyright 1922 by C. H. Beck'sche Verlagsbuchhandlung, Munich.

and upon things *in so far as they are dead,* that these experiences are involuntarily acquired. This is the difference between Cult and Myth, for at this level there is no boundary line between religion and the profane—all waking-consciousness *is* religion.

The decisive turn in the history of the higher life occurs when the *determination* of Nature (in order to be guided by it) changes into a *fixation*—that is, a purposed alteration of Nature. With this, technique becomes more or less sovereign and the instinctive prime-experience changes into a definitely "conscious" prime-*knowing.* Thought has emancipated itself from sensation. It is the *language of words* that brings about this epochal change. The liberation of speech from speaking gives rise to a stock of signs for communication-speech which are much more than identification-marks—they are *names* bound up with a sense of meaning, whereby man has the secret of numina (deities, nature-forces) in his power, and *number* (formulae, simple laws), whereby the inner form of the actual is abstracted from the accidental-sensuous.

With that, the system of identification-marks develops into a theory, a *picture* which detaches itself from the technique of the day[1]—whether this be a day of high-level Civilized technics or a day of simplest beginnings—by way of *abstraction,* as a piece of waking-consciousness uncommitted to activity. One "knows" what one wants, but much must have happened for one to have that knowledge, and we must make no mistake as to its character. By numerical experience man is enabled to switch the secret on and off, but he has not discovered it. The figure of the modern sorcerer—a switchboard with levers and labels at which the workman calls mighty effects into play by the pressure of a finger without possessing the slightest notion of their essence—is only the symbol of human technique in general. The picture of the light-world around us—in so far as we have developed it critically, analytically, as theory, as picture—is nothing but a switchboard of the kind, on which particular things are so labelled that by (so to say) pressing the appropriate button particular effects follow with certainty. The secret itself remains none the less oppressive on that account.[2] But through this technique the waking-consciousness does, all the same, intervene masterfully in the fact-world. Life *makes use* of thought as an "open sesame," and at the peak of many a Civilization, in its great cities, there arrives finally the moment when technical critique becomes tired of being life's servant and makes itself tyrant. The Western Culture is even now experiencing an orgy of this unbridled thought, and on a tragic scale.

Man has listened-in to the march of Nature and made notes of its

---

[1] And not vice versa.

[2] The "correctness" of physical data (i.e., their applicability never disproved up to date, and therefore ranking as an *interpretation*) is wholly independent of their technical value. An undoubtedly wrong, and even self-contradictory, theory may be more valuable for practical purposes than a "correct" and profound one, and physical science has long been careful to avoid applying the words "right" and "wrong" in the popular sense, and to regard their syntheses as images rather than flat formulae.

indices. He begins to imitate it by means and methods that utilize the laws of the cosmic pulse. He is emboldened to play the part of God, and it is easy to understand how the earliest preparers and experts of these artificial things—for it was here that art came to be, as *counter-concept to nature*—and how in particular the guardians of the smith's art, appeared to those around them as something uncanny and were regarded with awe or horror as the case might be. The stock of such discoveries grew and grew. Often they were made and forgotten and made again, were imitated, shunned, improved. But in the end they constituted for whole continents a store of *self-evident* means—fire, metal-working, instruments, arms, ploughs, boats, houses, animal-taming, and husbandry. Above all, the metals, to whose site in the earth primitive man is led by some uncannily mystical trait in him. Immemoriably old trade-routes lead to ore deposits that are kept secret, through the life of the settled countryside and over frequented seas, and along these, later, travel cults and ornaments and persistent legends of islands of tin and lands of gold. The primary trade of all is the metal trade, and with it the economics of production and of work are joined intrusively by a third—alien, venturesome, free-ranging over the lands.

On this foundation, now, arises the technique of the higher Cultures, expressive in quality and colour and passion of the whole soul of these major entities. It need hardly be said that Classical man, who felt himself and his environment alike Euclidean, set himself *a priori* in hostile opposition to the very idea of technique. If by "Classical" technique we mean something that (along with the rest that we comprehend in the adjective) rose with determined effort above the universal dead perfection of the Mycenaean age, then there was no Classical technique.[3] Its triremes were glorified row-boats, its catapults and onagers mere substitutes for arms and fists—not to be named in the same breath with the war-engines of Assyria and China—and as for Hero and his like, it was flukes and not discoveries that they achieved. They lacked the inner weight, the fatedness of their moment, the deep necessity. Here and there men played with data (and why not?) that probably came from the East, but no one devoted serious attention to them and, above all, no one made a real effort to introduce them into the ensemble-picture of life.

Very different is the Faustian technics, which with all its passion of the third dimension, and from earliest Gothic days, thrusts itself upon Nature, with the firm resolve to *be its master*. Here, and only here, is the connexion of insight and utilization a matter of course.[4] Theory is work-

---

[3] What Diels has managed to assemble in his work *Antike Technik* amounts to a comprehensive nullity. If we take away from it what belongs to the older Babylonian Civilization (such as water clocks and sun-dials) and to the younger Arabian Springtime (such as chemistry or the wonder-clock of Gaza), there is nothing left but devices, such as door-locks of a sort, that it would be an insult to attribute to any other Culture.

[4] The Chinese Culture, too, made almost all these European discoveries on its own account—including compass, telescope, printing, gunpowder, paper, porcelain—but the Chinese did not wrest, but *wheedled*, things out of Nature. No doubt he felt

ing hypothesis from the outset. The Classical investigator "contemplated" like Aristotle's deity, the Arabian sought as alchemist for magical means (such as the Philosophers' Stone) whereby to possess himself of Nature's treasures *without effort*,[5] but the Western strives to *direct* the world according to his will.

The Faustian inventor and discoverer is a unique type. The primitive force of his will, the brilliance of his visions, the steely energy of his practical ponderings, must appear queer and incomprehensible to anyone at the standpoint of another Culture, but for us they are in the blood. Our whole Culture has a discoverer's soul. To *dis*-cover that which is not seen, to draw it into the light-world of the inner eye so as to master it—that was its stubborn passion from the first days on. All its great inventions slowly ripened in the deeps, to emerge at last with the necessity of a Destiny. All of them were very nearly approached by the high-hearted, happy research of the early Gothic monks.[6] Here, if anywhere, the religious origins of all technical thought are manifested.[7] These meditative discoverers in their cells, who with prayers and fastings *wrung* God's secret out of him, felt that they were *serving* God thereby. Here is the Faust-figure, the grand symbol of a true discovering Culture. The *Scientia experimentalis*, as Roger Bacon was the first to call nature-research, the *insistent* questioning of Nature with levers and screws, began that of which the issue lies under our eyes as a countryside sprouting factory-chimneys and conveyor-towers. But for all of them, too, there was the truly Faustian danger of the Devil's having a hand in the game, the risk that he was leading them in spirit to that mountain on which he promises all the power of the earth. This is the significance of the *perpetuum mobile* dreamed of by those strange Dominicans like Petrus Peregrinus, which would wrest the almightiness from God. Again and again they succumbed to this ambition; they forced this secret out of God in order themselves to be God. They listened for the laws of the cosmic pulse in order to overpower it. And so they created the *idea of the machine* as a small cosmos obeying the will of man alone. But with that they over-passed the slender border-line whereat the reverent piety of others saw the beginning of sin, and on it, from Roger Bacon to Giordano Bruno, they came to grief. Ever and ever again, true belief has regarded the machine as of the Devil.

---

the advantages of his knowledge and turned it to account, but he did not hurl himself upon it to exploit it.

[5] It is the same spirit that distinguishes the Jewish, Parsee, Armenian, Greek, and Arab ideas of business from that of the Western peoples.

[6] Albertus Magnus lived on in legend as the great magician. Roger Bacon meditated upon steam-engines, steamships, and aircraft.

[7] According to Roger Bacon the "third rôle of science," which is not relative to the other sciences, consists in the power that makes it to search the secrets of nature, to discover past and future, and to produce so many marvellous results that power is assured to those who possess it. . . . The Church should take it into consideration in order to spare Christian blood in the struggle with the infidel and above all in preparation for the perils that will menace us in the days of Antichrist. [*Trans.*]

The passion of discovery declares itself as early as the Gothic architecture—compare with this the deliberate form-poverty of the Doric!—and is manifest throughout our music. Book-printing appeared, and the long-range weapon.[8] On the heels of Columbus and Copernicus come the telescope, the microscope, the chemical elements, and lastly the immense technological corpus of the early Baroque.

Then followed, however, simultaneously with Rationalism, the discovery of the steam-engine, which upset everything and transformed economic life from the foundations up. Till then nature had rendered services, but now she was tied to the yoke as *a slave*, and her work was as though in contempt measured by a standard of horse-power. We advanced from the muscle-force of the Negro, which was set to work in organized routines, to the organic reserves of the Earth's crust, where the life-forces of millennia lay stored as coal; and to-day we cast our eyes on inorganic nature, where water-forces are already being brought in to supplement coal. As the horse-powers run to millions and milliards, the numbers of the population increase and increase, on a scale that no other Culture ever thought possible. This growth is a *product of the Machine*, which insists on being used and directed, and to that end centuples the forces of each individual. For the sake of the machine, human life becomes precious. *Work* becomes the great word of ethical thinking; in the eighteenth century it loses its derogatory implication in all languages. The machine works and forces the man to co-operate. The entire Culture reaches a degree of activity such that the earth trembles under it.

And what now develops, in the space of hardly a century, is a drama of such greatness that the men of a future Culture, with other soul and other passions, will hardly be able to resist the conviction that "in those days" nature herself was tottering. The politics stride over cities and peoples; even the economics, deeply as they bite into the destinies of the plant and animal worlds, merely touch the fringe of life and efface themselves. But this technique will leave traces of its heyday behind it when all else is lost and forgotten. For this Faustian passion has altered the Face of the Earth.

This is the outward- and upward-straining life-feeling—true descendant, therefore, of the Gothic—as expressed in Goethe's Faust monologue when the steam-engine was yet young. The intoxicated soul wills to fly above space and Time. An ineffable longing tempts him to indefinable horizons. Man would free himself from the earth, rise into the infinite, leave the bonds of the body, and circle in the universe of space amongst the stars. That which the glowing and soaring inwardness of St. Bernard sought at the beginning, that which Grünewald and Rembrandt conceived in their backgrounds, and Beethoven in the trans-earthly tones of his last quartets, comes back now in the intellectual intoxication of the

---

[8] Greek fire was only to terrify and to ignite, but here the tense force of the gases of explosion are converted into energy of motion. Anyone who seriously compares the two does not understand the spirit of the Western technique.

inventions that crowd one upon another. Hence the fantastic traffic that crosses the continents in a few days, that puts itself across oceans in floating cities, that bores through mountains, rushes about in subterranean labyrinths, uses the steam-engine till its last possibilities have been exhausted, and then passes on to the gas-engine, and finally raises itself above the roads and railways and flies in the air; hence it is that the spoken word is sent in one moment over all the oceans; hence comes the ambition to break all records and beat all dimensions, to build giant halls for giant machines, vast ships and bridge-spans, buildings that deliriously scrape the clouds, fabulous forces pressed together to a focus to obey the hand of a child, stamping and quivering and droning works of steel and glass in which tiny man moves as unlimited monarch and, at the last, feels nature as beneath him.

And these machines become in their forms less and ever less human, more ascetic, mystic, esoteric. They weave the earth over with an infinite web of subtle forces, currents, and tensions. Their bodies become ever more and more immaterial, ever less noisy. The wheels, rollers, and levers are vocal no more. All that matters withdraws itself into the interior. Man has felt the machine to be devilish, and rightly. It signifies in the eyes of the believer the deposition of God. It delivers sacred Causality over to man and by him, with a sort of foreseeing omniscience, is set in motion, silent and irresistible.

II

NEVER SAVE HERE has a microcosm felt itself superior to its macrocosm, but here the little life-units have by the sheer force of their intellect made the unliving dependent upon themselves. It is a triumph, so far as we can see, unparalleled. Only this our Culture has achieved it, and perhaps only for a few centuries.

But for that very reason Faustian man has become *the slave of his creation*. His number, and the arrangement of life as he lives it, have been driven by the machine on to a path where there is no standing still and no turning back. The peasant, the hand-worker, even the merchant, appear suddenly as inessential in comparison with the *three great figures that the Machine has bred and trained up in the cause of its development: the entrepreneur, the engineer, and the factory-worker*. Out of a quite small branch of manual work—namely, the preparation-economy—there has grown up (*in this one Culture alone*) a mighty tree that casts its shadow over all the other vocations—namely, *the economy of the machine-industry*.[9] It forces the entrepreneur not less than the workman to obedi-

---

[9] Marx is quite right; it is one of the creations (and what is more, the proudest creation) of the bourgeoisie. But, spellbound as he is by the ancient-medieval-modern scheme, he has failed to note that it is only the bourgeoisie of this one single Culture that is master of the destiny of the Machine. So long as it dominates the earth, every

ence. *Both* become slaves, and not masters, of the machine, that now for the first time develops its devilish and occult power. But although the Socialistic theory of the present day has insisted upon looking only at the latter's contribution and has claimed the word "work" for him alone, it has all become possible only through the sovereign and decisive achievement of the former. The famous phrase concerning the "strong arm" that bids every wheel cease from running is a piece of wrong-headedness. To stop them—yes! but it does not need a worker to do that. To keep them running—no! The centre of this artificial and complicated realm of the Machine is the organizer and manager. The mind, not the hand, holds it together. But, for that very reason, to preserve the ever endangered structure, *one* figure is even more important than all the energy of enterprising master-men that make cities to grow out of the ground and alter the picture of the landscape; it is a figure that is apt to be forgotten in this conflict of politics—the *engineer*, the priest of the machine, the man who knows it. Not merely the importance, but the very existence of the industry depends upon the existence of the hundred thousand talented, rigorously schooled brains that command the technique and develop it onward and onward. The quiet engineer it is who is the machine's master and destiny. His thought is as possibility what the machine is as actuality. There have been fears, thoroughly materialistic fears, of the exhaustion of the coal-fields. But so long as there are worthy technical path-finders, dangers of this sort have no existence. When, and only when, the crop of recruits for this army fails—this army whose thought-work forms one inward unit with the work of the machine—the industry must flicker out in spite of all that managerial energy and the workers can do. Suppose that, in future generations, the most gifted minds were to find their soul's health more important than all the powers of this world; suppose that, under the influence of the metaphysic and mysticism that is taking the place of rationalism to-day, the very élite of intellect that is now concerned with the machine comes to be overpowered by a growing sense of its *Satanism* (it is the step from Roger Bacon to Bernard of Clairvaux)— then nothing can hinder the end of this grand drama that has been a play of intellects, with hands as mere auxiliaries.

The Western industry has diverted the ancient traditions of the other Cultures. The streams of economic life move towards the seats of King Coal and the great regions of raw material. Nature becomes ex-

---

non-European tries and will try to fathom the secret of this terrible weapon. Nevertheless, inwardly he abhors it, be he Indian or Japanese, Russian or Arab. It is something fundamental in the essence of the Magian soul that leads the Jew, as entrepreneur and engineer, to stand aside from the creation proper of machines and devote himself to the business side of their production. But so also the Russian looks with fear and hatred at this tyranny of wheels, cables, and rails, and if he adapts himself for to-day and to-morrow to the inevitable, yet there will come a time when he will *blot out the whole thing from his memory and his environment*, and create about himself a wholly new world, in which nothing of this Devil's technique is left.

hausted, the globe sacrificed to Faustian thinking in energies. The *work-ing* earth is the Faustian aspect of her, the aspect contemplated by the Faust of Part II, the supreme transfiguration of enterprising work—and contemplating, he dies. Nothing is so utterly antipodal to the motionless satiate being of the Classical Empire. It is the engineer who is remotest from the Classical law-thought, and he will see to it that his economy has *its own* law, wherein forces and efficiencies will take the place of Person and Thing.

III

BUT TITANIC, TOO, is the onslaught of money upon this intellectual force. Industry, too, is earth-bound like the yeoman. It has its station, and its materials stream up out of the earth. Only high finance is *wholly* free, wholly intangible. Since 1789 the banks, and with them the bourses, have developed themselves on the credit-needs of an industry growing ever more enormous, as a power on their own account, and they will (as money wills in every Civilization) to be the only power. The ancient wrestle between the productive and the acquisitive economies intensifies now into a silent gigantomachy of intellects, fought out in the lists of the world-cities. This battle is the despairing struggle of technical thought to maintain its liberty against money-thought.[1]

The dictature of money marches on, tending to its material peak, in the Faustian Civilization as in every other. And now something happens that is intelligible only to one who has penetrated to the essence of money. If it were anything tangible, then its existence would be for ever—but, as it is a form of thought, *it fades out as soon as it has thought its economic world to finality*, and has no more material upon which to feed. It thrust into the life of the yeoman's countryside and set the earth a-moving; its thought transformed every sort of handicraft; to-day it presses victoriously upon industry to make the productive work of entrepreneur and engineer and labourer alike its spoil. The machine with its human retinue, the real queen of this century, is in danger of succumbing to a stronger power. But with this, money, too, is at the end of its success, and the last conflict is at hand in which the Civilization receives its conclusive form—the conflict *between* money and blood.

The coming of Caesarism breaks the dictature of money and its political weapon democracy. After a long triumph of world-city econ-omy and its interests over political creative force, the political side of life manifests itself after all as the stronger of the two. The sword is victori-ous over the money, the master-will subdues again the plunderer-will. If

[1] Compared with this mighty contest between the two handfuls of steel-hard men of race and of immense intellect—which the simple citizen neither observes nor comprehends—the battle of mere interests between the employing class and the workers' Socialism sinks into insignificance when regarded from the distant world-historical view-point. The working-class movement is what its leaders *make* of it, and

we call these money-powers "Capitalism,"[2] then we may designate as Socialism the will to call into life a mighty politico-economic order that transcends all class interests, a system of *lofty* thoughtfulness and duty-sense that keeps the whole in fine condition for the decisive battle of its history, and this battle is also the battle of money and law. The *private* powers of the economy want free paths for their acquisition of great resources. No legislation must stand in their way. They want to make the laws themselves, in their interests, and to that end they make use of the tool they have made for themselves, democracy, the subsidized party. Law needs, in order to resist this onslaught, a high tradition and an ambition of strong families that finds its satisfaction not in the heaping-up of riches, but in the tasks of true rulership, above and beyond all money-advantage. *A power can be overthrown only by another power*, not by a principle, and no power that can confront money is left but this one. Money is overthrown and abolished only by blood. *Life* is alpha and omega, the cosmic onflow in microcosmic form. It is *the* fact of facts within the world-as-history. Before the irresistible rhythm of the generation-sequence, everything built up by the waking-consciousness in its intellectual world vanishes at the last. Ever in History it is life and life only—race-quality, the triumph of the will-to-power—and not the victory of truths, discoveries, or money that signifies. *World-history is the world court*, and it has ever decided in favour of the stronger, fuller, and more self-assured life—decreed to it, namely, the right to exist, regardless of whether its right would hold before a tribunal of waking-consciousness. Always it has sacrificed truth and justice to might and race, and passed doom of death upon men and peoples in whom truth was more than deeds, and justice than power. And so the drama of a high Culture—that wondrous world of deities, arts, thoughts, battles, cities—closes with the return of the pristine facts of the blood eternal that is one and the same as the ever-circling cosmic flow. The bright imaginative Waking-Being submerges itself into the silent service of Being, as the Chinese and Roman empires tell us. Time triumphs over Space, and it is Time whose inexorable movement embeds the ephemeral incident of the Culture, on this planet, in the incident of Man—a form wherein the incident life flows on for a time, while behind it all the streaming horizons of geological and stellar histories pile up in the light-world of our eyes.

For us, however, whom a Destiny has placed in this Culture and at this moment of its development—the moment when money is celebrating its last victories, and the Caesarism that is to succeed approaches with quiet, firm step—our direction, willed and obligatory at once, is set for us

---

hatred of the owner has long enlisted itself in the service of the bourse. Practical communism with its "class-war"—to-day a long obsolete and adulterated phrase—is nothing but the trusty henchman of big Capital, which knows perfectly well how to make use of it.

[2] In this sense the interest-politics of the workers' movements also belong to it, in that their object is not to overcome the money-values, but to possess them.

within narrow limits, and on any other terms life is not worth the living. We have not the freedom to reach to this or to that, but the freedom to do the necessary or to do nothing. And a task that historic necessity has set *will* be accomplished with the individual or against him.

Ducunt Fata volentem, nolentem trahunt.

J. W. N. Sullivan

BEETHOVEN:

The Last Quartets and the Final Stage

BEETHOVEN WAS ALREADY THINKING of writing a string quartet, a form he had neglected for thirteen years, when a letter came from Prince Galitzin requesting that he should compose three quartets at fifty ducats apiece. Beethoven accepted this offer in January, 1823, but the first quartet, in E flat major, Op. 127, was not finished until early in 1825. It was first performed on March 6, 1825. Two more quartets followed and were sent to the Prince. The Prince had paid for the first quartet, but he never paid Beethoven for the others. It was not until some years after the composer's death, as the result of very strong representations made to him, that the Prince paid over the rest of the money to Beethoven's nephew Carl. But, in writing the three quartets, Beethoven had by no means exhausted the ideas he could embody in this form, and he went on and completed two others, one in C sharp minor, Op. 131, and the other in F major, Op. 135. In these five quartets we have the greatest of Beethoven's music, and much of it is different in kind from any other music that he or anybody else ever wrote. In the last quartets, and particularly in the great three, those in A minor, B flat major, and C sharp minor, Beethoven is exploring new regions of consciousness. All the major, formative experiences of his life had been assimilated; life had nothing new to teach him. And his experience had, as we have seen, taken on a very high degree of organization, and to these organic wholes, formed very deep down in his consciousness, he had given expression

From *Beethoven: His Spiritual Development*, 1927. Copyright 1927 by J. W. N. Sullivan. Renewal copyright 1955 by Mrs. E. V. Sullivan.

again and again. But this inner world to which Beethoven had now retreated, although it no longer owed anything to fresh contacts with the
outer world, was nevertheless a living and developing world. It not only
contained elements which he had never before explored, but also elements
that had never before existed. The last quartets testify to a veritable
growth of consciousness, to a higher degree of consciousness, probably,
than is manifested anywhere else in art. The human consciousness is a
developing thing. It is nourished and fructified by experience but there
must be, in addition, an inner principle of growth. A marked increase of
consciousness, so far as the human race as a whole is concerned, seems to
take æons to manifest itself. But great artists appear who possess a
higher degree of consciousness than that enjoyed by the ordinary
man. And amongst such artists are some whose growth in awareness, in
sensibility, in power of co-ordination, is apparent during their lifetime.
In Beethoven such a process is very marked, more marked, probably, than
in the case of any other artist. His quite exceptional characteristics and
circumstances are partly responsible for this, and may serve to explain his
uniqueness. His faithfulness to his experience, his lack of malleability, his
deafness, and his emotional isolation from the world, were all favouring
conditions for the development of his inner life. This development, as
we have said, is very marked from the fifth to the ninth symphonies, for
example. The ninth symphony shows a way of apprehending reality, due
to the emergence in Beethoven of a new kind of awareness, that was
strictly impossible to the young Beethoven. It is a revelation of existence
as seen from the vantage point of a higher consciousness. In the ninth
symphony Beethoven has, in this respect, so far surpassed the norm of
great artists that he cannot influence them. The human mind may be
likened to some kind of multiple plant, here in full bloom, there still in
the bud. Different minds have flowered in different ways. Beethoven had
reached relative maturity in directions where those of us who respond to
him are still in the stage of embryonic growth. And in some people, it is
obvious, there is no germ of consciousness akin to the state of awareness
manifested by the late Beethoven. In his earlier works, however, he is
concerned with states of consciousness that most of us can share. For this
reason his earlier work has influenced other musicians, in content as well
as in form. But there is no music subsequent to Beethoven whose spiritual
content is of the order expressed in the ninth symphony. No other musician has ever risen to the state of awareness necessary to write the first
movement of that symphony, or possessed the power of synthesizing his
experience necessary to write its third movement. Beethoven has shown
that it is within the resources of music to express these stages of consciousness but, of the great followers of Beethoven, neither Wagner nor Brahms
has been in a position to profit by the demonstration. When we come to
the last quartets we find a still more remote spiritual content. We here
become aware not only of new syntheses of spiritual elements, but of

radically new elements. In these "strange seas of thought" Beethoven has discovered unsuspected islands and even continents.

The actual process of what we have called a growth of consciousness is extremely obscure. When we speak of a new synthesis of spiritual elements, whether these elements be emotions of states of awareness or whatever we choose to call them, we must remember that the synthesis corresponds to a definitely new state of consciousness and is not to be described by tabulating its elements. Thus the complex emotion, awe, to a person who has never felt it, does not become known through a knowledge of its constituents. Language, as we have had occasion to remark before, is poor in names for subjective states, and this poverty becomes particularly apparent when we try to describe such works of art as the late quartets. A spiritual synthesis, when we try to describe it, sometimes seems to contain contradictory elements. Thus a conscientious logician would probably hesitate to describe some emotional state as "gay melancholy." Yet, as a blunt description of the *alla tedesca* movement of the B flat quartet, it might pass. Neither word by itself would be in the least adequate. Both elements are present, not as contrasting, but strangely unified in one haunting phrase. And it would not be sufficient to say of the phrase that it is unique. All musical phrases are unique. Merely to say that the phrase is unique ignores the fact that it does suggest certain states rather than others. "Gay melancholy" may be contradictory and is certainly inadequate. But it is no more contradictory and is certainly less inadequate than "tender rage," or "virile weakness" or many other combinations would be.

The musical phrase we have referred to presents, in a simple form, one of the difficulties that face the writer who wishes to deal with the last string quartets. It is a difficulty which, to a greater or less extent, is involved in any description of a musical composition. But in the last string quartets spiritual experiences are communicated of which it is very difficult to mention even the elements. And yet it is just this music that most moves us and impresses us as containing the profoundest and most valuable experiences that any artist has yet conveyed. Our experience of the opening fugue of the C sharp minor quartet, for example, is surely one of the most pregnant and exalted that we know. Yet Wagner described this movement as the greatest expression of melancholy in all music. One may understand him saying this, and yet be utterly unable to agree with him. It is possible he did not agree with himself. That he heard more than melancholy in this movement we may be convinced, but for the something more he had no words. And yet the presence of that something more makes his description not only inadequate, but entirely erroneous. What is communicated to us in the first movement of the C sharp minor quartet has no more to do with melancholy than it has with joy. All art exists to communicate states of consciousness which are higher synthetic wholes than those of ordinary experience, but in these last quartets Beethoven is dealing with states for which there are no analogues in any other art. Regarding the content of some of his earlier work he could refer a questioner to Shakespeare. Regarding the content of these works he could refer him to nobody.

The first of the last quartets, in E flat major, stands rather apart from the next three, as does the last, in F major, Op. 135. The middle three quartets were worked upon almost simultaneously, they contain some of the same thematic material, they are sufficiently akin for movements originally destined for one to be transferred to another, and in each of them Beethoven abandons the four-movement sonata form. The first of these three quartets, in A minor, Op. 132, has five movements; the second, in B flat major, Op. 130, has six movements; and the third, in C sharp minor, Op. 131, has seven movements. Both Op. 127 and Op. 135 have the usual four-movement form. The middle three quartets are the greatest of the five and it is here that Beethoven the explorer is most clearly revealed. The reason why these quartets, particularly those in B flat major and C sharp minor, are not in sonata form, is made evident by their contents. The four-movement sonata form corresponds to a very fundamental and general psychological process, which is the reason why it is found so satisfactory and has been so often employed. The general scheme of a first movement, usually representing a conflict of some kind, followed by a meditative or consoling slow movement, and that by a section easing the way to a vigorous final statement, to the conclusion won, is, in its main lines, admirably adapted to exhibit an important and recurrent psychological process. The life-histories of many major psychological processes can be accommodated within this framework. But in the quartets we are discussing Beethoven's experience could not be presented in this form. The connection between the various movements is altogether more organic than that of the four-movement sonata form. In these quartets the movements radiate, as it were, from a central experience. They do not represent stages in a journey, each stage being independent and existing in its own right. They represent separate experiences, but the meaning they take on in the quartet is derived from their relation to a dominating, central experience. This is characteristic of the mystic vision, to which everything in the world appears unified in the light of one fundamental experience. In these quartets, then, Beethoven is not describing to us a spiritual history; he is presenting to us a vision of life. In each quartet many elements are surveyed, but from one central point of view. They are presented as apprehended by a special kind of awareness, they are seen in the light of one fundamental experience. It is not any kinship between the experiences described in the separate movements themselves, but the light in which they are seen, that gives to these works their profound homogeneity. Without this unity the quartets could only appear incoherent and capricious. And yet, although the unity possessed by these quartets is of this subtle kind, it is remarkable how generally it has been perceived. Although these quartets do not obey the usual criteria of coherence, they have been felt by nearly all musicians to be quite exceptionally organic. In both the B flat major and C sharp minor quartets Beethoven has given us, quite nakedly, the vision or experience from which the whole work proceeds. In the C sharp minor quartet this dominating experience is found in the fugue with which the work opens. In the B flat quartet it is found in the original last movement, the *Grosse Fuge,* now published separately as Op. 133.

The difference between these two quartets is profound. In the great fugue of the B flat quartet the experiences of life are seen as the conditions of creation and are accepted as such. The fugue has been called an expression of the reconciliation of freedom and necessity, or of assertion and submission, and the terms may pass since they suggest the state of consciousness that informs the fugue, a state in which the apparently opposing elements of life are seen as necessary and no longer in opposition. Beethoven had come to realize that his creative energy, which he at one time opposed to his destiny, in reality owed its very life to that destiny. It is not merely that he believed that the price was worth paying; he came to see it as necessary that a price should be paid. To be willing to suffer in order to create is one thing; to realize that one's creation necessitates one's suffering, that suffering is one of the greatest of God's gifts, is almost to reach a mystical solution of the problem of evil, a solution that it is probably for the good of the world that very few people will ever entertain. Yet, except in terms of this kind, we cannot represent to ourselves the spiritual content of the *Grosse Fuge.* The fugue opens with such an expression of unbridled energy and dominant will that it seems about to break the bounds of the string quartet. This vigorous, striving life is very different from the almost subhuman furious activity of the fugue of the Hammerclavier sonata, although it seems to promise an equally headlong course. But, with the entry of the opposing G flat major episode it changes its character. We become aware that a truly indescribable synthesis has been effected. There is no effect conveyed to us of anything being yielded up or sacrificed. Nevertheless, there is a change, a change that makes us conscious that opposites have been reconciled, although the fugue marches to its close in indestructible might. This fugue is certainly, as Bekker has rightly insisted, the crown and *raison d'être* of the whole B flat major quartet. The other movements of the quartet, although it would be incorrect to say that they point towards the fugue, find their resolution within it. For these movements are, regarded separately, quite amazingly various, and they are quite unrelated to one another. There is, in fact, no reason why there should not have been more of them, or why their order should not have been different. For they merely depict various aspects of experience, all of which find their true relation, their reason for existence, in the light of the culminating experience of the fugue. In the first movement Beethoven chooses the sonata form, for he has to present to us a familiar contrast, the joy and energy of creation springing from a substratum of sorrow and suffering. This, to him, was one of life's dominant characteristics, but how lightly he touches on it! This movement has something of that note of reminiscence, of remoteness, that becomes so familiar to us in the last quartets. The wonderful little Presto that follows is a hint, although a pretty broad hint, of that delight in purely musical fantasy that must have been one of Beethoven's compensations. The content of the Andante is less obvious, but the complete absence here of all "great effects," the purely daylight atmosphere and the loving care with which all the details are treated, suggests that Beethoven is here concerned with the norm of human life, that priceless existence that even he could, at times, share, where there are no great passions, no ecstasies, and no profound despairs. It is an agreeably diversified life and certainly to be envied; its greatest contrasts are never violent. The *alla danza tedesca* movement, which smiles through tears, is deservedly popular for its haunting embodiment of a very general human experience, an experience that Beethoven evidently thought important, and which he expresses with the most exquisite and unforgettable charm. But the Cavatina has the profoundest emotional content of all these movements. We have already said that the quality of its yearning is yearning for the unattainable, for that close human intimacy, that love and sympathy, that Beethoven never experienced. There is nothing reminiscent about this movement. Its poignancy is of an experience altogether living. The preceding movements all have the delicacy of reminiscence; the Cavatina has the reality of a contemporary experience. This is an experience which is carried alive into the apotheosis of the fugue, and, transformed, helps to give it its note of heroic passion. The fugue was found too long and difficult by contemporary performers and audiences, as it has been until quite recently by most performers and audiences. As a result of the protests aroused by this movement, Beethoven substituted for it the present finale, the last complete composition that he wrote. Its effect is to make the whole quartet purely "human." Its reckless joy, rising at moments to the point of ecstasy, suggests no transcendental imaginings. It does not belong to the same region of consciousness as the fugue. If it be regarded as having any kinship with that experience and therefore as being in some sort a proper culmination of the quartet, it can only have the sort of kinship that exists between an emotion and the thought that provokes that emotion. This state of dithyrambic joy may, as it were, be the emotional reaction to, the generally understandable indication of, the state of illumination reached in the fugue, but it is no substitute for it. It has been suggested that Beethoven's unexpected docility in yielding to the request of his publisher to substitute the present finale for the fugue was due to irony, and some have read irony into this last movement. But to Beethoven an excellent reason for writing a new finale was that he would get a few more ducats for doing so, and as for its effect on the quartet, there are indications that Beethoven, at this time, paid little attention to contemporary opinion, but had much more confidence in posterity. He knew exactly what he had done in the original version of this quartet and

OSWALD SPENGLER

photograph by Müller-Hilsdorf

LANGSTON HUGHES

photograph by Roy de Carava

he knew that the world would insist upon having it when it was ripe for it. In the meantime he bothered little about the lack of comprehension on the part of the musical amateurs of Vienna, and pocketed thankfully the extra ducats their insensibility brought him. For the rest he was willing to wait, for that his music would be a fructifying influence in a continually improving world he never had any doubt. Some years before he had written to a publisher, à propos of the Hammerclavier sonata, "Here is a sonata for you that will give the pianist something to do, and which will be played fifty years hence." He called it his greatest sonata, and he had spent immense pains on it. There is no question but that it existed in his mind as a perfectly organic unit. Yet at the same time he writes to Ries giving him *carte blanche* to leave out movements or to change their order if that will make the work more accessible to London audiences. That this indicates a certain lack of high expectations regarding the average "music lover" is pretty obvious but, considering that the quartet in B flat major is still never played in its original form, it is possible that he would have felt that very little higher demands could be made of that posterity he so much trusted.

The quartet in C sharp minor is the greatest of Beethoven's quartets, as he himself thought. It is also the most mystical of the quartets, and the one where the mystical vision is most perfectly sustained. It counts seven movements, but, regarded as an organic unity, it is the most complete of Beethoven's works. For the purposes of description, however, it is convenient to divide it into three parts. The opening fugue is the most superhuman piece of music that Beethoven has ever written. It is the completely unfaltering rendering into music of what we can only call the mystic vision. It has that serenity which, as Wagner said, speaking of these quartets, passes beyond beauty. Nowhere else in music are we made so aware, as here, of a state of consciousness surpassing our own, where our problems do not exist, and to which even our highest aspirations, those that we can formulate, provide no key. Those faint and troubling intimations we sometimes have of a vision different from and yet including our own, of a way of apprehending life, passionless, perfect and complete, that resolves all our discords, are here presented with the reality they had glimpsed. This impression of a superhuman knowledge, of a superhuman life being slowly frozen into shape, as it were, before our eyes, can be ambiguous. That passionless, remote calm can seem, as it did to Wagner, like a melancholy too profound for any tears. To Berlioz it was terrifying. To Beethoven himself it was the justification of, and the key to, life. In the light of this vision he surveys the world. That this vision was permanent with Beethoven is inconceivable. No men ever lived who could maintain such a state of illumination. This, we may be sure, is the last and greatest of Beethoven's spiritual discoveries, only to be grasped in the moments of his profoundest abstraction from the world. But it was sufficiently permanent to enable him to write the C sharp minor quartet in the light of it, a feat of concentration, of abstraction, of utter truthfulness, that is without equal. In the light of this experience we arrive, in the next movement, as a new-born creature in a new-born world. The virginal purity of this movement, its ethereal and crystalline quality, suggests to us a spirit not yet made flesh. After a brief introduction, which seems to usher in the act of incarnation, we find ourselves fully present in the warm, familiar human world. And yet how different it has become! The various aspects of experience that make up this human life, surveyed in the variations that follow, all have this different quality. They have the delicacy of shadows, but without their suggestion of impermanence. It is a transfigured world, where both our happiness and our prayers have become more pure and more simple. There is an indescribable lightness in this air; our bonds have become gossamer threads. And after floating through this outspread world we do, at that rapturous outbreak of trills in the last variation, rise up on wings and fly. And it is not only we, but all creation, that seems to be taking part in this exultant stirring. If ever a mystical vision of life has been presented in art it is here, in the sequence beginning with the fugue and ending with the last variation. It is this sequence, more than anything else in Beethoven's music, that convinces us that he had finally effected a synthesis of his whole experience. In these moments of illumination Beethoven had reached that state of consciousness that only the great mystics have ever reached, where there is no more discord. And in reaching it he retained the whole of his experience of life; he denied nothing. There follows an outbreak of the most exultant gaiety. There is no trace in the Scherzo of anything but the purest joy. Its most human quality is its humour, but humour so carefree and radiant is scarcely human. The adagio introduction to the finale has all the quality of a sorrowful awakening. It is as if the whole of the quartet preceding this movement had been a dream. But that, we are passionately convinced, cannot be true. The note of complete authenticity in that opening fugue cannot be mistaken. But it is certain that there is a withdrawal of the vision. It signifies, perhaps, a return from those heights on which no man may permanently live to this less real but more insistent world in which we are plunged in the last movement, a world where a heroism which is also pathetic marches to its end attended by yearning and pain. It may or it may not be of symbolic significance that Beethoven makes some use of the fugue theme in this last movement. But the character of the theme, as it occurs here, is entirely changed, and any symbolic significance it may have is not obvious.

Of the three great last quartets, the one in C sharp minor is the most unearthly and serene. The first of them, in A minor, is the least mystical and the one most full of human pain. It is, as a matter of historical fact, connected with a serious illness of Beethoven's and he himself wrote over the slow movement "Heiliger Dankgesang an die Gottheit eines Genesenen, in der lidischen Tonart." Acting on this hint the commentator A.-B. Marx sees in this quartet the description of a physical illness. This idea, as with so many apparently ridiculous "programmes" suggested by musical compositions, does, although inadequate, testify to certain genuine perceptions on the part of the commentator. The whole quartet may be taken as illustrating the normal aspect that life presented to the late Beethoven. Witness after witness testifies to the expression of profound sorrow that was habitual with him in the last years of his life, so that in mere contemplation of that dumb countenance the more emotional of them felt moved to tears. As we have said, we believe that in his most profound moments of insight and abstraction Beethoven was granted the solace of a more complete understanding. But such moments must have been comparatively rare, and could have occurred only in the midst of the artist's most profound isolation. We can well believe that no man ever saw the face of the transfigured Beethoven. But we believe that this man had suffered so greatly that the Beethoven men saw was the normal Beethoven of those days, poor, ill, stone-deaf, wretchedly housed, utterly alone, betrayed and abandoned by the one human being whose love he so desperately and pitifully craved. And from the depths of this man rose that solemn, pure and profound song of thanksgiving to the God-head. The yearning and the pain of the first movement (which ends, as only Beethoven would end, with what sounds like a startling and celestial trumpet call) is but little lightened in the second movement, where there reigns a spiritual weariness which is quite unmistakable. But again there comes that intimation of something celestial in an *alternativo* (that some writers find "curious" and others "humorous"!) where the first violin soars high over a pedal, and then comes the first moment of joy, real joy without any *arrière-pensé*, in the whole quartet. The first part is then repeated; the dominant mood is re-established. From this matrix rises the slow movement, the most heart-felt prayer from the most manly soul that has expressed itself in music. From this pure and sincere communion with his God there comes a quickened life, a rush of celestial joy, in the passage marked "Neue Kraft fühlend." The psychological resemblance between this transition and that in the second movement is obvious. Relief from pain, in this most pessimistic of Beethoven's quartets, comes only from above. Two main experiences form the texture of this quartet, exhaustion and defeat, and the new life bestowed as an act of grace from on high. With this "new strength" the next movement steps forth, but there is a wistfulness in its bravery. This is one of those movements, that occur only in the late Beethoven, where the very quality of the heroism reveals the heartache it is intended to conceal. This forlorn and lonely little march is marching to no victory. It is a gesture, brave but pathetic. With the *più allegro* section our forebodings are realized. Here is a shudder of realization, a resigned and hopeless cry, and we are again in the darkness of the struggle. Great waves of anguish seem to sweep over the struggling soul and at moments it seems that no resolution and faith can prevail against them. But a permanent strength, we may suppose, has come from those earlier celestial visions, from that pure and profound prayer, and the theme which before seemed to strive with difficulty against despair accelerates, until, in the final Presto, it rings out victoriously, but victor in a victory so hard-won that we are left with none of that feeling of exultant triumph with which we have watched so many of Beethoven's victories, but rather with a feeling of slightly incredulous relief, of thankfulness still tinged with doubt.

*   *   *

THERE SEEMS TO BE no reason to doubt that the great bulk of Beethoven's work is of permanent value. The greatest function of a work of art is to present us with a higher organization of experience. It is on this that its claim to "greatness" depends. It does not seem that the "greatness" and the "beauty" of a work of art are identical. What constitutes the beauty of a work of art is a hitherto unresolved problem with which, in this book, we are not concerned. That Beethoven's music is more beautiful than any other music we are not inclined to assert; that it is greater than any other music has been, on the whole, the general opinion ever since it appeared. Its greatness depends on what we have called its spiritual content, and this is something that the listener perceives directly, although he may be entirely unable to formulate it. Beethoven's work will live because of the permanent value, to the human race, of the experiences it communicates. These experiences are valuable because they are in the line of human development; they are experiences to which the race, in its evolutionary march, aspires. At a given period certain experiences may be current, and may be given popular artistic expression, which are not valuable. In our own day, for example, a certain nervous excitability and spiritual weariness, due to specific and essentially temporary causes, has informed a good deal of contemporary art. Small artists can flourish in an age which is not fit for heroes to live in. But such manifestations are of quite local importance. The great artist achieves a relative immortality because the experiences he deals with are as fundamental for humanity as are hunger, sex, and the succession of day and night. It does not follow that the experiences he communicates are elementary. They may belong to an order of consciousness that very few men have attained but, in that case, they must be in the line of human development; we must feel them as prophetic. Beethoven's late music communicates experiences that very few people can normally possess. But we value these experiences because we feel they are not freakish. They correspond to a spiritual synthesis which the race has not achieved but which, we may suppose, it is on the way to achieving. It is only the very greatest kind of artist who presents us with experiences that we recognize both as fundamental and as in advance of anything we have hitherto known. With such art we make contact, for a moment, with

The prophetic soul of the wide world
Dreaming on things to come.

It is to this kind of art that Beethoven's greatest music belongs and it is, perhaps, the greatest in that kind.

In Beethoven's earlier work we are dealing, for the most part, with experiences which are not only fundamental but universal. This is what is meant by some writers when they call this music more "objective" than his later work. The spiritual content of the most characteristic of Beethoven's "second period" work may be summed up as achievement through heroism in spite of suffering. This music is probably still what the bulk of listeners mean when they speak of Beethoven. To the majority of people suffering is still one of life's major characteristics, and it is that characteristic, more than any other, that determines our attitude towards life. The spiritual essence of life, as presented by Beethoven is, we feel, consistent with our deepest experiences, and the solution he presents is one consistent with our loftiest aspirations. This music has the note of authenticity. Its sorrow is real, and so is its heroism. The passionate reverence that so many thousands have felt for the author of this music (a phenomenon quite without parallel in the case of any other musician) is a testimony to the profundity, universality and genuineness of the experiences it communicates. No artist, more than Beethoven, has dealt with the things that most deeply concern mankind. And we can be encouraged and made hopeful by the solution he presents because he convinces us that he knows, in all their bitterness, the elements of the problem. What optimism this man preaches has, we feel, been earned. This attitude towards Beethoven is, and always has been, very general and, except on the basis of quite arbitrary theories about the meaninglessness of music, is perfectly justified. Beethoven could compose music "for the fun of it," but in all his greatest work he was concerned to make explicit, through the medium of his art, states of consciousness evoked by his profoundest experiences. For his ability to use his medium he would have to be ranked amongst the greatest composers; for the quality of what he expressed he is beyond comparison.

In Beethoven's personal history the attitude towards life characteristic of his "second period" was found to be insufficient. It is true that abandonment of the struggle, as preached by such a man as Schopenhauer, was never accepted by Beethoven. But it seems likely that he passed through a period when his resistance and endurance were attended by no hope. The fugue of the Hammerclavier sonata is informed with a most furious energy, but he would be a strange listener who should be inspired by it to anything that could be called courageous optimism. But in the ninth symphony we are aware that, although all the elements of the old problem are present, something new is being said. A synthesis has been achieved. Suffering no longer plays the part it did in the attitude of the young Beethoven. In listening to this symphony, and particularly its first and third movements, we have the feeling we have only with Beethoven's late music, that something hitherto unknown and yet that passionately matters to us, is being revealed. A new kind of awareness is

communicated to us. No elements of our experience are omitted, but the light in which they are presented transforms them. And in the last quartets it appears that quite new elements enter. The opening movement of the C sharp minor quartet seems to reveal an unsuspected possibility of the mind, to communicate to us a state of consciousness hardly analogous to anything we have previously experienced. Even the world of the ninth symphony contains nothing that so far surpasses the norm of human experience. Perhaps the only thing in Beethoven's music that would serve as a bridge to that unearthly experience is the last movement of the last pianoforte sonata. That great flight ends, we may suppose, on the threshold of the region from which the fugue proceeds.

It so happens that Beethoven's last complete work, the quartet in F major, Op. 135, makes a fitting end to his great series of explorations. It is the work of a man who is fundamentally at peace. It is the peace of a man who has known conflict, but whose conflicts are now reminiscent. This quality is most apparent in the last movement, with its motto "Muss es sein? Es muss sein!" According to Schindler this motto had its origin in a joke but, as used here, it is a summary of the great Beethovenian problem of destiny and submission. But Beethoven had found his solution of that problem, and he treats the old question here with the lightness, even the humour, of one to whom the issue is settled and familiar. There is no real conflict depicted in this last movement; the portentous question meets with a jovial, almost exultant answer, and the ending is one of perfect confidence. The question raised here is, indeed, seen in the light of the profound peace which dominates the slow movement of this quartet. If we may judge from this quartet, and also from Beethoven's actual last composition, the present finale of the B flat quartet, it would appear that at the end of his life the inner Beethoven, the Beethoven who expressed himself in music, was content.

The quartet in F, Op. 135, was finished at Gneixendorf ("the name sounds like the breaking of an axletree," said Beethoven), where Beethoven was staying during the late autumn of 1826 with his nephew in the house of his brother Johann. The purpose of this visit was to find a suitable asylum for the young man, who had recently left hospital after his attempt at suicide, until the time elapsed when he was due to join the army. The visit was not a success. Beethoven was morose and his nephew was irked by the restraints imposed upon him. From what we know of this visit it again becomes clear that Beethoven's music, at this time, proceeded in entire independence of the contemporary circumstances of his life. On December 2, Beethoven and his nephew returned to Vienna. Owing to exposure on the journey Beethoven arrived ill. A complication of diseases, amongst them dropsy, rapidly developed. The sick-room was appallingly dirty and uncared for, and the medical attention not very efficient. Beethoven was four times operated on for dropsy and then abandoned hope. Except for the bank shares, destined for his nephew, and which he therefore resolutely refused to sell, he had very little

money. He appealed for assistance to friends in England, and the Philharmonic Society responded by sending him one hundred pounds, a gift for which he was extremely grateful, but which he never lived to touch. Some of it was used afterwards to pay his funeral expenses. Otherwise, according to Schindler, he could not have been decently buried without selling one of the bank shares. During his illness Beethoven passed much of his time in reading Handel, whose complete works had been presented to him by Stumpff. He had a special liking for this composer. Indeed, he had said more than once that he placed Handel above all others. A reference to this reading, which also throws light on the attitude in which Beethoven awaited death, occurs in a letter by his physician, Dr. Wawruch, written after the fourth operation for dropsy.

> No words of comfort could brace him up, and when I promised him alleviation of his sufferings with the coming of the vitalizing weather of spring he answered with a smile, "My day's work is finished. If there were a physician could help me his name should be called Wonderful." This pathetic allusion to Handel's "Messiah" touched me so deeply that I had to confess its correctness to myself with profound emotion.

The end came some time after five o'clock on the afternoon of March 26, 1827. Beethoven had been unconscious for two days, and his death struggles were violent. His last moments are described by Hüttenbrenner, who, with Beethoven's sister-in-law, made one of the only two people present at the end. There had been a violent storm, and suddenly there was a lightning flash and a great crash of thunder. It seems to have aroused the dying man from his unconsciousness. He raised his clenched fist, opened his eyes and looked upwards for several seconds with a "very serious, threatening expression." As the hand dropped he fell back dead.

In this sketch of Beethoven's spiritual development we have regarded him chiefly as an explorer. What we may call his emotional nature was sensitive, discriminating, and profound, and his circumstances brought him an intimate acquaintance with the chief characteristics of life. His realization of the character of life was not hindered by insensitiveness, as was Wagner's, nor by religion, as was Bach's. There was nothing in this man, either natural or acquired, to blunt his perceptions. And he was not merely sensitive; he was not merely a reflecting mirror. His experiences took root and grew. An inner life of quite extraordinary intensity was in process of development till the very end. Other artists, of those few whose spirits were both sensitive and free, seem to have passed through similar stages of development. But perhaps even Shakespeare never reached that final stage of illumination that is expressed in some of Beethoven's late music. The other steps of the journey he knew, but Shakespeare never wrote his C sharp minor quartet. It is possible, indeed, that Beethoven's late music is unique, not only in music, but in the whole of art.

Although we have regarded Beethoven's music from its philosophic aspect, it is not for the purpose of deducing a philosophy from it. Beethoven's greatest music has meaning in the sense that it is not a mere pattern of sounds, but possesses a spiritual content; nevertheless, it does not in any sense express a philosophy. It expresses certain primary experiences as organized in the mind of this particular artist. But this organization of experience is utterly different from the organization of experience presented in a philosophy. It is an organization to which the criteria of logical coherence do not in the least apply. Beethoven's profoundest attitude towards life, as expressed in his music, owes nothing to the mediation of his intelligence. The synthesis of his experience that is achieved by a great artist proceeds according to laws of which we know almost nothing, but purely intellectual formulation plays a very small part in it. If Beethoven reached the state, as we believe he did, where he achieved the "submission" he felt to be so necessary, it was not through any process of reasoning. And his realization of the necessity of submission could not have been reached by any such process. As a crude analogy we may suggest that there are spiritual appetites, as there are bodily ones, necessary for development but which, like the sexual appetite, make their appearance only at a certain stage of growth. Comparatively few men, even amongst artists, manifest a true spiritual growth. Their attitude towards life is relatively fixed; it may be exemplified with more richness and subtlety as they mature, but it does not develop. Such a transition, as we find from Beethoven's "second" to his "third" period, where nothing is abandoned and yet where everything is changed, is extremely rare. Beethoven, therefore, although he preached no philosophy, is of philosophical importance because he adds one to the very few cases that exist of a genuine spiritual development. Such cases, it might be said, do nothing to help the development of mankind. Beethoven's music illustrates the development, but throws no light on the process by which it came about. But such revelations have a strangely haunting quality. We may be unable to earn for ourselves the capacity to utter the prayer of thanksgiving of the A minor quartet, or to reach the state of final serenity of the fugue of the C sharp minor quartet, but we can henceforth take but little account of attitudes towards life that leave no room for these experiences, attitudes which deny them or explain them away. And our conviction that these experiences are valuable, even to us, is reinforced by the whole bulk of Beethoven's work. If they stood alone these superhuman utterances might seem to us those of an oracle who was hardly a man. But we know, from the rest of his music, that Beethoven was a man who experienced all that we can experience, who suffered all that we can suffer. If, in the end, he seems to reach a state "above the battle" we also know that no man ever knew more bitterly what the battle is.

Miguel de Unamuno

THE MAN OF FLESH AND BONE

Homo sum; nihil humani a me alienum puto, said the Latin playwright. And I would rather say: *Nullum hominem a me alienum puto:* I am a man; no other man do I deem a stranger. For to me the adjective *humanus* is no less suspect than its abstract substantive *humanitas,* humanity. Neither the "human" nor "humanity," neither the simple adjective nor the substantivized adjective, but the concrete substantive—man. The man of flesh and bone; the man who is born, suffers, and dies—above all, who dies; the man who eats and drinks and plays and thinks and wills; the man who is seen and heard; the brother, the real brother.

For there is something else that is also called man, and he is the subject of many more or less scientific speculations. He is the legendary featherless biped, the ζῷον πολιτικόν of Aristotle, the social contractor of Rousseau, the *Homo economicus* of the Manchester school, the *Homo sapiens* of Linnaeus, or, if you like, the vertical mammal. A man neither of here nor there, neither of this age nor of another, who has neither sex nor country, who is, in brief, merely an idea. That is to say, a no-man.

Our man is the other man, the man of flesh and bone—I and you, my reader, and the other man over there, all of us who weigh upon the earth.

And this concrete man, this man of flesh and bone, is at once the subject and the supreme object of all philosophy, whether certain self-styled philosophers like it or not.

In most of the histories of philosophy that I know, philosophic systems are presented to us as if they grew out of one another and their authors, the philosophers, appear only as mere pretexts. The inward biography of the philosophers, of the men who philosophized, occupies a secondary place. And it is this, nevertheless, this inward biography, that explains most things to us.

It behoves us to say, before all, that philosophy lies closer to poetry than to science. All philosophic systems that have been constructed as a supreme concord of the final results of the individual sciences have in every age possessed much less consistency and less life than those which have expressed the integral desire of the spirit of their authors.

For the fact is that the sciences, important to us as they are and indeed indispensable for our life and thought, are in a certain sense more extraneous to us than philosophy. They fulfil a more objective end, that is to say, an end more external to ourselves. They are, at bottom, a matter of economics. A new scientific discovery, of the kind called theoretical, is like a mechanical discovery—that of the steam-engine, the telephone, the phonograph, or the aeroplane—a thing that is useful for something. Thus the telephone may be useful to us in enabling us to communicate at a distance with the woman we love. But she, what is she useful to us for? A man takes an electric tram to go to hear an opera and asks himself: Which is in this case more useful, the tram or the opera?

Philosophy answers to our need of forming a complete and unitary conception of the world and of life, and as a result of this conception, a feeling which gives birth to an inward attitude and even to an activity. But in fact this feeling, instead of being a consequence of this conception, is the cause of it. Our philosophy—that is, our mode of understanding or of not understanding the world and life—springs from our feeling towards life itself. And this, like everything affective, has subconscious, perhaps unconscious, roots.

It is not usually our ideas that make us optimists or pessimists, but it is our optimism or our pessimism, of physiological or perhaps pathological origin, as much the one as the other, that makes our ideas.

Man, they say, is a reasoning animal. I do not know why he has not been defined as an affective or feeling animal. Perhaps that which differentiates him from other animals is feeling rather than reason. More often I have seen a cat reason than laugh or weep. Perhaps it weeps or laughs inwardly—but then perhaps the crab also resolves equations of the second degree inwardly.

And thus in a philosopher what must most concern us is the man.

Man is an end, not a means. All civilization addresses itself to man, to each man, to each "I." What is this idol—call it Humanity or call it what you will—to which all men and each individual man must be sacrificed? For I sacrifice myself for my neighbours, for my fellow-countrymen, for my children, and these sacrifice themselves in their turn for theirs, and theirs again for those who come after them, and so on in a never-ending series of generations. And who receives the fruit of this sacrifice?

Those who talk to us about this fantastic sacrifice, this dedication without an object, are wont to talk to us also about the right to live. And what is this right to live? They tell me that I have come into the world to realize I know not what social end; but I feel that I, like each one of my fellows, am here to realize myself, to live.

Yes, yes, I see it all—an enormous social activity, a mighty civilization, an accumulation of science, of art, of industry, of morality, and afterwards, when we have filled the world with industrial marvels, with great factories, with roads, with museums, with libraries, we shall fall exhausted at the foot of it all, and it will endure—for whom? Was man made for science or was science made for man?

"Why," the reader will exclaim, "we are getting back to what the Catechism says: 'Q. For whom did God create the world? A. For man.'" Precisely—so ought the man who is a man to reply. The ant, if it took account of these matters and were a person, conscious of itself, would reply: "For the ant," and it would reply rightly. The world is made for consciousness, for each consciousness.

A human soul is worth all the universe, someone has said—I know not who, but it was excellently well said. A human soul, mind you! Not a human life. Not this life. And it is a fact that the less a man believes in the soul, that is to say, in his conscious immortality, personal and concrete, the more he will exaggerate the worth of this poor transitory life. Hence arises the effeminate sentimental feeling against war. True, a man ought not to wish to die, but it is the other, the eternal death, that he ought not to wish. "Whosoever will save his life shall lose it," says the Gospel; but it does not say "whosoever will save his soul," the immortal soul—the soul that we believe and wish to be immortal.

And all those definers of objectism do not realize, or rather do not wish to realize, that a man, in affirming his "I," his personal consciousness, affirms man, man concrete and real, affirms the true humanism—the humanism of man, not of the things of man—and in affirming man he affirms consciousness. For the only consciousness of which we have consciousness is that of man.

The world is for consciousness. Or rather this *for*, this notion of finality, and feeling rather than notion, this teleological feeling is born only where there is consciousness. Consciousness and finality are the same thing fundamentally.

If the sun possessed consciousness it would think, no doubt, that it lived in order to give light to the worlds; but it would also and above all think that the worlds existed in order that it might give them light and joy in giving them light and so live. And it would think well.

And all this tragic fight of man to save himself, this immortal craving for immortality which caused the man Kant to make that immortal leap[1] of which I have spoken, all this is simply a fight for consciousness.

[1] The leap from the "Critique of Pure Reason," in which he subjected the traditional proofs of the existence of God to a destructive analysis, to the "Critique

If consciousness is, as some inhuman thinker has said, nothing more than a flash of light between two eternities of darkness, then there is nothing more execrable than existence.

It is possible that someone will discover that everything that I am saying rests upon a contradiction, since sometimes I express a longing for immortality and at other times I say that this life does not possess the value that is attributed to it. Contradiction? To be sure! The contradiction of my heart that says Yes and of my head that says No. Of course there is contradiction. Who does not recollect those words of the Gospel: "Lord, I believe, help thou my unbelief"? Contradiction? Of course! For we only live upon contradictions and by them; life is tragedy, and the tragedy is perpetual struggle, without victory or the hope of victory; life is contradiction.

It is question, as you see, of an affective value, and against affective values reasons do not avail. For reasons are nothing more than reasons, that is to say, they are not even truths. There are definition-mongers—pedants by nature and by grace—who produce an effect upon me like that of a man who consoles a father for the loss of a son, dead in the prime of his life, by saying: "Patience, friend, we all must die." Would you think it strange if this father were irritated by such an ineptitude? For it is an ineptitude. How often may it not be said—

> *para penser cual tú, sólo es preciso*
> *no tener nada más que inteligencia?*[2]

There are, in fact, people who appear to think only with the brain or with whatever other organ may be the specific organ for thinking; while others think with the whole body and with the whole soul, with the blood, with the marrow of the bones, with the heart, with the lungs, with the belly, with the life. And the people who think only with the brain become definition-mongers; they become the professionals of thought. And you know what a professional is. . . .

If a philosopher is not a man, he is anything rather than a philosopher; he is, above all, a pedant, that is to say, a caricature of a man. The cultivation of any science—of chemistry, of physics, of geometry, of philology—may be, though within very narrow limits and restrictions, a work of differentiated specialization; but philosophy, like poetry, is either a work of integration and harmony or else it is mere philosophism, pseudo-philosophical erudition.

All knowledge has an ultimate object. Knowing for the sake of knowing is, say what you will, nothing but a solemn begging of the question. We learn a thing either for an immediate practical end, or in order to complete the rest of our knowledge. Even the ideas that appear

---

of Practical Reason," in which he reconstructed God, but the God of the conscience, the Author of the moral order. [*Trans.*]

[2] To think as you think, all that is necessary is to possess nothing more than intelligence. [*Trans.*]

to us most theoretical—that is to say, of least immediate application to the non-intellectual necessities of life—answer to an intellectual necessity, which is also a real necessity, to a principle of unity and continuity of consciousness. But just as scientific knowledge has its finality in the rest of our knowledge, the philosophy which we may be forced to choose has another extrinsic finality—it refers to our whole destiny, to our attitude towards life and the universe. And the most tragic problem of philosophy is that of reconciling intellectual necessities of the heart and the will. For it is just here that every philosophy that claims to resolve the eternal and tragic contradiction that is the very basis of our existence breaks down. But do all men confront this contradiction?

Little can he hoped for from a ruler, for example, who has not been preoccupied at some time or other, even if only in some dim way, with the first beginning and ultimate end of all things, and, above all, of men, with their first "why" and their ultimate "wherefore."

And this supreme preoccupation cannot be purely rational, it must be affective. It is not enough to think about our destiny, it must be felt. And the would-be leader of men who says and proclaims that he pays no heed to the things of the spirit, does not deserve to lead them. Which does not mean, of course, that any determinate solution is to be required of him. Solution? Is there, indeed, any?

For my part, I will never willingly yield myself, nor entrust my confidence, to any popular leader who has not a real conviction that the leader of a people is a leader of men—men of flesh and bone; men who are born, suffer, and, although they may not wish to die, die; men who are ends in themselves, not merely means; men who have to be themselves and not others; men, in short, who seek that which we call happiness. It is inhuman, for example, to sacrifice one generation of men to the generation following when there is no regard for the destiny of those sacrificed—not merely for their memory, for their names, but for themselves.

All this idea that a man lives in his children, or in his works, or in the universe, is but vague verbiage which satisfies only those who suffer from affective stupidity and who may, for the rest, be persons of a certain cerebral distinction. For it is possible to possess a great talent or what we call great talent, and yet to be stupid as far as the feelings are concerned, and even morally imbecile. There have been instances.

Those who are mentally talented and affectively stupid usually say that it is useless to seek to delve into the unknowable or to kick against the pricks. It is as if one should say to a man whose leg has been amputated that it is useless to think about it. And we all lack something; only some of us feel it and others do not. Or they pretend not to feel it, and then they are hypocrites.

There is something which, for want of a better name, we will call the tragic sense of life, which carries with it a whole conception of life itself and of the universe, a whole philosophy, more or less formulated, more or less conscious. And this sense may be possessed, and is possessed, not only by individual men but by whole peoples. And this sense does not flow from ideas but rather determines them, although afterwards, of course, these ideas react upon the sense and confirm it. Sometimes this sense may proceed from a casual illness—from dyspepsia, for example—but at other times it is constitutional. And it is useless to speak of men who are healthy and men who are unhealthy. Apart from there being no normal standard of health, nobody has proved that man is necessarily cheerful by nature. And, further, man, by the very fact of being man, of possessing consciousness, is, when compared with the ass or the crab, already a diseased animal. Consciousness is a disease.

Among men of flesh and bone there have been typical examples of those who possess the tragic sense of life. I recall now Marcus Aurelius, St. Augustine, Pascal, Rousseau, *René*, *Obermann*, Thomson,[3] Leopardi, Vigny, Lenau, Kleist, Amiel, Quental, Kierkegaard—men laden with wisdom rather than with knowledge.

And there are, I believe, also peoples who possess this tragic sense of life.

[3] James Thomson, author of "The City of Dreadful Night." [*Trans.*]

Joseph Wechsberg

THE FORMIDABLE MONSIEUR POINT

I always try to make every meal une petite merveille.

FERNAND POINT

I SHALL NEVER FORGET my first lunch at Fernand Point's Restaurant de la Pyramide in Vienne. That was a few years ago; the war was over, and France was slowly getting back to peacetime abnormalcy. My Parisian friends had stopped griping about the black market and rationing and were again discussing, passionately and at great length, the heady mysteries of *la grande cuisine*, which, next to women, has always been their favorite topic of conversation in times of content. My friends were "serious eaters"; they loved truly good food and scorned the snobbism of self-appointed "gourmets" and one-dish amateur cooks. They didn't consider themselves gourmets, but they would confide to each other, with the air of brokers divulging something hot in the market, the addresses of good restaurants.

The finest restaurant in France, and perhaps anywhere, it was agreed by my well-informed friends, was not in Paris. If I wanted to have the epicurean experience of my life, they assured me, I would have to go to Vienne, a town of twenty-three thousand inhabitants in the department of Isère, seventeen miles south of Lyon, at the confluence of the Rhône and Gère rivers. There I would find the Restaurant de la Pyramide and its proprietor, the great, the formidable, the one and only M. Point.

"Ah, Fernand Point!" said one of my French friends with a deep, reverent sigh. "The greatest epicures in France and Navarre sing his praises.

From *Blue Trout and Black Truffles*, 1953. Copyright 1951, 1953 by Joseph Wechsberg.

He's been given the highest eulogies by the gastronomic guide-books. France's most famous chefs call Point 'the King.' His *gratin d'écrevisses* is true perfection. And I once had a *volaille en vessie* there that . . ."

"Point's hors-d'œuvres alone are worth a trip to Vienne from anywhere in the world," someone else said. "He calls them hors-d'œuvres but they are a meal in themselves—and what a meal! There is a *pâté de lièvre chaud . . .*"

"Last year at Point's I had the best lunch I've had since Escoffier left the Ritz," a third friend told me matter-of-factly. This friend was a man of seventy-four years and three hundred and twenty pounds, and he had spent most of the former in increasing the latter with good food. "In short, you must go to Point's restaurant."

I objected mildly that I wasn't too much interested in the "show places" of *la grande cuisine*. France's restaurants are, by and large, the best in the world, I said, and I could see no reason for patronizing fancy establishments when there is such an astonishing number of small restaurants all over the country where one can get a delicious omelet, a succulent *blanquette de veau*, a fine Brie, and a bottle of honest *vin du pays* for the equivalent of a dollar and a half.

"Ah, but Point's restaurant is not a show place," my wise old friend said. "It is a temple for gastronomes who know that *la grande cuisine* must be well orchestrated, that it must be surrounded by careful details, ranging from the temperature of the dining-room to that of the wines, from the thinness of the pastry shells to that of the glasses, from the color of the fruits to that of—"

"All right," I said, "I'll go."

"But it's not a question of whether or not you will *go*," my friend said. "The question is, will Monsieur Point let you eat in his place? He has thrown out American millionaires and French ex-ministers when he didn't feel like serving them. Only last week a friend of mine called Monsieur Point long-distance and asked him to reserve a table for the next day. That, of course, was a mistake, because Monsieur Point usually insists on being notified at least three days beforehand. My friend gave his name—a *very* important name in French politics, I assure you. Ha! Monsieur Point pretended to be totally unimpressed and kept saying: 'Would you mind repeating the name?' Before long my friend had lost his celebrated poise and could only mumble that he was being recommended by the Aga Khan. And what do you think Monsieur Point said to that? He said: 'And who is the Aga Khan, if I may ask?' "

My friend chuckled. "But I think I can help you out with an introduction. I have a British friend, Monsieur Piperno, who happened to be among the Allied troops that liberated Vienne, and I'll have him give you a letter that will open all doors to you. Any friend of Monsieur Piperno's is treated royally at Point's. But be sure to call Monsieur Point well in advance to reserve your table. And, for heaven's sake, don't think of ordering your meal! You don't order at Point's. *He* tells *you* what to eat."

A few days later I received a note from my friend enclosing an amiable letter of introduction from a Mr. T. H. Piperno, and decided to put in a person-to-person call to M. Point without delay to reserve a table for lunch some day the following week. Finally, after some misunderstandings involving Point's name, my name, and the name of a girl, Denise something, who had a lovely way of yawning and seemed to be the long-distance operator in Vienne, I got hold of a man with a high, querulous voice who said yes, he was Point, and there were no tables available for the next week—or the next two weeks, for that matter.

I quickly said that I was a friend of Mr. Piperno's.

M. Point's voice abruptly dropped several notes as he said: "Oh!" Then he precipitately told me that I might come any day I liked, absolutely, it would be a pleasure, and how about tomorrow? And in whose name should the table be reserved?

I began to spell out my name, but M. Point must have got restless, because he said not to bother with the name—there would be a table. He hung up forthwith, without a good-by.

My friends in Paris had urged me to prepare myself for my monumental lunch by eating only extremely light food, and very little of it, during the preceding twenty-four hours, and I was hungry and cross when my overnight train pulled into Vienne early the following morning. A gentle rain was misting down upon the green trees of the town's miniature boulevards and blurring the outlines of the narrow, gray streets bordered by old, grimy houses and small, dark shops. I set out for the near-by Grand Hôtel du Nord, where, again on the advice of my friends, I had engaged a room.

"You'd better plan to spend the night," they had said. "No use trying to rush away. You have to relax after a meal at Point's."

There were only a few people on the street—pale, stockingless girls who were carrying small lunch boxes, and shabbily dressed men who looked as though they surely had never lunched or dined at Point's.

The Grand Hôtel du Nord, despite its name, was an unassuming establishment that did not indulge in such extravagances as elevators, a bathroom on every floor, and warm water after nine in the morning, but my room was clean and the comforter on my bed was filled with eiderdown. I had a pleasant view of two sides of a square—on one flank the town museum, on the other the Café du Commerce et des Voyageurs and its clients, all of them, I was sure, busy in lively discussions of politics, soccer, and the high cost of living. I washed up, read a newspaper I had bought at the station (politics, soccer, and the high cost of living), and finished my interrupted sleep.

When I awoke, it was getting on toward twelve o'clock, and nearly time for me to present myself at the Restaurant de la Pyramide. As I stepped into the street, I was stopped by a young man wearing a raincoat and a beret and carrying a pipe. He smiled at me like a Fuller Brush man, asked my pardon for his presumption, and informed me that he was Jean Lecutiez, an archæologist who had been sent to Vienne by the Ministry of National Education to dig up the ruins of the houses, temples, aqueducts, baths, and assorted monuments that the Romans left there two thousand years ago.

"I happened to be visiting my friend the desk clerk of your hotel as you came in, and I saw on the registration blotter that you were a writer," M. Lecutiez said. "Right away I told myself that I would make it my business to take you around."

I tried to protest, but he said: "Oh, don't worry—no bother at all. My two colleagues will carry on with the work. There are three of us archæologists here—a very old man, *un homme mûr* (a mature man), and myself."

M. Lecutiez prodded me energetically with the stem of his pipe. "You must realize, monsieur, that Vienne, the old Vienna Allobrogum, was the capital of the Allobroges in the first century B.C. Julius Cæsar established a colony here. Later the Romans went up north and founded Lugdunum, which eventually became Lyon. Naturally, the people in Lyon don't like to hear this, but it's true—"

"I'm sorry," I said. "That's wonderfully interesting, but I have a luncheon engagement at—"

M. Lecutiez ignored this interruption.

"Vienne, like Rome, is built around seven hills," he went on as he grasped my arm and relentlessly walked me away. "They are Levau, Mont Salomon, Mont Arnaud, Mont Pipet, Sainte-Blandine, Coupe Jarret, and Mont Saint-Just. I'll take you up on every one of them. Now, this afternoon we're going to start with—"

"It's almost lunch-time," I said. "How about an apéritif? Then I'll really have to run for my appointment."

"Thank you, I never drink," he said. "Would you like to see the pyramid?"

"Ah," I said. "That's exactly where I'm going. I'm lunching at Point's."

"The restaurant, *je m'en fiche*," said M. Lecutiez. "I mean the real pyramid, which for hundreds of years was commonly, and erroneously, thought to be the grave of Pontius Pilate. There is nothing like it anywhere. Come, it's no distance at all."

As we crossed the street, a wild bicyclist almost ran us down, but M. Lecutiez seemed not to notice.

"It was the great French architect Delorme who first stated that the pyramid dates from the fourth century and was the domed center of the *spina*, a longitudinal center wall, of a Roman circus, where chariot races were held. Now we turn here, and *voilà!*"

There before us, an island in the middle of the street, was the pyramid, a monument, perhaps fifty feet high, that looks like a giant metronome. Its square base is pierced by four arches. The thoroughfare it stands in is one of the drab, deserted side streets that one sees in so many small French towns.

"Excavations undertaken in 1854 by Constant Dufeu proved De-lorme completely right," M. Lecutiez went on, hardly pausing for breath. "We are indeed standing in the middle of what was once a vast Roman circus. It was a big arena, fifteen hundred feet long and . . ."

On the other side of the street, set in a ten-foot wall, was a gate, and beside it a black marble plate inscribed in red letters: "F. Point, Restau-rateur."

". . . and the chariots must have come from over there," M. Lecutiez was saying, pointing up the street. "They would pass right where we're standing, and then—"

"It's been a very instructive talk," I broke in, "and I am most grateful to you, but I must really go."

M. Lecutiez looked at me with a hurt expression, but I walked firmly across the street toward the gate in the wall. On the left the wall con-nected with a decrepit three-story building that looked as if it should have been condemned long before the Renaissance; on the right it joined a house that was considerably newer but was rather inconspicuous and in need of a coat of paint.

The rain had stopped and the sun had come out, but even under these favorable conditions the exterior of M. Point's temple for gas-tronomes presented a modest, unprepossessing appearance. Then I walked through the gate and found myself suddenly, without any transition, in another world.

I was in a lovely garden with clean gravel paths, green lawns, beds of flowers, and a terrace shaded by old maples and chestnuts, and covered with white tables and wicker chairs still wet from the rain. The courtyard walls of the building that I had thought should have been condemned were completely cloaked with ivy, which blended admirably with the beautifully landscaped grounds. To my right was a two-story house—the one that from the front I had thought was rather incon-spicuous and in need of a coat of paint. Its garden side was immaculate. The frames of its wide windows were freshly painted, and the whole building looked as clean and spruce as a Dutch sugar house.

I walked up three steps, scuffed my shoes on a mat, opened the big door, and entered the hall of what seemed to be a handsome country residence. On the wall were paintings and an old print of the pyramid bearing the caption: "*Un Monument Antique, Vulgairement Appelé le Tombeau de Pilate.*"

A man in a white jacket approached from the rear of the house, greeted me cheerfully, and took my raincoat and hung it on a hanger in the hall, as is the custom in French homes. This feeling of being in a home never left me while I was at Point's. I was ushered into a small, pleasantly furnished salon. The walls were hung with paintings and mirrors, a gold pendulum clock stood on a buffet, and a large glass-topped table sat in the middle of the room. On the table were champagne glasses and a half-empty magnum of champagne, and behind it was standing a huge man.

He must have been six feet three and weighed three hundred pounds. He had a longish, sad face, a vast double chin, a high forehead, dark hair, and melancholy eyes. I couldn't help thinking that one of M. Lecutiez's sybaritic Roman emperors had come to life. He wore a comfortably large suit and a big bow tie of black silk ornamented with a flowery design, like those the eccentric citizens of Montparnasse and flamboyant Italian tenors wore in the old days.

I introduced myself and we shook hands. I gave him Mr. Piperno's letter.

M. Point read it casually and shook hands with me again.

"Sit down!" he commanded with a magnificent gesture. "For the next few hours this house will be your home. I'm delighted you came early. Gives us a chance to talk and drink champagne. Quiet, Véronique!"

On a chair beside him a precisely clipped brown poodle was making hostile noises.

"Véronique belongs to the family," he said. "We also have a daughter, Marie-Josette. *Enfin!*" He filled two of the champagne glasses and said: "*A votre santé!*"

We drank.

"I like to start off my day with a glass of champagne," M. Point said. "I like to wind it up with champagne, too. To be frank, I also like a glass or two in between. It may not be the universal medicine for every disease, as my friends the champagne people in Reims and Épernay so often tell me, but it does you less harm than any other liquid. Pierre—our *sommelier*—and Madame Point and I go to the champagne district every year to buy. And, of course, to Burgundy, too. Last week we visited a great friend, the Marquise de la Tourette, the proprietor of one of the great Hermitage vineyards."

M. Point filled the glasses again. "*Ah, quelle grande dame!* She won't sell her wines in the commercial market. You have to be her friend, and you must literally force her into selling the stuff. She is over eighty, and every day she walks from her château to the church and back. Permit me to drink the health of the Marquise de la Tourette!"

While we were solemnly drinking the health of the Marquise, a man wearing a beret and the light-blue overalls and apron that are the uniform of France's winegrowers and *sommeliers* came in. He had a shriveled face that looked as though it had been chiseled out of a piece of seasoned wood.

"Ah, Pierre," said M. Point. "Monsieur, this is Pierre Chauvon, our *sommelier* and great connoisseur of that ever new miracle, wine."

The old man scratched his head under his beret with his left hand as he gave me his right.

"*Allons, allons, chef!*" he said, embarrassed but quite pleased. "You know a lot about wines yourself, and Madame Point knows even more. I assure you, monsieur," he said to me, "Madame is *épatante*. She is *très, très forte*. When we go to the vineyards and taste the wines, the wine-growers always look at her first. She's better than I am, and I certainly know my business."

He smiled, revealing a few side teeth and almost none in the front.

"Unfortunately, Madame always gets hungry around noon, and once you've eaten, your taste and judgment aren't reliable any more. I don't eat when we're out. Mustn't make a mistake, *chef, hein?*"

"Everybody calls me *chef* here," M. Point explained to me. "Never *patron*. They just won't forget that I used to be my own chef in the kitchen. Now I merely supervise things there, and my wife takes care of the clients in the dining-room. Well, Pierre, why don't we show our friend the cellar? Nothing to be ashamed of, is it?"

M. Point led the way out into the hall, through the kitchen, around a few corners, and down a stairway into a big, brightly lighted wine cellar with earthen walls. It was cool, and the dirt floor was as clean as much sweeping could make it. All along the walls were shelves on which bottles were stacked horizontally. Tacked to the lower left-hand corner of each shelf was a small label giving the place of origin and the vintage of the wine. In the center of the room was a table covered with baskets of fresh fruit—enormous pears, Calville apples, lush peaches, and aromatic *fraises de bois*, wild strawberries.

A roster of the wines in the cellar hung on one wall. It listed two hundred and nineteen names, in four columns. I remembered an article by one of France's leading wine experts which had called Point's cellar "incontestably the first in France." Glancing at random down the second column, I saw Richebourg '42, Romanée-Conti '35, Corton-Charlemagne '38, Les Grands-Échézeaux '42, Hermitage '98, Romanée-Conti '43, La Tache '43, Hermitage la Cour Blanche '06, Clos Vougeot '37, Vosne-Romanée '93, Corton-Charlemagne '42, La Tache '37, Romanée-Saint-Vivant '40, Pouilly '40, Montrachet '29, Richebourg '29, Chambolle-Musigny '21, Hermitage Blanc '70, Marc de Bourgogne '29, and Vire Chapitre '26. Among the Bordeaux was a Château Haut-Brion 1900, magnums of Château Lafite '69, Château Cos d'Estournel '07, and many, many others.

"What a mess!" said M. Point, waving his hands wildly at the chart. "We've always mixed them up—don't know why. Anyway, it's not a bad selection. We have all the great years of Château d'Yquem, back to 1874, and a lot of the fine years of Château Margaux and Château Lafite-Rothschild. You can see we're crowded in here. I had to rent a place down the street for Pierre to keep his champagnes in."

He pointed to a section of the shelves at my right.

"How do you like our cognacs?" he said.

They were impressive—cobweb-covered bottles of eighty-year-old

Otard and *hors-d'âge* Camus, along with batteries of gin, Scotch, apéritifs, and liqueurs.

M. Point slapped his stomach. "Before the war I refused to serve cocktails. Now they bring their own bottles if I don't serve them. My God, after a couple of those concoctions your palate can't distinguish an 1899 Château Margaux from 1949 fountain-pen ink! What's that you have, Pierre?"

The *sommelier* was examining a small bottle of the sort in which winegrowers send samples to merchants and restaurateurs. "The new Moulin-à-Vent," he said.

"We buy many wines by the barrel—*la pièce*," M. Point said, "and Pierre 'works' the wine, draining it from one barrel into another three times a year. The dregs remain in the old barrel. Pierre knows what he's doing. He wouldn't make a *soutirage*—as the process is called—while a south wind is blowing. The wind must be from the north. Right, Pierre?"

"*Bien sûr, chef.* I make three *soutirages* a year—in January, March, and September. Each barrel of Burgundy contains two hundred and twenty-five liters, and each barrel of Beaujolais two hundred and eighteen liters. When the wine is ready, I bottle it myself in my workroom. I've always done it. Had my own *bistro* in Lyon and would go to Burgundy three times a year to buy wines. Those were nice times, before my wife—"

He stopped and scratched his chin. "Ah, why warm up those old stories? I'm happy here now. I'm sixty-seven, and I hope to stay here until I die."

"*Allons, allons,* Pierre!" M. Point cried, and his high-pitched voice almost cracked. "What kind of talk is that? Go on, tell me how the wine is."

Pierre uncorked the sample bottle and took a big mouthful of the wine. He let it roll over and under his tongue, closed his eyes, and made a gargling sound. Then he spat on the floor.

"It'll be all right in three years," he said with authority.

"Good!" M. Point took my arm. "Let's go up to the kitchen and give some thought to your lunch."

The kitchen was large and cheery, with a white-tiled floor and walls. Copper pots hung from hooks on the ceiling, and silver trays were stacked on broad white tables. The ranges and slicing machines were so highly polished that they looked brand-new. M. Point told me that coal was used to cook everything except pastry, which was baked in an electric oven. At the rear of the kitchen were four refrigerators. Through their glass doors I could see hors-d'œuvres and butter in the first, rows of dressed chickens in the second, fillets of beef and veal tenderloin in the third, and potatoes, bunches of white asparagus, and other vegetables in the fourth.

The room was a busy place. Cooks and apprentices were washing vegetables, cutting meat, mixing sauces, and doing various other chores, but there was a total absence of haste or nervousness.

An elegant gray-haired man in a spotless chef's outfit joined us and was introduced to me as M. Paul Mercier, the *chef de cuisine.* "Do you like chicken, monsieur?" he asked me. He picked one up from a table. "All of ours come from the region of Bresse. Each is tagged with a silver label and a serial number. We store them in the refrigerator for four or five days after getting them, but we don't freeze them. They do a lot of freezing in America, don't they?"

"Malheureux, malheureux!" M. Point exclaimed, clasping his hands in deep unhappiness. "Of course they do a lot of freezing. It's such a hot country they have to, I am told. But you can't expect to get a good piece of chicken from a freezer. Here we keep everything just above the freezing point."

As he talked, his eyes roved over the kitchen, taking note of every bit of activity. "The main thing about cooking is to see that only the very best ingredients are used, and used as they should be. When you are interested in *la grande cuisine,* you can't think of money or you are licked from the start. Some well-known restaurants are run by men who are maîtres d'hôtel, not chefs. *Malheureux!* A maître d'hôtel wants to make money. A chef also wants to make money—but, above all, he wants to cook well. You must never be afraid of extra work. We have a man here who does nothing all day but press trout *mousse* through fine sieves —three or four times if necessary. And you have to go out yourself and get the ingredients. At six o'clock this morning Monsieur Mercier himself went to Lyon to buy the very freshest strawberries and asparagus he could find in the markets. And butter, naturally. How can anybody expect to cook well without using the finest butter? *Du beurre, du beurre, du beurre,* I keep telling my men—that's the secret of good cooking. The finest butter and lots of time."

I noticed that the bustle in the kitchen had subsided and that most of the undercooks were listening to M. Point with hushed attention.

M. Point solemnly raised his right hand and proclaimed: *"La grande cuisine* doesn't wait for the client. It is the client who must wait for *la grande cuisine."*

He stopped and looked around the kitchen.

"Allons, mes enfants!" he said, clapping his hands. "Let us go back to work."

These days, M. Point said to me, he rarely does any cooking himself, but his people work as well together as the members of the Boston Symphony. M. Point would arrive at the kitchen every morning before seven. He would spend several hours there, brooding, trying, tasting, mixing, experimenting, inventing. Unlike all other good chefs in France, M. Point is not satisfied merely to reproduce or improve the classic dishes of French cuisine. He belongs to the select, small group of kitchen immortals—like the great Carême, Montagné, and Escoffier—who *created* new dishes.

"*Je cherche, je cherche toujours,*" he said to me with a sigh. "I am always searching."

He ushered me through a doorway and took me into a small courtyard. "I want to show you our aquarium," he said.

The aquarium consisted of two square tanks. In one I saw a couple of dozen brook trout swimming around, and in the other a number of crayfish. The water in each tank was kept fresh by a flowing faucet.

M. Mercier joined us. "Are we going to serve Monsieur a trout?" he asked. "*Au bleu,* perhaps?"

"I haven't decided yet," M. Point said.

He turned to me. "So often our clients ask for what they call difficult things, with long and fancy names. People don't know that the most difficult and also the best dishes are the simple ones. What did you cook for your family on your last day off, Paul?"

"A *choucroute,*" M. Mercier said.

"There you are. Here is a great chef, who can cook a chicken in champagne with truffles the like of which has never before been tasted, and what does he cook for himself at home? A *choucroute*—cabbage, delicious soft ham, Alsatian sausage, and very young potatoes—and what could be better?"

He swallowed. I found myself swallowing too. My stomach was gnawing.

"But it takes experience," he said. "What looks easier than to make a *sauce béarnaise?* Butter, egg yolks, chopped shallots—nothing to it, is there? But years of practice are needed before you can do it right. Forget to watch for a single instant and it's gone, finished, lost. Everybody thinks he can fry eggs, and I suppose anybody can, but to fry them so they are soft and mellow throughout, not burned on the bottom and raw on top—*that* is art, my friend. Isn't that right, Paul?"

"Absolutely," said M. Mercier.

"Absolutely. Now, monsieur, let us return to the salon and think seriously about your lunch."

In the hall we encountered a slim, middle-aged woman, charming and well dressed. She was carrying an order pad under her arm. M. Point introduced me to his wife, Marie-Louise. "Our friends call her Mado," he said. "Our friends think I would be broke if it were not for Mado." His eyes were soft, and tender.

The financial operations of the House of Point have always mystified his friends, since he uses only the finest, costliest ingredients, yet charges prices lower than those of most high-class restaurants in Paris. His friends agree that Point might have gone bankrupt long ago but for his wife. "Mado" Point is one of those storybook wives—charming, elegant, efficient, always smiling, always ready to cheer up her husband. She acts as maître d'hôtel, purchasing agent, wine-taster, cashier, house physician, confidential secretary, and chronicler. Someday, she hopes, she will collect her husband's recipes and put them in a book for posterity's sake. This won't be easy. M. Point takes a dim view of the printed word and keeps "the elements" of his creations in his head, where they are no good to anyone else. Once he watched a new member of his kitchen staff for six months before he decided to confide to him the elements of an important recipe.

Mme Point smiled at me and whispered into M. Point's ear.

"Madame *who?*" he said. "No, no. Tell her we have no table. I don't want her. She smokes before dessert. The last time she was here she even smoked after the hors-d'œuvres."

He escorted me into his salon. The magnum was empty, and he called loudly for another. It was quickly brought in an ice bucket by a frightened young waiter. M. Point watched the youth sternly as he worked out the cork and stopped the flow of foam by pressing a silver spoon over the mouth of the bottle.

"A little trick," M. Point said. "Metal will stop the flow. Don't pour yet, Marcel. Always leave the bottle open in the ice bucket for a few minutes."

He gave a sad shrug and said the silly doctors objected to his drinking too much champagne.

"My legs hurt me," he said. "They claim I have water in my knees. Ignorants! How can it be water when I drink only champagne?"

M. Point was always on the lookout for fine champagne. Sometimes he would drink the private *cuvées* of the owners of the great champagne firms; but he is a discoverer at heart and enthusiastically propagates a small house that produces a good blend. Nothing would please him more than to find an airy *Cramant blanc de blancs,* so light that it seemed only bubbles and bouquet. He loves the honest *vin du pays* of the near-by Condrieu and Juliénas regions. He loves a glass of Beaujolais with his meal.

A drop of champagne had spilled on the tabletop, and the waiter, before leaving, carefully wiped it away with his napkin.

M. Point nodded in approval. "So many otherwise good restaurants in France don't teach their personnel the importance of the attention to detail that makes for flawless service," he said.

I saw Mme Point greeting four guests, and a waiter or two scurrying by in the hall. In a minute a boy in a white apron put his head in the door and said that a M. Godet was calling from Lyon about a reservation, and would M. Point—

For some reason this seemed to infuriate M. Point. He shooed the boy away, went to the door, and announced down the hall in a loud voice that he was about to have a glass of champagne and that he would be grateful if the world would leave him in peace for a few minutes. Then he shut the door, came back, and sat down.

"Too many people," he said. "Vienne is halfway between Paris and the Riviera, and everybody wants to stop over to break the monotony of

the trip. Not many Vienne people come here; most of my clients are
from the outside world. It's been that way ever since I opened the restaurant, twenty-nine years ago, when I was twenty-six years old."

He poured us each a glass of champagne and looked thoughtfully
into his.

"I was born near here, and I always wanted to cook. My father was a
chef. A very good chef. He made me start from the beginning—washing
dishes, waiting on tables, peeling potatoes. It's quite important to peel
them right, believe me. Then I learned to cook vegetables and make soups
and things like that, and after that I went to Paris. Remember Foyot's?
Ah, they had a great *saucier!* He taught me a lot. And for a long time I
worked at the Hôtel Bristol. I came back home in 1923 and bought this
place with my savings. It was just a shack and a few trees then. In time
Father and I added the second floor and a new kitchen, the wine cellar,
and the terrace. We had the garden landscaped and bought the adjoining
lot. Father died a few years ago. All this time I was doing the cuisine
myself, always learning, always trying to improve a little. I remember the
first dish I ever made in our kitchen, *petits pois à la Française* (green
peas). I burned them completely. We had a *prix-fixe* menu for five francs,
and I would stick to omelets, *navarin, poulet rôti*. Then I began to experiment with new things. The old customers ran away and no new ones
came in. The people of Lyon are thrifty; they thought they would have
to pay for the new building and the improvements. Word must have got
around, for suddenly they all came. In the thirties we would often have as
many as a hundred and thirty *couverts*. People would eat outside in the
garden and downstairs in the dining-room and upstairs on the terrace.
Mado was my maître d'hôtel. She never made a mistake. Nothing was
ever written down but no one's order got mixed up. I had the phone next
to my working-table in the kitchen; I would hold the phone with one
hand and prepare the *gratin* with the other. And all the time I would eat
well. You've got to love to eat well if you want to cook well. Whenever I
stop at a restaurant while traveling, I go and look at the chef. If he's a thin
fellow, I don't eat there. I've learned much about cooking, but I still have
far to go."

M. Point leaned back, reached into the drawer of a table behind him,
and pulled out a leather-bound book with a gold inscription on its cover:
"F. POINT, LIVRE D'OR."

"I started keeping this on the restaurant's tenth anniversary, in September 1933," he said. He handed it to me. On page 1 was a short note:
"*Quel excellent déjeuner!*" signed by the Aga Khan.

"He knows how to eat well," M. Point said, with a note of respect.

A couple of pages on, the Fratellinis, France's most famous clowns,
had written: "Today we have eaten at Lucullus's"; and Colette had written: "The trout was rosy, the wine was sparkling, the pâtisserie went
straight to my heart—and I am trying to lose weight! This is definitely

the last time I come here—*on ne m'y reprendra pas!*" Farther along there was an unfinished sentence by Léon Blum: *"Si j'en trouve encore la force après un tel déjeuner . . . !"* a drawing by Jean Cocteau, and an observation by Curnonsky: "Since cooking is without doubt the greatest art, I salute my dear Fernand Point as one of the greatest artists of our time!"

Nothing was entered from January 1940 until September 2, 1944. On the latter date someone had written: *"Premières Troupes Alliées—Merci 1000 Fois!"* over an excited, illegible signature. Below was the exclamation *"Vive la France!"* and the signatures of, among others, the Abbé de Pélissier, F.F.I., and Lieutenant Colonel H. C. Lodge, Jr., and Carl F. Gooding, "American jeep driver."

Several pages beyond I came upon a pasted-in letter, dated December 3, 1946, and typed on the stationery of the War Office (Room 900), Whitehall, London S.W. 1. It read: "Mr. Fernand Point: I have the honor to inform you that His Majesty the King has approved the award to you of the King's Medal for Courage in the Cause of Freedom, for your good services in France. . . ."

I asked M. Point about the letter. He shrugged and took the *livre d'or* away from me and threw it back into the drawer.

"No time for that. Time for lunch. If you will go into the dining-room, I'll step into the kitchen and see what can be done. I've thought it all out."

At the entrance to the dining-room I was taken in tow by Vincent, the cheerful headwaiter, who led me to a table. Mme Point came up with the order pad still under her arm. She gave me a long, speculative glance —the kind of glance that wives so often give their husbands' drinking companions—and then she smiled and said that she hoped I would have a nice lunch.

She went off and I looked around the dining-room. I had the feeling of being in a comfortable home in the country. The room wasn't so small as to give one a sense of being cooped up with a lot of other people (there were perhaps twenty-five or thirty other guests), and not so large as to give a feeling of mass production. There were pretty white curtains on all the windows. There were flowers inside the windows, but none on the tables. In the center of the room stood a long buffet covered high with stacks of big, ivory-colored plates, piles of silver, and rows of glasses. The curtains, and the plates, and the glasses, and the ashtrays bore the sign of the pyramid. Against one wall was a grandfather's clock. When I opened my white napkin of rough linen, it turned out to be almost the size of a small bedspread and exhaled the fragrance of fresh air and of the grass on which it had been dried in the sun.

A waiter placed one of the ivory-colored plates in front of me, and another waiter served me the first hors-d'œuvre, an excellent *pâté campagne en croûte*. French cooks are generally expert at baking an extremely light, buttery dough called *croûte*, but never before had I eaten *croûte* that almost dissolved in my mouth. When I had finished, the first waiter replaced my plate, fork, and knife with clean ones, and a third waiter served me a slice of *foie gras naturel truffé* embedded in a ring of *crème de foie gras.* The ritual of changing plates and silver was repeated after each hors-d'œuvre—hot sausage baked in a light pastry shell, accompanied by delicious *sauce piquante;* a *pâté* of pheasant; crackling hot cheese croissants; fresh asparagus (which M. Mercier must have bought in Lyon that morning), set off by a truly perfect *sauce hollandaise.*

A bottle of wine—an elegant, airy Montrachet—was brought in an ice bucket; the waiter filled my glass half full and gave it a gentle swirl to spread the bouquet. It was a great show and a fine wine. The last hors-d'œuvre was followed in person by M. Point, who informed me that I had now completed the "overture."

"The overture merely indicates the themes that will turn up later," he said. "A good meal must be as well constructed as a good play. As it progresses, it should gain in intensity, with the wines getting older and more full-bodied."

Having delivered himself of this pronouncement, he returned to the kitchen.

Whenever I think back to that lunch, I feel contentedly well fed; the memory of it alone seems almost enough to sustain life. The next course was *truite au porto,* which, the headwaiter told me, had been prepared by M. Point himself; brook trout boiled in water to which vinegar, pepper, salt, and bay leaf had been added, and then skinned, split in half, and filled with a ragout of truffles, mushrooms, and vegetables. With it came a sauce made of butter, cream, and port wine.

It was a masterpiece. I was by then entirely willing to take the word of my friends in Paris that Fernand Point is today France's greatest chef. The trout was followed by a breast of guinea hen with morels, in an egg sauce; a splendid Pont-l'Evêque; strawberry ice cream, made of *fraises de bois* that had been picked the same day; and an array of pâtisserie.

M. Point had chosen as a wine for the guinea hen a rich, full-bodied Château Lafite-Rothschild '24. And at the end of the meal, with my coffee, there was a Grande Fine Champagne '04, the taste of which I still remember vividly.

Later M. Point sat down at my table. The smell of good coffee and good cigars and the sound of soft, relaxed conversation drifted through the room.

M. Point acknowledged my praises with the casual air of a seasoned virtuoso who had expected nothing else.

"We always strive for near-perfection," he said.

The inevitable bottle of champagne in its ice bucket was whisked up to the table by the headwaiter, and two glasses were filled.

"Of course, I know that there is no such thing as perfection. But I always try to make every meal"—he closed his eyes, searching for the right words,—"*une petite merveille.* Now, you won't believe it, but I gave a lot of thought to your lunch. I said to myself: 'Maybe he should have a *sole aux nouilles* instead of the *truite au porto.*' I decided against it. It might have been too much, and I don't want my clients to eat too much. Only in bad restaurants is one urged to order a lot. *Enfin,* you are satisfied."

I said he could probably make a fortune if he opened a restaurant in Paris.

His face darkened as if making a fortune were the worst thing that could happen to him.

"Yes, my friends have been telling me that for years. But why should I leave? I belong here. I like my friends to come and stay with me here. My men like to work for me. We have thirteen men here in the dining-room, and eight cooks and two *pâtissiers,* under Paul Mercier, in the kitchen. Many of them have been with me for over twelve years, and some have been here a lot longer than that. They don't quit, as they do in Paris. Look at Vincent, here. He's been with me for twenty years—or is it twenty-one, Vincent?"

The gray-haired headwaiter filled the glasses again and gave the champagne bottle a twirl as he replaced it in its bucket.

"Twenty-one, *chef,*" he said, giving the chef a fond smile.

"You can't get rid of them," said M. Point. "I could throw Vincent out the door and he would come right back in through the window. No, *mon cher ami. Point ne bouge pas.* Point stays at the Pyramide."

He lifted his glass with forefinger and thumb, holding it at the base. "Let us drink to the Pyramide!"

"To the Pyramide!" I said.

Since then I've gone back to the Pyramide many times, undaunted by distances, borders, and customs guards. Each meal has been a memorable event—one of those rare moments when you know that it *couldn't* be any better. Repetition has intensified rather than dulled the delight of my first lunch at the restaurant.

Fernand Point is incontestably the greatest chef on earth. His perfection, like the perfection of Toscanini, is a blend of hard thinking, much work, and a dash of genius. At the Pyramide nothing is left to chance. M. Point isn't satisfied to use *poulet de Bresse,* the finest chicken in France. He "searches" until he finds the finest chicken in the Bresse region, which happens to be near Vienne. He has suppliers all over the fat French countryside who send him their choice products when they are "in season." I've eaten in his house the finest butter, the mildest caviar, the freshest sea fish, the tastiest sturgeon, the juiciest steak, the youngest vegetable, the daintiest woodcock, the ripest cheese, the best-flavored fruit.

Point's craving for perfection is evident at every stage of his work. When, after years of "searching," he finally arrived at his own recipe for *mousse* of brook trout—he adds a little *mousse* of chicken livers among many other mysterious things—he wasn't satisfied with the copper sieves that his emissaries had sent him from Paris. Instead he had special, extra-fine sieves made through which the delicate trout meat is strained not once but several times. The cooks in his kitchen work with a degree of perfection I have seen nowhere else outside a Swiss watch factory. When they make a *pâté* of pheasant, they wouldn't think of serving it in a *terrine*, as elsewhere; instead, they stuff a pheasant with the *pâté*. The "presentation" is no mere stage effect, but is calculated to enhance the supreme enjoyment of the dish. At the Pyramide they bake their own bread and *brioches,* and make their own sausages, which are served among the hors-d'œuvres. Point uses few spices and almost no garlic: he maintains that one must never make things too obvious. I remember a meal at which he served a special dish. He was pleased as a kid when no one present could accurately define what it was—a *mousse* made of carp's milt.

In spite of such precautions, many of his recipes have been copied, not too successfully, by imitators. When that happens, Point loses interest in the creation and stops serving it. Instead, he comes up with something new that surprises the finicky palates of France's gastronomes. Not long ago he gave a luncheon to two of France's finest chefs and served them *la Croustade de moules sur fond d'épinards et nappée d'une sauce crémeuse.* "It was not only wonderful to taste but a symphony of color," one of the chefs remembers. The other one told me, "Next to Point we are merely apprentices."

Point sees to it that his creations are properly appreciated. When he serves a delicate dish, such as his magnificent *gratin de queues d'écrevisses,* he asks his guests not to wait until all people at the same table are served. This may be bad manners according to the etiquette experts, but in the gastronomical etiquette of Fernand Point, it would be infinitely worse to let the *gratin de queues d'écrevisses* get cold. Recently he banned flowers from his tables because their scent was distracting. He doesn't approve of ladies who wear too much perfume when they sit down at the table. And he takes a dim view of restaurants that thrive on two or three *specialités de la maison.*

"Every good cook can design five or ten different meals," he said to me once. "But to change your menu every day, and to prepare three hundred and fifty meals a year—that's difficult."

M. Point is a generous grand-seigneur in the old style, who loves the company of enthusiastic fellow eaters. His friends claim that he keeps his restaurant mainly because it gives him a chance to entertain his friends. M. Point is particularly touched by the loyalty of some friends who don't care about his food and come to the Pyramide to see *him.* One of them, a local citizen, is a heavy though not discriminating eater.

"Il vient ici pour se nourir" (he comes here to feed himself), Point says, with a chuckle. That anybody should come to the Pyramide to *eat,* instead of to taste, enjoy, appreciate, dream, amuses him no end,

As you come in, you will be offered a glass of champagne. Hold it with forefinger and thumb, at the bottom, thumb up—never by the stem! Raise your glass and drink to the Pyramide. M. Point appreciates little things like that. He has mastered three words of English: "yes, sir," and "darling," and uses them as indiscriminately as a Hollywood producer.

At the Pyramide I've never been offered the same dish twice. Mme Point has an uncanny memory for menus and remembers what you ate there as long as two years ago. M. Point claims that a meal must be "composed and orchestrated" like a symphony. It should start with light dishes and proceed to heavier ones, with the accent on the specialties of the particular season—whatever best fish, fowl, game, fruit, cheese happen to be available at the moment.

Point's closest friends agree that the best day to eat at the Pyramide is Tuesday. On Tuesdays the restaurant is closed, and Point himself goes down to the kitchen to cook for his family and his friends. He makes what he calls a "simple" dish, a *blanquette de veau à l'ancienne*, or a beef stew in Chambertin (he uses vintage wines for cooking), or his inimitable *gratin dauphinois*—but it's the simplicity and delicacy of a Mozart symphony. The coffee is perfect, which is rare in France, and there are surprises even when the liqueurs arrive. Lately M. Point has been experimenting with flavors. Last spring he placed an empty glass bottle over a small pear hanging from a tree. During the summer the pear grew inside the bottle, as in a glass house. In the autumn Point took the ripe pear off the tree—by that time it had become too large to be removed from inside the bottle—and added pure alcohol. The result is the finest, strongest pear liqueur that was ever caught in a bottle. The label says: "POIRE EST CELUI QUI N'EN BOIT POINT."

One October day, when the leaves of the chestnut trees in his garden were playing the colors of a Cézanne painting, M. Point composed and orchestrated this lunch for us:

PÂTÉ CHAUD DE CANETON AU CHAMBERTIN

BRIOCHE DE FOIE GRAS

TERRINE DES GRIVES AU GENIÈVRE

MOUSSE DE TRUITES

HUÎTRES CHAUDES GRATINÉES

GRATIN DE QUEUES D'ÉCREVISSES NANTUA

PERDREAUX CASSEROLE

CHOUCROUTE, PURÉE DE POMMES

LES FROMAGES DE ST. MARCELLIN ET DE BRIE

GÂTEAU SUCCÈS MARJOLAINE

GLACES PYRAMIDE

MIGNARDISES POINT

POIRES CARDINAL

CORBEILLES DE FRUITS DE LA VALLÉE DU RHÔNE

Cramant blanc de blancs 1949

Condrieu 1950
Juliénas 1949 (en carafe)
Moulin-à-Vent 1945
La Romanée-Conti 1929
Pommery 1945 (en magnum)

I never asked M. Point to give me the recipe of one of his creations. What's the use? It would be like attempting to play the cello by watching Pablo Casals.

But I didn't finish the story of my first lunch at the Pyramide. M. Point and I had drunk a considerable number of champagne toasts—to France; to the United States; to Escoffier; to Dom Pérignon, who put the bubbles in champagne; to the memorable day when M. Point prepared his first *truite au porto;* and there were many toasts in between "to the Pyramide!" I was beginning to master the difficult trick of holding my flute-shaped glass at its base, with forefinger and thumb. It was with a delicious feeling of lightheadedness and supreme contentment that, in the late afternoon, I paid my bill, bid an affectionate farewell to M. Point, and went out into the garden.

It had rained again, but now the sun was shining. The earth had a strong smell of mushrooms and flowers. I headed back to my hotel.

At the corner of the Cours Président Wilson, I ran smack into M. Lecutiez. He was talking to an unworldly-looking, white-bearded patriarch, who I presumed was the oldest of the three archæologists, but M. Lecutiez introduced him to me as *l'homme mûr,* the mature man. He said good-by to his colleague and seized my arm with great enthusiasm.

"I've been waiting for you!" he said, waving his pipe happily. "We've got lots of things to do. We still have time to climb at least three of Vienne's seven hills."

I said that he must excuse me, because I was hardly able to make the Grand Hôtel du Nord, having just had lunch at M. Point's.

"Monsieur Point has a very interesting place," M. Lecutiez said.

"Interesting?" I said. "He has the finest restaurant this side of paradise. The Pyramide is a triumph to French civilization, like Notre-Dame or the Château of Versailles—"

"Oh, I don't mean that," M. Lecutiez broke in. "I don't give a damn about the restaurant. I care only for antiquities, you know, and Monsieur Point has plenty of them buried under his place. When they landscaped his garden ten years ago, they came across a couple of first-class Roman sculptures. I wish we could take over Monsieur Point's place and start digging in earnest. I'll bet there are any number of marvelous relics under his wine cellar."

WALLACE STEVENS
copyright Rollie McKenna

ELINOR WYLIE
photograph by Brown Brothers

989

Verse

HERE IS A MERE CLUTCH, not a true anthology, of poetry. The intent is simple: to exhibit what one American publishing house has done to give us access to genuinely first-order poetry (Eliot, Pound, Stevens); to good second-order poetry (the youthful Graves, Housman, Bynner, Ransom, Hughes, Wylie, Lawrence); and to younger men (Roethke, Snodgrass, Meredith). I have also included a pair of masterpieces of light verse, by Belloc and Newman Levy, plus a couple of exquisite translations by Arthur Waley and Frank O'Connor.

Any American publisher (and there are several) who accepts and prints fine verse loses money. (There is an occasional exception, as in the case of Robert Frost.) Such publishers are in effect making a voluntary contribution to Western culture. If our Internal Revenue Service had any intelligence it would grant such publishers a special tax deduction.

Hilaire Belloc

THE BAD CHILD'S
BOOK OF BEASTS

[Illustrated by B.T.B.]

TO

MASTER EVELYN BELL

of Oxford

Evelyn Bell,
I love you well.

INTRODUCTION

I CALL you bad, my little child,
  Upon the title page,
Because a manner rude and wild
  Is common at your age.

The Moral of this priceless work
  (If rightly understood)
Will make you—from a little Turk—
  Unnaturally good.

Do not as evil children do,
  Who on the slightest grounds
Will imitate

    the Kangaroo,
With wild unmeaning bounds:

Do not as children badly bred,
  Who eat like little Hogs,
And when they have to go to bed
  Will whine like Puppy Dogs:

Who take their manners from the Ape,
  Their habits from the Bear,
Indulge the loud unseemly jape,
  And never brush their hair.

But so control your actions that
Your friends may all repeat.

"This child is dainty as the Cat,
And as the Owl discreet."

THE YAK

As a friend to the children

commend me the Yak.

You will find it exactly the thing:
It will carry and fetch,

you can ride on its back,
Or lead it about

with a string.

The Tartar who dwells on the plains of Thibet
(A desolate region of snow)

Has for centuries made it a nursery pet,
    And surely the Tartar should know!
Then tell your papa where the Yak can be got,

And if he is awfully rich
He will buy you the creature—

or else

(I cannot be positive which.)   he will *not*.

THE POLAR BEAR

The Polar Bear is unaware

Of cold that cuts me through:
For why? He has a coat of hair
I wish I had one too!

THE LION

The Lion, the Lion, he dwells in the waste,
He has a big head and a very small waist;

But his shoulders are stark, and his jaws they are grim,
And a good little child will not play with him.

THE TIGER

The Tiger on the other hand,

is kittenish and mild,
He makes a pretty playfellow for any little child;

And mothers of large families (who claim to common sense)

Will find a Tiger well repays the trouble and expense.

THE DROMEDARY

The Dromedary is a cheerful bird:

I cannot say the same about the Kurd.

THE WHALE

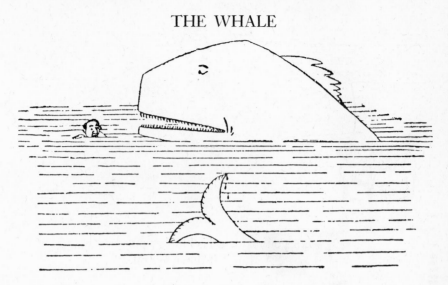

The Whale that wanders round the Pole
Is not

a table fish.
You cannot bake or boil him whole
Nor serve him in a dish;

But you may cut his blubber up
And melt it down for oil.

And so replace

the colza bean
(A product of the soil).

These facts should all be noted down
And ruminated on,

By every boy in Oxford town
Who wants to be a Don.

THE CAMEL

"The Ship of the Desert."

THE HIPPOPOTAMUS

I shoot the Hippopotamus

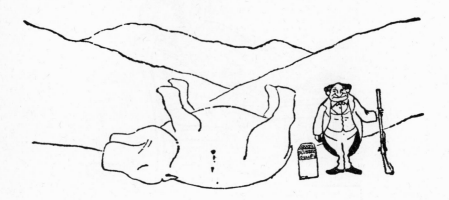

with bullets made of platinum,

Because if I use leaden ones

his hide is sure to flatten 'em.

THE DODO

The Dodo used

to walk around,

And take the sun and air.
The sun yet warms his native ground—
The Dodo is not there!

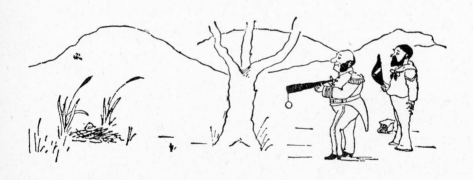

The voice which used to squawk and squeak
Is now for ever dumb—

Yet may you see his bones and
All in the Mu-se-um.

THE MARMOZET

The species Man and Marmozet
Are intimately linked;

The Marmozet survives as yet,
But Men are all extinct.

THE CAMELOPARD

The Camelopard, it is said
By travellers (who never lie),

He cannot stretch out straight in bed
Because he is so high.
The clouds surround his lofty head,
His hornlets touch the sky.

How shall
I hunt
I

this quadruped?
cannot tell!
Not I!

(A picture of how people try
And fail to hit that head so high.)

I'll buy a little parachute
(A common parachute with wings),
I'll fill it full of arrowroot
And other necessary things,

And I will slay this fearful brute
With stones and sticks and guns and slings.

(A picture of

how people shoot
With comfort from a parachute.)

THE LEARNED FISH

This learned Fish has not sufficient brains
To go into the water when it rains.

THE ELEPHANT

When people call this beast to mind,

They marvel more and more
At such a

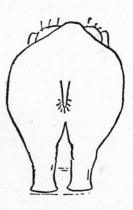

LITTLE tail behind,

So LARGE a trunk before.

THE BIG BABOON

The Big Baboon is found upon
The plains of Cariboo:

He goes about

with nothing on
(A shocking thing to do).

But if he

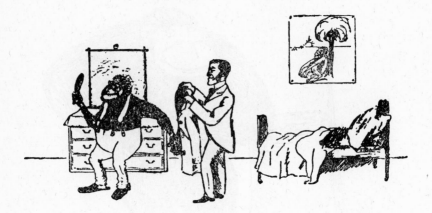

dressed respectably
And let his whiskers grow,

How like this Big Baboon would be

To Mister So-and-so!

THE RHINOCEROS

Rhinoceros, your hide looks all undone,

You do not take my fancy in the least:

You have a horn where other brutes have none:
Rhinoceros, you are an ugly beast.

THE FROG

Be kind and tender to the Frog,

And do not call him names,
As "Slimy skin," or "Polly-wog,"
Or likewise "Ugly James,"
Or "Gap-a-grin," or "Toad-gone-wrong,"
Or "Bill Bandy-knees":

The Frog is justly sensitive
To epithets like these.

No animal will more repay
A treatment kind and fair;
At least

so lonely people say
Who keep a frog (and, by the way,
They are extremely rare).

Oh! My!

Witter Bynner

A Farmer Remembers Lincoln

"Lincoln?—
Well, I was in the old Second Maine,
The first regiment in Washington from the Pine Tree State.
Of course I didn't get the butt of the clip;
We was there for guardin' Washington—
We was all green.

"I ain't never ben to but one theatre in my life—
I didn't know how to behave.
I ain't never ben since.
I can see as plain as my hat the box where he sat in
When he was shot.
I can tell you, sir, there was a panic
When we found our President was in the shape he was in!
Never saw a soldier in the world but what liked him.

"Yes, sir. His looks was kind o' hard to forget.
He was a spare man,
An old farmer.
Everything was all right, you know,
But he wan't a smooth-appearin' man at all—
Not in no ways;
Thin-faced, long-necked,
And a swellin' kind of a thick lip like.

From *Grenstone Poems: A Sequence*, 1926. Copyright 1926 by Alfred A. Knopf, Inc.
Renewal copyright 1954 by Witter Bynner.

"And he was a jolly old fellow—always cheerful;
He wan't so high but the boys could talk to him their own ways.
While I was servin' at the hospital,
He'd come in and say, "You look nice in here,"
Praise us up, you know.
And he'd bend over and talk to the boys—
And he'd talk so good to 'em—so close—
That's why I call him a farmer.
I don't mean that everything about him wasn't all right, you understand,
It's just—well, I was a farmer—
And he was my neighbour, anybody's neighbour.

"I guess even you young folks would 'a' liked him."

T. S. Eliot

The Love Song of J. Alfred Prufrock

S'io credesse che mia risposta fosse
A persona che mai tornasse al mondo,
Questa fiamma staria senza piu scosse.
Ma perciocche giammai di questo fondo
Non torno vivo alcun, s'i'odo il vero,
Senza tema d'infamia ti rispondo.

Let us go then, you and I,
When the evening is spread out against the sky
Like a patient etherized upon a table;
Let us go, through certain half-deserted streets,
The muttering retreats
Of restless nights in one-night cheap hotels
And sawdust restaurants with oyster-shells:
Streets that follow like a tedious argument
Of insidious intent
To lead you to an overwhelming question. . . .
Oh, do not ask, "What is it?"
Let us go and make our visit.

In the room the women come and go
Talking of Michelangelo.

The yellow fog that rubs its back upon the window-panes,
The yellow smoke that rubs its muzzle on the window-panes
Licked its tongue into the corners of the evening,

Lingered upon the pools that stand in drains,
Let fall upon its back the soot that falls from chimneys,
Slipped by the terrace, made a sudden leap,
And seeing that it was a soft October night,
Curled once about the house, and fell asleep.

And indeed there will be time
For the yellow smoke that slides along the street,
Rubbing its back upon the window-panes;
There will be time, there will be time
To prepare a face to meet the faces that you meet;
There will be time to murder and create,
And time for all the works and days of hands
That lift and drop a question on your plate;
Time for you and time for me,
And time yet for a hundred indecisions,
And for a hundred visions and revisions,
Before the taking of a toast and tea.

In the room the women come and go
Talking of Michelangelo.

And indeed there will be time
To wonder, "Do I dare?" and, "Do I dare?"
Time to turn back and descend the stair,
With a bald spot in the middle of my hair—
(They will say: "How his hair is growing thin!")
My morning coat, my collar mounting firmly to the chin,
My necktie rich and modest, but asserted by a simple pin—
(They will say: "But how his arms and legs are thin!")
Do I dare
Disturb the universe?
In a minute there is time
For decisions and revisions which a minute will reverse.

For I have known them all already, known them all:
Have known the evenings, mornings, afternoons,
I have measured out my life with coffee spoons;
I know the voices dying with a dying fall
Beneath the music from a farther room.
    So how should I presume?

And I have known the eyes already, known them all—
The eyes that fix you in a formulated phrase,
And when I am formulated, sprawling on a pin,
When I am pinned and wriggling on the wall,
Then how should I begin
To spit out all the butt-ends of my days and ways?
    And how should I presume?

And I have known the arms already, known them all—
Arms that are braceleted and white and bare
(But in the lamplight, downed with light brown hair!)
Is it perfume from a dress
That makes me so digress?
Arms that lie along a table, or wrap about a shawl.
    And should I then presume?
    And how should I begin?

                      .   .   .   .   .   .

Shall I say, I have gone at dusk through narrow streets
And watched the smoke that rises from the pipes
Of lonely men in shirt-sleeves, leaning out of windows? . . .

I should have been a pair of ragged claws
Scuttling across the floors of silent seas.

                      .   .   .   .   .   .

And the afternoon, the evening, sleeps so peacefully!
Smoothed by long fingers,
Asleep . . . tired . . . or it malingers,
Stretched on the floor, here beside you and me.
Should I, after tea and cakes and ices,
Have the strength to force the moment to its crisis?
But though I have wept and fasted, wept and prayed,
Though I have seen my head (grown slightly bald) brought in upon a
        platter,
I am no prophet—and here's no great matter;
I have seen the moment of my greatness flicker,
And I have seen the eternal Footman hold my coat, and snicker,
And in short, I was afraid.

And would it have been worth it, after all,
After the cups, the marmalade, the tea,

Among the porcelain, among some talk of you and me,
Would it have been worth while,
To have bitten off the matter with a smile,
To have squeezed the universe into a ball
To roll it toward some overwhelming question,
To say: "I am Lazarus, come from the dead,
Come back to tell you all, I shall tell you all"—
If one, settling a pillow by her head,
  Should say: "That is not what I meant at all;
  That is not it, at all."

And would it have been worth it, after all,
Would it have been worth while,
After the sunsets and the dooryards and the sprinkled streets,
After the novels, after the teacups, after the skirts that trail along the
    floor—
And this, and so much more?—
It is impossible to say just what I mean!
But as if a magic lantern threw the nerves in patterns on a screen:
Would it have been worth while
If one, settling a pillow or throwing off a shawl,
And turning toward the window, should say:
  "That is not it at all,
  That is not what I meant, at all."

              .   .   .   .

No! I am not Prince Hamlet, nor was meant to be;
Am an attendant lord, one that will do
To swell a progress, start a scene or two,
Advise the prince; no doubt, an easy tool,
Deferential, glad to be of use,
Politic, cautious, and meticulous;
Full of high sentence, but a bit obtuse;
At times, indeed, almost ridiculous—
Almost, at times, the Fool.

I grow old . . . I grow old . . .
I shall wear the bottoms of my trousers rolled.

Shall I part my hair behind? Do I dare to eat a peach?
I shall wear white flannel trousers, and walk upon the beach.
I have heard the mermaids singing, each to each.

I do not think that they will sing to me.

I have seen them riding seaward on the waves
Combing the white hair of the waves blown back
When the wind blows the water white and black.

We have lingered in the chambers of the sea
By sea-girls wreathed with seaweed red and brown
Till human voices wake us, and we drown.

Robert Graves

Lost Love

His eyes are quickened so with grief,
He can watch a grass or leaf
Every instant grow; he can
Clearly through a flint wall see,
Or watch the startled spirit flee
From the throat of a dead man.
Across two counties he can hear,
And catch your words before you speak.
The woodlouse or the maggot's weak
Clamour rings in his sad ear;
And noise so slight it would surpass
Credence:—drinking sound of grass,
Worm talk, clashing jaws of moth
Chumbling holes in cloth:
The groan of ants who undertake
Gigantic loads for honour's sake,
Their sinews creak, their breath comes thin:
Whir of spiders when they spin,
And minute whispering, mumbling, sighs
Of idle grubs and flies.
This man is quickened so with grief,
He wanders god-like or like thief
Inside and out, below, above,
Without relief seeking lost love.

Apples and Water

Dust in a cloud, blinding weather,
   Drums that rattle and roar!
A mother and daughter stood together
   Beside their cottage door.

"Mother, the heavens are bright like brass,
   The dust is shaken high,
With labouring breath the soldiers pass,
   Their lips are cracked and dry.

"Mother, I'll throw them apples down,
   I'll bring them pails of water."
The mother turned with an angry frown
   Holding back her daughter.

"But mother, see, they faint with thirst,
   They march away to die,"
"Ah, sweet, had I but known at first
   Their throats are always dry.

"There is no water can supply them
   In western streams that flow,
There is no fruit can satisfy them
   On orchard trees that grow.

"Once in my youth I gave, poor fool,
   A soldier apples and water,
So may I die before you cool
   Your father's drouth, my daughter."

From *Country Sentiment*, 1920. Copyright 1920 by International Authors N. V. Reprinted by permission of Willis Kingsley Wing.

A. E. Housman

[FROM More Poems]

Here dead lie we because we did not choose
To live and shame the land from which we sprung.
Life, to be sure, is nothing much to lose;
But young men think it is, and we were young.

Parta Quies

Good-night; ensured release,
Imperishable peace,
    Have these for yours,
While sea abides, and land,
And earth's foundations stand,
    And heaven endures.

When earth's foundations flee,
Nor sky nor land nor sea
    At all is found,
Content you, let them burn:
It is not your concern;
    Sleep on, sleep sound.

Langston Hughes

Kid Sleepy

Listen, Kid Sleepy,
Don't you want to run around
To the other side of the house
Where the shade is?
It's sunny here
And your skin'll turn
A reddish-purple in the sun.

Kid Sleepy said,
I don't care.

Listen, Kid Sleepy,
Don't you want to get up
And go to work down-
Town somewhere
To earn enough
For lunches and car fare?

Kid Sleepy said,
I don't care.

Or would you rather,
Kid Sleepy, just
Stay here?

Rather just
Stay here.

50–50

I'm all alone in this world, she said,
Ain't got nobody to share my bed,
Ain't got nobody to hold my hand—
The truth of the matter's
I ain't got no man.

Big Boy opened his mouth and said,
Trouble with you is
You ain't got no head!
If you had a head and used your mind
You could have *me* with you
All the time.

She answered, Babe, what must I do?

He said, Share your bed—
And your money, too.

D. H. Lawrence

Don'ts—

Fight your little fight, my boy
fight and be a man.
Don't be a good little, good little boy
being as good as you can

and agreeing with all the mealy-mouthed, mealy-mouthed
truths that the sly trot out
to protect themselves and their greedy-mouthed, greedy-mouthed
cowardice, every old lout.

Don't live up to the dear little girl who costs
you your manhood, and makes you pay.
Nor the dear old mater who so proudly boasts
that you'll make your way.

Don't earn golden opinions, opinions golden,
or at least worth Treasury notes,
from all sorts of men; don't be beholden
to the herd inside the pen.

Don't long to have dear little, dear little boys
whom you'll have to educate
to earn their living; nor yet girls, sweet joys
who will find it so hard to mate.

Nor a dear little home, with its cost, its cost
that you have to pay,

From *Pansies: Poems*, 1929. Copyright 1929 by D. H. Lawrence.

earning your living while your life is lost
and dull death comes in a day.

Don't be sucked in by the su-superior,
don't swallow the culture bait,
don't drink, don't drink and get beerier and beerier,
do learn to discriminate.

Do hold yourself together, and fight
with a hit-hit here and a hit-hit there,
and a comfortable feeling at night
that you've let in a little air.

A little fresh air in the money sty,
knocked a little hole in the holy prison,
done your own little bit, made your own little try
that the risen Christ should *be* risen.

Newman Levy

[*Illustrated by Rea Irvin*]

Carmen

In Spain, where the courtly Castilian hidalgo twangs lightly
each night his romantic guitar,
Where the castanets clink on the gay piazetta, and strains of
fandangoes are heard from afar,
There lived, I am told, a bold hussy named Carmen, a pampered
young vamp full of devil and guile.
Cigarette and cigar men were smitten with Carmen; from near and
from far men were caught with her smile.
Now one day it happened she got in a scrap and proceeded to beat
up a girl in the shop,
Till someone suggested they have her arrested, and though she protested they called in a cop.

From *Opera Guyed*, 1923. Copyright 1923 by Alfred A. Knopf, Inc. Renewal copyright 1950 by Newman Levy.

In command of the guard was a shavetail named José, a valiant young don
with a weakness for janes,

And so great was her beauty this bold second loot he could not do his
duty and put her in chains.

"I'm sorry, my dear, to appear to arrest you,—at best you are hardly much
more than a kid.

If I let you go, say, there'll be some exposé. But beat it," said José. And
beat it she did.

The scene now is changed to a strange sort of tavern—a hangout of
gypsies, a rough kind of dive,

And Carmen, who *can* sing, is warbling and dancing, awaiting her date the
late loot to arrive.

In comes Escamillo the toreadoro and sings his great solo 'mid plaudits
and cheers,

And when he concludes, after three or four encores, the gypsies depart
and Don José appears.

These gypsy companions of Carmen are smugglers, the worst band of
bandits and cutthroats in Spain.

And José, we know well's A.W.O.L. Says he "Since that's so, well I guess
I'll remain."

The gypsies depart to the heart of the mountains, and with them goes
José who's grouchy and sore.

For Carmen, the flirt, has deserted poor José, and transferred her love to
the toreador.

And as he sits sulking he sees Escamillo. A challenge is passed and they
draw out their knives.

Till José, though lighter, disarms the bull fighter and near kills the
blighter when Carmen arrives.

Now comes Micaela, Don José's young sweetheart, a nice-looking blonde
without much in her dome.

Says she, "Do you know, kid, your ma's kinder low, kid?" Says José,
"Let's go, kid," and follows her home.

At last we arrive at the day of the bull fight; the grand stand is packed
and the bleachers are full;

A picturesque scene, a square near the arena, the Plaza del Toro or Place
of the Bull.

Dark-skinned señoritas with fans and mantillas, and haughty Castilians in
festive array;

And dolled out to charm men, suspecting no harm, enters, last of all,
Carmen to witness the fray.

But here's our friend José who seizes her bridle. A wild homicidal glint
gleams in his eye.

He's mad and disgusted and cries out, "You've busted the heart that once
    trusted you. Wed me or die!"
Though Carmen is frightened at how this scene might end, I'm forced to
    admit she is game to the last.
She says to him "Banish the notion and vanish. *Vamos!*" which is Spanish
    for "run away fast."
A scream and a struggle! She reels and she staggers, for Don José's
    dagger's plunged deep in her breast.
No more will she flirt in her old way, that's certain. So ring down the cur-
    tain, poor Carmen's at rest.

William Meredith

The Open Sea

We say the sea is lonely; better say
Ourselves are lonesome creatures whom the sea
Gives neither yes nor no for company.

Oh, there are people, all right, settled in the sea—
It is as populous as Maine today—
But no one who will give you the time of day.

A man who asks there of his family
Or a friend or teacher gets a cold reply
Or finds him dead against that vast majority.

Nor does it signify that people who stay
Very long, bereaved or not, at the edge of the sea
Hear the drowned folk call: that is mere fancy,

They are speechless. And the famous noise of sea,
Which a poet has beautifully told us in our day,
Is hardly a sound to speak comfort to the lonely.

Although not yet a man given to prayer, I pray
For each creature lost since the start at sea,
And give thanks it was not I, nor yet one close to me.

From *The Open Sea and Other Poems*, 1957. Copyright 1953, © 1957 by William
Meredith. Originally published in *The Hudson Review*.

Frank O'Connor

[TRANSLATOR]

The Scholar and the Cat

This, one of the most beautiful poems of the early Middle Ages, was found in a manuscript in Austria. I have hinted at the rhyme-scheme of the Irish, which displaces the accent in alternate lines. Robin Flower's well-known translation in the metre of "Twinkle, twinkle, little star" ignores the slowness of the original, which approximates more to iambic pentameter.

Each of us pursues his trade,
I and Pangur my comrade,
His whole fancy on the hunt,
And mine for learning ardent.

More than fame I love to be
Among my books and study,
Pangur does not grudge me it,
Content with his own merit.

When—a heavenly time!—we are
In our small room together
Each of us has his own sport
And asks no greater comfort.

While he sets his round sharp eye
On the wall of my study

From *Kings, Lords, and Commons,* 1959. Copyright © 1959 by Frank O'Connor.

I turn mine, though lost its edge,
On the great wall of knowledge.

Now a mouse drops in his net
After some mighty onset
While into my bag I cram
Some difficult darksome problem.

When a mouse comes to the kill
Pangur exults, a marvel!
I have when some secret's won
My hour of exultation.

Though we work for days and years
Neither the other hinders;
Each is competent and hence
Enjoys his skill in silence.

Master of the death of mice,
He keeps in daily practice,
I too, making dark things clear,
Am of my trade a master.

Ezra Pound

Further Instructions

Come, my songs, let us express our baser passions,
Let us express our envy of the man with a steady job and no worry about
    the future.
You are very idle, my songs.
I fear you will come to a bad end.
You stand about in the streets,
You loiter at the corners and bus-stops,
You do next to nothing at all.

You do not even express our inner nobilities,
You will come to a very bad end.

And I?
I have gone half cracked,
I have talked to you so much that
           I almost see you about me,
Insolent little beasts, shameless, devoid of clothing!

But you, newest song of the lot,
You are not old enough to have done much mischief,
I will get you a green coat out of China
With dragons worked upon it,
I will get you the scarlet silk trousers
From the statue of the infant Christ at Santa Maria Novella,
Lest they say we are lacking in taste,
Or that there is no caste in this family.

The River-Merchant's Wife:
A Letter

While my hair was still cut straight across my forehead
I played about the front gate, pulling flowers.
You came by on bamboo stilts, playing horse,
You walked about my seat, playing with blue plums.
And we went on living in the village of Chokan:
Two small people, without dislike or suspicion.

At fourteen I married My Lord you.
I never laughed, being bashful.
Lowering my head, I looked at the wall.
Called to, a thousand times, I never looked back.

At fifteen I stopped scowling,
I desired my dust to be mingled with yours
Forever and forever and forever.
Why should I climb the look out?

At sixteen you departed,
You went into far Ku-to-Yen, by the river of swirling eddies,
And you have been gone five months.
The monkeys make sorrowful noise overhead.
You dragged your feet when you went out.
By the gate now, the moss is grown, the different mosses,
Too deep to clear them away!
The leaves fall early this autumn, in wind.
The paired butterflies are already yellow with August
Over the grass in the West garden;
They hurt me.
I grow older.
If you are coming down through the narrows of the river Kiang,
Please let me know beforehand,
And I will come out to meet you
        As far as Cho-fu-Sa.

by Rihaku
8th century A.D.

ΔΏΡΙΑ

Be in me as the eternal moods
            of the bleak wind, and not
As transient things are—
            gaiety of flowers.
Have me in the strong loneliness
            of sunless cliffs
And of grey waters.
                        Let the gods speak softly of us
In days hereafter,
                        The shadowy flowers of Orcus
Remember Thee.

John Crowe Ransom

Here Lies a Lady

Here lies a lady of beauty and high degree.
Of chills and fever she died, of fever and chills,
The delight of her husband, her aunt, an infant of three,
And of medicos marveling sweetly on her ills.

For either she burned, and her confident eyes would blaze,
And her fingers fly in a manner to puzzle their heads—
What was she making? Why, nothing; she sat in a maze
Of old scraps of laces, snipped into curious shreds—

Or this would pass, and the light of her fire decline
Till she lay discouraged and cold, like a thin stalk white and blown,
And would not open her eyes, to kisses, to wine;
The sixth of these states was her last; the cold settled down.

Sweet ladies, long may ye bloom, and toughly I hope ye may thole,
But was she not lucky? In flowers and lace and mourning,
In love and great honor we bade God rest her soul
After six little spaces of chill, and six of burning.

Captain Carpenter

Captain Carpenter rose up in his prime
Put on his pistols and went riding out
But had got wellnigh nowhere at that time
Till he fell in with ladies in a rout.

It was a pretty lady and all her train
That played with him so sweetly but before
An hour she'd taken a sword with all her main
And twined him of his nose for evermore.

Captain Carpenter mounted up one day
And rode straightway into a stranger rogue
That looked unchristian but be that as may
The Captain did not wait upon prologue.

But drew upon him out of his great heart
The other swung against him with a club
And cracked his two legs at the shinny part
And let him roll and stick like any tub.

Captain Carpenter rode many a time
From male and female took he sundry harms
He met the wife of Satan crying "I'm
The she-wolf bids you shall bear no more arms."

Their strokes and counters whistled in the wind
I wish he had delivered half his blows
But where she should have made off like a hind
The bitch bit off his arms at the elbows.

And Captain Carpenter parted with his ears
To a black devil that used him in this wise
O Jesus ere his threescore and ten years
Another had plucked out his sweet blue eyes.

Captain Carpenter got up on his roan
And sallied from the gate in hell's despite
I heard him asking in the grimmest tone
If any enemy yet there was to fight?

"To any adversary it is fame
If he risk to be wounded by my tongue
Or burnt in two beneath my red heart's flame
Such are the perils he is cast among.

"But if he can he has a pretty choice
From an anatomy with little to lose
Whether he cut my tongue and take my voice
Or whether it be my round red heart he choose."

It was the neatest knave that ever was seen
Stepping in perfume from his lady's bower
Who at this word put in his merry mien
And fell on Captain Carpenter like a tower.

I would not knock old fellows in the dust
But there lay Captain Carpenter on his back
His weapons were the old heart in his bust
And a blade shook between rotten teeth alack.

The rogue in scarlet and grey soon knew his mind
He wished to get his trophy and depart
With gentle apology and touch refined
He pierced him and produced the Captain's heart.

God's mercy rest on Captain Carpenter now
I thought him Sirs an honest gentleman
Citizen husband soldier and scholar enow
Let jangling kites eat of him if they can.

But God's deep curses follow after those
That shore him of his goodly nose and ears
His legs and strong arms at the two elbows
And eyes that had not watered seventy years.

The curse of hell upon the sleek upstart
That got the Captain finally on his back
And took the red red vitals of his heart
And made the kites to whet their beaks clack clack.

Theodore Roethke

To My Sister

O my sister remember the stars the tears the trains
The woods in spring the leaves the scented lanes
Recall the gradual dark the snow's unmeasured fall
The naked fields the cloud's immaculate folds
Recount each childhood pleasure: the skies of azure
The pageantry of wings the eye's bright treasure.

Keep faith with present joys refuse to choose
Defer the vice of flesh the irrevocable choice
Cherish the eyes the proud incredible poise
Walk boldly my sister but do not deign to give
Remain secure from pain preserve thy hate thy heart.

The Bat

By day the bat is cousin to the mouse.
He likes the attic of an aging house.

His fingers make a hat about his head.
His pulse beat is so slow we think him dead.

He loops in crazy figures half the night
Among the trees that face the corner light.

But when he brushes up against a screen,
We are afraid of what our eyes have seen:

For something is amiss or out of place
When mice with wings can wear a human face.

W. D. Snodgrass

April Inventory

The green catalpa tree has turned
All white; the cherry blooms once more.
In one whole year I haven't learned
A blessed thing they pay you for.
The blossoms snow down in my hair;
The trees and I will soon be bare

The trees have more than I to spare.
The sleek, expensive girls I teach,
Younger and pinker every year,
Bloom gradually out of reach.
The pear tree lets its petals drop
Like dandruff on a tabletop.

The girls have grown so young by now
I have to nudge myself to stare.
This year they smile and mind me how
My teeth are falling with my hair.
In thirty years I may not get
Younger, shrewder, or out of debt.

The tenth time, just a year ago,
I made myself a little list
Of all the things I'd ought to know,
Then told my parents, analyst,
And everyone who's trusted me
I'd be substantial, presently.

I haven't read one book about
A book or memorized one plot.
Or found a mind I did not doubt.
I learned one date. And then forgot.
And one by one the solid scholars
Get the degrees, the jobs, the dollars.

And smile above their starchy collars.
I taught my classes Whitehead's notions;
One lovely girl, a song of Mahler's.
Lacking a source-book or promotions,
I showed one child the colors of
A luna moth and how to love.

I taught myself to name my name,
To bark back, loosen love and crying;
To ease my woman so she came,
To ease an old man who was dying.
I have not learned how often I
Can win, can love, but choose to die.

I have not learned there is a lie
Love shall be blonder, slimmer, younger;
That my equivocating eye
Loves only by my body's hunger;
That I have forces, true to feel,
Or that the lovely world is real.

While scholars speak authority
And wear their ulcers on their sleeves,
My eyes in spectacles shall see
These trees procure and spend their leaves.
There is a value underneath
The gold and silver in my teeth.

Though trees turn bare and girls turn wives,
We shall afford our costly seasons;
There is a gentleness survives
That will outspeak and has its reasons.
There is a loveliness exists,
Preserves us, not for specialists.

Wallace Stevens

Peter Quince at the Clavier

I

Just as my fingers on these keys
Make music, so the selfsame sounds
On my spirit make a music, too.

Music is feeling, then, not sound;
And thus it is that what I feel,
Here in this room, desiring you,

Thinking of your blue-shadowed silk,
Is music. It is like the strain
Waked in the elders by Susanna.

Of a green evening, clear and warm,
She bathed in her still garden, while
The red-eyed elders watching, felt

The basses of their beings throb
In witching chords, and their thin blood
Pulse pizzicati of Hosanna.

II

In the green water, clear and warm,
Susanna lay.
She searched
The touch of springs,

And found
Concealed imaginings,
She sighed,
For so much melody.

Upon the bank, she stood
In the cool
Of spent emotions.
She felt, among the leaves,
The dew
Of old devotions.

She walked upon the grass,
Still quavering.
The winds were like her maids,
On timid feet,
Fetching her woven scarves,
Yet wavering.

A breath upon her hand
Muted the night.
She turned—
A cymbal crashed,
And roaring horns.

III

Soon, with a noise like tambourines,
Came her attendant Byzantines.

They wondered why Susanna cried
Against the elders by her side;

And as they whispered, the refrain
Was like a willow swept by rain.

Anon, their lamps' uplifted flame
Revealed Susanna and her shame.

And then, the simpering Byzantines
Fled, with a noise like tambourines.

IV

Beauty is momentary in the mind—
The fitful tracing of a portal;
But in the flesh it is immortal.
The body dies; the body's beauty lives.
So evenings die, in their green going,
A wave, interminably flowing.
So gardens die, their meek breath scenting
The cowl of winter, done repenting.
So maidens die, to the auroral
Celebration of a maiden's choral.
Susanna's music touched the bawdy strings
Of those white elders; but, escaping,
Left only Death's ironic scraping.
Now, in its immortality, it plays
On the clear viol of her memory,
And makes a constant sacrament of praise.

The House Was Quiet and the World Was Calm

The house was quiet and the world was calm.
The reader became the book; and summer night

Was like the conscious being of the book.
The house was quiet and the world was calm.

The words were spoken as if there was no book,
Except that the reader leaned above the page,

Wanted to lean, wanted much most to be
The scholar to whom his book is true, to whom

The summer night is like a perfection of thought.
The house was quiet because it had to be.

The quiet was part of the meaning, part of the mind:
The access of perfection to the page.

And the world was calm. The truth in a calm world,
In which there is no other meaning, itself

Is calm, itself is summer and night, itself
Is the reader leaning late and reading there.

From *Transport to Summer*, 1947. Copyright 1947 by Wallace Stevens.

The Rock

I

Seventy Years Later

It is an illusion that we were ever alive,
Lived in the houses of mothers, arranged ourselves
By our own motions in a freedom of air.

Regard the freedom of seventy years ago.
It is no longer air. The houses still stand,
Though they are rigid in rigid emptiness.

Even our shadows, their shadows, no longer remain.
The lives these lived in the mind are at an end.
They never were . . . The sounds of the guitar

Were not and are not. Absurd. The words spoken
Were not and are not. It is not to be believed.
The meeting at noon at the edge of the field seems like

An invention, an embrace between one desperate clod
And another in a fantastic consciousness,
In a queer assertion of humanity:

A theorem proposed between the two—
Two figures in a nature of the sun,
In the sun's design of its own happiness,

As if nothingness contained a métier,
A vital assumption, an impermanence
In its permanent cold, an illusion so desired

That the green leaves came and covered the high rock,
That the lilacs came and bloomed, like a blindness cleaned,
Exclaiming bright sight, as it was satisfied,

In a birth of sight. The blooming and the musk
Were being alive, an incessant being alive,
A particular of being, that gross universe.

II
The Poem as Icon

It is not enough to cover the rock with leaves.
We must be cured of it by a cure of the ground
Or a cure of ourselves, that is equal to a cure

Of the ground, a cure beyond forgetfulness.
And yet the leaves, if they broke into bud,
If they broke into bloom, if they bore fruit,

And if we ate the incipient colorings
Of their fresh culls might be a cure of the ground.
The fiction of the leaves is the icon

Of the poem, the figuration of blessedness,
And the icon is the man. The pearled chaplet of spring,
The magnum wreath of summer, time's autumn snood,

Its copy of the sun, these cover the rock.
These leaves are the poem, the icon and the man.
These are a cure of the ground and of ourselves,

In the predicate that there is nothing else.
They bud and bloom and bear their fruit without change.
They are more than leaves that cover the barren rock

They bud the whitest eye, the pallidest sprout,
New senses in the engenderings of sense,
The desire to be at the end of distances,

The body quickened and the mind in root.
They bloom as a man loves, as he lives in love.
They bear their fruit so that the year is known,

As if its understanding was brown skin,
The honey in its pulp, the final found,
The plenty of the year and of the world.

In this plenty, the poem makes meanings of the rock,
Of such mixed motion and such imagery
That its barrenness becomes a thousand things

And so exists no more. This is the cure
Of leaves and of the ground and of ourselves.
His words are both the icon and the man.

III
Forms of the Rock in a Night-Hymn

The rock is the gray particular of man's life,
The stone from which he rises, up—and—ho,
The step to the bleaker depths of his descents . . .

The rock is the stern particular of the air,
The mirror of the planets, one by one,
But through man's eye, their silent rhapsodist,

Turquoise the rock, at odious evening bright
With redness that sticks fast to evil dreams;
The difficult rightness of half-risen day.

The rock is the habitation of the whole,
Its strength and measure, that which is near, point A
In a perspective that begins again

At B: the origin of the mango's rind.
It is the rock where tranquil must adduce
Its tranquil self, the main of things, the mind,

The starting point of the human and the end,
That in which space itself is contained, the gate
To the enclosure, day, the things illumined

By day, night and that which night illumines,
Night and its midnight-minting fragrances,
Night's hymn of the rock, as in a vivid sleep.

Of Modern Poetry

The poem of the mind in the act of finding
What will suffice. It has not always had
To find: the scene was set; it repeated what
Was in the script.
               Then the theatre was changed
To something else. Its past was a souvenir.
It has to be living, to learn the speech of the place.
It has to face the men of the time and to meet
The women of the time. It has to think about war
And it has to find what will suffice. It has
To construct a new stage. It has to be on that stage
And, like an insatiable actor, slowly and
With meditation, speak words that in the ear,
In the delicatest ear of the mind, repeat,
Exactly, that which it wants to hear, at the sound
Of which, an invisible audience listens,
Not to the play, but to itself, expressed
In an emotion as of two people, as of two
Emotions becoming one. The actor is
A metaphysician in the dark, twanging
An instrument, twanging a wiry string that gives
Sounds passing through sudden rightnesses, wholly
Containing the mind, below which it cannot descend,
Beyond which it has no will to rise.
                    It must
Be the finding of a satisfaction, and may
Be of a man skating, a woman dancing, a woman
Combing. The poem of the act of the mind.

From *Parts of a World*, 1942. Copyright 1942 by Wallace Stevens.

Arthur Waley

[TRANSLATOR]

On the Birth of His Son

by Su Tung-p'o (A.D. 1036–1101)

Families, when a child is born,
Want it to be intelligent.
I, through intelligence,
Having wrecked my whole life,
Only hope the baby will prove
Ignorant and stupid.
Then he will crown a tranquil life
By becoming a Cabinet Minister.

From *Translations from the Chinese*, 1941. Copyright 1941 by Alfred A. Knopf, Inc.

Elinor Wylie

The Eagle and the Mole

Avoid the reeking herd,
Shun the polluted flock,
Live like that stoic bird,
The eagle of the rock.

The huddled warmth of crowds
Begets and fosters hate;
He keeps, above the clouds,
His cliff inviolate.

When flocks are folded warm,
And herds to shelter run,
He sails above the storm,
He stares into the sun.

If in the eagle's track
Your sinews cannot leap,
Avoid the lathered pack,
Turn from the steaming sheep.

If you would keep your soul
From spotted sight or sound,
Live like the velvet mole;
Go burrow underground.

From *Nets to Catch the Wind*, 1921. Copyright 1921 by Alfred A. Knopf, Inc. Renewal copyright 1949 by William Rose Benét.

And there hold intercourse
With roots of trees and stones,
With rivers at their source,
And disembodied bones.

Address to My Soul

My soul, be not disturbed
By planetary war;
Remain securely orbed
In this contracted star.

Fear not, pathetic flame;
Your sustenance is doubt:
Glassed in translucent dream
They cannot snuff you out.

Wear water, or a mask
Of unapparent cloud;
Be brave and never ask
A more defunctive shroud.

The universal points
Are shrunk into a flower;
Between its delicate joints
Chaos keeps no power.

The pure integral form,
Austere and silver-dark,
Is balanced on the storm
In its predestined arc.

Small as a sphere of rain
It slides along the groove
Whose path is furrowed plain
Among the suns that move.

The shapes of April buds
Outlive the phantom year:
Upon the void at odds
The dewdrop falls severe.

Five-petalled flame, be cold:
Be firm, dissolving star:
Accept the stricter mould
That makes you singular.

A Complete List of Authors,

CLASSIC AND CONTEMPORARY,

PUBLISHED OVER THE BORZOI IMPRINT, 1915–1965

*[including the authors and editors of special limited edi-
tions, reissues, collections of correspondence, and classics]*

Daniel Aaron (ed.)
Kobo Abé
Peter Abelard
Gerald Abraham
Peter Abrahams
Lawrence Edwin Abt (ed.)
A. H. Adair
Ansel Adams
Brooks Adams
Cleve F. Adams
John Adams
John Quincy Adams
Léonie Adams
Randolph G. Adams (ed.)
Edward Adler
Conrad Aiken
Henry David Aiken
Henry G. Aikman
AJO
Antonio de Alarcón
P. A. de Alarcón
Don Juan Ruiz de Alarcón y
  Mendoza
Alastair
George Albee
Mark Aldanov
Richard Aldington

James Aldridge
Sholom Aleichem
Franz Alexander
William Alfred
Anne Allardice
Eric W. Allen
H. Warner Allen
Johannes Allen
James Z. Alner
Antony Alpers
Hollis Alpert
Richard Altick
Corrado Alvaro
Jorge Amado
Eric Ambler
Kay Ambrose
Emmanuel Anati
Hans Christian Andersen
Bern Anderson
Nels Anderson
Raymond W. Anderson
Marius André
George Gordon Andrews
Leonid Andreyev
Ivo Andrić
Jerzy Andrzejewski
Claude Anet

Andrew Angarsky
L. L. B. Angas
Joseph Warner Angell (ed.)
Paul Angle
Charles Angoff
Jens Anker
Russell Annabel
Katharine Anthony
Etienne Antonelli
Benjamin Appel
C. J. Apperley
John T. Appleby
Paul H. Appleby
William Archer
Germán Arciniegas
Walter Arensberg
Philippe Ariès
Jean Ariss
Merle Armitage
Anne W. Armstrong
Harold Armstrong
Martin Armstrong
William Armstrong
Alma C. Arnold
Elliott Arnold
Frederick B. Artz
Michael Artzibashef
Newton Arvin (ed.)
Herbert Asbury
Bernard Ash
Percy Ashley
James Aston
Alex Atkinson
J. Brooks Atkinson
Margaret Atkinson
William Attwood
Marjorie Auerbach
Emile Augier
Garry August
Autolycus (Leonard Bacon)
Kay Avery
C. C. Ayer
Margaret Ayer
Azorín

Dwight V. Babcock
F. Lawrence Babcock, Jr.
I. Babel
G. L. Bach
Carol Bache
Ingeborg Bachmann
Lawrence P. Bachmann
Leonard Bacon
Walter Bagehot
Enid Bagnold

Frank Bailey
John R. Baker
Laura Nelson Baker
Nina Brown Baker
Russell Baker
John L. Balderston
Robert Baldick (ed.)
Cyrus LeRoy Baldridge
Hanson W. Baldwin
James Baldwin
Robert F. Bales (ed.)
Albert G. A. Balz
Honoré de Balzac
Herman Bang
Francis Hyde Bangs
Michael Banner
Nina Lloyd Banning
Jules Barbey d'Aurevilly
Maurice Baring
Lena Barksdale
Joseph W. Barlow
Harry Elmer Barnes
Lincoln Barnett
Maginel Wright Barney
T. Alexander Barns
P. T. Barnum
Pío Baroja
Stanley Baron
Leighton Barret (adapter)
Lawrence Barrett
Lillian Barrett
Margaret Barrington
Milton L. Barron
Henry Barry
Ruhl Jacob Bartlett (ed.)
Vernon Bartlett
William Warren Bartley III
Ralph Barton
Libushka Bartusek
Victor Basch
Henry Bassett
John Spencer Bassett
Lionel Bataillon
Ernest Sutherland Bates
H. E. Bates
Claire Batigne
Georgina Battiscombe
W. W. Bauer
Betty Baum
Franklin Le Van Baumer (ed.)
Richard G. Baumhoff
Maurice Baumont
René Bazin
Carleton Beals
Louis H. Bean

Charles A. Beard
C. W. Beaumont
Simone de Beauvoir
Simone Beck
Warren Beck
Carl L. Becker
May Lamberton Becker (ed.)
Peter Beckford
William Beebe (ed.)
Sir Thomas Beecham
Samuel H. Beer
Thomas Beer
Max Beerbohm
Brendan Behan
Jeanne Behrend (ed.)
Jack Belden
Ben Belitt
Aubrey F. G. Bell
Clair H. Bell
Coral Bell
James Warner Bellah
Leopold Bellak (ed.)
Hilaire Belloc
Emma S. Bellows
George W. Bellows
Samuel Flagg Bemis
Effie Bendann
William Rose Benét
Frans G. Bengtsson
René Benjamin
Joan Bennett
John W. Bennett
Peggy Bennett
Alexandre Benois
Pierre Benoît
Isaac Benrubi
E. C. Bentley
Robert Benton
Walter Benton
Konrad Bercovici
Bernard Berenson
John Beresford
Ragnar Berg
John Berger
Hjalmar Bergman
Ray Bergman
Arthur F. Beringause
Hector Berlioz
Count Folke Bernadotte
Josephine B. Bernhard
Aline Bernstein
Herman Bernstein
Charles Walter Berry
Alfred Bertholet
Louisette Bertholle

Pierre Berton
Anthony Bertram
Elsa Beskow
Adolfo Best-Maugard
Arthur Bestor
H. L. Betten
Audrey White Beyer
Geoffrey Bibby
Henri Bidou
Libero Bigiaretti
Alfred Hoyt Bill
June Bingham
Wilfred E. Binkley
Ottwell Binns
John Peale Bishop
Morris Bishop
Karl Bjarnhof
Edwin Björkman
Lou Blachly
Cyril E. Black
Hugo L. Black
Irma Simonton Black
Algernon Blackwood
George Blake
Peter Blake
Russell Blankenship
Vicente Blasco-Ibáñez
Horace Bleackley (ed.)
Rudi Blesh
Alberto Blest-Gana
Bruce Bliven
Bror von Blixen-Finecke
Herbert A. Bloch
Marc Bloch
Libbie Block
Morton Wilfred Bloomfield
Dorothy Blumenstock
Edmund Blunden
Wilfrid Blunt
Wilfrid Scawen Blunt
C. A. Bodelsen
Maxwell Bodenheim
Jacob Böhme
P. Boissonnade
Curtis Bok
Ben Zion Bokser
Luis A. Bolin
Hector Bolitho
Herbert Eugene Bolton
James Bone
Charles Bonner
Mary Graham Bonner
T. D. Bonner
Arna Bontemps
Percy Boomer

Bradford Allen Booth (ed.)
Edward Townsend Booth
Ernest Booth
Clare Boothe
Josef Bor
Mary Borden
Edgar F. Borgatta (ed.)
Hal Borland
François Bourlière
Elizabeth Bowen
Robert O. Bowen
Ella Shannon Bowles
Jane Bowles
William Dodgson Bowman
C. R. Boxer
Neith Boyce
Ernest Boyd
William Boyd (ed.)
David D. Boyden
Kay Boyle
René Boylesve
Charles Brackett
Malcolm Bradbury
William Bradford
Phillips Bradley (ed.)
William Aspenwall Bradley
Claude Bragdon
Melvin Bragg
Paul C. Bragg
Christianna Brand
Oscar Brand
Karl Brandi
Wilfred Brandon
Otto Braun
Benjamin Brawley
Marie Bregendahl
Joseph Breitbach
J. V. Breitwieser
Frederick Hazlitt Brennan
Barbara Brenner
Paul Brewster (ed.)
Carl Bridenbaugh
Ann Bridge
Robert Bridges
Howard M. Brier
Barbara Briggs
A. A. Brill
John Malcolm Brinnin
Peter Brinson
Emma L. Brock
Max Brod
Fawn M. Brodie
George D. Brodsky
D. W. Brogan
Winifred Bromhall

Emily Brontë
Jocelyn Brooke
Alden Brooks
Cleanth Brooks
Paul Brooks
Walter R. Brooks
Brigid Brophy
D. C. Brown
E. K. Brown
Harry Brown
Hilton Brown
Louise Fargo Brown
Sherman W. Brown
Gawen Brownrigg
Ferdinand Bruckner
René Brunet
Emma Beatrice Brunner
Laurids Bruun
George S. Bryan
Johannes Buchholtz
Blossom Budney
Frederick Buechner
Raymond Leslie Buell
Remo Bufano
Gerald Bullett
Hans von Bülow
Ivan Bunin
John Bunzel
Madeleine Bunzel
José Gou Burgell
Roger Burlingame
A. R. Burn
Dana Burnet
Constance Buel Burnett
W. R. Burnett
Arthur Robert Burns
Jean Burton
John W. Burton
Sir Richard F. Burton
Margaret Just Butcher
George F. Butler
Dorothy Gilman Butters
L. H. Dudley Buxton
Hugh Byas
Raymond T. Bye
Witter Bynner
Robert Byron

Feldwebel C . . .
Coulson T. Cade
Sylvanus Cadwallader
Joseph Caillaux
James M. Cain
Huntington Cairns (ed.)
Clinch Calkins

Raymond E. Callahan
Harold Callender
Dion Clayton Calthrop
M. D. Calvocoressi
Kenneth Neill Cameron (ed.)
Raymond R. Camp
Alexander Campbell
Alfred S. Campbell
Harriette R. Campbell
Albert Camus
Elias Canetti
Alyce Canfield
Jimmy Cannon
Francis Carco
Arthur H. Carhart
Clancy Carlile
John Roy Carlson
Harry J. Carman
Carl Carmer
Mosco Carner
Hans Carossa
Francis Carpenter
Alejo Carpentier
Archie Carr
Edward Hallett Carr
José Suárez Carreño
Sally Carrighar
George Barr Carson, Jr.
Otto Cartellieri
John Carter
Mary L. Caruso
Giacomo Casanova
W. J. Cash
Marquis Boni de Castellane
Arturo Castiglioni
Michel del Castillo
Willa Cather
G. E. G. Catlin
William B. Catton
Paul Cauer (ed.)
David Causey
Henry Céard
C. W. Ceram
Miguel de Cervantes
Lynwood M. Chace
Henry Chafetz
Feodor I. Chaliapin
Narcissa Chamberlain
Raymond Chandler
Walter Chandoha (ed.)
Frederick Chapman
Maristan Chapman
Victor Chapot
Warren Chappell
Gerda Charles

Remy Charlip
Annie Vivanti Chartres
Abram Chasins
François-René de Chateaubriand
Anton Chekhov
Cora Cheney
Sheldon Cheney
Louis Cheslock (ed.)
Haakon Chevalier
Abel Chevalley
Samuel C. Chew
Edward P. Cheyney
Donald Barr Chidsey
Julia Child
C. M. Child (ed.)
Nellise Child
V. Gordon Childe
Frédéric François Chopin
Henry F. Chorley
Samuel Chotzinoff
Eric Chou
Eugene Christian
Anatole Chujoy
Creighton Churchill
Robert Churchill
Verne Chute
Bert Claflin
James Gordon Clapp
Louise A. K. S. Clappe
Emily Clark
John Grahame Clark
John Maurice Clark
Clyde B. Clason
Robert Glass Cleland
Elizabeth Clemons
Logan Clendening
James Cleugh
Winston Clewes
W. K. Clifford
Allan S. Clifton
Hans Cloos
Ben C. Clough
Harold Clurman
John F. Coar
Grace Stone Coates
Elizabeth J. Coatsworth
William Cobbett
Alvin Langdon Coburn
Cornelius Cofyn
Elliot E. Cohen (ed.)
George D. H. Cole
Margaret Cole
Taylor Cole (ed.)
Manning Coles
Glenna Collett

John Collier
Susan Colling
Dale Collins
Maurice Collis
Joel Colton
Anne Colver
Henry Steele Commager
John R. Commons
Ivy Compton-Burnett
Helen B. Condon
Herbert Wheaton Congdon
Grace Hazard Conkling
Rearden Conner
M. Benjamin de Constant (ed.)
Alonso de Contreras
J. Gregory Conway
Cecil M. Cook
Marion Belden Cook
Alistair Cooke
Muriel Cooke
C. H. Cooley
Carleton S. Coon
James Fenimore Cooper
A. E. Coppard
Chester Cornish
Igor Caesar Count Corti
Frederick Baron Corvo
Edward S. Corwin
March Cost
Adolfo Costa du Rels
R. N. Coudenhove-Kalergi
Father Louis Coulange
G. G. Coulton
John Cournos
Geoffrey Cousins
John Cousins
Walter Coutu
Miguel Covarrubias
Adrian Cowell
Henry Cowell
Sidney Cox
George Harmon Coxe
Mildred Cram
C. Gregory Crampton
Charles Edward Crane
Stephen Crane
Adelaide Crapsey
Algernon Sidney Crapsey
John V. Craven
Finla Goff Crawford (ed.)
Jack R. Crawford
Nelson Antrim Crawford
Lawrence A. Cremin
Angelo Crespi
Benedetto Croce

Rupert Croft-Cooke
Maurice Croiset
Anthony Cronin
William F. Crosby
Margaret Crosland
Russel Crouse
Alice Crow
Lester D. Crow
Chester T. Crowell
J. R. Crowell
Joseph Crozier
Richard S. Crutchfield
Anne Culver
William Cummings
Charles Greene Cumston
Caroline Cunningham
Richard Curle
Dale Curran
Richard N. Current
Isabel Currier
Alice Turner Curtis
C. P. Curtis, Jr.
James Curtis
Marguerite Curtis
Paul A. Curtis
Mina K. Curtiss
Thomas Quinn Curtiss (ed.)
Frank Hamilton Cushing
Lin Cutler

James McBride Dabbs
Eugène Dabit
Virginius Dabney
Roald Dahl
Edwin F. Dakin (ed.)
Chester Dale
Maude Dale
Morris Dallett
Hugh Dalton
G. Ezra Dane (ed.)
Henry Daniel-Rops
Harriet McDoual Daniels
Pierre Daninos
Dante Alighieri
Esther Birdsall Darling
Henry Darlington (ed.)
R. D. Darrell
James Daugherty (ed.)
Jocelyn Davey
Elizabeth David
Eugene Davidson
G. D. G. Davies
Robertson Davies
Thomas A. Davies
William H. Davies

Allan Davis
Hallam Walker Davis
Coningsby Dawson
C. A. Dawson-Scott
Clarence Day
Frank B. Deakin
Agnes Louise Dean
Gordon Dean
Vera Micheles Dean
L. J. deBekker
Angie Debo
Edith de Born
J. Declareuil
Warwick Deeping
Daniel Defoe
Alfred de Grazia
Ludwig Dehio
David Cornel DeJong
Dola de Jong
E. M. Delafield
Walter de la Mare
L. Delaporte
Mazo de la Roche
Aubert de la Rue
Paul Delarue
Lillian de la Torre
Floyd Dell
Sidney Dell
Lester del Ray
Peter de Mendelssohn
Frank Denman
Geoffrey Dennis
Ludwell Denny
Alan Dent (ed.)
John Yerbury Dent
W. Deonna
Peter de Polnay
Dan De Quille
Richard de Rochemont
José Luís Martín Descalzo
Jean Descola
Leo Deuel
Gwen Dew
Elisabeth Anthony Dexter
Robert Cloutman Dexter
Everett Dick
Charles Dickens
J. Dickenson (ed.)
Edward R. Dickson (ed.)
Charles Diehl
Irving Dilliard (ed.)
Benjamin Disraeli
John V. Dittemore
Beulah Marie Dix
Valentine Dobrée

Heimito von Doderer
Johannes Dogigli
Maurice Dolbier
Gene d'Olive
David Donald
Stanley F. Donath
Hobart Donavan
Maurice Donnay
Joseph Donon
José Donoso
Jacques Dorey
Iris Dornfeld
Edward Doro
Feodor Dostoevsky
Lord Alfred Douglas
Harry G. Dowdall
Clifford Dowdey
Olin Downes
Elizabeth Downs
Donald Marquand Dozer (ed.)
A. B. Drachmann
Ernest G. Draper
Nancy Draper
Elizabeth Dresser
Tom Driberg
Pierre Drieu La Rochelle
John Drinkwater
Leonard Drohan
Isabel Drummond
Friedrich Duerrenmatt
Anne Duffield
R. L. Duffus
Alfred Duggan
Winifred Duke
Glenn S. Dumke (ed.)
Ethel S. Dummer
Barrows Dunham
Charles T. Duncan (ed.)
Alan Dunn
Henri Dupré
Jimmy Durante
Theo Durrant
Olav Duun
James Henry Duveen
Roger Duvoisin
W. A. Dwiggins
Edwin Erich Dwinger
Hugh L. Dwyer
Ossip Dymov
James Dyson

Harriet Ide Eager
Solomon Eagle (J. C. Squire)
Lawrence Earl
Roger East

Max Eastman
David Easton
Dorothy Easton
John Easton
Walter Prichard Eaton
Charlotte Ebener
Irmengarde Eberle
Alcide Ebray
Eça de Queiros
Marriner S. Eccles
José Echegaray
Hans von Eckardt
H. S. Ede
Leon Edel
Vera Edelstadt
F. Edgar (ed.)
Lucile Selk Edgerston
Dorothy Edwards
Ilya Ehrenburg
Albert Ehrenstein
Alfred Einstein
Lewis Einstein
Philip Eisenberg
Karl Ekman
Samuel Milton Elam
Robert H. Elias
T. S. Eliot
Juliette Elkon
Vilhelm Ellermann
Kathleen Morrow Elliot
William Yandell Elliott
Elmer Ellis
Mary Grosvenor Ellsworth
Jacques Ellul
Robert P. Elmer
Jefferson Elmore
Arthur Eloesser
Lord Elton
Sven Elvestad
Carl Engel
William Engel
Stuart D. Engstrand
Abraham Epstein
Phoebe Erickson
David B. Ericson
Richard Eriksen
Albert Erlande
Margaret S. Ernst
John Erskine
John J. Espey
Aurelio M. Espinosa (ed.)
Gabrielle Estivals
Bergen Evans
George Heberton Evans, Jr.
Jean Evans

John Evans
W. A. Evans
Hal G. Evarts
David Ewen (ed.)
Max Ewing
Mordecai Ezekiel

Doris Faber
Alfred Fabre-Luce
Clifton Fadiman (ed.)
Peter Faecke
William Fain
Nan Fairbrother
Paul Farmer
Michael Farrell
Julian Farren
I. Hadfield Farthing
Nathan Fasten
Elie Faure
Joan Lee Faust (ed.)
Lucien Febvre
Harry H. Fein
Herbert Feis
T. R. Feiwel
Rose Feld
Floyd M. Feldman
William Fellner
Harold W. Felton
Phyllis R. Fenner
Ernest Fenollosa
Charles W. Ferguson
Erna Fergusson
Harvey Fergusson
Friedrich Wilhelm Fernau
Michael Fessier
Arthur Davison Ficke
A. Fielding
Henry Fielding
R. Welldon Finn
Alex Fischer
Jacques Fischer
Max Fischer
Rudolph Fisher
Sidney Nettleton Fisher
Earl E. Fisk (ed.)
G. W. Fitch
Constantine FitzGibbon
Ardo Flakkeberg
Harry W. Flannery
Gustave Flaubert
James Elroy Flecker
J. S. Fletcher
Svend Fleuron
James Thomas Flexner
Alexander Clarence Flick

Timothy Flint
Barbara Newhall Follett
Wilson Follett
Clarita de Forceville
Ford Madox Ford
Guy J. Forgue
E. M. Forster
Robert S. Forsythe (ed.)
Jan Fortune
John Fothergill
Georges de la Fouchardière
C. E. Fox
Fannie Ferber Fox
Sidney A. Fox
Osmond K. Fraenkel
André François
Bernard Frank
Bruno Frank
John P. Frank
Philipp Frank
Gilbert Frankau
Viktor E. Frankl
John Hope Franklin
Herbert F. Fraser
D. F. Fraser-Harris
E. Franklin Frazier
Ray Frazier
John T. Frederick
Frank Freidel
Richard Müller Freienfels
Sigmund Freud
Gilberto Freyre
Donald Friede
Egon Friedell
Robert Frost
Ralph Frye
Walter René Fuerst
George W. Fuller
Henry B. Fuller
René Fülöp-Miller
Rocco Fumento
Bess Furman
Clifton Joseph Furness (ed.)
Edwin Fussell
Futabatei
T. R. Fyvel

Dennis Gabor
A. Gagarine (ed.)
Otto Willi Gail
Pierre-Dominique Gaisseau
Hans Gal
Iago Galdston
Zona Gale
Paul Gallico

Donald Gallup (ed.)
Alfred Ganachilly
Harry Gannes
Rudolph Ganz
Jorge García-Granados
Wayne Gard
Elizabeth Garner
David Garnett
Edward Garnett
Richard Garnett
Morris E. Garnsey
John A. Garraty
V. M. Garshin
Viola Gerard Garvin
Beverley Gasner
Jim Gasque
Paul Gates
Robert Gathorne-Hardy (ed.)
Pola Gauguin
Théophile Gautier
Peter Gay
Zhenya Gay
Mark Gayn
Emile Gebhart
Gustaf af Geijerstam
Stanley Geist
Roland Gelatt
M. Dorothy George
W. H. George
William Gerhardi
Ira Gershwin
Friedrich Gerstäcker
Waguih Ghali
C. Virgil Gheorghiu
G. S. Ghurye
Robert Gibbons
Kahlil Gibran
William Gibson
André Gide
Charles Gide
Stephen Gilbert
Stuart Gilbert
Sir W. S. Gilbert
James Edward Gillespie
Edmund Gilligan
Margaret Gilmour
Arnold Gingrich
Jean Giono
Lawrence H. Gipson
Jean Giraudoux
José María Gironella
R. C. Givler
Milton Glaser
Shirley Glaser
Alexander von Gleichen-Russwurm

Marion Glendining
Isa Glenn
Gustave Glotz
Eleanor Glueck
Sheldon Glueck
Count Arthur de Gobineau
Scott Goddard (ed.)
Jon Godden
Rumer Godden
William Godwin
Johann Wolfgang von Goethe
Nikolai Gogol
Robert S. Gold
Isaac Goldberg
Grace B. Golden
Alexander A. Goldenweiser
Louis Golding
Emma Goldman
Eric F. Goldman
William Goldman
Carlo Goldoni
Claire Goll
Ivan Goncharov
Edmond de Goncourt
Jules de Goncourt
G. P. Gooch
Earle Goodenow
Philip Goodman
Geraint Goodwin
John B. L. Goodwin
Frank Goodwyn
Michel Gordey
Matthew Gordon
Wendell C. Gordon
Geoffrey Gorer
Maxim Gorky
William P. Gottlieb
Fruma Gottschalk
Louis Gottschalk
Louis Moreau Gottschalk
Sir Ernest Gowers
Juan Goytisolo
Carl H. Grabo
Oskar Maria Graf
Stephen Graham
Marcel Granet
Shirley Ann Grau
John Graves
Ralph Graves
Robert Graves
Cecil Gray
George W. Gray
James Gray
Horace Greeley
Fletcher M. Green (ed.)

John Greenway
Martin Gregor-Dellin
John Gregory
Albert Grenier
Roger Grenier
Nordahl Grieg
Edward Grierson
Jacob Grimm
Wilhelm Grimm
A. J. Grodin
J. A. Grohusko
Maurice Grosser
George Grossmith
Weedon Grossmith
René Grousset
Russell Clark Grove
Adolf Grünbaum
Paul Gsell
Philip Guedalla
Albert J. Guérard
Charles Guignebert
João Guimarães Rosa
Luther Halsey Gulick
Peggy Gulick
Gunnar Gunnarsson
Gösta Gustaf-Janson
Anne Guy
René Guyon
Martín Luís Guzmán

Magnhild Haalke
Berta Hader
Elmer Hader
John M. Hadley
Victor Wolfgang von Hagen
B. H. Haggin
Richard Hakluyt
Bolton Hall (ed.)
Carroll D. Hall
David Hall
Gertrude Hall
H. Duncan Hall
Leland Hall
Tom Hall
Wilbur Hall
William Hall
Johannes Haller
Mauritz A. Hallgren
Nancy Hallinan
Philip Hamburger
Hugh M. Hamill, Jr. (ed.)
Katharine Hamill
Thomas J. Hamilton
Walton Hamilton
Otto Hammann

Dag Hammarskjöld
Oscar Hammerstein II
Dashiell Hammett
Kenneth R. Hammond
John Hampson
Knut Hamsun
Learned Hand
Oscar Handlin
Lewis Hanke (ed.)
Frank H. Hankins
Whitney J. Hanks
James Hanley
Earl Parker Hanson
Simon Harcourt-Smith
Walter Harding
A. Paul Hare (ed.)
Marjory Gane Harkness
Oswald H. Harland
René d'Harnoncourt
Headley Harpers
Margaret Case Harriman
Alan Harrington
Harry Rowland Harris
Herbert Harris
Mark Harris
Seymour E. Harris
J. B. Harris-Burland
John B. Harrison
Richard Edes Harrison
Tom Harrisson
Jean-Paul Harroy
Jeffrey Hart (ed.)
Dorothy Hartley
Eugene L. Hartley
L. P. Hartley
Samuel W. Hartwell
Alexander Harvey
Peggy Harvey
Francis Haskell
H. J. Haskell
M. L. Haskins
A. W. Haslett
Macdonald Hastings
Owen Hatteras
Ludwig Hatvany
Einar Haugen
Arnold Hauser
Ernest A. Hauser
Manfred Hausmann
Jacquetta Hawkes (ed.)
Desmond Hawkins
Nancy Hawkins
Gessner G. Hawley
Hildegarde Hawthorne
Nathaniel Hawthorne

Sara Henderson Hay
Sterling Hayden
H. Gordon Hayes
Donald Hayne
Williams Haynes
H. R. Hays
Harold M. Hays
Charles W. Hayward
Shirley Hazzard
William Healy
Ben Hecht
Herbert Heckmann
Helen Hedrick
Werner Hegemann
Konrad Heiden
Verner von Heidenstam
Van Campen Heilner
Michael A. Heilperin
John Held, Jr.
Otto Heller
George S. Hellman
Lillian Hellman
E. C. Helmreich
Daniel Henderson
Gertrude Henderson
Ives Hendrick
James Henle
Lewis Herber
A. P. Herbert
Joseph Hergesheimer
Yuri Herman
Booton Herndon
Hubert Herring
Karl M. Herrligkoffer
Edward A. Herron
John Hersey
Francis S. Herskovits
Melville J. Herskovits
Alexander Herzen
William B. Hesseltine
Charles H. Hession
A. L. Hetherington
Agnes Danforth Hewes
Laurence Hewes
W. W. Hewett
Dorothy Hewlett
Elinor Wallace Hiatt
William Hickey
Edward Higbee
Charles F. Higham
Gilbert Highet
John Hightower
Herbert Hill (ed.)
Russell Hill
Harold Newcomb Hillebrand

Wilhelmine von Hillern
Alan Hillgarth
May Hillman
Robert Hillyer
William Hurd Hillyer
Chester Himes
L. G. Hines
Pamela Hinkson
Richard W. Hinton
A. William Hire
Edwin W. Hirsch
Robin Hiscock
Alger Hiss
Sir Samuel Hoare
Adam Hobhouse
R. L. Hobson
James Lansdale Hodson
Charles Hoffman
Paul Hoffman
Ross J. S. Hoffman
Richard Hofstadter
Lancelot Hogben
Hajo Holborn
Stewart H. Holbrook
Arthur N. Holcombe
Bob Holland
Dan Holland
Marion Holland
Ray P. Holland
Lee M. Hollander
W. Eugene Hollon
Emory Holloway
Charles S. Holmes
Henry Wyman Holmes
Helge Holst
George C. Homans
Homer
Léon Homo
Sidney Hook
Forrestine Hooker
Eileen Hooton-Smith
Arthur Hopkins
E. O. Hoppé
Horace
Sidney Horler
David Horowitz
J. F. Horrabin
I. M. Hotep
Leslie Hotson
James E. Householder
A. E. Housman
Louis How
Kathleen Howard
Ed Howe
Cyrus Hoy

Rosemary Hoyland
Nancy Hoyt
Clément Huart
Lindley Williams Hubbell
Henri Hubert
Robert Norman Hubner
Evariste-Régis Huc
Ricarda Huch
Bryce D. Hudgins
Stephen Hudson
W. H. Hudson
H. Stuart Hughes
Langston Hughes
Margaret M. Hughes (ed.)
Richard Hughes
Kathryn Hulme
Martin A. S. Hume
S. Hume
William Humphrey
R. A. Humphreys (ed.)
Howard Hunt
Morton M. Hunt
Dard Hunter
Bernard F. Huppé
Fannie Hurst
L. M. Hussey
Ernest Hutcheson
Emily Grant Hutchings
Vere Hutchinson
Bruce Hutchison
Julian Huxley
Albert M. Hyamson
Harold M. Hyman
Stanley Edgar Hyman

Harold L. Ickes
Nobutaka Ike
Jeremy Ingalls
Rex Ingram
Helge Ingstad
Hammond Innes
Nella Innes
Dahlov Ipcar
Robert Irving
Will Irwin
Panaït Istrati
Sumner Ives

S. W. Jackman (ed.)
Christopher S. Jackson
Frederick Jackson
Holbrook Jackson
Robert H. Jackson
J. P. Jacobsen
Dan Jacobson

B. L. Jacot
Philip Jaffe
Henry James
Paul James
Walter James
Storm Jameson
Harriet Janis
A. Jardé
Louise Llewellyn Jarecka
Randall Jarrell
Leland Hamilton Jenks
Randolph Jenks
Axel Jensen
Johannes V. Jensen
Merrill Jensen
Edgar Jepson
F. Tennyson Jesse
Edward Alden Jewell
Joachim Joesten
John of Salisbury
Orrick Johns
Alvin Johnson
E. Bishop Johnson
Gerald W. Johnson
Harold E. Johnson
James Weldon Johnson
Maurice C. Johnson
Pamela Hansford Johnson
R. Brimley Johnson (ed.)
W. Bolingbroke Johnson
Walter Johnson
Johanna Johnston
Oliver M. Johnston
Klaus W. Jonas
Evan Jones
Idwal Jones
Llewellyn Jones
Timothy Angus Jones
W. Tudor Jones
Ben Jonson
Mildred Jordan
Alvin M. Josephy, Jr.
Pierre Jouguet
Jorge Juan
Frances Judge
Jan Juta
Réné Juta

Bruce Kafaroff
Franz Kafka
Wood Kahler
Fritz Kahn
Joan Kahn
Dunbar von Kalckreuth

Aino Kallas
Godmundur Kamban
Yasaku Kamekura (ed.)
Jack Kaminsky
Henry Kane
J. Robert Kantor
Julius Kapp
I. J. Kapstein
David Karp
Yousuf Karsh
Rafael Karsten
Raden Adjeng Kartini
Erich Kästner
George N. Kates
Norman Katkov
Masuo Kato
Adele T. Katz
Leo Katz
Betty Katzoff
George S. Kaufman
Maxine Kaufman
Yasunari Kawabata
Sheila Kaye-Smith
Edmund Keeley (ed.)
Hugh Ll. Keenleyside
Henning Kehler
Emery Kelen
A. G. Keller
Ethel May Kelley
Leon Kellner
Charles E. Kelly
Fred C. Kelly
Wallace McElroy Kelly
Frances Anne Kemble
Coleridge Kennard
Mildred Kennedy
Frank R. Kent
Joseph Kerman
Walter Kerr
Madeleine Kerwin
Joseph Kessel
John Kettlewell
Irmgard Keun
Charles E. Key
V. O. Key, Jr.
John Maynard Keynes
John Oliver Killens
Alice Mary Kimball
Kim Yong Ik
C. Daly King
Mrs. Francis King
William B. King
Hugh Kingsmill (ed.)
Eugene Kinkead
Bruce Kinloch

Philip Kinsley
Andrew Kippis
Michael Kirby
R. G. Kirk
Lincoln Kirstein
Egon Erwin Kisch
Samuel Klaus (ed.)
A. M. Klein
Lenore Klein
Rolf Klep
Clyde K. Kluckhohn
Percy Knauth
Nigel Kneale
William S. Knickerbocker
Bruce W. Knight
Charles R. Knight
Clayton Knight
Grant C. Knight
John Alden Knight
Werner Knop
Edwin H. Knopf
Mildred O. Knopf
John Knowler
William Knowlton
Karl Kobald
John Kobler (ed.)
Adrienne Koch
Erich Koch-Weser
Ursula Koering
Jack Kofoed
Julilly H. Kohler
Otto Koischwitz
Irving Kolodin
Manuel Komroff
Hans Koningsberger
Nicholas Kopeloff
Alexander Kornilov
Anatol Kovarsky
S. Kracauer
H. A. Kramers
George Philip Krapp
David Krech
Hilda Sidney Krech
Alfred Kreymborg
Rosalyn Krokover
Tom Kromer
Louis Kronenberger
P. A. Kropotkin
Peter Krott
John Allen Krout
Joseph Wood Krutch
Erich Kuby
Delia Kuhn
Ferdinand Kuhn
Winifred Kupper

Harold Kurtz
Elizabeth Kytle

Pierre de Labriolle
Phyllis La Farge
Anand Lall
René Lalou
Louis Laloy
Harold Lamb
Millard Lampell
Rom Landau
Charles Landery
Wanda Landowska
Catherine Landreth
Margaret Lane
Wheaton J. Lane
William Thomas Lane
William L. Langer
Elisabeth Langgässer
Henry Wysham Lanier
Vittorio Lanternari
David Glass Larg
Margaret Larkin
Hanna Astrup Larsen
J. Anker Larsen
Nella Larsen
Christopher Lasch
Bruno Lasker
Edward Lasker
Harold D. Lasswell
Barbara Latham
Thérèse Louis Latour
Stefanie Lauer
Marcus Lauesen
Margaret Laurence
William L. Laurence
Jonreed Lauritzen
James Laver
D. H. Lawrence
Frieda Lawrence
Robert Lawson
Halldór Laxness
Jack Thomas Leahy
F. R. Leavis
Norbert Lebermann
Charlotte Lederer
Norbert Lederer
C. P. Lee
Carl A. Lefevre (ed.)
Helen E. Lefevre (ed.)
Louis Le Fevre
Marcel Légaut
John Lehmann
Avery Leiserson
Joaquim G. Leithäuser

C. A. Lejeune
Georges Lemaitre
Jacques Lemarchand
H. R. Lenormand
Elbert Lenrow (ed.)
Lois Lenski
Richard W. Leopold
Albert Lepawsky
Leo Lerman
M. Y. Lermontov
Mervyn LeRoy
Don D. Lescohier
Nikolai Leskov
Larry Lesueur
Meridel Le Sueur
Francis Ellington Leupp
Paul Levack
E. Frances Le Valley
Aaron Levenstein
Carlo Levi
Harry Levin
Jack Levin
J. J. Levison
Beryl Harold Levy
H. Levy
Harry Levy
Hyman Levy
John Levy
Newman Levy
Lucien Lévy-Bruhl
John Lewellen
Beth Lewis
Edith Lewis
Ewart Lewis
May Lewis
Oscar Lewis
Roger Lewis
Roy Lewis
Wilmarth Lewis
Wyndham Lewis
Sam A. Lewisohn
Walter Libby
Alexis Lichine
A. J. Liebling
Richard G. Lillard
C. Lindeman
Howard Lindsay
Arthur S. Link
Lilo Linke
Eric Linklater
Ralph Linton
John Thomas Lister (ed.)
Donald J. Lloyd
E. M. H. Lloyd
Margaret Lloyd

Lobagola
Adolphe Lods
Norah Lofts
John Logan
Remie Lohse
Helen Lombard
Eula Long
Edward Loomis
Frederic Loomis
Sándor Lorand
The Earl Loreburn
Ferdinand Lot
Pierre Loti
Paul-Louis
G. Constant Lounsbery
Arthur Lourié
William Lovett
Walter Lowenfels (ed.)
Max Lowenthal
H. T. Lowe-Porter
Mrs. Belloc Lowndes
Marion Lowndes
Susan Lowndes
Torcuato Luca de Tena
Anthony M. Ludovici
Mabel Dodge Luhan
Katharine Du Pre Lumpkin
Dudley Cammett Lunt
Emilio Lussu
Hermann Lutz
Bohun Lynch
John Lynch (ed.)
Eugene Lyons
Luella Lyons
Stella H. Lyons

Carleton Mabee
Mary Frost Mabon
Wilson MacArthur
F. F. MacCabe
Ross Macdonald
Malcolm MacDonald
Syl MacDowell
Haldane MacFall
Arthur Machen
Elisabeth MacIntyre
Robert M. MacIver
Connie Mack
Gerstle Mack
Orin Mack
J. W. Mackail
Percy MacKaye
Compton Mackenzie
Donald A. Mackenzie
Archibald MacLeish

Leroy MacLeod
William Christie MacLeod
Francis MacManus
Denis Mack Smith
Louis Madelin
Marcus Magill
Maurice Magnes
Edward M. Maisel
Ralph H. Major
John M. Maki
Alida Malkus
Eduardo Mallea
Jerre Mangione
Don M. Mankiewicz
Heinrich Mann
Klaus Mann
Thomas Mann
Grete Mannheim
Ethel Mannin
Olivia Manning
Katherine Mansfield
Florence Maple
Josef Marais
Leslie A. Marchand
Ludwig Marcuse
Arthur J. Marder
Kurt W. Marek (C. W. Ceram)
Paul Margueritte
Victor Margueritte
Marie, Queen of Roumania
Johannes Maringer
Irving Mark (ed.)
Gene Markey
Virgil Markham
John Marks
Mickey Klar Marks
Louis Marlow
Frederick Marryat
Bruce Marshall
May Davies Martenet
Charles E. Martin
John Bartlow Martin
Judith Martin
Kingsley Martin
Philip L. Martin
Harry Martinson
Emmanuel de Martonne
Daniel Gregory Mason
Jeanne Massey
Loys Masson
René Masson
C. F. G. Masterman
Dexter Masters
Nicholas A. Masters
Powys Mathers

David Mathew
Albert Mathiez
T. S. Matthews
F. O. Matthiessen
Michel Matveev
Angus Maude
W. Somerset Maugham
Guy de Maupassant
André Maurois
Simone André Maurois
Chester C. Maxey
William Maxwell
Henry F. May
Robert L. May
Gustav Mayer
Morrow Mayo
Claire McAllister
Edwin McArthur
Henry McBride
James L. McCamy
Davida McCaslin
William McCleery
Robert G. McCloskey (ed.)
John McClure
Grant McConnell
Anne O'Hare McCormick
Chester Charlton McCown
Horace McCoy
Walt McDougall
Thomas P. McElroy, Jr.
Thomas F. McGann (ed.)
James L. McGaugh
Edgar W. McInnis
Margaret McKenny
Robert McLaughlin
Geoffrey McNeill-Moss
Faith McNulty
James Lowell McPherson
W. S. Meadmore
S. P. Meek
Arthur Meeker
Anne Sinclair Mehdevi
Julius Meier-Graefe
Franklin J. Meine (ed.)
Marguerite F. Melcher
Wilfrid Mellers
William Brown Meloney
Herman Melville
August Mencken (ed.)
H. L. Mencken
Johann Burkhard Mencken
Karl A. Menninger
David William Meredith
William Meredith
Frederick Merk

Robert Merle
Eve Merriam
Frances Merrill
Francis E. Merrill
James Merrill
Jean Merrill
Mason Merrill
W. S. Merwin
Gladys Meyer
Henry J. Meyer
Joseph Meyouhas
Drew Middleton
Earl Schenck Miers
Ejnar Mikkelsen
Betty Miles
Hamish Miles
Darius Milhaud
George Millar
Kenneth Millar (Ross Macdonald)
David Hunter Miller
Martha Miller
May Merrill Miller
Philip L. Miller
S. M. Miller
Sarah Gertrude Millin
Walter Millis
A. A. Milne
Lorus J. Milne
Margery Milne
Czeslaw Milosz
Alfred Milotte
Rose Laura Mincieli
Gabriel Miró
Hope Mirrlees
Prince Mirsky
Jeannette Mirsky
Robert Jay Misch
Yukio Mishima
Donald W. Mitchell
Frederick Mitchell
Gladys Mitchell
Horace Mitchell
Kate L. Mitchell
Alice-Leone Moats
Vilhelm Moberg
Philip Moeller
Pierre Moinot
Raymond Moley
Nicholas Monsarrat
Helen A. Monsell
Derek Monsey
Michel de Montaigne
Count Max Montgelas
Rutherford Montgomery

Henry de Montherlant
Beni Montresor
Richard Moody
Anne Carroll Moore
Ruth Moore
Malcolm Moos
Johanna Moosdorf
Paul Morand
George Soulie de Morant
Elsa Morante
Nicolas Mordvinoff
Albert H. Morehead
A. Moret
Charles Morgan
Jacques de Morgan
William Thomas Morgan
Hans J. Morgenthau
Zsigmond Móricz
James Morier
Relman Morin
Samuel Eliot Morison
Stanley Morison
Morley, Viscount of Blackburn
Felix Morley
Magnus Mörner (ed.)
Lady Ottoline Morrell
Constance Lily Morris
Desmond Morris
Ira Morris
Ivan Morris
Richard B. Morris
Terry Morris
Wright Morris
Herbert Morrison
Elizabeth H. Morrow
John Morse
Richard M. Morse (ed.)
A. Russell Mortenson
Raymond Mortimer
David Morton
Warren Moscow
Richard Count du Moulin-Eckart
Thomas Moult
R. B. Mowat
Edgar Ansel Mowrer
Helen Parker Mudgett
Edwin Muir
P. H. Muir
Ramsay Muir
William Mulder
Herbert J. Muller
F. Müller-Lyer
Multatuli
Ernest Mundt
C. K. Munro

James Munro
Ruth Munroe
Martha E. Munzer
Margaret E. Murie
Paul L. Murphy
D. L. Murray
Henry A. Murray
John Murray IV
John Middleton Murry
Michael A. Musmanno
Barrows Mussey
Abraham Myerson
Gerald Mygatt (ed.)
Ethelyn Myhre

Nancy Nance
Adele Gutman Nathan
George Jean Nathan
Robert Nathan
Friedrich Naumann
Ivan Nazhivin
Peter Nehemkis
Einar Nerman
L. M. Nesbitt
Israel Nestyev
Anthony Netboy
Alfred Neumann
Robert Neumann
Otto Neurath
Allan Nevins
Henry Woodd Nevinson
Marion I. Newbigin
P. H. Newby
Nancy Newhall
Ernest Newman
Vera Newman
Leonard D. Newmark
Arthur Percival Newton (ed.)
Ian Niall
Basil Nicholson
Robert Nicolson
Tobia Nicotra
Walter Niemann
Friedrich Wilhelm Nietzsche
Walter Nigg
Peter Nisser
Raymond B. Nixon
Ivor Noël Hume
Bruno Nordang
Erik Nordenskiöld
Charles Norman
Dorothy Norman
Gertrude Norman
Gunilla Norris
A. Novikoff-Priboy

Sidney L. Nyburg
Russel Blaine Nye

Helen Oakley
Edna O'Brien
Frank O'Brien
Justin O'Brien
Charles O'Connell
Frank O'Connor
Harvey O'Connor
Jack O'Connor
Liam O'Flaherty
C. K. Ogden (ed.)
William Ogilvie
Kate Richards O'Hare
Helen D. Olds
John Rathbone Oliver
Alfred Ollivant
Edwin Olmstead
Frederick Law Olmsted
Sigurd F. Olson
Walter O'Meara
Hermann Oncken
Rose O'Neill
Harriet de Onís
Shohei Ooka
James Oppenheim
A. R. Orage
A. F. K. Organski
Katherine Organski
Iris Origo
Clyde Ormond
Fernando Ortiz
Jiro Osaragi
Paul Osborn
H. Wilder Osborne
Arthur Osburn
K. G. Ossiannilsson
Margaret Otto
P. D. Ouspensky
Bonaro Wilkinson Overstreet
Richard C. Overton
Jeanne Owen
Jesse M. Owen
Robert Owen
Hamilton Owens (ed.)
Harry J. Owens

Don Paarlberg
Robert Pack
Stanley Hart Page
Thomas Paine
Sidney Painter
Compton Pakenham
Marco Pallis

Ricardo Palma
Leonard R. Palmer
Robert R. Palmer
Winthrop Palmer (ed.)
E. Sylvia Pankhurst
Vera Panova
Sir Bernard Pares
Goffredo Parise
E. H. Parker
Henry Bamford Parkes
Winthrop Parkhurst
Maurice Parmelee
Randall Parrish
Edward Abbott Parry
Hubert Parsons
Philip A. Parsons
Margaret Parton
Ben Partridge
Simon Nelson Patten
Elliot H. Paul
Louis Paul
Hertha Pauli
Hilah Paulmier (ed.)
Gerald Pawle
Robert Payne
Raymond Pearl
Frank A. Pearson
F. R. Pearson
Hendry Peart
Martin W. Peck
Rachel Peden
William Peden (ed.)
E. Allison Peers
Creighton Peet
Angelo M. Pellegrini
Murdock Pemberton
Walker Percy
William Alexander Percy
Margery Perham
James E. Perkins
Edmond Perrier
Ralph Barton Perry
W. J. Perry (ed.)
Roland Pertwee
Julia Peterkin
Samuel Peterson
Mary Petty
Ruth Shepard Phelps
Charles-Louis Philippe
Morris Philipson
Robert Pick
Marmaduke Pickthall
Mariano Picón-Salas
Gerard Piel
Bessie Louise Pierce

Donn Pierce
Jean de Pierrefeu
Léon Pierre-Quint
Stuart Piggott
Gunnar Pihl
Frederick B. Pike (ed.)
Boris Pilniak
Edgcumb Pinchon
Ping-Chia Kuo
E. G. Pinkham
H. Beam Piper
Eugene Pittard
E. B. Place (ed.)
Sylvia Plath
June Platt
Jean Plattard
Theodor Plivier
J. H. Plumb (ed.)
Edgar Allan Poe
James Kerr Pollock
Earl Pomeroy
Pont of Punch
Clifford H. Pope
James Pope-Hennessy
Odon Por
Catherine Porter
Cole Porter
G. Portigliotti
Raymond Postgate
Leo Postman (ed.)
William S. A. Pott
Frederik Poulsen
Ezra Pound
Guy de Pourtalès
T. F. Powys
Edward J. Pratt
Theodore Pratt
Mario Praz
Edgar Prestage (ed.)
Robert Presthus
Abbé Prévost
George Madison Priest (ed.)
V. S. Pritchett
Serge Prokofieff
Madame Simone Prunier
Alan Pryce-Jones
Stanislaw Przybyszewski
Sandor Puder
René Puissesseau
Carlton W. Pullin
L. Pumpelly
Samuel Putnam

Thomas Quale
Francisco de Quevedo-Villegas

Arthur Hobson Quinn (ed.)
Ricardo Quintana
Joaquín Alvarez Quintero
Serafín Alvarez Quintero

Max Radin
Graciliano Ramos
Christopher Rand
Paul Rand
Vera Randal
Edward C. Randall
Vance Randolph
Otto Rank
John Crowe Ransom
Samson Raphaelson
Vilhelm Rasmussen
Fannie E. Ratchford (ed.)
Walther Rathenau
Gino A. Ratti
Margaret Rau
M. E. Ravage
Wade Ray
Conyers Read
Evelyn Read
P. H. Reaney
René Antoine Ferchault de Réaumur
Paul Reboux
Arthur B. Recknagel
John Redfield
Fritz Redlich
Alves Redol
Lillian J. Redstone
Ruth Reed
Robert Reeves
Rosser Reeves
Adolf Reichwein
J. H. S. Reid
V. S. Reid
Anna Reiner
Edwin O. Reischauer
Alexei Remizov
G. Renard
Kuno Renatus
Renzo Rendi
Theodore Repard
James Reston
Gabriele Reuter
Alfonso Reyes
Ladislas Reymont
E. A. Rheinhardt
Jean Rhys
D. T. Rice
Stuart A. Rice
Paul Richard
Dorothy M. Richardson

William L. Richardson
Clément Richer
Conrad Richter
Edgell Rickword
A. de Ridder
Roberto Ridolfi
Robert Rienow
Oskar von Riesemann
Felix Riesenberg, Jr.
Shepard Rifkin
Eugenio Rignano
Thad W. Riker
Nikolay Rimsky-Korsakov
Barbara Ring
William L. Riordan
J. Fred Rippy
W. H. R. Rivers
Herman Robbers
Harold Robbins
Roland Wells Robbins
Grace Robert
Joseph C. Robert
J. W. Roberts
Morley Roberts
Ben Robertson
R. B. Robertson
L. Robin
T. H. Robsjohn-Gibbings
John Rock
Richard Rodgers
Robert E. Roeder
Theodore Roethke
Charles Elkins Rogers (ed.)
Leigh Rogers
Lindsay Rogers
Géza Róheim
Feodor Rojankovsky
Milton Rokeach
Alfred B. Rollins, Jr.
Jules Romains
Eleanor Roosevelt
Kermit Roosevelt
Waverley Root
Ropshin (Boris Savinkov)
Forrest Rosaire
Arnold M. Rose
Caroline Rose
Baron Rosen
Norma Stahl Rosen
Arthur Rosenberg
James N. Rosenberg
S. L. Millard Rosenberg
Henry M. Rosenthal
Lawrence K. Rosinger
Nancy Wilson Ross

Patricia Fent Ross
Clinton Rossiter
Thomas Rourke
Jean-Jacques Rousseau
Carl T. Rowan
Margaret Rowlett
Jules Roy
Josiah Royce
Naomi Royde-Smith
Harry C. Rubicam, Jr.
Marion Rubinstein
Frederick Rudolph
Maximilian J. Rudwin (ed.)
Rogers D. Rusk
Lord Russell of Liverpool
Franklin Russell
John Russell
Kent Ruth
Albert Rutherston
Marion Crowell Ryder
Robert Rylee
Morrie Ryskind

Ernesto Sábato
Abram Leon Sachar
Maurice Sachs
Paul J. Sachs
Edward Sackville-West
M. T. H. Sadleir
Miloš Safránek
Nayantara Sahgal
Giles St. Aubyn
Georges de Saint-Foix
George Saintsbury
Robert H. Salisbury
C. C. Sallustius
Max Saltmarsh
Luigi Salvatorelli
Anne Samstag
Gordon Samstag
Maurice Samuel
Elaine Sanceau
Florencio Sánchez
Aksel Sandemose
Ivan T. Sanderson
Samuel Sandmel
Mari Sandoz
John Sanford
G. B. Sansom
Bert R. Sappenfield
Charles Sarolea
Jean-Paul Sartre
Siegfried Sassoon
Max Savelle
Boris Savinkov

Joel Sayre
Richard Schaap
Hyman Judah Schachtel
Samuel B. Schaeffer
Aaron Schaffer (ed.)
August Ludolf Schaumann
Israel Scheffler
Karl Scheffler
Harry N. Scheiber (ed.)
Erich Schenk
Rita Scherman
René Schickele
Oscar Schisgall
Johannes Schlaf
Arthur M. Schlesinger
G. Warren Schloat, Jr.
F. G. G. Schmidt
Heinrich Schnee
Arthur Schnitzler
Max Schoen
Hermann Schoenen
Richard Schoenwald
Herbert Scholfield
Harold C. Schonberg
Georg Schreiber
Hermann Schreiber
Franz Schubert
Frederick L. Schuman
Cathleen Schurr
Kurt Schuschnigg
Eugene Schwaab (ed.)
Earl Schwalje
Marjory Schwalje
Bernard Schwartz
H. Stanley Schwarz
Leopold Schwarzschild
Leonardo Sciascia
William Lutley Sclater
Margaret C. Scoggin
Barbara Ann Scott
Dustin C. Scott
Harold P. Scott
J. D. Scott
Sir J. G. Scott
John A. Scott (ed.)
Florida Scott-Maxwell
C. K. Scott Moncrieff (ed.)
William Seagle
Ronald Searle
Murray Seasongood
Robert C. Sedgwick
René Sédillot
Henri Sée
Rayner Seelig
Simon Segal

Madame de Ségur
Marjorie Allen Seiffert
Charles Seignobos
David Sentner
Elizabeth Shepley Sergeant
Victor Seroff
Jean-Jacques Servan-Schreiber
Eric Sevareid
Bill Severn
Sue Severn
Beatrice Kean Seymour
L. T. Shackelford, Jr.
Don Cameron Shafer
P. Morton Shand
Jon Beck Shank
Robert Shankland
Edward Shanks
Robert Shaplen
Judith Shatnoff
Archer H. Shaw
George Bernard Shaw
Joseph T. Shaw
Vincent Sheean
Percy Bysshe Shelley
Odell Shepard
William R. Shepherd
Philip Sherrard (ed.)
E. Spencer Shew
M. P. Shiel
Charles Howard Shinn
Maynard Shipley
Margaret Shipton
Peter Shiraeff
William L. Shirer
Dame Shirley (Louise A. K. S. Clappe)
Mikhail Sholokhov
Miriam Lubell Shrifte
Richard Harrison Shryock
Mary Francis Shura
N. K. E. Sidhanta
Elie Siegmeister
Eduard Sievers (ed.)
Donald K. Silks
F. E. Sillanpää
Alan Sillitoe
A. T. W. Simeons
Natasha Simkhovitch
Francis Butler Simkins
André L. Simon
Herbert A. Simon
Alyse Simpson
Charles Simpson
Elizabeth Simpson
Helen Simpson
Howard R. Simpson

Joseph Sinel
Caroline Singer
Charles Singer
I. B. Singer
I. J. Singer
Marcus George Singer
Curt Siodmak
Edith Sitwell
Osbert Sitwell
Sacheverell Sitwell
Sigfrid Siwertz
George Sklar
Arne Skouen
Georgi Skrebitsky
Charles E. Slaughter
Jean Slaughter
Sumner H. Slichter
Harry Slochower
Donald Smalley (ed.)
Susan Dabney Smedes
Agnes Smedley
V. V. Smidovich
Bernard Smith (ed.)
Bradley Smith
Dulcie L. Smith
E. Cadwallader Smith
Henry Ladd Smith
Howard K. Smith
James M. Smith (ed.)
Louis M. Smith
Page Smith
Red Smith
Richard Austin Smith
Susan Smith
T. Lynn Smith (ed.)
T. V. Smith
Donald W. Smithburg
Lee J. Smits
Dame Ethel Smyth
William H. Smyth
W. D. Snodgrass
Ronni Solbert
Mario Soldati
Feodor Sologub
Vladimir Soloviev
Felix Somary
Anne Somerhausen
John Sommerfield
Virginia Sorensen
Philippe Soupault
D. H. Southgate
Benn Sowerby
Muriel Spark
Richard Specht
Thomas Spence

Cornelia Spencer
R. E. Spencer
Oswald Spengler
Bella Spewack
Samuel Spewack
Leonora Speyer
Hyman Spotnitz
Elizabeth Sprigge
Samuel N. Spring
Constance Spry
J. C. Squire
Ann Stafford
Robert Wooster Stallman (ed.)
Kenneth M. Stampp
Harold Stannard
Freya Stark
Marion L. Starkey
Chester G. Starr
Louis M. Starr
Ethelbert Stauffer
Hal Steed
Byron Steel
Hermann Stegemann
Wallace Stegner
Henry Steig
William Steig
Erwin Stein
Charlotte Steiner
Gary A. Steiner
George Steiner
Stendhal
Ruth Stephan
G. B. Stern
Philip Van Doren Stern
Emma Gelders Sterne
Laurence Sterne
Carl Sternheim
Ettie Stettheimer
Elizabeth Welty Stevens
Harry Stevens (ed.)
James Stevens
Wallace Stevens
Friedrich Stieve
Hart Stilwell
G. Harry Stine
Curwen Stoddart
Eugenia Stone
William S. Stone
Marian Storm
Theodor Storm
Rex Stout (ed.)
A. Monroe Stowe
Leland Stowe
Michael Straight
Julian Strange

Michael Strange
Anna R. Stratton
Nathan Straus
Richard Strauss
Julian Street
Arthur Stringer
Hudson Strode (ed.)
Leslie Winter Strom
L. A. G. Strong
Luís de Sttau Monteiro
Francis Stuart
Roland Stucki
Ruth Suckow
Sidney C. Sufrin
Samuel Sugden
J. W. N. Sullivan
Richard E. Sullivan
Montague Summers
Margaret Sutton
Italo Svevo
Jonathan Swift
Frank Swinnerton
Christopher Sykes
Wilbur Owen Sypherd (ed.)
Harold C. Syrett
Marie Syrkin
Magda Szabo
Berta Szeps
Joseph Szigeti

Robert A. Taft
Genevieve Taggard
Harald Tandrup
Junichiro Tanizaki
Frank Tannenbaum
Roberts Tapley
Valeriy Tarsis
Robert Joyce Tasker
Algernon Tassin
Gus Tavo
A. J. P. Taylor
Allan Taylor
Bayard Taylor
Bert Leston Taylor
Carl C. Taylor
Elizabeth Taylor
Maurice Taylor
Sara Teasdale
E. W. Tedlock, Jr. (ed.)
Helen Tee-Van
Janet Teissier du Cros
Walter Magnes Teller
Marguerite Templeton
Viscount Templewood
    (Sir Samuel Hoare)

Joseph Tenenbaurr
Helmut de Terra
Manuel Romero De Terreros
John Tettemer
Jean Tharaud
Jerome Tharaud
Mary Dixon Thayer
Rudolf Thiel
Frank Thiess
Angela Thirkell
Ludwig Thoma
Benjamin P. Thomas
Calvin Thomas
Dorothy Thomas
Dorothy Swaine Thomas
Edward J. Thomas
Elizabeth Marshall Thomas
Gertrude Z. Thomas
Jerry Thomas
Paul B. Thomas
William I. Thomas
Edward Thompson
James Westfall Thompson
Kenneth W. Thompson
Victor A. Thompson
Warren S. Thompson
David Thomson
Gladys Scott Thomson
Virgil Thomson
Willard Thorp
Berenice Thorpe
James Throneburg
Richard Thruelsen (ed.)
James Thurber
H. C. Thurnau
Eunice Tietjens
Freeman Tilden
Germaine Tillion
William York Tindall
Lance O. Tingay
Helen Tinyanova
Barry J. Titus
James A. Tobey
Alexis de Tocqueville
Ruthven Todd
Ernst Toller
Cyril J. H. Tolley
Alexei Tolstoy
Alexis K. Tolstoy
Leo Tolstoy
Josef Toman
H. M. Tomlinson
Angela Tonks
Frances Toor
Ellen Torelle

Jules Toutain
Frank Townshend
Francis Toye
Pierre l'Espagnol de la Tramerye
B. Traven
Jerome D. Travers
Henry Treece
J. B. Trend
Alvin Tresselt
John Trevena
André Tridon
W. B. Trites
Anthony Trollope
Mrs. Frances Trollope
Philip Truex
David B. Truman
Dalton Trumbo
Kyoson Tsuchida
Gilbert M. Tucker
Nathaniel Beverley Tucker
Frederick Goddard Tuckerman
Rexford G. Tugwell (ed.)
Jim Tully
Melvin M. Tumin
Ivan Turgenev
Charlotte Turgeon
George Kibbe Turner
Ralph E. Turner
W. J. Turner
Robert Turney
Godfrey E. Turton
Warren Tute
Charles H. Tutt
Mark Twain
Anne Tyler
Nedra Tyre
Ross Tyrell
Leopold Tyrmand

Manuel Ugarte
John E. Uhler (ed.)
William H. Ukers
Antonio de Ulloa
Joseph N. Ulman
Miguel de Unamuno
A. C. Underwood
Sigrid Undset
Fritz von Unruh
Jean Starr Untermeyer
Louis Untermeyer
John Updike
Arturo Uslar Pietri

Horace Annesley Vachell
Roger Vailland

Veit Valentin
Paul Valéry
Pasteur Vallery-Radot
Arthur T. Vanderbilt
J. J. Van der Leeuw
Carl Van Doren
Harold A. Van Dorn
John Van Druten
Peggy van Praagh
Alexander Van Rensselaer
Gustave L. Van Roosbroeck
V. A. Van Sickle
Lord Vansittart
Carl Van Vechten
H. B. van Wesep
Dimitry Varley
A. V. Vasiliev
Vassilis Vassilikos
Gabor Vaszary
Agnes Carr Vaughn
J. Alvarez del Vayo
Vernon Venable
J. Vendryes
Franco Venturi
Vikenty Veressayev
A. Hyatt Verrill
Peter Viereck
Antonio Ruiz Vilaplana
Henry Villard
Oswald Garrison Villard
Mary Villarejo
Villiers de L'Isle-Adam
Harold M. Vinacke
Paul Vinogradoff
Helen Wolff Vogel
Joseph Vogel
Julie Vogelstein (ed.)
Vicomte de Vogüé
Ambroise Vollard
Rudolph Von Abele
Boris Voyetekhov
E. L. Voynich (ed.)

Charles Wagley
Charles A. Wagner
Constance Wagner
Philip M. Wagner
Richard Wagner
Dorothy Wagstaff
John Wain
Arthur Edward Waite
Arthur Waley
Frank Walker
Franklin Walker
Mabel Gregory Walker

A. B. Walkley
Irving Wallace
Schuyler C. Wallace
Graham Wallas
William English Walling
Wilson D. Wallis
Leo Walmsley
Mary Walsh
Bruno Walter
Hedda Walther
Arthur Walworth
James P. Warburg
Phyllis Ward
Harry R. Warfel
Rex Warner
Sunny B. Warner
Sylvia Townsend Warner
Lella Warren
Henrie Waste
Philip F. Waterman
Lawrence Edward Watkin
Hope Brister Watkins
Maurine Watkins
E. L. Grant Watson
Nancy Dingman Watson
Alexander Watt
Gwendoline Watts
John V. A. Weaver
Joseph Wechsberg
Alfred von Wegerer
Mary H. Weik
Henry Weinberg
Herbert Weinstock
Franz C. Weiskopf
Alden W. Welch
John Welcome
Anna Mary Wells
H. G. Wells
Robert Wells
Joel Carl Welty
Edward Wenham
Alexander Werth
Albert Richard Wetjen
G. Weulersse
John Wexley
Don Wharton
Carl I. Wheat
Harry Grove Wheat
William Morton Wheeler
Joseph Wheless
Maurine Whipple
Bessie F. White
David Omar White
Elizabeth Brett White
Newman Ivey White

Robb White
Walter F. White
William C. White
William Wallace Whitelock (ed.)
Raoul Whitfield
Alvin Whitley
Walt Whitman
Courtney Whitney
Adam Gowans Whyte
Alban G. Widgery
Ernst von Wildenbruch
Hugh Wiley
Bonaro Wilkinson
Louis Wilkinson
William B. Willcox
Cornelius W. Willemse
M. M. Willey
Cora Lenore Williams
Frank J. Williams
Gertrude Marvin Williams
Glanville Williams
Greer Williams
Harold Williams
James Mickel Williams
John H. Williams
Robin M. Williams, Jr.
T. Harry Williams
Ursula Moray Williams
Jefferson Williamson
Joanne S. Williamson
Irene Cooper Willis
Edmund Wilson
Esther Wilson
Hazel Wilson
James Herbert Wilson (ed.)
J. Tuzo Wilson
Romer Wilson
William K. Wimsatt, Jr.
Edgar Wind
Mary Day Winn
Anne Goodwin Winslow
Thyra Samter Winslow
Oscar Osburn Winther
Thomas J. Wise
William Wise
Bernard W. Wishy
Carl Wittke
Bernard Wolfe
Bertram D. Wolfe
Humbert Wolfe
Linnie Marsh Wolfe
Charlotte Wolff
Theodor Wolff

Johan Wøller
Goesta Wollin
Adelaide H. Wonsetler
John C. Wonsetler
Harrie Wood
James N. Wood
Marni Wood
Noel Woodin
W. E. Woodward
Regina J. Woody
Ronald Woolmer
Basil Woon
William Wordsworth
Kathryn Worth
Marjorie Worthington
F. R. Worts (ed.)
Arnold Wright
Cedric Wright
Louis B. Wright
Elinor Wylie
Philip Wylie
Lee Wyndham
Fred E. M. B. Wynne

William Yandell
Kenneth Yasuda
Elizabeth Yates
Dorr Yeager
Samuel Yellen
Eiji Yoshikawa
Barbara Young
Catherine Young
Francis Brett Young
Kimball Young
Roland Young

George Zabriskie
Paul A. Zahl
Ernst Zahn
Harry Zarchy
Jeanette Zarchy
Jacob Zeitlin (ed.)
Stefan Zeromski
Edwin H. Zeydel
E. R. Zietlow
Carl Zigrosser
John Lee Zimmerman
Howard Zinn
Hans Zinsser
Florian Znaniecki
Emile Zola
Don José Zorrilla